GEOLOGY OF NORTHERN CALIFORNIA

EDGAR H. BAILEY, *Editor*
United States Geological Survey

BULLETIN 190
California Division
of
Mines and Geology
Ferry Building, San Francisco
1966

State of California
EDMUND G. BROWN, *Governor*

The Resources Agency
HUGO FISHER, *Administrator*

Department of Conservation
IAN CAMPBELL, *Director*

DIVISION OF MINES AND GEOLOGY
IAN CAMPBELL, *State Geologist*

BULLETIN 190

Price $6.00

CONTENTS

CONTENTS—Continued

PAGE

CONTENTS—Continued

PAGE

CONTENTS—Continued

PAGE

CONTENTS—Continued

PAGE

CONTENTS—Continued

PAGE

CONTENTS—Continued

PREFACE

The National Meetings of the Geological Society of America often furnish the impetus required for the assembling of the most recent geological information available for the region surrounding the host city. The publication of this data provides a background for geologists from other areas and permits them to get the most out of field excursions run in connection with the meetings. The value of this short-term use of a geologic summary of the region, however, is greatly exceeded by the continuing year-after-year use of the publication by mining and petroleum geologists, regional planners, engineers, faculties and students of universities, and other research geologists, as well as those who are seeking only to learn more about the world in which they live. Bulletin 170, *The Geology of Southern California,* edited by R. H. Jahns and issued in connection with the Geological Society of America meeting in Los Angeles in November 1954, has proved to have just such continuing value; in fact, it has recently been reprinted. This bulletin on *The Geology of Northern California,* being issued in connection with the Geological Society of America meeting in San Francisco in November 1966, treats the geology of the other half of the State and doubtless will prove to be equally useful.

The content and organization of this bulletin is largely that which seemed to be most appropriate after helpful discussions with many geologic colleagues. Limitations of both time and money led to restricting the authors to a planned number of pages and to illustrations of page size or smaller, but it is likely that in many cases this has resulted in a better product. The selection of authors of articles and leaders for the field trips was made with the guidance of an advisory committee consisting of W. R. Dickinson, of Stanford University; G. B. Oakeshott, of the California Division of Mines and Geology; P. D. Snavely, of the U.S. Geological Survey; and C. A. Wahrhaftig, of the University of California at Berkeley. For most, but not all, topics the geologist selected as the committee's first choice was able to contribute. Numerous other authors and topics also were considered, but for practical reasons we felt they would have to be omitted, even though we recognized that their inclusion might have improved the bulletin and made it more complete.

Although the controlling factor in the selection of authors was a desire to obtain the most qualified geologist available, regardless of his affiliation, the resulting selection involved representatives of universities and colleges, State and Federal organizations, and private industries. Included are geologists from the University of California at Berkeley (2), at Davis (2), and at Scripps Institution of Oceanography (1), San Jose State College (2), University of Nevada (1), Stanford University (4), University of Southern California (1), University of Hawaii (1), Califorina Academy of Sciences (1), California Division of Mines and Geology (8), U.S. Coast and Geodetic Survey (2), U.S. Geological Survey (15), petroleum companies (2), and mining companies (2).

To the contributing authors, who generally managed to submit their manuscripts not long after their deadline, took my editorial sniping in good grace, promptly and accurately reviewed illustrations and proof, and put forth a real effort to make this bulletin a summary of the Geology of Northern California that is scientifically accurate, generally understandable, and a pleasure to read, I offer my sincere appreciation.

Many people other than the authors also have contributed to this volume, and in the aggregate their contribution in time probably exceeds that of the authors. Most of the tedious work of collating, editing, drafting, and some of the proofing was done by the staff at the U.S. Geological Survey office in Menlo Park, and the help of this experienced group not only greatly facilitated the preparation of this bulletin but also significantly enhanced its quality. Many hundred pages of manuscript were accurately typed and retyped by Frances LeBaker, Mary L. Brannock, Vera P. Campbell, Irene Jiminez, and Beatrice L. Sanders. The staff of the Area Publication Unit of the Survey, under the supervision of Henry Berg, aided immensely by reviewing articles and references, checking for consistent editorial policy, and proofreading. Particular thanks are due to Catherine C. Campbell, Alice A. Parcel, and Cornelia Kline for manuscript reviewing, to Sumi W. Sumida for assistance with bibliography, and to Susan McMurray and Warnette Ching for proofreading. Rudolph W. Kopf, of the Geologic Names Review Staff, offered a great deal of technical assistance and helpful guidance regarding the usage of geologic names and proper stratigraphic terminology.

Final copy for many of the illustrations was also made in the Menlo Park office of the U.S. Geological Survey. We are indebted to Esther T. McDermott, most ably assisted by Faye Koonce and Fidelia R. Portillo, for carefully preparing most of the line drawings and maps that so enhance this bulletin. We are equally grateful to Norman Prime and Christopher Utter for fine photocopying of the drafting and many of the photographs. Paul Y. W. Ho skillfully retouched some of the photographs and spliced others for panoramas.

The complete cooperation of the staff of the California Division of Mines and Geology throughout every stage in the preparation of this bulletin, from its initial conception to its final delivery, contributed greatly to its quality. Ian Campbell, State Geologist, actively supported its publication both by his own personal interest and by offering the assistance of members of his staff. Gordon B. Oakeshott and Tom E. Gay deserve special thanks for technical aid and advice, but many others also contributed. Some finished drafting was prepared by Merl Smith and his staff. Final assembly of the bulletin and many other editorial matters were adeptly handled by Mary Hill, who also contributed several of the most attractive photographs.

Students of California geology now have available bulletins on the geology of both southern California and northern California, which will aid greatly in understanding the geologic history of the State. Neither of these bulletins, however, provides an entirely satisfying geologic account, because neither presents an integrated report describing what events were occurring simultaneously throughout the whole of either area through geologic time. This is not the fault of the authors, who have prepared excellent summary articles on the topics on which they agreed to write; perhaps it is a necessary consequence of publication limitations or the need for multiple authorship to cope with the complex and diverse geology in an area as large as even half of the State. Regardless of the cause, each bulletin consists chiefly of separate discussions of the geology of smaller individual areas, ranging in size from less than a quadrangle to a province, with little mention of what is beyond that limited area. But even though geologic provinces are distinct and each tells a different story, what happens in one province—be it erosion, deposition, intrusion, or tectonism—does affect bordering provinces. In reaching an understanding of these relations, authoritative province summaries, such as presented here and in Bulletin 170, are a necessary first step, especially now that the literature has become so voluminous and geologists so specialized. With this step accomplished, it is hoped that we can look forward to still broader concepts regarding the interplay of geologic events among the provinces of this State, and to early publication of a truly integrated geologic history of the entire State of California.

EDGAR H. BAILEY, *Editor*
U.S. Geological Survey
Menlo Park, California

SCOPE AND ARRANGEMENT OF THE BULLETIN

California is readily divisible into natural provinces, each of which has characteristic geography and topography, reflecting fundamental differences in geology, see figure 1. The geologic history for each province is different from that of its neighbor, and consequently the rocks, structures, mineral deposits, and geomorphology also are different. Six of these provinces—Klamath Mountains, Cascade Range, Modoc Plateau, Sierra Nevada, Great Valley, and Coast Ranges—comprise the area that is generally regarded as northern California. In addition, two small parts of the Great Basin province that penetrate into the northeastern corner of the state are also included in northern California. The much larger part of the Great Basin province that extends in California north from the Mojave desert to Mono Lake has closer geologic affinities, as well as cultural ties, to southern California and is generally considered as a part of southern California even though its northern extremity is farther north than San Francisco.

Following an historical summary of State geologic maps of California, there is a chapter devoted to each of the provinces, or in one case to a group of related provinces, and the leading article for each chapter is a summary of the main geologic features of the province prepared by a specialist in that area. Supplementing these summary articles are shorter papers treating some geologic aspect of the province of particular interest, either because it is unusual, recently discovered, or of economic importance.

The area beneath the sea offshore from northern California has attracted considerable interest in recent years because of its potential for oil and other mineral resources. It is treated herein in much the same manner as the onshore geologic provinces, though it is recognized that the part extending out to the base of the continental slope is in reality just a submerged part of the Coast Ranges province.

No discussion of the geology of California, especially northern California, can be considered as complete without some special treatment of its best known, and most feared, geologic structure—the great San Andreas fault. It is the subject of three articles, two of which present strongly opposed views of the total amount of offset along the fault, while the third presents new data that indicate how fast the blocks on each side of the fault are now moving relative to each other.

The geology at depths below those penetrated by mines or drill holes is always speculative, being either based on downward projections of known geology or on geophysical measurements. The wealth of new geophysical data that has become available in recent years provides new insight into deep crustal structures, and we can expect much more information will become available soon because of the much larger geophysical programs now underway. The information on the crustal structure of northern California now available from geophysical measurements—gravity, magnetic, and seismic—is summarized by articles prepared by experts in each of these fields.

Lastly, a series of roadlogs is included to aid geologists taking guided field trips that are being run in connection with the National Meeting in San Francisco of The Geologic Society of America. The logs are all written, however, in such a fashion that they will provide the information necessary for one to observe and learn about the geology along the route even on a self-guided tour.

Figure 1. Relief map of California showing the natural provinces.

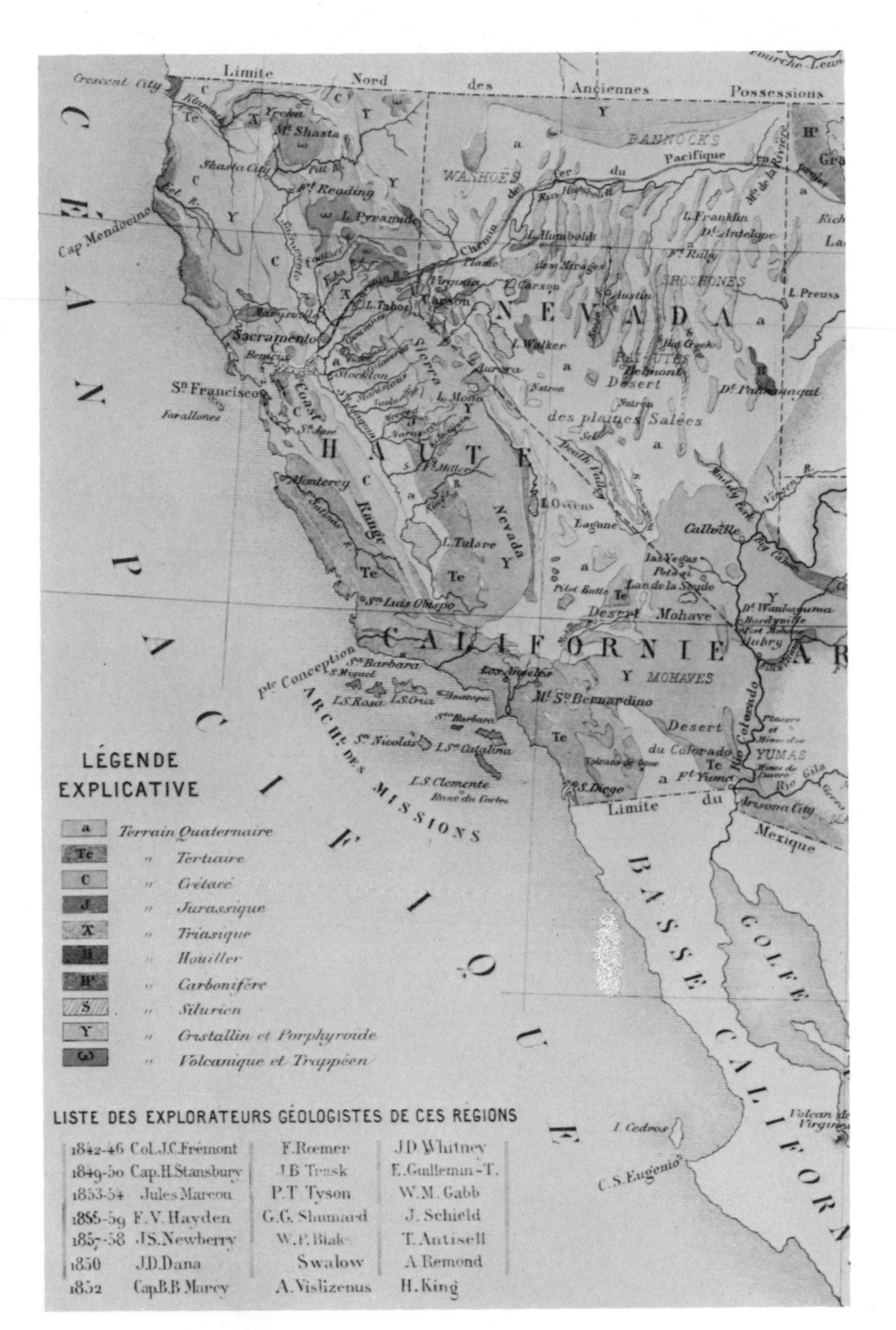

Geologic map of California and Nevada: being a portion of Esquisse géologique des anciennes possessions mexicaines du nord incorporées a la fédération des États-Unis. Echelle de $\frac{1}{8,000,000}$. 1867. From E. Guillemin-Tarayre, *Mission scientifique au Mexique et dans l'Amérique centrale . . . Paris, 1871.*

CHAPTER I
INTRODUCTION

Page

From Cadwalader Ringgold, U.S.N., *A series of charts, with sailing directions . . .* 1852.

STATE GEOLOGIC MAPS OF CALIFORNIA—A BRIEF HISTORY

By Charles W. Jennings
California Division of Mines and Geology, San Francisco

It has been more than 125 years since the first geologic map of a part of California was published, and nearly 100 years have passed since the first geologic map of the entire State was prepared. In order to appreciate more fully our modern geologic maps, it is desirable to refer to the earlier maps and compare the development and progress through the years. Great advances are expected, but often current concepts considered as recent developments are found upon investigation to have had their seeds sown long ago.

The history of geologic exploration and mapping in California is a colorful and significant one, closely associated with the economic and social development of the "Golden State." California, early in its history, became a training ground for many illustrious pioneers in the field of geology. This is not at all surprising, considering the wide diversity and complexity of the geology and its fabulous mineral wealth.

The first geologic explorations in California were closely associated with the search for gold, and, secondly and relatedly, with the surveys for railroad routes to the Pacific. After the railroads were built and the gold hysteria had lessened, geologic mapping in the State proceeded in a more orderly fashion as the Federal and State surveys gathered information for the continued economic development of the State. Beginning at the turn of the century, the University of California and Stanford University began to make important contributions to the understanding of the geology of California, especially in basic geologic research. Later, all of these groups, plus petroleum and other mineral exploration companies, pushed the frontiers of California geologic mapping further back until there remain today but few areas for which there exists little or no geologic mapping.

The following discussion of the history of California geology focusses on those pioneers who prepared the first geologic maps on a statewide scale. No attempt has been made to include all those who labored in the field in various corners of the State and upon whose information the geologic map compilers often had to depend. For the history of those stalwart men, whose work was often done under conditions of hardship impossible to imagine today, the reader should consult such references as F. M. Anderson's "Pioneers in the geology of California" (1932); George P. Merrill's "Contributions to the history of American geology" (1906); and V. L. VanderHoof's "History of geologic investigation in the Bay region" (1954).

THE FIRST GEOLOGIC MAPS—1826, 1850

The honor for the first geologic map of any part of California goes to Lieut. Edward Belcher for his "Geological plan for the port of San Francisco" prepared in 1826 and published in 1839. This map accompanies a geologic report by Rev. Buckland (1839) that is included in the volume entitled "The zoology of Captain Beechey's voyage" (fig. 1). This is a most remarkable geologic and topographic map made with exceptional skill. It was surveyed only 17 years after William Maclure, "the father of American geology," produced, in 1809, the earliest attempt at a geologic map of the United States (a map of the region east of the Mississippi River).

The first map of a relatively large segment of California on which an attempt was made to show the distribution of rock types, and the first report that attempted to treat the geology of much of the State, was prepared by Philip T. Tyson and published by the U. S. Government in 1850. This map, entitled "Geological reconnaissances in California," accompanied his report "Geology and topography of California" which was published as Senate Executive Document 47, and privately the following year under the title "Geology and industrial resources of California."

The publication of this official report was of great importance, for with the discovery of gold in California in 1848 there had arisen an intense demand for information on the geology of this practically unknown region. Tyson, a private citizen having geological training, came to California soon after the discovery of gold. Upon his return to Baltimore, he offered to Col. J. J. Abert, of the Bureau of Topographical Engineers, a copy of the memoir he made during his visit west. Abert submitted the report to the Senate for publication in compliance with their request for any recent reports concerning the geology and topography of California.

Tyson's geologic map included the central part of the State and was highly generalized and uncolored, perhaps barely qualifying as a geologic map. Word descriptions lettered on the map were employed in an attempt to show the distribution of various rock types. It was, nevertheless, the first attempt at a regional geologic analysis of the State, and together with the report and eight cross sections constituted a notable effort to describe the geology of California.

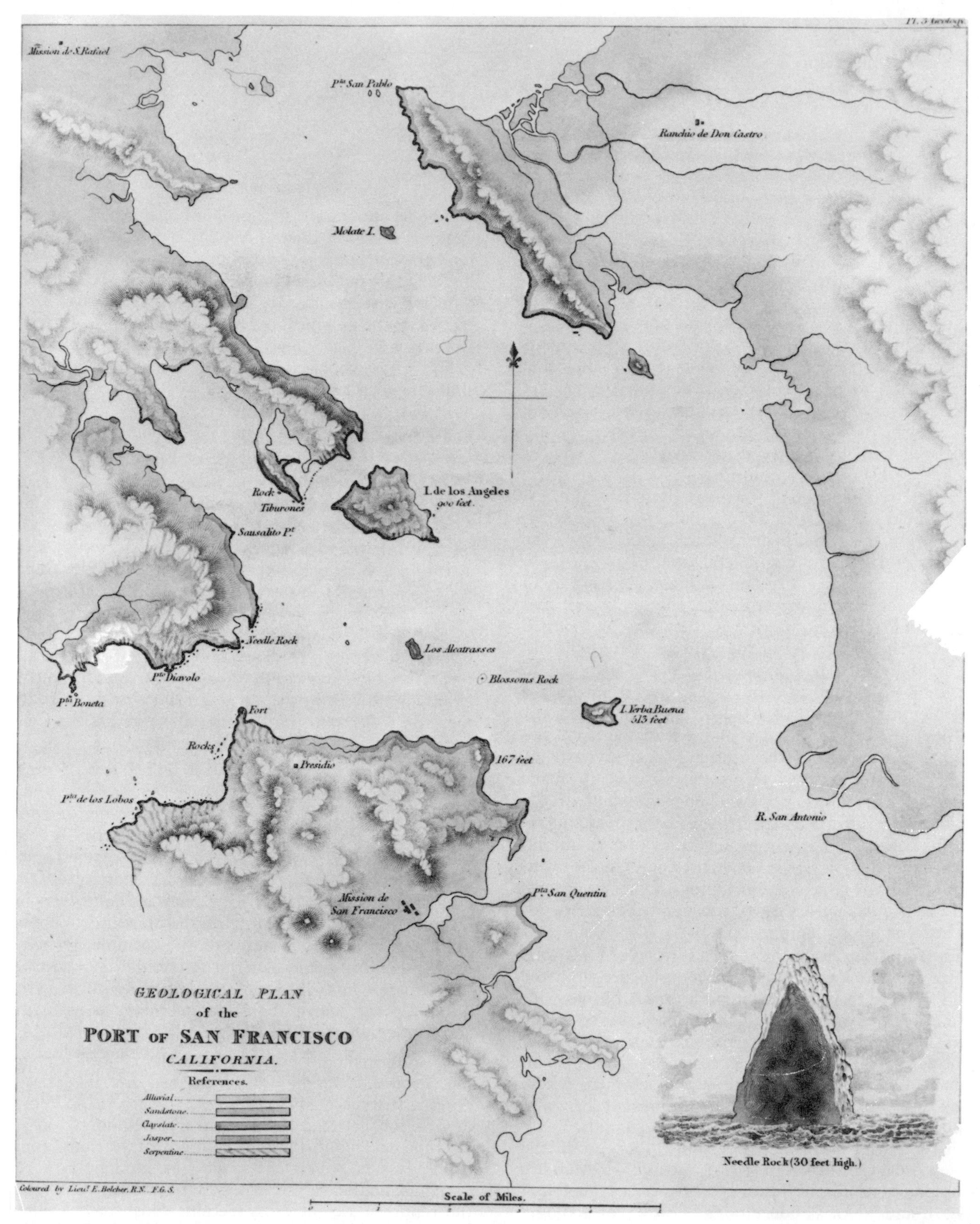

Figure 1. First geologic map of an area of California, surveyed in 1826 by Lieut. Belcher of His Majesty's Ship *Blossom,* with the assistance of Ship's Surgeon, Alex Collie. This hand-colored map of the headlands surrounding San Francisco Bay depicts five geologic units, including serpentine, jasper, claystone, sandstone, and alluvium.

Tyson's report was principally concerned with warning overadventurous gold seekers and investors, and he was quite prophetic when he stated:

> Notwithstanding the seeming brilliancy of the golden prospects, the full development of those branches of industry embraced under the general head of agriculture, in connexion with the arts by which its products are elaborated, is far more important to the *permanent* prosperity of the country than its precious metals can ever become.

MAPS OF THE RAILROAD EXPLORATIONS

In 1853 and 1854, in accordance with Acts of Congress, a number of expeditions were sent out by the Secretary of War, Jefferson Davis, to explore routes for a railroad from the Mississippi River to the Pacific Ocean. These expeditions were under the command of army officers, but nearly all included one or more geologists or naturalists. The resulting reports comprise the monumental "Pacific Railroad Reports"—12 large volumes (sometimes bound as 13 volumes), many beautifully illustrated with geologic maps and engravings. Volumes V and VII contain most of the reports of geological observations made in California—by William Blake and Thomas Antisell, respectively. Shorter accounts of California geology by Jules Marcou appear in Volume III, and by John S. Newberry in Volume VI.

William P. Blake was associated with the Pacific Railroad Survey from 1853 until 1856, and during this time traversed a very large part of the State. He soon became the most extensive writer and accurate observer of the geology of California. Volume V, containing Blake's "Geological Report," published in 1857, is still thought provoking and very entertaining. It is beautifully illustrated with numerous engravings of scenic views and natural history. Among the various maps of this volume is the first geologic map that specifically and exclusively pertains to California. The map is highly generalized and many areas are left blank for lack of information, the result of the rapid nature of the reconnaissance. Nevertheless, utilizing a legend of nine units, a broad brush treatment of the State shows the following units: Granitic and metamorphic; Erupted granite and syenite; Serpentine, trap, greenstone, and porphyry; Basaltic lava; Metamorphic slates; White and crystalline limestone; Tertiary and Quaternary (Tertiary rocks generally covered by Quaternary wash and detritus); Tertiary (including the San Francisco Sandstone); and Alluvium.

The 40-mile-to-the-inch base map, prepared by Lt. Williamson, is about as crude as the geologic mapping. It shows Lake Tahoe (here called Lake Bonpland)[1] as one of the smallest lakes in the California-Nevada area, whereas actually it is one of the largest. The lake is also shown entirely in Nevada (here labeled as Utah, as it was then part of the Utah Territory). However, the coastline is well surveyed. An interesting geographical feature located in the embayment of the coast between San Pedro and San Diego is labeled "Earthquake Bay," probably in recognition of the shattering earthquake of 1812 during which 40 lives were lost at Mission San Juan Capistrano.

The geology depicted on the base map is colored by hand. A comparison with the same map plate in other copies of the Railroad Reports shows that the coloring was in wide variance, not only in hue, but in location from map to map—not an uncommon failing of the hand-colored geologic maps published in the old reports.

Blake's larger scale maps of smaller regions in the same volume are much more carefully constructed, and one in particular, a "Geological map of the vicinity of San Francisco" (at a scale of about 2¼ miles-to-the-inch) merits a description. On it six lithologic units were employed and shown lithographed in color —one of the earliest colored maps to be so printed. The units include Serpentine, Trap, San Francisco Sandstone, Metamorphosed sandstone, Alluvial, and Blown sand dunes. Ages are not indicated on the map, probably because of the great uncertainty, but some speculations are made in the text. The "San Francisco Sandstone," the most widespread unit in the area comprising essentially the Jurassic-Cretaceous "Franciscan Formation" of today, is considered to be probably Tertiary and possibly partly Upper Cretaceous.

Blake's accounts on California geology are not confined to the Pacific Railroad Reports, but include reports published over many years in various journals and government documents. His published contributions to California geology total at least seventy. Blake deserves grateful recognition for his accurate and honest reporting done under circumstances of great hardship.

In 1855, Jules Marcou, a native of France, published in French and German scientific journals a colored map of the "United States and the British Provinces of North America." This map is the first geological map of the whole country from the Atlantic to the Pacific Oceans, and is the first map showing geology for the entire State of California. However, much of the geology depicted must have come from some psychic source, for at that time large areas of California were still totally unexplored. Marcou had been the geologist on Lt. Whipple's party of the 1853–54 Railroad Survey, which started in Arkansas, entered California at Needles, and terminated at Los Angeles. His observations along this 2,000 mile route, that approximately followed the 35th parallel, are represented on a geologic strip map and cross section—both remarkably well executed and representing some of the best geological work found in the volumes of Railroad

[1] According to Gudde (1960), the lake was discovered by Lt. Frémont and his skilled German topographer, Charles Preuss, in 1844, and first went by the name of "Mountain Lake." Later Frémont named it Lake Bonpland in honor of the French botanist who had accompanied Humboldt on his great journey to South America. In 1854 friends of the Governor of California succeeded in naming it Lake Bigler in his honor. However, during the Civil War, Bigler was an outspoken secessionist, and a movement was started to change the name of the lake to its Washoe Indian name, understood to be Tahoe—meaning "big water."

Reports. However, this would hardly have given him the information to interpret the geology of the whole State! Consequently, Blake (1856) strongly criticized Marcou's 1855 map and had this to say about the California portion:

> Commencing on the Pacific coast, the peninsula of San Francisco is represented as composed of erupted and metamorphic rocks, being colored the same as the Sierra Nevada and Appalachians. The rocks of that peninsula, and on both sides of the Golden Gate, are chiefly sandstone and shale, and the same formation extends along the shores of the Bay to and beyond San Jose. Not only the extent and position, but the lithological characters of these rocks are discussed in a published report (Williamson, R. S., 1855, Preliminary geological report on the Pacific Railroad Route, surveyed by Lieut R. S. Williamson in California: House Doc. 129, Washington, D. C.) which was in the hands of the author of the map previous to its publication. The representation of the granitic rocks is not confined to the end of the peninsula, but is continued southward to the western shores of the Tulare lakes where the formations are chiefly miocene tertiary, the eruptive rocks scarcely appearing.
>
> The promontory called Point Pinos, which forms the headland of the Bay of Monterey, is represented as tertiary, while a porphyritic granite constitutes the whole point and forms the coastline south to the Bay of San Carlos, and is probably continuous southward to San Luis Obispo; forming a high and unbroken line of coast, all of which is colored tertiary on the map. Casting the eye further south, we find the color denoting the eruptive and metamorphic rocks again usurping the place which should be colored tertiary, at Point Conception, which consists of beds of conglomerate and sandstone.
>
> The broad alluvial tract at the head of the Gulf of California—the Colorado desert—is made to extend nearly due north and parallel with the Colorado to the Soda Lake (near Baker, ed.). The published description of this valley gives its direction as northwest and southeast, extending to the foot of San Bernardine Mountain.

MAP OF THE COUNTRY WEST OF THE MISSISSIPPI RIVER—1857

The U. S.-Mexican Boundary Survey, conducted in 1855–56, under the direction of Major W. H. Emory, was for the primary purpose of "running and marking the boundary line under the Treaty of Guadalupe Hidalgo." It was also commissioned with the task of making "an examination of the country contiguous to the line to ascertain its practicability for a railroad route to the Pacific, as well as collect information in reference to the agricultural and mineral resources and such other subjects as would give a correct knowledge of the physical character of the country and its present occupants." Dr. C. C. Parry was the Survey's botanist and geologist, Arthur Schott his assistant.

The results of this survey were published in 1857, and were a significant contribution to the understanding of the geology of southernmost California. The report also included a very interesting hand-colored geological map of the Mississippi Valley and the country westward to the Pacific. This map was prepared by James Hall of New York, who acted as the Survey's geological consultant, and who also reported upon the fossils and rocks collected by the Survey. Hall's map was published at a scale of 1:6,000,000, and includes within its borders California and all of the western territories. It is of historical interest because it shows how little was definitely known about the geology of the region. The entire Sierra Nevada was shown as "Metamorphic," as well as was most of the Transverse and Peninsular Ranges. The bulk of the northern Coast Ranges is shown as "Lava and other igneous rocks" and an interesting "Desert Quaternary" unit is used to show areas in the Sacramento Valley, the northern coast, and an area along the coast near San Diego. Much of California is shown unmapped and that which is shown, is, we now know, mostly incorrect. The base map is also very crude—for example, hachures for the Sierra Nevada are not shown; Lake Tahoe (or Lac Bonpland) is missing; San Pedro is identified, whereas Los Angeles is not. It is difficult to understand why such an inferior base map was used, especially when a very excellent topographical map made by Major Emory of exactly the same territory and on the same scale was published in the same report!

FRANCE EXPLORES CALIFORNIA AND NEVADA—1867

The next geological map of California deserving of mention in this chronological description is a remarkable one, and possesses a very interesting history. This map, prepared by Edmond Guillemin-Tarayre in 1867 and published in Paris in 1871, is but one of 17 beautiful plates accompanying an obscure volume entitled "Description des anciennes possessions Mexicaines du nord, Mission Scientifique au Mexique et dane l'Amérique Central, Géologic." This publication apparently is Volume 2 of several volumes describing the geological, botanical, archeological, zoological, and linguistic researches of a French scientific mission to Mexico, California, and Nevada. The geology volume was the first to be published, and is confined to California and Nevada; however, it very strangely was left unfinished for the text stops abruptly after 216 pages, in the middle of a hyphenated word!

It is interesting to note that this geologic map and volume on geology are not listed in the earliest bibliographies of geologic maps of California. For example, they are not mentioned in Marcou's "Catalog of geological maps of America" (U.S. Geol. Survey Bull. No. 7) published in 1884, or Vodges' "Bibliography relating to the geology, paleontology, and mineral resources of California" (California State Mining Bur. Bull. No. 10) published in 1896. Although the U.S. Geological Survey's "Geologic literature on North America, 1785 to 1918", published in 1923, enters Guillemin's publications, and these are consequently picked up and relisted by later indexes, nothing could

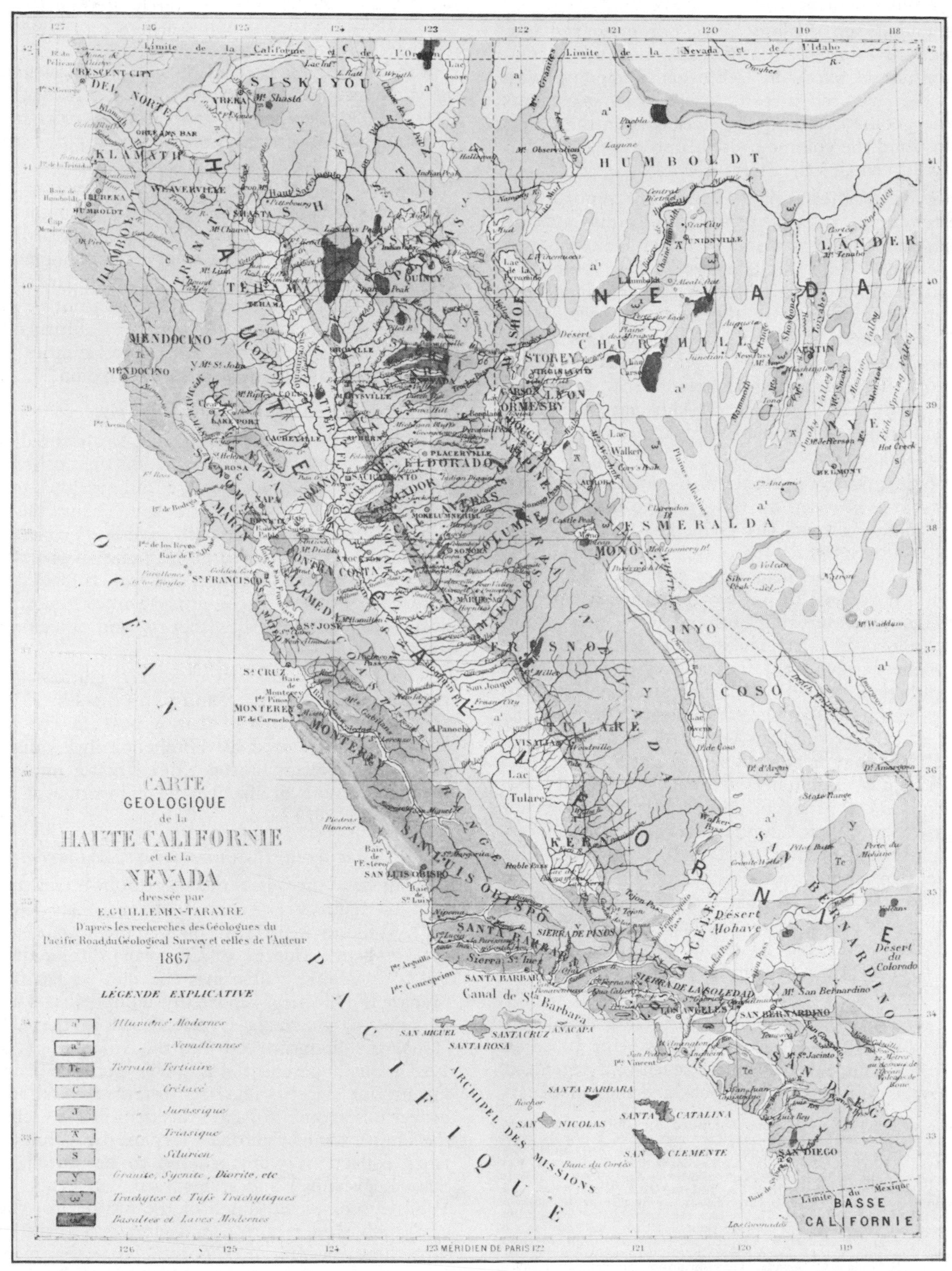

Figure 2. The first color-lithographed geologic map focusing on California (and part of Nevada), prepared by Edmond Guillemin-Tarayre in 1867. This remarkable map, published in Paris as part of the report of a French scientific mission to Mexico and the "ancient Mexican possessions of the north", has heretofore remained virtually unknown in American literature.

be found in the American literature about this geologist and this excellent scientific survey.[2]

The volume on geology (1871) is organized into two sections—the first on Nevada, and the second (and unfinished part) on California. Beginning with geographical data on these states, succeeding chapters treat the geology, mining districts, and metallurgical processes, and the volume ends abruptly in a discussion of the gold veins of the Sierra Nevada.

However, it is the plates which are probably of greatest interest to us—seven on California, nine on Nevada, and one of the southwestern United States. The California plates include two hand-colored geologic maps of parts of California (an area in central California, and an area in the southern part of the State), a colored lithographic geologic map, and a metallurgic map of California and Nevada, and four engravings. The engravings illustrate cross sections of Sierran gold mines, the New Almaden quicksilver mine, and mining equipment used in the recovery of gold and quicksilver.

A notation on the geologic map of California indicates that it was based on the geologic investigations of the Pacific Railroad, the Geological Survey (California's Whitney Survey), and the observations of the author (fig. 2). The map bears the date 1867. The geology is portrayed in a most impressive manner by ten geologic units utilizing both color lithography and letter symbols, the latter making it easier to correctly identify the various units, not always easy to do on early geologic maps. All of California is depicted by geologic map units, but the southeastern corner of the state is cut off by the map border. The base map on which the geology is plotted is very good for its time. It identifies a large number of towns, rivers, and lakes, and indicates the names of the counties but does not attempt to show their boundaries. The geologic interpretation is remarkably good. In most respects this geologic map is much more accurate than any of the maps presented prior to that time, and was not surpassed by any other geologic map of the State for several years following its publication. What a pity that such an informative map should have been buried for so long in an obscure foreign publication!

The accompanying "metallurgic" (sic) map bears the same date, 1867, and is credited as being based on the "latest documents." Using a seven-unit legend, it portrays the gold-, silver-, copper-, and mercury-bearing belts, the lignite basins, the bituminous shales, and mineral springs—a most remarkable attempt to emphasize and locate the economic geology of the State at such an early date!

The colored plate entitled "Geological sketch map of the metalliferous regions of California," scale 1:1,000,000, encompasses central California. It is interesting to note that the text states that this map has been constructed from the observations of Tyson, Trask, various members of the Geological Survey (California's Whitney Survey), and from the reconnaissance of the French scientific mission. Mr. Rémond of the California Geological Survey was singled out as a source of information on the boundaries of the Tertiary strata. This map stands in contrast to another plate, at the same scale, of southern California (Santa Barbara, Los Angeles, and San Diego Counties) which is referred to in the title as the "oil region."

NINTH CENSUS MAP—1872

In 1872, Charles H. Hitchcock, Professor of Geology at Dartmouth College, with the assistance of W. P. Blake, published a colored lithographed geologic map of the United States to accompany the Ninth U.S. Census report. The part covering California was compiled by Blake, based on his personal observations, the Pacific Railroad Reports and reports made for railroad corporations, the Whitney Survey reports, Clarence King's 40th Parallel Reports, and other unnamed sources.

This map was the first of several editions, another appearing the same year, and two others in 1874. The considerable differences that appear in the various editions are described by Hitchcock in his discussion of geological maps of the United States published in the Transactions of the American Institute of Mining Engineers (1887).

THE MISSING WHITNEY SURVEY MAP—1873?

A mystery surrounds the whereabouts of a geologic map of California prepared by the State Geologist J. D. Whitney in 1873. In his statement of progress of the Geological Survey of California during the years 1872–73, Whitney describes the map as having been prepared. This map, reportedly compiled at a scale of 36 miles to the inch, is referenced in the U.S.G.S. "Geologic literature on North America" (Nickles, 1923), but apparently was never published, and the manuscript map has not been found. Several attempts by various people to locate this map in the archives of the University of California (where the Whitney Survey's collections were ordered to be stored by the State Legislature) and at Harvard University (where Whitney completed much of the writing for the Survey's published reports), and elsewhere, have proved to be unsuccessful. It is possible that this map rests forgotten in a drawer or box, and hopefully, someday, someone will recognize this important map and announce its discovery.

[2] From two French publications, one published by Guillemin in 1869, "Exploration minéralogique des régiones mexicaines, suivie de notes archeologiques et ethnographiques," and the other, his obituary by P. Rivet (1920), we learn that Guillemin, a mining engineer, was a member of the scientific expedition to Mexico (including California and Nevada) from 1864 to 1866. Judging from these dates, and recalling the ill-fated French intervention in Mexico with Emperor Maximillian during 1863–1867, we can see the probable relationship between the French scientific expedition of which Guillemin was a part, and France's interest in the economic aspects of the Mexican region. Guillemin started his research in the very active mining districts of California and Nevada, later continuing his work in Mexico. His departure from Mexico in 1866 must have been premature and probably occurred as a result of the existing adverse political climate. Surely any Frenchman in Mexico at that time must have been considered *persona non grata*. By 1867 the French troops had withdrawn, and Maximillian was captured and executed.

Photo 1. An 1864 field party of the Whitney Survey. Left to right, James Gardner, mining engineer; Richard Cotter, packer; William Brewer, party chief; and Clarence King, geologist. *Courtesy U.S. Geological Survey.*

Although Whitney's geological map of California has vanished, his survey was nevertheless a milestone in the development of an understanding of the geology of the State. It produced a monumental amount of information, eventually published in 8 large volumes—2 on geology, 2 on paleontology, 2 on botany, 1 on fossil plants, and 1 on ornithology. In addition, work of the Survey resulted in the publication of a number of topographic maps, including the classic "Map of California and Nevada" (18 miles to the inch), a volume on the auriferous gravels of the Sierra Nevada, and several guidebooks to Yosemite. The "auriferous gravels" report, written by Whitney after his retirement and the abolishment of the California Geological Survey, was published by the Museum of Comparative Zoology at Harvard in 1880. It contains the only geologic maps by the California Geological Survey ever made public. It is interesting to note, however, that in 1877, the famous New York lithographer, Julius Bien, sought to have the California Legislature publish an atlas of Whitney's topographic and geologic maps, but the legislature turned a deaf ear to the appeal for funds and nothing came of the proposal (Wheat, 1963, p. 333).

The Whitney Survey faced enormous difficulties—both in the field and in the legislative halls of Sacramento. Although the act of 1860, naming Josiah Dwight Whitney as state geologist, directed him

> ". . . to make an accurate and complete Geological Survey of the State, and to furnish in his Report of the same, proper maps and diagrams thereof, with a full and scientific description of its rocks, fossils, soils, and minerals, and of its botanical and zoological productions,"

it seems that almost immediately Whitney ran into resistance in the legislature and had to spend an enormous amount of time defending his survey and fighting for appropriations to continue. The Survey lasted from 1860 until 1873. It included on its staff an impressive array of talent, including such men as William H. Brewer, Clarence King, Charles Hoffmann, William Gabb, James T. Gardner, James G. Cooper, and William Ashburner[3] (photo 1).

MARCOU'S MAP OF CALIFORNIA—1883

Following the Whitney Geological Survey, there was published in 1883, a geologic map of California by the remarkable and energetic Jules Marcou (fig. 3). This map, published in the Bulletin of the Geological Society of France, accompanied a report on the geology of California. The map incorporated the interesting dates 1854–75 in the title; however, it appears that these dates do not signify 22 years of work in California by the author, but refer instead to his association with the Pacific Railroad Survey in 1854 and with the Wheeler Survey West of the 100th Meridian in 1875. During the intervening years Marcou was out of the State, and for five of those years out of the country.

This page-size map, at a scale of 1:6,000,000, shows in colored lithography, nine geologic units for a large part of the state. As was typical of most of the geologic maps of the time, no letter symbols were utilized and recognition of the various units on the map is often very trying. One unit (Carboniferous) is difficult, if not impossible, to locate on the map. The distribution of volcanic rocks in the state is quite good for its time. The distribution of the granitic-metamorphic rocks ("Syenite et Roches metamorphiques") is fairly good in the Sierra Nevada and Transverse Ranges, but quite poor in the southern Coast Ranges. It is surprising that Marcou, a paleontologist, recognized Cretaceous rocks in only one small area (near Redding), while Guillemin (1871) recognized the extent of Cretaceous strata much more accurately.

It is interesting to note that the year following Marcou's 1883 publication, the U. S. Geological Survey, in its 5th Annual Report, published a "Map of the United States exhibiting the present status of knowledge relating to areal distribution of geologic groups" by W. J. McGee. This map, surprisingly enough, does not show any geology for California and the other western states, the Survey apparently preferring to ignore all earlier maps including Marcou's. This infuriated Marcou (1892), as indicated by his severe criticism of Mr. McGee, and indeed of the entire U. S. Geological Survey from Director Powell on down!

HITCHCOCK'S MAPS OF THE U.S.—1887

Charles H. Hitchcock again published a geologic map of the United States (including a part of Canada), which appeared together with his description of geological maps of the United States in the Transactions of the American Institute of Mining Engineers, 1887. This map was based upon the map by McGee, but most of the parts not colored on that map were filled in with data from other sources. Nearly all of California is colored on the map, with only a small blank area in the southeastern part of the state. The general distribution of the rocks as we know them today is quite good, although it is surprising that the Sierran and other granitic rocks are shown as Archean (no Mesozoic granitic rocks recognized in the legend!). The map was lithographed by Julius Bien of New York, and follows the colors adopted by the 3rd International Geological Congress of 1885. It is a very handsome geologic map and contains surprisingly abundant information on the geology of California.

[3] Brewer returned to Yale as Professor of Agriculture and played an important part in the development of soil science. King, who came to Whitney as a volunteer assistant, later organized and directed the 40th Parallel Survey, and, at the age of 37, became the first Director of the U. S. Geological Survey. Hoffmann may well be called the father of modern American topographic surveying having developed the methods used by the Federal survey. Gabb, paleontologist of the Survey, had helped lay the groundwork for the understanding of the Triassic, Cretaceous, and Tertiary of California, before dying at the age of 39. Gardner joined King in the Survey of the 40th Parallel and later was connected with the Hayden Surveys. Cooper, trained as a physician, became noted as a zoologist and paleontologist and published a number of papers including several on Cretaceous and Tertiary fossils. Ashburner, after leaving the Whitney Survey, practiced as a mining engineer and became a regent of the University of California and a trustee of Stanford University.

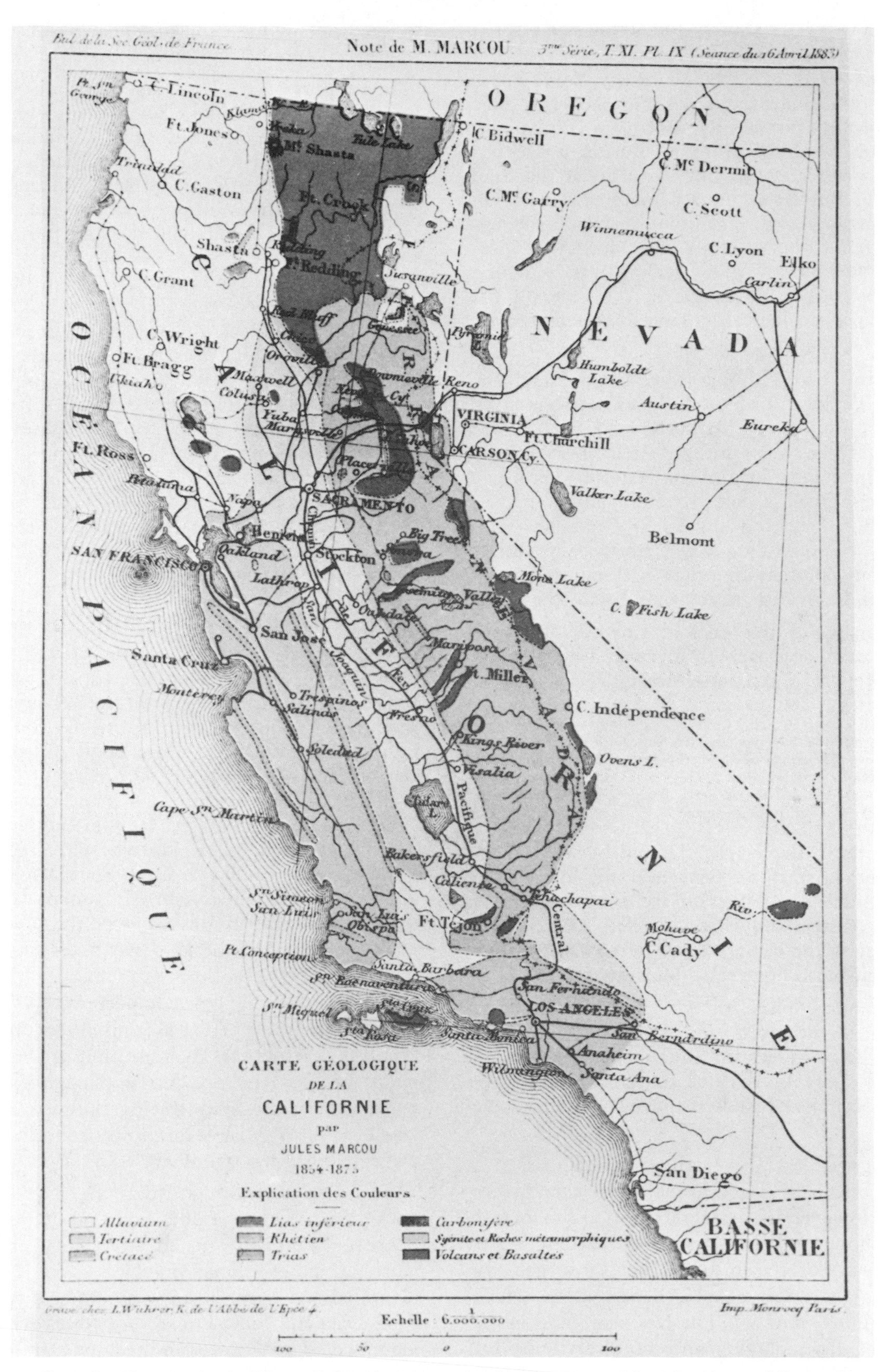

Figure 3. The second color-lithographed geologic map of California. Prepared by Jules Marcou following his explorations in California in 1854 and 1875, this map was published in the Bulletin of the Geological Society of France in 1883.

FIRST LARGE-SCALE STATEWIDE GEOLOGIC MAP OF CALIFORNIA—1891

In 1880, six years after the Whitney Survey was discontinued, the State again felt the need for some formal organization to provide information on its mineral wealth; thus the State Mining Bureau was established. Care was taken this time to place at the head of the Mining Bureau a "State Mineralogist," not an "academic" geologist or paleontologist, which the legislature had felt to be so impractical during the preceding Whitney Survey! This feeling was so strong that not until 1961 was the title of the Chief of the State's principal geological organization changed to that of State Geologist.

In 1891, the State Mining Bureau published the largest scale geologic map of California prepared to that time. This map, on the scale of 1:750,000 (12 miles to the inch), was entitled "Preliminary mineralogical and geological map of the State of California" and was lithographed in color by the well-known San Francisco firm of Britton and Rey.[4] Beginning with this map, the responsibility of preparing and publishing succeeding editions of large-scale statewide geologic maps of California has remained with the State.

The authorship of this geologic map is quite obscure; the closest approach to a credit line is found in the 10th Report of the State Mineralogist where on page 21 it states:

> H. I. Willey, ex-State Surveyor-General, was engineer in charge of the Preliminary Geological and Mineralogical Map, the topographical and other work thereon being executed by Mr. Julius Henkenius, who received aid in the geological and mineralogical locatings (sic) from the Field Assistants.[5]

On the map itself, the words "Drawn by J. C. Henkenius" appear in small lettering near the lower edge of the map, while the names of the five members of the board of trustees and William Irelan, State Mineralogist, appear in the elaborate title of the map drawn in a large hand with numerous flourishes.

The economic emphasis of this map is quite apparent, not only in the word "mineralogical" in its title but by the choice of certain units in the legend such as Auriferous gravels, Auriferous slates, and Limestone. The locations of known mineral deposits were also plotted.

The geology appears very crude, especially as it is plotted on a much larger scale map than ever before attempted. However, the general relationship of the eight units shown is better than on preceding maps. The compiler(s) of this map did not show geology for those regions poorly explored and about which little was definitely known. The base map used in the preparation of this geologic map is noteworthy in that it was presented as "the first map replete in topography ever made of California."

In a report on the "Springs of California" published by the U.S. Geological Survey in 1915, there is a "Lithologic map of California" compiled by G. A. Waring. Though not issued as a state geologic map, this small scale map (1:2,000,000), utilizing five cartographic units, showed the distribution of the principal geologic groups throughout the state more completely than any map to that date. The map notes that the rock distribution shown was compiled from published and unpublished data of the U.S. Geological Survey, and from the 1891 Geologic map of California published by the State Mining Bureau. An accompanying map on the same scale shows the locations of springs and faults. The faults are reported as taken from the atlas accompanying the report of the State Earthquake Investigation Commission (Lawson and others, 1908), This 1908 fault map is probably the first published map of the state to show faults. Faults were not depicted on any of the earlier described state geologic maps, nor on the succeeding geologic map of California published in 1916.

RECONNAISANCE GEOLOGIC MAP OF CALIFORNIA—1916

Twenty-five years after the 1891 "Preliminary mineralogical and geological map of the State of California," the next edition of the geological map was published. The preparation of this map had been commissioned by the State Mineralogist, Fletcher Hamilton, to James Perrin Smith, Professor of Paleontology at Stanford University. This map was published in 1916, together with a brief bulletin entitled "The geologic formations of California with reconnaissance geologic map" (Bull. 72, Calif. State Mining Bureau). This interesting bulletin briefly summarized the geologic mapping accomplished since the preceding 1891 map, and described the 1916 map as essentially a report of progress. The author states that . . . "he is well aware that there are many imperfections. Certain areas have not been mapped at all, and others only in a general way." However, an inspection of the map shows color and contacts have been applied uniformly to the entire area of the State leaving the map user without any clue as to what was known and what had been projected into the unknown.

The map legend consisted of 21 geologic units, with the Mother Lode and oil fields especially delineated—probably in an attempt to give the map more of an economic emphasis. The 21 units are identified and organized by age and, in addition, the Franciscan and Santa Lucia Formations are specifically identified. The Franciscan is shown as Jurassic and separated from other rocks of Jurassic age. The Jurassic designation was in contrast to the previously accepted Cretaceous assignment by Whitney, Becker.

[4] Many of the most important early maps and views of San Francisco and California were published by this firm.

[5] H. W. Fairbanks, W. A. Goodyear, and W. L. Watts were among the "assistants"; thus, very able men contributed to the making of this map.

and Lawson. This was in keeping with the then current views of H. W. Fairbanks (1898) and the descriptions of fossils at Slate's Springs in the Santa Lucia Mountains by C. H. Davis (1913). Later work clearly established the fossils as Late Cretaceous, and as a result the strata at Slate's Springs were excluded from the Franciscan Formation by N. L. Taliaferro (1943) who assiduously adhered to a Jurassic age assignment for the Franciscan.

The progress portrayed on the 1916 map was largely a result of the monumental work done by the U.S. Geological Survey in the Sierra Nevada, the Coast Ranges, and the oil regions. Such illustrious Survey geologists as W. H. Turner, Waldemar Lindgren, J. S. Diller, and F. L. Ransome became synonymous with the Gold Belt studies, and H. W. Fairbanks, Ralph Arnold, H. R. Johnson, Robert Anderson, and R. W. Pack became the leading authorities on the Coast Ranges and oil areas. Additionally, many significant contributions were made by Professor A. C. Lawson and graduate students at the University of California, and by Professor J. C. Branner and his students at Stanford University.

FAULT MAP OF CALIFORNIA—1923

Although not a geologic map in the usual sense, it would seem appropriate to mention here the relatively large-scale (1:500,000) "Fault map of California," prepared by Bailey Willis and H. O. Wood and published by the Seismological Society of America in 1923. This map, in the words of Willis, was . . ."designed to show the lines on which earthquakes may occur and which, therefore, should be avoided by structures liable to damage by earthquakes." On it, Willis attempted to differentiate active faults from "probably active faults" and "dead faults". However, the criteria used differed significantly in the northern and central California map area compiled by Willis, from those of the southern California area, compiled by Wood. Wood considered as active faults those on which there had been some movement within historic time, or upon which recent surface dislocation could be found. Willis, on the other hand, associated faults with the growth of mountains and considered that "any fault related to a growing mountain is reasonably subject to the suspicion of being an active fault in the sense that a slip may occur." Unfortunately, many mountains in northern California were interpreted on physiographic evidence alone as being bounded by faults. Nevertheless, it remained as the largest scale map of the entire State showing faults until the next geologic map of California was published by the State Division of Mines in 1938.

O. P. JENKINS GEOLOGIC MAP OF CALIFORNIA—1938

The 1:500,000-scale geologic map of California, published in 1938, represented 9 years of careful coordination of geological research by Olaf P. Jenkins, then Chief Geologist of the Division of Mines. Being of much larger scale than any previous geologic map of the State, considerably more detail was shown, and the geologic boundaries were drawn with much greater precision, care being taken to follow the source data accurately. Unlike many of the earlier maps, blank places were left for areas which had not been mapped adequately, and little attempt was made at predicting or at conjuring what the geology might be. The largest blank areas of the map appeared in the northwestern part of the State—in the Northern Coast Ranges and the Klamath Mountains. Large unmapped areas also were left in the southern Sierra Nevada and in the desert areas of southeastern California. For the first time, faults were depicted together with the areal distribution of rocks on a map of the entire State.

When work on preparing this new geologic map of California was started in 1929, the U.S. Geological Survey desired to cooperate, since it had undertaken the task of making a new geologic map of the United States. The Survey prepared a map of California under the direction of George W. Stose in Washington, D.C., who used data from all available sources, including those gathered by Jenkins in San Francisco and sent to Washington. The correlation and adjustment of the map units of the various authors, and the assembling of a comprehensive legend for the State map were done by Stose with the cooperation of Jenkins at the scale of 1:500,000. The resulting Stose-Jenkins map, however, was not published on its original scale, but was incorporated in the geologic map of the United States, published in 1932, in somewhat generalized form for this much smaller scale (1:2,500,000).

Subsequently, as much new geologic information was obtained, new thoughts developed concerning the preparation of a 1:500,000-scale geologic map, and it was decided to completely recompile the map. An appropriation was obtained from the Federal Public Works Administration, for assisting technical projects during the depression period of the 1930's, and from this fund came salaries for two additional geologists to work on the map under the direction of the California Division of Mines. E. Wayne Galliher was assigned the task of compiling the complex geology of the Coast Ranges and also contributed some field work. Burt Beverly was responsible for most of the photographic reduction, the transcribing, and drafting of the final map.

Eighty-one different cartographic units were employed on the Jenkins 1938 map. Marine rocks were distinguished from continental beds, and the rocks were classified into periods of the Paleozoic and Mesozoic, and into periods and epochs of the Cenozoic. In addition, the Franciscan and Knoxville were treated separately because so much of the Coast Ranges is comprised of rocks of these formations.

NEW GEOLOGIC ATLAS OF CALIFORNIA

The California Division of Mines and Geology is now engaged in preparing and publishing the fourth large-scale geologic map of the entire State. This map, taking the form of an atlas, will consist of 27 map sheets, each at a scale of 1:250,000. One hundred and twenty-four cartographic units are being used. The preparation of uncolored maps on this scale began in 1952, and the first sheet, lithographed in color, was published in 1958. By late 1965 more than two-thirds of the sheets had been printed and were being widely used.

The Geologic Atlas of California presents the results of more than 140 years of geologic mapping in the State, starting from the geologic sketch map of San Francisco Bay area by Lt. Belcher, prepared in 1826. Today, very few completely unmapped areas remain, even though several large areas have been mapped only in a reconnaissance fashion. We are, therefore, just beginning to understand the areal distribution of the rock types in California. We know even less about the gross structure of the State, although we now have a much better understanding of the major fault patterns. Nevertheless, much of this knowledge has been gained only very recently and much still remains to be done.

Hence, no State geologic map can endure as a final and finished product. Each edition essentially represents a progress report. At the same time that we carefully map the unexplored or reconnaissanced areas, other areas are being studied in greater detail and mapped on larger and still larger scales to satisfy special needs. With the increasing wealth of new information, we recognize that our current State map series will soon require revision. With this revision in details will come a better understanding of the broad geologic framework and more accurate answers concerning the forces which are responsible for the development of geologic structures, as well as some of the answers to mysteries of ore deposition and control. Therefore, the work of preparing more accurate geologic maps has continued and will continue as long as we search for a better understanding of the environment in which we live.

REFERENCES

Anderson, F. M., 1933, Pioneers in the geology of California, *in* Shedd, Solon, Bibliography of the geology and mineral resources of California to December 31, 1930: California Div. Mines Bull. 104, p. 1–24.

Blake, W. P., 1856, Review of a portion of the geological map of the United States and British Provinces by Jules Marcou: Am. Jour. Sci., 2d ser., v. 22, no. 66, p. 383–388.

—— 1857, Geological report, *in* Williamson, R. S., Report on exploration for railroad route from Mississippi River to Pacific Ocean in 1853: U.S. Pacific R.R. Explor. (U.S., 33d Cong., 2d sess., Sen. Ex. Doc. 78 and H. Ex. Doc. 91), v. 5, pt. 2, 310 p.

Buckland, W., 1839, Geology, *in* The zoology of Captain Beechey's voyage: London, Henry G. Bohn, p. 157–180.

Davis, C. H., 1913, New species from the Santa Lucia Mountains, California, with a discussion of the Jurassic age of the slates at Slate Springs: Jour. Geology, v. 21, p. 453–458.

Emory, W. H., 1857, Report on the United States and Mexican boundary survey * * * : U.S. 34th Cong., 1st sess., Sen. Ex. Doc. 108 and H. Ex. Doc. 135, 258, 174 p.

Fairbanks, H. W., 1898, Geology of a portion of the southern Coast Ranges: Jour. Geology, v. 6, no. 6, p. 551–576.

Gudde, E. G., 1960, California place names; the origin and etymology of current geographical names, 2d ed.: California Univ. Press, Berkeley, 383 p.

Guillemin-Tarayre, Edmond, 1869, Exploration minéralogique des régiones mexicaines, suivie de notes archeologiques et ethnographiques: Paris, Imprimerie Impériale.

—— 1871, Description des anciennes possessions mexicaines du nord: Paris, France, Mission Sci. au Mexique et dans l'Amérique Centrale, Géologie, pt. 2, 216 p.

Hitchcock, C. H., 1872, Description of the geological map [of the United States]: U.S. Ninth Census, v. 3, p. 754–756.

—— 1887, The geological map of the United States and part of Canada 1886, *in* The geological map of the United States: Am. Inst. Mining Engineers Trans., v. 15, p. 465–488.

Lawson, A. C., and others, 1908, The California earthquake of April 18, 1906—report of the State Earthquake Investigation Commission: Carnegie Inst. Washington Pub. 87, Atlas, 25 maps and seismograms.

Marcou, Jules, 1855, Résumé explicatif d'une carte géologique des États-Unis et des provinces anglaises de l'Amérique du Nord, avec un profil géologique allant de la vallée du Mississippi aux côtes du Pacifique, et un planche de fossiles: Soc. Géol. France Bull., 2d ser., v. 12, p. 813–936.

—— 1855, Ueber die Geologische der Vereinigten Staaten und der Englischen Provinzen von Nord-Amerika: Petermann's Mitt., v. 1, p. 149–159.

—— 1883, Note sur la géologie de la Californie: Soc. Géol. France Bull., 3d ser., v. 11, p. 407–435.

—— 1892, The geological map of the United States and the United States Geological Survey: Cambridge, Mass., 56 p.

Marcou, Jules, and Marcou, J. B., 1884, Mapoteca geologica americana, a catalogue of geological maps of America (North and South), 1752–1881: U.S. Geol. Survey Bull. 7, 184 p.

Merrill, G. P., 1906, Contributions to the history of American geology: U.S. Natl. Mus. Ann. Rept. 1904, p. 189–733.

Nickles, J. M., 1923, Geologic literature on North America, 1785–1918: U.S. Geol. Survey Bull. 746, 1167 p.

Rivet, P., 1920, Edmond Guillemin-Tarayre (nécrologie): Jour. Soc. Americanistes, n.s., v. 12, p. 236–238.

Smith, J. P., 1916, The geologic formations of California with reconnaissance geologic map: California State Mining Bur. Bull. 72, 47 p.

Taliaferro, N. L., 1943, Franciscan-Knoxville problem: Am. Assoc. Petroleum Geologists Bull., v. 27, no. 2, p. 109–219.

Tyson, P. T., 1850, * * * information in relation to the geology and topography of California: U.S. 31st Cong., 1st sess., Sen. Ex. Doc. 47, p. 1–74, map and sections.

—— 1851, Geology and industrial resources of California: Baltimore, Md., 127, 37 p.

VanderHoof, V. L., 1954, History of geologic investigation in the bay region, *in* Geologic guidebook of the San Francisco Bay counties: California Div. Mines Bull. 154, p. 109–116.

Vodges, A. W., 1896, A bibliography relating to the geology, paleontology, and mineral resources of California: California Mining Bur. Bull. 10, 121 p.

Waring, G. A., 1915, Springs of California: U.S. Geol. Survey Water-Supply Paper 338, 410 p.

Wheat, C. I., 1963, Mapping the transmississippi West: San Francisco, Inst. Hist. Cartography, v. 5, pt. 2.

Whitney, J. D., 1873, Statement of the progress of the geological survey of California during the years 1872–3: [Sacramento], 14 p.

—— 1880, The auriferous gravels of the Sierra Nevada of California: Harvard Coll. Mus. Comp. Zoology, Mem. 6, no. 1, 659 p.

Willis, Bailey, 1923, A fault map of California: Seismol. Soc. America Bull., v. 13, no. 1, p. 1–12.

CHAPTER II
KLAMATH MOUNTAINS PROVINCE

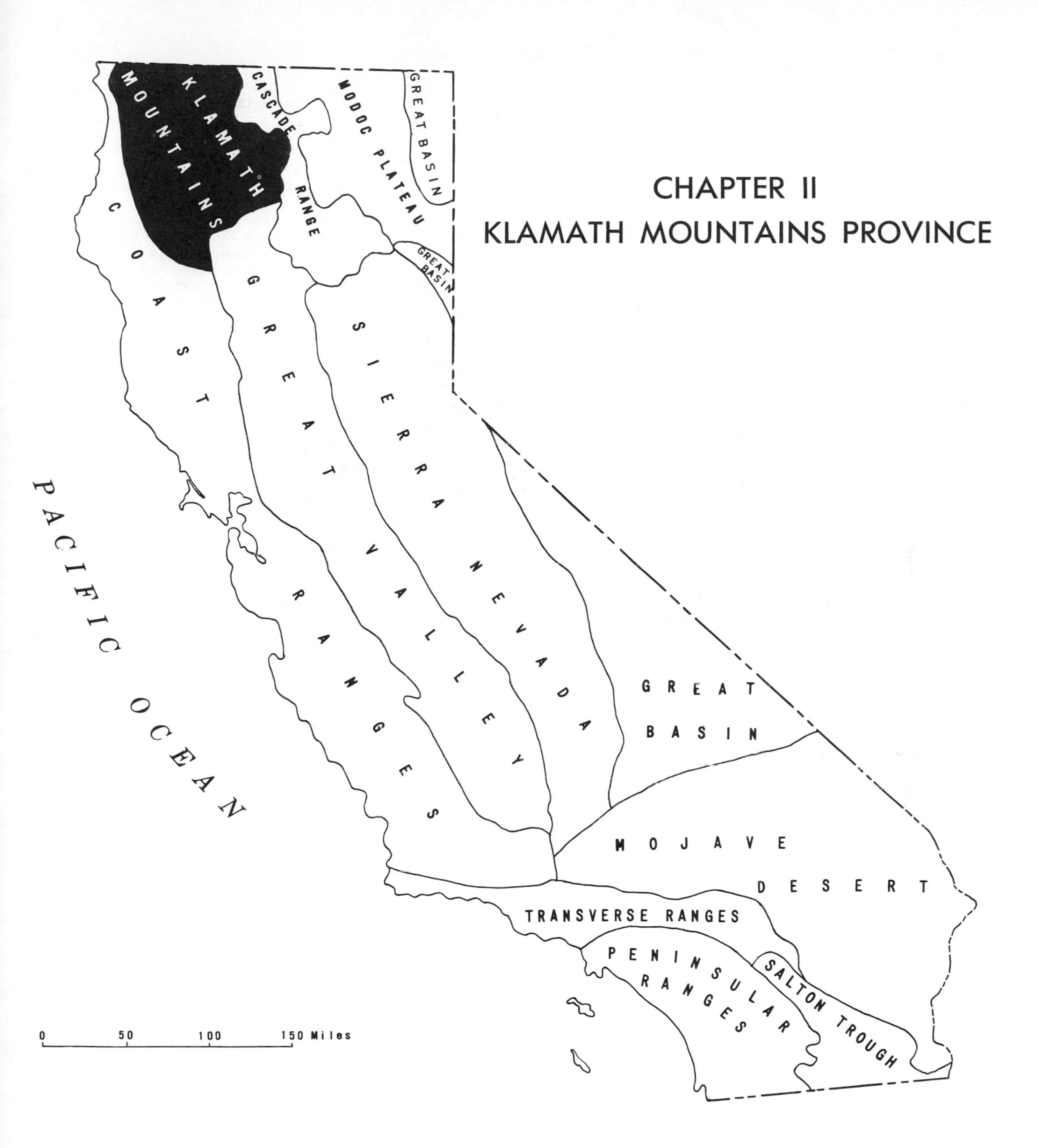

Page

GEOLOGY OF THE KLAMATH MOUNTAINS PROVINCE *

By William P. Irwin
U.S. Geological Survey, Menlo Park, California

The Klamath Mountains geologic province covers an elongate north-trending area of approximately 11,800 square miles in northwestern California and southwestern Oregon. This article, however, deals chiefly with the part that lies in California. The province embraces many individual mountain ranges, among which in California are the Trinity, South Fork, Salmon, Trinity Alps, Scott, Scott Bar, and Marble Mountains. The Siskiyou Mountains occupy a large area on both sides of the boundary between California and Oregon. Northward from the Siskiyou Mountains the terrane becomes increasingly subdued and individual ranges less distinct.

Accordant summit levels and highly dissected oldland surfaces are striking features of many of the ranges in the Klamath Mountains. The crestlines generally reach altitudes between 5,000 and 7,000 feet, and locally culminate in peaks as high as 9,000 feet above sea level. Features indicating former glaciation are seen along many of the crests, but the glaciers themselves are now virtually extinct.

The slopes of most of the ranges are heavily timbered with fir and pine, particularly in the western part of the province. The thick forest cover is due largely to a heavy rainfall that occurs mostly during the winter months. Most of the rainfall drains westward to the ocean through deep canyons of the Klamath and Trinity Rivers in California and the Rogue River and its tributaries in Oregon. The drainage is transverse to the lithic and structural grain of the province. The easternmost part of the area in California is drained to the south by the Sacramento River.

The Klamath Mountains lie generally between U.S. Highway 101 on the west and U.S. 99 on the east, except where U.S. 99 diagonally crosses the province in Oregon. Roads crossing the province from west to east, connecting U.S. 101 to U.S. 99, are U.S. 199 from Crescent City to Grants Pass, U.S. 299 from Arcata to Redding, and California Route 36 from near Fortuna to Red Bluff. California Route 96 is the principal access to much of the area that lies between U.S. 199 and U.S. 299.

The province is thinly populated, the largest towns being Roseburg (pop. 11,467) and Grants Pass (pop. 10,118) in Oregon. Larger centers of population nearby include Medford, Ore., and Redding, Calif., on the east, and Eureka, Calif., on the west. Settlement of the area began with the discovery of gold in the southern part of the province in 1848. Production of gold and other metalliferous commodities was the chief industry until the early 1900's. Lumbering is now the principal industry.

Many geologists have contributed to our knowledge of the stratigraphy and structure of the Klamath Mountains, but space limitations do not allow mention of all of them. Of the early work, the contributions of J. S. Diller of the U.S. Geological Survey have had the most profound and lasting influence. During the late 1800's and early 1900's, Diller mapped several 30-minute quadrangles in Oregon and California, of which the most important is perhaps the Redding quadrangle. His stratigraphic column of the Redding area has well withstood the test of time, having required only minor modification in later years. During the early 1900's, O. H. Hershey examined mines and prospected in the area, and his talent for understanding regional geologic relations led to important contributions. Much of the eastern part of the Klamath Mountains in California was mapped in reconnaissance by geologists of the Southern Pacific Railroad during the early 1900's and again in the 1950's.

Much of the early work, particularly that of Hershey, suffered from the lack of adequate base maps. All of the area is now covered by modern topographic maps at a scale of 1:62,500. During the 1930's and 1940's, several 30-minute and 15-minute quadrangles, mostly in Oregon, were mapped by the U.S. Geological Survey. This work was done chiefly under the direction of F. G. Wells, who was assisted notably by P. E. Hotz, G. W. Walker, H. L. James, and F. W. Cater, among others. Refinements in the Paleozoic and lower Mesozoic part of Diller's stratigraphic column were made in the Shasta district near Redding by A. R. Kinkel, Jr., W. E. Hall, J. P. Albers, and J. F. Robertson of the U.S. Geological Survey during the late 1940's and early 1950's. Farther east, the Upper Mesozoic part of Diller's stratigraphic column was modified by A. F. Sanborn of Stanford University. Reconnaissance mapping of the hitherto unmapped parts of the Klamath Mountains in California, chiefly the western part, was done by W. P. Irwin and D. B. Tatlock during the middle 1950's. During the late 1950's the work begun by the U.S. Geological Survey in the Shasta district was extended to the west by Albers in the French Gulch quadrangle, and still

* Publication authorized by the Director, U.S. Geological Survey.

farther west by Irwin in the Weaverville quadrangle. Adjacent areas along a belt of metamorphic rocks in the central Klamath Mountains were studied for Ph.D. theses by D. P. Cox and P. W. Lipman of Stanford University, and by G. A. Davis, M. J. Holdaway, and W. D. Romey of the University of California at Berkeley. Other studies as Ph.D. theses at Stanford University include those by W. P. Pratt and C. K. Seyfert, Jr., in the central part of the province, and by M. C. Blake, Jr., along the southern boundary of the province.

The principal rocks of the Klamath Mountains are eugeosynclinal and plutonic rocks that were involved in the Nevadan (Late Jurassic) orogeny. For purpose of discussion they are distinguished from younger rocks by use of the term "subjacent." Rocks younger than the Nevadan orogeny surround the Klamath Mountains and occur within the province as small patches at a few places. They were deposited on the subjacent rocks with great unconformity, and are referred to by use of the term "superjacent."

Figure 1. Map of northwestern California showing outline of Klamath Mountains province, major drainage, towns and routes of travel.

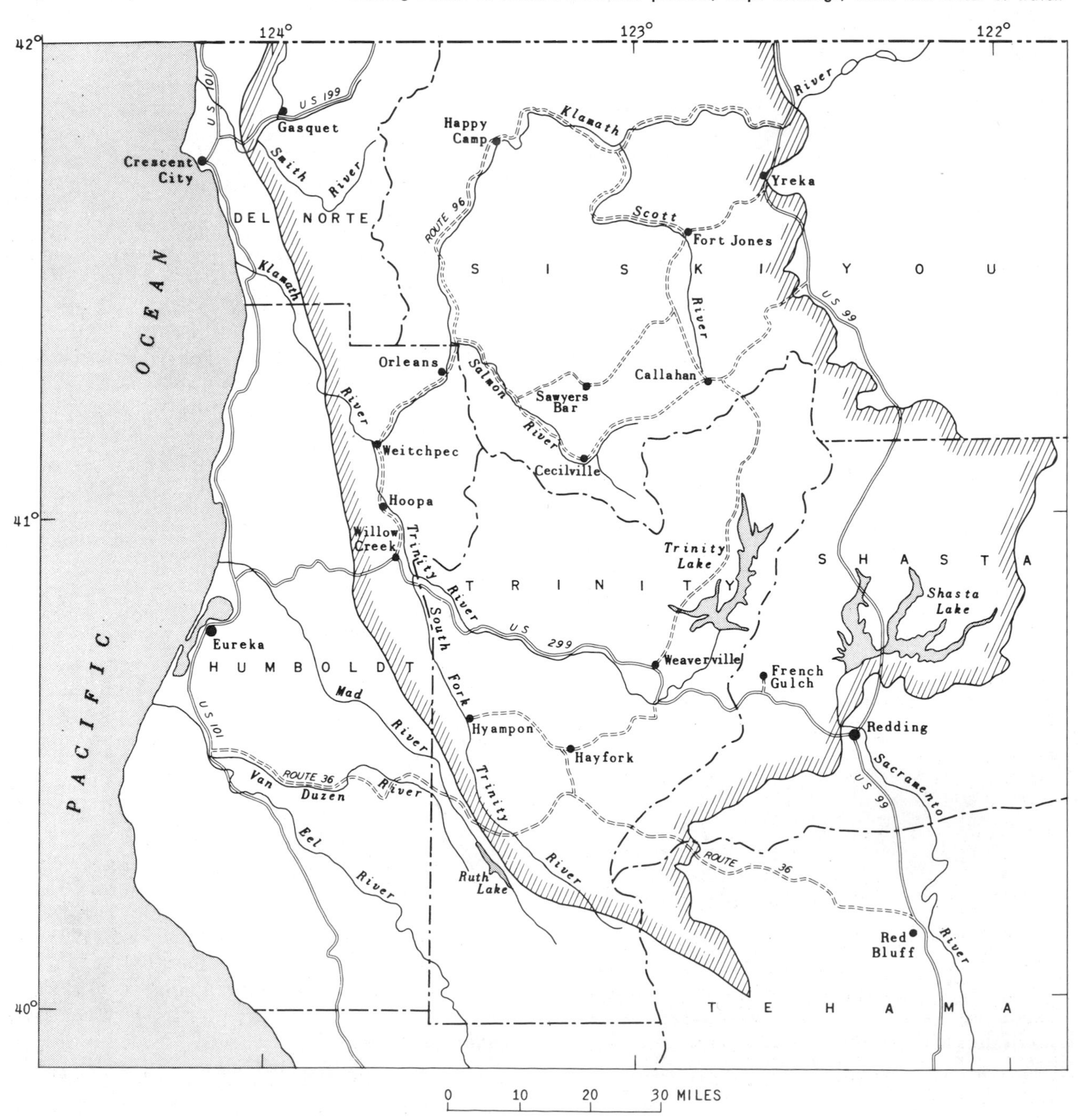

SUBJACENT ROCKS

The subjacent eugeosynclinal rocks range from Ordovician to Late Jurassic (Kimmeridgian) in age. They consist of graywacke sandstones, mudstones, greenstones, radiolarian cherts, and relatively minor limestone, as well as metamorphic equivalents of the foregoing rock types and abundant granitic and ultramafic intrusives. Their pattern of distribution is one of concentric, rudely arcuate belts, which from east to west are referred to as the eastern Klamath,[1] central metamorphic, western Paleozoic and Triassic, and western Jurassic belts (fig. 2). In all the belts except the eastern Klamath, a few outliers of rocks of adjacent belts are found. The arcuate pattern of lithic belts is emphasized by linear bodies of ultramafic rock that tend to be concentrated along boundaries between the belts. Some bodies of granitic rock also are linear, and conform to the arcuate pattern.

Eastern Klamath Belt

The gross aspect of the eastern Klamath belt is that of an eastward-dipping, essentially homoclinal sequence that to the west is deformed and terminated against ultramafic rocks. The strata of the belt constitute, in the aggregate, a column 40,000 to 50,000 feet thick, and represent the time from Ordovician to Jurassic (fig. 3). Those of Ordovician and Silurian age are exposed only in an isolated northern part of the belt (fig. 2). Probable extensions of the belt, northeast into Oregon and southeast toward the Sierra Nevada, are concealed by a mantle of superjacent rocks.

Central Metamorphic Belt

The central metamorphic belt consists chiefly of the Salmon Hornblende Schist and Abrams Mica Schist.[2] Inasmuch as the rocks of the central metamorphic belt are described in detail in the next article of this volume, only the gross features will be given here.

The rocks of the central metamorphic belt are generally separated from those of the eastern Klamath belt by ultramafic rocks, and are in fault contact along the western border with rocks of the western Paleozoic and Triassic belt. Windows in the Salmon expose the Stuart Fork Formation (Davis and Lipman, 1962). A few small outliers of Bragdon Formation of the eastern Klamath belt occur within the southern part of the metamorphic terrane and are separated from the metamorphic rocks either by ultramafic rocks or by faults. The metamorphic rocks are intruded by abundant granitic rocks of Jurassic age. At the southern end of the belt, the metamorphic rocks are overlain with great unconformity by Cretaceous superjacent rocks.

The age of the rocks of the central metamorphic belt is problematic. The stratigraphic relations between the schists and the rocks of known age in adjacent belts are not known, nor is debris from the metamorphic terrane known to be present in any of the other subjacent formations. Isotopic ages ranging from 270 ± 10 m.y. to 329 ± 13 m.y., obtained on hornblende from the Salmon and on muscovite from the Abrams, indicate a Carboniferous age of metamorphism, and it has been suggested that these schists may be metamorphic equivalents of Carboniferous or older strata of the eastern Klamath belt (Lanphere and Irwin, 1965). Metamorphism accompanying the tectonic development of the arcuate belt seems a more likely hypothesis than the uplifting and refolding of an ancient metamorphic terrane that existed prior to deposition of the oldest strata of the eastern Klamath belt.

Western Paleozoic and Triassic Belt

The western Paleozoic and Triassic belt is a structurally complex eugeosynclinal terrane. It consists mainly of phyllitic detrital rocks, rhythmically thin-bedded radiolarian chert, mafic volcanic rocks, and lenses of coarsely crystalline limestone. These rocks are abundantly intruded by ultramafic and granitic rocks. The interlayered rocks generally are metamorphosed to a grade low in the greenschist facies, but in some large areas, such as in Scott Bar quadrangle (Pratt, 1964), and parts of Condrey Mountain (P. E. Hotz, oral communication, 1965) and Sawyers Bar quadrangles (Seyfert, 1964), grades as high as amphibolite facies are attained. A large area of schists in the Condrey Mountain and Seiad Valley quadrangles previously were shown (Irwin, 1960) as an outlier of the central metamorphic belt, but these schists are now thought most likely to be metamorphic equivalents of rocks of the western Paleozoic and Triassic belt (P. E. Hotz, oral communication, 1965) with which they are included in figure 12.

Remarkably few fossil localities are known in the western Paleozoic and Triassic belt. Fossils in limestone lenses at sparsely scattered localities were collected during the early days of reconnaissance, chiefly by Diller. In general, these were considered Devonian along the western side of the belt and Carboniferous along the eastern side (Diller, 1903b). However, most of these fossils were later found to be either of indeterminate age or of an age greatly different from that originally assigned (Wells, Hotz, and Cater, 1949; Merriam, 1961; Silberling and Irwin, 1962). Few localities of fossils now considered of determinate age are known. Several limestone lenses within a few miles of the eastern boundary along the southern part of the belt contain fusulinids of Late Pennsylvania(?) and Early Permian ages (Irwin, 1960, p. 26; 1963). An ammonite collected from limestone in the southeastern part of the belt is considered middle or Late Permian in age (Miller, Furnish, and Clark, 1957,

[1] The name "eastern Klamath belt" supersedes the name "eastern Paleozoic belt" (Irwin, 1960), and refers to all the Paleozoic and subjacent Mesozoic strata of the Klamath Mountains east of the central metamorphic belt.

[2] The name Abrams Mica Schist as used herein is restricted to dominantly micaceous schists that are coextensive with the Salmon Hornblende Schist and that have shared a similar metamorphic and tectonic history with the Salmon. It differs from the original Abrams Mica Schist of Hershey (1901) by exclusion of rocks named the Stuart Fork Formation by Davis and Lipman (1962).

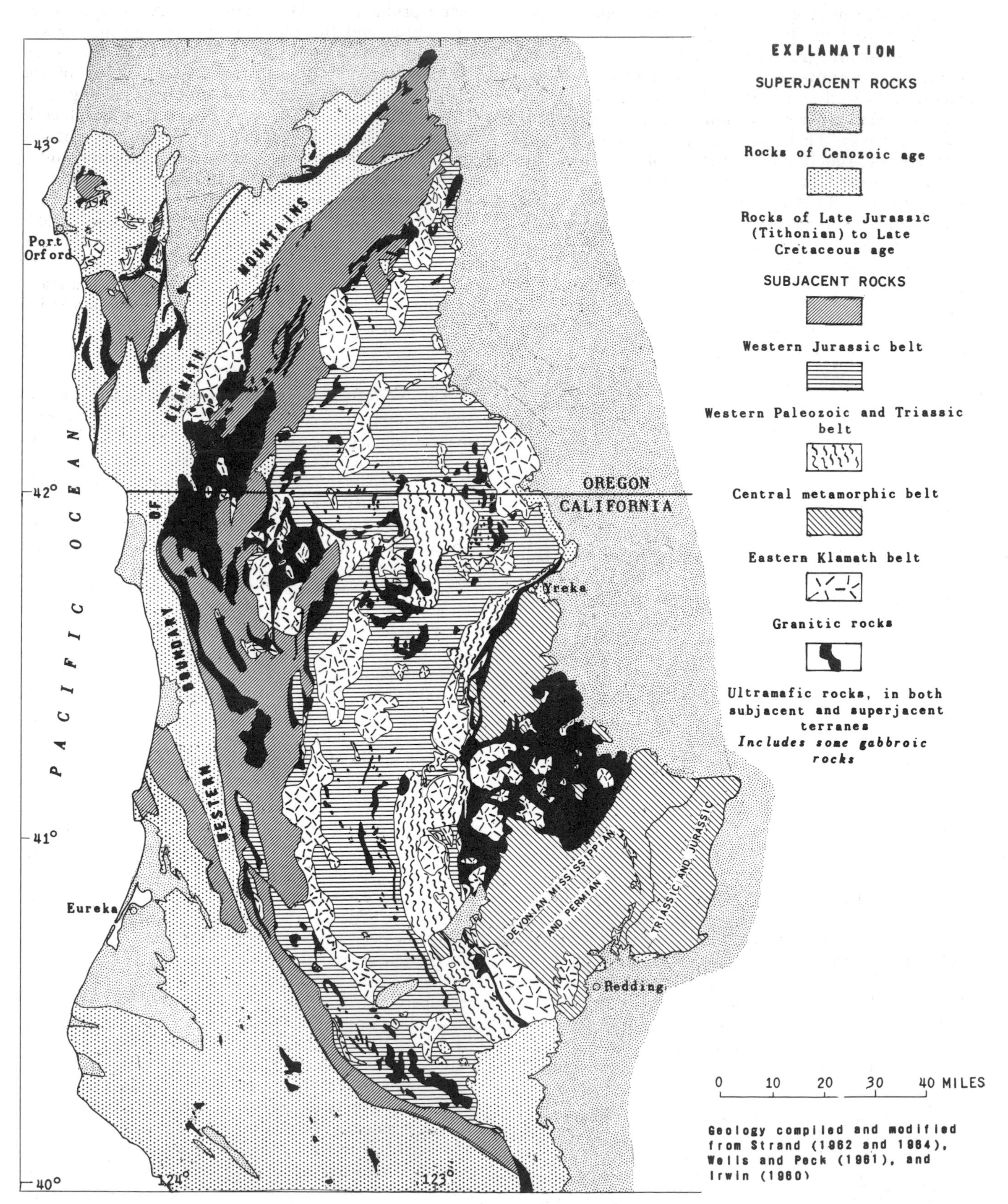

Figure 2. Geologic map of northwestern California and southwestern Oregon.

Figure 3. Stratigraphic column of subjacent formations of the eastern Klamath Mountains, California.

Age	Formation	Thickness in feet	General features	References
Jurassic	Potem Formation	1,000	Argillite and tuffaceous sandstones, with minor beds of conglomerate, pyroclastics, and limestone. Lower beds are probably Early Jurassic. Upper beds are Middle Jurassic (Bajocian). Upper limit not exposed. Overlain by post-Jurassic rocks with great unconformity.	Diller (1906) Sanborn (1960)
	Bagley Andesite	700	Andesitic flows and pyroclastics. Overlies and interfingers with lower part of Potem Formation according to Sanborn.	Diller (1906) Sanborn (1953, 1960)
	Arvison Formation of Sanborn (1953)	5,090	Interbedded volcanic breccia, conglomerate, tuff, and minor andesitic lava flows. Fossil fragments in many tuff and sandstone beds. Ammonites indicate Early Jurassic (Sinemurian) age. Probably gradational contact with Potem Formation.	Sanborn (1960)
Triassic	Modin Formation	5,500	Basal member of volcanic conglomerate, breccia, tuff, and porphyry, with limestone fragments from the Hosselkus. Middle member is massive fossiliferous limestones and calcareous sandstones. Upper member is dark thin-bedded argillite with interbedded andesitic pyroclastic rocks. Formation considered Jurassic by Diller. Probably unconformable beneath Arvison Formation.	Diller (1906) Sanborn (1960)
	Brock Shale	400	Dark massive argillite interlayered with tuff or tuffaceous sandstone. Locally fossiliferous. Thought to be Late Triassic (Norian) in age. Probably unconformable with overlying Modin Formation.	Diller (1906) Sanborn (1960)
	Hosselkus Limestone	0–250	Thin-bedded to massive light-gray limestone. Fossils indicate Late Triassic (Karnian) age. Conformable with underlying Pit Formation and overlying Brock Shale. May be lenticular bodies.	Sanborn (1960) Albers and Robertson (1961)
	Pit Formation	2,000–4,400	Predominantly dark shale and siltstone, with abundant lenses of metadacite and quartz-keratophyre tuffs. Includes lenses of limestone and lava flows. Fossils in limestones, including brachiopods, ammonites, and belemnites, indicate Middle and Late Triassic age. Generally overlies, but partly intertongues with, Bully Hill Rhyolite.	Albers and Robertson (1961)
	Bully Hill Rhyolite	100–2,500	Lava flows and pyroclastic rocks, with subordinate hypabyssal intrusive bodies. Contacts gradational; interbedded with and intrusive into Dekkas Andesite below, and interbedded with Pit Formation above.	Albers and Robertson (1961)
Permian	Dekkas Andesite	1,000–3,500	Chiefly fragmental lava and pyroclastic rocks, but includes mudstone and tuffaceous sandstone. Interfingers with underlying Nosoni Formation. Fossils in tuffaceous beds indicate Permian (Capitan) age, but formation probably ranges into Triassic.	Albers and Robertson (1961)
	Nosoni Formation	0–2,000	Mudstone and fine-grained tuff, with minor coarse mafic pyroclastic rocks and lava. Fusulinids, brachiopods, and bryozoans are common. Formation separated from McCloud Limestone, locally by mafic intrusion and elsewhere by disconformity.	Albers and Robertson (1961)
	McCloud Limestone	0–2,500	Thin-bedded to massive light-gray limestone, with local beds and nodules of chert. Abundant corals and fusulinids indicate Wolfcamp and probable Leonard (Early Permian) age. Relations to adjacent younger and older formations not clear, owing to mafic intrusions along much of the contacts.	Albers and Robertson (1961)
Pennsylvanian / Mississippian	Baird Formation	3,000–5,000	Pyroclastic rocks, mudstone, and keratophyre flows in lower part; siliceous mudstone, with minor limestone, chert, and tuff in middle part; and greenstone, quartz keratophyre, and mafic pyroclastic rocks and flow breccia in upper part. Abundant shallow-water marine fossils from middle part indicate Visean age. Uppermost part contains Early Pennsylvanian fusulinids.	Albers and Robertson (1961) Skinner and Wilde (1965)
Mississippian	Bragdon Formation	6,000±	Interbedded shale and sandstone, with grit and chert-pebble conglomerate abundant in upper part. Minor pyroclastic rocks and radiolarian chert. Fossils sparse. Essentially conformable with overlying Baird Formation. Rests variably on Kennett Formation, Balaklala Rhyolite, or Copley Greenstone.	Diller (1906) Kinkel, Hall, Albers (1956) Albers and Robertson (1961) Albers (1964) Irwin (1963)
Devonian	Kennett Formation	0–400	Dark, thin-bedded, siliceous mudstone and tuff. Limestone in upper part. Fossils from mudstone and limestone include corals and brachiopods of late Middle Devonian age. In places is structurally conformable with overlying Bragdon Formation. Rests in Balaklala Rhyolite in some places, and on Copley Greenstone in others. Thin or absent in westernmost part of belt.	Kinkel, Hall, Albers (1956) Albers and Robertson (1961) Albers (1964)
	Balaklala Rhyolite	0–3,500	Light-colored quartz-keratophyre flows and pyroclastics. Conformable with, and grades upward into Kennett Formation. Greatly variable thickness. Thin or absent in westernmost part of the belt. Nonfossiliferous. Presumably Middle Devonian.	Kinkel, Hall, Albers (1956) Albers and Robertson (1961) Albers (1964)
Devonian(?)	Copley Greenstone	3,700+	Keratophyric and spilitic pillow lavas and pyroclastic rocks. Intertongues with overlying Balaklala Rhyolite. Overlain in some places by Kennett Formation, and in others by Bragdon Formation. Nonfossiliferous. Probably Middle Devonian. Base not exposed.	Kinkel, Hall, Albers (1956) Albers and Robertson (1961) Albers (1964)
Silurian	Gazelle Formation	2,400+	Siliceous graywackes, mudstone, chert-pebble conglomerate, tuff, and limestone. Limestone contains corals, brachiopods, and trilobites indicative of Middle and Late(?) Silurian age. Graptolites in shale indicate latest Early or Middle Silurian. Devonian rocks in Grouse Creek area, formerly included in Gazelle (Merriam, 1961) should be excluded (Merriam, oral communication, 1965). Fault contacts with Duzel Formation.	Wells, Walker, Merriam (1959) Churkin and Langenheim (1960) Churkin (1961, 1965) Merriam (1961)
Ordovician(?)	Duzel Formation	1,250+	Thinly layered phyllitic graywacke, locally with radiolarian chert and limestone. Limestone has large coral and brachiopod fauna. Top and bottom of formation not known. Locally small overturned folds. Formation involved in northward-plunging synclinorium, and locally thrust over Gazelle Formation.	Wells, Walker, Merriam (1959)

p. 1062–1063). Ammonites of Late Triassic (Karnian) age were found in limestone on the boundary between Trinity and Tehama Counties in the extreme southern part of the belt (Silberling and Irwin, 1962). Fossils suggesting a Silurian and Devonian age are found at a single locality near the center of the belt (Merriam, 1961). In Oregon, fossils collected by Diller (1914a), in addition to more recent collections, are now considered to be of Mesozoic age, probably Late Triassic (Wells, Hotz, and Cater, 1949, p. 4).

Names such as the Blue Chert and Lower Slate Series of Hershey (1901, 1906, 1911), the Chanchelulla Formation of Hinds (1932), the Grayback Formation of Maxon (1933), and the Applegate Group of Wells and others (1949) have been applied to the aggregate assemblage of rocks at several places in the western Paleozoic and Triassic terrane. However, meaningful subdivision into formations has not been accomplished, nor are the stratigraphic relations of the rocks known from one area to another. Correlation between rocks of the western Paleozoic and Triassic belt and those in the more systematic sequence of the eastern Klamath belt has not been established, except that one might broadly correlate the Permian and Triassic limestones of the western belt with the McCloud and Hosselkus Limestones (fig. 3) of the eastern Klamath belt.

Photo 1. Pillow structure in Copley Greenstone, exposed near the mouth of Deadwood Creek in northeastern Weaverville quadrangle.

Western Jurassic Belt

The most westerly lithic belt of the Klamath Mountains includes the Galice Formation of slaty detrital rocks and the schist typical of South Fork Mountain. The Galice Formation crops out generally in the eastern part of the belt, and the schists occupy a band along the western boundary. When the western Jurassic belt was originally outlined (Irwin, 1960), the schist of South Fork Mountain was thought likely to be metamorphosed Galice Formation. Later work has cast doubt on this relation, as well as on the validity of considering the schist of South Fork Mountain to be a part of the subjacent terrane.

The Galice Formation was named by Diller (1907, p. 403) for exposures of dark slaty mudstone and subordinate sandstone and conglomerate along Galice Creek in southwestern Oregon. It was redefined to include considerable intercalated volcanic rock (Wells, Hotz, and Cater, 1949, p. 4).

In California the Galice Formation has been studied in the Gasquet quadrangle adjacent to the Oregon border. There, the formation is described (Cater and Wells, 1953, p. 86) as consisting of a lower metavolcanic unit and an upper metasedimentary unit. The lower unit consists mostly of meta-andesite flows and breccias and is thought to be at least 7,000 feet thick. The metasedimentary unit is chiefly slaty mudstone with interbedded graywacke. The graywacke is generally fine to medium grained and ranges from gray to green where unweathered. It consists principally of angular grains of plagioclase, quartz, augite, hornblende, chlorite, epidote, micas, fragments of volcanic rocks, quartzite, shale, shards of devitrified glass, and minor carbonaceous and argillaceous material (Cater and Wells, 1953, p. 91). The thickness of the metasedimentary unit in Gasquet quadrangle is estimated to be at least 3,000 feet. Thicknesses as great as 15,000 feet are reported in Oregon (Wells, Hotz, and Cater, 1949, p. 7).

The Galice is the youngest known subjacent formation, and generally is considered to be correlative with the Mariposa Slate of the Sierra Nevada. It contains the Late Jurassic pelecypod *Buchia concentrica* (Sowerby) which ranges from late Oxfordian to middle Kimmeridgian (Imlay, 1959, p. 157 and fig. 36). None of the formation can be much younger than middle Kimmeridgian, as the Galice was deformed during the Nevadan orogeny, and as some superjacent strata are as old as latest Jurassic (Tithonian). The age of the oldest part of the Galice is obscure, and stratigraphic relations between the Galice and older formations are not known. Exposures of detrital rocks that are largely phyllitic were mapped in reconnaissance (Irwin, 1960) southward from the Gasquet quadrangle for nearly the remaining length of the Klamath Mountains. These were tentatively correlated with the Galice Formation on the basis of continuity of the gross lithology, but fossils were not found for establishing a correlative age.

Schist forms a narrow selvage along much of the 150-mile length of the western and southern boundary of the Klamath Mountains in California (fig. 4). It generally occupies the crest and eastern slope of South Fork Mountain, a remarkably long and even-crested

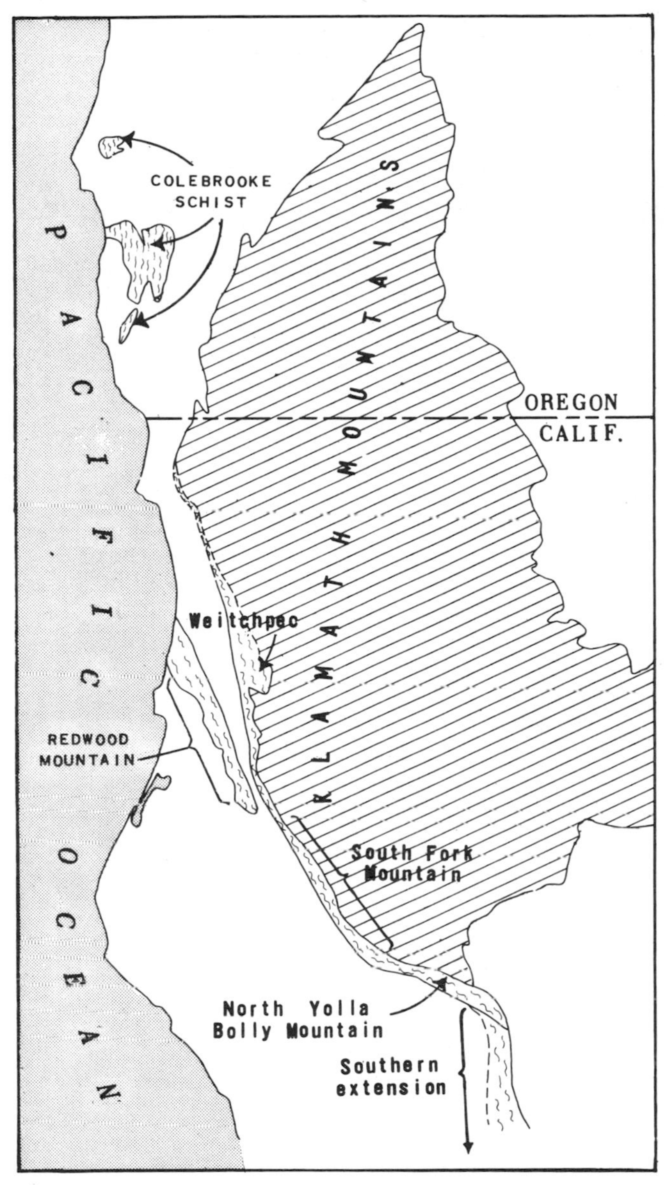

Figure 4. Distribution of South Fork Mountain and related schists. Southern extension (after Ghent, 1965, and Blake, 1965) is an area of rocks considered at least in part equivalent to schist of South Fork Mountain.

ridge that trends northwest, forming the western boundary of the Klamath Mountains for nearly 50 miles in Trinity and Humboldt Counties. At the south end of South Fork Mountain, the schist abruptly changes trend and continues more nearly eastward along Black Rock and Yolla Bolly Mountains toward the Sacramento Valley. In the Coast Ranges west of the Klamath Mountains, the schist occurs as a shorter parallel band along Redwood Mountain.

Diller (1903b, p. 343) synonymously referred to the schist as the southwestern belt of schists and the South Fork Mountain belt of schists. At Weitchpec, near the confluence of the Trinity and Klamath Rivers, the schist was named the Weitchpec Schists (Hershey, 1903, p. 357; 1906, p. 63), and in southwestern Blue Lake quadrangle, the Kerr Ranch Schist (Ogle and Manning, 1950, p. 13). For convenience, Irwin (1960, p. 29) informally referred to these schists collectively as the South Fork Mountain schist, as they are herein. They were included as part of the western Jurassic belt of the Klamath Mountains, because they were thought to be not only a part of the subjacent terrane but probably a metamorphic equivalent of the Galice Formation.

Although the length of exposure of South Fork Mountain schist is impressive, it is only part of a narrow belt of low-grade metamorphic rock that is virtually 300 miles long. South of Yolla Bolly Mountains, semischists and schists follow the boundary between the Coast Ranges and Sacramento Valley for more than 50 miles. These were described as metamorphosed Franciscan(?) rocks of the Coast Ranges (Irwin, 1960). In southwestern Oregon, the northern extension of the belt of low-grade metamorphic rocks is the Colebrooke Schist, which Diller (1903a, p. 2) considered equivalent to the schist of South Fork Mountain.

The South Fork Mountain schist is typically a well-foliated quartz-mica schist, and locally includes thick layers of chlorite-epidote-albite metavolcanic rock. Some of the metavolcanic layers contain thin crossite- or glaucophane-rich layers. The rocks have been folded twice. The first folding appears to be along northwest-trending axes, with axial planes dipping to the northeast. Superimposed on these are eastward trending folds that most commonly plunge gently to the east. The double folding results in much of the schist being complexly contorted and in an intricate distribution of outcrops of the metavolcanic rock. Study of the schist is greatly hampered by dense forest cover and abundant debris.

Similar relations in the Yolla Bolly Mountain portion of the South Fork Mountain schist belt are described in detail by Blake (1965). Lithologic similarity of the South Fork Mountain schist to quartz-mica schist and metavolcanic rock of the Colebrooke Schist has been observed by Blake and Irwin, as well as by others.

Doubt as to the affiliation of the South Fork Mountain schist with the subjacent terrane of the Klamath Mountains was first raised by Blake and Ghent (1965), who consider the schist to have a closer affinity with the post-Nevadan Franciscan rocks of the Coast Ranges. Along the south side of the Yolla Bolly Mountain, Blake (1965) found an essentially complete gradation from South Fork Mountain schist to semischist and platy graywacke of the belt of metamorphosed Franciscan rocks of Irwin (1960). Farther south in the belt of metamorphosed Franciscan, Ghent (1965) found a similar metamorphic gradation, with quartz-mica schist and metavolcanic rock similar to that of the South Fork and Yolla Bolly Mountains. At both of these localities, as well as along South Fork Mountain,

Photo 2. View of the remarkably uniform summit level along the southern part of South Fork Mountain, looking northeast (left) to southeast (right) from Mount Lassic (Signal Peak) in the northern Coast Ranges. The same vantage point was visited by Diller (1902, p. 18), who considered the long, even crest of South Fork Mountain to be one of the best developed portions of the Klamath peneplain. The terrane between South Fork Mountain and Mount Lassic is chiefly Franciscan rocks. Black Lassic Peak is dominantly graywacke and shale; Red Lassic is mainly greenstone. Much of the terrane in the foreground is sharply folded ultramafic rock. North Yolla Bolly Mountain is along the southeasterly extension of the belt of schist of South Fork Mountain, toward the Sacramento Valley. Bully Choop Mountain, 45 miles distant in the southeast corner of the Weaverville quadrangle, is along the easternmost ultramafic belt of the Klamath Mountains.

the range in metamorphic grade is comparable to the Chlorite 1 through Chlorite 3 subzones defined by Turner (1938). The rocks of higher grade are thought to overlie those of lower grade, and although the transition from one zone to another is essentially gradational, both Blake (1965) and Ghent (1965, p. 388) consider that the rocks of higher metamorphic grade have been thrust over those of lower grade. Fossils have not been found in the rocks of higher metamorphic grade typical of the South Fork Mountain schist, but in the lower-grade rocks that seem gradational with the schist, pelecypods of Early Cretaceous (Valanginian) age have been found (Irwin, 1960; Ghent, 1963; Blake, 1965).

Ultramafic Rocks

Ultramafic rocks are an abundant component of the subjacent terrane, and generally crop out as bodies whose linear trends accentuate the arcuate structure of the Klamath Mountains (fig. 5). They are chiefly peridotite, but varieties range from pyroxenite to dunite. Generally these rocks are serpentinized, and at many places, principally along their borders, they are highly sheared. The ultramafic rocks are widely distributed throughout much of the province but are significantly absent within the South Fork Mountain schist and eastern Klamath terranes. Abundant gabbroic rocks are included in areas of ultramafic rock shown on figures 2 and 5. They are structurally associated with the ultramafic rock, and not with the granitic rocks, but whether they are genetically related to the ultramafic rock is not clear.

The largest ultramafic body separates the eastern Klamath terrane from rocks of the central metamorphic belt. Its arcuate western boundary is virtually continuous for 100 miles in length, and disappears beneath a mantle of superjacent strata at both ends. The northeasterly extent beneath the young volcanic rocks of the Cascade province is not known, but to the southeast the ultramafic body probably continues beneath a mantle of Cretaceous and younger superjacent strata of the Great Valley and is perhaps represented by a line of discontinuous ultramafic bodies along the western front of the Sierra Nevada. In the Klamath Mountains this impressive exposure is thought to be the eroded lip of an ultramafic sheet whose roots lie buried to the east beneath rocks of the eastern Klamath belt (Irwin and Lipman, 1962). The broad area of ultramafic rock that extends eastward from the arcuate exposure, and which generally separates Ordovician and Silurian strata from Devonian and younger strata of the eastern Klamath belt, is interpreted as a broad arch in the ultramafic sheet from which the once-overlying strata of the eastern Klamath belt are largely eroded. The ultramafic sheet is grossly discordant with the layered rocks of the eastern Klamath belt; in the northern part it is in contact with Ordovician and Silurian strata, and in the southern part with Devonian and Mississippian strata. This sheet is of considerable tectonic significance, as it seems most likely to have deep roots that perhaps connect with the mantle. It is the most easterly ultramafic rock in the Klamath Mountains, and it separates a thick section of Ordovician to Late Jurassic strata on the east from metamorphic rocks of Carboniferous or older age to the west.

Although linear bodies of ultramafic rock are numerous west of the central metamorphic belt, their structural relations to the enclosing rocks are not clear in most cases. The largest and best known of these is the Josephine peridotite body (Wells and others,

1949), which crops out over a broad area of northern Del Norte County and adjacent parts of Oregon along the western border of the province. In southern Del Norte County, the Josephine body continues as a narrow linear exposure; farther south, it may be represented by numerous discontinuous bodies that follow the same general trend along the western border of the province in Humboldt and Trinity Counties. The Josephine body generally intrudes the Galice Formation (Cater and Wells, 1953) but along much of its western side it is in fault contact either with Franciscan rocks (shown as Dothan Formation by Cater and Wells, 1953) or with phyllitic rocks that in reconnaisance were tentatively assigned (Irwin, 1960) to the Galice Formation. The structure is not clear, but some of the relations and topograhpic expression of the Josephine body suggest that it too may be a sheet. Owing to the uncertainty of the earlier assignment of both the South Fork Mountain schist and the phyllitic rock west of the Josephine body to the subjacent terrane, the Josephine body and its possible southern extension may more closely delineate the western boundary of the province than heretofore considered.

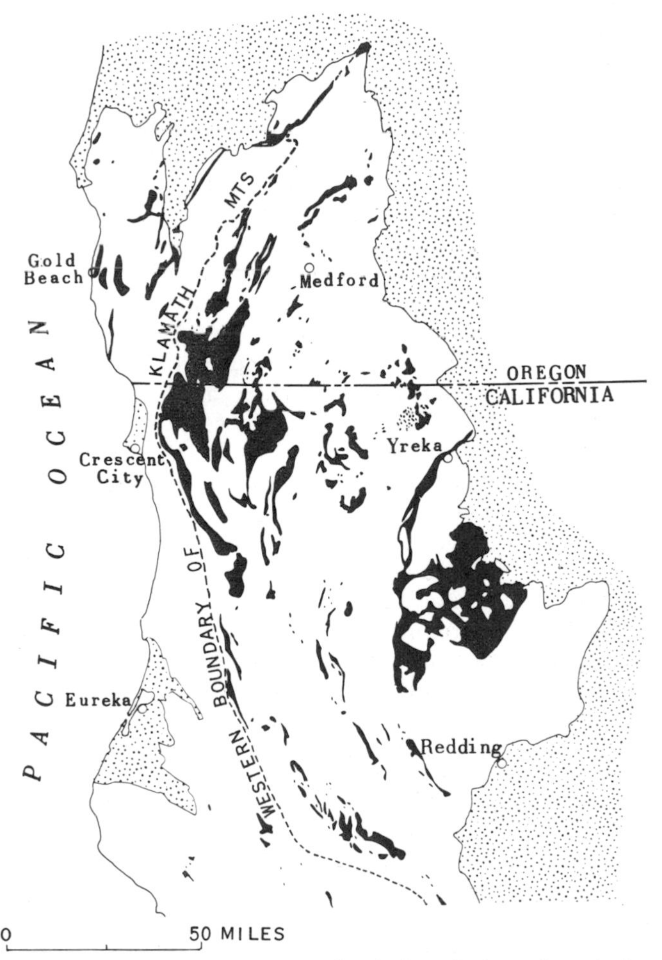

Figure 5. Map showing arcuate distribution of ultramafic rocks in Klamath Mountains of California and Oregon. Ultramafic rocks shown as solid black areas. Mantle of Cenozoic rocks shown as stippled areas.

It is not known with certainty that the ultramafic bodies of the subjacent terrane were emplaced during a single part of geologic time. Nor is it known whether they intruded as many separate bodies, or—taking an extreme view—whether they are dislocated parts of an essentially single great ultramafic sheet that transgressed successively younger strata from the eastern Klamath to the western Jurassic belt. Most of the larger ultramafic bodies of the Klamath Mountains are clearly part of the subjacent terrane, as they are cut by granitic rocks that are reasonably certain to have intruded during the Nevadan orogeny. Notably, the easternmost ultramafic sheet is intruded by the Shasta Bally batholith and related dikes, and a few inclusions of ultramafic rock are found in the batholith. However, the earlier limit to the age of this sheet is not closely fixed, as the youngest strata known with certainty to be cut by the sheet are Mississippian. In contrast, emplacement of the Josephine peridotite body can be dated closely, as it intrudes the Galice Formation (Late Jurassic) and is intruded by Nevadan plutons (Cater and Wells, 1953). Although evidence for closely dating the emplacement of most of the ultramafic bodies is not at hand, a tentative designation of Late Jurassic (Nevadan) is permissive.

Granitic Rocks

Granitic plutons and associated dikes are widespread in the Klamath Mountains but are not uniformly distributed among the several lithic belts. They range widely in composition, but quartz diorite predominates. Plutons are most abundant in the western Paleozoic and Triassic belt and are much more sparse in the eastern Klamath belt. None is known in the South Fork Mountain schist. As the granitic rocks are discussed in detail in the next article in this volume, only a few of their regional aspects will be given here.

The apparent scarcity of granitic plutons in the eastern Klamath belt may result from the plutons not reaching to as high a level through the eastern Klamath strata as in the belts to the west. Abundant granitic plutons are exposed in the broad area of ultramafic rock that separates the Ordovician and Silurian from younger strata of the eastern Klamath belt but are sparse in the adjacent strata. This suggests the possibility that the ultramafic sheet, which presumably extends for some distance beneath the strata of the eastern Klamath belt, exerted some control over the emplacement of the granitic plutons, and that granitic plutons may be concealed beneath much of the Ordovician and younger strata. The Shasta Bally batholith, the largest pluton in the eastern Klamath belt, is eroded only to shallow depth, as indicated by arch-forming flow structures (Albers, 1964) and erosional remnants of an original cap of the contact metamorphosed Bragdon Formation (Irwin, 1963). Albers and Robertson (1961, p. 50) have suggested that several smaller stocks are eminences rising above the general level of an intrusive mass that may underlie the entire area. Other features that may point to concealed plutons in the eastern Klamath belt are the important base-metal sulfide deposits of the East- and West-Shasta districts and abundant gold-bearing quartz veins along the Devonian-Mississippian boundary.

Photo 3. Metabasalt member of schist of South Fork Mountain in southeastern Pickett Peak quadrangle. Open folds plunge gently to northeast, away from viewer, and are of second generation. Mineral lineation trends from left to right across trend of open folds.

The granitic plutons of the Klamath Mountains are generally thought to have intruded during the Nevadan (Late Jurassic) orogeny. There is little evidence of intrusion earlier than Late Jurassic, and none of later intrusion. The youngest strata of the subjacent terrane, the Galice Formation of Late Jurassic (Kimmeridgian) age, are intruded by granitic rocks, as are those of older Mesozoic and Paleozoic ages. The superjacent strata, the oldest of which are Late Jurassic (Tithonian), are not intruded. Multiple intrusions have been described by Hinds (1932) and Maxson (1933), among others, but no field evidence has been found to indicate two or more distinct and widely spaced periods of granitic intrusion.

Potassium-argon ages measured on biotite from several plutons in the south-central Klamath Mountains range from 127 to 133 m.y. (Curtis and others, 1958; Davis, 1963; Lanphere and Irwin, 1965), and an age of 128 m.y. was similarly measured on hornblende from the Shasta Bally batholith (Lanphere and Irwin, 1965). Ages of 141 and 146 m.y. are reported for biotite from a pluton in an outlier of subjacent rocks in southwestern Oregon (Dott, 1964). All of these are considered minimum ages, and at best only approximate the age of emplacement of the respective plutons. All are permissive of a Late Jurassic age of emplacement. The span in age from 127 to 146 does not necessarily indicate a 19 m.y. period of intrusive activity. The only evidence for plutonic intrusion in the Klamath Mountains prior to the Late Jurassic is a potassium-argon age of 215 m.y. measured on hornblende (Mineral Information Service, 1965, p. 16) from a small granitic stock that intrudes Mississippian strata of the eastern Klamath belt.

There is no field evidence in the Klamath Mountains that granitic plutons intruded during the Cretaceous. Nor can the youngest of the isotopic dates be used to support a Cretaceous age for the plutons based on the 135-m.y. (Kulp, 1961) or 136-m.y. (Casey, 1964) assignment for the age of the Jurassic-Cretaceous boundary. Isotopic dates obtained on both biotite and hornblende from the Shasta Bally batholith are all younger than 135 m.y. Nevertheless, the batholith is part of a subjacent terrane that is overlain with great unconformity by a blanket of fossiliferous strata that internally are essentially conformable and that range in age from Late Jurassic (Tithonian) to Late Cretaceous. Of this superjacent blanket, the oldest strata that are actually seen to lie on the eroded roof of the batholith are Early Cretaceous, but it is untenable to consider that the batholith intruded after deposition of the Late Jurassic (Tithonian) strata that only a few miles distant to the south are conformable beneath the Lower Cretaceous. Granitic cobbles are uncommon in the older superjacent strata, but in the Wilbur Springs quadrangle two granitic cobbles were collected from near the Jurassic-Cretaceous stratigraphic boundary below the *Buchia crassicollis* zone (E. H. Bailey and D. L. Jones, oral communication, 1965). A potassium-argon age of 138 m.y. (hornblende) was determined for one cobble, and 141 m.y. (biotite) and 152 m.y. (hornblende) for the other (M. A. Lanphere, 1965, oral communication). These ages agree within analytical uncertainty with the ages of Nevadan plutons in the Klamath Mountains, and suggest that plutons from which these ages are obtained were being eroded by the end of the Jurassic.

The lithic and structural trends of the southern Klamath Mountains correspond to those of the northern Sierra Nevada; at the north end of the Great Valley the continuity of Nevadan and older rocks between the two provinces is concealed by a wide area of Cretaceous superjacent strata. The superjacent strata apparently are not intruded by granitic plutons. Thus, abundant Cretaceous plutons indicated by isotopic age dates in the Sierra Nevada must not follow the same lithic and structural trend as the Late Jurassic orogenic belt of the Klamath Mountains and Sierra Nevada and must represent an orogenic pulse that is younger and distinct from that of the Nevadan orogeny.

SUPERJACENT ROCKS

The oldest rocks exposed unconformably on the subjacent terrane of the Klamath Mountains are well-bedded marine sedimentary deposits of Cretaceous age. Within the province they are preserved as several relatively small erosional remnants. These deposits are correlative and doubtless once continuous with a sedimentary prism of similar strata, the Great Valley sequence (Bailey, Irwin, and Jones, 1965), which laps onto the subjacent terrane at the southeast border of the Klamath Mountains, and which crops out for several hundred miles to the south along the west side of the Great Valley. The erosional remnants in the Klamath Mountains, which are restricted to the Cretaceous and are at most about 2,000 feet thick, represent the thinning edge of the sedimentary prism that, along the Great Valley, ranges from Late Jurassic (Tithonian) to Late Cretaceous and attains a thickness of approximately 40,000 feet. The entire prism of strata of the Great Valley sequence is considered superjacent with respect to rocks involved in the Nevadan (Late Jurassic) orogeny.

The Cretaceous of the Klamath Mountains consists of mudstone, sandstone, and conglomerate, which generally are well bedded and firmly indurated. The beds commonly range from a fraction of an inch to a few feet in thickness. Some are graded, and at a few places sole markings can be seen. The sandstone consists of poorly sorted angular grains of quartz, feldspar, and lithic fragments. Similar to sandstones of much of the Great Valley sequence, some of the feldspar grains are potassium-bearing varieties. Where the local stratigraphy is known, conglomerate is most abundant in the lower part of the section. The clasts are most commonly chert and other resistant fine-grained rock. At the Reading Creek locality, a conglomerate bed near the base of the section consists almost entirely of fragments of mica schist that must have come from the large area of schist now exposed nearby.

Fossils are abundant locally in several of the patches of Cretaceous strata. They are chiefly pelecypods and ammonites of Early Cretaceous (Hauterivian) age (Anderson, 1938; Imlay, 1960; D. L. Jones, written communication, 1964), but at the Big Bar locality *Buchia crassicollis* (Keyserling) of the Valanginian Stage of the Early Cretaceous was found (R. W. Imlay, written communication, 1958). Fossils of Late Cretaceous age are said to occur at a locality just south of Hayfork and at another on the east side of Hyampom Valley, but this has not been verified.

Strata that are correlative with the younger part of the Great Valley sequence crop out in a narrow band along the northeastern boundary of the Klamath Mountains in California and Oregon. These are referred to the Hornbrook Formation (Peck, Imlay, and Popenoe, 1956) and range from at least as old as Cenomanian to late Campanian in age. They consist chiefly of bluish-grey siltstone, buff-weathering sandstone, and minor conglomerate that lie unconformably on the metamorphic and granitic rocks of the Klamath Mountains. The beds dip northeastward at angles between 10° and 30°, and they are believed to continue northeastward under the lavas of the Cascade Range.

Tertiary rocks are found at few places within the Klamath Mountains, although they are abundant along the northern and eastern borders of the province. The most important of those within the province in California are continental detrital rocks of the Weaverville Formation, which crop out in only a few small areas in the southern part of the province and are probably Oligocene in age. A few thin patches of marine sedimentary rocks of the Wimer Formation of late Miocene age occur on crests of ridges in the northwesternmost part of California.

The Weaverville Formation was named by Hinds (1932, p. 115), but had been described in earlier reports by Diller (1902, 1911, 1914b). It was studied by MacGinitie (1937) with particular reference to well-preserved fossil plants. The formation was once mined for placer gold and for coal, and in the past few years has been prospected for phosphate.

The principal areas of the Weaverville Formation are in the vicinity of Weaverville and Hayfork, with smaller areas at Reading Creek, Hyampom, and Big Bar. Small patches of possibly related strata are at Corral Bottom, Clark Creek, Buckhorn Creek in the northern part of Hyampom quadrangle, and on the northwest side of Hoopa Valley.

The formation includes beds of sandstone, shale, conglomerate, tuff, and lignite that are thought to have been deposited on flood plains with widespread swampy lakes (MacGinitie, 1937, p. 102). Some may be estuarine (Diller, 1902, p. 43). Much of the detritus came from nearby highlands, as shown by coarse conglomerate that consists in the Weaverville area almost entirely of fragments of Salmon Hornblende Schist from the adjacent metamorphic terrane. Carbonaceous fragments are found throughout much of the formation, and locally, such as at Hyampom, lignite forms beds as thick as 16 feet (MacGinitie, 1937, p. 96). At the Reading Creek area, the lignite and fine-grained sedimentary rocks form the lower part of the section; the upper part is predominantly conglomerate (Irwin, 1963). There, as at Hyampom, Hayfork, and Big Bar, small tonnages of lignitic coal have been mined. Some of the tuffaceous shales of the Weaverville Formation near Hyampom locally contain as much as 20 percent P_2O_5 (Lydon, 1964).

Fossil plants found in some of the shale and light-colored tuffaceous beds were first considered Miocene (Diller, 1902, p. 41–45), and later thought to be chiefly Eocene (Hinds, 1932, p. 79, 114–116). However, a more thorough study of the flora by MacGinitie (1937) suggests an Oligocene age.

The areas of Weaverville Formation are in many places bounded by steep faults. In some areas the formation rests with angular unconformity on Cretaceous strata and elsewhere on pre-Nevadan rocks. Typically, the Weaverville is deformed by open folds with limbs dipping 5° to 20°, but beds along some major faults are steep or nearly vertical. The thickness of the formation is about 1,900 feet at Reading Creek, probably not less than 2,000 feet at Hayfork, and about 1,100 feet at Hyampom; at Big Bar it is a little less than 500 feet but neither the top nor the bottom of the section is exposed (MacGinitie, 1937).

Marine sedimentary beds of Miocene age occur as small patches on ridge tops near the western boundary of the Klamath Mountains in Del Norte County. They were named the Wymer Beds by Diller (1902, p. 32–33), and have since been renamed Wimer Formation by Maxson (1933, p. 134; see Wilmarth, 1938, p. 2347). The formation consists of not more than 150 feet of nearly horizontal beds of friable shale, sandstone, and conglomerate that weathers yellow and red in color (Maxson, 1933, p. 134). Imprints of mollusks and plants are abundant locally in the beds, and according to F. H. Knowlton (in Diller, 1902, p. 33) and Maxson (1933, p. 135), these fossils indicate that the formation is late Miocene in age.

Gravels that occur only at the same general altitude as the Wimer and that fill channels cut into the Wimer and older formations in the Gasquet quadrangle are described by Cater and Wells (1953, p. 104–105). These gravels are poorly sorted and include clay as well as boulders. Some of the pebbles and boulders are fresh and hard, but others are thoroughly weathered and crumble easily. They are thought to have been deposited shortly after emergence of the Wimer Formation and to be of late Miocene or early Pliocene age. Similar gravels that occur for 2½ miles along the crest of a high ridge northwest of Hoopa Valley were considered by Diller (1902, p. 52–54) to have been deposited in an ancient bed of the Klamath River.

QUATERNARY DEPOSITS

Alluvial deposits of sand and gravel occur along the courses of the major rivers and their tributaries, both in the beds of the streams and on terrace remnants of earlier levels. The only broad area of valley fill within the province is Scott Valley, where alluvial fan deposits attain a probable thickness of 400 feet (Olmsted, 1956, p. 28–29). In most other valleys of significant breadth in the Klamath Mountains, such as Weaverville, Hayfork, Hyampom, and Hoopa Valleys, Quaternary alluvium is only a thin, patchy veneer.

Early interest in the gravel was caused by the discovery of placer gold at the mouth of Reading Creek in 1848, which rapidly led to prospecting and settlement throughout the entire province. Owing to continued economic interest in the gravels, they were studied along the upper reaches of the Trinity River by Diller (1911 and 1914b). Terraces along the South Fork of the Salmon River have been described by Hershey (1903) in an attempt to relate them to several glacial stages; those along the Smith River are described by Cater and Wells (1953, p. 105–106, 124).

Some of the terrace deposits are perched as high as 400 feet above the present streams and are more than 100 feet thick. Many have been well exposed during hydraulic placer-mining operations, with old streamcut surfaces on the bedrock being exhumed. At the Union Hill mine near Douglas City, the gravels filled an ancient loop in Weaver Creek (see Irwin, 1963). According to Diller (1911, p. 26–27), who examined the deposit when the exposures were relatively new, the upper 115 feet of the deposit is reddish, poorly stratified clay, sand, and gravel, which is underlain by 19 feet of blue gravels, sand, and clay, with a thin carbonaceous layer at the base. Fossil bones and shells, associated with the carbonaceous layer, indicate a Pleistocene age. The bones are of mammoths, deer, and ground sloths. The shells are similar to those of living fresh-water species (Diller, 1911, p. 27).

Evidence of alpine glaciation is abundant along the higher ranges of the Klamath Mountains, but the glaciers are extinct except for two glacierets covering several acres in the Trinity Alps (Sharp, 1960, p. 337–338). Cirques, bedrock basins, marshy meadows, and U-shaped valleys are common features of the landscape

Photo 4. View looking southwest (left) to northwest (right) from Elk Camp in northern Gasquet quadrangle, showing accordant summit levels of the Klamath peneplain in Del Norte County. Terrane is chiefly ultramafic rock. Lateritic soil on some of the upland surfaces has been prospected for nickel. *Photo by P. E. Hotz.*

in the higher parts of many of the mountains (see Davis, 1933, p. 215, figs. 19, 20; Hinds, 1952, p. 139–142, fig. 100; Irwin, 1960, photo 14). Small lakes associated with these features are generally at altitudes above 6,000 feet in the eastern part of the province and above 5,000 feet along the boundary between Siskiyou and Del Norte Counties in the western part. Near the south end of South Fork Mountain, cirques occur below Chinquapin Butte at an altitude of 5,200 feet on the east side of the ridge. On the north side of North Yolla Bolly Mountain are several small cirque lakes, and polished and striated surfaces extend down to an altitude at least as low as 5,600 feet (Blake, 1965).

The only modern detailed study of glaciation in the Klamath Mountains was in the Trinity Alps area by Sharp (1960). He recognized four glacial episodes, of which the three youngest are probably Wisconsin and the oldest probably pre-Wisconsin. Some less compelling evidence suggesting both younger and possibly considerably older glaciation also was found. During the youngest episode there were at least 30 valley glaciers in the Trinity Alps area. The glaciers were shorter and had a higher terminus in successively younger stages. The longest glacier—thought to have been about 13.7 miles long—occupied the valley of Swift Creek during the pre-Wisconsin episode (Sharp, 1960, table 6). Associated with the glaciers were numerous moraines, as well as debris flows that extended down the valleys from the glaciers.

STRUCTURE

The arcuate, concentric distribution of the lithic belts of subjacent rocks is the most obvious gross structural aspect of the Klamath Mountains. The lithic belts generally are separated by faults, or by linear ultramafic bodies or granitic plutons. The strata most commonly dip eastward, and small-scale isoclinal folds with eastward-dipping axial planes are reported in all belts. For the few areas where major folds are mapped, the fold axes are essentially parallel to the arcuate pattern of the lithic belts. Some of the major folds are isoclinal with eastward-dipping axial planes. Outliers of rocks of adjacent belts are found in all except the eastern Klamath belt. The foregoing features are interpreted to result from compressional forces normal to the arcuate trend, with westward overriding of low-angle thrust plates. This mechanism was operative during at least two major pulses—one pulse in the Klamath terrane during the Nevadan orogeny and a second pulse that delineated the general western boundary of the subjacent terrane during a younger age, probably Late Cretaceous. A third pulse during the Carboniferous may be suggested by the isotopic ages of Salmon and Abrams schists.

Structural relations are shown on the schematic cross section (fig. 6). For simplicity, the granitic plutons are not shown, nor are the many high-angle faults that would complicate portrayal of gross relations between lithic units.

The eastern Klamath belt (fig. 6) is an essentially eastward-dipping stratigraphic sequence that to the west, in its older part near the ultramafic sheet, is highly deformed by folding and faulting. Within the sequence, however, an anomalous situation exists along the boundary between Baird Formation and McCloud Limestone (fig. 6, locality 1). The boundary generally conforms to the arcuate regional pattern, but as pointed out by J. P. Albers (oral communication, 1965), the Baird and older strata are more highly deformed and intruded by dikes and sills than are the younger strata to the east. A faunal hiatus that may represent most of Pennsylvanian time is reported by Skinner and Wilde (1965) to occur between the uppermost (Early Pennsylvanian) part of the Baird and the McCloud (Permian). Although Skinner and Wilde report seeing little or no evidence of a physical break, much of the boundary is the locus of intrusion of discontinuous bodies of mafic quartz diorite in which much of the McCloud is engulfed (Albers and Robertson, 1961). The general scarcity of rocks of Pennsylvanian age in eugeosynclinal sections of the Pacific Coast indicates an interruption of marine deposition during much of the Pennsylvanian, and the restricted intrusion of mafic quartz diorite along the Baird-McCloud boundary suggests a major fault.

Nearer to the ultramafic sheet along the western boundary, the Mississippian and older Paleozoic strata of the eastern Klamath belt are folded and highly dislocated along steep faults. Here the arcuate regional structural trend is not as clearly defined as elsewhere, and in the French Gulch quadrangle the local structure is dominated by the Shasta Bally batholith and other plutonic intrusives (see Albers, 1964, fig. 5). The contact between the Bragdon Formation and underlying rocks is of particular interest in the French Gulch quadrangle, as it is thought to be a low-angle thrust fault over a wide area (fig. 6, locality 2), with neither the direction nor amount of displacement known (Albers, 1964, p. 62–63).

Along much of the western boundary of the eastern Klamath belt, the ultramafic sheet and adjacent rocks are folded into an antiformal structure. The axes of the antiform and other major folds in the central metamorphic belt are generally parallel to the arcuate trend of the belt along its entire length.

In Weaverville quadrangle (Irwin, 1963), the Bragdon Formation and Copley Greenstone wrap over the crest of the antiformal fold, and the Copley is progressively cut out toward the west by the ultramafic sheet (fig. 6, locality 3). Near the latitude where the antiformal fold is crossed by the Trinity River, the Bragdon is separated from underlying schist of the central metamorphic belt in the breached core of the fold only by the ultramafic sheet, which here is less than 200 feet thick and nearly horizontal. The structural horizon represented by the ultramafic sheet and the overlying Bragdon Formation occurs to the west only as two outliers within the confines of the central

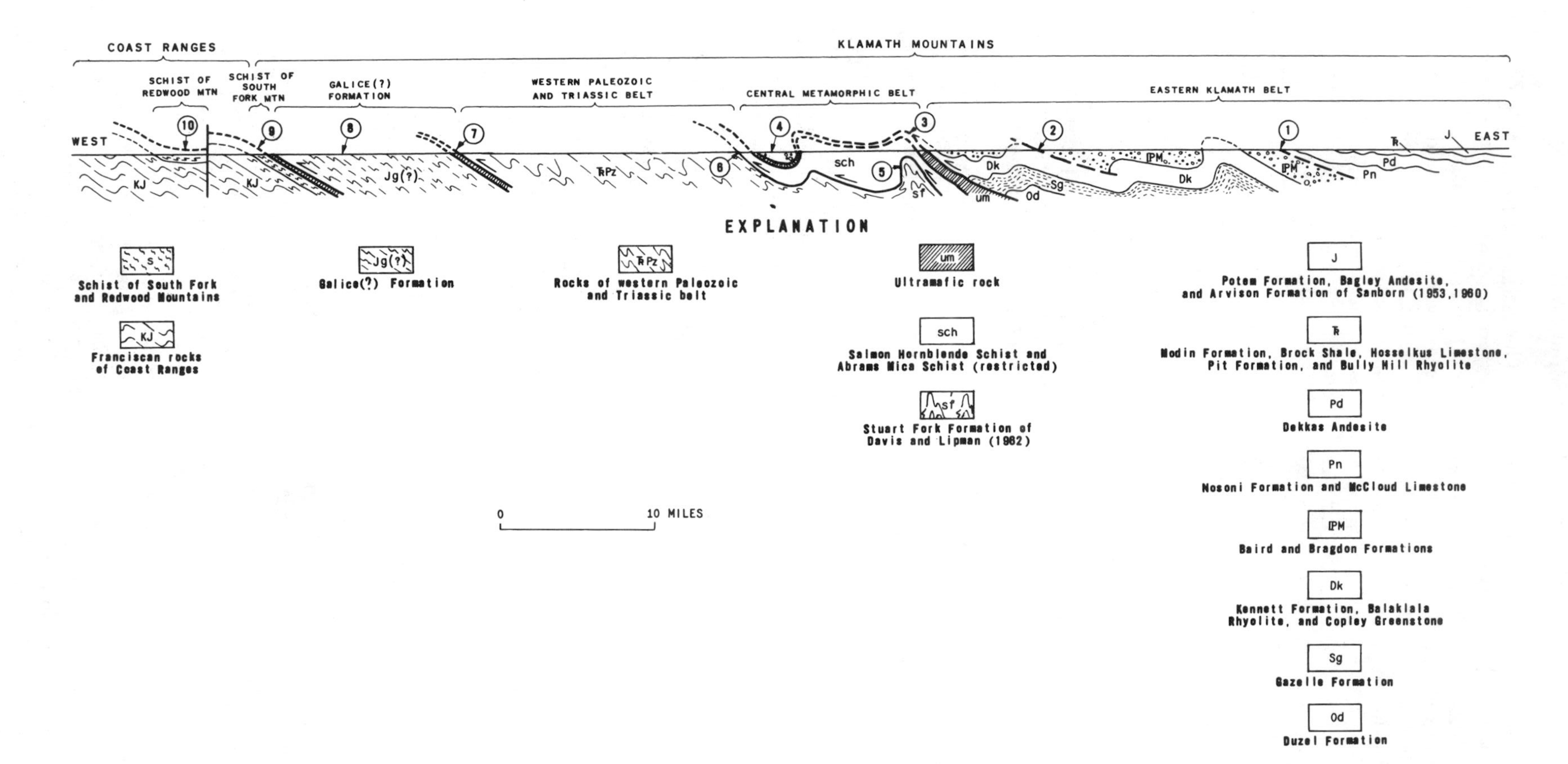

Figure 6. Schematic section across Klamath Mountains and part of northern Coast Ranges of California. Numbers in circles show location of items referred to in text. Granitic plutons are not shown.

metamorphic belt, one in Weaverville quadrangle (fig. 6, locality 4) and a smaller one at the south end of the belt at the Cretaceous overlap. As described earlier in this paper and elsewhere (Irwin and Lipman, 1962; Irwin, 1964), the ultramafic sheet is thought to have intruded a regional fault along which the rocks of the eastern Klamath belt are thrust westward over rocks of the central metamorphic belt.

In the Trinity Alps, north of Weaverville quadrangle, the rocks in the eastern part of the metamorphic belt are described (Davis and Lipman, 1962; Davis, 1964) as isoclinally folded into a north-trending antiformal structure that is steeply overturned to the west. The rocks that underlie the Salmon Hornblende Schist in the breached core of the fold (fig. 6, locality 5) are of anomalously low metamorphic grade, and are thought to be correlative with rocks of the western Paleozoic and Triassic belt. The contact between the rocks of the core and the overlying Salmon Hornblende Schist is considered a folded thrust fault along which the rocks of the central metamorphic belt are displaced a minimum of 15 miles across rocks of the western Paleozoic and Triassic belt (Davis, 1965). Farther north along the metamorphic belt, in the areas studied by Holdaway (1962) and Romey (1962), the dominant fold structures continue parallel to the trend of the belt except where they are deflected by intrusions of granitic plutons.

The western boundary of the metamorphic belt was thought by Hershey (1906, p. 58) to be a regional fault along which the schists were thrust westward over rocks of the western Paleozoic and Triassic belt, and this general idea (fig. 6, locality 6) is substantiated to some extent by more recent work of others. In Helena quadrangle the boundary is a thrust fault that dips 40° to 50° to the east, and, where well exposed, Salmon Hornblende Schist on the hanging wall is separated from rocks of the western Paleozoic and Triassic belt by a shear zone a few inches in width (Cox, 1956, p. 103). To the north in Cecilville quadrangle, G. A. Davis (written communication, 1963) also reports that the boundary is a thrust fault, and that the Salmon is thrust over rocks of the western Paleozoic and Triassic belt. To the south in Weaverville quadrangle, east-dipping shear planes and phyllonite zones that suggest thrusting are locally abundant near the boundary, but much of what may earlier have been a thrust boundary is perhaps modified by high-angle normal faults. Relations along the northern part of the metamorphic belt (Holdaway, 1962) also suggest a thrust fault. However, the general boundary would indeed seem to be fundamentally the lip of a thrust if, as suggested by Davis and Lipman (1962), the rocks of anomalously low metamorphic grade (Stuart Fork Formation) in the core of a major antiformal fold are in thrust contact with overlying Salmon Hornblende Schist and are correlative with rocks of the western Paleozoic and Triassic belt.

The regional structure of the western Paleozoic and Triassic belt is little known but obviously complex. The belt has been mapped in detail at only a few places, and even at those places an understanding of the structure has been hindered by a lack of adequate stratigraphic data. However, the trends of certain linear lithic units, particularly belts of discontinuous limestone lenses (Diller, 1903b; Irwin, 1960, p. 23), are parallel to the belt, and indicate that the regional structural axis also is parallel. Axes of numerous minor folds in Permian strata west of the metamorphic rocks in Weaverville quadrangle generally trend northwest and are subhorizontal. In western Helena quadrangle, the strata trend north to northwest, generally dip eastward, and have abundant small folds whose axes strike north to northwest (Cox, 1956, p. 98). In Sawyers Bar quadrangle to the north, the strata are described by Seyfert (1964) as isoclinally folded, with axial planes dipping steeply east and fold axes plunging gently south. Here the folds range from several feet to several thousand feet across and are remarkably continuous along their trend.

The western boundary of the western Paleozoic and Triassic belt was early recognized as a major structural break, which in northern Humboldt County and northward in California was called the Orleans fault by Hershey (1906). During reconnaissance (Irwin, 1960), the rocks of the belt seemed virtually everywhere to be separated from younger rocks to the west either by ultramafic and granitic rocks or by faults. Although Hershey's Orleans fault corresponds to some extent to the western boundary of the western Paleozoic and Triassic belt, some parts of the trace of the fault as drawn by Hershey (1911) differ markedly from the boundary of the belt as drawn later (Irwin, 1960, pl. 1). Hershey stated that the Orleans fault dipped steeply east, and although he referred to the Orleans fault as a thrust fault, it was clearly in the sense of a high-angle reverse fault.

There is little positive evidence to refute Hershey's concept of an overall high-angle character of the faulting along much of the western boundary of the belt. At some localities, however, the fault is seen to dip gently eastward (fig. 6, locality 7). One of these is on a major spur ridge east of Hoopa. There the boundary is marked by a serpentine mass that is laced by abundant shear planes that dip gently eastward and that includes lenses of rodingite parallel to the shear planes. In addition to local suggestions of a gentle easterly dip of the fault boundary, several outliers of rocks similar to the rocks of the western Paleozoic and Triassic belt lie west of the boundary. Linear exposures of ultramafic rock form boundaries of some of these outliers, and owing in part to the structural significance attributed to ultramafic bodies in the Klamath Mountains and Coast Ranges (Irwin, 1964), these outliers are postulated to be klippen detached from a thrust plate of western Paleozoic and Triassic rocks that overrode rocks of the western Jurassic belt. The western boundary of the western Paleozoic and Triassic belt, although now perhaps marked by steep faults along much of its length, may fundamentally be the upturned edge of a low-angle thrust plate that once was continuous with outliers to the west.

The most obvious structure of sedimentary rocks of the western Jurassic belt is a slaty cleavage that commonly dips toward the eastern boundary (fig. 6, locality 8). The Galice Formation in Gasquet quadrangle (Cater and Wells, 1953) is deformed by north- to northeast-trending folds, parallel to the gross structural axis of the province, that are steeply overturned to the west. These are associated with high-angle reverse faults that are parallel to the axial planes of the folds. Faults with other trends postdate the folds and reverse faults but are thought to belong to the same (Nevadan) period of deformation. South of Gasquet quadrangle, the rocks tentatively assigned to the Galice Formation appear more phyllitic than to the north, and although the bedding and cleavage is commonly parallel to the long axis of the belt, the area has not been studied sufficiently for the structure to be known.

The problematic South Fork Mountain schist (fig. 6, locality 9) forms the western boundary of much of the Galice(?) Formation in California. The principal structural axis is essentially parallel to the trend of the belt, as shown by northwest-trending isoclinal primary folds that are overturned to the west. The primary folds are modified by secondary folds whose axes trend eastward. Metamorphism of the parent rock occurred during the primary folding. Regardless of whether the schist formed from Galice Formation or from Franciscan rocks, the general structural pattern resembles that of the lithic belts to the east and probably resulted from similar although perhaps younger (Late Cretaceous?) directed crustal stresses. Outliers of the schist that occur to the west along Redwood Mountain (fig. 6, locality 10) and in southwestern Oregon (Colebrooke Schist) are most readily explained as klippen (Irwin, 1964).

The inferred pre-Tertiary thrust structures are shown schematically in plan on figure 7. The lithic belts of the Klamath Mountains are considered thrust plates that successsively overlap adjacent plates to the west. Isolated patches of rocks correlative with a spe-

Photo 5. View to northeast across McCloud River Arm of Shasta Lake. Large area of light colored outcrop is McCloud Limestone, separated from underlying Baird Formation (darker slopes near lake) by band of intrusive mafic quartz diorite. Approximate position of intrusive contact between McCloud and quartz diorite is shown by black line. Beds in McCloud Limestone strike northwest across northeasterly trace of intrusive contact. Dark peak in right background is Horse Mountain, which consists of Dekkas Andesite. *Photo by J. P. Albers.*

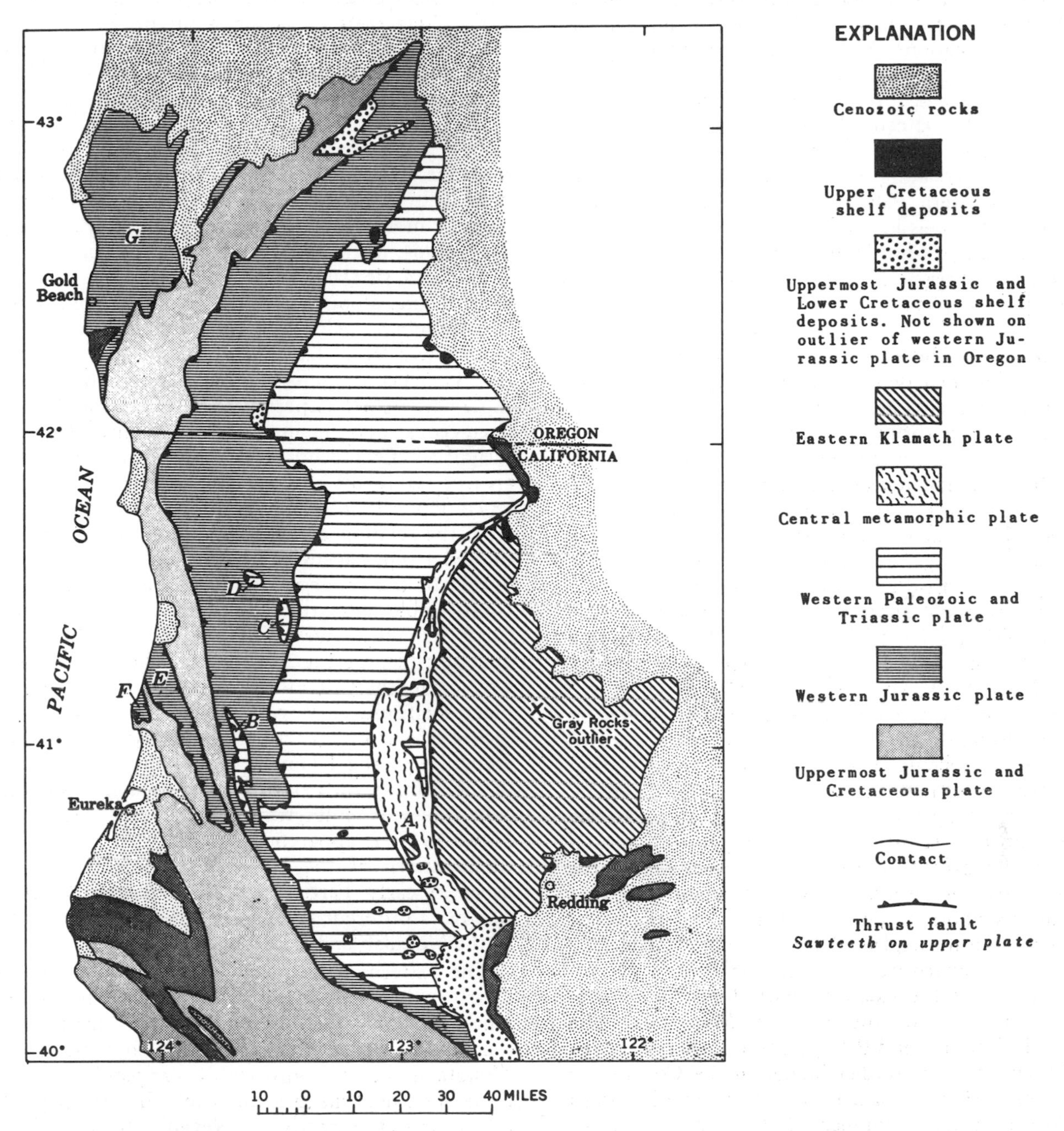

Figure 7. Principal postulated thrust plates of the Klamath Mountains and adjacent Coast Ranges. Thrust outliers are indicated by letter symbol: A, Oregon Mountain; B, Willow Creek; C, Prospect Hill; D, Flint Valley; E, Redwood Mountain; F, Patricks Point; and G, southwestern Oregon.

cific belt are interpreted to be thrust outliers (klippen) or windows of the plate to which the correlative rocks have been assigned. The granitic and ultramafic rocks are not outlined on the sketch, and are included arbitrarily with individual thrust plates. Although ultramafic rock intruded between certain of the thrust plates, its inclusion with individual plates does not in most cases seriously distort the outlines of the thrust plates shown on figure 7. An exception is the outline of the eastern Klamath plate, which here includes the erosional lip and exposed crest of the broad arch in the ultramafic sheet. Thus the eastern Klamath plate as shown on figure 7 suggests a reconstruction of the strata that formerly bridged the broad arch of ultramafic rocks. Because of this, the position of the Gray Rocks outlier, which forms part of this bridge, is shown only by a symbol.

The central metamorphic plate lies below the eastern Klamath plate and above the western Paleozoic and Triassic plate. The Oregon Mountain outlier (Bragdon Formation) of the eastern Klamath plate rests on the central metamorphic plate, and, as suggested by Davis and Lipman (1962), windows at several places along the central metamorphic plate expose portions (Stuart Fork Formation) of the underlying western Paleozoic and Triassic plate. Along its western border the western Paleozoic and Triassic plate lies on the western Jurassic plate, with the Willow Creek, Prospect Hill, and Flint Valley outliers of the western Paleozoic and Triassic plate presumably resting on the western Jurassic plate.

These thrust plates are depositionally overlapped at the south end of the Klamath Mountains by the prism of superjacent shelf deposits of the Great Valley, and thus are older than Late Jurassic (Tithonian) in age. Whether all these thrust plates were developed during a single brief orogenic episode is not clear. However, if all the relevant ultramafic rocks were emplaced during a single brief span of time in the Late Jurassic, between the middle Kimmeridgian and Tithonian Stages, a similar age span seems likely for the major thrusting. The thrusting, the emplacement of the Klamath ultramafic sheets, and the intrusion of granitic batholiths are tentatively considered closely timed sequential events of the Nevadan orogeny.

The South Fork Mountain and related schists are included with the western Jurassic plate as shown on figure 7, although rather than actually being part of the subjacent terrane, they may have formed from post-Nevadan (Franciscan) rocks through tectonic overpressure along the sole of a thrust. Owing to the thinness of this schistose rind, the gross structural picture is not greatly affected by whether the rind is directly above or directly below the thrust. In either case, the distribution and other features of the schist are mostly readily explained by the subjacent terrane being thrust westward over post-Nevadan (Franciscan) rocks of the Coast Ranges along the general western boundary of the Klamath Mountains. The Redwood Mountain and Patrick Point outliers of schist in California and the outlier including the Colebrooke Schist and other subjacent rocks in southwestern Oregon are shown as klippen of the western Jurassic plate.

The post-Nevadan eugeosynclinal (Franciscan) rocks along the west side of South Fork Mountain contain Early Cretaceous fossils. Even excluding the possibility of the South Fork Mountain schist being formed from these rocks, they are metamorphosed at least to the Chlorite 2 subzone in a narrow belt alongside the schist. It is noteworthy that in the Klamath Mountains only a few miles to the east of these metamorphosed post-Nevadan rocks, patches of Cretaceous strata of equivalent age but of a shelf facies lie depositionally on thrust plates of pre-Nevadan rocks. The metamorphism indicates that the thrusting along the western boundary of the Klamath Mountains was later than Early Cretaceous, and the abrupt change in facies of Early Cretaceous rocks across the province boundary suggests great horizontal translation along the thrust.

The thrust along the western boundary of the Klamath Mountains seems essentially continuous with the thrust fault along the west side of the Sacramento Valley, along which shelf deposits of the Great Valley sequence are thrust westward over eugeosynclinal Franciscan rocks with a horizontal translation of 50 miles or more (Irwin, 1964, p. 6–7; Bailey, Irwin, and Jones, 1964, p. 163–165). By analogy, horizontal translation of a similar order of magnitude is postulated for thrusting along the western boundary of the Klamath Mountains. Although the thrusting in both cases clearly was later than Early Cretaceous, a post-early Late Cretaceous age is suggested by a juxtaposition of superjacent shelf deposits of Late Jurassic and Early Cretaceous age against eugeosynclinal deposits of early Late Cretaceous age in the San Francisco Bay area of California and the Roseburg area of Oregon.

An upper limit to the age of the thrusting is inferred from the relation of Late Cretaceous shelf deposits to the older superjacent strata. In the Great Valley, deposition of the superjacent shelf deposits was virtually conformable into the late Late Cretaceous. In the Coast Ranges, however, the relation is one of great unconformity at the few places where the late Late Cretaceous shelf deposits are known to occur on the older shelf and eugeosynclinal rocks.

Post-Mesozoic structures generally are difficult to recognize in the Klamath Mountains, mainly because of the scarcity of Tertiary strata in which post-Mesozoic folds or faults would be readily distinguished. However, it is apparent that the gross arcuate structural pattern of the Klamath Mountains was established by early Tertiary and that subsequent deformation has a different style and was less intense than that of the Nevadan and Late Cretaceous.

The pattern of Cenozoic deformation, however, is clearly evident in the area covered by the Weaverville Formation of Oligocene(?) age. This formation, the oldest Tertiary deposit in the southern Klamath Mountains, lies unconformably on patches of Cretaceous shelf deposits at some places, but at other places nearby it rests directly on Nevadan terrane. This relation indicates that by Oligocene(?) time the Cretaceous deposits, which presumably once mantled much of the Nevadan terrane, had been mostly stripped off. It is not clear whether the stripping was accomplished principally during the latest Cretaceous or during the earliest Tertiary, but the profound denudation of the subjacent terrane may have furnished detritus for the Tyee Formation, which is as thick as 10,000 feet and is widely distributed in coastal Oregon (Snavely and Wagner, 1964).

The Weaverville Formation and associated patches of Cretaceous rocks are preserved chiefly as depressed blocks bordered by a series of northeast-trending Ter-

Photo 6. View of La Grange fault, looking northeast along U. S. Highway 299 in northwest corner of Weaverville quadrangle. Hillside to left of highway is exhumed footwall surface of fault, consisting of Salmon Schist with thin capping of mylonite. Approximate dip-slope trace of fault is shown by black line in right background. Rocks in background beyond trace of fault are chiefly highly-sheared Abrams Schist of hanging-wall block.

tiary faults. These faults are abundant throughout a northeast-trending zone that is at least 30 miles long and 10 miles wide. Other Tertiary faults that border the Weaverville Formation commonly trend northwest. Most of the Tertiary faults appear to be high-angle normal faults and some have a vertical displacement of several thousand feet.

The La Grange fault, one of the most important Tertiary faults, essentially defines the northwestern limit of the zone of recognizable northeast-trending faults. The footwall surface of this fault is remarkably well exposed where it has been exhumed at the La Grange hydraulic mine in the northwest corner of the Weaverville quadrangle. The fault here forms the northern end of the Oregon Mountain outlier of Bragdon Formation, which, along with the Abrams Mica Schist and the Weaverville Formation constitutes the hanging wall block. From the mine the fault extends for more than 10 miles northeast, forming the northwest boundary of the largest area of Weaverville Formation, and for most of this distance the footwall is Salmon Hornblende Schist.

REFERENCES

Albers, J. P., 1964, Geology of the French Gulch quadrangle, Shasta and Trinity Counties, California: U.S. Geol. Survey Bull. 1141-J, p. J1–J70.

Albers, J. P., and Robertson, J. F., 1961, Geology and ore deposits of east Shasta copper-zinc district, Shasta County, California: U.S. Geol. Survey Prof. Paper 338, 107 p.

Anderson, F. M., 1938, Lower Cretaceous deposits in California and Oregon: Geol. Soc. America Spec. Paper 16, 339 p.

Bailey, E. H., Irwin, W. P., and Jones, D. L., 1964, Franciscan and related rocks, and their significance in the geology of western California: California Div. Mines and Geology Bull. 183, 177 p.

Blake, M. C., Jr., 1965, Structure and petrology of low-grade metamorphic rocks, blueschist facies, Yolla Bolly area, northern California: Stanford Univ., Stanford, Calif., Ph.D. thesis, 92 p.

Blake, M. C., Jr., and Ghent, E. D., 1965, Regional glaucophane-schist-facies metamorphism in the northern Coast Ranges of California [abs.]: Geol. Soc. America Spec. Paper 82, p. 241.

Casey, Raymond, 1964, The Cretaceous Period, *in* The Phanerozoic time-scale: Geol. Soc. London Quart. Jour., v. 120S, p. 193–202.

Cater, F. W., Jr., and Wells, F. G., 1953, Geology and mineral resources of the Gasquet quadrangle, California-Oregon: U.S. Geol. Survey Bull. 995-C, p. 79–133.

Churkin, Michael, Jr., 1961, Silurian trilobites from the Klamath Mountains, California: Jour. Paleontology, v. 35, no. 1, p. 168–175.

—— 1965, First occurrence of graptolites in the Klamath Mountains, California: U.S. Geol. Survey Prof. Paper 525-C, p. C72–C73.

Churkin, Michael, Jr., and Langenheim, R. L., Jr., 1960, Silurian strata of the Klamath Mountains, California: Am. Jour. Sci., v. 258, no. 4, p. 258–273.

Cox, D. P., 1956, Geology of the Helena quadrangle, Trinity County, California: Stanford Univ., Stanford, Calif., Ph.D. thesis, 123 p.

Curtis, G. H., Evernden, J. F., and Lipson, J. I., 1958, Age determination of some granitic rocks in California by the potassium-argon method: California Div. Mines Spec. Rept. 54, 16 p.

Davis, G. A., 1963, Structure and mode of emplacement of Caribou Mountain pluton, Klamath Mountains, California: Geol. Soc. America Bull., v. 74, no. 3, p. 331–348.

—— 1965, Regional Mesozoic thrusting in the south-central Klamath Mountains of California [abs.]: Geol. Soc. America Spec. Paper 82, p. 248.

Davis, G. A., and Lipman, P. W., 1962, Revised structural sequence of pre-Cretaceous metamorphic rocks in the southern Klamath Mountains, California: Geol. Soc. America Bull., v. 73, no. 12, p. 1547–1552.

Davis, W. M., 1933, The lakes of California: California Jour. Mines and Geology, v. 29, nos. 1, 2, p. 175–236.

Diller, J. S., 1902, Topographic development of the Klamath Mountains: U.S. Geol. Survey Bull. 196, 69 p.

—— 1903a, Description of the Port Orford quadrangle [Oregon]: U.S. Geol. Survey Geol. Atlas, Folio 89, 6 p.

—— 1903b, Klamath Mountain section: Am. Jour. Sci., 4th ser., v. 15, p. 342–362.

—— 1906, Description of the Redding quadrangle [California]: U.S. Geol. Survey Geol. Atlas, Folio 138, 14 p.

—— 1907, The Mesozoic sediments of southwestern Oregon: Am. Jour. Sci., 4th ser., v. 23, p. 401–421.

—— 1911, The auriferous gravels of the Trinity River basin, California: U.S. Geol. Survey Bull. 470, p. 11–29.

—— 1914a, Mineral resources of southwestern Oregon: U.S. Geol. Survey Bull. 546, 147 p.

—— 1914b, Auriferous gravels in the Weaverville quadrangle, California: U.S. Geol. Survey Bull. 540, p. 11–21.

Dott, R. H., Jr., 1964, Classic Nevadan Orogenesis in southwestern Oregon [abs.]: Geol. Soc. America Spec. Paper 76, p. 197–198.

Ghent, E. D., 1963, Fossil evidence for maximum age of metamorphism in part of the Franciscan Formation, northern Coast Ranges, California: California Div. Mines and Geology Spec. Rept. 82, p. 41.

—— 1965, Glaucophane-schist facies metamorphism in the Black Butte area, northern Coast Ranges, California: Am. Jour. Sci., v. 263, no. 5, p. 385–400.

Hershey, O. H., 1901, Metamorphic formations of northwestern California: Am. Geologist, v. 27, p. 225–245.

—— 1903, The relation between certain river terraces and the glacial series in northwestern California: Jour. Geology, v. 11, p. 431–458.

—— 1906, Some western Klamath stratigraphy: Am. Jour. Sci., 4th ser., v. 21, p. 58–66.

—— 1911, Del Norte County [California] geology: Mineral and Sci., Press, v. 102, p. 468.

Hinds, N. E. A., 1932, Paleozoic eruptive rocks of the southern Klamath Mountains, California: California Univ., Dept. Geol. Sci. Bull., v. 20, no. 11, p. 375–410.

—— 1952, Evolution of the California landscape: California Div. Mines Bull. 158, 240 p.

Holdaway, M. J., 1962, Petrology and structure of metamorphic and igneous rocks of parts of northern Coffee Creek and Cecilville quadrangles, Klamath Mountains, California: California Univ., Berkeley, Ph.D. thesis, 202 p.

Imlay, R. W., 1959, Succession and speciation of the pelecypod *Aucella:* U.S. Geol. Survey Prof. Paper 314-G, p. 155–169.

—— 1960, Ammonites of Early Cretaceous (Valanginian and Hauterivian) from the Pacific Coast States: U.S. Geol. Survey Prof. Paper 334-F, p. 167–228.

Irwin, W. P., 1960, Geologic reconnaissance of the northern Coast Ranges and Klamath Mountains, California, with a summary of the mineral resources: California Div. Mines Bull. 179, 80 p.

—— 1963, Preliminary geologic map of the Weaverville quadrangle, California: U.S. Geol. Survey Mineral Inv. Field Studies Map MF-275, scale 1:62,500.

—— 1964, Late Mesozoic orogenies in the ultramafic belts of northwestern California and southwestern Oregon: U.S. Geol. Survey Prof. Paper 501-C, p. C1–C9.

Irwin, W. P., and Lipman, P.W., 1962, A regional ultramafic sheet in eastern Klamath Mountains, California: U.S. Geol. Survey Prof. Paper 450-C, art. 67, p. C18–C21.

Kinkel, A. R., Jr., Hall, W. E., and Albers, J. P., 1956, Geology and base-metal deposits of West Shasta copper-zinc district, Shasta County, California: U.S. Geol. Survey Prof. Paper 285, 156 p.

Kulp, J. L., 1961, Geologic time scale: Science, v. 133, no. 3459, p. 1105–1114.

Lanphere, M. A., and Irwin, W. P., 1965, Carboniferous isotopic age of metamorphism of the Salmon Hornblende Schist and Abrams Mica Schist, southern Klamath Mountains, California: U.S. Geol. Survey Prof. Paper 525-D, p. D27–D33.

Lydon, P. A., 1964, Unusual phosphatic rock: California Div. Mines and Geology, Mineral Inf. Service, v. 17, no. 5, p. 65–74.

MacGinitie, H. D., 1937, The flora of the Weaverville beds of Trinity County, California, *in* Sanborn, E. I., Eocene flora of Western America: Carnegie Inst. Washington Pub. 465, Contr. Paleontology, p. 84–151.

Maxson, J. H., 1933, Economic geology of portions of Del Norte and Siskiyou Counties, northwesternmost California: California Jour. Mines and Geology, v. 29, nos. 1, 2, p. 123–160.

Merriam, C. W., 1961, Silurian and Devonian rocks of the Klamath Mountains, California: U.S. Geol. Survey Prof. Paper 424-C, art. 216, p. C188–C190.

Miller, A. K., Furnish, W. M., Jr., and Clark, D. L., 1957, Permian ammonoids from western United States: Jour. Paleontology, v. 31, no. 6, p. 1057–1068.

Mineral Information Service, 1965, California Div. Mines and Geology, v. 18, no. 1, 19 p.

Olmsted, F. H., 1956, Summary of ground-water conditions in northwestern California, *in* Water resources, Appendix of Natural resources of northwestern California, preliminary report: U.S. Geol. Survey, U.S. Dept. Interior Pacific Southwest Field Comm., 93 p.

Peck, D. L., Imlay, R. W., and Popenoe, W. P., 1956, Upper Cretaceous rocks of parts of southwestern Oregon and northern California: Am. Assoc. Petroleum Geologists Bull., v. 40, no. 8, p. 1968–1984.

Pratt, W. P., 1964, Jurassic(?) regional metamorphism in the Marble Mountains, northern California [abs.]: Geol. Soc. America Spec. Paper 82, Ann. Mtg., Miami, Fla., 1964, Program, p. 154.

Romey, W. D., 1962, Geology of a part of the Etna Quadrangle, Siskiyou County, California: California Univ., Berkeley, Ph.D. thesis.

Sanborn, A. F., 1953, Geology and paleontology of a part of the Big Bend quadrangle, Shasta County, California [abs.]: Stanford Univ. Abs. Dissert., 1951–52, v. 27, p. 436–437.

—— 1960, Geology and paleontology of the southwest quarter of the Big Bend quadrangle, Shasta County, California: California Div. Mines Spec. Rept. 63, 26 p.

Seyfert, C. K., Jr., 1964, Geology of the Sawyers Bar area, Klamath Mountains, northern California: Stanford Univ., Stanford, Calif., Ph.D. thesis, 277 p.

Sharp, R. P., 1960, Pleistocene glaciation in the Trinity Alps of northern California: Am. Jour. Sci., v. 258, no. 5, p. 305–340.

Silberling, N. J., and Irwin, W. P., 1962, Triassic fossils from the southern Klamath Mountains, California: U.S. Geol. Survey Prof. Paper 450-B, art. 23, p. B60–B61.

Skinner, J. W., and Wilde, G. L., 1965, Permian biostratigraphy and fusulinid faunas of the Shasta Lake area, northern California: Kansas Univ., Harold N. Fiske Mem. Papers. (In press)

Snavely, P. D., Jr., and Wagner, H. C., 1964, Geologic sketch of northwestern Oregon: U.S. Geol. Survey Bull. 1181-M, 17 p.

Strand, R. G., 1962, Geologic map of California, Olaf P. Jenkins edition, Redding sheet: California Div. Mines and Geology.

—— 1964, Geologic map of California, Olaf P. Jenkins edition, Weed sheet: California Div. Mines and Geology.

Turner, F. J., 1938, Progressive regional metamorphism in southern New Zealand: Geol. Mag., v. 75, p. 160–174.

Wells, F. G., Hotz, P. E., and Cater, F. W., Jr., 1949, Preliminary description of the geology of the Kerby quadrangle, Oregon: Oregon Dept. Geology and Mineral Industries Bull. 40, 23 p.

Wells, F. G., and Peck, D. L., 1961, Geologic map of Oregon west of the 121st meridian: U.S. Geol. Survey Misc. Geol. Inv. Map I-325.

Wells, F. G., Walker, G. W., and Merriam, C. W., 1959, Upper Ordovician(?) and Upper Silurian formations of the northern Klamath Mountains, California: Geol. Soc. America Bull., v. 70, no. 5, p. 645–649.

Wilmarth, M. G., 1938, Lexicon of geologic names of the United States (including Alaska): U.S. Geol. Survey Bull. 896, pts. 1 and 2, 2396 p.

METAMORPHIC AND GRANITIC HISTORY OF THE KLAMATH MOUNTAINS

By Gregory A. Davis
University of Southern California, Los Angeles

INTRODUCTION

The orogenic history of the Klamath geological province as indicated by the age, duration, and areal extent of metamorphic and plutonic igneous events is poorly known. Detailed geologic studies of the last decade cover only about 25 percent of the California portion of the province, largely its central and southeastern areas. High relief, thick vegetative cover, and limited accessibility other than by trail has discouraged and hindered field work in the Klamath Mountains, as has structural complexity and a lack of distinctive marker units within many portions of this former eugeosynclinal terrane. Nevertheless, as in other formerly neglected areas of "basement rocks," detailed field studies coupled with an increasing use of radiometric dating have begun to decipher the Klamath geological record—one considerably more complex than that envisioned by Diller, Hershey, Hinds, and other geological pioneers of the province.

Following Irwin's terminology (1960) the Klamath province can be divided into four arcuate north-south lithic belts or subprovinces named from east to west, respectively: the eastern Paleozoic, the central metamorphic, the western Paleozoic and Triassic, and the western Jurassic subprovinces (fig. 1). Several revisions in Irwin's lithic belt designations which appear warranted on the basis of recent studies are discussed below.

Regionally metamorphosed rocks of variable grade are present in all four Klamath subprovinces, but only the central metamorphic and western Paleozoic and Triassic subprovinces are composed wholly of metamorphic rocks (exclusive of igneous intrusive bodies). Metamorphic relationships within the Klamath Mountains are complex because of several factors. At least two distinct periods of regional metamorphism can be recognized in the province, one late Paleozoic and the other Jurassic, but the extent of areal overlap between the two is unknown. This polymetamorphic history coupled with the widespread distribution throughout the province of nondistinctive and poorly fossiliferous eugeosynclinal parental rocks, for example, cherts, shales, and mafic volcanic rocks, makes it difficult, without radiometric dating, to assign a particular metamorphic terrane to a particular metamorphic event or to correlate one terrane with another.

Metamorphic relationships between subprovinces are further complicated by the tectonic nature of the subprovince boundaries. In the southeastern quarter of the Klamath Mountains these boundaries are major thrust zones between metamorphic terranes of different grade. Near Cecilville, California (fig. 1), where three of the four Klamath subprovinces are tectonically superposed, the structural and metamorphic sequence, bottom to top, is as follows: (1) the western Paleozoic and Triassic subprovince (lower greenschist facies); (2) the central metamorphic subprovince (upper greenschist and almandine-amphibolite facies); (3) the eastern Paleozoic subprovince (lower greenschist facies). Serpentinized peridotites of the sill-like Trinity ultramafic pluton separate the eastern Paleozoic subprovince from the underlying central metamorphic subprovince in this area, as elsewhere over a total area of approximately 1,000 square miles.

EASTERN PALEOZOIC SUBPROVINCE

Metamorphic relationships in the northern half of the eastern Paleozoic subprovince have been previously described by Wells and others (1959), Churkin and Langenheim (1960), and Davis and others (1965); regional metamorphism in the southern half of the subprovince has been discussed by Kinkel and others (1956) and Albers and Robertson (1961). The boundaries of the subprovince (fig. 1) are essentially those defined by Irwin (1960) except for two recently discovered klippen lying above central metamorphic rocks near Weaverville (Irwin, 1963) and Cecilville (Davis, work in progress).

In the northern part of the subprovince metamorphic relationships are uncertain for lack of detailed study. Sedimentary rocks of the oldest known unit, the Duzel Formation (Upper Ordovician and/or Lower Silurian), exhibit a variable degree of metamorphic recrystallization. Rocks of the formation near Callahan exhibit only incipient recrystallization within a few hundred yards of some ultramafic contacts. To the north and east, however, low-grade metamorphism is more complete and muscovite-chlorite-bearing phyllites, semischists, and phyllitic graywackes are widespread. Further to the east these rocks overlie unmetamorphosed Middle to Late Silurian sedimentary rocks of the Gazelle Formation along the Mallethead thrust fault (Churkin and Langenheim, 1960).

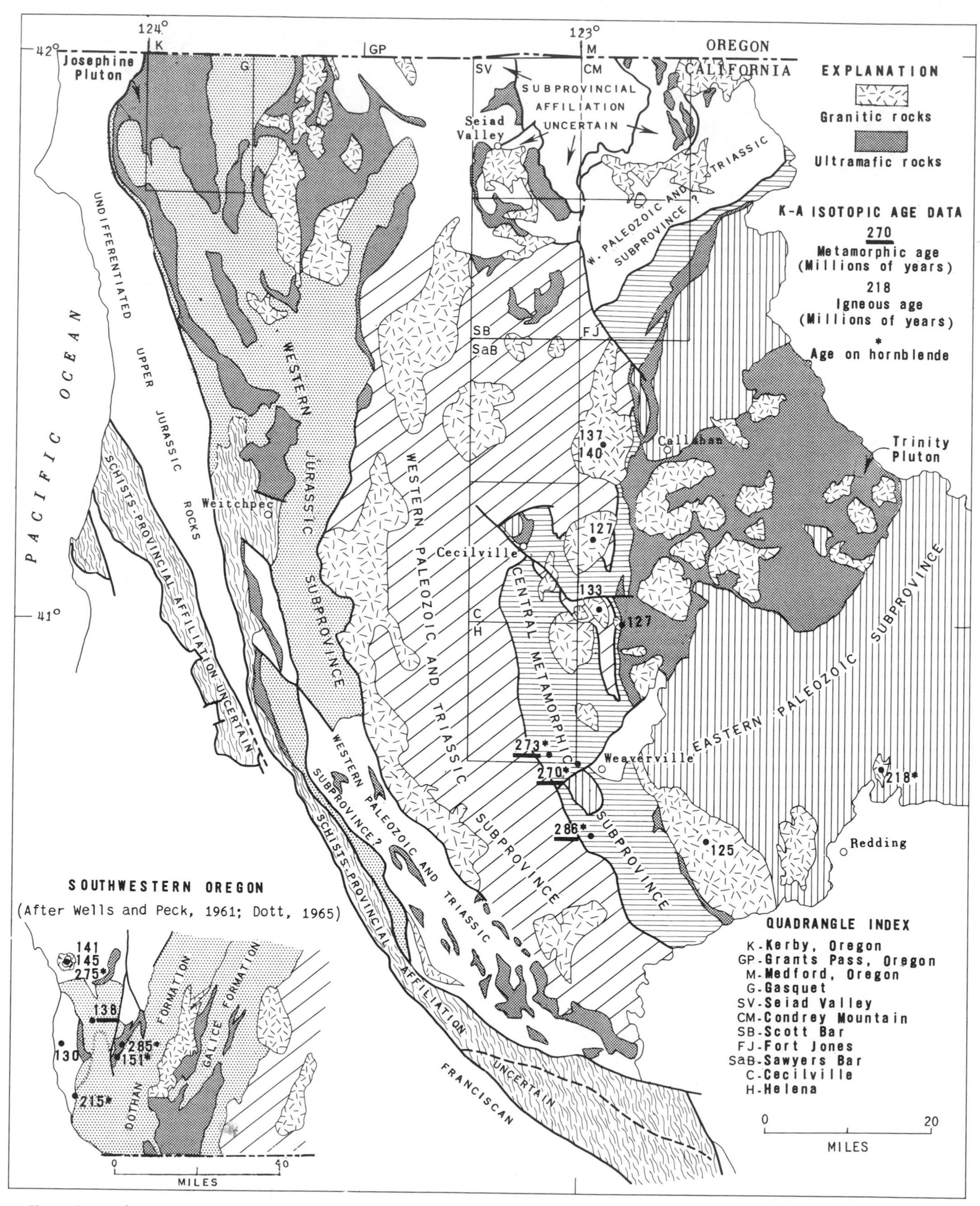

Figure 1. Geologic index map of the Klamath province, northwestern California, showing available isotopic age data, with inset map of southwestern Oregon showing additional isotopic ages. Index map modified after Weed (1963) and Redding (1962) sheets, Geologic Map of California.

Sedimentary rocks of the Mississippian Bragdon and Kennett Formations in the southern part of the subprovince are typically unmetamorphosed, except near pluton contacts, but Kinkel and others (1956) report that incipient to low-grade regional metamorphism has affected mafic volcanic rocks of the Middle Devonian(?) Copley Greenstone. Volcanic textures in Copley greenstones are usually preserved, although original mineral assemblages have been replaced by chlorite, epidote, albite, and carbonates. The grade of greenschist facies metamorphism and the prevalence of foliated rocks decrease eastward.

Regional metamorphism of the Copley Greenstone under conditions of the greenschist facies should not be equated with Late Jurassic albitization of some eastern Paleozoic rocks which is described by Kinkel and others (1956, p. 74) as "later and . . . unrelated in time to the formation of albite in the . . . Copley greenstone." Regional albitization and chloritization unaccompanied by the development of foliation produced rocks such as spilites, keratophyres, and albite granites, and affected all Jurassic and pre-Jurassic formations in the southern part of the province, including the Pit River and Mule Mountain granitic stocks. The latter stock was albitized after its emplacement into metamorphosed and foliated Copley greenstones (Kinkel and others, 1956, p. 47, 57), thus indicating a polymetamorphic history for the southern portion of the subprovince.

CENTRAL METAMORPHIC SUBPROVINCE

Metamorphic rocks within the central metamorphic subprovince were first described by O. H. Hershey (1901) as the Abrams Mica Schist and Salmon Hornblende Schist of probable Precambrian age. Studies in the Trinity Alps area north of Weaverville by Davis and Lipman (1962) led to revision of Hershey's schist nomenclature. The Abrams Mica Schist was recognized as a composite unit including metasedimentary rocks both above and below the Salmon Hornblende Schist, which were renamed the Grouse Ridge and Stuart Fork Formations, respectively. Because the Stuart Fork Formation is of lower regional metamorphic grade than the overlying Salmon and Grouse Ridge units, Davis and Lipman postulated the Stuart Fork-Salmon contact to be a major low-angle thrust fault and proposed a tentative correlation of the Stuart Fork Formation with low-grade metamorphic rocks in the adjacent western Paleozoic and Triassic subprovince. Subsequent work by Davis (1964) has confirmed the tectonic nature of the Stuart Fork-Salmon contact and the correlation of Stuart Fork rocks with those of the western Paleozoic and Triassic subprovince. Areas of Stuart Fork rocks within the boundaries of the central metamorphic subprovince are interpreted as fensters in a regional thrust plate of Salmon and Grouse Ridge rocks (fig. 1).

Detailed accounts of the petrology of the Grouse Ridge and Salmon Formations in the central part of the central metamorphic subprovince have been given by Davis, Holdaway, Lipman, and Romey (1965) and by Holdaway (1965). The metamorphic history of the Salmon and Grouse Ridge Formations includes progressive regional metamorphism under conditions of the upper greenschist and almandine-amphibolite facies, and incomplete, static retrogressive metamorphism under conditions of the lower greenschist facies. Rocks of the subprovince are characterized by complete recrystallization, the elimination of primary textures and structures, and the development of foliated and lineated metamorphic fabrics.

A simple increase in regional metamorphic grade of subprovince rocks from west to east as previously described (Davis and others, 1965) is no longer tenable, although D. P. Cox (Ph.D. thesis, Stanford Univ., 1956, p. 12–13) has described such a variation in the central Helena quadrangle where a calcic albite to oligoclase transition is present in Salmon hornblende schists. Grouse Ridge rocks in the area east and northeast of Cecilville, and most Salmon schists north of the Browns Meadow fault, contain clear, primary albite and other minerals characteristic of the upper greenschist facies. Oligoclase or albite-epidote pseudomorphs of calcic plagioclase, however, are widely distributed in recently discovered Grouse Ridge rocks south of Cecilville, as well as in those of the type locality along the eastern border of the central metamorphic subprovince.

Regional metamorphism of the Salmon Hornblende Schist, and therefore of the Grouse Ridge Formation, has been determined by Lanphere and Irwin (1965) as Late Pennsylvanian to Early Permian on the basis of three potassium-argon dates on hornblende from schists in the Weaverville area (270, 273, and 286 m.y., revised dates, M. A. Lanphere, written communication, 1965). The age and origin of the later, retrogressive metamorphic event are not known.

WESTERN PALEOZOIC AND TRIASSIC SUBPROVINCE

The few published accounts of metamorphic relationships in the western Paleozoic and Triassic subprovince include papers by Wells (1956) and Wells and associates in southern Oregon (1940, 1949), reconnaissance work in California by Irwin (1960), and studies of the Stuart Fork Formation within and adjacent to the central metamorphic subprovince (Davis and Lipman, 1962; Davis and others, 1965). Metasedimentary and metavolcanic rocks of the subprovince include, from south to north, the Chanchelulla Formation (Hinds, 1933), the Stuart Fork Formation, and the Applegate Group (Wells and others, 1949). Because of incomplete mapping and a paucity of fossils within rocks of the subprovince, the stratigraphic relationships between these units are not known.

Within southern Oregon and in the Cecilville and Helena quadrangles, California (fig. 1), the characteristic grade of regional metamorphism is that of the lower greenschist facies (chlorite subfacies). Primary tectures and structures are widespread in all rock types. Pillow structures, and vesicular, porphyritic, and pyroclastic textures are commonly preserved in metabasalts and meta-andesites, although original mineral constituents have been altered to assemblages of albite, actinolite, epidote, chlorite, and carbonates. In interlayered rocks of sedimentary origin the effects of metamorphic recrystallization are generally most obvious in limestones (increase in grain size) and argillaceous rocks (development of cleavage).

Glaucophane- and lawsonite-bearing rocks representative of the glaucophane schist facies have been found to date at two localities within the subprovince. A small isolated outcrop of fine-grained glaucophane-lawsonite schist was discovered by D. P. Cox (Ph.D. thesis, Stanford Univ., 1956, p. 27) within metasedimentary rocks in the southwestern corner of the Helena quadrangle. The writer has mapped a separate, more extensive occurrence of glaucophane-lawsonite phyllites, schists, and nonfoliated rocks in the Cecilville and Helena quadrangles. Here a north-south belt of glaucophanitic rocks 1,500–2,000 feet wide and 8–9 miles long crosses the quadrangle boundary approximately 1 mile west of the fault contact between the western Paleozoic and Triassic and central metamorphic subprovinces. The belt is bordered on eastern and western sides by low-grade metasedimentary and mafic metavolcanic rocks in which primary textures and structures are well preserved and mineral assemblages are those of the chlorite subfacies of the greenschists facies. In contrast, rocks within the glaucophane schist belt are generally characterized by penetrative deformation and most, although not all, are foliated. At the northern end of the belt 1 mile north of the Salmon-Trinity drainage divide glaucophane-lawsonite-bearing rocks grade into sheared greenstones and metasedimentary rocks. Petrologic study of the rocks of the belt is in progress.

Metamorphic rocks within the biotite subfacies of the greenschist facies are present in the Sawyers Bar quadrangle to the north of the Cecilville quadrangle and locally in areas south of Cecilville. Lipman (*in* Davis and others, 1965) reports albite and biotite in metacherts in the southern part of the Stuart Fork fenster within the central metamorphic subprovince. Biotite is also a constituent of schistose metacherts within 1,000–2,500 feet of the thrust contact with the central metamorphic subprovince in the Cecilville quadrangle south of Cecilville. At even greater distances (up to 4,000 feet) below the thrust plate recrystallization of metacherts becomes apparent in the field and a penetrative slip surface is first noted. Within the thrust zone the muscovite-biotite-quartz schists, locally phyllonitized, are tectonically intermixed with foliated and unfoliated metavolcanic rocks of the subprovince and phyllonitized Salmon hornblende schists.

The increase in grade of metasedimentary rocks upwards from chlorite to biotite subfacies towards the thrust plate can be attributed either to dislocational metamorphism within the thrust zone or to thermal effects on low-grade rocks produced by the tectonic emplacement over them *during* regional metamorphism of a metamorphic sheet of higher temperature (almandine-amphibolite facies). The biotite in metacherts in the southern part of the Stuart Fork fenster may also be related to thrust faulting, or it may represent an increase to the east in the grade of regional metamorphism which has affected the subprovince.

Most of the northern half of the Sawyers Bar quadrangle lies within a biotite zone in which metasedimentary and some metavolcanic rocks contain the distinctive assemblage of biotite and albite (C. K. Seyfert, Ph.D. thesis, Stanford Univ., 1965). Biotite-albite-bearing rocks grade northwards into oligoclase or andesine-bearing rocks of the almandine-amphibolite facies. The facies transition approximates in position the northern boundary of the Sawyers Bar quadrangle with the Scott Bar quadrangle. Seyfert (*op. cit.*, p. 42) believes that the presence of biotitic metamorphic rocks in the Sawyers Bar quadrangle is "at least in part" due to the large number of granitic plutons in the area, but the continued increase in grade to the north, where granitic plutons are absent, is indicative that the variation is predominantly regional in nature and independent of subsequent plutonism.

W. P. Pratt (Ph.D. thesis, Stanford Univ., 1964) reports that the assemblage andesine (or oligoclase)-hornblende-epidote is representative of mafic metavolcanic rocks found throughout the Marble Mountains area in the Scott Bar quadrangle. In many of the mafic metavolcanic rocks relict porphyritic and pyroclastic textures are present, although most rocks of both sedimentary and volcanic origin have a faint to well-developed foliation. A general increase in the degree of foliation development eastwards across the quadrangle is reported by Pratt (*op. cit.*, p. 79), but even within foliated sequences there are structural domains in which foliation is absent or only poorly developed and relict textures and structures are preserved. Retrogressive effects of a localized nature, including the saussuritization of plagioclase, are noted by Pratt in some rocks of the Marble Mountains terrane.

In summary, rocks of the western Paleozoic and Triassic subprovince within California increase in regional metamorphic grade northwards across the Helena, Cecilville, Sawyers Bar, and Scott Bar quadrangles from the lower greenschist facies to the almandine-amphibolite facies. No major structural breaks across this portion of the subprovince have been mapped so that metasedimentary and metavolcanic rocks within this area probably constitute a continuous terrane from the structural standpoint. In the writer's opinion, however, the extension of the sub-

Photo 1. Trinity Dam. *Photo by Phil Merrit.*

province to the east of the Scott Bar quadrangle and north to the type area of the Applegate Group in southern Oregon has not yet been demonstrated. Accordingly, metamorphic and structural relationships within the area which includes the Seiad Valley, Condrey Mountain, and Fort Jones 15-minute quadrangles, California, and the southern portions of the 30-minute Grants Pass and Medford quadrangles, Oregon, are described separately below.

SEIAD VALLEY—CONDREY MOUNTAIN—FORT JONES AREA

The writer is indebted to Preston E. Hotz and to Gordon L. Medaris, whose work in the Condrey Mountain and Seiad Valley quadrangles, respectively, is in large part the basis for the following discussion; both studies are in progress at the time of this writing and findings reported herein are subject to revision.

Approximately 250 square miles of the central part of the Seiad Valley-Condrey Mountain area along the Oregon-California border are underlain by highly foliated, low-grade schists of the greenschist facies (fig. 1). This schist unit, which appears to be the lowermost unit in the region in a structural sense, has been previously referred to as the "old schists" (Wells and others, 1940) and the "pre-Upper Triassic schists" (Wells, 1956). Hotz (written communication, 1965) describes rocks of the unit as of two main types: quartz-muscovite schists, commonly graphitic, and chlorite-actinolite-epidote schists. The age of the schists, as for all metamorphic rocks in the vicinity, is unknown.

The low-grade schists are apparently completely surrounded and in tectonic contact with metavolcanic and metasedimentary rocks assignable to the almandine-amphibolite facies. These higher grade rocks include in the Condrey Mountain quadrangle a lower member of oligoclase or andesine-bearing hornblende schists and an upper, largely metasedimentary, member of muscovite-biotite phyllites and schists, quartzites, marbles, and hornblende schists. Both members are extensively intruded by serpentinized ultramafic rocks, in contrast to the central greenschist terrane which is nearly barren of ultramafic intrusions. Hornblende schists in the northeastern corner of the Scott Bar quadrangle mapped by Pratt (Ph.D. thesis, Stanford Univ., 1964) as the Townsend Gulch Schist probably occupy a structural position comparable to the lower member of hornblende schists in the Condrey Mountain quadrangle.

Hotz (written communication, 1965) describes the contact between the low-grade schists and the higher grade rocks to the east as a moderate to steeply dipping reverse fault along which the higher grade rocks have moved over the schists of greenschist facies. Medaris (personal communication, 1965) reports that the western contact of the greenschist terrane with ultramafic rocks, hornblende schists, and amphibolites north of Seiad Valley is a west-dipping fault.

Boundary relationships of the high-grade rocks with metamorphic units at greater distances from the greenschist terrane are not yet completely clear. Amphibolites in the Seiad Valley area appear to grade downwards into epidote-hornblende schists of lower metamorphic grade and upwards into lower grade rocks of the Applegate Group (Medaris, personal communication, 1965). A transition between rocks of the Applegate Group and rocks of the almandine-amphibolite facies in the Grants Pass quadrangle north of the greenschist terrane has also been reported by Wells (1956). In the Condrey Mountain area the high-grade rocks are overlain, along a thrust fault in the few areas where the contact is exposed and is not occupied by igneous intrusions, by interlayered metavolcanic and metasedimentary rocks of similar grade which pass eastwards and southwards into weakly metamorphosed argillites, slates, cherts, and mafic volcanic rocks (Hotz, written communication, 1965). These low-grade rocks probably extend southwards into the Fort Jones quadrangle where they are in fault contact, approximately along the Scott Bar-Fort Jones quadrangle boundary, with the high-grade rocks of the Marble Mountains area described above. They have been correlated with the Applegate Group by Wells and others (1959) and included within the western Paleozoic and Triassic subprovince by Irwin (1964), although neither correlation can as yet be proved.

In summary, a highly foliated, low-grade metamorphic terrane (greenschist facies) along the Oregon-California border is surrounded tectonically, and possibly overlain, by higher grade metamorphic rocks (almandine-amphibolite facies). A gradation outwards from rocks of the almandine-amphibolite facies to weakly metamorphosed volcanic and sedimentary rocks is reported to the west, north, and east of the central greenschist terrane, although structural relationships between the high-grade and outer low-grade rocks apparently vary. If metasedimentary and metavolcanic rocks of the almandine-amphiobolite facies in the Marble Mountains overlie the Townsend Gulch Schist, as Pratt postulates (Ph.D. thesis, Stanford Univ., 1965), then the decrease in grade of regional metamorphism south of the Marble Mountains may be of similar nature to that noted on all other sides of the central greenschist terrane.

The central greenschist or "old schists" terrane has been correlated with the central metamorphic subprovince by Irwin (1960, 1964), although its structural position and metamorphic grade are not those this writer would expect if the correlation is valid. Irwin (1964) has assigned the higher grade rocks which border (and overlie?) the central terrane to the western Paleozoic and Triassic subprovince. Gradations reported between rocks of the almandine-amphibolite facies and lower grade rocks of the Applegate Group in the Seiad Valley and Grants Pass quadrangle support this correlation, but additional confirmation of the gradational relationship is needed in light of conflicting relationships elsewhere.

Sequential and petrologic similarities exist between rocks of the almandine-amphibolite facies of the Scott Bar, Condrey Mountain, and Seiad Valley quadrangles, and the Salmon-Grouse Ridge sequence of the central metamorphic subprovince. It is doubtful, however, that the two areas of high-grade rocks are at present structurally continuous, although the possibility does exist that both metamorphic sequences were originally derived from common parental rocks during the same metamorphic event. Lack of structural continuity between the two areas is indicated by the observation that low-grade rocks which appear to grade into or to overlie the northern high-grade terrane are overthrust by rocks of the central metamorphic subprovince near Cecilville, and probably along the southern boundary of the Condrey Mountain quadrangle (fig. 1).

WESTERN JURASSIC SUBPROVINCE

The western Jurassic subprovince, within California the least studied of the four Klamath subprovinces, was defined by Irwin (1960) to include the Galice Formation of middle Late Jurassic age and what he believed to be its locally developed metamorphic equivalents, the South Fork Mountain, Weitchpec, Kerr Ranch, and Colebrooke schists. A thick sequence of volcanic and metavolcanic rocks below sedimentary and metasedimentary rocks of the Galice Formation is particularly well developed in southwestern Oregon. This sequence was originally mapped by Wells and Walker (1953) as the Rogue Formation, but was later included within the Galice Formation by Cater and Wells (1954).

The position of the western boundary of the subprovince, and hence the western boundary of the Klamath province, is still subject to question. R. H. Dott, to whom appreciation is extended for the use of material unpublished at the time of this writing, has presented strong evidence (1965) that the Dothan Formation of southwestern Oregon properly belongs to the western Jurassic belt and is probably older than the Galice Formation which borders it to the east (fig. 1). Dott's position, accepted in this paper, contrasts with that of Irwin (1960, 1964) who assigns the Dothan Formation to the Coast Range province.

Within California the western boundary of the subprovince is drawn by Irwin (1960, 1964), to include a narrow, fault-bounded belt of low-grade schists, the South Fork Mountain Schist, which separates Franciscan rocks on the northern Coast Ranges from Galice(?) rocks for nearly 120 miles (fig. 1). Serpentinized ultramafic rocks are present along much of the eastern fault contact of both the South Fork Mountain Schist and similar schists which extend southward from South Fork Mountain along the western side of the Sacramento Valley. These schists, at least from South Fork Mountain to the south, generally have lawsonite- and aragonite-bearing mineral assemblages characteristic of the glaucophane schist facies (Blake and Ghent, 1964; Ghent, 1965). Irwin (1960, p. 29) assigns the South Fork Mountain Schist to the Klamath province since schists exposed near Weitchpec and believed to be the northern part of the South Fork Mountain belt grade into slates and phyllites correlated with the Galice Formation. At the southern end of the belt, however, Ghent (1965) believes that the schists of South Fork Mountain are continuous with those to the south which he and others, including Irwin (1960, fig. 3), tentatively assign to the Franciscan Formation. The metamorphism of these southern schists is younger than Klamath metamorphic events dated elsewhere. Blake and Ghent (1964, p. 31) report that "Late Jurassic and Early Cretaceous fossils were found in lawsonite- and aragonite-bearing metagraywackes at four separate localities, indicating a post-Early Cretaceous period of metamorphism."

Throughout the western Jurassic subprovince the presence of slates, phyllites, and altered graywackes and volcanic rocks attests to widespread, but low-grade regional metamorphism. Locally, higher grade and more thoroughly recrystallized rocks are found, including schists, gneisses, and amphibolites. Gradations between such rocks and parental rocks in the Dothan and Galice Formations have been described in a number of areas. In the Collier Butte-Agness area of southwestern Oregon micaceous and chloritic schists of the Colebrooke Formation grade southward across the Rogue River into sandstones, mudstones, conglomerates, and greenstones of the Dothan Formation (Dott, 1965). Metamorphism of the Colebrooke Formation has been radiometrically dated at 138 m.y. (whole rock potassium-argon date on quartz-mica schist; Dott, 1965). This Late Jurassic date is in agreement with other limiting evidence on the time of metamorphism: a radiometric age of unmetamorphosed Dothan rhyolite of 149 m.y. (whole rock potassium-argon; Dott, 1965), and the unconformable relationship between Colebrooke metamorphic rocks and unmetamorphosed late Late Jurassic (Portlandian) conglomerates of the Myrtle Formation in an area about 25 miles north of Agness (R. H. Dott, Jr., written communication, 1965).

In the 15-minute Galice quadrangle, Oregon, to the northeast of the Collier Butte area, low-grade, mafic to silicic metavolcanic rocks of the Rogue Member of the Galice Formation grade into amphibole gneisses, quartz schists, and quartz-garnet-mica gneisses with mineral assemblages characteristic of the upper greenschist and almandine-amphibolite facies (Wells and Walker, 1953). These rocks extend southward into the 30-minute Kerby quadrangle, Oregon, where they were originally described as being older than the Galice Formation and possibly correlative with high-grade metamorphic equivalents of the Applegate Group in the Medford quadrangle (Wells and others, 1949). Their subsequent recognition as metamorphic equivalents of the Galice Formation points out the difficulties of correlating one metamorphic unit with another solely on the basis of petrologic similarities.

REGIONAL METAMORPHISM AND ULTRAMAFIC INTRUSIONS

A recurring problem in Klamath geological studies and one of importance in this discussion is the relationship between metamorphism of regional type and the intrusion of ultramafic rocks. The problem arises from the close spatial association of most of the higher grade Klamath metamorphic terranes with ultramafic intrusions, although ultramafic rocks also intrude Klamath terranes where metamorphism has not occurred or is only of low grade. As examples of the former association, schists, gneisses, and amphibolites of the almandine-amphibolite facies are bordered or extensively intruded by ultramafic rocks in the Galice and Kerby quadrangles in the western Jurassic subprovince, in the Condrey Mountain-Seiad Valley-Marble Mountains area, and in the central metamorphic subprovince (Grouse Ridge Formation).

It is the variability of contact relationships between ultramafic and surrounding country rocks both on a regional scale and in given local areas, that has obscured possible genetic relationships between ultramafic intrusions and the foliated metamorphic rocks which border them at some localities. For example, high-grade metamorphic equivalents of the Galice Formation in the Galice and Kerby quadrangles are present only along the contacts of a narrow apophysis of the extensive Josephine peridotite sheet. Nevertheless, the metamorphic rocks are only discontinuously present along the apophysis (Wells and others, 1949); there is no consistent relationship between width of the apophysis and width of the belt of metamorphic rocks (up to 2 miles), and similar rocks are not found adjacent to other apophyses of the same pluton in this area. Metamorphic effects are not present in Galice rocks along the main contact of the Josephine pluton in the Gasquet quadrangle of California immediately to the south (Cater and Wells, 1954, p. 98, 112).

The most striking spatial association between ultramafic intrusions and metamorphic rocks of moderate to high grade is in the metamorphic terrane which surrounds the low-grade "old schists" of the California-Oregon border area (see, for example, the geologic map of the Medford quadrangle, Oregon, Wells, 1956, or the Weed sheet of the *Geologic Map of California*, Strand, 1963). C. K. Seyfert (Ph.D. thesis, Stanford Univ., 1965, p. 166) has postulated that the presence of rocks of the almandine-amphibolite facies in the Marble Mountains of the Scott Bar quadrangle may be due to metamorphic effects from the numerous large ultramafic bodies in the area. W. P. Pratt (Ph.D. thesis, Stanford Univ., 1964, p. 74), however, has concluded that intrusion of the major ultramafic bodies in the Scott Bar quadrangle probably postdated regional metamorphism.

Near Seiad Valley the metamorphic grade in metavolcanic rocks increases both up and down structure towards a large sill-like peridotite body in the Red Butte-Kangaroo Mountain area (G. Medaris, personal communication, 1965). Amphibolites (almandine-amphibolite facies) surround the largely unserpentinized ultramafic body on all sites except along the eastern fault contact with the "old schists," and pyroxene granulites are locally developed at the intrusive contact. Medaris believes that there is a close time relationship between regional metamorphism, penetrative deformation of the metamorphic rocks, and ultramafic emplacement in the Seiad Valley area, and that the higher grades of metamorphism are very likely related to the peridotite intrusion at Red Butte. The amphibolitic rocks which border the peridotite appear to this writer to be very similar to recrystallized hornblende schists found within contact aureoles of some granitic plutons in the central metamorphic subprovince.

One of the largest ultramafic bodies in the Klamath province is the sheetlike Trinity pluton which separates the central metamorphic and eastern Paleozoic subprovinces. Lipman (1964) has postulated that contact metamorphism acting downward from the Trinity pluton might account for metamorphic relationships observed below the peridotite sheet, principally (1) the lower grade of the Stuart Fork Formation as opposed to that of overlying units, and (2) the coarser grain size of Grouse Ridge amphibolites as compared with Salmon schists of comparable composition. A tectonic alternative for explaining these relationships has been offered elsewhere (Davis and others, 1965), although Hershey (1901, p. 240) considered the problem of metamorphism of country rocks by the Trinity pluton in another light—the absence of metamorphism or appreciable metamorphism of eastern Paleozoic rocks (his "Devono-Carboniferous" series) above the ultramafic pluton. In Hershey's words:

> "It would be too remarkable a case of selection to suppose that the peridotyte converted thousands of feet of strata into mica and hornblende schists in one area, and that in an immediately adjoining area . . . failed to develop . . . even a narrow contact zone of similar schist. The inference is unavoidable that the schists are a distinct series, as a whole much more highly metamorphosed than the Devono-Carboniferous, and that at least to the extent that their alteration exceeds that of the other series, the metamorphism is not due to the intrusion of peridotyte."

The mobility of ultramafic rock masses, during primary emplacement and secondary or "cold" intrusion related to later deformation, seriously complicates metamorphic-ultramafic relationships. The absence of a metamorphic contact zone along a particular ultramafic contact can be attributed, for example, to disruption and "erosion" of contact rocks by primary or secondary movements within the ultramafic body (cf. P. W. Lipman, Ph.D., thesis, Stanford Univ., 1962, p. 67), or alternatively, to a location at present of the ultramafic rocks which has resulted from secondary intrusion and is far removed from the original site of emplacement where metamorphic effects might be found.

There appears to be no consistent relationship between the development of foliated metamorphic rocks and the degree of serpentinization of ultramafic bodies in contact with them. In the Kerby quadrangle serpentinites and unserpentinized peridotites occur in contact with both metamorphosed and unmetamorphosed rocks of the Galice Formation (Wells and others, 1949, map). Ultramafic intrusions within gneisses and amphibolites in the Medford quadrangle are predominantly serpentinized (Wells, 1956), whereas metamorphic rocks of similar grade and structural position in the Seiad Valley area are intruded by peridotites which are largely unserpentinized. These variable relationships may result from factors difficult to assess, such as the extent and effects of secondary intrusion, or the size, shape, and level of exposure of partly serpentinized ultramafic bodies.

It is the writer's opinion, and one which will no doubt be contested, that the variations in regional metamorphic grade previously noted for the three easternmost Klamath subprovinces and the Seiad Valley-Condrey Mountain area are due to factors operative prior to ultramafic emplacement in these areas and unrelated to it. Localized upgrading of regionally metamorphosed rocks by contact metamorphism does appear to have occurred adjacent to some large and predominantly unserpentinized peridotitic plutons, as for example, in the Seiad Valley area and adjacent to the Josephine pluton in the Kerby and Galice quadrangles (although in this latter example tectonic and intrusive complications of original contact relationships between ultramafic and metamorphic rocks appear likely).

GRANITIC INTRUSIONS

Granitic intrusions are present throughout the Klamath province, but particularly concentrated within a central or axial zone which excludes most of the western Jurassic and eastern Paleozoic subprovinces (fig. 1). The plutons of the province are typically of dioritic, quartz-dioritic, or granodioritic composition, although gabbros and quartz monzonites represent compositional extremes present in some intrusions. Compositional variations within single plutons have been attributed by different authors to multiple intrusion, assimilation of wall rocks, and magmatic differentiation *in situ* and at depth prior to emplacement. Many of the larger Klamath plutons are composite bodies, with the outer intrusive units characteristically the oldest and most mafic in composition.

Within the central metamorphic subprovince the rocks of most plutons exhibit much higher Na_2O/K_2O ratios than do calc-alkaline granitic rocks of comparable silica percentage from the Sierra Nevada batholith. Reasons for this differentiation trend toward sodic rocks of trondhjemitic composition have been discussed by Moore (1959), Davis (1963), and Lipman (1963), but the matter is at present unresolved, as is the areal extent within the Klamath Mountains of such differentiation. The English Peak batholith in the Sawyers Bar quadrangle, for example, exhibits a normal calc-alkaline trend of compositional variation from gabbros to quartz monzonites (C. K. Seyfert, Ph.D. thesis, Stanford Univ., 1965).

Granitic plutons in the Klamath Mountains are generally aligned with their long axes parallel to the north-south arcuate trend of the province. Their predominant mode of emplacement as indicated by largely concordant contacts and the deflection of country rock structures around them was by forceful intrusion. Most of the more equidimensional plutons studied to date are domical in internal form (cf. Davis and others, 1965, pl. 1). The more elongate plutons, which seem particularly characteristic of the western Paleozoic and Triassic subprovince, are probably sheetlike in shape. One such dioritic intrusion in the Kerby quadrangle is described by Wells and others (1949) as a sill, 20 miles long, 13,000–20,000 feet thick, and dipping to the east at approximately 60°. The sill has been emplaced along the contact zone between the Dothan Formation and the overlying Josephine peridotite sheet. Another sill-like granitic pluton, ranging from gabbro to quartz diorite in composition, is present in the southern part of the Condrey Mountain quadrangle (P. Hotz, written communication, 1965). This southward-dipping intrusion also follows a major contact, probably a thrust fault, between hornblende schists and higher, weakly metamorphosed sedimentary and volcanic rocks.

On the basis of general geological relationships the age of the granitic plutons in the Klamath Mountains has been considered as Late Jurassic or Early Cretaceous by most geologists (cf. Irwin, 1960). Recent potassium-argon age dating of Klamath granitic rocks has partly supported this supposition, but has also revealed the presence within the province of granitic rocks considerably older than Late Jurassic.

The existence of widespread plutonism in the Klamath province during the Late Jurassic is indicated by potassium-argon dates from rocks of granitic plutons in the central metamorphic subprovince and the western Jurassic subprovince in southwestern Oregon (fig. 1). Six biotite-determined dates on five plutons in the former subprovince range from 125 m.y. to 140 m.y. (Davis and others, 1965); across the Klamath province in southwestern Oregon, Dott (1965) reports dates of 130 m.y., 141–145 m.y. (biotite), and 151 m.y. (hornblende) for the diorites of the Grizzly Mountain, Pearse Peak, and Collier Butte plutons, respectively. Four of the six dates determined from biotites in granitic rocks of the central metamorphic subprovince are Early Cretaceous using Kulp's 1961 time-scale, but geological relationships would seem to require that even the youngest of the dated plutons, the Shasta Bally batholith, be Late Jurassic in age (Irwin, 1960, p. 57–58). Recent studies on potassium-argon dating of biotite have indicated that biotite ages are typically younger and geologically less reliable than dates from hornblendes in the same specimens (Kistler and others, 1965; Hart, 1964).

Hornblende-determined pre-Jurassic dates on dioritic rocks in the northwestern and southeastern corners of the Klamath province, together with similar radiometric ages for the Salmon Hornblende Schist in the central metamorphic subprovince, indicate an earlier Klamath orogenic episode of unexpectedly broad areal extent. Hornblende from the Pit River Diorite in the southern part of the eastern Paleozoic subprovince has been dated as Early to Middle Triassic in age (218 m.y., Evans, 1965). A comparable early age for the nearby Mule Mountain stock appears reasonable, since both it and the Pit River stock were regionally albitized prior to Late Jurassic emplacement of the Shasta Bally batholith (Kinkel and others, 1956, p. 47).

Horneblende dates of 285 m.y., 275 m.y., and 215 m.y. are cited by Dott (1965) for the Saddle Mountain Diorite, the Pearse Peak Diorite, and a mafic dike rock in southwestern Oregon, respectively. The dates appear to be anomalously old for rocks apparently intrusive into the western Jurassic subprovince, but their striking similarity to dates on the Pit River Diorite and the Salmon Hornblende Schist (286 m.y. to 218 m.y.) lends them credence. Dott (1965) has suggested that the dike rock and the Saddle Mountain Diorite may be old crustal material brought up along fault zones in the ultramafic rock with which they are associated. Field relationships of the Pearse Peak Diorite, however, are described by Dott as inconsistent with this explanation. An alternative explanation for the Pearse Peak pluton is that dioritic basement rocks of Paleozoic age were remobilized and intruded to higher crustal levels during Late Jurassic orogeny. This possibility would be in accord with the younger, biotite-defined age for the Pearse Peak pluton (141 m.y. to 145 m.y.) and other radiometric evidence for Late Jurassic metamorphism and igneous intrusion in the southwestern Oregon area.

CONCLUSIONS

Too little is yet known, as the preceding discussion shows, to draw an adequate synthesis of the metamorphic and plutonic history of the Klamath Mountains. The incomplete picture which has begun to emerge, however, is of two major provincewide periods of regional metamorphism, deformation, and igneous intrusion—the first broadly dated isotopically as Late Pennsylvanian to Early or Middle Triassic, and the second as Late Jurassic.

The existence of the older orogenic period in the westernmost part of the province can at present only be inferred from several anomalously old radiometric dates, but across the province metamorphic rocks of the central metamorphic subprovince are Late Pennsylvanian to Early Permian in age on the basis of limited isotopic age data. The original extent of the metamorphic terrane of which the Salmon and Grouse Ridge Formations are part cannot be determined with certainty, since the central metamorphic subprovince is an allochthonous plate which overlies the western Paleozoic and Triassic subprovince and is in turn overlain by the eastern Paleozoic subprovince. Nevertheless, a tentative reconstruction of the Late Paleozoic metamorphic terrane can be hazarded in the limited light of present knowledge, with the admitted possibility that future studies, particularly geochronologic, may require its revision.

In the southeastern Klamath Mountains south of lat 41°15′ N., a broadly symmetrical terrane can be discerned in which metamorphic grade generally decreases to the east and to the west from the almandine and staurolite zones of regional metamorphism in the central metamorphic subprovince. Rocks of the western Paleozoic and Triassic subprovince are only incipiently metamorphosed in the westernmost portions of the Helena and Cecilville quadrangles, metamorphosed to chlorite zone assemblages to the east, and possibly regionally metamorphosed to biotite zone assemblages in the Stuart Fork fenster farther east. In the southern part of the eastern Paleozoic subprovince chlorite zone assemblages in the Copley Greenstone are more widespread in western areas than in eastern.

This crude, but apparently real symmetry of decreasing metamorphic grade in rocks to both east and west of the central metamorphic subprovince is indicative that rocks of all three subprovinces were affected by the Late Paleozoic regional metamorphism dated in rocks of the central subprovince. The minimum east-west width of the postulated Late Paleozoic metamorphic terrane prior to its disruption and telescoping by westward thrusting must have been on the order of 50 miles, although the absence of some zones in this reconstruction, e.g. the biotite zone between the central metamorphic and eastern Paleozoic subprovinces, suggests that the terrane was substantially wider. In the Cecilville area minimum thrust displacements of the central metamorphic and eastern Paleozoic subprovinces are estimated by the writer to be 15–20 and 20 miles, respectively.

If, to the contrary, regional metamorphism in the western Paleozoic and Triassic and eastern Paleozoic subprovinces was Late Jurassic in age, as has generally been believed, then the older rocks of the central metamorphic subprovince between them do not clearly exhibit its effects. Retrogressive mineral assemblages are present in rocks of the central subprovince, but they are only incompletely developed—particularly so in the lower subprovince unit, the Salmon Hornblende

Schist. In addition, retrogression was not accompanied by the penetrative deformation responsible for the development of foliated rocks in the adjoining subprovinces. If rock units in the eastern Paleozoic subprovince were not regionally metamorphosed until the Late Jurassic, as Kinkel and others claim (1956, p. 65), then it is difficult to explain the absence of earlier metamorphic effects on Paleozoic units, such as the Copley Greenstone, which are older than the dated metamorphic event in the central metamorphic subprovince. The absence in the southeastern Klamath area of other rocks belonging to the Late Paleozoic terrane only partially represented by the moderate to high-grade Salmon and Grouse Ridge Formations is also difficult to explain in terms of Jurassic regional metamorphism only of the adjacent subprovinces. These problems can be resolved if the metamorphic rocks of the three subprovinces are considered to represent disrupted portions of a single Late Paleozoic terrane.

Late Paleozoic regional metamorphism of the Copley Greenstone does not seem at odds with known geological relationships, and Irwin (1960, p. 20) has previously commented on the possibility that the Salmon Hornblende Schist and Copley Greenstone were metamorphosed at the same time. As described above, regional metamorphism of the Copley Greenstone under conditions of the greenschist facies preceded both Late Jurassic regional albitization and the earlier emplacement (Triassic?) of the Mule Mountain stock.

Detailed structural and petrologic studies of the Stuart Fork Formation of the western Paleozoic and Triassic subprovince indicate that its regional metamorphism and accompanying deformation were contemporaneous with that of the Salmon and Grouse Ridge Formations (Davis and others, 1965). The principal barrier to accepting Late Paleozoic metamorphism of the western Paleozoic and Triassic subprovince is the presumed Triassic age of many of its rocks. Despite its name, however, the writer can find no reference to undoubted Triassic rocks within the California portion of the subprovince, and direct correlation of subprovince rocks within California with poorly dated rocks of the Upper Triassic(?) Applegate Group of southern Oregon (Wells and others, 1949) has not yet been demonstrated. Fossiliferous rocks within the subprovince are not abundant, but Late Pennsylvanian(?), Early Permian, and Middle or Late Permian fossils have been found at several California localities (Irwin, 1960, p. 26; 1963). A Silurian-Devonian fossil occurrence about 10 miles west-northwest of Cecilville has been described by Merriam (1961). Irwin (1960, p. 26) reports the presence of fossiliferous Middle or Late Triassic rocks at the extreme southern end of the subprovince, but the structurally complex area of the locality has been mapped only in brief reconnaissance and cannot, in the writer's opinion, be shown to be structurally continuous with that portion of the western Paleozoic and "Triassic" subprovince discussed above (fig. 1).

The disruption of the postulated Late Paleozoic metamorphic terrane by westward thrust faulting, and the emplacement of the Trinity ultramafic sheet between the central metamorphic and eastern Paleozoic thrust plates during thrusting are believed by the writer to have occurred during late stages of the Late Paleozoic metamorphism. An upper age limit on thrusting of the eastern Paleozoic plate is tentatively established by the Early to Middle Triassic age of the Pit River stock which intrudes Early Permian limestones of the plate, although it could be argued that the stock is part of the plate. Middle and (or) Late Triassic to Middle Jurassic stratigraphic units are present in the eastern Paleozoic subprovince, but are separated from Middle Permian rocks of the plate by a probable disconformity (Dott, 1961, p. 578), the hiatus of which brackets the time of intrusion of the Pit River stock. South of Lake Shasta the Pit Formation (Middle and/or Late Triassic) is reported to overlie the Dekkas Andesite (Middle and Upper(?) Permian) "with apparent structural discordance" by Albers and Robertson (1961, p. 35), although these authors believe the Dekkas Andesite-Bully Hill Rhyolite-Pit Formation sequence in the East Shasta Lake area to be conformable.

Briefly, evidence for concluding contemporaneity of late stages of regional metamorphism, thrust faulting, and emplacement of the Trinity pluton includes: the crystalloblastic fabric of Salmon phyllonites in the basal thrust zone of the central metamorphic plate, apparent structural homogeneity between Salmon schists within the plate and their phyllonitic equivalents at its base, an increase in metamorphic grade of low-grade rocks immediately below the central plate, and the incorporation of serpentinites from the Trinity ultramafic sheet within Grouse Ridge rocks prior to cessation of regional metamorphism under conditions of the almandine-amphibolite facies. The last relationship is particularly important in ascertaining the age of the Trinity pluton, previously considered Late Jurassic in age (Irwin, 1960; 1964) because ultramafic rocks intruded the Galice Formation in the western Jurassic subprovince at that time. Ultramafic intrusion in central and northeastern Oregon, however, can be dated stratigraphically as post-Early Permian and pre-Late Triassic (Thayer and Brown, 1964, p. 1257). Emplacement of ultramafic and gabbroic rocks in Oregon during this interval was associated with regional metamorphism and "was followed closely by intrusion of quartz diorite and albite granite" (*ibid.*, p. 1257). A close parallel can thus be drawn between metamorphism and Permo-Triassic intrusive activity in Oregon, and metamorphism and a presumed Trinity ultramafic-Pit River (and Mule Mountain?) granitic intrusive sequence in the southeastern Klamath Mountains.

The ages of regional metamorphism, igneous intrusion, and probable thrust faulting in the Seiad Valley, Condrey Mountain, and Marble Mountains areas are not known, but it is difficult to separate this region in terms of its gross tectonic style and its metamorphic and plutonic characteristics from the southeastern Klamath area.

Late Jurassic orogeny in the Klamath Mountains appears to have been particularly pronounced in the western area of the province. In addition to strong deformation this area experienced regional metamorphism (e.g., formation of the Colebrook Schist), widespread ultramafic intrusion (e.g., the Josephine peridotite sheet), and granitic intrusion. Most of the granitic plutons now exposed in the Klamath province were probably emplaced at this time, although the full extent of Permo-Triassic plutonism will never be known in those areas where younger Triassic and Jurassic rocks are exposed. Late Jurassic orogenic effects in the southeastern quarter of the province were apparently limited to regional albitization, widespread granitic intrustion, and open folding.

REFERENCES

Albers, J. P., and Robertson, J. F., 1961, Geology and ore deposits of east Shasta copper-zinc district, Shasta County, California: U.S. Geol. Survey Prof. Paper 338, 107 p.

Blake, M. C., Jr., and Ghent, E. D., 1964, Regional glaucophane-schist-facies metamorphism in the northern Coast Ranges of California [abs.]: Geol. Soc. America, Cordilleran Sec., 60th Ann. Mtg., Seattle 1964, Program, p. 21.

Cater, F. W., Jr., and Wells, F. G., 1953, Geology and mineral resources of the Gasquet quadrangle, California-Oregon: U.S. Geol. Survey Bull. 995-C, p. 79–133.

Churkin, Michael, and Langenheim, R. L., 1960, Silurian strata of the Klamath Mountains, California: Am. Jour. Sci., v. 258, no. 4, p. 258–273.

Davis, G. A., 1963, Structure and mode of emplacement of Caribou Mountain pluton, Klamath Mountains, California: Geol. Soc. America Bull., v. 74, no. 3, p. 331–348.

—— 1964, Regional Mesozoic thrusting in the south-central Klamath Mountains of California [abs.]: Geol. Soc. America, Cordilleran Sec., 60th Ann. Mtg., Seattle 1964, Program, p. 28.

Davis, G. A., and Lipman, P. W., 1962, Revised structural sequence of pre-Cretaceous metamorphic rocks in the southern Klamath Mountains, California: Geol. Soc. America Bull., v. 73, no. 12, p. 1547–1552.

Davis, G. A., Holdaway, M. J., Lipman, P. W., and Romey, W. D., 1965, Structure, metamorphism, and plutonism in the south-central Klamath Mountains, California: Geol. Soc. America Bull., v. 76 no. 8, p. 933–966.

Dott, R. H., Jr., 1961, Permo-Triassic diastrophism in the western Cordilleran region: Am. Jour. Sci., v. 259, no. 8, p. 561–582.

—— 1965, Mesozoic-Cenozoic tectonic history of the southwestern Oregon coast in relation to Cordilleran orogenesis: Jour. Geophys. Research, v. 70, no. 18, p. 4687–4707.

Evans, J. R., 1965, Geology and petrology of the McCloud Limestone in the South Gray Rocks area, Shasta County, California [abs.]: Geol. Soc. America, Cordilleran Sec., 61st Ann. Mtg., Fresno 1965, p. 22–23.

Ghent, E. D., 1965, Glaucophane-schist facies metamorphism in the Black Butte area, northern Coast Ranges, California: Am. Jour. Sci., v. 263, no. 5, p. 385–400.

Hart, S. R., 1964, The petrology and isotopic-mineral age relations of a contact zone in the Front Range, Colorado: Jour. Geology, v. 72, no. 5, p. 493–525.

Hershey, O. H., 1901, Metamorphic formations of northwestern California: Am. Geologist, v. 27, p. 225–245

Hinds, N. E. A., 1933, Geologic formations of the Redding-Weaverville districts, northern California: California Jour. Mines and Geology, v. 29, nos. 1-2, p. 76–122.

Holdaway, M. J., 1965, Basic regional metamorphic rocks in part of the Klamath Mountains, northern California: Am. Mineralogist, v. 50, p. 953–977.

Irwin, W. P., 1960, Geologic reconnaissance of the northern Coast Ranges and Klamath Mountains, California, with a summary of the mineral resources: California Div. Mines Bull. 179, 80 p.

—— 1963, Preliminary geologic map of the Weaverville quadrangle, California: U.S. Geol. Survey Mineral Inv. Field Studies Map MF-275, scale 1:62,500.

—— 1964, Late Mesozoic orogenies in the ultramafic belts of northwestern California and southwestern Oregon: U.S. Geol. Survey Prof. Paper 501-C, p. C1–C9.

Kinkel, A. R., Jr., Hall, W. E., and Albers, J. P., 1956, Geology and base-metal deposits of West Shasta copper-zinc district, Shasta County, California: U.S. Geol. Survey Prof. Paper 285, 156 p.

Kistler, R. W., Bateman, P. C., and Brannock, W. W., 1965, Isotopic ages of minerals from granitic rocks of the central Sierra Nevada and Inyo Mountains, California: Geol. Soc. America Bull., v. 76, no. 2, p. 155–164.

Kulp, J. L., 1961, Geologic time scale: Science, v. 133, no. 3459, p. 1105–1114.

Lanphere, M. A., and Irwin, W. P., 1965, Isotopic age of Salmon and Abrams Schists, Klamath Mountains, California [abs.]: Geol. Soc. America, Cordilleran Sec., 61st Ann. Mtg., Fresno 1965, p. 33.

Lipman, P. W., 1963, Gibson Peak pluton: a discordant composite intrusion in the southeastern Trinity Alps, northern California: Geol. Soc. America Bull., v. 74, no. 10, p. 1259–1280.

—— 1964, Structure and origin of an ultramafic pluton in the Klamath Mountains, California: Am. Jour. Sci., v. 262, no. 2, p. 199–222.

Merriam, C. W., 1961, Silurian and Devonian rocks of the Klamath Mountains, California: U.S. Geol. Survey Prof. Paper 424-C, p. C188–C189.

Moore, J. G., 1959, The quartz diorite boundary line in the western United States: Jour. Geology, v. 67, no. 2, p. 198–210.

Strand, R. G., 1963, Geologic map of California, Olaf P. Jenkins edition, Weed sheet: California Div. Mines and Geology, scale 1:250,000.

Thayer, T. P., and Brown, C. E., 1964, Pre-Tertiary orogenic and plutonic intrusive activity in central and northeastern Oregon: Geol. Soc. America Bull., v. 75, no. 12, p. 1255–1262.

Wells, F. G., 1956, Geology of the Medford quadrangle, Oregon-California: U.S. Geol. Survey Geol. Quad. Map GQ-89, scale 1:96,000.

Wells, F. G., and others, 1940, Preliminary geologic map of the Grants Pass quadrangle, Oregon: Oregon Dept. Geology and Mineral Industries, scale 1:96,000.

Wells, F. G., and Peck, D. L., 1961, Geologic map of Oregon west of the 121st meridian: U.S. Geol. Survey Misc. Geol. Inv. Map I-325.

Wells, F. G., and Walker, G. W., 1953, Geology of the Galice quadrangle, Oregon: U.S. Geol. Survey Geol. Quad. Map [GQ-25], scale 1:62,500.

Wells, F. G., Hotz, P. E., and Cater, F. W., 1949, Preliminary description of the geology of the Kerby quadrangle, Oregon: Oregon Dept. Geology and Mineral Industries Bull., v. 40, 23 p.

Wells, F. G., Walker, G. W., and Merriam, C. W., 1959, Upper Ordovician(?) and Upper Silurian formations of the northern Klamath Mountains, California: Geol. Soc. America Bull., v. 70, no. 5, p. 645–649.

ECONOMIC DEPOSITS OF THE KLAMATH MOUNTAINS *

By John P. Albers
U.S. Geological Survey, Menlo Park, California

INTRODUCTION

The metallic substances that have been produced from the Klamath Mountains of California (fig. 1) include gold, copper, zinc, pyrites, lead, silver, chromite, quicksilver, iron, platinum, and manganese. Limestone (for cement), sand, gravel, building stone, crushed rock, brick, rubble, and riprap are the important nonmetallic products. In 1965 these nonmetallic materials and quicksilver were the principal mineral products of the province. Table 1 summarizes the approximate total production of the major mineral commodities from 1880 through 1963; figures 2 and 3 show graphically the annual production trend of these commodities.

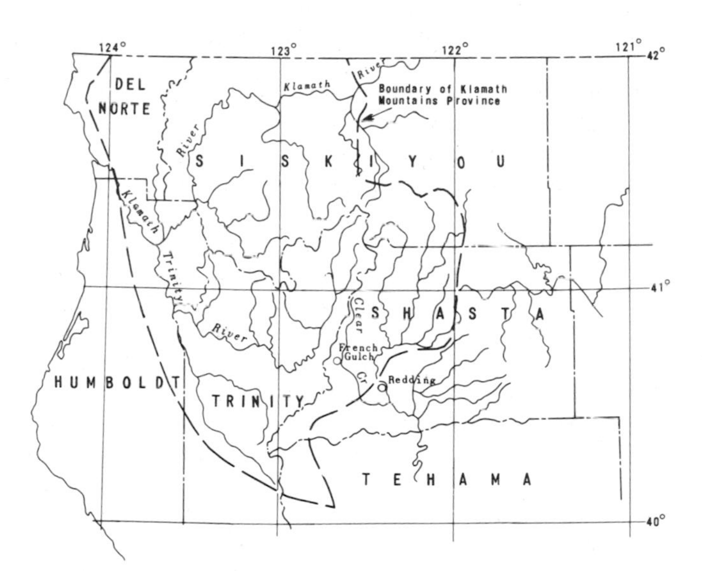

Figure 1. Index map showing location of physical features referred to in text.

For purposes of discussion, the economic deposits are subdivided as follows: (1) deposits found in ultramafic igneous rocks (chromite, asbestos, and nickel); (2) deposits found chiefly in metamorphosed sedimentary and volcanic rocks, and inferred to be genetically related to the intrusion of granitic rocks, (gold, silver, copper, lead, zinc, pyrites, iron); (3) deposits inferred to be associated elsewhere with late volcanic activity (quicksilver); and (4) deposits concentrated by sedimentary processes (managanese, placer gold and platinum, and the building materials).

The building materials will not be discussed in this paper and only brief mention will be made of placer deposits and manganese. Occurrences of antimony, arsenic, clay, graphite, molybdenite, ocher, talc, tin, and tungsten are also known in the Klamath Mountains, but production is negligible, and thus the occurrences of these materials will not be described.

DEPOSITS FOUND IN ULTRAMAFIC IGNEOUS ROCKS

Chromite.—Chromite has been produced from the Klamath Mountains only during World Wars I and II, when access to foreign sources was more difficult, and during the 1950's, when the U.S. Government purchased chromite at incentive prices for the national strategic mineral stockpile. At other times domestic chromite has been unable to compete with foreign sources.

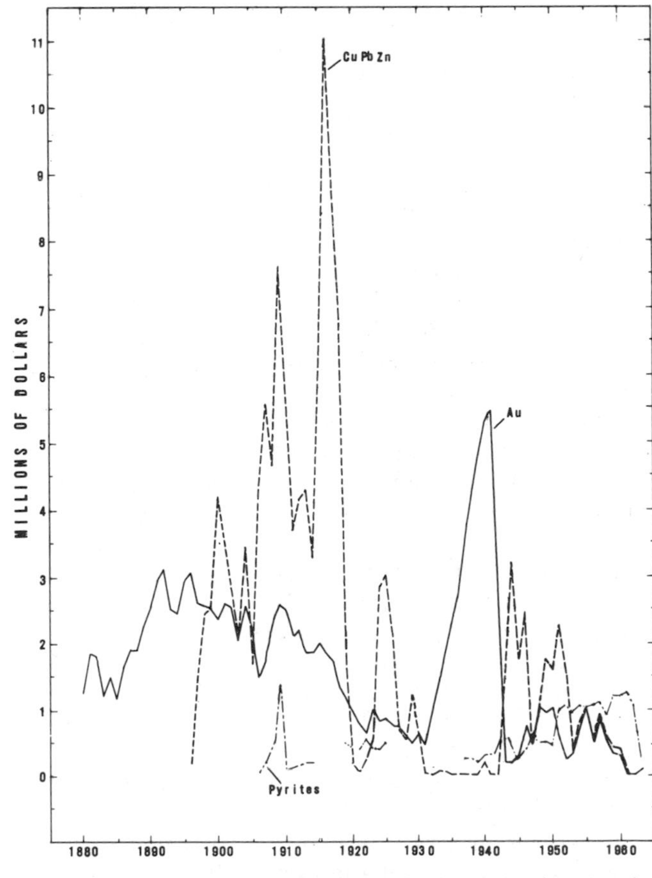

Figure 2. Production of gold, copper, lead, zinc, and pyrites between 1880 and 1963, in millions of dollars.

* Publication authorized by the Director, U.S. Geological Survey.

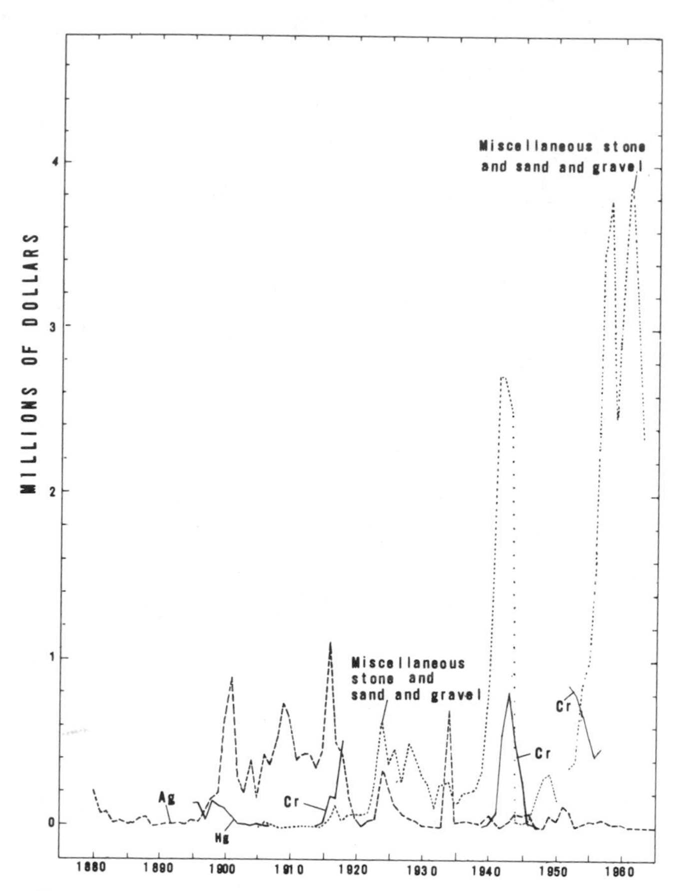

Figure 3. Production of chromite, silver, stone, sand and gravel, and quicksilver between 1880 and 1963, in millions of dollars.

Because of the interest in chromite during World War II, the more important deposits in the Klamath Mountains were intensively studied during that period by the U.S. Geological Survey. The following description is summarized largely from reports by Allen (1941); Wells, Cater, and Rynearson (1946); Wells, Smith, Rynearson, and Livermore (1949); and Wells and Cater (1950).

Chromite is found exclusively in ultramafic igneous rocks and in serpentine derived from them. The distribution of ultramafic rocks and the location of the principal chromite deposits is shown on figure 4. The ultramafic rock generally forms sill-like tabular bodies that lie parallel to bedding or foliation in the intruded rocks. Individual ultramafic masses are commonly composed of more or less discrete bodies of several different rock types—saxonite, dunite, lherzolite, pyroxenite, and hornblendite. The chromite occurs in tabular or lenticular bodies of dunite that may be any size or shape and may occur anywhere within an ultramafic mass. The dunite is composed of at least 95 percent olivine and less than 5 percent pyroxene.

Wells and others (1949, p. 26) describe dunite in weathered outcrops of the eastern Klamaths as characterized by a yellowish-red color, a smooth fine-grained surface, protruding scattered grains of chromite or magnetite, and an irregular jointing. Unaltered dunite has a ragged uneven fracture, a glassy to oily luster, and is light yellowish green to grayish green on the fresh surface. Highly serpentinized dunite, however, has a conchoidal fracture, a waxy or corneous luster, and is bluish green to greenish black. Under the microscope, dunite shows interlocking angular grains of olivine from 0.5 to 1.0 mm in diameter, and enstatite, augite, and hornblende in minor amounts. Serpentine is common along cracks and cleavages and as rinds around olivine grains in dunite. Serpentine may also surround chromite grains, forming an association that is of great importance in crushing the ore.

Chromite occurs in various degrees of concentration within dunite—from tabular or podlike aggregates of almost solid chromite to deposits containing only a few percent of chromite as disseminated grains. Thus two general types of chromite deposits are recognized: (1) pod, and (2) disseminated. The pod deposits consist of clean ore that can be mined, sorted, and shipped as lump ore. Almost all the deposits of Del Norte County in the western Klamaths are this type. Ore has been shipped from about 50 pod deposits which yielded from 5 to 20,000 tons each. Pod deposits commonly occur in shear zones, which may be as much as several hundred feet wide and several miles long. Allen (1941, p. 103) points out that elongate masses of chromite may be horizontal and parallel to the trend of a shear zone or may be inclined at any angle up to 90°. Deposits of the disseminated type are composed of chromite grains scattered through dunite or serpentine derived from dunite. The chromite may range in concentration from accessory amounts to as much as 80 percent of the rock. Deposits of disseminated ore range in size from a few tons to more than 200,000 tons. The largest disseminated deposit is the Seiad Creek or Mountain View deposit in the eastern Klamaths which according to Wells and others (1946, p. 33) measures 1,300 feet long by 250 feet wide and 250 feet down dip. Most of the chromite in the Klamaths, in both pod and disseminated deposits, is of metallurgical grade, with a Cr/Fe ratio of 2.50 or higher and a Cr_2O_3 content in excess of 45 percent. The richer pod deposits have yielded most of the ore to date, but ore reserves are mostly in disseminated deposits.

Geologists who have studied the chromite deposits of the Klamaths generally agree that the chromite was formed syngenetically with the enclosing ultramafic rock. Allen (1941, p. 103), in discussing chromite in California, states that most of the chromite bodies were emplaced late in the magmatic cycle, in some cases while differentiation was still going on. Wells and others (1949, p. 34), on the basis of detailed studies of structures in the ore and studies of internal structures of the enclosing ultramafic rock masses in the Seiad Valley-McGuffy Creek area, conclude that the chromite was as truly a component of the original ultramafic magma as the olivine and pyroxene. In their view the chromite crystallized early and accumulated

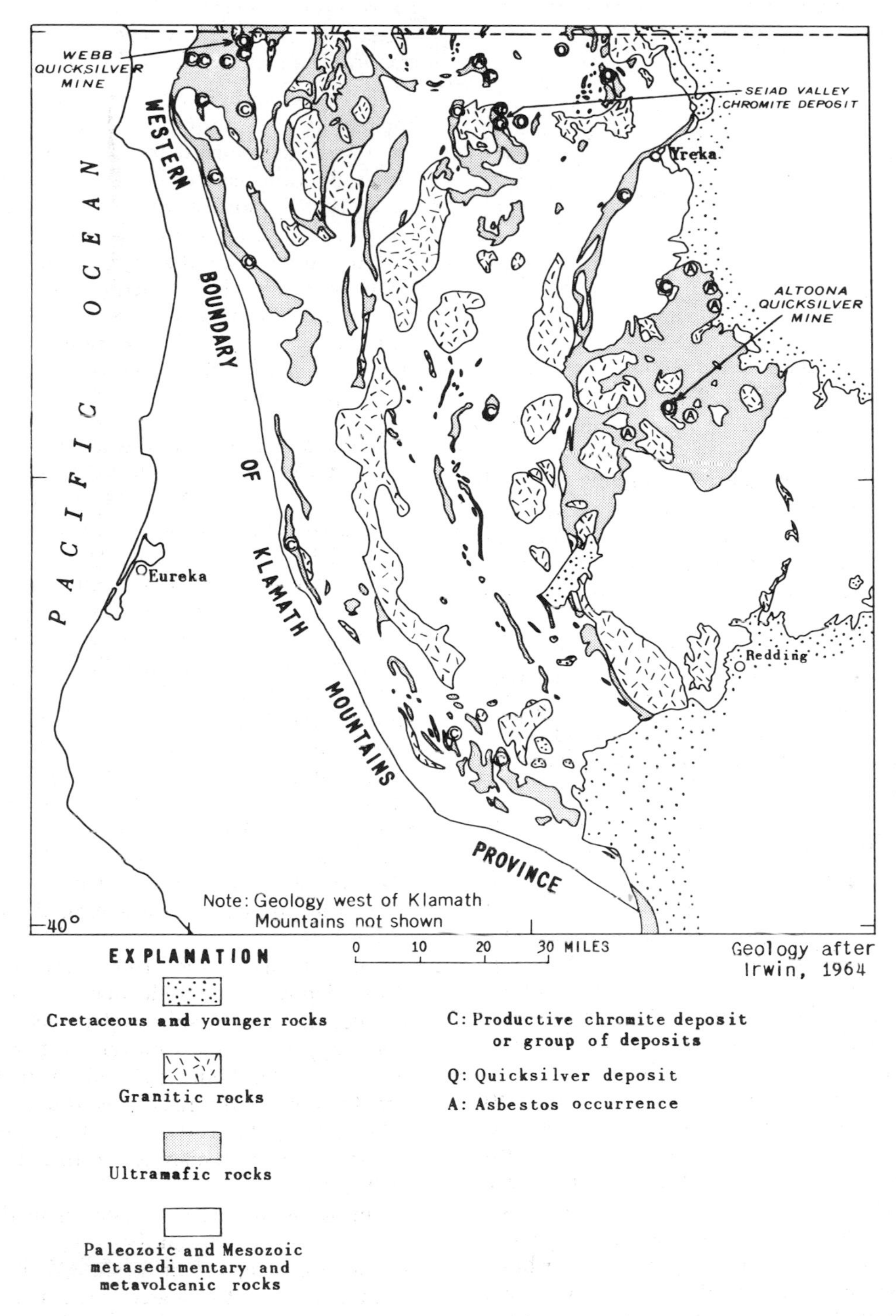

Figure 4. Distribution of chromite, asbestos, and quicksilver deposits in the Klamath Mountains of California.

Table 1. Approximate value of principal mineral commodities produced in the Klamath Mountains from 1880 through 1963

Commodity	Value
Gold	$140,127,320
Copper, lead, and zinc	139,503,044
Miscellaneous stone[1]	42,030,009
Pyrites[2]	21,178,850
Silver	13,046,907
Chromite	8,975,260
Mercury[3]	1,310,796
Platinum	185,830
Total	$366,358,016

(Data from U.S. Bureau of Mines Mineral Yearbooks and California Division of Mines and Geology publications.)

[1] Includes sand and gravel; excludes brick and cement.

[2] Data in part from Mountain Copper Company of California.

[3] Trinity County only.

in certain zones within the melt to form chromite-rich layers and bodies. They also think that crystallization of most of the chromite, much of the olivine, and some of the pyroxene was completed when the crystal-bearing mush moved from its crystallization chamber into its present position.

Because chromite is syngenetic with ultramafic rock, which was emplaced before the granitic rocks with which most of the epigenetic mineral deposits are believed to be related, it is inferred that the chromite ore bodies represent the oldest mineral deposits in the Klamath Mountains.

Asbestos.—Occurrences of asbestos are fairly numerous in the Klamath Mountains but the quantity mined to date is insignificant. Nearly all occurrences are in serpentine derived from peridotite (fig. 4). Two types of asbestos are found: (1) chrysotile or cross-fiber asbestos; and (2) amphibole (tremolite) or slip-fiber asbestos. Chrysotile has the higher tensile strength and therefore has a higher value. The chrysotile deposits commonly consist of a small zone of closely spaced veins that range in thickness from a fraction of an inch to about an inch. The fibers are oriented at right angles to the vein walls. The amphibole asbestos veins, on the other hand, are commonly along shear zones a few inches wide and have fibers oriented more or less parallel to vein walls. In a few places the amphibole veins contain lenticular pockets of fiber several feet wide. Rice (1957) describes a vein at the Sylvester mine, in Shasta County, which had a maximum width of 30 inches and was mined over a length of at least 110 feet. Owing to a limited market and the expense of handling, few amphibole veins are worked to depths greater than 25 feet. It appears that a successful amphibole asbestos industry in the Klamaths would depend on the discovery of deposits having a minimum strike length of several hundred feet.

Although the spatial relationship of both chrysotile and amphibole asbestos deposits to serpentine is clear, the genetic relationship is uncertain. The occurrence of asbestos in veins and shear zones indicates an epigenetic origin, possibly related to the process of serpentinization or to the intrusion of granitic rocks.

Nickel.—Ferruginous nickeliferous lateritic soils—formed by weathering of ultramafic rocks in place—are rather widespread in the Klamath Mountains but no production has yet been realized. Hotz (1964) believed that the soils were formed by chemical weathering in a climate characterized by alternate wet and dry seasons—similar to that prevailing today. The most likely time of their formation is post-Miocene to Pleistocene. Because the deposits are small, are low grade, and have a scattered distribution in a rugged and relatively isolated terrain, they are unlikely to be exploited in the foreseeable future.

DEPOSITS CHIEFLY IN METAMORPHOSED SEDIMENTARY AND VOLCANIC ROCKS AND INFERRED TO BE GENETICALLY RELATED TO GRANITIC ROCKS

Gold.—Gold ranks as the principal mineral product of the Klamath Mountains. Approximately $140 million worth of gold has been produced since 1880 (table 1); in addition at least several million dollars worth was mined between 1848 and 1880.

As shown by figure 1, gold production reached an early peak of about $3 million in 1894 and then declined irregularly to less than $1 million annually during the 1920's. Then, in the 1930's, stimulated by the Great Depression which drove many people into prospecting, and by a substantial rise in price from $20.67 to $35.00 a fine ounce in 1934, production rose sharply and reached a peak of about $5.5 million in 1941. World War II resulted in a very sharp decline; since 1943 production has averaged well under $1 million a year.

The gold has come from three main sources: (1) placer deposits; (2) lode deposits; and (3) as a by-product of massive sulfide deposits mined chiefly for their copper content, and from gossan derived from massive sulfide. About $12 million of the $140 million total has come from massive sulfides. Of the remaining $128 million, about 70 percent has come from placer deposits, and the remainder from lode deposits (Irwin, 1960, p. 64).

During the first few years after its discovery in 1848 gold was produced mainly from placer deposits. The first lode mining began at the Washington mine (fig. 5) in 1852, but for many years the output of lodes was far below that of the rich gulches and bench gravels (Ferguson, 1914, p. 33). Lode mining increased in relative importance in the 1880's and probably yielded at least as much gold as placer mining until World War I. During the 1930's the great bulk of the gold produced was from dredging operations. Fineness of gold in the Klamaths has averaged about 850.

Placer deposits are located mainly along the Trinity and Klamath Rivers and their tributaries and along Clear Creek. Pleistocene gravels and gravels of the Tertiary Weaverville Formation have also yielded sig-

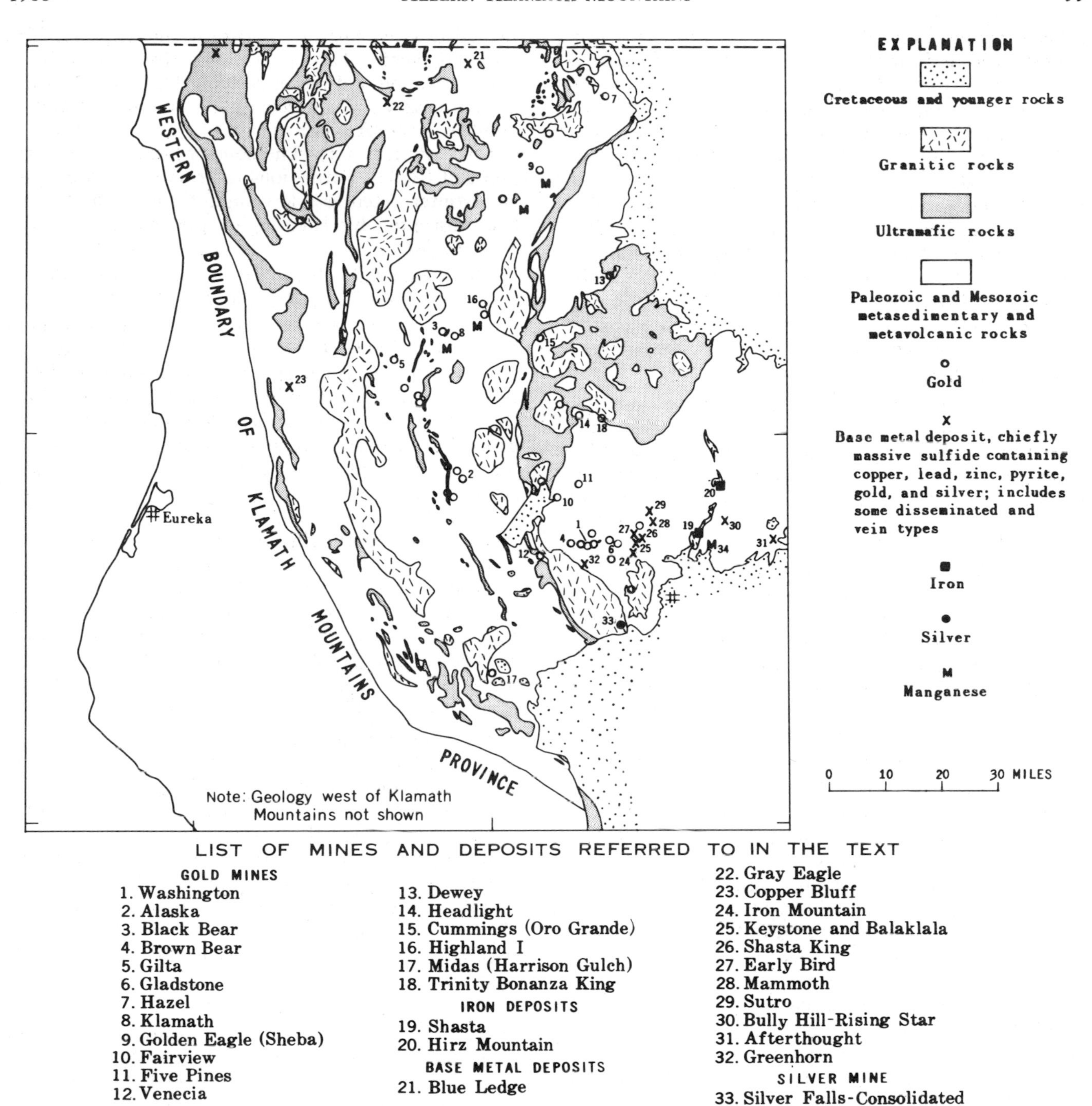

LIST OF MINES AND DEPOSITS REFERRED TO IN THE TEXT

GOLD MINES

1. Washington
2. Alaska
3. Black Bear
4. Brown Bear
5. Gilta
6. Gladstone
7. Hazel
8. Klamath
9. Golden Eagle (Sheba)
10. Fairview
11. Five Pines
12. Venecia
13. Dewey
14. Headlight
15. Cummings (Oro Grande)
16. Highland I
17. Midas (Harrison Gulch)
18. Trinity Bonanza King

IRON DEPOSITS

19. Shasta
20. Hirz Mountain

BASE METAL DEPOSITS

21. Blue Ledge
22. Gray Eagle
23. Copper Bluff
24. Iron Mountain
25. Keystone and Balaklala
26. Shasta King
27. Early Bird
28. Mammoth
29. Sutro
30. Bully Hill-Rising Star
31. Afterthought
32. Greenhorn

SILVER MINE

33. Silver Falls-Consolidated

MANGANESE MINE

34. Shasta Copper mine

Figure 5. Distribution of gold lodes, iron, base metal, silver, and manganese deposits in the Klamath Mountains of California.

nificant amounts of gold. The gold in all these placer deposits was derived from eroded segments of the lode deposits described below.

No overall study of the lode deposits of the Klamath Mountains has been made. However, geologists of the U.S. Geological Survey (MacDonald, 1913; Ferguson, 1914; and Albers, 1961, 1964) have studied individual districts and groups of districts, and geologists and engineers of the California Division of Mines and Geology have reported on the geology of individual mines, mainly on a county basis (Brown, 1916; Averill, 1931, 1933, 1935, 1941). The summary description of the principal kinds of deposits given below is based partly on these writings and partly on the writer's knowledge of the region.

Figure 5 shows that most of the principal lode deposits lie in an arcuate belt that parallels the gross structural grain in the central part of the Klamaths. They are predominantly in weakly metamorphosed sedimentary and volcanic rocks of Paleozoic age, and the great majority are closely associated with dike-like or sill-like bodies of a porphyry known by local miners as "birdseye" porphyry. This porphyry differs somewhat in composition from place to place and includes two principal rock types—diorite porphyry and dacite porphyry. Overall, the "birdseye" porphyry bears a strong affinity to the quartz diorite and granodiorite plutonic rocks of the Klamath Mountains and appears to be genetically related to the plutons. In addition to the "birdseye" porphyry, dikes of quartz porphyry are commonly associated with gold lodes in the southeastern part of the region.

The principal lode deposits are veins that occur in the following geologic environments: (1) steeply dipping veins in black carbonaceous shale or slate (Alaska, Black Bear, Brown Bear, Gilta, Gladstone, Hazel, and Klamath deposits are examples); (2) steeply dipping veins in greenstone that underlies shale or slate in much of the region (Golden Eagle, formerly Sheba, deposit); (3) gently dipping veinlike deposits along faulted contacts between shale and greenstone (Fairview, Five Pines, Venecia, and Washington deposits); (4) steeply or gently dipping veins in "birdseye" porphyry dikes or quartz porphyry dikes (Dewey and Headlight deposits); and (5) steeply dipping dikes in schists and miscellaneous rock types (Cummings, formerly Oro Grande, Highland I, Midas, and Trinity Bonanza King deposits).

Several of the five types of deposits may be found within an individual district. Such a district is the French Gulch-Deadwood district, which has yielded at least 800,000 ounces of gold. It contains some of the largest producing mines representing at least three of the five types of deposits. The district lies about 20 miles northwest of Redding in the southern part of the region and is in an eastward-trending highly fractured belt about 9 miles long and a mile wide. It includes the Brown Bear mine at its western end and the Gladstone mine at its eastern end (fig. 5). The rocks are chiefly shaly rocks of the Mississippian Bragdon Formation and the underlying Devonian(?) Copley Greenstone, which delineates an eastward-trending archlike structure just north of the fractured belt (Albers, 1961, p. C1). The contact between the Bragdon and Copley Formations is structurally discordant and is interpreted as a low-angle thrust fault that has been disrupted by later high-angle faulting (Albers, 1964, p. J62).

The Shasta Bally batholith of silicic quartz diorite and granodiorite intrudes the Bragdon and Copley Formations about a mile west of the French Gulch-Deadwood district. In the western part of the district numerous "birdseye" porphyry dikes intrude the Bragdon Formation and locally form sill-like bodies along the contact between the Bragdon and Copley. One group of these dikes is similar in composition to the Shasta Bally batholith, and at least one dike is also similar in texture. Because of the similarity the dikes are regarded as offshoots from the batholith, and a salient of the batholith is inferred to extend in an easterly direction beneath the fractured, intruded, and mineralized belt (Albers, 1961, p. C2). Most fractures trend parallel to the belt and are thought to be at least in part tension fractures formed by the upward push of the magma of the salient. Subsequently, many of the fractures controlled the emplacement of "birdseye" porphyry dikes and quartz veins.

The types of lodes in the French Gulch-Deadwood district include: (1) steeply dipping quartz and quartz-calcite veins in shaly rocks of the Bragdon Formation; (2) gently to moderately dipping quartz and quartz-calcite veins along the thrust contact between the Bragdon and Copley Formations; and (3) veins in the "birdseye" porphyry dikes and sills. In addition, a fourth type of deposit—steeply dipping quartz veins in greenstone—occurs in at least one mine in the district (Washington) but has accounted for very little production.

Most gold has come from the steeply dipping veins in the Bragdon Formation. Workings of the two largest mines—Brown Bear and Gladstone—as well as several other mines, are on such veins, and although some workings are more than 1,000 feet deep they have not penetrated the Copley Greenstone contact. On the other hand, most gold from the intervening Washington mine (fig. 5) has come from lodes along the contact between the Bragdon and Copley Formations. The "birdseye" porphyry dikes and sills that are abundant in the Brown Bear and other mines of the western part of the district are in many places cut by gold-bearing quartz veins. Quartz porphyry dikes and sills —the soda granite porphyry of Ferguson (1914)—are also common in the western part of the district. No "birdseye" porphyry is known in the mines of the eastern part of the district but some quartz porphyry has been reported in the Gladstone mine.

The ore shoots in the steeply dipping veins at the Brown Bear and other mines in the district are commonly at the intersection of veins which have opposing dips or at the intersection of veins with contacts between shale and porphyry. The two principal veins at the Brown Bear mine are essentially parallel in strike but intersect in places because of variable and opposing dips. Subsidiary veins also intersect the main veins. Nearly horizontal ore shoots are thus formed along the line of intersection at two main levels in the mine. In contrast to the highly productive, steeply dipping veins in the Bragdon Formation, similar steep veins in the Copley Greenstone, as in the deeper levels of the Washington mine, are commonly narrow and of poor grade; only at the contact with the shale of the Bragdon are they productive.

Much of the richest gold ore within the Bragdon was reportedly along contacts between the quartz veins and black slickensided graphitic shale, or associated with inclusions of graphitic shale in the vein, suggesting the importance of graphitic material as a precipitating agent for gold. This importance of carbon or graphite as a precipitating agent has been noted by Hershey (1910) and Ferguson (1914, p. 40–43). Ferguson thought that the pocket gold deposits of the Klamath Mountains, found mainly at the contact between the Copley and Bragdon Formations, were of surficial origin, formed as a result of precipitation of gold from surficial waters where these waters first came in contact with graphitic material of the Bragdon. According to this interpretation the gold was taken into solution by surface waters from pyritized zones in greenstone in the presence of manganese oxide. Although this may be a valid hypothesis for the origin of some pockets, it seems to the writer that to be effective the depositional process would require ascending surficial solutions, inasmuch as the shaly rocks overlie the greenstone. A preferred interpretation is that the gold was deposited by rising hydrothermal solutions at and above the contact between greenstone and overlying shaly rocks. By this interpretation the gold in steeply dipping veins within the Bragdon, or in veins cutting "birdseye" porphyry dikes in the Bragdon, represents a residue in solutions that must have come past the more favorable contact between Copley and Bragdon. Therefore the possibility that additional ore will be found at depth in mines such as the Brown Bear and Gladstone that have not penetrated as deep as the Copley Greenstone appears promising.

The mineral composition of veins shows little variation. Quartz is the chief gangue mineral, calcite and mica are present in minor amounts, and locally manganese oxide occurs near the surface. Pyrite, galena, sphalerite, arsenopyrite, and less common chalcopyrite are the sulfides. Gold occurs mainly as free gold but also occurs in the sulfide minerals.

If the inference that the porphyry dike rocks in the western part of the French Gulch-Deadwood district are offshoots from an underlying salient of the Shasta Bally batholith is correct, it appears highly probable that the gold-bearing quartz veins originated from the same magmatic source. The veins are apparently controlled by the same eastward-trending fracture system that controls the dikes, and are at least slightly younger than the dikes. The veins are interpreted as residual fluids rising from the cooling batholith salient along reopened fractures of the same system that had previously given access to the dikes. As the veins traversed the Copley Greenstone little gold was deposited except in small pockets, but where the solutions encountered graphitic material at and above the Copley-Bragdon contact, gold was precipitated, particularly at the intersections of fractures where graphitic material was abundant.

Elsewhere in the Klamath Mountains many of the best gold mines are in a geologic environment grossly similar to that of the French Gulch district. However, a few gold lodes are in schistose rocks, as the Midas (Harrison Gulch) deposit in the extreme southern part of the region, and the Bonanza King deposit in the east-central part (fig. 5). As in the French Gulch-Deadwood district, the principal ore is free gold in quartz or quartz-calcite veins. Tellurides are reported in a few localities.

"Birdseye" porphyry dikes are associated with many but not all the deposits throughout the Klamath Mountains. The importance of the "birdseye" porphyry dikes was recognized by MacDonald (1913, p. 19), who, in discussing the Carrville district of the central Klamath Mountains, advised prospectors to search all contacts of "birdseye" porphyry dikes. The close association between gold lodes and porphyry dikes in so many localities strongly suggests a genetic relationship. It seems equally clear that the "birdseye" porphyry dikes are offshoots from large plutonic bodies as previously described in the French Gulch-Deadwood district. Probably the gold-bearing quartz and quartz-calcite veins came from the same magmatic source and followed very nearly the same fracture systems as the dikes.

The outcrop pattern (fig. 5) suggests that silicic plutonic rocks may lie at relatively shallow depth beneath much of the eastern part of the Klamaths where most of the gold lodes occur. Therefore those lodes that have no associated "birdseye" porphyry dikes may have been derived from plutonic rocks at depth. The only condition necessary for their formation was a fracture system allowing access of mineralizing fluids from the plutonic bodies to the host rocks.

Iron.—Only two iron ore deposits of economic significance are known in the Klamath Mountains province. These are the Shasta and Hirz Mountain deposits along the McCloud River arm of Shasta Lake a few miles north of Redding (fig. 5). Iron ore was produced on a small scale from the Shasta deposit inter-

Photo 1. Aerial photo of Redding and the Trinity Alps.

mittently between 1907 and 1926, and several hundred thousand tons were mined during the period 1942–1944 for use as ballast by the U.S. Navy. No production has been realized from the Hirz Mountain deposit. Both deposits are contact metasomatic replacement deposits localized along contacts between the Permian McCloud and Nosoni Formations and an irregular large dikelike body of quartz diorite. The ore occurs as a replacement of the McCloud and Nosoni Formations and also as a replacement of the quartz diorite. It consists chiefly of magnetite accompanied by garnet and epidote. For a more complete description of these deposits the reader may refer to Lamey (1948a, 1948b).

Massive sulfides and replacement veins.—The base metals, particularly copper, and to a much lesser extent zinc and lead, rank with gold as the chief mineral products of the Klamath Mountains (table 1), and well over 90 percent of these base metals have come from massive sulfide deposits of the West Shasta and East Shasta copper-zinc districts in the eastern part of the region. The remaining base-metal production is mainly from the Blue Ledge and Gray Eagle replacement vein deposits near the Oregon border, and the Copper Bluff deposit in the western part of the province.

The first massive sulfide deposits were discovered in the 1860's, and during the early years their oxidized outcrops were worked for precious metal content. Beginning in 1896 and for more than 20 years thereafter, the unoxidized sulfide ore was exploited, and a large mining industry grew up in the area north of Redding. The massive sulfides were direct smelted during most of this period, and copper along with some gold and silver were the only metals recovered. Zinc was successfully recovered from some ores in 1918, and thereafter was an important product of the district. Lead production has been relatively insignificant.

As shown in figure 2, the production of base metals reached a high of $11 million (nearly all from copper) in 1917 and declined sharply to virtually nothing in 1920. During the 1930's about 2.6 million tons of gossan derived from oxidation of massive sulfide at the Iron Mountain deposit (fig. 5) was treated for its gold content, and from 1948 until 1962 the same deposit yielded pyrite from which sulfur was extracted for use in making sulfuric acid. In all, the Iron Mountain mine in the West Shasta district was a continuous producer of mineral products for a period of more than 65 years, and it (as well as the other massive sulfide mines) was of prime importance in the economic development of northern California.

Important deposits in addition to Iron Mountain are the Mammoth, Balaklala, Keystone, Early Bird, Shasta King, and Sutro (fig. 5); these make up the West Shasta copper-zinc district which has yielded the bulk of the production. The Bully Hill-Rising Star and Afterthought mines make up the East Shasta copper-zinc district (fig. 5). Both districts have been studied in detail in recent years by the U.S. Geological Survey (Kinkel, Hall, and Albers, 1956; Albers and Robertson, 1961). The Greenhorn mine is another fairly large massive sulfide deposit that lies a few miles west of the West Shasta district.

The massive sulfide deposits of the West Shasta copper-zinc district lie in a belt about 9 miles long, 1 mile wide and trending N. 25° E. All the deposits are in an altered silicic volcanic rock unit of Devonian age called the Balaklala Rhyolite. The deposits lie at a more or less consistent stratigraphic position within the formation, beneath a layer of pyroclastic rocks in some places, and in other places beneath a coarsely porphyritic facies of rhyolite that is the stratigraphic equivalent of the pyroclastic beds. The massive sulfide bodies are mainly lenses, pods, or cigar-shaped masses. They are in sharp contact with wallrocks which are everywhere altered and more or less pyritized. The length and width of massive sulfide bodies are commonly 2 to 10 times the thickness, and except at the extreme north end of the district the long axes of the sulfide bodies are essentially horizontal. The bodies range in size from a few thousand tons to more than 5 million tons. However, the several discrete bodies mined at Iron Mountain were, before faulting and erosion, a continuous mass about 4,500 feet long and containing perhaps 25 million tons of massive sulfide.

Although the sulfide bodies are everywhere in sharp contact with the wallrocks, the contacts are not frozen. Typically, a thin seam of gouge separates massive sulfide from wallrock. In many localities the evidence is clear that the sulfide has replaced the enclosing host rocks. A fault set striking about N. 70° E. across the N. 25° E. grain of the district is older than the mineralization and probably provided the main feeder channels for the sulfide ore. All the ore bodies are near these faults but not all are adjacent to them. Some ore bodies in the West Shasta district are on or near the axes of folds in the host rock, but there seems to be no preference for anticlines or synclines; in any case not all sulfide bodies show a preference for folds.

The massive sulfide ore is typically 90 to 95 percent sulfide minerals—dominantly pyrite, with lesser amounts of chalcopyrite, sphalerite, quartz, and calcite. The ore has a brassy appearance and is generally structureless. The average grain size is about half a millimeter, but locally it is much coarser. Much of the massive sulfide is essentially pyrite that contains very little chalcopyrite or sphalerite. This low-grade copper ore has been mined at Iron Mountain for its sulfur, but elsewhere in the district it has been treated as waste during mining operations. The low-grade massive pyrite occurs as separate bodies and also as parts of ore bodies that contain copper and zinc values high enough to be mined as base-metal ore. The copper content of ore mined for copper ranged from 2 to 7.5 percent. Zinc content ranged as high as 21.1 percent in parts of the Mammoth mine, but the content of this metal is extremely variable and would probably average well under 5 percent in the base-metal ore mined throughout the district. No lead is present in the West Shasta sulfide ores, but most of the ore contained 0.02 to 0.06 ounce of gold and 1 to 8 ounces of silver per ton.

Kinkel, Hall, and Albers (1956, p. 93), as well as other geologists who have worked in the West Shasta district, believe that the massive sulfide deposits formed by replacement of the Balaklala Rhyolite. Perhaps the most convincing evidence for this is the presence in a few places of relict quartz phenocrysts of the replaced host rock in the massive sulfide ore. Other evidence in the sulfide is local banding, which is probably inherited from foliation in the enveloping host rock. Also, the abundant disseminated pyrite that occurs throughout the district is clearly replacement in origin. The ore controls in summary are: (1) favorable stratigraphic position in the Balaklala Rhyolite; (2) the N. 70° E. trending premineralization feeder faults; and (3) in local areas, secondary foliation in the host rock. The deposits are probably late Jurassic or possibly very early Cretaceous in age.

The source of the solutions that deposited the massive sulfides is unknown. However, the district lies at the north end of a large stock of altered quartz diorite (fig. 5) and only a few miles from the Shasta Bally batholith. Either of these bodies may continue at depth beneath the West Shasta district and either could have supplied the mineralizing fluids. The metallic constituents could have come from the plutonic masses themselves or could have been derived in large part from the Copley Greenstone that lies at depth beneath the mineralized belt. Computations based on spectrographic analyses indicate that the Copley Greenstone and rocks of similar character in the stratigraphic section contain roughly 1 million tons of metallic copper and over 2 million tons of metallic zinc per cubic mile. These rocks are strongly and pervasively altered, and large amounts of material have been added and removed by metasomatic processes. Probably at least 5 to 10 cubic miles of greenstone lie directly beneath the West Shasta district; only a small percentage of their copper and zinc need to have migrated from the greenstone and been concentrated in the sulfide deposits to account for the 340,000 tons of copper and 30,000 tons of zinc that the ore bodies have yielded.

The speculations in the preceding paragraph apply if—as the available evidence seems to indicate—the deposits are strictly epigenetic. However, the evidence for epigenetic origin is not conclusive, and the idea that massive sulfide deposits of this type may be syngenetic is gaining favor among some geologists. It is possible that the sulfides were precipitated in a submarine environment in stagnant waters heavily laden with metallic exhalations from a nearby volcanic source. Such a syngenetic origin, however, would seem to require some redistribution of the sulfides during a subsequent orogeny to account for the epigenetic relationships observed.

The massive sulfide deposits in the East Shasta copper-zinc district are much smaller than those in the West Shasta district and have yielded only about 15 percent as much base metal—about 30,000 tons of copper and 25,000 tons of zinc. The assay of mined ore averages about 15 to 20 percent zinc, 3 percent copper, 0 to 2 percent lead, 5 ounces silver, and 0.03 ounce gold per ton. The deposits occur as lenses that replace two rock units of Triassic age—an altered silicic volcanic rock unit called the Bully Hill Rhyolite, and the Pit Formation consisting of shale and tuff. Most of the sulfide lenses are tabular and steeply inclined. A few are cigar shaped. They range in size from a few inches to as much as 400 feet in greatest dimension. The largest lenses have a maximum thickness of 35 to 40 feet. Most lenses are clearly controlled by shear zones, and they lie generally parallel to schistosity or bedding in the host rocks. Their walls are either frozen to the country rock or are separated from it by a layer of clayey gouge. The walls of most sulfide lenses are sharp and smooth, but the edges, in contrast, are commonly irregular. Some lenses taper to a knife edge. Others pinch out in many thin layers or sheets extending a few inches to a few feet into the host rock. Much of the sulfide ore is banded, and in places near the edges of lenses the banding parallels bedding or schistosity in the host rock. Both the banding and the presence of structurally oriented horsts of country rock enclosed in sulfide lenses are convincing evidence of a replacement origin for the sulfide.

Much of the sulfide ore is fine grained; it consists of intimate mixtures of pyrite, sphalerite, chalcopyrite, galena, and tetrahedrite-tennantite. Quartz, barite, calcite, anhydrite, and gypsum are the principal gangue minerals. In general the proportion of gangue minerals to sulfides is appreciably higher than in the West Shasta deposits, and the proportion of pyrite to other sulfide is much lower. The problem of the origin of mineralizing solutions and the source of the base metals is essentially the same as in the West Shasta district. The closest plutonic rock outcrops are two small stocks of altered quartz diorite about 5 miles away on either side of the deposits, but possibly these stocks are merely eminences rising from a subjacent mass concealed at a depth of a few thousand feet beneath the deposits.

The occurrence of massive sulfide deposits in formations of vastly different age (Devonian and Triassic) within the restricted area of the West and East Shasta copper-zinc districts is additional strong evidence favoring an epigenetic origin for both the West and East Shasta deposits. It is highly improbable that identical conditions conducive to the formation of syngenetic massive sulfides had been repeated in an area with such an active tectonic and depositional history.

The Blue Ledge mine, near the California-Oregon border (fig. 5), has yielded about 11,151 tons of ore containing 12.12 percent copper, 0.092 ounce of gold, and 5.24 ounces of silver per ton (Hundhausen, 1947, p. 5). Most of the production was during World War I. The deposit is a replacement vein that dips about 60° W. in quartz-muscovite schist. Although the deposit consists of fairly massive sulfide (pyrite, pyrrhotite, chalcopyrite, and sphalerite), it is not strictly the massive sulfide type of deposit because of its veinlike form. The vein is 1,300 feet long, 5 feet thick, and has been followed to a depth of 350 feet.

A second deposit with production of some significance in the northern part of the area is the Gray Eagle mine (fig. 5). According to Brown (1916, p. 818), this deposit is a vein 10 to 80 feet thick that strikes northwest and dips 45° northeast. An ore shoot over 300 feet long consists of chalcopyrite and pyrite. The ore carries from 2.5 to 18 percent copper and $1.50 per ton in gold. The surface outcrop is marked by a gossan.

The Copper Bluff deposit in the western Klamaths (fig. 5) is a bedded replacement deposit in chlorite schist beneath a black carbonaceous phyllite (H. K. Stager, written communication, 1959). The ore has an average thickness of 5 feet. During the 1950's about 10,000 tons of ore milled had an average gross value of $6.50 per ton. Silicic plutonic rocks crop out no closer than 4 or 5 miles from any of the three deposits mentioned above. Hence there may or may not be a genetic relation between these deposits and the emplacement of plutonic rocks.

Silver.—About $13 million worth of silver has been recovered from ore mined in the Klamath Mountains. Most of this ore was produced from the massive sulfide deposits in the West and East Shasta copper-zinc districts.

The only silver mine of any consequence is the Silver Falls-Consolidated mine about 12 miles southwest of Redding (fig. 5). This mine was discovered about 1866, and most of its production was achieved prior to 1900. Veins striking N. 45° E. to N. 60° E. are from 10 inches to 2 feet wide and dip steeply. The veins are in quartz diorite of the Shasta Bally batholith. According to Tucker (1923, p. 313) the silver-bearing mineral is tetrahedrite, associated with galena, pyrite, sphalerite, chalcopyrite, and gold. A few other silver-bearing veins near the Silver Falls-Consolidated deposit are also known.

All are along fractures in the Shasta Bally batholith and are inferred to be genetically related to the batholith.

DEPOSITS INFERRED TO BE ASSOCIATED WITH LATE VOLCANIC ACTIVITY

Quicksilver.—Occurrences of quicksilver are found at several widely scattered localities in the Klamath Mountains, but the only deposit having significant production is the Altoona mine in the east-central part of the area (fig. 4). This deposit, discovered in 1871, has a recorded production of about 34,000 flasks, mostly recovered prior to 1900, and significant reserves of good grade ore reportedly still remain. The geology of the deposit has been reported on by Swinney (1950). More recently the deposit was explored under a Defense Minerals Exploration Administration contract, and much of the material below is taken from H. K. Stager (written communication, 1958), who studied the geology in connection with the exploration work.

The ore bodies are along steeply dipping shear zones up to 30 feet wide that cut altered porphyritic diorite and serpentinized peridotite. The ore bodies are found only in diorite. They are tabular lenses that average 5 feet thick and are as much as 270 feet long and extend down dip as much as 300 feet. The diorite host is intensely altered and replaced by quartz and carbonates. The resulting rock resembles the silica-carbonate rock of Coast Range quicksilver deposits. Ore minerals are cinnabar and native mercury. The cinnabar is in small crystals disseminated in the sheared and altered diorite and as veinlets and fracture coatings. Native mercury is common in vugs and cinnabar-lined cavities in the rock, and some vugs have yielded as much as several pounds of native mercury. Gangue minerals are ankerite, pyrite, barite, quartz, and clay minerals. The two main types of ore are an altered diorite type and a carbonate type. Although both types may be found in the same shear zone, most of the production has come from the diorite type.

Of the several other localities in the Klamath Mountains where quicksilver is known to occur (see Irwin, 1960, p. 72) one of the most promising is the Webb deposit in the extreme northwestern part of the area. According to Cater and Wells (1953) this deposit is on a shear zone in serpentinized saxonite intruded by small irregular bodies of diorite and by felsite dikes. Production has been very small.

The age and genesis of quicksilver deposits in the Klamath Mountains cannot be directly determined from the observed relations. The quicksilver deposits in the California Coast Ranges to the west and south are generally regarded as post-Miocene in age and are genetically related to late Tertiary or Quaternary volcanism. However, there are no known volcanic centers near the Klamath Mountains deposits.

DEPOSITS CONCENTRATED BY SEDIMENTARY PROCESSES

The mineral commodities genetically associated with sedimentary processes include placer gold and platinum, building materials, and manganese. Placer gold, important historically, has been discussed earlier; platinum was produced from placer deposits intermittently. Stone and sand and gravel are important economic commodities, as shown by figure 3, but the occurrence of mineable deposits will not be discussed here as it depends more on economic factors than on geologic relations.

Manganese.—Although numerous occurrences of manganese are known in the area, production has been negligible. A small production has come mostly from the Shasta Copper mine (fig. 5) where about 1,000 tons of ore containing 27 percent manganese was produced. Most of the deposits are associated with bedded chert in greenstone or schist. The primary manganese mineral is the silicate rhodonite, which cannot under present technologic conditions be utilized as ore, and which oxidizes slowly, yielding only small shallow pockets of manganese oxide. The individual manganese deposits are described by Trask and others (1950).

REFERENCES

Albers, J. P., 1961, Gold deposits in the French Gulch-Deadwood district, Shasta and Trinity Counties, California: U.S. Geol. Survey Prof. Paper 424-C, art. 147, p. C1–C4.

—— 1964, Geology of the French Gulch quadrangle, Shasta and Trinity Counties, California: U.S. Geol. Survey Bull. 1141-J, p. J1–J70.

—— 196__, Economic geology of the French Gulch quadrangle: California Div. Mines and Geology Spec. Rept. (In press)

Albers, J. P., and Robertson, J. F., 1961, Geology and ore deposits of east Shasta copper-zinc district, Shasta County, California: U.S. Geol. Survey Prof. Paper 338, 107 p.

Allen, J. E., 1941, Geologic investigation of the chromite deposits of California: California Jour. Mines and Geology, v. 37, no. 1, p. 101–167.

Averill, C. V., 1931, Preliminary report on economic geology of the Shasta quadrangle: California Div. Mines, 27th Rept. State Mineralogist, no. 1, p. 2–65.

—— 1933, Gold deposits of the Redding and Weaverville quadrangles [California]: California Jour. Mines and Geology, v. 29, nos. 1, 2, p. 2–73.

—— 1935, Mines and mineral resources of Siskiyou County [California]: California Jour. Mines and Geology, v. 31, no. 3, p. 255–338.

—— 1941, Mineral resources of Trinity County: California Jour. Mines and Geology, v. 37, no. 1, p. 8–90.

Brown, G. C., 1916, The counties of Shasta, Siskiyou, Trinity: California Mining Bur., 14th Rept. State Mineralogist (1913–1914), pt. 6, p. 745–925.

Cater, F. W., Jr., and Wells, F. G., 1953, Geology and mineral resources of the Gasquet quadrangle, California-Oregon: U.S. Geol. Survey Bull. 995-C, p. 79–133.

Ferguson, H. G., 1914, Gold lodes of the Weaverville quadrangle, California: U.S. Geol. Survey Bull. 540-A, p. 22–79.

Hershey, O. H., 1910, Origin of gold "pockets" in northern California: Mining and Sci. Press, v. 101, p. 741–742.

Hotz, P. E., 1964, Nickeliferous laterites in southwestern Oregon and northwestern California: Econ. Geology, v. 59, no. 3, p. 355–396.

Hundhausen, R. J., 1947, Blue Ledge copper-zinc mine, Siskiyou County, California: U.S. Bur. Mines Rept. Inv. 4124, 16 p.

Irwin, W. P., 1960, Geologic reconnaissance of the northern Coast Ranges and Klamath Mountains, California, with a summary of the mineral resources: California Div. Mines Bull. 179, 80 p.

—— 1964, Late Mesozoic orogenies in the ultramafic belts of northwestern California and southwestern Oregon: U.S. Geol. Survey Prof. Paper 501-C, p. C1–C9.

Kinkel, A. R., Jr., Hall, W. E., and Albers, J. P., 1956, Geology and base-metal deposits of the West Shasta copper-zinc district, Shasta County, California: U.S. Geol. Survey Prof. Paper 285, 156 p.

Lamey, C. A., 1948a, Hirz Mountain iron-ore deposits, Shasta County, California: California Div. Mines Bull. 129, p. 129–136.

—— 1948b, Shasta and California iron-ore deposits, Shasta County, California: California Div. Mines Bull. 129, p. 137–164.

MacDonald, D. F., 1913, Notes on the gold lodes of the Carrville district, Trinity County, California: U.S. Geol. Survey Bull. 530, p. 9–41.

Rice, S. J., 1957, Asbestos, *in* Wright, L. A., ed., Mineral commodities of California: California Div. Mines Bull. 176, p. 49–58.

Swinney, C. M., 1950, The Altoona quicksilver mine, Trinity County, California: California Jour. Mines and Geology, v. 46, no. 3, p. 395–404.

Trask, P. D., and others, 1950, Geologic description of the manganese deposits of California: California Div. Mines Bull. 152, 378 p.

Tucker, W. B., 1923, Silver lodes of the South Fork mining district, Shasta County: California Mining Bur., 18th Rept. State Mineralogist, pt. 7, p. 313–321.

Wells, F. G., and Cater, F. W., Jr., 1950, Chromite deposits of Siskiyou County, California: California Div. Mines Bull. 134, pt. 1, chap. 2, p. 77–127.

Wells, F. G., Cater, F. W., Jr., and Rynearson, G. A., 1946, Chromite deposits of Del Norte County, California: California Div. Mines Bull. 134, pt. 1, chap. 1, p. 1–76.

Wells, F. G., Smith, C T., Rynearson, G. A., and Livermore, J. S., 1949, Chromite deposits near Seiad and McGuffy Creeks, Siskiyou County, California: U.S. Geol. Survey Bull. 948-B, p. 19–62.

Photo 2. Castle Crags, Shasta County.

CHAPTER III

CASCADE RANGE, MODOC PLATEAU AND GREAT BASIN PROVINCES

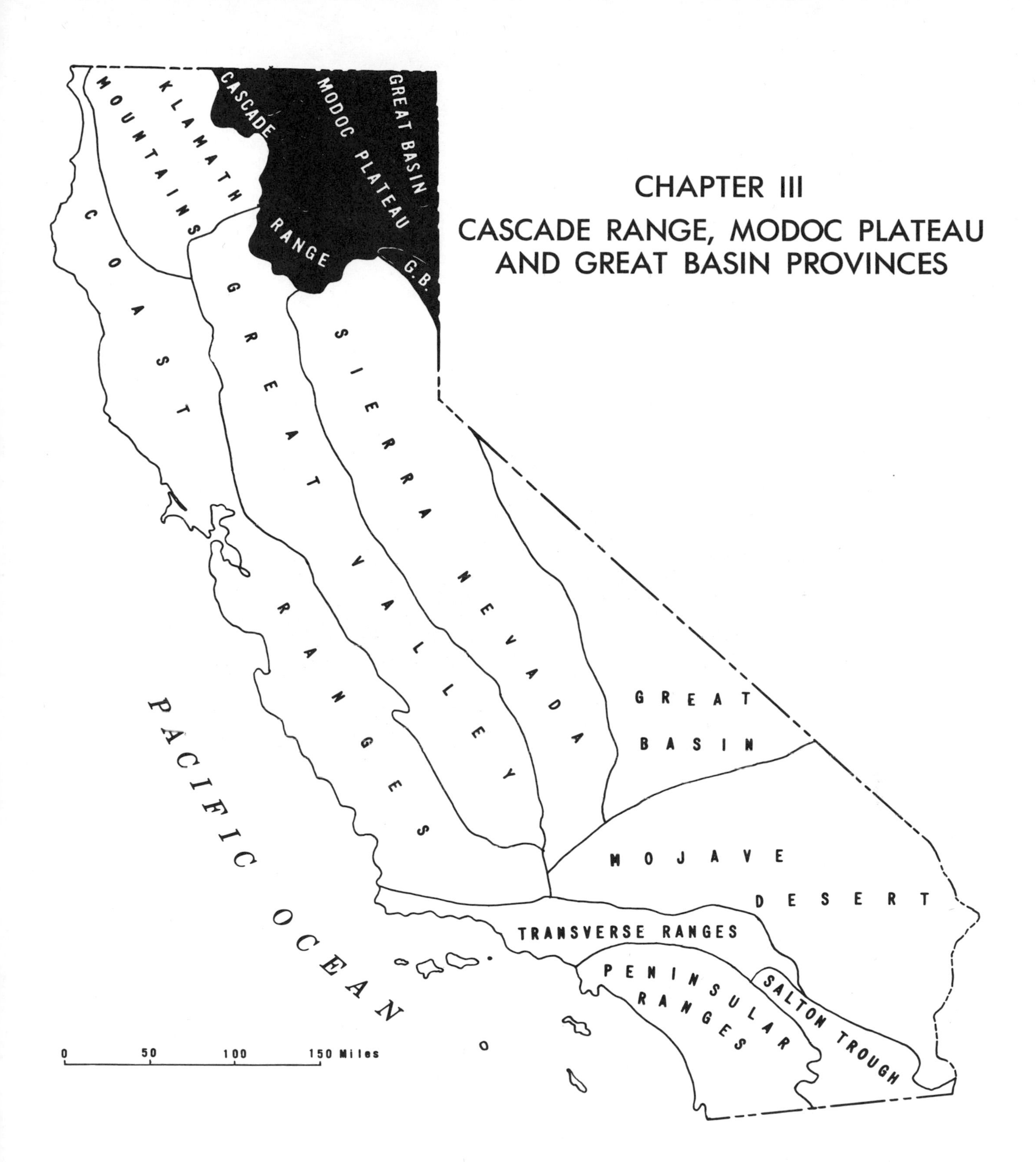

Page

Cone Mountain.

GEOLOGY OF THE CASCADE RANGE AND MODOC PLATEAU *

By Gordon A. Macdonald
U.S. Geological Survey and Hawaii Institute of Geophysics,
University of Hawaii, Honolulu, Hawaii

Most of the northeastern corner of California, north of the Sierra Nevada, is included in the physiographic provinces of the Cascade Mountains and the Modoc Plateau. The Cascade Range extends northward through Oregon and Washington into British Columbia, and the Modoc Plateau extends into Oregon and southeastward into Nevada. Most of the Cascade Range is a fairly well-defined province, but in northern California the separation between it and the Modoc Plateau becomes indefinite. The block-faulting characteristic of the Modoc region extends into the Cascade Range, and the rocks characteristic of the two provinces are intermingled. The division between the Modoc Plateau and the Great Basin, which borders it on the east, also is vague. Both regions consist of fault-block mountain ranges separated by flat-floored basins, and similar rocks are present on both sides of the boundary.

The outstanding characteristics of the Modoc region are the dominance of volcanism so recent that the constructional volcanic landforms are still clearly preserved and the presence of broad interrange areas of nearly flat basalt plains. It is the basalt plains that have given rise to the designation "plateau"; however, the region as a whole is far from being the high, essentially undiversified plain that the term usually implies.

At the southern end of the region, the rocks of the Cascade Range and the Modoc Plateau overlap the metamorphic and plutonic rocks of the Sierra Nevada; 50 miles to the northwest, similar rocks emerge from beneath the Cascade volcanics at the edge of the Klamath Mountains province. The broad depression extending northeast across the Sierra Nevada-Klamath orogenic belt, originally recognized by von Richthofen (1868), was called the "Lassen Strait," by Diller (1895a, 1897), who believed it to have been a seaway that in Cretaceous time connected the marine basin of California with that of east-central Oregon. Sediments deposited in the southwestern end of the strait are represented by sandstones of the Chico Formation (Upper Cretaceous) which underlie the volcanic rocks of the Cascade Range along the eastern edge of the Sacramento Valley. Probably this depression persisted—though above sea level and disrupted by volcanism and faulting—through much of Tertiary time. Although the plutonic and metamorphic rocks are nowhere exposed within it except in a small area adjacent to Eagle Lake, there can be no serious doubt that they underlie the volcanics throughout the area of the depression.

Throughout most of its extent, from northern California into Washington, the Cascade Range trends slightly east of north. However, at Mount Shasta, 40 miles south of the California boundary, the trend abruptly changes to southeastward. (It is perhaps worth noting that the Sutter Buttes, 150 miles to the south, lie approximately on the extension of the main Cascade trend.) The change in trend of the Cascade Range takes place approximately at the north edge of the "Lassen Strait," where it intersects the Klamath-Sierra Nevada belt; the trend of the southern part of the range is parallel to, and probably controlled by, the underlying Sierra Nevada structures. The southern portion of the range is almost isolated from the northern part by a projection of metamorphic rocks of the Klamath province. Within this portion of the Cascade Range, almost certainly underlain by the older orogenic belt of the Sierra Nevada, the variation in rock types and the incidence of varieties more acidic than andesite appears to be greater than in the northern portion of the range, except for the eastern outliers of the Medicine Lake Highland in California and the Newberry Volcano in Oregon.

Although it is distinctly to the east of the Cascade Range as a whole (fig. 1), the Medicine Lake Highland is generally regarded as an eastward bulge of the Cascade province (Hinds, 1952, p. 129). As Anderson (1941, p. 350) has pointed out, however, the Medicine Lake volcano, like the similarly outlying Newberry Volcano (Williams, 1935), differs somewhat from the typical volcanoes of the High Cascades. Situated in the plateau region, rather than in the Cascade belt of orogenic volcanism, these volcanoes may represent an evolution of stray Cascade-type magmas under different tectonic conditions.

Following Diller's (1895a, 1906) excellent pioneer work in the southeastern part of the region, the amount of geological work that has been done in the Cascade and Modoc provinces of California is surprisingly little. The areas are shown on a scale of 1:250,000 on the Weed, Alturas, Redding, and Westwood sheets of the Geologic Map of California (California Div. Mines, 1958–1964), but published mapping on a larger scale is limited to a few widely separated areas. Within the Cascade Range these include, near the south end, the Lassen Volcanic National Park (Williams, 1932a)

* Publication authorized by the Director, U.S. Geological Survey.

and the region just to the north (Macdonald, 1963, 1964), and the Macdoel quadrangle (1:125,000) just south of the Oregon border (Williams, 1949). Between these, the region in the immediate vicinity of Mount Shasta has also been described and mapped in a reconnaissance fashion (Williams, 1932b, 1934). The Medicine Lake Highland has been studied and mapped by Anderson (1941), but within the Modoc region proper, the only published mapping on a larger scale is on the area immediately adjacent to Lassen Volcanic National Park (Macdonald, 1964, 1965), in and near the Pit River valley near Alturas (Ford and others, 1963), and near Eagle Lake (Gester, 1962). Unpublished studies have been made of the area south and west of Lassen Volcanic National Park by G. H. Curtis and T. A. Wilson, of the University of California; and reconnaissance studies (unpublished) of many other areas have been made by Q. A. Aune, C. W. Chesterman, T. E. Gay, Jr., P. A. Lydon, and V. C. McMath of the California Division of Mines and Geology. George W. Walker, of the U.S. Geological Survey, who studied parts of the northern Modoc Plateau while preparing the State Geologic Map of Oregon, has generously supplied information for this paper, and information for the section on Cretaceous rocks was supplied by D. L. Jones, of the U. S. Geological Survey.

A generalized geologic map of the northeastern part of California accompanies the article by T. E. Gay, Jr., on the economic mineral deposits of the Cascade Range, Modoc Plateau, and Great Basin regions of northeastern California.

I wish to thank Q. A. Aune, and especially T. E. Gay, Jr., of the California Division of Mines and Geology, for their constructive criticism of the manuscript of this article and for their aid in collecting and preparing the illustrations.

CASCADE RANGE

The Cascade Range in Oregon is conveniently divided into the Western Cascade Range and the High Cascade Range (Callaghan, 1933; Peck and others, 1964). The rocks of the Western Cascade Range include lava flows and beds of pyroclastic debris, and in places interbedded nonmarine and shallow marine sediments, gradually accumulated in a slowly sinking trough to a thickness of more than 10,000 feet. Their age ranges from late Eocene to Pliocene (Peck, 1964). In composition, they are predominantly pyroxene andesite but range from olivine basalt to rhyolite. Rocks of the Western Cascade are underlain by Eocene sedimentary rocks of the Umpqua Formation and are unconformably overlain by Pliocene to Recent volcanic rocks of the High Cascade Range. The latter are predominantly pyroxene andesite, but range in composition from olivine basalt to dacite. Early eruptions in the High Cascade were almost wholly basaltic andesite and basalt, producing fluid lava flows that spread to great distances and built a broad, gently sloping ridge that consisted largely of coalescing small shield volcanoes and fissure-type flows. Pyroclastic material was comparatively small in amount. In time, however, the predominant lavas became more siliceous, the proportion of explosive eruption increased, and on the earlier ridge of lavas were built the great composite volcanoes that form the conspicuous peaks of the present Cascade Range. Rarely, domes of dacite were formed. Occasional basaltic eruptions, largely from eccentric and independent vents, appear to have taken place throughout the period of building of the big cones and to have continued afterward.

Volcanic rocks in the Western Cascade Range differ from those of most of the High Cascade Range primarily in greater variety of petrographic types, larger proportion of pyroclastic rocks, and a pervasive chloritic alteration that gives a characteristic greenish hue to most of the rocks. The alteration was probably related to the period of folding and uplift of the Western Cascade, followed by erosion, that preceded the building of the High Cascade, and particularly to the small intrusions of gabbroic to quartz monzonitic composition.

The northern part of the Cascade Range in California is much like that in Oregon. Upper Cretaceous and Eocene sedimentary rocks are succeeded by greenish volcanics of the Western Cascade series which were faulted and tilted eastward and northeastward at about the end of the Miocene (Williams, 1949, p. 14). Erosion destroyed the constructional volcanic landforms and reduced the region to one of rolling hills before renewed volcanism built the High Cascade. Southward the volcanic rocks of the Western Cascade are overlapped by those of the High Cascade, and south of the Shasta region rocks belonging to the Western Cascade series have not been recognized, although volcanic rocks overlain by Pliocene diatomite in the gorge of the Pit River may be equivalent to part of them in age. In the region northwest of Mount Lassen the upper Pliocene Tuscan Formation rests directly on Cretaceous and Eocene sedimentary rocks, and the Western Cascade volcanics are absent.

As in Oregon, the lower part of the High Cascade sequence in California consists largely of pyroxene andesite, with lesser amounts of basalt and minor amounts of hornblende andesite and dacite. Although erosion has destroyed the original topography, these lavas appear to have built a broad ridge with few, if any, big cones. Most of the lavas are probably of latest Pliocene age (Macdonald, 1963). In the region southwest of Lassen Volcanic National Park, however, some of them are of pre-Tuscan age (Wilson, 1961). Continuing volcanism became more concentrated at distinct centers, and more individualized cones were built, some of which are shield volcanoes and some composite cones. The latter included the largest of the volcanic mountains, such as Brokeoff Volcano (Mount Tehama), which collapsed to form the caldera in which

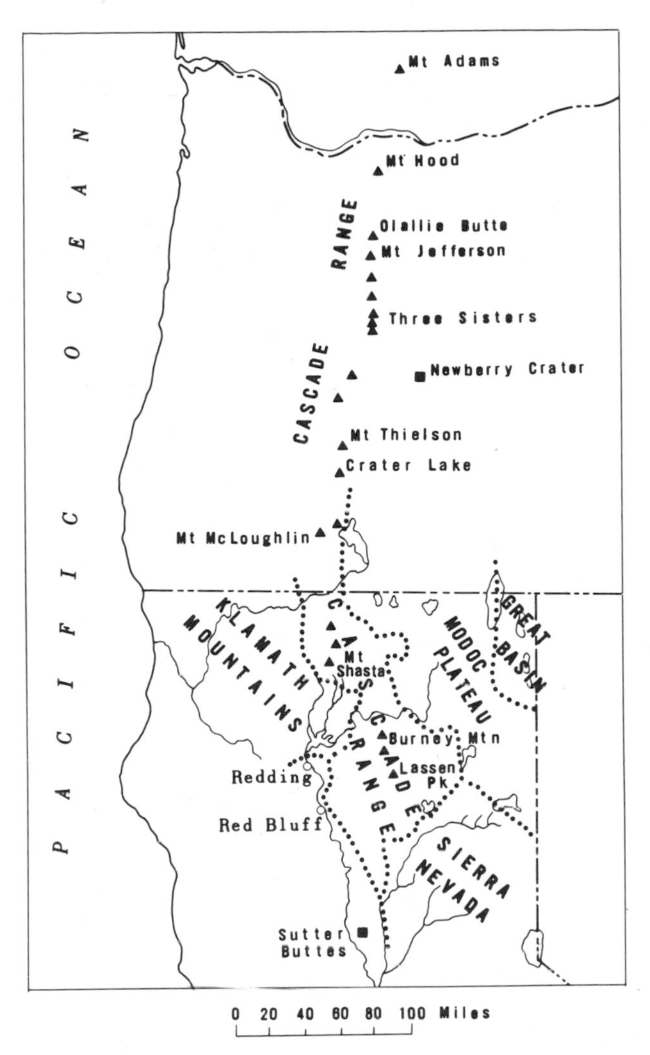

Figure 1. *Map of a part of northern California, western Oregon, and southern Washington, showing the principal peaks of the Cascade Range and Sutter Buttes lying farther south along the same trend.*

Lassen Peak was later built, Magee Mountain (Crater Peak), Burney Mountain, and Mount Shasta (fig. 1). In the Lassen region, volcanism culminated in the eruption of several dacite domes, some of them only a few hundred years old, and at Medicine Lake, flows and domes of rhyolite obsidian were erupted. Contemporaneously, basaltic volcanism continued with the eruption of such flows and associated cinder cones as the Callahan and Burnt Lava flows near Medicine Lake, and the Hat Creek and Cinder Cone flows in the Lassen region.

With eruptions at Cinder Cone in 1851 and Lassen Peak in 1914–17, and a possible eruption at Medicine Lake in 1910 (Finch, 1928), the Cascade Range of California must be regarded as a region of still-active volcanism.

Cretaceous and Early Tertiary Sedimentary Rocks

Rocks of Late Cretaceous age are exposed at many places along the east side of the Sacramento Valley from near Folsom, west of the central Sierra Nevada, to the area east of Redding; and from the vicinity of Shasta Valley, northwest of Mount Shasta, to and beyond the northern boundary of the State. In these areas they rest unconformably on the pre-Cretaceous rocks of the Sierra Nevada-Klamath Mountains complex. They have been referred to as the Chico Formation at Chico and Butte Creeks in Butte County and as the Hornbrook Formation in northern Siskiyou County (Popenoe and others, 1960).

The Chico Formation consists of massive gray, buff-weathering, arkosic sandstone, dark-gray to black shales, and beds of conglomerate, particularly near the base. In the type locality at Chico Creek, where it is 4,000 feet thick, it has yielded a varied fauna of ammonites, gastropods, and pelecypods ranging in age from Coniacian to Campanian.

East and north of Redding, a similar thickness of Upper Cretaceous rocks has been described by Popenoe (1943). The lithologies present are much like those at Chico Creek, but although the time of deposition of the rocks in the two areas overlaps considerably, the section at Redding spans a slightly older segment of the Late Cretaceous.

In the Hornbrook area near the California-Oregon boundary, the Cretaceous rocks consist of about 5,000 feet of conglomerate, sandstone, and siltstone. The oldest unit, which rests unconformably on granitic and metamorphic rocks, contains marine fossils (Turonian to Coniacian), but part of the overlying conglomeratic sandstone is nonmarine. These rocks are in turn overlain by 5,000 feet of marine siltstone, with some sandy interbeds. This silty sequence was long regarded as a part of the widespread Eocene Umpqua Formation, but it has been found to contain Late Cretaceous fossils in its upper part (Jones, 1959). About 5 miles south of Ager, in exposures near the western edge of the Copco quadrangle, the section contains a bed of coal, in places as much as 6 feet thick, that was at one time mined. Fossils discovered in overlying shales confirm the Cretaceous age of the coal beds, formerly regarded as Eocene. Thus, no rocks that can be positively assigned to the Umpqua Formation of early to middle Eocene age (Baldwin, 1964) are known in the California part of the Cascade Range or Modoc Plateau provinces. The Late Cretaceous in this area was a period of shallow marine sedimentation with some nonmarine deposition, in part on swampy flood plains in the northern area. Marine deposition in northeastern California terminated in the latest Cretaceous, and there is no depositional record for the Paleocene or earliest Eocene.

Deposition in late Eocene time is recorded by the Montgomery Creek Formation (Williams, 1932a; Anderson and Russell, 1939), which was originally included by Diller (1895a) in the Ione Formation. The Montgomery Creek Formation is exposed along the east side of the Sacramento Valley from near Shingletown, 25 miles east-southeast of Redding, northward

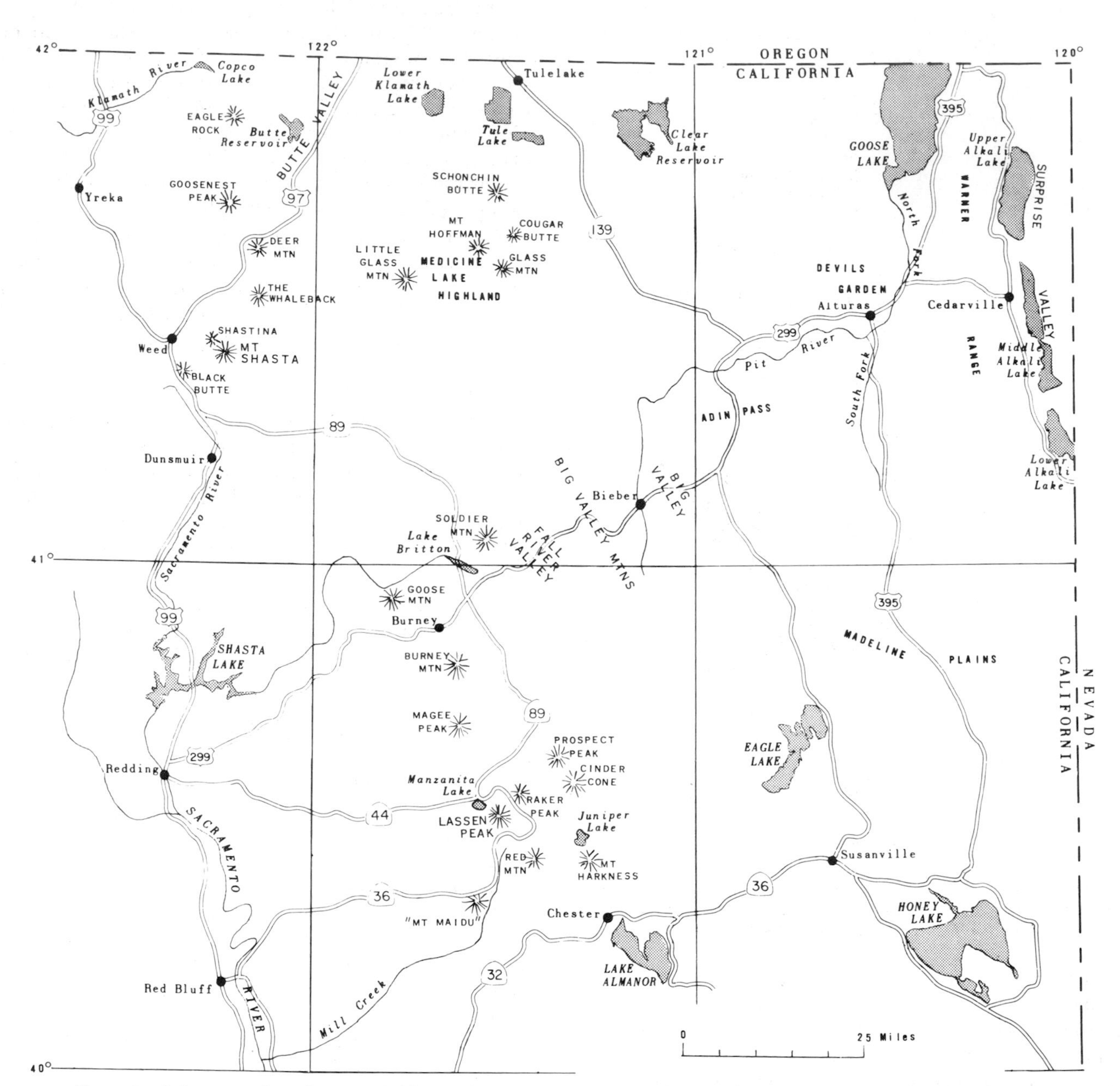

Figure 2. Index map of northeastern California showing the principal physiographic features referred to in the text.

for about 50 miles to the upper drainage basin of Kosk Creek in the Big Bend quadrangle. It is extensively exposed along the Pit River near Big Bend, and some of the best and most easily accessible exposures are along Highway 299 (fig. 2) just east of Montgomery Creek, where sandstones and conglomerates in a big highway cut contain fossil leaves. In most places the Montgomery Creek Formation consists predominantly of pale-gray massive sandstone, weathering to buff, that is locally much channeled and cross-bedded and commonly contains scattered pebbles and pebbly lenses. Thick beds of conglomerate, and less commonly of silty shale, are present in places. Locally, as along Coal Creek in the Whitmore quadrangle, the formation contains thin beds of poor-grade coal that have been mined to a small extent in the past. Fragments of petrified wood are common in some areas. The sandstones are poor in ferromagnesian minerals, and in general are weakly cemented. Their weak consolidation results in poor exposures; and where valleys have been cut into them, the poor consolidation commonly produces extensive landsliding of overlying more resistant rocks such as breccias or andesitic lava flows of the upper Pliocene Tuscan Formation. Typically, the Montgomery Creek Formation rests unconformably on Upper Cretaceous sedimentary rocks and is overlain unconformably by Pliocene volcanic rocks.

Figure 3. Index map of same area as figure 2, showing location of quadrangles and principal geographic features mentioned in the text.

Western Cascade Volcanic Series

The rocks of the Western Cascade volcanic series form a nearly continuous belt extending along the western foothills of the Cascade Range for 45 miles south of the State boundary, and scattered outcrops for another 10 miles. They are exposed along Highway 99 just west of Weed, but are better seen along the road extending eastward along the Klamath River from Hornbrook to Copco Lake. The following description is largely summarized from the report by Williams (1949, p. 20–32).

Near the State boundary, the exposed thickness of the Western Cascade volcanics is not less than 12,000 feet, and may be as much as 15,000 feet. In the northern part of the Yreka quadrangle, a few thin beds of volcanic conglomerate and sandstone of the Colestin Formation (upper Eocene) rest unconformably on the Hornbrook Formation at the base of the Western Cascade series, but farther south these are absent and the lowest lavas rest directly on the Hornbrook Formation or overlap it to rest on the pre-Cretaceous plutonic and metamorphic basement. A few lenses of tuffaceous sandstone and volcanic conglomerate are interbedded with the volcanics at higher stratigraphic levels, and coal and carbonaceous shale are present east of Little Shasta. The volcanic rocks include both lava flows and fragmental deposits, the latter being in part direct products of volcanic explosion and in part mudflow deposits.

The lava flows are mostly pyroxene andesite, generally with hypersthene more abundant than augite. Some contain a small amount of olivine, commonly replaced by serpentine or iddingsite, or by a mixture of magnetite and hematite or goethite. A small amount of cristobalite or tridymite generally is present in the groundmass. Most flows are between 10 and 30 feet thick, but a few exceed 100 feet. Most are dense to sparingly vesicular, and most have a well-developed platy jointing that results from shearing in the flow as slight movement continues during the last stages of consolidation. Hornblende andesites and hornblende-bearing pyroxene andesites are relatively rare, as are flows of dacite. The Western Cascade lavas in northern California are less altered than many of those in Oregon, possibly, Williams suggests, because of the absence of subvolcanic dioritic stocks and related mineralized belts. Particularly in the upper part of the series, however, many of the andesites are propylitized, the feldspars being partly altered to kaolin and the pyroxenes replaced by calcite, chlorite, and limonite. In many andesites, veins and amygdules of opal and chalcedony are abundant, and silicified wood may be found in the intercalated tuffs, as at Agate Flat, in the north center of the Copco quadrangle, just south of the State boundary.

Pyroclastic rocks include well-stratified andesitic tuff-breccias and lapilli tuffs, basaltic agglomerates composed of rounded lapilli and bombs, and tuffs of andesitic, basaltic, dacitic, and rhyolitic composition. Rhyolitic tuffs are found chiefly in the upper part of the series. Well-bedded rhyolitic lapilli tuffs of air-laid origin reach a thickness of nearly 500 feet near the head of Shovel Creek in the northern part of the Macdoel (1:62,500) quadrangle; and dense dust-textured tuffs reach a similar thickness near the head of Little Bogus Creek in the center of the Copco quadrangle. Near Bogus School a bed of rhyolitic tuff, traceable for more than 5 miles, varies from an incoherent rock, rich in pumice fragments up to an inch long, to a compact crystal-vitric tuff nearly devoid of pumice fragments. In places, particularly near the base, it is streaky and welded. The rock is an ignimbrite formed by an incandescent ash flow. A quarter of a mile north of Bogus Creek, a vertical dike of glassy rhyolite 10 feet thick, closely resembling the dense crystal-vitric tuff, cuts the bottom of the bed. This dike is considered to be the filling of a fissure that gave vent to the tuff in the same manner as the eruption of the "sand flow" of 1912 in the Valley of Ten Thousand Smokes in Alaska (Williams, 1949, p. 25). Welded dacite tuff near the eastern foot of Miller Mountain, in the west-central part of The Whaleback quadrangle, is considered by Williams to belong to the Western Cascade series and to unconformably underlie basalt of the High Cascade series.

At Sheep Rock, south of Miller Mountain, beds of coarse andesitic tuff-breccia containing angular to subangular blocks up to 4 feet across in a tuffaceous matrix reach a thickness of 1,600 feet. Individual layers, some of them more than 100 feet thick, show only a very crude bedding. The deposits resemble those of the Tuscan Formation in the Cascade Range and the Mehrten Formation (Miocene and Pliocene) in the Sierra Nevada (Curtis, 1957), and like them, are interpreted as being the products of volcanic mudflows. Similar deposits are found northwest of Little Shasta, on the south side of Bogus Mountain, and along the Klamath River south of Brush Creek, in the northwest portion of the Copco quadrangle.

Several rhyolite domes are found in the vicinity of Little Shasta, and volcanic necks and plugs of andesite and basalt occur near the lower end of Copco Lake and in Shasta Valley. Two necks at Agate Flat are oval in plan, elongated north-south, and approximately 2,000 by 1,000 feet across. One of the andesite necks, at the hairpin turn of the Klamath River a mile below the Copco Dam, is noteworthy for the presence of aegirine in veinlets that also contain zeolites and magnetite and as an alteration product of other pyroxenes close to the edge of the veinlets (Williams, 1949, p. 29). Another of the necks has marginal ring dikes that dip outward at angles of 60°–80°.

Near the end of the Miocene, the entire Cascade belt is believed to have been upheaved, perhaps partly by arching, but partly by roughly north-south faulting that produced high east-facing scarps like the one 2,000 feet high described by Thayer (1936, p. 708) near Mount Jefferson in Oregon. Similar fault scarps are believed by Williams (1942, p. 29) to have formed and been buried by later High Cascade lavas near Crater Lake, Oregon; others may have formed in the region just north of Mount Shasta (Williams, 1949, p. 52). Still other faults formed horsts along the eastern side of Shasta Valley and one bordering Shasta Valley near Yellow Butte (Dwinnell Reservoir quadrangle) must have had a throw of more than 10,000 feet (Williams, 1949, p. 53). Whether any corresponding displacements took place in the portion of the Cascade Range south of Mount Shasta is not known. The fact that the northwesterly trend of this portion of the range coincides with the direction of Sierra Nevada-Klamath Mountains structures that are believed to underlie it suggests that south of Mount Shasta the Cascade Range may have shared the history of uplift of the Sierra Nevada, rather than that of the main, northern portion of the Cascade Range.

Some time after the upheaval of the main Cascade Range, fissures were opened on or near the crest of the ridge, and along them new magma rose to the surface to build the High Cascade volcanoes during Pliocene to Recent times (Williams, 1949, p. 35). The new vents appear to have been located somewhat to the east of those that supplied the lava of the Western Cascade Range (Peck and others, 1964, p. 50). The building of the Cascade Range south of Mount Shasta must have been coeval with that of the High Cascade Range farther north.

Tuscan Formation

The Tuscan Formation is exposed continuously for 65 miles along the east side of the Sacramento Valley, from near Oroville to 15 miles north of Red Bluff, with smaller isolated areas east of Redding. It has been shown by Anderson (1933a) to consist largely of breccias formed by lahars, or volcanic mudflows. The eastern part of the Tuscan consists almost entirely of tuff-breccia, in beds ranging from about 40 to 100 feet thick, and the entire accumulation averages about 1,000 feet in thickness. Along Mill Creek Canyon, southwest of Lassen Peak, its thickness is about 1,500 feet (Q. A. Aune, oral communication, 1965). Toward its western edge, interbedded volcanic conglomerates, sands, and tuffs appear, and still farther west it interdigitates with the strictly sedimentary Tehama Formation (Anderson and Russell, 1939, p. 232). Its southern portion rests on the western slope of the Sierra Nevada and overlaps the Sierran metamorphic and plutonic complex, but its northern portion forms part of the western slope of the southern Cascade Range.

Interbedded in the lower part of the Tuscan Formation in the southern part of the area, east of Red Bluff, and with the Tehama Formation on the west side of the Sacramento Valley, is 40 to 100 feet of gray, white, or pink dacite tuff containing fragments of pumice up to a few inches across in a matrix of glass and crystal shards. The massive and unsorted character of the deposit and the cleanness of the pumice vesicles indicates the ash-flow origin of the deposit. Even clearer is the evidence along Bear Creek, in the Millville quadrangle, east of Redding, where the tuff is in places more than 200 feet thick and much of it is thoroughly welded, with the elongate black glass "flames" characteristic of ignimbrite. This tuff is known as the Nomlaki Tuff Member (Russell and VanderHoof, 1931, p. 12–15). Vertebrate fossils in the Tehama Formation 10 feet above the Nomlaki indicate a late Pliocene age for the Tehama and Tuscan Formations and the intercalated Nomlaki. This age is confirmed by a potassium-argon age of 3.3 m.y. for the tuff along Bear Creek (Everndon, et al., 1964). It appears probable, however, that the tuff along Bear Creek was derived from a different source than that farther south.

Individual blocks in Tuscan breccia generally range from 1 to 6 inches across, but scattered blocks are commonly as much as 5 feet thick. Many are vesicular, and most were quite certainly derived from lava flows. Erosion of the formation results in removal of the finer material and concentration of the larger blocks on the surface, forming the broad stony plains crossed by the highways running northeastward from Chico and eastward from Red Bluff and Redding. Cross sections of the breccias are well displayed near Highway 32, along Deer Creek northeast of Chico, along Highway 36 east of Red Bluff, and less spectacularly along Highway 44 and the Millville-Whitmore Road east of Redding.

In the main southern area the blocks in the breccia are predominantly basalt, with lesser amounts of andesite; but in the smaller northern area, they are predominantly andesitic and dacitic, except locally along Bear Creek, where basalt is again abundant (Anderson, 1933a, p. 228). The difference in the prevalent type of rock among the blocks suggests different sources for the breccias of the southern and northern areas, and Lydon (1961) believes that the Tuscan Formation is derived from at least four different sources: one near Butt Mountain, 9 miles southwest of Lake Almanor, and nearly due east of Red Bluff; one near Mineral, 10 miles south-southwest of Lassen Peak; one east of Whitmore, 30 miles east of Redding; and another, less certain, a few miles farther north, west of Burney. All of these sources lie within the Cascade Range, and the Tuscan Formation, including the Nomlaki Tuff Member, almost surely is to be regarded as a unit within the High Cascade volcanic series. Along the edge of the Sacramento Valley east of Redding, it is the oldest unit, resting directly on the Montgomery Creek and Chico Formations, but in the Mineral area it is underlain by a thin series of basic lava flows.

In the area east of Redding, the Tuscan Formation, with its interbedded late Pliocene (3.3-m.y.) Nomlaki Tuff Member, serves to limit the maximum age of the overlying lavas, and these in turn indicate a limiting age for the widespread Burney (or so-called Warner) Basalt in the part of the Modoc Plateau just to the east. In other areas, however, the Tuscan Formation may range through a considerable age span. Q. A. Aune (oral communication, 1965) states that along Antelope Creek, in the Red Bluff quadrangle east of Red Bluff, the upper layers of the Tuscan Formation are nearly horizontal, whereas the lower layers are deformed nearly as much as the underlying Cretaceous strata. He suggests that the lower part of the Tuscan in that area may be considerably older than the late Pliocene age generally accepted for the formation.

High Cascade Volcanic Series

The time of beginning of High Cascade volcanism is difficult to date precisely. In the region north of Mount Shasta the oldest of the High Cascade rocks are younger than the Miocene rocks of the Western Cascades and older than other rocks that are in turn overlain by Pleistocene glacial moraines. They have been referred to the Pliocene, but there is no assurance that the moraines in question are not wholly of late Pleistocene age, and hence that the older lavas themselves may not have been erupted in the Pleistocene. Near the south end of the Cascade Range, northwest of Lassen Peak, andesite lava flows of the High Cascade rest on the Tuscan Formation (Macdonald, 1963), which is of latest Pliocene age (Axelrod, 1957,

p. 27). These andesites cannot, therefore, be older than latest Pliocene. They have, however, been much eroded, and the original constructional volcanic landforms on them have been destroyed to a considerably greater degree than on the oldest High Cascade lavas between Mount Shasta and the Oregon boundary. Consequently, it appears unlikely that the latter are older than latest Pliocene, and they are more probably of Pleistocene age. The basic lava flows that underlie the Tuscan formation near Mineral are probably the oldest exposed rocks in the High Cascade Range of California. Conversely, only relatively minor amounts of volcanic rock appear to be later in age than the youngest glaciation. The building of the High Cascade took place largely in Pliocene and Pleistocene times.

Williams (1949, p. 35) writes,

> "Throughout the southern part of the High Cascades in Oregon and California, Pliocene and early Pleistocene times were characterized by the growth of a north-south chain of large, flattish shield volcanoes built by quiet effusions of fluid olivine basalt and basaltic andesite. Great diversity had marked the behavior and products of the volcanoes that produced the Western Cascade series; on the contrary, the volcanoes now to be described [between Mount Shasta and the Oregon border in the Macdoel and The Whaleback quadrangles] were extremely uniform in their activity; fragmental explosions seldom interrupted the quiet outflow of lava, and the flows themselves varied only slightly in composition despite their wide extent."

The volcanoes include Miller Mountain, Ball Mountain, and the Eagle Rock shield. On the eastern edge of the area a series of similar broad cones, including Mount Hebron, south of Butte Valley, the McGavin Peak and Secret Spring Mountain, north of Butte Valley, are cut by faults of large displacement that represent the edge of the block-faulted Modoc Plateau. The only signs of explosive activity are a few thin beds of cinders intercalated with the flows on Secret Spring Mountain, and the remains of cinder (scoria) cones on the summits of Horsethief Butte, Ball Mountain, and a small shield north of the Copco Dam. Slightly younger than the basaltic shields is a series of thick flows of hornblende andesite and dacite(?) erupted from the Haight Mountain volcano, in the Bray quadrangle, just northeast of Mount Shasta, probably soon followed by the pyroxene andesites of Deer Mountain, Willow Creek Mountain, and the early andesite flows of Mount Shasta. These rocks contain abundant phenocrysts of hypersthene, augite, and labradorite in a pilotaxitic groundmass, with a little tridymite and cristobalite lining cavities. They resemble the principal types of andesite composing many of the big cones of the High Cascade (Williams, 1949, p. 40). Still later, eruptions of andesite built the Goosenest volcano, olivine basalt flows built the steep-sided cone of The Whaleback volcano, and finally floods of olivine basalt issued from fissures to pour down the valley of Alder Creek and spread over large parts of the floors of Butte and Shasta Valleys. Small flows of this group dammed the Klamath River to form a lake, at least 35 feet deeper than the present Copco Lake, whose shorelines are marked by conspicuous deposits of diatomite.

The history of Mount Shasta itself will be outlined on a later page.

The sequence of events in the area just north of Lassen Volcanic National Park is in general much the same as that deduced by Williams in the region north of Mount Shasta, outlined above. The earliest lavas, which rest on breccias of the Tuscan Formation, are pyroxene andesites associated with small amounts of hornblende andesite and dacite. These masses, presumably of latest Pliocene age, are deeply eroded, with resultant complete obliteration of constructional forms, and the position of former vents is indicated only by a few small intrusive plugs and a few cindercone remnants. The predominant lavas are two-pyroxene andesites, commonly with small phenocrysts of feldspar and often of hypersthene. Scattered small phenocrysts of olivine are present in some flows, and at Latour Butte blocky augite phenocrysts as much as 1 cm long are abundant. These andesites were gently folded on east-northeast-trending axes and were slightly eroded before they were covered locally by olivine-bearing basalts and basaltic andesites considered to be of very early Pleistocene age.

Both the andesites and the basalts were then broken by a series of northwest- to north-trending faults. Next came a succession of eruptions of basalt, basaltic andesite, and andesite that built a series of small shields and lava cones. Some of the andesites, such as those of Table and Badger Mountains, at the north edge of Lassen Volcanic National Park, are very siliceous despite their very dark color and decidedly basaltic aspect in the field. The Burney Basalt, a "plateau" basalt, rests against the base of the Badger Mountain shield. Next came a series of eruptions of andesite that built somewhat larger cones, including Crater Peak (generally known locally as Magee Mountain), and the Brokeoff (Tehama) Volcano that later collapsed to form the caldera in which Lassen Peak and its associated domes were built. The construction of the big composite cones was followed by the extrusion of domes and thick flows of dacite.

Through later Pleistocene and Recent time, basalt, basaltic andesite, andesite, and dacite have been erupted more or less simultaneously. Many of the basalt flows are of very large volume and extent, and in range of types are identical to the flows of the Modoc region to the northeast. One such flow, near Whitmore, covers an area of about 25 square miles. Another extends nearly 30 miles, from near the northwest corner of Lassen Volcanic National Park to about 2 miles southeast of Millville, nearly parallel to Highway 44 for most of that distance. It covers an area of more than 50 square miles; and its volume exceeds 1 cubic mile, and may be as great as 2.

A feature of this region that deserves special mention is the very widespread occurrence of quartz xenocrysts in the lavas. They are most common in the late basalts, such as the well-known quartz basalt of Cinder Cone in the Prospect Peak quadrangle (Finch and Anderson, 1930), but they are found in both basalts and andesites ranging in age from late Pliocene to Recent. They can be found in the basalt along Highway 89 in the pass just north of the Manzanita Lake entrance to Lassen Volcanic National Park and are abundant at Red Lake Mountain, a mile to the northwest. Not uncommonly they are several inches across, and some of them clearly show the comb structure characteristic of many quartz veins. There seems to be little question that they are fragments of veins picked up by the magma in its rise through the underlying basement of crystalline rocks. Some show no signs of reaction with the enclosing magma, but others are rounded and enclosed in thin reaction rims of pyroxene.

The region south and west of Lassen Volcanic National Park has been studied and described by T. A. Wilson (1961). After the deposition of the Tuscan breccias a big strato-volcano, named by Wilson Mount Maidu, rose around a vent located at Battle Creek Meadows, near Mineral, in the Lassen Peak quadrangle. The growth of the cone was contemporaneous with that of the Brokeoff Volcano, just to the northeast. Early eruptions of basaltic andesite were followed by later ones of pyroxene andesite and dacite. This was followed, some 1½ m.y. ago (potassium-argon age by G. S. Curtis), by the eruption of two enormous flows of rhyolite from fissures on the lower slopes of the composite cone. One flow is exposed along Blue Ridge and Snoqualmie Gulch, 7 miles northwest of Mineral, and the other on the Mill Creek Plateau, 5 miles southeast of Mineral, but both are accessible only by minor country roads. These remarkable flows cover an area of about 78 square miles. Their average thickness is nearly 500 feet and their maximum thickness exceeds 800 feet. The total volume is about 7.6 cubic miles! They were followed by eruption of glowing dacite avalanches, probably from the same fissures that gave vent to the more westerly of the rhyolite flows. These avalanche deposits of pumice tuff-breccia range from 100 to 200 feet thick. Their present area is about 21 square miles, but large amounts of the easily eroded material have been stripped away, and the original area was probably two or three times as great. The original volume of the avalanche deposits was probably at least 1½ cubic miles. With the eruption of more than 8 cubic miles of rhyolite and dacite magma from its lower flanks, it is small wonder that the summit of Mount Maidu volcano collapsed to form a caldera! Later came a series of basalt eruptions that built shield volcanoes with summit cinder cones, or cinder cones with associated lava flows. One of the latter is Inskip Hill, the edge of which is crossed by Highway 36 about 20 miles east of Red Bluff.

Little information is available on the part of the Cascade Range between Mount Shasta and the row of quadrangles (Whitmore, Manzanita Lake, and Prospect Peak) which include the northern part of Lassen Volcanic National Park. The stratigraphic relationships appear to be much like those described for the parts of the range to the north and south except that in part the basic lavas rest directly on the pre-Cretaceous rocks of the Klamath Mountains. Along Highway 299 west of Burney, on the Hatchet Mountain grade that ascends the fault scarp at the east side of the range, are exposed a series of mudflow breccias which appear to be too high in the volcanic sequence to be equivalent to the Tuscan Formation. On the same highway, 0.2 mile uphill from the 4,000-foot altitude marker, massive glowing-avalanche deposits contain numerous fragments of white to cream-colored pumice up to 6 inches long. Similar deposits, exposed for half a mile westward, commonly contain many fragments of andesite and dacite. The same or similar beds, one of them containing many dark irregular bombs and lapilli of andesitic cinder, are conspicuously displayed in roadcuts and a quarry just west of Hatchet Mountain summit, interbedded with flows of andesite. These rocks appear to be of about the same age as the folded, very late Pliocene volcanic rocks in the Manzanita Lake quadrangle.

The Hatchet Mountain fault, west of Burney, appears to be older than the basaltic shield of Goose Mountain (northeast Montgomery Creek quadrangle), which is built against the base of the scarp. The cone of Burney Mountain, one of the major peaks in this part of the range, appears to be built almost entirely of block-lava flows of basaltic andesite, though it may, like Magee Mountain just to the south, have a pyroclastic core (Macdonald, 1963). Burney Mountain shows no sign of having been glaciated, and at least its carapace is probably of Recent age, though it appears to be older than the twin cinder cones and associated basalt lava flows at its southeast base.

Just north of the Pit River, the andesites and basalts mapped by Powers (1932, pl. 1) along the east edge of the Cascade Range as his massive lava group also appear to be equivalent, at least in part, to the late Pliocene volcanic rocks of the Manzanita Lake and Whitmore quadrangles. Their original surface forms have been destroyed by erosion and they have been severely glaciated, but they are less deformed than the nearby rocks of probable Miocene age of the Cedarville Series of Russell (1928) in the Modoc Plateau and have been regarded by Powers (1932, p. 259-260) as probably of Pliocene age.

A series of interbedded basaltic and andesitic lava flows, mudflow deposits, volcanic sediments, and a little diatomite are exposed along the gorge of the Pit River west of Lake Britton (Aune, 1964, p. 187) and dip in general 15°–30° northeastward. They are overlain unconformably by diatomaceous sediments deposited in a lake that occupied the site of the present Lake Britton but was considerably more extensive. According to G. Dallas Hanna, the diatoms in these sediments are of Pliocene age, probably not younger

Photo 1. Mount Shasta. *Photo by G. Dallas Hanna.*

than middle Pliocene (Aune, 1964, p. 187). On that basis, Aune infers a Miocene age for the volcanic rocks along the Pit River gorge. The latter rocks resemble those of the Cedarville Series a few miles to the east, in Fort Mountain (southeastern Pondosa quadrangle) and its southward continuation, and probably should be correlated with them. Further work probably will demonstrate that the late Pliocene and Pleistocene volcanics of the Cascade Range have here buried one of the fault blocks of the Cedarville Series characteristic of the Modoc province.

Mount Shasta.—The beautiful double cone of Mount Shasta is the largest of the Cascade volcanoes. From a base about 17 miles in diameter, it rises to an altitude of 14,162 feet, some 10,000 feet above the average level of its surroundings. Its volume is about 80 cubic miles. The slope of the cone diminishes from about 35° near the summit to 5° near the base. The geology of Mount Shasta has been described by Diller (1895b) and Williams (1932b, 1934); the following account is taken largely from the papers by Williams.

To the south and west, the lavas of Mount Shasta rest in part on older (late Pliocene?) andesites of the High Cascades and slightly altered volcanics of the Western Cascades, and in part on metamorphic and plutonic rocks of the Klamath Mountains complex. Haystack Butte, in the southeast corner of the Dwinnell Reservoir quadrangle, 10 miles north-northwest of the summit of the mountain, is a steptoe of the latter rocks projecting through basalt and andesite flows of Mount Shasta. To the east, the Shasta flows disappear beneath a cover of later volcanics.

The main cone of Mount Shasta is so young that only its outermost part is exposed by erosion. The deepest canyon, that of Mud Creek, on the southeast flank, has cut into it only about 1,500 feet. The visible portion of the cone consists, according to Williams, almost entirely of massive, poorly banded, moderately vesicular lava. Individual flows attain a thickness of 200 feet but average only about 50 feet; apparently all originated from the single central vent. Block lava and aa flows are rare and largely confined to the upper part of the cone. The lavas of the basal part of the cone are predominantly basaltic andesite, whereas the later lavas of the upper part are predominantly pyroxene andesite, with a lesser amount of dacite. Some of the latest flows contain basaltic hornblende, and the very summit of the mountain consists of solfatarized dacite. Pyroclastic materials are present only in small proportion. Fragmental beds in the walls of Mud Creek Canyon, which are among the oldest exposed rocks of the cone, appear to be mudflow deposits, and Williams comments (1934, p. 231) that mudflows must have been numerous and extensive during the rise of the main cone of Shasta, in the Pleistocene Epoch, when much of its surface was covered with glaciers.

Late in the history of the volcano, a fissure opened across the cone in a nearly north-south direction, and along it eruptions formed a series of domes and cinder cones with associated lava flows. Gray Butte and the McKenzie Buttes, on the south side of the mountain, are domes belonging to this series, and nearby Red Butte and Signal Butte (formerly called Bear Butte) are cinder cones. Gray Butte is hornblende-pyroxene andesite, and the McKenzie Buttes are glassy dacite. On the north flank of the mountain, in northwestern Shasta quadrangle, the two prominent hills just southwest of North Gate are dacitic domes on the same line of fissuring, and North Gate itself marks the vent of a young flow of basalt that overlaps the western edge of The Whaleback shield volcano. About 2.5 miles east-northeast of North Gate, a mile south of Military Pass, is the steep blocky front of a slightly older flow of andesite that originated on the upper slope of the main cone in the vicinity of the present Hotlum Glacier.

At the southwestern base of Mount Shasta, just west of the line of vents mentioned above, is Everitt Hill, a shield volcano with a small cinder cone at its summit. Flows of basaltic andesite from this vent extend southwestward down the canyon of the Sacramento River for more than 40 miles (Williams, 1934, p. 235). The columnar-jointed lava, at places overlying river gravels, is well exposed in cuts along Highway 99. At Shasta Springs, in the northeastern corner of the Dunsmuir quadrangle, a large volume of water issues from the base of this flow, where it is perched by underlying stream-laid sediments.

Also very late in the history of the volcano, and possibly at about the same time as the development of the north-south fissure, an east-west fissure opened on the western flank of the mountain. Eruptions along this fissure built a small lava-and-cinder cone a mile west of the summit, and shortly afterward short thick flows of pyroxene andesite began to erupt from another vent half a mile farther west, building the lateral cone of Shastina, which eventually grew to nearly rival the main cone in height. The last eruptions of Shastina built two small domes and a small dikelike plug of hornblende andesite within the crater. Extending from a deep notch in the crater rim down the western slope of Shastina is Diller Canyon, a V-shaped gash averaging about a quarter of a mile across and as much as 400 feet deep. Williams (1934, p. 236) suggests that it may have been formed by violent downward-directed explosions and glowing avalanches resembling those of Mount Pelée in 1902, which followed the rise of the domes in the crater. The explosions and resulting avalanches may have been guided by a preexisting fracture. The sides of the canyon and the surface near its distal end are mantled with angular blocks of hornblende andesite like that of the domes, almost certainly deposited by avalanches, but at temperatures too low to produce bread-crusting of the blocks or alteration of the hornblende crystals on their surfaces (Williams, 1934, p. 236). No doubt the avalanches modified the form of the mountain slope, but whether they alone could have formed the great gash remains in doubt.

The domes in the crater of Shastina are of postglacial age, their surfaces being wholly unmodified by ice action, although most of the surface of Shasta and Shastina was covered by Pleistocene glaciers. On the west, ice descended to the level of the valley at the base of the mountain, and on the east ice from the Shasta center extended outward over the Modoc Plateau. Evidence of only one stage of glaciation has been recognized, but since the mountain was probably in active growth throughout the Pleistocene, deposits of earlier glacial stages have probably been buried by later lavas.

At present, the Wintun Glacier, on the east side of the mountain, extends down to an altitude of about 9,125 feet, and on the northwest slope the Whitney Glacier reaches about 9,850 feet. The glaciers of Mount Shasta have been shrinking rapidly during recent decades. In 1934 Williams estimated that they covered an area of slightly more than 3 square miles, whereas in 1954 they covered only about 2 square miles. In 1895 Diller reported the length of the Konwakiton Glacier, on the south slope of the mountain, to be about 5 miles, but its present length is scarcely more than 0.25 mile. Edward Stuhl estimated that during the year 1924 alone the length of the glacier decreased three-eighths of a mile (Williams, 1934, p. 252). Rapid melting of the snow and ice during dry years results in torrents of water which issue from the snout of the glacier and rush down the canyon of Mud Creek. Undermining of the canyon walls, formed of old mudflow breccias, sometimes results in landslips that form temporary dams, which may then be breached to release floods that travel down the canyon to overflow and spread mudflow debris over the lower slopes of the mountain.

Probably even later than the domes in the crater of Shastina is a series of block-lava flows of pyroxene andesite erupted from progressively lower vents on the west flank of the cone, covering an area of nearly 20 square miles. Like the summit domes, these flows are of postglacial age, one of the earliest of them issuing from vents in the side of the terminal moraine of the Whitney Glacier. In the walls of Whitney and Bolam Canyons, moraines are exposed beneath the lava flows. The surfaces of the flows are almost perfectly preserved, and the youngest of them probably are not more than a few hundreds of years old.

At the west-southwest base of Mount Shasta, between the towns of Mount Shasta and Weed, Highway 99 skirts the base of Black Butte, a dome of hornblende andesite. The mountain is about 2,500 feet high and 1.5 miles in basal diameter, and owes its almost perfectly conical form to the great banks of crumble breccia that completely mantle the solid core of the dome except for a few crags near the top.

The latest eruptions of Mount Shasta appear to have been from the summit vent of the main cone; they produced a deposit of hypersthene andesite pumice and cinder containing blocks, lapilli, and bombs of dark glassy andesite. This deposit mantles the cirque heads and forms the Red Banks on the south side of the summit crater (Williams, 1934, p. 231). The final explosion, which covered the upper part of the mountain with a thin layer of brown pumice, may have taken place in 1786, when an eruption apparently in the general location of Mount Shasta was recorded by La Perouse as he cruised along the coast (Finch, 1930).

Photo 2. Shasta Mountain. From the Wilkes Exploring Expedition, in the mid–19th century.

At present, the summit crater of Mount Shasta is filled by a snowfield about 600 feet across, with a small acid hot spring at its margin. When the mountain was first climbed by E. D. Pearce in 1854, there were about a dozen such springs, emitting prominent clouds of steam (Williams, 1934, p. 239). The spring water contains free sulfuric acid, and ranges in temperature between about 166°F and 184°F, depending on weather and the amount of dilution by melt water from snow. The rocks within and around the crater are partly opalized and otherwise altered by solfataric action.

Lassen Peak region.—Many of the rocks and structures of the region around Lassen Peak are directly continuous with those of the Manzanita Lake and Prospect Peak quadrangles (Macdonald, 1963, 1964), mentioned above. Although the oldest rocks of the Lassen region are isolated from those to the north by intervening younger volcanics, they can be correlated with them with considerable certainty. The rocks named the Juniper Andesites by Williams (1932a) are similar petrographically and in degree of deformation and erosion to the late Pliocene andesites of the more northerly region, and both are clearly overlain by the almost-continuously-exposed Eastern Basalts. The earlier Willow Lake Basalts of Williams (1932a) are probably equivalent to Pliocene volcanic rocks in the region northeast of Lassen Volcanic National Park.

The geology of Lassen Volcanic National Park has been studied in detail by Williams, and we cannot do better than to quote his extended summary (Williams, 1932a, p. 216–219):

"The earliest activity seems to be recorded in the Willow Lake basalts exposed along the southern border of the Park, but of the source of these lavas nothing is at present known. They were followed by the eruption of a thick series of platy pyroxene andesites, here termed the Juniper lavas, which extend westward from Juniper Lake for a distance of some four miles. Possibly these flows issued from vents that lie concealed beneath later ejecta in the region lying to the east of the Park. At about the same time a series of black, porphyritic lavas—the Twin Lakes andesites—poured out from a number of vents on the Central Plateau, flooding an area of at least 30 square miles * * *. Petrographically, these Twin Lakes andesites are peculiar by reason of their content of quartz xenocrysts, a feature deserving especial mention in view of the fact that the lavas lie adjacent to the recently erupted quartz basalt of Cinder Cone * * *.

"At some time following the extrusion of the Twin Lakes andesites, vents opened in the vicinity of White Mountain [northwestern corner of the Mount Harkness quadrangle] and pyroxene andesite flows poured from it, chiefly to the south and east, extending for some five miles as far as the head of Warner Valley. To these flows the name Flatiron andesites has been applied. By this time the whole eastern portion of the Park seems to have been transformed into a relatively flat lava plain, conspicuously devoid of pyroclastic accumulations.

"The next event was a renewal of activity immediately to the east of the Park, whereby thick flows of pyroxene basalt—the Eastern basalts—were poured out onto the Juniper andesites. Subsequent erosion of these basalts, which may not have extended much farther west than at present, produced the rugged hills that limit the Park on the east. Toward the close of this phase of activity there were many important pyroclastic eruptions, and possibly about the same time—the exact chronology is open to doubt—andesitic and basaltic cones were active along the northern boundary of the Park, in the vicinity of Badger and Table Mountains.

"Meanwhile an enormous volcano had gradually been rising in the southwest corner of the Park, ultimately attaining a height of about 11,000 feet and a diameter of perhaps 15 miles. For this volcano the name Brokeoff Cone has been adopted. [This term is equivalent to the name "Tehama Volcano" used by other writers.] There is no means of telling when the cone commenced activity, but not improbably it was in existence when the Willow Lake basalts were being erupted. However that may be, most if not all of its exposed flows appear to be later than the Flatiron lavas. In a general way it may be said that the earliest of the Brokeoff lavas are augite andesites, above which follow hypersthene andesites interbedded, toward the top of the cone, with much tuff and breccia. The principal vent of this great volcano lay in the neighborhood of Supan's (Tophet) Springs [now Sulphur Works].

"At some period during the later history of the Brokeoff cone, fluid lavas were being erupted from four shield volcanoes of Hawaiian type, situated one at each corner of the Central Plateau, namely Raker and Prospect peaks, Red Mountain, and Mount Harkness. By that time the Juniper and Flatiron andesites had been deeply denuded so that the new lavas poured over an uneven surface, many of them spilling down the sides of large valleys. Excepting Raker Peak, which is composed of pyroxene andesite, each of these broad, low cones or "shields" consists of pyroxene basalt, and all four are surmounted by well preserved cinder cones that rise within central, summit craters.

"The eruptions of Red Mountain had entirely ceased when an irregular body of rhyolite was intruded into the cone at its northern base; likewise the Raker Peak volcano had long been dormant when a steep-sided, endogenous dome of hornblende-mica dacite was protruded through its southern flank * * *

Photo 3. Lassen crater on June 2, 1914. *Photo by B. F. Loomis.*

Photo 4. Lassen crater, eruption of September 29, 1914. *Photo by B. F. Loomis.*

Photo 5. Lassen Peak June 11, 1915. *Photo by B. F. Loomis.*

Photo 6. Volcanic bomb from Lassen Peak eruption, 1915. *Photo by B. F. Loomis.*

Photo 7. Lassen "mud flow" May 24, 1915. *Photo by B. F. Loomis.*

"Approximately at this time a new vent opened on the northeast slope of the Brokeoff cone, probably close to, if not immediately beneath the [present] edifice of Lassen Peak. As far as can be judged from the meager evidence this event was unheralded by strong pyroclastic explosions. From this new crater streams of fluid dacite flowed radially, but chiefly toward the north, piling up lava to a thickness of 1,500 feet. These are the black, glassy, beautifully columnar lavas that now encircle Lassen Peak, here referred to as the pre-Lassen dacites. If they are studied from the base upward, it will be found that their content of basic inclusions increases more or less regularly until in the topmost dacites of Loomis Peak [2 miles west of Lassen Peak] the inclusions may constitute as much as half the total volume. Mention is here made of this phenomenon because the dacite of Lassen Peak itself is likewise heavily charged with similar basic inclusions. Without doubt the large, almost structureless mass of Lassen represents a crater filling or plug-dome of Peléan type. The fluid, gas-rich magma has escaped from the crater to form the pre-Lassen flows; subsequently the gas-poor dacite, carrying with it abundant fragments from the hornblendic, basic crust of the magma reservoir, welled up sluggishly to build Lassen Peak. As the lava rose, partly solid and partly viscous, the margins of the dome were abraded and polished against the walls of the vent and the surface of the growing pile crumbled continually so as to construct enormous banks of talus.

"Smaller domes of viscous dacite rose to the south of Lassen Peak—at Bumpass Mountain, Mount Helen, Eagle Peak, and Vulcan's Castle—and some were connected with short, stumpy flows. Perhaps at this time also the dacite domes of Morgan and Boy Scout Hills were protruded through the southern base of the Brokeoff Volcano, and the dome of White Mountain was upheaved through the vents from which the Flatiron andesites had long before been erupted. Perhaps the domes that border Lost Creek also originated at this time. All these domes must have risen with great rapidity compared with the rate of growth of the earlier strato-volcanoes.

"Whether or not the emission of so much dacite was the immediate cause cannot be determined, but for some reason this phase of activity was succeeded by the collapse of the summit of the Brokeoff cone along a series of more or less vertical faults, thereby producing a vast caldera, approximately 2½ square miles in extent. In its mode of origin this caldera therefore simulates that of Crater Lake, Oregon. Many of the principal hot springs of the Lassen region are to be found within this faulted caldera of the Brokeoff cone.

"Lassen Peak had probably risen to its present height when a parasitic vent, Crescent Crater, erupted flows of dacite from its northeast flank. Then, about 200 years ago, a line of dacite cones developed at the northwest base of Lassen, from which showers of tuff and pumice were exploded. Two more or less cylindrical bodies of viscous dacite, each about a mile in diameter, were subsequently protruded through these cones and now form the Chaos Crags. Hardly had the later, northern dome of dacite been emplaced, having risen some 1,800 feet, than steam explosions issued from its northern base, causing that whole side of the mass to collapse and precipitating a great avalanche of angular blocks which lie strewn over an area of 2½ square miles, a wilderness of debris known as the Chaos Jumbles * * *

"The complicated history of Cinder Cone, in the northeast part of the Park, commenced with violent pyroclastic explosions, producing not merely the cone itself but mantling an area of more than 30 square miles with a sheet of fine ejecta. Possibly this occurred about 500 A.D. Subsequently blocky flows of quartz basalt were erupted and after these had been partly concealed by the products of further explosions, there were at least two

Photo 8. Lassen Peak eruption, 1915. *Photo courtesy of Oakland Tribune.*

Photo 9. Cinder Cone, Lassen Volcanic National Park. This area was in eruption in the 1850s. *Photo by Mary Hill.*

Photo 10. Chaos Crags, Chaos Jumbles. *Photo by Robert Stinnett, courtesy of Oakland Tribune.*

Photo 11. Manzanita Lake and Lassen Peak. *Photo by Mary Hill.*

Photo 12. Lassen Peak. *Photo by Mary Hill.*

more eruptions of blocky lava, the latest of which is reliably dated as occurring in 1851.

"Steam was seen to be rising from the domes of the Chaos Crags as late as 1857, but no further important eruptions took place in this region until May, 1914, when Lassen itself burst into activity. For a year explosions recurred at irregular intervals. In May, 1915, a mass of lava rose into the summit crater, spilling over the rim on the northwest and northeast sides and causing extensive mud flows by the melting of the snows. On May 22, a horizontal blast issued from the northeast side of the crater, resulting in further damage along the headwaters of Hat and Lost creeks. Thereafter activity declined, finally ending in the summer of 1917. Since that date the volcano has lain dormant."

Heath (1960) has shown that the Chaos Jumbles were produced by several, probably three, separate avalanches. His date of approximately 1700 A.D. for the formation of the last portion of the Jumbles, based on tree-ring counts and an estimate of the time required for establishment of vegetation on the deposit, is a good confirmation of Williams' earlier estimate of approximately 200 years for the age of the deposit.

Another event late in the history of the volcano was a glowing avalanche that swept down the valley of Manzanita Creek, northwest of Lassen Peak, depositing an unsorted mass of pale-gray to white dacite blocks and weakly breadcrusted pumice bombs in a matrix of dacite ash (Macdonald, 1963). The deposit can be seen at the Sunset Campground, west of Manzanita Lake, and a small remnant crosses the highway just outside the Manzanita Lake entrance to the National Park, where it rests on the Chaos Jumbles. Charcoal fragments from the deposit close to the campground yield a C^{14} age of less than 200 years (Rubin and Alexander, 1960, p. 156). The avalanche appears to have come from Lassen Peak but may have occurred at about the time of the last eruption of the Chaos Crags.

Brief mention should also be made of the pumice ejected during the 1915 eruption of Lassen Peak. The pumice is conspicuously banded, with light streaks of dacite and dark ones of andesite. The bands appear to represent two distinct magmas, imperfectly mixed at the time of eruption (Macdonald and Katsura, 1965). Many blocks of this banded pumice can be found in the vicinity of the Devastated Area parking lot, near the eastern base of Lassen Peak.

Several groups of hot springs and fumaroles exist in and near Lassen Volcanic National Park. Supan's Springs, at the Sulphur Works, on Highway 89 near the south entrance of the park, issue from andesite flows and breccias of the Brokeoff Volcano within the caldera, as also do others along Mill Creek and its tributaries, Sulphur Creek and Little Hot Springs Valley. The springs and fumaroles of Bumpass Hell occupy a basin between the dacite dome of Bumpass Mountain and the andesites of Brokeoff Mountain. Most of the springs contain small amounts (19 to 436 mg/l) of sulfuric acid, derived from the oxidation of H_2S in rising magmatic gases, either directly, or by oxidation of native sulfur that is in turn derived from H_2S (Day and Allen, 1925, p. 113, 138). In each spring area the highest temperature of the water generally is close to the boiling temperature at the altitude of the particular spring or fumarole—91° to 92°C at Bumpass Hell and Supan's Springs—but fumarole temperatures as high as 117.5°C have been observed. Depending largely on the abundance of the water supply, the springs vary from clear pulsating springs to mud pots, the spattering of the latter sometimes building enclosing cones to form mud volcanoes. There are no true geysers. The rocks around the springs are altered, ultimately largely to opal and kaolin, accompanied by minor amounts of alunite (Anderson, 1935). The structures and textures of the original rocks are often almost perfectly preserved in the opalized residuals. Where acidity is comparatively high, nearly pure opal is formed, but where it is lower, kaolin is the principal product. In addition to opal, kaolin, and alunite, the sediments in the springs and along their drainage channels contain sulfur, pyrite, tridymite, and quartz. The two latter minerals may be in part residual from the original rocks but appear to have been formed partly within the hot springs.

The area of solfataric alteration within the Brokeoff caldera is approximately 5 square miles and is much more extensive than the present hot-spring basins (Williams, 1932a, p. 259). Solfataric and hot-spring activity seems to have been at one time much more widespread than it now is.

Studies by R. W. Bowers and L. C. Pakiser over an area of 4,000 square miles in the southern Cascade Range and adjoining Modoc Plateau have demonstrated an area of negative gravity anomaly that is centered in the Lassen region and extends southeastward into the Lake Almanor basin (Pakiser, 1964). The gravity low, which covers an area of about 2,000 square miles, has a maximum amplitude of 70 mgals and a steep gradient of 8 mgals per mile on the western side. Pakiser finds that it can be explained by a volume of about 15,000 km^3 of light material in the outer part of the earth's crust, with a density contrast between it and the enclosing rocks of 0.2 grams per cm^3. Possible explanations of the low-density mass include: (1) a batholith of silicic rock beneath the volcanic rocks; (2) a thick accumulation of sedimentary rocks beneath the volcanic rocks, deposited in the Lassen Strait; (3) a low-density mass caused by thermal expansion of crustal rocks resulting from volcanic heat; (4) a volcano-tectonic depression filled with light volcanic rock. All four may contribute to the deficiency of gravity in the area. Certainly, heating of adjacent rocks must have occurred during the rise of magma through the volcanic conduits, and Pakiser (1964, p. 618) considers that this may explain the local gravity lows observed in the vicinity of some of the volcanoes, such as Lassen and West Prospect Peaks. Also, petrographic evidence suggests the fusion of crustal material to supply some of the erupted lavas (Macdonald and Katsura, 1965, p. 479–480), which may have resulted in the formation of a low-density batholithic mass beneath the area. Partly because of the steep gravity gradient on the western edge of the region, the fourth explanation appears the most likely for the major part of the anomaly (Pakiser, 1964, p. 618). Pakiser makes the reasonable suggestion that the sunken region was the source of the Nomlaki Tuff and that large volumes of low-density ash and other volcanic material were deposited in the subsiding structure. Similar deficiencies of gravity are found at many collapse calderas and volcano-tectonic depressions in continental regions.

Medicine Lake Highland.—The Medicine Lake area (Medicine Lake and adjacent quadrangles) has been studied by C. A. Anderson, and the following brief account is abstracted from his report (1941).

The oldest rocks in the region are a series of fragmental deposits of basaltic and andesitic composition, correlated by Powers (1932, p. 259) with the Cedarville Series in the Warner Mountains, 60 miles to the east. Similar rocks are widespread in the Modoc region north, east, and south of Medicine Lake. They have been block faulted, and the lower parts of the fault blocks buried by the widespread "plateau" basalts referred to by both Powers and Anderson as the Warner Basalt. Both the Cedarville Series and the Warner Basalt will be discussed in the section on the Modoc Plateau; it will suffice here to say that they appear to be the basement on which the rocks of the Medicine Lake Highland accumulated.

Northwest of the Highland, the Warner Basalt is covered by a sheet of massive andesite tuff. Near Dock Well, 7 miles northwest of Medicine Lake, the tuff is more than 200 feet thick, with no visible stratification. It ranges from gray to pink or buff in color, and contains pumice fragments commonly up to an inch across, in places up to 3 inches across, in a fine

Photo 13. Bumpass Hell, Lassen Volcanic National Park. *Photo by Mary Hill.*

Photo 14. Devils Kitchen, Lassen Volcanic National Park. *Photo by Mary Hill.*

silty matrix. Some of the pumice lapilli are flattened and stretched, and the glass is partly devitrified. In places the tuff is slightly welded (Anderson, 1941, p. 356). There appears to be little question that it is the product of a glowing avalanche (pumice and ash flow). Its source is unknown, but probably it is genetically related to flows and domes of platy rhyolite and rhyolite obsidian that crop out at nine places around the base of the Medicine Lake volcano. These obsidians are locally spherulitic, and in the mass between Cougar Butte and the road from Lava Beds National Monument to Tionesta (Timber Mountain quadrangle), lines of spherulites give it a pronounced parallel structure. At the same locality, lithophysae are lined with cristobalite and small black tablets of fayalite (Anderson, 1941, p. 356). At one place on the north slope of the Highland, a small mass of stony dacite overlies the obsidian. The distribution of the rhyolites indicates that they are related to a volcanic center beneath the present Highland.

West of Medicine Lake Highland, a group of cones, as much as 1,000 feet high, are built of very massive basalt containing conspicuous phenocrysts of white plagioclase and reddish-brown altered olivine. Some of the lava flows must have been quite viscous, since the north side of the cone a mile northwest of Pumice Stone Mountain consists of a series of superimposed flows, each ending in a steep front, giving the slope a terraced aspect (Anderson, 1941, p. 357). The massive basalts are probably of about the same age as the rhyolites mentioned in the last paragraph.

The growth of the present Highland began with the eruption of rather fluid pyroxene andesites, which gradually built up a broad shield volcano some 20 miles across, with a slope of only about 3°. No intercalated pyroclastic material is found. The flows consist of a dark-gray vesicular surface portion, 3 to 6 feet thick, terminating sharply against an interior medium to light-gray dense portion characterized by conspicuous platy jointing. The earliest lavas contain 2 or 3 percent of small phenocrysts of yellowish olivine, whereas the later ones are generally olivine free. The platy andesites overlie the massive basalts, the andesite tuff, and the rhyolites. They are best exposed on the northwest side of the Highland, but most of the shield has been buried beneath later volcanics.

The ultimate height of the shield was probably about 2,500 feet, but Anderson (1941, p. 352, 359–362) concludes that after the growth of the shield its summit collapsed to form a caldera 6 miles long and 4 miles wide, with its rim some 500 feet below the level of the former summit. Lava then rose along the arcuate marginal fractures, poured as flows into the caldera, and built cones that eventually surmounted the caldera rim and allowed some of the later flows to pour down the outer slope of the shield. The result was a series of eight separate rim volcanoes around the caldera which have completely hidden the former caldera boundaries. The present lake basin is the depression left between these rim cones.

The earliest postcaldera lavas were platy olivine-free andesites, resembling the last precaldera lavas. Later these gave way to olivine andesites, dacites, and rhyolites. The eruptions of platy andesite built ridges around the north, west, and south of the basin, the northern one capped by four cinder cones. A small mass of perlitic rhyolite is associated with the andesite in the western ridge. Presumably a similar, but somewhat lower, ridge was built on the east side of the basin, since its lavas are exposed northwest of Mount Hoffmann, but it is largely hidden by later volcanics of three separate complexes: Red Shale Butte, and Lyons Peak, both about 5 miles east of Medicine Lake, and Mount Hoffmann, 2 miles east of Medicine Lake. Volcanic activity in the Red Shale Butte complex started with eruption of platy olivine andesites resembling the early lavas of the underlying shield. These were followed by the Lake basalt of Powers (1932) —a flow of coarsely porphyritic olivine basalt that poured into the central basin and now forms the eastern and northeastern margins of Medicine Lake. The Lake basalt contains numerous phenocrysts of white plagioclase along with those of yellow-green olivine. It was followed by platy andesites, resembling those in the ridges north and south of the basin that built Red Shale Butte and Lyons Peak. In the latter complex, some of the lavas are dacitic and contain large amounts of brownish glass. In contrast, the Mount Hoffmann complex consists largely of silicic lavas, predominantly rhyolites, with basalt flows at the base:

> "The Mount Hoffmann complex is essentially a circular table built up by successive outpourings of very viscous perlitic rhyolite, each flow ranging from 50 to 150 feet in thickness * * *. The closing stages of activity at the summit were marked by the eruption of a short eastern tongue of perlitic rhyolite, about 100 feet in thickness, followed by the protrusion of a dome about 200 feet high above the short flow. The two, combined, form a topographic dome some 300 feet above the circular table. (Anderson, 1941 p. 356.)
>
> "The picture during the late Pleistocene was undoubtedly that of a northern ridge of platy andesite passing into the circular table of Mount Hoffmann perlitic rhyolite, separated by an ice cap from the Red Shale Butte complex of basalt and platy andesites, which in turn was separated from the Medicine Mountain platy andesites by a second ice cap. A third covering of ice occupied the broad ridge of platy andesites west of the summit basin * * *. As the ice disappeared, Medicine Lake came into existence, filling the summit basin. Continued volcanic activity produced cones and lava flows, and most of the later products show weak or no glaciated surfaces and for that reason have been related to the Recent * * *." (Anderson, 1941, p. 367.)

More than 100 basaltic cinder cones, ranging in age from late Pleistocene to Recent, are present in the 400-square-mile area of Anderson's map. They are scattered over the entire Highland, on the floor and rim of the summit basin as well as on the outer slopes of the old shield, and on the surrounding plateau. The cones in the summit basin and on the rim "stand alone" (Anderson, 1941, p. 368), but most of the others are accompanied by lava flows. Great floods of basaltic lava were poured from vents on the north, east, and south flanks of the Highland. These were termed the Modoc Basalt by Powers (1932, p. 272). They include the flows of the Lava Beds National Monument.

> "In many places the Modoc basalt flows emerged from fissures bearing no relationship to cinder cones. One of the most striking examples is on the road north of High Hole Crater [on the southeast flank of the Highland], where a fissure supplied part of the lava for the Burnt Lava flow. [The rest of the flow came from High Hole Crater.] Another good example can be seen * * * east of Lava Camp (on the northern flank of the Highland), where three fissures discharged basalt to the northern lava field." (Anderson, 1941, p. 368.)

Flows of the Modoc Basalt include nearly aphyric rocks, containing only a few small phenocrysts of olivine and an intersertal texture that may be seen with the hand lens, and porphyritic rocks with conspicuous plagioclase phenocrysts in a dark-gray aphanitic, microcrystalline, hyalo-ophitic to hyalopilitic, rarely intergranular or intersertal, groundmass. The basalts of the latter type grade into andesites. Flows of the first type include both pahoehoe and aa, with pahoehoe predominant. The flows of the second type are nearly all aa, grading into block lava, and are commonly younger than those of the first type. The flows of the Lava Beds National Monument will be discussed in the next section.

Three very recent basaltic lava flows on the flanks of the Medicine Lake Highland are singled out for special mention. All three are largely aa, but locally have pahoehoe and block-lava surfaces. Possibly the oldest of the three is the flow called the Callahan flow by Peacock (1931, p. 269). It covers about 10 square miles on the lower northern slope of the Highland. The Paint Pot Crater flow (Anderson, 1941, p. 371), just southwest of Little Glass Mountain on the southwest flank of the Highland, has an area of only about 1 square mile. Its source, Paint Pot Crater, is a basalt cinder cone mantled with a thick layer of white pumice from the eruption of Little Glass Mountain. Pumice Stone Mountain, just to the north, is an older basaltic cinder cone similarly covered by pumice. Most picturesque and youngest in appearance is the Burnt Lava flow (Peacock, 1931, p. 269–270) on the southern flank of the Highland, easily accessible by the road that leads southeastward from Medicine Lake. The lava issued from the vent marked by the cinder cone of High Hole Crater and from a fissure just to the north. The lava field covers an area of about 14 square miles, but consists of at least two flows of different age (Finch, 1933): The older is a highly oxidized aa exposed near the south end of the field, and the younger consists of pahoehoe partly overridden by aa which has buried a large part of the older flow. The lava is basaltic in appearance, but chemically it is a basaltic andesite, with a silica content of more than 55 percent and a color index of less than 30. The same is true of many other flows in the Modoc Basalt and other young basaltic flows of the Modoc Plateau.

Very late in the history of the Medicine Lake Highland came a series of silicic eruptions. These include: A black, glassy to stony flow of dacite poured out on the floor of the summit basin just north of Medicine Lake, where it covers about 1 square mile; another dacite flow in the gap between Mount Hoffmann and Red Shale Butte; another slightly older one east of Glass Mountain; a flow of perlitic rhyolite on the northeast flank of Mount Hoffmann; a small mass of rhyolite obsidian on the northwest rim of the summit basin; and the two striking masses of rhyolite obsidian that form Glass Mountain and Little Glass Mountain. The Little Glass Mountain eruption began with explosions that showered pumice over the surrounding country. Fragments of pumice can be found as far away as 15 miles to the southwest. Probably a cone of pumice was built around the vent, but it was either destroyed or wholly buried by the ensuing flows. Two separate flows were extruded, the second completely burying the first except at the northeast corner. An excellent view of them can be had from the summit of Little Mount Hoffmann, which is accessible by car. The flow is roughly rectangular and averages a little more than 1½ miles across. Its margins are 50 to nearly 200 feet high, and it is probably more than 500 feet thick in the middle. Its volume probably exceeds 0.1 cubic mile.

The history of Glass Mountain is more complex (Anderson, 1933b; Chesterman, 1955). The first event was the opening of a fissure trending N. 30° W., along which explosions built at least seven cones of pumice, the largest at the site of the present Glass Mountain. The surrounding area, particularly to the northeast, was showered with pumice. Ten miles from the vents the pumice layer is several inches thick, and near Glass Mountain it is as much as 60 feet thick, with pumice blocks up to 2 feet in diameter. At the other cones, finely vesicular glass rose in the vents, forming domes, most of which breached the cone walls and flowed a short distance beyond. At Glass Mountain a much larger flow issued, pouring mostly eastward to form a flow 3½ miles long which was split into two tongues by the slightly older mass of dacite mentioned above. The eastern tongues are of stony dacite containing numerous inclusions of olivine basalt. The dacite passes abruptly into rhyolitic obsidian through a transition zone in which both rock types are present, the main part of the flow consisting of rhyolitic obsidian devoid of basaltic inclusions (Anderson, 1941, p. 375–376). At the end of the eruption, the lava was so viscous that it was pushed up into a small dome. Renewed activity resulted in a second, smaller flow that partly covered the first. Both obsidian flows have pumiceous to scoriaceous surface phases and dense glassy interiors. The final stage of activity consisted in the rise of a dome of microvesicular rhyolitic glass, a quarter of a mile in diameter and 150 feet high, whose summit bristles with partly collapsed spines.

Photo 15. Little Glass Mountain and Mount Shasta from Little Mount Hoffman. *Photo by Mary Hill.*

North of Glass Mountain two beds of pumice are separated by 6 to 12 inches of soil, showing that the eruptions were interrupted by a considerable period of quiescence. The upper pumice ranges in thickness from a few feet to 30 feet, and contains upright trunks of ponderosa pines that were rooted in the soil layer on the lower pumice (Chesterman, 1955). Growth rings indicate that the largest trees were at least 225 years old at the time they were killed by the upper pumice fall; the interval between the two pumice falls—making allowance for the time required to establish plant growth—is estimated by Chesterman to have been around 300 to 350 years. Radiocarbon age determinations made by W. F. Libby on the tree trunks, give a maximum of 1,660 ± 300 years and a minimum of 1,107 ± 380 years, with an average of 1,360 ± 240 years (Chesterman, 1955). The upper pumice thus has a probable age of about 1,400 years and the lower about 1,700 years.

Was the Glass Mountain obsidian flow the last eruptive activity in the Medicine Lake region? All of the young basalt flows mentioned above have bits of pumice and rhyolitic obsidian scattered over their surfaces, and the Callahan and Paint Pot Crater flows are almost unquestionably older than the last silicic eruptions. On the more recent part of the Burnt Lava flow, however, the pumice is very small in amount, and has probably been blown onto the lava by the wind. The flow is close to Glass Mountain, and if it had been present at the time of the eruption that produced the last thick fall of Glass Mountain pumice, the amount of pumice on the flow would be much greater. Adjacent older lavas and islands within the flow have much more pumice on their surfaces, and the pumice can hardly have been removed from the exceedingly rough surface of the Burnt Lava flow by running water. The largest trees growing on the older part of the Burnt Lava flow have been estimated to be only 300 years old, and the surface of the younger part is so fresh in appearance that Finch (1933) considered that it could easily be less than 300 years old. Charcoal samples from a tree stump buried by the flow give an age of only 200 ± 200 years (Ives and others, 1964, p. 49). It appears probable that at least the younger part of the Burnt Lava flow is more recent than the big eruption of Glass Mountain. The same conclusion has been arrived at independently by C. W. Chesterman (written communication, 1965).

Even this may not have been the last eruption! Finch (1928) cites a report of a light ash fall that coated leaves of plants in the nearby area in 1910 and suggests that the ash may have come from a small explosive eruption of Glass Mountain.

Lava Beds National Monument.—Although the area of the Lava Beds National Monument is geologically most closely related to the Modoc Plateau, the area is located immediately north of the Medicine Lake Highland, and it is convenient to discuss the two contiguously. The rocks of the Monument are the Modoc Basalt of Recent age. Most of the surface is covered with pahoehoe flows containing numerous lava tubes, some of which served as shelters for Captain Jack and

Photo 16. Schonchin Butte, Modoc Lava Beds. *Photo by Mary Hill.*

his band of Modoc Indians during the Modoc War of 1872–73. Of the 300 lava tubes known within the Monument, about 130 have been explored; they range from a few feet to about 75 feet in diameter. Some have two or three levels, separated by nearly horizontal septa formed by the freezing of the surface of the lava stream in the tube during a pause in the lowering of the surface of the stream toward the end of the eruption. In the lower levels of some caves percolating water freezes during the winter to form ice that persists, only partly melted, through the next summer. Lava stalactites are common on the roofs of the caves, and occasional stalagmites are found on the floors. Quite commonly, an increase in the viscosity of the last fluid lava moving through the tube has resulted in a change of the lava to aa and the formation of a layer of aa clinker on the floor of the pahoehoe tube. The roofs of some tunnels have collapsed to form long winding trenches, 20 to 50 feet deep and 50 to 100 feet wide (Stearns, 1928), with occasional short uncollapsed sections forming natural arches. Tumuli (pressure domes) are present on the pahoehoe flow surfaces, and ropy surface is preserved in places, but most of the surfaces are smooth or billowy.

Less abundant than pahoehoes are flows of aa, such as the Devils Homestead flow, that is visible from the highway 6 miles north of the Monument Headquarters. Others include the flow from Schonchin Butte,

Photo 17. Lava flows from Schonchin Butte. *Photo by Mary Hill.*

a small flow from Black Crater 2 miles to the northwest, and in the southwestern corner of the Monument part of the Callahan flow (known also as the Black Lava flow).

About a dozen cinder cones, 50 to 700 feet high, lie within the Monument, and were formed by moderately explosive Strombolian-type eruptions at the vents of some of the flows. Perhaps the best example is Schonchin Butte, just east of the highway 2 miles northwest of Monument headquarters. Elsewhere, the eruptions were less explosive and built spatter cones, commonly in lines along fissure vents. A good example of these is the Fleener Chimneys, 0.8 miles west of the highway on a branch road 2 miles northwest of Schonchin Butte—a row of spatter cones built by Hawaiian-type eruption at the vents of the Devils Homestead lava flow. Some other spatter and driblet cones are rootless hornitos, built by escape of gas-charged lava through holes in the roofs of underlying lava tubes. Mammoth Crater, on the road to Medicine Lake at the south border of the Monument, was formed by the collapse of the summit of a lava-armored cinder cone as a result of lava draining from the underlying conduit through a tube in the cone wall.

Prisoners Rock, at the Petroglyph Section, a few miles northeast of the main part of the Monument, is a remnant of a cone of palagonite tuff, dissected by sub-aerial erosion and cliffed by the waves of ancient Tule Lake. Just north of it lies another similar cone. These cones resemble Diamond Head and Punchbowl, in Honolulu, and Fort Rock and nearby cones in central Oregon, and like them were formed by phreatomagmatic explosions where rising basaltic magma encountered water. The cones appear to be older than most or all of the lava flows in the main part of the Monument.

Some of the flows in the Monument, particularly the Devils Homestead flow, appear to be very recent. However, all of them have bits of silicic pumice scattered over their surfaces and are probably older than the last silicic eruptions in the adjoining Medicine Lake area. By comparison with flows in other regions, Stearns (1928, p. 253) estimated that none of them are younger than 5,000 years.

At the northwest edge of the Monument, Gillem Bluff is an excellent example of one of the recent fault scarps that are widely distributed over the Modoc Plateau. It is one of three east-facing scarps that form the western side of the Tule Lake basin.

MODOC PLATEAU

The Modoc region consists of a series of northwest- to north-trending block-faulted ranges, with the intervening basins filled with broad-spreading "plateau" basalt flows, or with small shield volcanoes, steeper sided lava or composite cones, cinder cones, and lake deposits resulting from disruption of the drainage by faulting or volcanism. The oldest rocks are of Miocene, or possibly of Oligocene age, and the youngest are Recent. Although the faulting culminated in late Miocene or Pliocene, it has continued into Recent time. The Modoc region is best regarded as a part of the Great Basin province that has been flooded by volcanics, which are perhaps related to the Cascade volcanic province.

Cedarville Series

Petrographically, the Warner Range, which adjoins the Modoc Plateau on the east, is a part of the Modoc Plateau province. The oldest rocks recognized in the Warner Range constitute the Cedarville Series of Russell (1928, p. 402–416), divided by him into lower and upper units consisting largely of andesitic fragmental beds, separated by a middle lava member. The lower and upper units consist mainly of tuffs, tuff-breccias and agglomerates, ignimbrites, and mudflow deposits, with a subordinate amount of intercalated andesite lava flows. The lower unit contains an abundant middle Oligocene flora and a rhinoceros jaw of probable early Miocene age (Gay, 1959, p. 6), and the upper member is of late Miocene age (LaMotte, 1936).

The oldest rocks in the Modoc region are exposed only in the relatively uplifted fault blocks and have been tilted, commonly between 20° and 30°. Because of similarity in lithology and structural relationships, Powers (1932, p. 258–259) correlated them with the type Cedarville Series of the Warner Range, but

Photo 18. Interior of lava tube, Modoc Lava Beds. ***Photo by Mary Hill.***

pointed out that in general there is no indication whether the rocks of the Modoc Plateau are equivalent to the lower or upper unit of the Cedarville, or to both. A middle Miocene flora is present in lake sediments intercalated with the volcanics in the mountains between Canby and Adin (Gay, 1959, p. 6).

Little can be added to Powers' (1932, p. 258–259) description of the Cedarville Series of the Modoc région:

> "The oldest series of volcanic rocks of the area was recognized in the field by the abundance of pyroclastic material, tilted and warped structure, and the gentle slopes eroded on its non-resistant pyroclastic members. The series shows great range in lithology: basaltic flows, intrusives, and pyroclastics; andesitic flows and pyroclastics; and rhyolitic intrusives and pyroclastics * * *. The basalt is typically dark gray to black and has a fine-grained, compact texture. Most of the specimens collected have the ophitic or intersertal texture common to the typical plateau basalt * * *. They are notable for the presence of chlorophaeite which is not found in the younger basalts of the area * * *. A few of the basalts show an intergranular texture * * *.
>
> "Andesitic members are most abundant in the series, and of these the pyroclastic rocks predominate. The lava specimens collected are all pyroxene andesites with both hypersthene and augite as phenocrysts. Fragments of hornblende andesite are found in detrital material.
>
> "Rhyolites are represented chiefly by beds of pumice-tuff. Fragments of pumice three to four inches in diameter are included in a matrix of smaller fragments of the same material. One dike of compact, reddish felsite was found which shows a brecciated border zone cemented by colorless to white opal."

Some of the fragmental beds are the tops and bottoms of block-lava flows, and others are mudflow deposits, rather than "pyroclastic" rocks in the sense of being direct deposits from explosive activity. Blocky flow tops and bottoms are well exposed in cuts on Highway 299 half a mile east of the Pit No. 1 Powerhouse, interbedded with massive to platy central portions of the flows. Irregular tongues of the massive lava intrude the breccias. Near the top of the same highway grade, a segment of a red cinder cone is interbedded with the lava flows. Mudflows of the Cedarville Series are well exposed in cuts along Highway 299, 8 miles northeast of Alturas.

Rhyolite and rhyolite obsidian in the region near Hambone, and at various places within the area of the Warner Basalt farther northeast, may belong to the Cedarville Series.

At Hayden Hill, 15 miles south-southeast of Adin, gold was formerly mined from an epithermal deposit in silicified rhyolite tuff. Gold-bearing veins are also present in andesitic volcanic rocks in the Winters district, southwest of Alturas, and in rhyolitic rocks in the High Grade district, northeast of Alturas (Clark, 1957, p. 219).

Sedimentary rocks are intercalated with volcanic rocks of the Cedarville in some areas. Along Highway 299, where it climbs the western flank of the Big Valley Mountains at the east side of Fall River Valley, rhyolitic tuff and tuffaceous sandstone, as well as mudflow breccias, are exposed. Miocene lake beds, including diatomite, crop out farther north in the same range, in the mountains to the northeast, at some other localities in that area (Gay, 1959, p. 5), and in the vicinity of the Madeline Plains 45 miles southeast of Alturas.

The Cedarville is probably equivalent in age to predominantly volcanic formations, such as the Ingalls, Delleker, and Bonta Formations of Durrell (1959), in the northern Sierra Nevada and adjacent parts of the Great Basin.

Pliocene Rocks Other Than Warner Basalt

About the end of the Miocene Epoch, the Modoc Plateau region was shattered by tectonic movements, and rocks of the Cedarville Series were broken, tilted, and elevated into a series of mountain ranges by faulting. The drainage system was disrupted, and in the basins between the ranges, a series of fresh-water lakes were formed in which sediments accumulated. Volcanism continued, and lava flows, subaerial and water-laid ash beds, mudflow deposits, and the deposits of incandescent ash flows (ignimbrites) were mingled with the sediments. In some places the accumulations were wholly sedimentary, elsewhere volcanic layers were intercalated with the sedimentary rocks, and in still other places the sequence is nearly or entirely volcanic. The lava flows are predominantly mafic, being basalts and basaltic andesites; the pyroclastic rocks are predominantly rhyolitic.

Pliocene lake beds are exposed along the valley of the Pit River for more than 20 miles west of Alturas, for an equal distance southward along the South Fork of the Pit River, and for 10 miles northeastward along the North Fork. These have been called the Alturas Formation by Dorf (1930, p. 6, 23). They include diatomite, diatomaceous and tuffaceous silty and sandy shale, siltstone, and sandstone. Locally, strongly current-bedded sandstone and conglomerate are probably of fluviatile, rather than lacustrine, origin. The lake beds contain a middle Pliocene flora and Pliocene mammalian remains (Gay, 1959, p. 6). Interbedded with the sediments southwest of Alturas are layers of ignimbrite containing many lumps of pumice. They can be seen along Highway 299, 8 to 10 miles west of Alturas, and in the plateau escarpment to the north. South of the highway a layer of welded ignimbrite locally forms the resistant caprock of the Alturas Formation, where less resistant overlying lake beds have been eroded away. A second, slightly less welded layer lies a few feet lower in the section. The rock has been quarried for building stone, and the cut stone can be seen in the Elks Club building (the former railway station) in Alturas. Similar ignimbrites are associated with lava flows, mudflow deposits, and sediments in the mountains farther west, between Canby and Adin. In a bed well exposed in a highway cut 0.9 mile south of Adin Pass, some of the lumps of pumice are more than a foot long. In the same cut, mudflows of ignimbritic debris grade in their upper parts into poorly bedded material reworked by water.

Rattlesnake Butte, 10 miles west of Alturas, the type locality of the Alturas Formation (Dorf, 1930), marks the site of a volcanic vent. The sedimentary beds are steeply upturned around the central basaltic neck. The age of the vent may have been either late Pliocene or early Pleistocene.

According to G. W. Walker (oral communication, 1965), the uppermost beds that are generally included in the Alturas Formation north and west of Alturas are nearly horizontal and locally are separated by an angular unconformity from the lower part of the formation. The latter, which contains the beds of ignimbrite mentioned above, was faulted and gently folded, and was eroded before the deposition of the upper beds. In places, however, no unconformity can be found, and sedimentation was probably essentially continuous throughout the period of accumulation of the formation. The upper, horizontal beds contain upper Pliocene gastropods and Pliocene or Pleistocene mouse teeth (Gay, 1959, p. 6). Local deformation and erosion in some areas appears to have been concomitant with continued sedimentation in other nearby areas.

Diatomaceous lake beds are well exposed also around Lake Britton, 10 miles north of Burney, and along the valley of the Pit River for 5 miles east of the lake. They are well displayed where Highway 89 crosses the lake, and where Highway 299 crosses Hat Creek. Diatoms from these deposits have been studied by G. Dallas Hanna, who states that they are of middle and late Pliocene age. Similar sediments are found along the valley of Willow Creek, southwest of Lower Klamath Lake and northwest of the Medicine Lake Highland. Still farther northwest, near the village of Dorris, sandstones and conglomerates contain nonmarine gastropods of late Pliocene age (Hanna and Gester, 1963).

In most areas the lake beds were slightly tilted and eroded before they were overlain by the Warner Basalt (see next section). Along Highway 299, about 7 miles northeast of Alturas, white pumice-lapilli tuffs appear to belong to the Alturas Formation, although they are tilted at angles greater than 30°. They are closely similar to nearly horizontal lapilli tuffs in the Alturas Formation a few miles farther west. In the area northeast of Alturas they exhibit striking conical erosional forms, resembling haystacks or beehives, as much as 20 feet in basal diameter and 30 feet high.

In the southwestern part of the Modoc region, just north of Lassen Volcanic National Park, the uplifted fault blocks are composed of andesite lava flows identical with, and unquestionably correlative with, the post-Tuscan lavas of the adjacent Cascade Range. Farther eastward, in the Harvey Mountain and Little Valley quadrangles, similar fault blocks consist of basalt and olivine basalt. The very late Pliocene andesitic volcanism in the Cascade Range gave way eastward to basaltic volcanism. In both areas the bases of the fault blocks are submerged in the Burney (Warner) Basalt.

In the southeastern part of the Modoc Plateau region, many small shields of basalt and basaltic andesite, although considerably eroded, still retain their general constructional form. These appear to be certainly younger than the Pliocene rocks in the fault blocks, which have not only been much more disrupted by faulting but also have suffered much more erosion. They are nevertheless older than the widespread Warner Basalt and older than Pleistocene lake beds, and are regarded as of late Pliocene or Pliocene and Pleistocene age. As examples there may be mentioned Roop Mountain, 10 miles west-northwest of Susanville, and several mountains lying between Honey Lake and the Madeline Plains. Just north of Lake Britton, Soldier Mountain is one of this group, resting against the Cedarville Series of the Fort Mountain fault block.

Warner Basalt

The plateau basalt that is widely distributed between the fault-block ranges of the Modoc region is commonly referred to as the Warner Basalt of Russell (1928). It was named in the Warner Mountains, where R. J. Russell found a sheet of basalt capping the Cedarville Series; but Russell (1928, p. 416) believed that the same basalt was the most widespread unit in the Modoc Lava-Bed quadrangle to the west. This was accepted by Powers (1932, p. 266) and Anderson (1941, p. 353), though both Fuller (1931, p. 115) and Anderson recognized that it might not be possible to group all of the "plateau" basalt of the area into a single stratigraphic unit. Actually, considerable variation in both the degree of weathering and the thickness of the ashy soil cover on the basalt at different places, as well as other differences in geological relationships, indicate that there is considerable difference in age of the basalt from one place to another, and it is preferable to use local formation names until the correlation of the basalts throughout the region can be more firmly established. The name Burney Basalt has been used in this way for the plateau basalt in the Prospect Peak and Harvey Mountain quadrangles (Macdonald, 1964, 1965) and in the Burney and Little Valley quadrangles just to the north, and the name Gardens Basalt has been used by Ford and others (1963) in the area just northwest of Alturas. For the purpose of this report, however, Russell's name Warner Basalt is herein retained as a collective term for the petrographically and structurally similar lavas throughout the region, without any specific implication as to contemporaneity.

In the Warner Mountains the Warner Basalt overlies the tilted upper Cedarville Series conformably, but throughout the rest of the region it rests against the eroded edges of fault blocks composed of tilted Cedarville and younger rocks. Since the upper Cedarville is of probable late Miocene age, the Warner Basalt in the Warner Range cannot be older than late Miocene, but the lack of any structural deformation between it and the underlying rocks suggests that there may not be any great difference in their ages. Both have been tilted westward with the uplift of the Warner Mountains fault block and the basalt appears to be overlain by Pliocene volcanic rocks and lake-bed deposits of the Alturas Formation. The latter is in turn deformed, eroded, and locally overlain by a later series of lake-bed deposits, which in turn is capped by a plateau basalt not older than latest Pliocene and probably of Pleistocene age (Gardens Basalt of Ford and others, 1963). In the vicinity of Lake Britton also, basalt like that of the Warner rests on lower or middle Pliocene lake-bed deposits. On Highway 89, 0.8 mile north of the bridge across Lake Britton, the lower 10 to 15 feet of the basalt consists of pillow lava and associated hyaloclastite formed by granulation of the hot lava where it entered water. The lava is conformable with the bedding in the underlying sediments, and poorly consolidated sediment was squeezed up into the fragmental base of the lava. It is thus unlikely that the age of this lava is very different from that of the underlying sediment. Elsewhere, however, as along Highway 299 a mile west of the Hat Creek bridge, Warner Basalt can be seen resting unconformably on the same series of lake-bed deposits, which had been slightly tilted and eroded before they were covered by the lava flows. Thus even in the small area immediately around Lake Britton, there appears to be a considerable range in the age of the basalts. Farther south, at the north end of the Sierra Nevada, Warner Basalt lies unconformably on the Penman Formation, which is probably of early Pliocene age (Durrell, 1959, p. 177–180). All that can be certainly said of these lavas is that they are later than the sediments; they could conceivably be as old as middle Pliocene. In the western part of the Prospect Peak quadrangle, however, the Burney Basalt rests against the eroded edges of fault blocks of andesite that is in turn younger than the Tuscan Formation, of late late Pliocene age, and it appears very unlikely that the Burney Basalt is older than very early Pleistocene. Thus flows of the Warner Basalt probably range from Miocene to Pleistocene in age. Gay and Aune (1958, footnote to stratigraphic table on explanatory data sheet) came to the same conclusion.

The largest continuous exposure of the Warner Basalt is that of the Gardens Basalt on the high plateau, commonly called The Gardens or The Devils Garden, that stretches from Alturas westward more than 20 miles and northward more than 25 miles, with extensions reaching far westward and northward on the south and northeast side of Clear Lake Reservoir. The total area of the plateau is in the vicinity of 700 square miles. Other extensive areas of Warner Basalt are found in other parts of the region. On Highway 299 one drives from west of Burney to the rim of Hat Creek Valley, a distance of 9 miles, continuously over the surface of the Burney Basalt.

The thickness of the Warner Basalt varies considerably, even over short distances. In the edge of the plateau near Alturas, the Warner Basalt ranges in thickness from 15 to more than 360 feet (Russell, 1928, p. 418–419). Powers (1932, p. 267) believes that the average thickness in the area mapped by him is probably a little more than 100 feet. Individual flow units range from less than 2 feet to more than 50 feet, and probably average 4 to 5 feet. Thin units are vesicular throughout, but thick ones may be very dense in their middle and lower parts. Pipestem vesicles are common at the base of flow units, but in the upper parts the vesicles tend to be spheroidal, with forms characteristic of pahoehoe. The surface forms of the flows also are typical of pahoehoe. The surface as a whole is gently undulating, the undulations being mostly part of the original surface, but to a lesser degree the result of later faulting. In some areas tumuli are common. Ropy surfaces can be seen in places.

In some areas, as on the plateau just east of the Hat Creek fault scarp in the Prospect Peak quadrangle, the vents of the Warner Basalt are marked by small- to moderate-sized cinder cones. Elsewhere, very low shields, sometimes with small amounts of spatter still preserved near their summits, were built over the vents. For the most part, however, the vents were probably fissures along which only very small amounts of spatter accumulated, as at the vents of the Recent Hat Creek flow, described on a later page. Most of these vent structures have since been destroyed by weathering and erosion, or were buried by outwelling lava in a late stage of the eruption, and they can no longer be found.

In hand specimens the Warner Basalt generally is medium to light gray, with strikingly coarse grain and, under the hand lens, with a distinctly diabasic appearance. Small yellowish-green grains of olivine are abundant in most specimens, and occasionally small phenocrysts of feldspar are present. Under the microscope, the texture is usually intergranular to subophitic, with pale-brown augite occupying the interstices between the feldspar grains. Chemically, the rocks are undersaturated, containing normative olivine, and are moderately high to very high in alumina. In two analyses listed by Anderson (1941, p. 387) alumina is 18.5 and 18.2 percent, and total alkalies approximately 2.3 percent, with potash very low. A sample collected in a railway cut at Tionesta by C. W. Chesterman contains 18.5 percent Al_2O_3 (Yoder and Tilley, 1962, p. 362). However, one collected by Kuno (1965, p. 306) from the basalt overlying bright-red soil in the cut on Highway 395, just east of the Pit River bridge 3½ miles northeast of Alturas, contains only 16.8 percent Al_2O_3.

The most characteristic feature of the Warner Basalt is diktytaxitic structure (Fuller, 1931, p. 116), in which many open spaces exist in the network of plagioclase plates, as though a late-stage fluid had drained away from between them. Actually, although diktytaxitic structure is very common in the Warner Basalt, it is not always present; furthermore, it is present in many other basalts in the area, both older and younger than the Warner, as in some basalts of the Cedarville Series, and among the upper Pleistocene and Recent flows, both in the Modoc Plateau region, and in the Cascade Range. It appears to be characteristic of high-alumina basalts in which feldspar reaches saturation and starts to crystallize at an early stage of cooling, rather than of any particular stratigraphic or structural unit. The uniformity in texture and mineral composition of rocks of this magma type, throughout the period from Miocene to Recent, is striking and noteworthy.

Pleistocene and Recent Volcanic Rocks Other Than Warner Basalt

In the region just northeast and east of Lassen Volcanic National Park, there are many small shield volcanoes and lava flows associated with cinder cones, and some steeper lava cones that are younger than the widespread plateau basalts. The rocks range from olivine basalt, through basalt, to basaltic andesite and andesite. Among the steeper cones are Prospect and West Prospect Peaks, at the north edge of Lassen National Park, and Sugarloaf, on the west edge of Hat Creek Valley a few miles farther north. All three have cinder cones at their summits. These volcanoes are close to the Cascade Range, and perhaps should be included with it. Farther east the cones are all flatter, and most of them are typical shields of Icelandic type. Among them are Cal Mountain, Cone Mountain, and Crater Lake Mountain, just north of Highway 44 in the Harvey Mountain quadrangle. Many of them, like Cone Mountain, are crowned by a small cinder cone. Crater Lake Mountain is a typical shield, 6 miles across, containing at its summit a double collapse crater that holds a small lake. South of the highway, rows of cinder cones aligned in a north-northwest direction mark the vents of basaltic block-lava flows, the steep edges of which can be seen near the highway. Northward and eastward the abundance of post-Warner volcanic rocks decreases, and volcanoes later than the Gardens Basalt are nearly absent in the northeastern quarter of the Modoc Plateau region.

East of Highway 89, and 6 miles southeast of its junction with Highway 299, Cinder Butte is a shield built against the base of the Hat Creek fault scarp. The position of the vent was probably controlled by one of the faults of the Hat Creek system. Another shield, 9 miles to the northeast and visible from the lookout point on Highway 299 above the Pit River Falls, appears to have been the source of the lava flow that descended the Pit River canyon at that point and now constitutes the ledge of the falls. Like that of Cinder Butte, the vent that fed the shield appears to have been localized by a fault belonging, in this case, to the Butte Creek system.

It has already been pointed out that the volcanics of the Lava Beds National Monument belong to the Modoc Plateau region rather than to the Cascade Range or the Medicine Lake Highland. Actually, however, it may be more accurate to consider that the Modoc and Cascade provinces overlapped during Quaternary time. Certainly, in the region just northwest of Lassen Volcanic National Park, the late Pleistocene and Recent basalt and quartz basalt flows are identical in type to those found to the east in the Modoc region, and except for the quartz inclusions in some flows, are very much like the Warner Basalt.

Some of the eruptions in the Modoc Plateau region are very recent, though with the exception of that of Cinder Cone in the northeastern corner of Lassen Volcanic National Park, mentioned earlier, none of them are historic. On a line extending northwestward from Cinder Cone, a flow of basalt block lava from a vent between Prospect and West Prospect Peaks is so very fresh, and its surface is so well preserved, that it cannot be more than a few thousand years old. On the same line lie the vents of the Hat Creek flow, believed by Anderson (1940) to be less than 2,000 years old. The flow occupies the floor of Hat Creek Valley from south of Old Station northward for more than 16 miles. Highway 89 lies on its surface or close to its edge for most of its length. The flow is pahoehoe, with a typical undulating surface, in part ropy, and with many tumuli. Some of the latter are conspicuously displayed along Highway 44 where it crosses the flow east of its junction with Highway 89. Along much of the eastern margin of the flow is a scarp, up to 15 feet high. Although it lies along the base of the Hat Creek fault scarp, the scarp on the flow is not due to recently renewed movement on the fault, but is a slump scarp resulting from lowering of the surface of the central part of the flow as the lava drained away down the valley and shrank due to loss of gas and cooling. The Subway Cave is one of several similar caves known in the flow (Evans, 1963). It is part of the main feeding tube of the flow, formed by the draining away of lava out of the tube at the end of the eruption. It can be followed for a distance of 2,300 feet, and in places is as much as 50 feet in diameter and 16 feet high. The flat floor, which represents the congealed surface of the last fluid lava that flowed through the tube, in places shows the clinkery surface characteristic of aa—a common feature in pahoehoe tubes. The Hat Creek flow is a fissure eruption. Its vents lie along a line trending slightly west of north a mile southwest of Old Station. Spatter cones built along the fissure range from a few feet to 30 feet high.

The lava surfaces north and east of Hambone Butte, 25 miles north of Lake Britton, are very fresh and well preserved, and may be nearly as young as the Hat Creek flow. The lava appears to have come from a vent, or vents, on the south flank of the Medicine Lake Highland.

Quaternary Sedimentary Rocks

Faulting and volcanism were essentially continuous in the Modoc Plateau region from Miocene to Recent time. These, together with climatic changes, brought about disruptions of drainage and changes of stream gradient and regimen, which in turn resulted in the formation of lakes and the deposition of lake and stream sediments. The sedimentary deposits include fanglomerates, stream-laid alluvium and terrace deposits, and tuffaceous sandy, silty, and diatomaceous lake beds, and, in the high mountains, glacial moraines and outwash. Lake deposits occupy broad areas in the Fall River Valley, Big Valley, the valley of the South Fork of the Pit River, the Madeline Plains, around the north end of Lake Almanor, the region around the Klamath and Tule Lakes, and smaller areas in other basins. Still other basins that appear to be wholly floored by alluvium may be underlain by lake deposits. Deposition of both lake sediments and alluvium is continuing in these basins today.

Structure

The dominant structure of the Modoc Plateau region is the very large number of northwest- to north-trending faults (fig. 4), many of which are so recent that the scarps are still well preserved. Most of the faults are normal, with little or no suggestion of strike slip; but Gay (1959, p. 5) and his coworkers have found evidence of major right-lateral movement on the Likely fault, which extends southeastward from near Canby for 50 miles, to the northeastern part of the Madeline Plains. (See California Div. Mines, 1958, Alturas sheet, Geologic Map of California.) Along this fault, sag ponds and offset drainage lines are still visible. On the normal faults, either the east or the west side may be downthrown. Some fault blocks are tilted, with a visible fault scarp on only one side, but others are bounded by fault scarps on both sides. The amount of displacement varies from a few feet to more than 1,000 feet. Striking fault scarps are so numerous that it is difficult to single out any for special mention. Among them are: the scarp more than 1,300 feet high on the east side of Lookout Mountain, 5 miles north of Burney; the step-fault scarp 1,800 feet high on the west side of Fort Mountain, 3 miles northeast of the Highway 89 bridge over Lake Britton; the scarp ascended by Highway 299 at the east edge of Fall River Valley; the 2,000-foot scarp on the west side of Mahogony Mountain, east of Highway 97, 7 miles south of Dorris; the series of spectacular east-facing scarps west of Tule Lake that are visible from Lava Beds National Monument; and the series of scarps near Highway 139 southeast of Tule Lake. A low, but beautifully preserved, scarp is visible just east of Highway 89 about 4½ miles north of its junction with Highway 299.

The fault scarp along the east side of Hat Creek Valley also deserves special comment. At its highest point, the scarp, which is clearly visible from Highway 89 and is ascended by Highway 44, rises more than 1,000 feet above the surface of the Hat Creek lava flow. The fault is a complex system of subparallel *en echelon* fractures, the displacement increasing on one as it decreases on the adjacent one, with the blocks between them commonly constituting inclined ramps (fig. 4). The Butte Creek fault system, 3 miles farther east, shows a similar pattern (Macdonald, 1964). Fre-

Figure 4. Topographic map of part of the Prospect Peak quadrangle, showing the Hat Creek fault scarp along the eastern edge of Hat Creek Valley. The plateau on the right of the scarp is capped with Burney Basalt. Sugarloaf Peak, on the left, is a late Pleistocene cone built largely of andesite block lava flows. The valley is floored by the Hat Creek lava flow, which only a few thousand years ago poured out of inconspicuous vents located 2 miles north of the south boundary and 1 mile east of the west boundary of the figure.

quent small earthquakes are reported from the Hat Creek region, indicating that the Hat Creek fault probably is still active.

Hydrology

Brief mention should be made of some of the features of the hydrology. Throughout much of the region, the high permeability of the surface rocks, typical of basaltic terranes, results in a nearly complete lack of surface drainage. However, the underlying rocks are commonly much less permeable, and the rocks of the Cascade Range constitute a barrier to the westward movement of the ground water. The result is a water table that ranges in altitude from about 4,000 to 4,100 feet through much of the Modoc Plateau region. Above about 4,000 feet, the Pit River and its tributaries and many of the other streams are losing water to the ground, but below that altitude they are gaining water (R. H. Dale, oral communication, 1965).

Lost Creek disappears completely within a short distance of the place where it flows onto the surface of that Hat Creek lava flow, and Hat Creek itself loses large amounts of water to the same lava flow along the upper part of the valley; but the water appears again at the Rising River springs (eastern side of the Burney quadrangle), where the lower end of Hat Creek Valley is blocked by less permeable older rocks. The upper stretches of Burney Creek lose water to the permeable Burney Basalt and a mile above Burney Falls the streambed is usually completely dry; but 200 million gallons of water issue daily from the streambed within five-eighths of a mile above the falls and in the face of the falls in McArthur-Burney Falls State Park, where the base of the lava is exposed resting on the less permeable rocks beneath.

The Fall River Springs, 7 miles north of Fall River Mills, is one of the largest spring groups in the United States, with a flow of about 1,290,000,000 gallons a day. This huge discharge is particularly striking in view of the low rainfall in the surrounding region. Studies of groundwater gradients by the U.S. Geological Survey indicate that the water is moving southward from the Tule Lake and Clear Lake Reservoir areas, 50 miles to the north, beneath and around the Medicine Lake Highland (R. H. Dale, oral communication, 1965).

REFERENCES

Anderson, C. A., 1933a, The Tuscan formation of northern California, with a discussion concerning the origin of volcanic breccias: California Univ. Dept. Geol. Sci. Bull., v. 23, no. 7, p. 215–276.

—— 1933b, Volcanic history of Glass Mountain, northern California: Am. Jour. Sci., 5th ser., v. 26, no. 155, p. 485–506.

—— 1935, Alteration of the lavas surrounding the hot springs in Lassen Volcanic National Park: Am. Mineralogist, v. 20, no. 4, p. 240–252.

—— 1940, Hat Creek lava flow [California]: Am. Jour. Sci., v. 238, no. 7, p. 477–492.

—— 1941, Volcanoes of the Medicine Lake highland, California: California Univ. Dept. Geol. Sci. Bull., v. 25, no. 7, p. 347–422.

Anderson, C. A., and Russell, R. D., 1939, Tertiary formations of northern Sacramento Valley, California: California Jour. Mines and Geology, v. 35, no. 3, p. 219–253.

Aune, Q. A., 1964, A trip to Burney Falls: California Div. Mines and Geology Mineral Inf. Service, v. 17, no. 10, p. 183–191.

Axelrod, D. I., 1957, Late Tertiary floras and the Sierra Nevada uplift [California-Nevada]: Geol. Soc. America Bull., v. 68, no. 1, p. 19–45.

Baldwin, E. M., 1964, Thrust faulting in the Roseburg area, Oregon: Oregon Dept. Geology and Mineral Industries, The Ore Bin, v. 26, p. 176–184.

California Division of Mines, 1959, Geology of northeastern California: California Div. Mines Mineral Inf. Service, v. 12, no. 6, p. 1–7.

Callaghan, Eugene, 1933, Some features of the volcanic sequence in the Cascade Range in Oregon: Am. Geophys. Union Trans., 14th Ann. Mtg., p. 243–249.

Chesterman, C. W., 1955, Age of the obsidian flow at Glass Mountain, Siskiyou County, California: Am. Jour. Sci., v. 253, no. 7, p. 418–424.

Clark, W. B., 1957, Gold, *in* Mineral commodities of California—geologic occurrence, economic development, and utilization of the state's mineral resources: California Div. Mines Bull. 176, p. 215–226.

Curtis, G. H., 1957, Mode of origin of pyroclastic debris in the Mehrten formation of the Sierra Nevada: California Univ. Dept. Geol. Sci. Bull., v. 29, no. 9, p. 453–502.

Day, A. L., and Allen, E. T., 1925, The volcanic activity and hot springs of Lassen Peak [California]: Carnegie Inst. Washington Pub. 360, 190 p.

Diller, J. S., 1889, Geology of the Lassen Peak district [California]: U.S. Geol. Survey, 8th Ann. Rept., pt. 1, p. 395–432.

—— 1893, Cretaceous and early Tertiary of northern California and Oregon: Geol. Soc. America Bull., v. 4, p. 205–224.

—— 1895a, Description of the Lassen Peak sheet, California: U.S. Geol. Survey Geol. Atlas, Folio 15, 4 p.

—— 1895b, Mount Shasta—a typical volcano: Natl. Geog. Soc., Mon. 1, no. 8, p. 237–268.

—— 1906, Description of the Redding quadrangle, California: U.S. Geol. Survey Geol. Atlas, Folio 138, 14 p.

Dorf, Erling, 1933, Pliocene floras of California: Carnegie Inst. Washington Pub. 412, p. 1–112.

Durrell, Cordell, 1959, Tertiary stratigraphy of the Blairsden quadrangle, Plumas County, California: California Univ. Pubs. Geol. Sci., v. 43, no. 3, p. 161–192.

Evans, J. R., 1963, Geology of some lava tubes, Shasta County: California Div. Mines and Geology Mineral Inf. Service, v. 16, no. 3, p. 1–7.

Evernden, J. F., Savage, D. E., Curtis, G. H., and James, G. T., 1964, Potassium-argon dates and the Cenozoic mammalian chronology of North America: Am. Jour. Sci., v. 262, no. 2, p. 145–198.

Finch, R. H., 1928, Lassen Report No. 14: The Volcano Letter, no. 161, p. 1.

—— 1930, Activity of a California volcano in 1786: The Volcano Letter, no. 308, p. 3.

—— 1933, Burnt lava flow in northern California: Zeitschr. Vulkanologie, v. 15, no. 3, p. 180–183.

Finch, R. H., and Anderson, C. A., 1930, The quartz basalt eruptions of Cinder Cone, Lassen Volcanic National Park, California: California Univ. Dept. Geol. Sci. Bull., v. 19, no. 10, p. 245–273.

Ford, R. S., Soderstrand, J. N., Franson, R. E., Beach, F. H., Feingold, S. A., Hail, W. R., Iwamura, T. I., and Swanson, A. A., 1963, Northeastern counties ground water investigation: California Dept. Water Resources Bull. 98, v. 1, text, 246 p., v. 2, plates.

Fuller, R. E., 1931, The geomorphology and volcanic sequence of Steens Mountain in southeastern Oregon: Washington Univ. Geology Pub., v. 3, no. 1, p. 1–130.

Gay, T. E., Jr., and Aune, Q. A., 1958, Geologic map of California, Olaf P. Jenkins edition, Alturas sheet: California Div. Mines, scale 1:250,000.

Gester, G. C., 1962, The geological history of Eagle Lake, Lassen County, California: California Acad. Sci., Occasional Papers 34, 29 p.

Hanna, G. D., and Gester, G. C., 1963, Pliocene lake beds near Dorris, California: California Acad. Sci., Occasional Papers 42, 17 p.

Heath, J. P., 1960, Repeated avalanches at Chaos Jumbles, Lassen Volcanic National Park: Am. Jour. Sci., v. 258, no. 10, p. 744–751.

Hinds, N. E. A., 1952, Evolution of the California landscape: California Div. Mines Bull. 158, 240 p.

Ives, P. C., Levin, Betsy, Robinson, R. D., and Rubin, Meyer, 1964, U.S. Geological Survey radiocarbon dates VII: Am. Jour. Sci., Radiocarbon Supp., v. 6, p. 37–76.

Jones, D. L., 1959, Stratigraphy of Upper Cretaceous rocks in the Yreka-Hornbrook area, northern California [abs.]: Geol. Soc. America Bull., v. 70, no. 12, pt. 2, p. 1726–1727.

Kuno, H., 1965, Fractionation trends of basalt magmas in lava flows: Jour. Petrology [Oxford], v. 6, no. 2, p. 302–321.

LaMotte, R. S., 1936, The upper Cedarville flora of northwestern Nevada and adjacent California: Carnegie Inst. Washington Pub. 455, Contrib. Paleontology 5, p. 57–142.

Lydon, P. A., 1961, Sources of the Tuscan formation in northern California [abs.]: Geol. Soc. America Spec. Paper 68, p. 40.

Macdonald, G. A., 1963, Geology of the Manzanita Lake quadrangle, California: U.S. Geol. Survey Geol. Quad. Map GQ-248, scale 1:62,500.

—— 1964, Geology of the Prospect Peak quadrangle, California: U.S. Geol. Survey Geol. Quad. Map GQ-345, scale 1:62,500.

—— 1965, Geologic map of the Harvey Mountain quadrangle, California: U.S. Geol. Survey Geol. Quad. Map GQ-443, scale 1:62,500.

Macdonald, G. A., and Katsura, Takashi, 1965, Eruption of Lassen Peak, Cascade Range, California, in 1915—example of mixed magmas: Geol. Soc. America Bull., v. 76, no. 5, p. 475–482.

Pakiser, L. C., 1964, Gravity, volcanism, and crustal structures in the southern Cascade Range, California: Geol. Soc. America Bull., v. 75, p. 611–620.

Peacock, M. A., 1931, The Modoc lava field, northern California: Geog. Rev., v. 21, no. 2, p. 259–275.

Peck, D. L., Griggs, A. B., Schlicker, H. G., Wells, F. G., and Dole, H. M., 1964, Geology of the central and northern parts of the western Cascade Range in Oregon: U.S. Geol. Survey Prof. Paper 449, 56 p.

Popenoe, W. P., 1943, Cretaceous, east side Sacramento Valley, Shasta and Butte Counties, California: Am. Assoc. Petrol. Geol. Bull., v. 27, no. 3, p. 306–312.

Popenoe, W. P., Imlay, R. W., and Murphy, M. A., 1960, Correlation of the Cretaceous formations of the Pacific Coast (United States and northwestern Mexico): Geol. Soc. America Bull., v. 71, no. 10, p. 1491–1540.

Powers, H. A., 1932, The lavas of the Modoc Lava Bed quadrangle, California: Am. Mineralogist, v. 17, no. 7, p. 253–294.

Richthofen, Ferdinand von, 1868, The natural system of volcanic rocks: California Acad. Sci. Mem., pt. 2, 98 p.

Rubin, Meyer, and Alexander, Corrione, 1960, U.S. Geological Survey radiocarbon dates V: Am. Jour. Sci., Radiocarbon Supp., v. 2, p. 129–185.

Russell, R. D., and VanderHoof, V. L., 1931, A vertebrate fauna from a new Pliocene formation in northern California: California Univ. Dept. Geol. Sci. Bull., v. 20, no. 2, p. 11–21.

Russell, R. J., 1928, Basin Range structure and stratigraphy of the Warner Range, northeastern California: California Univ., Dept. Geol. Sci. Bull., v. 17, no. 11, p. 387–496.

Snavely, P. D., Jr., and Wagner, H. C., 1963, Tertiary geologic history of western Oregon and Washington: Washington Div. Mines and Geology Rept. Inv. 22, 25 p.

Stearns, H. T., 1928, Lava Beds National Monument, California: Geog. Soc. Philadelphia Bull., v. 26, no. 4, p. 239–253.

Thayer, T. P., 1936, Structure of the North Santiam River section of the Cascade Mountains in Oregon: Jour. Geology, v. 44, no. 6, p. 701–716.

Wells, F. G., 1956, Geology of the Medford quadrangle, Oregon-California: U.S. Geol. Survey Geol. Quad. Map GQ-89, scale 1:96,000.

Williams, Howel, 1932a, Geology of the Lassen Volcanic National Park, California: California Univ. Dept. Geol. Sci. Bull., v. 21, no. 9, p. 195–385.

—— 1932b, Mount Shasta, a Cascade volcano: Jour. Geology, v. 40, no. 5, p. 417–429.

—— 1934, Mount Shasta, California: Zeitschr. Vulkanologie, v. 15, no. 4, p. 225–253.

—— 1935, Newberry volcano of central Oregon: Geol. Soc. America Bull., v. 46, no. 2, p. 253–304.

—— 1942, The geology of Crater Lake National Park, Oregon, with a reconnaissance of the Cascade Range southward to Mount Shasta: Carnegie Inst. Washington Pub. 540, 162 p.

—— 1949, Geology of the Macdoel quadrangle [California]: California Div. Mines Bull. 151, p. 7–60.

Wilson, T. A., 1961, The geology near Mineral, California: California Univ., Berkeley, M.S. thesis.

Yoder, H. S., Jr., and Tilley, C. E., 1962, Origin of basalt magmas—an experimental study of natural and synthetic rock systems: Jour. Petrology [Oxford], v. 3, no. 3, p. 342–532.

Photo 19. Basalt pillow lava (Warner basalt) resting on diatomaceous lake sediments along Highway 89 just north of the bridge across Lake Britton. The pillows lie in a matrix of hyaloclastite. Diatomite has squeezed up into the fragmental base of the flow.

Photo 20. Hornito (rootless spatter cone) built on the surface of a pahoehoe lava flow in Lava Beds National Monument.

ECONOMIC MINERAL DEPOSITS OF THE CASCADE RANGE, MODOC PLATEAU, AND GREAT BASIN REGION OF NORTHEASTERN CALIFORNIA

By Thomas E. Gay, Jr.
California Division of Mines and Geology, San Francisco

The minerals industry of this region—about 16,500 square miles comprising the northeastern corner of California—is dominated by three factors: (1) A narrow range in variety of rocks, which are predominantly Cenozoic basalt and andesite, with local lake-laid sedimentary rocks; (2) a low population density both in and about the region, creating but minor local market demand, and (3) the lack of known commercial deposits of any mineral commodities except pumice, volcanic cinders, and peat suitable for mining and shipping to more distant population centers. Although transportation routes through the region are not numerous, rail and highway routes are more than adequate to meet the foreseeable demand for hauling mineral products.

The principal mineral commodities of the region, all of which are directly related to its volcanic terrane, are volcanic cinders, pumice and pumicite, and crushed stone—used for railroad ballast, lightweight aggregate, and regular aggregate, respectively. Volcanic products of potential importance are tuffaceous stone, for dimension stone; perlite, for lightweight aggregate; and obsidian, sought by rock collectors for decorative purposes. Numerous areas of hot springs, related to recent volcanic activity in the region, are possible sources of geothermal power, but none has been developed so far.

Photo 1. Indian mortars and pestles made from volcanic rock. Modoc Lava Bed Museum. *Photo by Mary Hill.*

Metallic commodities are notably lacking in the region, although three minor gold districts, minor showings of quicksilver, scattered traces of copper, and one small uranium deposit are known.

Lakebed deposits include peat that is being utilized, diatomite as yet unused, and salt which has not been recovered for many years. Stream and flood-plain deposits of sand and gravel are used locally for aggregate, but their chemical reactivity owing to excessive glass creates a problem. Mainly of historical interest are minor showings of low-grade coal; local common clay deposits formerly used for brick; spring-deposited limestone once burned for local use as mortar; and various siliceous materials, such as jasper and petrified wood, sought by rock collectors.

METALLIC MINERAL COMMODITIES

Copper

Colorful showings of secondary copper minerals in local altered zones in andesitic rocks have encouraged minor prospecting at half a dozen localities in the region, but no production has resulted.

Gold

The Hayden Hill gold-mining district in Lassen County and the High Grade and Winters districts in Modoc County have yielded about $3,500,000 in gold and silver, mostly in the early 1900's; however, all have long been inactive.

At Hayden Hill, steeply dipping veins, 1 to 25 ft wide, cut Tertiary rhyolitic tuff and breccia. Free gold, valued up to $14 per ounce (1915), occurs in iron-stained and manganese-rich gouge and ochre seams. Workings, as long as 4,500 ft on the level, and as deep as 835 ft, followed veins containing oreshoots which were reported to be enriched by concentration by descending waters. An estimated total of about $2,500,000 in gold, with minor silver, was recovered from 1880 to 1911, and about $50,000 was won during the latest period of activity, 1924 to 1934.

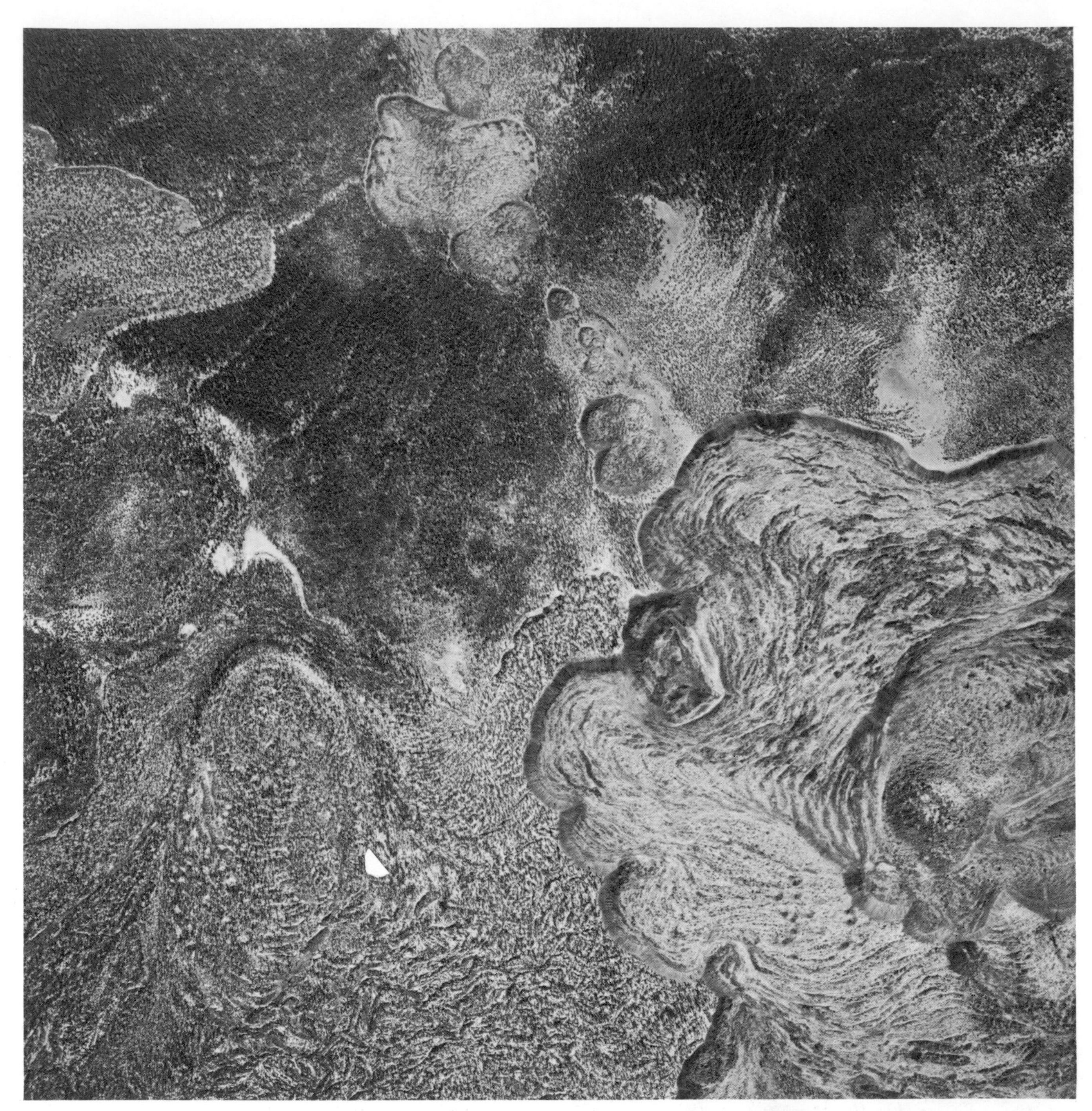

Photo 2. Air photo of Medicine Lake Highland area, showing lava flows.

Figure 1 (opposite). Geologic map of portions of Cascade Range, Modoc Plateau, and Great Basin provinces in northeastern California. Modified from Weed (1964), Alturas (1958), Redding (1962), Westwood (1960), and Chico (1962) sheets of Geologic Map of California.

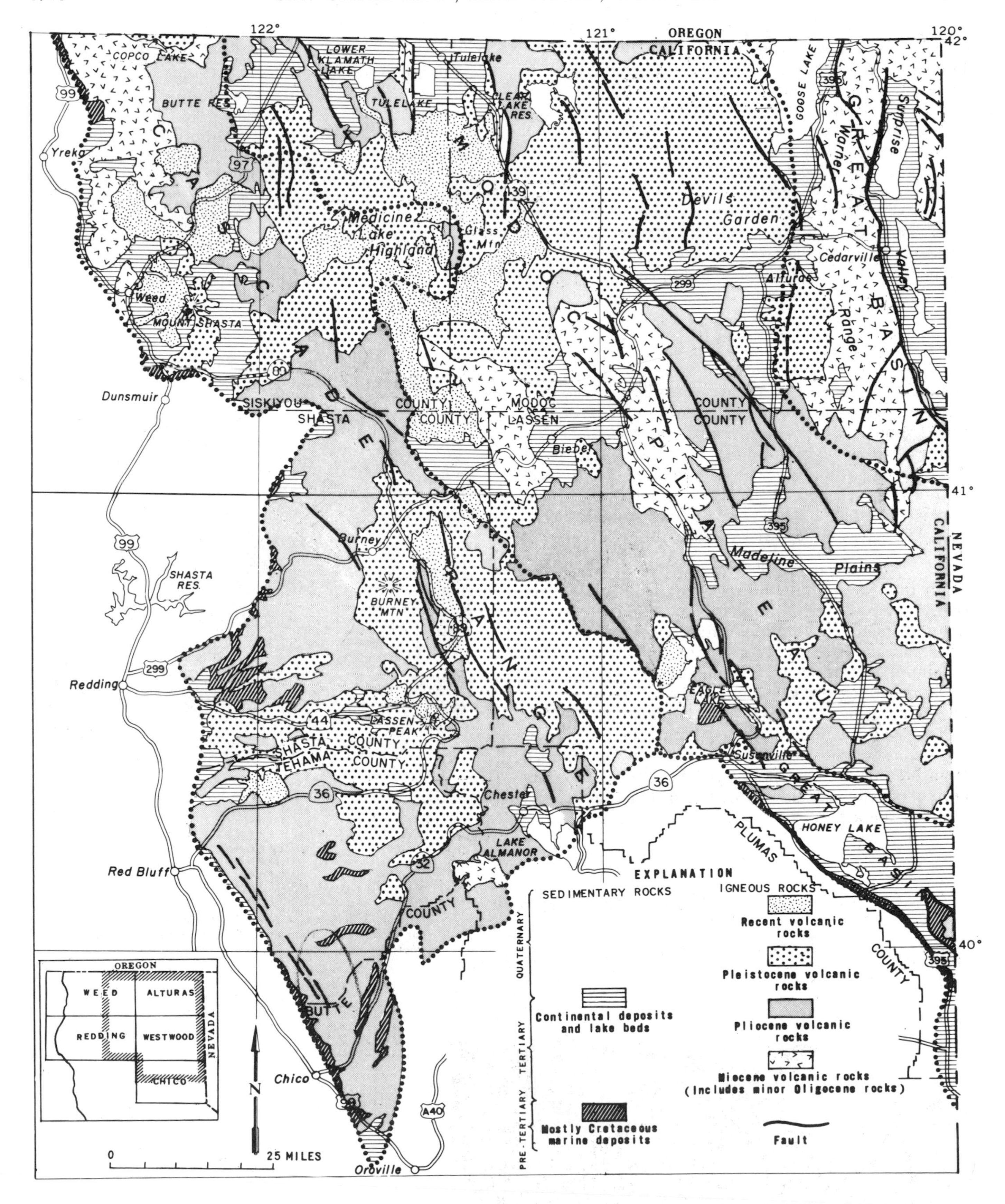
122°
121°
120°
42°
41°
40°
OREGON
CALIFORNIA
NEVADA
CALIFORNIA
COPCO LAKE
LOWER KLAMATH LAKE
Tulelake
TULELAKE
CLEAR LAKE RES.
BUTTE RES.
GOOSE LAKE
Yreka
Medicine Lake Highland
Glass Mtn
Devils Garden
Warner
Surprise
Valley
Range
Cedarville
Alturas
Weed
MOUNT SHASTA
Dunsmuir
SISKIYOU COUNTY
SHASTA COUNTY
MODOC COUNTY
LASSEN COUNTY
Bieber
Burney
Madeline Plains
SHASTA RES.
BURNEY MTN
Redding
LASSEN PEAK
SHASTA COUNTY
TEHAMA COUNTY
EAGLE LAKE
Susanville
Chester
HONEY LAKE
PLUMAS COUNTY
LAKE ALMANOR
Red Bluff
BUTTE COUNTY
Chico
Oroville
99
97
139
299
395
89
44
36
32
A40
CASCADE RANGE
MODOC PLATEAU
GREAT BASIN
N
0
25 MILES
OREGON
WEED
ALTURAS
REDDING
WESTWOOD
CHICO
NEVADA
EXPLANATION
SEDIMENTARY ROCKS
IGNEOUS ROCKS
QUATERNARY
TERTIARY
PRE-TERTIARY
Recent volcanic rocks
Pleistocene volcanic rocks
Continental deposits and lake beds
Pliocene volcanic rocks
Miocene volcanic rocks (Includes minor Oligocene rocks)
Mostly Cretaceous marine deposits
Fault

At High Grade, in the northern Warner Range, rich but discontinuous oreshoots were found within a hundred feet of the surface. Gold occurred mainly in narrow stringers in quartz-filled, steeply dipping silicified breccia zones and veins in Tertiary rhyolite. Despite enthusiastic promotion of the camp in 1909–11, its productivity was about $75,000 from 1910 to 1919, and perhaps $10,000 from 1931 to 1934. Since 1934 it has been essentially inactive.

The Winters district, near Adin Summit, comprises only the Lost Cabin mine, which in the early 1900's yielded about $10,000 from oxidized gold-bearing ore occurring in sheared calcite- and quartz-filled brecciated zones in Tertiary andesite.

Quicksilver

At several localities along the east side of Goose Lake, Modoc County, traces of cinnabar occur with chalcedonic silica as vein and seam fillings in brecciated, iron-stained, Tertiary rhyolite and interbedded tuff. Despite furnaces (now ruins) built in the 1940's and earlier at three localities, and local reports of "several flasks" of quicksilver produced from small rich pockets reached by shallow workings, no production is recorded. Exploration, though sporadic in recent years, was underway in mid-1965.

Uranium

On the Nevada line, northeast of Hallelujah Junction, Lassen County, autunite and other secondary uranium minerals occur in tuffaceous to sandy Tertiary lakebeds that overlap granitic basement. The uranium minerals occur disseminated and in seams, but are concentrated in and near woody and leafy organic material that is scattered in the lakebeds. In the late 1950's, open pit mining yielded a number of carloads of ore, averaging about 0.5 percent U_2O_3, shipped from Nevada to Salt Lake City, Utah. Exploration has been active in 1964 and 1965, but production, if any, is undetermined.

NONMETALLIC MINERAL COMMODITIES

Calcite (optical)

On the lower east slopes of the Warner Range, Modoc County, calcite pods and veins as much as 2 ft thick yield clear optical-grade calcite, suitable for making polarizing prisms and other precision optical equipment. The calcite occurs in Miocene andesitic tuff-breccia of the Cedarville Series in two localities, just west of Cedarville, and 2 miles north of Eagleville. About 1,000 ounces of optical calcite from the more southerly location were sold in 1920 and 1921. This shipment included usable crystals as large as 12 inches. An additional undetermined quantity was recovered from this deposit during World War II for use in gunsights. In the late 1940's about 1,000 pounds of chemically pure calcite from the same deposit were sold as a standardizing agent for testing acids, but no subsequent production is known.

Photo 3 (left) and 4 (above). Mining volcanic rock for garden stone from the Little Glass Mountain area. ***Photo by Mary Hill.***

Photo 5. Face of an obsidian flow, Siskiyou County. *Photo by Charles W. Chesterman.*

Clay

Common clay, mostly alluvial soil, was quarried in the late 1800's, from several localities near the early towns of the region; it was burned in field kilns to make bricks for local buildings.

Coal

Thin seams of low-grade coal, and many weathered-out fragments, occur in Tertiary lakebeds and volcanic sedimentary rocks in various parts of the region, but not in commercial quantity or quality.

Decorative Stone

Various decorative limy spring deposits and siliceous rocks such as jasper, chalcedony, and petrified wood, are hunted by mineral collectors ("rockhounds") in the region. Obsidian also is sought, but it is discussed separately in this article as it has another use. Favorite collecting localities are in the eastern desertlike areas, especially near hot springs, in the Warner Range, and in parts of the terrain underlain by the Tuscan Formation.

Diatomite

Some of the lakebed deposits scattered throughout the region, and ranging in age from Early Tertiary to Recent, contain potentially commercial deposits of diatomaceous earth. These deposits are from a few feet to several hundred feet thick, and some are exposed over tens of square miles. Varying amounts of volcanic ash are present in many of the localities, but portions of most of the deposits are relatively pure diatomite and potentially usable. Some deposits are partly covered by thin basalt flows.

These diatomite deposits have not been completely surveyed or analyzed for potential usefulness, and no diatomite from this region has been sold commercially, although freshwater lakebed diatomite has been quarried in Oregon and in Nevada.

The principal diatomite deposits of the region are the Pliocene beds around Lake Britton, northeast Shasta County, and in Willow Creek Valley, northeast Siskiyou County. Less extensive exposures occur near Alturas, Modoc County; near Day, southwest Modoc County; near Karlo and Long Valley, Lassen County; and adjacent to Copco and Lower Klamath Lakes, Siskiyou County.

Hot Springs

A large number of hot springs found throughout the region apparently are related to the recency of volcanic eruptive activity and the abundance of faulting. The 28 hot springs shown on figure 2 are all described by Waring (1915, p. 115–144) as hotter than 90°F. In 1963 sources of geothermal power were sought by exploratory drilling about 2 miles north of Lake City, in Surprise Valley, about half a mile west of the area of recently active mud volcanos described by White (1955), but no development resulted.

Limestone

Small vein and spring deposits of limestone, of variable purity, were quarried and burned to make lime

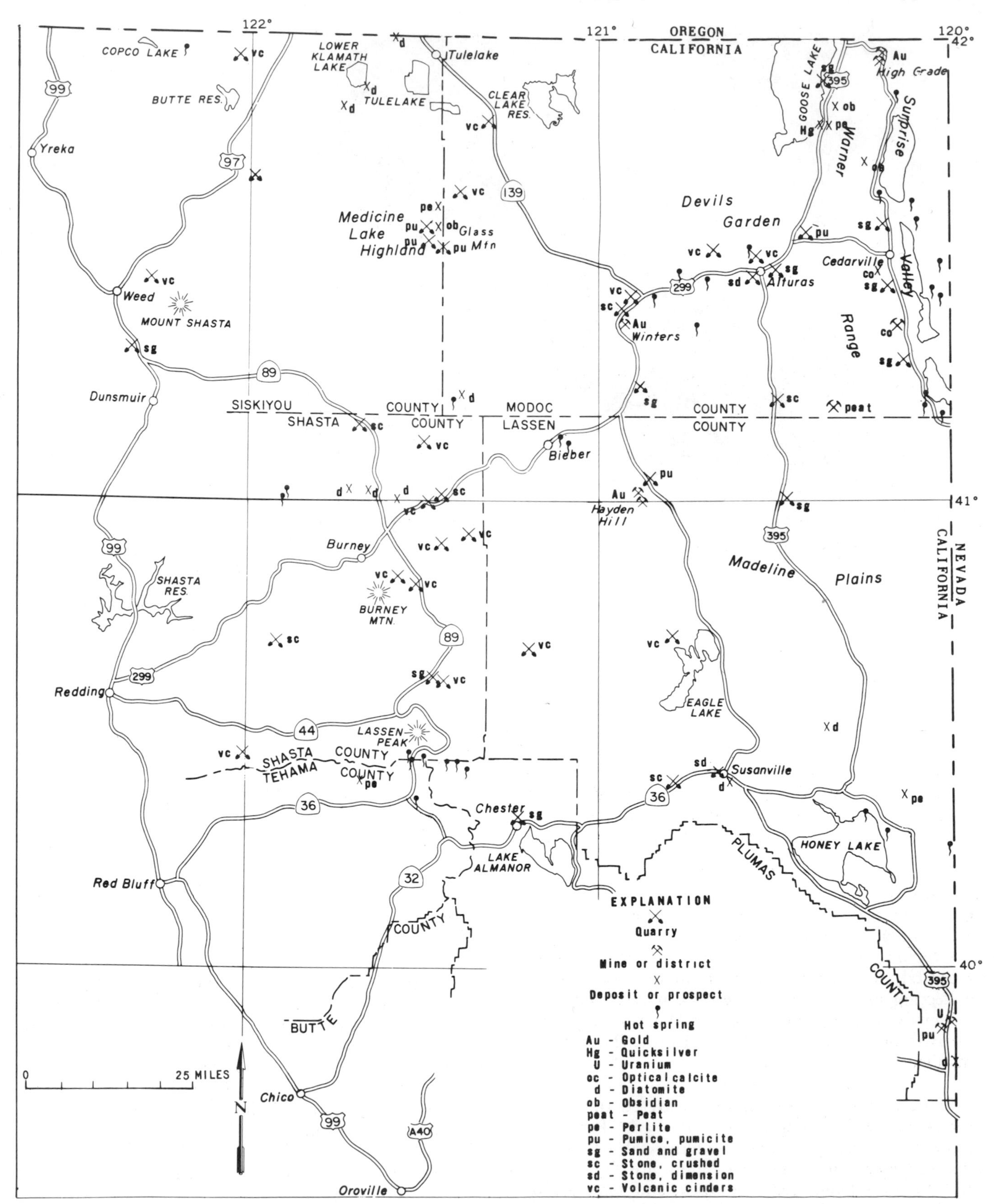

Figure 2. Map showing the location of hot springs and deposits of economic mineral commodities in northeastern California.

mortar for local building in various towns of the region, mainly during the 1800's.

Obsidian

Quaternary obsidian masses in the Medicine Lake Highland and in the Warner Range are sites of avid mineral-collector activity. Chatoyant ("rainbow") obsidian and red-streaked obsidian from the Warner Range are especially prized for cutting and polishing. Apparently, several thousand dollars worth of obsidian from the Warner Range was sold in the 1960's, and a large number of claims were staked covering desirable deposits. An unusual development came in the early 1950's, when several large pieces of clear obsidian from Glass Mountain, Siskiyou County, were cut and polished to make experimental industrial mirrors.

Peat

Recent accumulations of hypnum peat moss in the Pleistocene lake basin of Jess Valley, Modoc County, are the only source of peat moss in California. The usable peat layer is about 300 acres in area and about 3½ ft thick, lying beneath a foot of overburden. The deposit, which has been mined since 1939, yields in excess of 10,000 tons of peat moss a year. After the overburden is stripped, the peat is piled to dry for 2 months, then screened, shredded, and bagged in 80-pound bales at Likely for truck and rail shipment. The peat moss is used throughout California and seven western states for soil conditioner.

Perlite

Four deposits of perlite in the region were prospected and tested for lightweight aggregate in the late 1940's, but no production has resulted. These deposits are perlitic phases of Tertiary rhyolitic intrusions and flows, two at Sugar Hill, Modoc County; one at Cougar Butte, northeast Siskiyou County; and one at Hot Springs Peak, north of Honey Lake, Lassen County. A number of other perlite deposits that have not been tested occur with rhyolitic rocks in the region; one of the largest is in Battle Creek Canyon, Tehama County.

The first perlite to be tested for commercial expansibility in California was several hundred tons from Sugar Hill, shipped to Campbell, Santa Clara County, for the test in 1947. The availability of good quality perlite in large, uniform deposits much closer to the main centers of use, is mainly responsible for the lack of utilization of these more remote deposits.

Petroleum and Gas

Cretaceous and Early Tertiary units that yield gas in the Great Central Valley Province, also contain gas where they project eastward beneath the Tuscan Formation in the Cascade Province (Safonov, 1952, p. 96). Indicated favorable structures east of Cottonwood, northeast of Red Bluff, and east and northeast of Corning have been drilled in a few places, but no production has resulted.

Pozzolan

The rhyolitic Nomlaki Tuff, and other tuffs in the Tuscan Formation, have been discussed by Faick (1963, p. 714–717) as potential sources of natural pozzolan. Other occurrences of vitric tuffs and siliceous volcanic sediments scattered through the region may also be suitable for use as pozzolan should a market develop.

Pumice and Pumicite

About 30,000 tons of pumice and pumicite (about one-third of California's annual production) are mined each year in this region, with almost all coming from deposits at Glass Mountain, eastern Siskiyou County. The quarrying of pumice and pumicite (particles of pumice smaller than 4 mm) began in this region in the mid 1940's and through 1965 totaled about 500,000 tons. The deposits of the Glass Mountain area consist of loosely consolidated grayish-white rhyolite pumice tuff breccia of Recent age. The tuff breccia occurs in a blanket that ranges in thickness from 1 to 60 feet, and extends over about 10 square miles northeast of Medicine Lake Highland, eastern Siskiyou and western Modoc Counties.

After the overgrowth and thin soil overburden is removed, the pumice is quarried in broad pits by scraper loaders, and trucked about 10 miles to Tionesta for screening and rail shipment, or to pumice block plants near Perez, Modoc County. About 75 percent of the pumice is made into blocks in the area, for shipment throughout northern California and Oregon; about 25 percent is shipped in bulk to the San Francisco area, where it also is used to make lightweight building block. Sized pumice costs about $2.20 per short ton at the railhead.

Several hundred tons of pumice scouring blocks are sawed each year from a pumiceous obsidian crust atop Glass Mountain.

Salt

Brine pumped by windmills from shallow wells and ponds in unconsolidated Recent lake sediments east of Middle Surprise Lake once yielded a small tonnage of crude salt by solar evaporation. The salt was used locally for stock feed in the early 1900's; the salt works has been inactive since 1925, and is almost obliterated.

Sand and Gravel

Most towns throughout the region have local sources of sand and gravel used in small noncommercial quantities for portland cement concrete and asphalt concrete aggregate. Owing to its high content of glassy volcanic rocks, much of the sand and gravel in the region is too reactive for high-specification portland cement concrete, although it is commonly used for less exacting purposes in local road construction. Highway-building contracts commonly specify crushed stone, or require sand and gravel hauled from deposits outside this region—especially for curbs, gutters, and bridges.

Photo 6. Volcanic cinder quarry on the southeast side of East Sand Butte near Tionesta, Modoc County. Layering represents repeated volcanic outbursts. Solid blocks of rock on quarry floor and in quarry face represent fragments of volcanic bombs. The cinders from this cone are used for railroad construction. Observer faces north. *Photo by Charles W. Chesterman.*

The region's principal sources of sand and gravel are local stream alluvium in various localities; deltaic lake terrace deposits in Goose Lake, Surprise, and Honey Lake Valleys, and in the Madeline Plains; and Quaternary flood-plain gravels near Alturas and Chester.

Stone, Crushed

Like sand and gravel, and volcanic cinders, crushed stone is produced and used throughout the region in undetermined tonnages, with almost all being used for asphalt concrete aggregate and road building material. Various Tertiary and Quaternary basalt and andesite flows are sources of high-specification crushed stone throughout the region; notable quarries are at Canby Bridge and Likely, Modoc County. Decomposed granitic rock is quarried for road and fill purposes in Honey Lake Valley, Lassen County, and elsewhere Tertiary andesitic tuff breccias and vent agglomerates are sources of crushed stone for road building uses.

Stone, Dimension

In the 1800's and early 1900's, small tonnages of Tertiary tuffs and tuff breccias near Alturas, Modoc County, and Susanville, Lassen County, were quarried for local use in a few public and commercial buildings. None of these quarries has been active for several decades.

Volcanic Cinders

Cinder cones at about 20 localities in northeastern Shasta County, eastern Siskiyou County, and western Modoc County, have been sources of about 5 million tons of volcanic cinders since large-scale quarrying began in this area in the early 1930's. Production from the region has been about 140,000 tons of volcanic cinders each year for the past decade—about two-thirds to three-fourths of California's annual production.

The cinders at most cones are red, gray, or black basaltic to andesitic scoria fragments. The cinders are layered as they originally fell and are accompanied by scattered volcanic bombs. Most of the cones that have yielded cinders are Pleistocene, but a few are Recent.

Quarrying operations are typically simple: After removal of thin overburden, the loosely consolidated cinders are scraped and loaded into trucks for the haul to market. Sometimes the raw cinders are screened to remove bombs and agglutinated clumps. The immense tonnages quarried for railroad ballast at Kegg, Siskiyou County, and East Sand Butte, Modoc County, were loaded directly on railroad cars in the pits.

The main tonnage of volcanic cinders from this region has been used for railroad ballast, although this has been decreasing in the past decade; a lesser but growing tonnage, from cones throughout the region, is used as road material—fill, asphaltic concrete aggregate, and surfacing material. Smaller tonnages, but also notably increasing over the past decade, are used as lightweight aggregate in building blocks: the cones at Hotlum, near Yreka, Siskiyou County, and Poison Lake, near Susanville, Lassen County, are the main sources of volcanic cinders used for building blocks.

REFERENCES

Averill, C. V., 1936, Mineral resources of Modoc County: California Jour. Mines and Geology, v. 32, no. 4, p. 445–457.

Averill, C. V., and Erwin, H. D., 1936, Mineral resources of Lassen County: California Jour. Mines and Geology, v. 32, no. 4, p. 405–444.

Chesterman, C. W., 1956, Pumice, pumicite, and volcanic cinders in California: California Div. Mines Bull. 174, p. 3–97.

Faick, J. H., 1963, Geology and technology of some natural pozzolans in north-central California: Econ. Geology, v. 58, no. 5, p. 702–719.

Hill, J. M., 1915, Some mining districts in northeastern California and northwestern Nevada: U.S. Geol. Survey Bull. 594, 200 p.

Lydon, P. A., and O'Brien, J. C., 196___, Mines and mineral resources of Shasta County: California Div. Mines and Geology, County Rept. (In press)

Ross, C. P., 1941, Some quicksilver prospects in adjacent parts of Nevada, California, and Oregon: U.S. Geol. Survey Bull. 931-B, p. 23–37.

Safonov, Anatole, 1962, The Challenge of the Sacramento Valley, California, *in* Bowen, O. E., ed., Geologic guide to the gas and oil fields of northern California: California Div. Mines and Geology Bull. 181, p. 77–97.

Stearns, N. D., Stearns, H. T., and Waring, G. A., 1937, Thermal springs in the United States: U.S. Geol. Survey Water-Supply Paper 679-B, p. 59–206.

Tucker, W. B., 1919, Lassen County and Modoc County: California Mining Bur., 15th Rept. State Mineralogist, pt. 2, chaps. 2–3, p. 226–253.

Waring, G. A., 1915, Springs of California: U.S. Geol. Survey Water-Supply Paper 338, 410 p.

White, D. E., 1955, Violent mud-volcano eruption of Lake City hot springs, northeastern California: Geol. Soc. America Bull., v. 66, no. 9, p. 1109–1130.

CHAPTER IV
SIERRA NEVADA PROVINCE

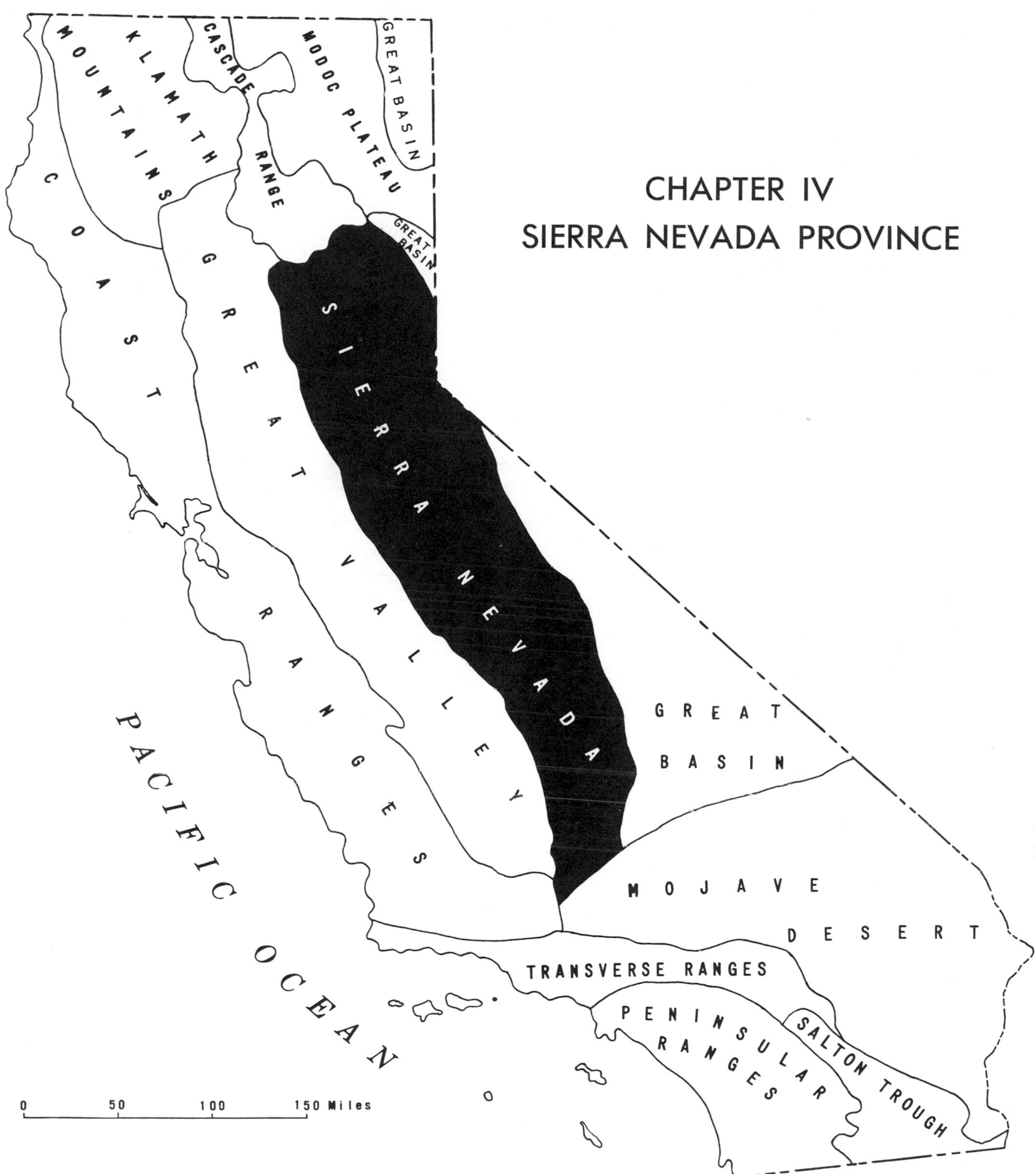

Mount Lyell group, and the source of the Tuolumne River. From J. D. Whitney, *The Yosemite Guide-Book,* 1870.

GEOLOGY OF THE SIERRA NEVADA

By Paul C. Bateman and Clyde Wahrhaftig *
U.S. Geological Survey, Menlo Park, California;
U.S.G.S. and University of California, Berkeley

The Sierra Nevada is a strongly asymmetric mountain range with a long gentle western slope and a high and steep eastern escarpment. It is 50 to 80 miles wide, and it runs west of north through eastern California for more than 400 miles—from the Mojave Desert on the south to the Cascade Range and the Modoc Plateau on the north (pl. 1). Mount Whitney, in the southeastern part of the range, attains a height of 14,495 feet and is the highest point in the conterminous United States. The "High Sierra," a spectacular span of the crestal region, which extends north from Mount Whitney for about a hundred miles, is a glaciated region characterized by numerous lakes and a procession of 13,000- and 14,000-foot peaks.

The range is a tremendous physical barrier to the passage of moisture eastward from the Pacific. Polar front cyclones expand adiabatically as they pass over the Sierra Nevada during the winter and cool well below their dewpoint. Most of the moisture that was obtained during the passage of warm air masses across the Pacific is precipitated as snow, which is preserved as a heavy snow pack at high altitudes and in the shade of the forests at lower elevations until late spring or summer. On the east side of the Sierra Nevada the descending air is warmed adiabatically and can hold more moisture than it contains. Hence the arid valleys of the Great Basin are "lands of little rain."

But the Sierra Nevada is more than a physical and climatic barrier; until recently it has been a remarkably effective barrier to geologic thought. Its towering eastern escarpment has been a boundary for thinking about problems in the Great Basin; and geologists working in the Great Valley, the Coast Ranges, or even along the west slope of the Sierra Nevada itself, have seldom looked eastward for correlations. Even now, we are only on the threshold of understanding the tremendous role the Sierra Nevada has played in the geologic history of the West.

GENERAL GEOLOGIC RELATIONS

The Sierra Nevada is a huge block of the earth's crust that has broken free on the east along the Sierra Nevada fault system and been tilted westward. It is overlapped on the west by sedimentary rocks of the Great Valley and on the north by volcanic sheets extending south from the Cascade Range. A blanket of volcanic material caps large areas in the north part of the range.

Most of the south half of the Sierra Nevada and the eastern part of the north half are composed of plutonic (chiefly granitic) rocks of Mesozoic age. These rocks constitute the Sierra Nevada batholith, which is part of a more or less continuous belt of plutonic rocks that extends from Baja California northward through the Peninsular Ranges and the Mojave Desert, through the Sierra Nevada at an acute angle to the long axis of the range, and into western Nevada; it may continue at depth beneath the volcanic rocks of the Snake River Plains and connect with the Idaho batholith.

In the north half of the range the batholith is flanked on the west by the western metamorphic belt, a terrane of strongly deformed and metamorphosed sedimentary and volcanic rocks of Paleozoic and Mesozoic age. The famed Mother Lode passes through the heart of this belt. Farther south, scattered remnants of metamorphic rock are found within the batholith, especially in the western foothills and along the crest in the east-central Sierra Nevada. The batholith extends eastward to the east edge of the range, but in the south half of the range one can look eastward across Owens Valley to the wall rocks on the east side of the batholith making up the White and Inyo Mountains.

The story of the Sierra Nevada is in four overlapping parts: (1) a long period in the Paleozoic when the area was mostly under the sea receiving sediments; (2) a shorter period during the Mesozoic when the Paleozoic strata were downwarped into a gigantic complexly faulted synclinorium which was filled with contemporaneous volcanic and sedimentary detritus, strongly deformed, intruded repeatedly by granitic masses, and eroded to a depth of 9 to 17 miles; (3) a period of relative stability in the early Cenozoic; and (4) a period of uplift, tilting, and faulting, preceded and accompanied by volcanic activity, in the late Cenozoic.

MILESTONES OF GEOLOGIC STUDY

The early literature of the Sierra Nevada is replete with the names of geologic "greats" who were lured into attacking some of its vexing problems—names such as John Muir, J. D. Whitney, Clarence King, Joseph Le Conte, A. C. "Andy" Lawson, Adolph Knopf, Waldemar Lindgren, F. L. Ransome, W. H.

* Publication authorized by the Director, U.S. Geological Survey. Bateman prepared the parts of the report that deal with the bedrock geology and Wahrhaftig the parts that deal with the Cenozoic geology.

Turner, and François Matthes. The first geologic studies were begun a little more than a hundred years ago by the Geological Survey of California, headed by J. D. Whitney. In the Sierra Nevada, geologists of the "Whitney Survey" devoted their attentions chiefly to the "gold belt" of the metamorphic western foothills and to reconnaissance of the still largely unknown higher granitic country to the east and southeast (Whitney, 1865). In 1886 Waldemar Lindgren and H. W. Turner, under the direction of G. F. Becker, were assigned by the U.S. Geological Survey to study the "gold belt," and between 1894 and 1900 Lindgren and Turner, together with F. L. Ransome who had joined them later, published 12 regular folios and 1 special folio, which together are known as the "gold belt" folios (Lindgren, Turner, and Ransome, 1894–1900). In terms of the time expended in fieldwork and report preparation measured against magnitude and value, these folios are truly a remarkable achievement. They were followed, in 1911, by Lindgren's report, "The Tertiary gravels of the Sierra Nevada." In 1915 Adolph Knopf undertook a study of the Mother Lode System (Knopf, 1929); in 1932 H. G. Ferguson and R. W. Gannet published on the gold quartz veins of the Alleghany district; and in 1940 W. D. Johnston published the results of a study of the Grass Valley gold district.

These publications provided much information on the character and distribution of the rocks in the western metamorphic belt, but the extremely complex stratigraphy and structure of the belt remained obscure. N. L. Taliaferro made some progress in unraveling the structure and stratigraphy, chiefly by applying criteria indicating the top directions of beds (1943), and the continued use of these criteria to determine the order of superposition has been a principal tool in most subsequent work (Clark, 1964). Recently students at the University of California at Berkeley have applied statistical methods of structural analysis to selected small areas (Parker, 1961; Baird, 1962; Best, 1963; Christensen, 1963), and this technique also aids in building up a knowledge of the structure and stratigraphy.

Adolph Knopf's study in 1912 and 1913 of the eastern Sierra Nevada and the Inyo Mountains (1918) was the first publication to deal with a large area of the Sierra Nevada batholith. Even though a reconnaissance study, it showed that the batholith is composed of many separate granitic intrusive bodies and clearly pointed the way for further work. Even earlier, probably prior to 1910, H. W. Turner had mapped parts of the Yosemite and Mount Lyell 30-minute quadrangles, which together span the batholith, but the mapping was never completed. Turner's maps did serve, however, as the start for a bedrock map of the Yosemite region that was prepared by F. C. Calkins (1930) in connection with a study of its physiographic development by François Matthes. Calkins' map accurately shows the separate granitic intrusive rocks in the Yosemite region, and his brief accompanying text includes descriptions of field relations that establish the sequence of intrusion. This map served as the base for Ernst Cloos' (1936) well-known study of the primary structures of the granitic rocks, "Der Sierra Nevada pluton," and also provided a test for age determinations of rocks by the potassium-argon (K-Ar) method (Curtis and others, 1958).

In 1934 E. B. Mayo published the results of studies in the Laurel and Convict Basins of the eastern Sierra Nevada, and in 1937, 1941, and 1947 he published the results of reconnaissance structural studies of the granitic rocks of the eastern Sierra Nevada.

Just before World War II, Durrell (1940) and Macdonald (1941) published reports that deal with sizeable areas in the western foothills south of the western metamorphic belt. These authors were concerned primarily with the structure and metamorphism of the metamorphic rocks, but also made an effort to distinguish the different granitic rocks. About the same time, Miller and Webb (1940) published a map and description of the Kernville 30-minute quadrangle in the southern part of the Sierra Nevada. Somewhat later Ross (1958) published a report on the bedrock geology of a part of Sequoia National Park, and Hamilton (1956a, 1956b) published the results of studies in the Huntington Lake area of the central Sierra Nevada.

During World War II, geologists of the U.S. Geological Survey investigated the tungsten deposits of the Sierra Nevada, and at the end of the war undertook regional studies of some of the more productive areas in the central Sierra Nevada. Noteworthy reports and maps dealing with the geology of the central part of the range are those of Krauskopf, 1953; Rinehart and Ross, 1957, 1964; Bateman, 1956, 1965; Moore, 1963. In 1963 the geologists of the U.S. Geological Survey then working in the Sierra Nevada published a synthesis of the geology of the central part of the Sierra Nevada batholith between parallels lat 36°45′ and 38°00′ N., where the Survey has made most of its studies and is continuing its investigations (Bateman and others, 1963). This report includes documentation supporting the hypothesis held by many geologists that the batholith is intruded into the axial region of a synclinorium. Important studies of the satellitic intrusive bodies in the western metamorphic belt have been made by Hietenan (1951), Compton (1955), and Best (1963). Studies of the Sierra Nevada made since the late 1950's have been aided by the new methods of dating granitic and volcanic rocks isotopically (Curtis and others, 1958; Kistler and others, 1965; Hurley and others, 1965).

The study of the Cenozoic rocks of the Sierra Nevada began at an early date for the practical reason that the gold-bearing gravels in the stream beds and on interstream divides are of Cenozoic age. The flood of miners during the Gold Rush of 1849 quickly exhausted the rich placers along the riverbeds and spread over the flat ridgetops, where high gravels were found and prospected. As early as 1849, P. T. Tyson, a geological traveler, inferred from these high gravels 2,000 feet of Tertiary uplift in the Sierra Nevada (Whitney, 1880, p. 66). J. B. Trask, M. D., the first State Geologist, in a report published in 1853, described the mining of these high bench gravels and deduced from their distribution that they had been deposited by an ancient stream flowing northward athwart the present drainage.

Mining of these bench gravels was probably the major industry of the State during the latter decades of the 19th century. The gravels were mined by two methods. Where exposed they were "hydraulicked" by playing jets of water under high pressure upon the gravel banks and washing the dislodged material through sluice boxes, where the gold was trapped on riffles and the waste was discharged into the present stream beds. Where thick volcanic overburden made hydraulicking impracticable, mining was conducted by driving horizontal tunnels, called drifts, through the gold-bearing gravel at the base of the channels. Needless to say, the ability to predict the course and slope of the gravel channels, and particularly of the gold-bearing "leads" at the base of the gravels, was of immense importance to the miners, and the scientific study of the auriferous gravels began early. This study was promoted, in turn, by the great wealth of exposures and information that was made available as the hydraulic mines ate away at the banks of gravel, exposing the ancient river beds, and as the drift mines explored the courses of the ancient rivers beneath their volcanic cover. In the areas downstream from the mines the hydraulic operation was immensely destructive of agricultural land and navigable channels, because of the vast quantities of gravel that were poured into the river systems; and hydraulicking was greatly curtailed by court action in 1884 and virtually ceased by 1905. Drift mining has been carried on sporadically until recent years, but its heyday of activity was the latter part of the 19th century.

The first great summary of the geology of the auriferous gravels was that of J. D. Whitney (1880) and was based largely on the investigations of the Whitney Survey of 1860 to 1874, although 2 years earlier Leo Lesquereux (1878) had published the results of his monumental study of the fossil plants of the auriferous gravels. Whitney's report contains a wealth of information on the distribution and character of the gravels as exposed up to that time, and also an extended discussion of the Calaveras skull, which was then regarded as the most convincing evidence for the existence of "Pliocene Man" in North America.

Joseph Le Conte (1880, 1886) concluded that the auriferous gravels indicated that the Sierra Nevada had been uplifted and titlted westward, while Whitney (1880, p. 317) contended that the Sierra had not been uplifted since the gravels were deposited. Ross E. Browne (1890) attempted the first scientific test of Whitney's and Le Conte's opposed theories by making a careful study of the auriferous gravels of the Forest Hill Divide and comparing the gradients of the variously directed segments of the ancient streambeds. Within the limits of error of the scanty information then available, he could find no significant difference in the slopes of the stream segments that trended in different directions, and he concluded, reasonably enough, that there had been no tilting of the Sierra Nevada since the gravels were deposited!

The systematic geologic mapping of the Gold Belt by Lindgren, Turner, and Ransome of the U.S. Geological Survey, between 1886 and 1900, included a study of the distribution and character of the Tertiary gravels and the volcanic rocks that overlie them. Lindgren's (1911) paper on the Tertiary gravels of the Sierra Nevada is still the standard work on Cenozoic history of the northern part of the range. An interesting sidelight of this paper is the final disposal of the question of the Calaveras skull, which had been causing controversy ever since it was discovered (Bret Harte, 1887). One of Lindgren's assistants, J. M. Boutwell, made a special trip to the discovery site and obtained from one of the original perpetrators the confession that it was a practical joke played upon a local physician and amateur scientist, thus confirming Bret Harte's estimate of the situation.

Since Lindgren's day, little geologic work has been done on the auriferous gravels, although the formations along the west edge of the foothills, into which the gravels are thought to grade, have been studied by Dickerson (1916), Allen (1929), Clark and Anderson (1938), and Creely (1955). The fossil floras from the gravels, originally studied by Lesquereux and Knowlton in collections whose stratigraphic relations were uncertain, have been recollected and restudied by Potbury (1937), MacGinitie (1941), Condit (1944a, 1944b) and Axelrod (1944). The few vertebrate remains that have been found have been studied by Wood (1960), VanderHoof (1933), and Stirton and Goeriz (1942).

Hard volcanic debris (generally rhyolitic ash flows and andesitic mudflows) that overlies and locally cuts off the auriferous channel gravels was called by the miners "cement" or "cement rock," but its volcanic origin was early recognized. Lava flows intercalated with the andesitic mudflows formed sinuous table mountains that excited the admiration of early California travelers and were described extensively in Whitney's reports. Between 1886 and 1900 Turner and Ransome did much petrographic work on the Cenozoic volcanic rocks, Ransome (1898) coining the term "latite" to describe the rocks of the Stanislaus Table Mountain. The volcanic formations of the northern Sierra Nevada were named by Piper and others (1939) and have been the subject of investigation by Durrell (1959), Curtis (1954), Wilshire (1957), and Slemmons (1953). Gilbert (1938, 1941) has investigated Upper Cenozoic volcanic rocks on the east side of the Sierra Nevada south of Mono Lake, and Thompson and White (1964) and Birkeland (1963) have investigated similar rocks north of Lake Tahoe.

Glaciation of the Sierra Nevada was recognized as early as 1863 by J. D. Whitney; shortly thereafter Clarence King and J. T. Gardiner, who were then also with the Whitney Survey, recognized extensive evidence of glaciation near Yosemite Valley. Both Whitney and King, however, maintained that the valley was structural in origin and not the result of glacial erosion. John Muir published in 1872, 1874, and 1880 a vivid account of the evidence for a glacial origin of Yosemite Valley (Colby, 1950), and Joseph Le Conte (1873) described evidence for glaciation in the northern Sierra Nevada.

I. C. Russell (1889)described the Quaternary history of the Mono Basin, and showed that the existing glaciers are not shrunken remnants of the Pleistocene ice sheets but formed after a period of complete disappearance of the ice. Glacial deposits are shown on the U.S. Geological Survey folios published between 1896 and 1900. H. W. Turner, in 1900, published a report on the Pleistocene geology of part of the Sierra Nevada, in which he concluded that Yosemite Valley is a river valley controlled by jointing but somewhat modified by ice. He also showed that there had been two periods of glaciation in the Sierra Nevada, separated by a long interglacial period. In 1904 A. C. Lawson mapped the extent of glaciers in the upper Kern Basin, and between 1905 and 1907 W. D. Johnston, who had been Russell's topographer, recognized in the Walker River drainage three glacial advances.

Modern work on the glacial geology of the Sierra Nevada began with the studies of François E. Matthes (1930, 1960, 1965) and Eliot Blackwelder (1931). Blackwelder recognized four glacial stages on the east side of the Sierra, and Matthes recognized three on the west side; although they consulted frequently in the field, they were unable to agree on a correlation across the Sierra Nevada. Later, W. C. Putnam mapped the moraines in the Mono Basin (1949, 1950) and the Rock Creek-McGee Mountain area (1960a, 1960b, 1962).

Birman (1954, 1964) traced glacial deposits from the upper San Joaquin on the west side of the range to Rock Creek on the east side, establishing a correlation. Sharp and Birman (1963) refined the later history of glaciation, adding two new glaciations. Subdivision along the east margin of the San Joaquin Valley using soil-stratigraphic techniques on the alluvium, which is largely of glacial outwash origin, promises to give a complete sequence of glaciations on the west side (Davis and Hall, 1959; Arkley, 1962a, 1962b; Janda, 1965a, 1965b).

The glacial chronology of the Truckee area has been mapped by Birkeland (1964) who also effected a tie with the lake stratigraphy of the Lahontan Basin by tracing catastrophic flood deposits from Lake Tahoe down the Truckee River canyon (1965).

Investigation of glacial geology is being continued by Birkeland in the Tahoe area, Malcolm Clark in the West Walker Basin, R. P. Sharp along the east side of the Sierra Nevada south of Bridgeport, R. J. Janda in the San Joaquin Basin, and J. H. Birman in Sequoia National Park.

The amount and time of uplift and tilting of the Sierra Nevada, and the date of the eastern boundary faulting, have been under investigation since the early work on the problem by Whitney, King, and Le Conte. In his 1911 paper, Lindgren summarized the evidence for uplift and tilting, and Louderback (1924) placed this uplift in late Pliocene time. Hudson (1955, 1960) questioned Lindgren's main conclusion—that the Sierra has been tilted as though it was a rigid block—and by his own method of calculation arrived at an amount of uplift much less than that of Lindgren. Axelrod (1957), from a study of the floras on the east side of the Sierra, concluded that in early Pliocene time the range could have been no higher than Lindgren claimed. The evidence for tilting in the Sierra Nevada has recently been reviewed by Christensen (1966) who also agrees with Lindgren.

As the auriferous gravels and extensive volcanic deposits are lacking in the Sierra Nevada south of the Tuolumne, geologists in the southern area have had to rely on physiographic evidence of uplift. A. C. Lawson (1904) recognized three stages of uplift and partial peneplanation in the Kern Canyon region. Knopf (1918) traced the ancient erosion surfaces recognized by Lawson northward along the east side of the range. Matthes (1930) found evidence for three stages of uplift and erosion in the Yosemite region and traced these into the San Joaquin drainage (Matthes, 1960). He also added to the erosion surfaces recognized by Lawson in the Whitney area (Matthes, 1937, 1965). Webb (1946) showed that the Kern Canyon fault had not been active in late Cenozoic time. Axelrod (1962; Axelrod and Ting, 1961) attempted to date the erosion surfaces in the Sierra Nevada by study of pollen-bearing sediments on them. Recently the validity of summit flats, benches, and nickpoints on stream profiles, as indicators of former base level and uplift, has been challenged by Wahrhaftig (1965e) who believes they can form in granitic terrane at any altitude independent of regional base level.

In the past few years, two techniques of dating and correlation have been applied to the volcanic rocks of the Sierra Nevada: potassium-argon dating (Evernden, Curtis, and Kistler, 1957; Dalrymple, 1963, 1964a, 1964b; Evernden, Savage, Curtis, and James, 1964; Dalrymple, Cox, and Doell, 1965), and dating by means of identification of the geomagnetic polarity epochs, which consist of intervals of about 0.7–1.5 million years during which the polarity of the earth's magnetic field was either as it is now (normal) or reversed (Doell, Dalrymple, and Cox, 1966). Used together to check each other, and as an extension of the costly potassium-argon dating by the relatively cheap paleomagnetic method, these techniques are providing new insights into the age of uplift and downcutting, the time of glaciation, and the nature of the deformation in the Sierra Nevada during Cenozoic time.

Interest in the crustal structure beneath the Sierra Nevada began in 1936 when Lawson published a paper "The Sierra Nevada in the light of isostasy." In a comment on Lawson's paper, Byerly (1938) inferred a root beneath the Sierra Nevada from delay in the arrival time at stations east of the range in response to earthquake waves that originated west and northwest of the range. Eaton (1963, p. 5805) has made seismic refraction measurements across the northern part of the range that indicate this root may extend to a depth of about 45 km near Lake Tahoe, and Eaton and Healy (1963) have made similar measurements across the high central part that indicate the root here extends to depths of at least 50 km. Mikumo (1965) has confirmed the existence and approximate depth of the root.

Extensive gravity measurements reported by Oliver (1960, 1965), Oliver and Mabey (1963), and Oliver, Pakiser, and Kane (1961) show eastward decrease in Bouguer gravity values by larger amounts than classical treatment of the data requires for isostatic equilibrium; part, and perhaps all, of the excess decrease reflects eastward decrease in the average density of the surface rocks.

Pakiser, Press, and Kane (1960) have investigated the structure of the Mono Basin east of the Sierra Nevada using gravimetric, magnetic, and seismic techniques, and Pakiser, Kane, and Jackson (1964) have similarly investigated the subsurface structure of the Owens Valley region. In 1964 Thompson and Talwani published two papers in which they presented an interpretation of the subcrustal structure of the Sierra Nevada and bordering regions.

Aeromagnetic maps of part of the western metamorphic belt (Henderson and Bass, 1953) and of Long Valley and northern Owens Valley (Henderson, White, and others, 1963) have been published, and others have been made but not published.

Wollenberg and Smith (1964) have begun study of the distribution of uranium, thorium, and potassium in the granitic rocks of the central Sierra Nevada, in order to determine the radiogenic heat yield of the surface rocks. In 1964 and 1965 several borings to measure heat flow were made by investigators of the U.S. Geological Survey and Harvard University, but none of the results was published by the end of 1965.

PREBATHOLITHIC "FRAMEWORK" ROCKS

The Sierra Nevada batholith was intruded into a framework of Paleozoic and early Mesozoic strata which are preserved in the walls of the batholith and in roof pendants, septa, and inclusions within the batholith (pl. 1). The rocks that form the west wall of the batholith are exposed in the western metamorphic belt, but the east contact of the batholith is hidden beneath surficial deposits of Cenozoic age. However, the composition, structure, and age of the eastern wall rocks are shown in a narrow belt of roof pendants that extends southeast from Bridgeport to Independence and in the White and Inyo Mountains east of Owens Valley. The Paleozoic strata indicate a transition from miogeosynclinal facies east of the batholith to eugeosynclinal facies west of the batholith. Most of the Mesozoic strata are eugeosynclinal, but a belt of roof pendants of possible Triassic age extending southeast from Huntington Lake contains miogeosynclinal strata (fig. 1).

Paleozoic Rocks

All the Paleozoic systems are represented in the White and Inyo Mountains east of the Sierra Nevada. There, 26,000 feet of fossiliferous strata of Paleozoic age rest with structural conformity on 13,000 feet of strata that have yielded no fossils and are presumed to be of late Precambrian age. The upper Precambrian and Lower Cambrian strata are composed of fine clastic sediments and carbonate rocks, chiefly dolomite in the Precambrian and limestone in the Lower Cambrian. The Paleozoic strata of Middle Cambrian and younger age are dominantly carbonate in the southern Inyo Mountains, but include some quartzite, siltstone, and shale. Northward the amount of siliceous and argillaceous clastic material increases, and the amount of carbonate decreases, particularly in the Mississipian and Pennsylvania strata.

Paleozoic rocks in the roof pendants of the eastern Sierra Nevada contain much smaller amounts of carbonate rock than those of the White and Inyo Mountains. They consist largely of fine-grained, thin-bedded siliceous hornfelses derived from siltstone, mudstone, and shale. Interbedded with the siliceous hornfelses are subordinate amounts of metamorphosed limestone, orthoquartzite that is locally calcareous, chert, and calcareous or dolomitic siltstone. The most complete Paleozoic section in the eastern Sierra Nevada is in the Mount Morrison roof pendant (fig. 1) and is more than 32,000 feet thick (Rinehart and Ross, 1964, p. 1). The lower part of the sequence contains fossils of Early to Middle or Late Ordovician age and consists of 19,100 feet of alternating thin-bedded siliceous and pelitic hornfels, marble, slate, metachert, and thick-bedded calcareous orthoquartzite. An upper part that contains fossils of Pennsylvanian and Permian(?) age consists of about 7,300 feet of siliceous hornfels and some limestone.

Through most of the length of the western metamorphic belt, Paleozoic strata occupy the eastern part of the belt and lie adjacent to the batholith, but north of lat 39° N. a narrow strip of Mesozoic strata lies between the Paleozoic strata and the batholith. The Paleozoic strata are generally in fault contact on the west

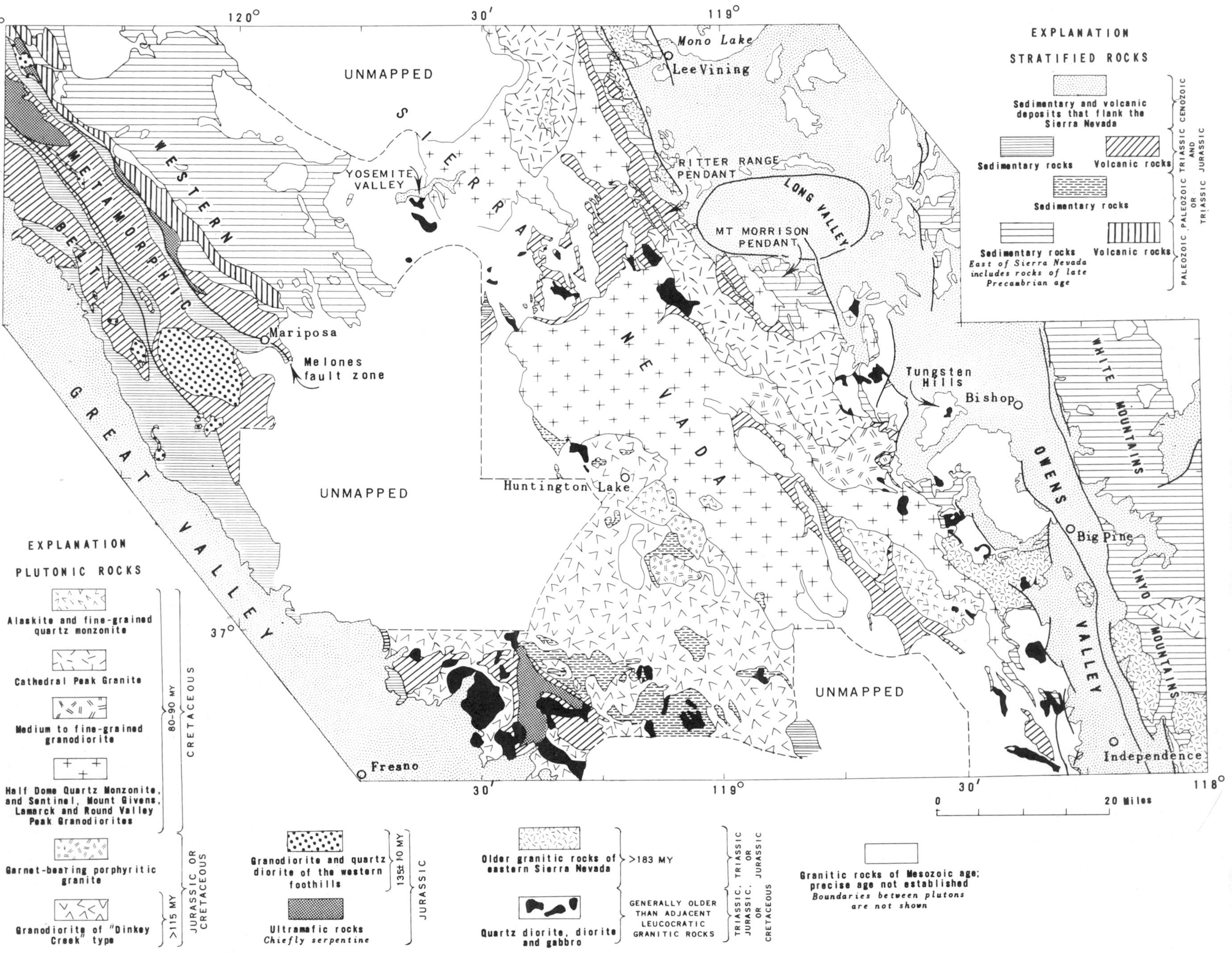

Figure 1. Geologic map across the central Sierra Nevada showing the distribution of the plutonic and metamorphic rocks. Modified from Pl. 1, U.S. Geol. Survey Prof. Paper 414D.

with Mesozoic strata. The Melones fault zone (Clark, 1964, p. 7) is the bounding structure in the south half of the belt, and a westerly branching strand of that fault is the bounding structure in the north half.

Most of the Paleozoic strata in the western metamorphic belt have been referred to the Calaveras Formation, which contains sparse fossils of Permian age in its upper part but which is predominantly unfossiliferous. In the Taylorsville region at the north end of the belt, Diller (1908) divided the Paleozoic strata into 11 formations, and McMath in the following article in this bulletin has recognized 8 formations above a thrust fault and 5 formations below, 4 of which are the same as those above the thrust. Fossils of Permian and Early Mississippian age have been collected from these rocks, and the stratigraphically lowest formation, the Shoo Fly Formation, is believed to be, at least in part, of Silurian(?) age (Clark and others, 1962). Farther south, in the vicinity of the American River, Lindgren (1900) divided the Paleozoic strata into five formations. Clark and others (1962) abandoned Lindgren's Blue Canyon Formation reassigning its rocks to the Shoo Fly Formation as defined in the Taylorsville area.

In the southern part of the western metamorphic belt, the most extensive Paleozoic rocks are black carbonaceous phyllite and schist with thinly interbedded chert, but lenses of mafic volcanic rocks and limestone are widespread and locally attain thicknesses of several thousand feet. In the northern part of the region, mafic volcanic rocks, slate, and sandstone constitute about equal parts of the Paleozoic section.

Mesozoic Stratified Rocks

Strata of Mesozoic age crop out in several northwest-trending belts that parallel the long axis of the batholith and the regional grain. In the eastern Sierra Nevada a group of roof pendants that contain Mesozoic strata extends for more than 150 miles. In the western metamorphic belt the most extensive Mesozoic strata lie along the west side, west of the Paleozoic strata, but a shorter and narrower strip lies between the north half of the strip of Paleozoic strata and the Sierra Nevada batholith. In addition, at least part of the miogeosynclinal strata in roof pendants that extend from near Huntington Lake for about 65 miles southeast through the heart of the batholith may be of Mesozoic age.

The Mesozoic strata in the belt of pendants through the east side of the batholith consist chiefly of metavolcanic rocks and graywacke-type sedimentary rocks that were derived chiefly from the volcanic rocks. These rocks weather gray and contrast strongly with the nearby hornfelsed miogeosynclinal Paleozoic strata, which weather reddish brown. Pyroclastic rocks of felsic to intermediate composition, which are the most common rocks, are interlayered with mafic flows and cut by hypabyssal intrusives. Thin beds of epiclastic rocks are sporadically scattered throughout the metavolcanic sequence. The thickest section of Mesozoic strata in the eastern Sierra Nevada is exposed in the Ritter Range roof pendant where about 30,000 feet of metamorphosed pyroclastic rocks of intermediate to felsic composition stratigraphically overlie rocks of Paleozoic age (Huber and Rinehart, 1965). The presence of graded beds, crossbeds, limestone lenses, ashflow tuffs, and accretionary lapilli indicates varied environments of deposition, including both subaqueous and subaerial. Early Jurassic fossils have been collected from a locality about 10,000 feet stratigraphically above the lower contact with Paleozoic rocks. Middle or Upper Jurassic or even Cretaceous strata may be present in the 20,000 feet of unfossiliferous strata that overlie the fossiliferous zone. A Permian age of 230 to 265 million years by the rubidium-strontium whole-rock method of age dating was reported by C. E. Hedge (U.S. Geol. Survey Prof. Paper 501, 1964, p. A114) for strongly foliated volcanic strata beneath the fossil zone; it suggests that Triassic rocks may be missing in this sequence and that volcanism may have begun before the end of the Paleozoic. However, in the southern Inyo Mountains about 1,800 feet of fossiliferous marine limestone and shale of medial Early to earliest Middle Triassic (early Anisian) age are overlain, possibly unconformably, by unfossiliferous interbedded continental volcanic and sedimentary strata that probably have a thickness in excess of 6,000 feet (Merriam, 1963, p. 28–31; N. J. Silberling, written communication, 1962), showing that volcanism did not begin there until Middle Triassic at the earliest.

All of the Mesozoic strata of the western metamorphic belt appear to have been deposited in a marine environment. The Mesozoic strata contain volcanics, as do the Paleozoic, and the differences between the rocks of the two systems are much less conspicuous here than in the roof pendants of the eastern Sierra Nevada. Both Triassic and Jurassic fossils have been collected from the western metamorphic belt, but Jurassic fossils are more common, and Jurassic strata are far more widespread than Triassic. The extensive belt of Mesozoic strata along the west side of the western metamorphic belt has yielded only Late Jurassic fossils, and the strata are generally considered to be restricted to the Late Jurassic (Clark, 1964, p. 15–31), although Eric and others (1955) and Taliaferro (1943) have allowed for the possibility that the Logtown Ridge and Cosumnes Formations, which constitute the Amador Group, may be in part of Middle Jurassic age. The belt includes sequences of epiclastic rocks, largely slate, graywacke, and conglomerate, commonly interbedded with volcanic rocks and in some places intertonguing with them. The graywacke and conglomerate of all formations are similar in composition; the most abundant clasts are volcanic rocks, slate, and chert, but fragments of metamorphic rocks, plutonic rocks, and quartzite are widespread. The various

Photo 1. The metamorphosed strata of the Sierra Nevada are complexly folded. A (above)—Gently plunging fold in hornfels and marble. B (below)—Chevron folds in tuffaceous slate.

volcanic formations also have many features in common; most are composed largely of andesitic(?) tuff and volcanic breccia, but basaltic lavas, in part having pillow structure, form thick sequences locally. Felsic volcanic rocks, such as occur in the Mesozoic of the eastern Sierra Nevada, are found locally but are uncommon.

In the Taylorsville region at the north end of the western metamorphic belt Upper Triassic strata are present (Diller, 1908), and, farther south at the American River, a lens of probable Triassic strata unconformably overlies the Shoo Fly Formation of Silurian(?) age and is unconformably overlain by the Sailor Canyon Formation of Early and Middle Jurassic age (Clark and others, 1962). The Upper Triassic strata of the Taylorsville region (Diller, 1908) consists of two formations, the Hosselkus Limestone and the Swearinger Slate, with a combined thickness of about 1,100 feet, according to McMath (this bulletin). Early to Late Jurassic marine strata of Mount Jura in the Taylorsville region have been divided by Crickmay (1933) into 14 formations with a combined thickness of about 13,000 feet. Farther south, in the vicinity of the American River, the Lower and Middle Jurassic Sailor Canyon Formation consists of at least 10,000 feet of graywacke, andesitic(?) tuff, and siltstone.

Structure of the "Framework" Rocks

The Paleozoic and Mesozoic strata of the Sierra Nevada have been complexly folded and faulted, and beds, cleavage, and lineations, including fold axes, are commonly steep or vertical (photo 1). A predominance of opposing, inward-facing top directions in the strata on the two sides of the range define a complexly faulted synclinorium. This synclinorium is not readily apparent in the patterns of geologic maps chiefly because strike faults of large displacement interrupt the sequence of strata in the western metamorphic belt. Apparently the axis of the synclinorium lies between miogeosynclinal Paleozoic strata on the east and eugeosynclinal strata on the west. The axial part of the synclinorium is occupied by the granitic rocks of the Sierra Nevada batholith. It trends N. 40° W. in the central Sierra Nevada, but probably bends to northward in the northern Sierra Nevada. The east side of the batholith follows approximately the east side of the volcanogenic and epiclastic Triassic and Jurassic strata. The eastern limit of the synclinorium is marked by a belt of Precambrian and Cambrian rocks that extends from the White Mountains southeastward into the Death Valley region and beyond. The western limit presumably lies beneath the Cretaceous and Tertiary strata of the Great Valley. An interesting speculation is that the sharply arcuate pattern of outcrops of Precambrian rock along the east and south sides of the Mojave Desert (pl. 1) may result from a southeastward continuation of the synclinorium.

From the belt of older rocks that extends between the White Mountains and Death Valley, the strata on the east side of the batholith are progressively younger westward. The range-front faults that bound Owens Valley and the east side of the central Sierra Nevada strike obliquely across the major structures in these Paleozoic and Mesozoic strata. The strata east of the White and Inyo Mountains, and in many remnants within the Sierra Nevada batholith, are strongly folded and faulted, causing repetitions of formations, but in the Mount Morrison and Ritter Range pendants of the eastern Sierra Nevada the gross structure is homoclinal, and bedding tops face west across more than 50,000 feet of vertical or steeply dipping strata ranging in age from Ordovician to Jurassic. Folds in the western part of the Ritter Range pendant may be related to the axial region of the synclinorium.

In the western metamorphic belt the gross distribution of strata resulting from the development of the synclinorium has been reversed by movement along steeply dipping fault zones of large displacement, and the Paleozoic strata lie between two belts of Mesozoic strata (see pl. 1). The internal structure of individual fault blocks is, in general, homoclinal, and most bedding tops face east; the dip of the beds is generally more than 60° eastward (Clark, 1964, p. 44). The homoclinal structure is interrupted in parts of the belt by both isoclinal and open folds, but the east limbs of anticlines commonly are longer than the west limbs, and the older strata in a fault block generally are exposed near its west side and the younger strata near its east side.

Unconformities have been recognized both within and between the Paleozoic and Mesozoic units, and they indicate repeated movement since middle Paleozoic time. The geometry of the structures of the "framework" rocks also indicates that the strata have been deformed either during several different episodes or during a single complex episode. Minor folds with steeply dipping axes are common and represent either refolding of earlier folds that were initially formed with subhorizontal axes or else folds that were formed in strata that had been previously so folded as to have steep dips. Some terranes contain two or more axial surfaces of systematically different orientation.

The Sierra Nevada lies within the Cordilleran mobile belt and its rocks reflect part of the deformation that has taken place there since mid-Paleozoic time. Probably the faulted synclinorium began to take form in Permian or Triassic time, and intermittent disturbances occurred through the Jurassic. The very severe disturbance that took place near the close of the Jurassic and caused the principal folds in the Upper Jurassic strata of the western metamorphic belt is referred to as the Nevadan orogeny, but both earlier and later disturbances are known to have occurred. Unconformities in the Taylorsville region indicate disturbances between the Silurian and Mississippian, and at the end of the Permian, Triassic, and Jurassic (McMath, this bulletin); and, in the eastern and central parts of the range, folds of two periods of deforma-

Photo 2. Contact between porphyritic and equigranular quartz monzonite.

tion antedate a third set that appears to have been formed during the Late Jurassic Nevadan orogeny. Kistler (in press) believes the earlier deformations occurred during the Late Permian and in the Early or Middle Triassic. In the western metamorphic belt, Clark (1964, p. 44) has recognized a stage of deformation that occurred after the principal folding of the Upper Jurassic strata. This deformation is characterized by the development of slip cleavage, steeply dipping minor folds, and steeply dipping lineations. Clark believes the large faults in the western metamorphic belt formed during this deformation, probably by strike-slip movement. The presence of ultramafic rocks, especially serpentine, along these faults suggests deep penetration, possibly penetration into the upper mantle.

The major deformation of the stratified rocks took place in parts of the range before the emplacement of the adjacent plutonic rocks, but locally plutons have been affected by regional deformation, indicating an overlap of the period of regional deformation with that of magma emplacement. For example, in the Goddard roof pendant of the east-central Sierra Nevada (fig. 1), a second deformation of the metamorphic rocks has affected plutons that were intruded after the first deformation. Farther west the eastern margin of the granodiorite of "Dinkey Creek" type, one of the largest plutons in the western Sierra Nevada, was intensely sheared and lineated before the emplacement of the Mount Givens Granodiorite which is the largest pluton in the central part of the range. Some of the plutons within the western metamorphic belt also were sheared during the second deformation.

The strata in the western metamorphic belt, except where adjacent to the batholith or smaller intrusive bodies, exhibit greenschist facies regional metamorphism. East of the batholith, in the White and Inyo Mountains, the only evidence of regional metamorphism is the presence of slaty cleavage in some pelitic and calcareous rocks. The strata adjacent to intrusive bodies and in remnants within the batholith are chiefly in the hornblende hornfels facies of contact metamorphism, although in the inner aureoles of some plutons that were intruded at unusually high temperatures the minerals sillimanite and brucite indicate the next higher pyroxene hornfels facies.

THE BATHOLITH

The batholith has been studied most intensively across the central part, between the 37th and 38th parallels of latitude (fig. 1), and much of the following discussion pertains specifically to that area (Bateman and others, 1963). However, the rest of the batholith appears to be very similar. The batholith is composed chiefly of quartz-bearing granitic rocks ranging in composition from quartz diorite to alaskite, but includes scattered smaller masses of darker and older plutonic rocks and remnants of metamorphosed sedimentary and volcanic rocks. Rocks in the compositional range of quartz monzonite and granodiorite predominate and are about equally abundant.

Mafic Rocks

The oldest and most mafic rocks of the batholith are small bodies of diorite, quartz diorite, and hornblende gabbro, which have been aptly called by Mayo (1941, p. 1010) "basic forerunners" or simply "forerunners." Their distribution is reminiscent of the metamorphic rocks, for they occur as small inclusions of small roof pendants within individual plutons or more silicic rock or as septa between plutons. Commonly they are associated with metamorphic rocks, and many are crowded with metamorphic inclusions. This intimate association with the metamorphic rocks probably results from the mafic plutonic rocks being the first to be emplaced, and consequently coming in contact with the metamorphic rocks on all sides. The original sizes and shapes of most masses were destroyed by later granitic intrusives, which tore them apart and recrystallized, granitized, and assimilated their fragments. Partly as a result of original differences, and partly because of subsequent modification, the mafic plutonic rocks are heterogeneous in composition and texture. Very likely they include rocks of diverse origin, some having been mafic volcanic or calcareous sedimentary rocks. Many bodies of dark granodiorite and some bodies of quartz diorite may be hybrids of more silicic granitic rocks and diorite, hornblende gabbro, or amphibolite. The fabric of these suspected hybrid rocks is generally highly irregular; some rocks are very coarse grained and in places contain poikilitic hornblende crystals an inch or more long.

Larger Features of the Granitic Rocks

The more leucocratic granitic rocks, which make up the bulk of the batholith, are in discrete masses or plutons, which are in sharp contact with one another or are separated by thin septa of metamorphic or mafic igneous rock. Individual plutons vary greatly in size; their outcrop area ranges from less than a square mile to more than 500 sq mi. The limits of many of the large plutons have not yet been delineated. On the whole the batholith appears to consist of a few large plutons and a great many smaller ones, which are grouped between the large plutons (fig. 1). All of the large plutons, and some of the smaller ones, are elongate in a northwesterly direction, parallel with the long direction of the batholith, but many of the small plutons are elongate in other directions or are rounded or irregularly shaped.

The major plutons in the western part of the batholith are generally older than those along the crest of the range, and in the Yosemite region Calkins (1930) has mapped two series of granitic formations in which the plutons are successively younger toward the east. Nevertheless, the pattern of intrusion is more complicated than a simple west-to-east sequence of emplacement.

Isotopic dates of plutons in the central Sierra Nevada indicate three widely separated epochs of plutonism at > 183 m.y. and probably no more than 210 m.y. (Late Triassic or Early Jurassic), 124–136 m.y. (Late Jurassic), and 80–90 m.y. (early Late Cretaceous). In addition, one large plutonic formation in the western half of the batholith, granodiorite of "Dinkey Creek" type (fig. 1), is at least 115 m.y. old, but may not be as old as Late Jurassic. The ages of many mapped plutons have not been established in terms of meaningful isotopic dates, and some plutons may have been emplaced in epochs of magmatism that have not yet been recognized. Although it is possible that the isotopic dates are simply points along a period of continuous magmatism, it is difficult to conceive of a parent magma continuing to exist for more than 100 m.y. It seems more likely that magma was generated at intervals within this time span.

The isotopic dates, together with intrusive relations observed in the field, indicate that plutons of similar ages are distributed not haphazardly but in geographic belts. The plutons of Late Triassic or Early Jurassic age lie along the east side of the batholith, and they may be closely related to isolated plutons of about the same age span farther east and southeast in the Inyo and Argus Mountains (Ross, 1965, p. O46–O48; Hall and MacKevitt, 1962, p. 30–31). Plutons of known Late Jurassic age in the central Sierra Nevada are confined to the western metamorphic belt, and it is likely that some plutons in the west side of the batholith are also of that age. The Late Cretaceous plutons constitute a belt, which averages about 25 miles in width, extending along and just west of the Sierran

Photo 3. Intrusive breccia. A (left)—Fragmentation of metamorphic rock by granitic magma. B (right)—Fragmentation of early quartz diorite by later quartz monzonite.

Photo 4. Felsic dikes in hornblende gabbro. Parent to dikes is quartz monzonite in foreground.

crest. This belt is interrupted south of Yosemite by a cross septum of metamorphic and pre-Late Cretaceous plutonic rocks, which provides a window into an earlier period in the development of the batholith.

Bateman and others (1963, p. D38) have listed ten relations, which taken together indicate that the major part of the granitic rocks crystallized from melts. These include such relations as sharp contacts of plutons with wall rocks and with one another, dikes and inclusions along contacts between plutons from which the relative ages of the plutons can be determined with consistent results, finer grain size in apophyses and in the margins of some plutons, wall-rock geometry that suggests dislocation by the emplacement of plutons, and dilated walls of aschistic dikes. The plutons are pictured as having moved upward from a deeper source region, much like salt domes, because molten granitic magma has a significantly lower specific gravity than rock of the same composition. As the plutons rose, the country rock is believed to have settled downward around the magma, thus providing room for its continued upward migration. Conceivably, some plutons may have become entirely detached from their source region and be underlain by country rock, but no field evidence for downward bottoming of plutons has been found.

The relative importance of several processes in the emplacement of the plutons has been only incompletely evaluated. Wall-rock deformation indicates that rising magma squeezed the wall and roof rocks aside and upward. Stoping appears to have been important locally, but there is little evidence in support of stoping as the principal mechanism of emplacement. Processes of granitization and assimilation have operated on a small scale where the wall and roof rocks were amphibolites or other mafic rock, but these processes are of possible quantitative importance only in terranes of mafic volcanic rocks. Melting and assimilation of pelitic rocks has not been proved, but very likely has taken place and may have been of considerable importance.

Broad chemical and mineralogic changes take place across the batholith. In general, the granitic rocks are

Photo 5. An exceptional abundance of K-feldspar phenocrysts in the marginal part of a pluton of prophyritic quartz monzonite.

more mafic toward the west and more silicic toward the east, but this is a gross trend, and some silicic plutons occur in the western half of the range and some mafic plutons are within the eastern half. The simple explanation that the more felsic rocks in the east half of the range are differentiates of the more mafic rocks in the west half does not hold for several reasons: (1) Lengthy time gaps probably exist between the different age groups. (2) Large granodiorite and quartz diorite plutons in the west half of the range are accompanied by younger and more felsic plutons, which are older than the large granodiorite and quartz monzonite plutons in the east side of the range. (3) The limited analytic data now available indicate systematically lower K_2O/Na_2O ratios in the Jurassic granitic rocks of the western part of the range than in either the Cretaceous or the Early Jurassic or Late Triassic rocks farther east.

Textures of the Granitic Rocks

The granitic rocks of the central Sierra Nevada have been grouped into formations and less formal units on the basis of similarity of composition, texture, and intrusive relations or other evidence of relative age (Bateman and others, 1963, p. D13). Each of the granitic rocks is characterized by a "typical appearance," which is determined largely by grain size, content of dark minerals, and texture. Except for uncommon local variants the granitic rocks are medium grained; hypidiomorphic-granular; equigranular, seriate, or porphyritic; and contain 2 to 20 percent of dark minerals.

The average grain size of most nonporphyritic rocks, and of the groundmass of the commoner porphyritic ones, is from 1 to 5 mm. Phenocrysts range widely in size; some K-feldspar phenocrysts are several inches long. Grain size is partly dependent on the size and shape of the pluton; the average grain size of large plutons is generally greater than that of smaller ones of the same composition. Equigranular rocks are commoner than porphyritic or seriate ones, but rocks with all three textures are well represented.

Photo 6. Flattened mafic inclusions in granodiorite.

The porphyritic rocks can be placed in two groups, those with phenocrysts of K-feldspar and those with phenocrysts of other minerals but none of K-feldspar. The phenocrysts of larger plutons generally are K-feldspar, whereas those in finer grained dikes, marginal rocks, and apophyses are generally minerals that crystallized early, such as hornblende or plagioclase. Phenocrysts of K-feldspar are largely restricted to rocks of intermediate to calcic quartz monzonite or potassic granodiorite composition. They cannot be explained in the same way as phenocrysts of most other minerals, which are formed early, because their many inclusions of other minerals show that they formed during the later rather than the earlier stages of crystallization. Nevertheless, dimensional orientation of K-feldspar phenocrysts near external contacts and in dikes shows that they were formed before the complete consolidation of the granitic rock. The presence of K-feldspar porphyroblasts in certain wall rocks and inclusions, which appear to be exactly like K-feldspar phenocrysts in contiguous granitic rock indicates pressure-temperature conditions like those in the magma, but does not indicate that the phenocrysts in granitic rock are porphyroblasts.

Mafic Inclusions

Many granitic rocks of mafic quartz monzonite, granodiorite, or quartz diorite composition contain mafic inclusions, which have greatest dimensions of a few inches to a few feet. In any given area the inclusions are generally all of about the same size and shape, but both size and shape vary from pluton to pluton and even from place to place within the same pluton. Commonly the mafic inclusions appear elongate in outcrop and are disc-shaped in three dimensions, but in some places they are subrounded or irregular in shape. Probably many are triaxial, but the difference between the two axes that lie in the plane of flattening generally is too small to determine. Spindles have been reported, but in most places they have resulted from postconsolidation cataclastic deformation (photo 6).

In many plutons mafic inclusions are progressively flatter toward the margins of the pluton—a relationship that suggests the inclusions were soft when they were suspended in the granitic magma and were shaped by movements of the magma. To obtain disclike shapes probably requires stretching in all directions parallel to the disc, and could occur in the marginal part of a pluton during emplacement as a result of growth brought about by the continuing introduction of magma into the central part of the pluton. Triaxial mafic inclusions could result from unequal stretching in the plane of flattening.

Mafic inclusions are present in quantity only in the granitic rocks that contain hornblende, although not all hornblende-bearing granitic rocks contain mafic

Photo 7. Joints in granitic rocks. A (above)—Deep slot eroded along joint in coarse-grained quartz monzonite. B (opposite)—Closely spaced orthogonal joints in medium-grained alaskite.

Photo 7B.

inclusions. Where the composition of a pluton changes and becomes more felsic, both hornblende and mafic inclusions may disappear. For example, many concentricially zoned plutons contain abundant hornblende and strongly flattened mafic inclusions near their margins but are free of both hornblende and mafic inclusions in their interiors. This relationship suggests strongly that mafic inclusions were stable only in magmas in which hornblende also was stable.

Primary Foliation and Lineation

Many of the granitic rocks are conspicuously foliated, and in others foliation can be determined by careful observation, but some felsic quartz monzonites and alaskites have no megascopically discernible foliation. Foliation is shown by flattened mafic inclusions and by the preferred orientation of tabular and prismatic minerals. Where both flattened inclusions and minerals with preferred orientation are present in the same pluton, they define foliations that are grossly parallel. However, the foliation defined by the preferred orientation of minerals may show minor irregularities that are not reflected in the foliation defined by the mafic inclusions. The preferred orientation of minerals doubtless results from the same movements of the enclosing magma that shaped the mafic inclusions, but because the minerals are smaller than the inclusions they were more sensitive to minor or local movements within the magma. Linear structure is best shown by preferred orientation of elongate minerals, especially hornblende, but in a few places is shown by a systematically longer direction within the plane of flattening of the mafic inclusions.

Compositional Zoning Within Plutons

Some granitic plutons are obviously compositionally zoned, and others not obviously zoned are found on careful study to show systematic variation in composition from place to place. Compositional zoning is shown by variations in the amount of all of the major constituents, but is most readily evident in the field from variation in the content of mafic minerals. The simplest and best method of determining zoning in the laboratory is to measure the specific gravities of systematically collected hand specimens. Zoning is generally either concentric or lateral. Concentrically zoned plutons generally are more felsic in the cores and more mafic toward the margins. Laterally zoned plutons are more felsic toward one side or one end—more commonly toward one end. Some very large plutons exhibit patchy or streaky zoning. Some compositional zoning can be related to contamination by wall rocks, but much zoning, particularly concentric zoning, is independent of the composition of the wall rocks and probably represents differentiation processes within the magma. Much work remains to be done in defining the mineralogical and chemical changes that take place in plutons, in relating these changes to field observations of wall rocks and inclusions, and in interpreting these with the aid of pertinent experimental studies of melts of granitic composition.

Regional Joints

A regional system of conjugate joints is conspicuous in the eastern Sierra Nevada but indistinct in the western part of the range. These joints dip steeply and are not to be confused with the gently dipping sheeting that is subparallel with topographic surfaces and doubtless related to the physiographic development of the landscape; nor are they to be confused with cooling joints, which can be identified only where occupied by dikes and dike swarms. In the eastern part of the range joints are strongly reflected in the topography in many places. On the floors of glaciated valleys and basins, and in regions of low relief, such as the Tungsten and Alabama Hills at the base of the eastern escarpment, linear depressions follow joints; even in deeply dissected regions straight segments of streams commonly are joint controlled. Detailed examination of a few areas in the western part of the range reveals that joints also are common there but are indistinct and not reflected in the topography. Why joints are more conspicuous in the eastern than in the western part of the range has not been satisfactorily explained. One possibility is that the development of sheeting may tend to suppress the opening of steep joints. For example, the magnificent domes of the Yosemite regions owe their forms to exfoliation sheeting and to the fact that steep joints have not opened. Domes are notably lacking east of the Sierran crest where joints are conspicuous. Another possibility is that the steep eastern escarpment provides a free face that permits joints to open toward it.

The joints are regional and are not confined to specific plutons—they cross boundaries between plutons, commonly with little or no deflection. Generally it is possible to identify two principal sets almost at right angles, one set striking northeast and the other northwest. The direction of strike changes somewhat from place to place; where this occurs, the strike of both sets generally changes so as to maintain the right-angle relationship.

Commonly the joints in a given set are nearly parallel, but in some places nearly parallel joints cross one another. Most joints are straight or gently curved, and where a significant change takes place in the strike of a joint set, the joints of one strike generally interfinger with the joints of another strike. Some individual joints can be traced for several miles. The spacing between the joints ranges from less than an inch to hundreds or even thousands of feet. Regional differences in spacing exist, but within a given region the spacing of the joints appears to be primarily a function of the average grain size of the rocks—the widest spacing is in the coarsest rocks. Thus the spacing of joints developed under constant stress conditions is roughly proportional to the number of mineral entities between joints. The most conspicuous joints are widely spaced, because where the joints are closely spaced the rock breaks into rubble, and systems of linear depressions do not form.

The facts that the joint pattern is regional and that the joint sets are continuous across boundaries between plutons indicates that the joints formed after consolidation of the entire batholith. The joints are also pre-Eocene in age, because the thick zone of weathering in the granitic rocks beneath the Eocene auriferous gravels extends downward into the unweathered rock along the joints. Furthermore, dikes of andesite, feeders to the Miocene and Pliocene Mehrten Formation, are intruded along the joints.

SPECULATIONS ON THE ORIGIN OF THE BATHOLITH

The localization of the batholith in the axial region of a synclinorium of great size and depth compels serious consideration of the hypothesis that the granitic magmas were generated by the melting of sialic rocks of the upper crust as a result of their being depressed into deeper regions of high temperature. Experimental studies show that at atmospheric pressure sialic rocks begin to melt fractionally at 960°C, but that an increase in water-vapor pressure causes the melting temperature to drop spectacularly (Tuttle and Bowen, 1958). At pressures above 1 kilobar and in the presence of enough water to saturate any amount of magma that may be generated, melting begins at temperatures between 600° and 700°C, the temperature varying inversely with the pressure. If certain other substances, such as fluorine or chlorine, are present, the temperature at which melting begins is lowered further.

The first melt is composed chiefly of normative quartz, orthoclase, and albite, in proportions that are different at different pressures of water vapor; this melt probably is saturated or nearly saturated with water. To form more calcic magma more of the source rock must be melted, which requires higher temperatures. To form magma of quartz diorite composition requires a temperature increase of about 200°C above the temperature of the beginning of melting if the melt is water saturated, and more if undersaturated. Because the amount of water soluble in magma may be quite high (about 10 percent by weight at 5 kilobars) and because the source rock is unlikely to contain more than a few percent of water at most, magmas of quartz monzonite, granodiorite, and quartz diorite are probably undersaturated with water. These considerations indicate that a temperature of 1,000°C or more is required to produce a granitic magma with normative plagioclase of An_{40} composition.

The depth at which sialic rocks can be expected to melt to granitic magma is difficult to evaluate because our present knowledge of the generation and distribution of heat in the earth is still in a primitive state. In stable parts of the crust where all the heat is carried to the surface by conduction, temperatures of 600° to 700°C may be attained at depths of 30 to 50 km, but a temperature of 1,000°C may not be reached at depths twice as great. However, the situation in a downfolding synclinorium is not ordinary because the crustal rock is greatly thickened in the downfold. Sialic rocks generally produce more heat than basaltic rocks, and the heat production in a downfolded sialic layer thickened two or three times may be of sufficient magnitude to cause melting to occur in the lower part of the downfold (A. H. Lachenbruch, oral communication, 1965). Measurements of the heat being produced in the exposed framework rocks by radioactivity would make possible some limiting calculations, but have not yet been made. Another possible source for heat is by upward movement of hotter material from deeper levels either by intrusion or by convection within the mantle. Convection currents in the mantle have been postulated by Vening Meinesz (1934), Griggs (1939), and many others in connection with the formation of deep geosynclinal troughs.

The model that emerges from these considerations is a magma zone that begins at a depth of 30 to 50 km and extends downward to the lowest level of depressed sial. At the top of the zone of melting, the ratio of hydrous felsic magma to solid rock is probably very small. If no migration of material occurs within the zone of melting, the ratio of magma to rock increases downward, and the melt is progressively less hydrous and richer in calcium, iron, and magnesium. Very likely, however, this model would be modified by diffusion of water from the hydrous upper part downward into the less hydrous lower part, and possibly also by convective circulation in the more completely fluid lower part, which would cause homogenization of the magma.

In terms of a developing synclinorium, the first magma would form when the lowest sialic rocks were depressed into the zone of melting. Further depression of these same rocks would cause additional melting to form a magma richer in calcium, iron, and magnesium, and poorer in water. At the same time, new magma would form at the top of the melting zone in higher rocks. Because the density of granitic magma is significantly less than granitic rock of the same composition, the magma would tend to work upward in the manner of a salt intrusion, exploiting lines of structural weakness wherever possible. Some magma would perhaps break through to the surface in volcanic eruptions, but much of it would crystallize at depth as plutons—which is what happened. Closely related sequences of granitic rocks that are successively more felsic with age and concentrically zoned plutons that are progressively more felsic toward the center indicate magmatic differentiation during emplacement from parent magma of granodiorite or quartz diorite composition. However, some compositional differences in genetically related sequences, especially among the volcanic rocks, may reflect differences in parent magmas formed at different depths in the zone of melting.

In the Sierra Nevada, the rocks that were melted doubtless included upper Precambrian, Paleozoic, and Mesozoic strata, but a major source of material probably was the underlying Precambrian. In the Death Valley region the Precambrian terrane is composed of quartzose and micaceous schist, amphibolite, and granitic gneiss. In addition to these sialic rocks, femic material from the lower crust and perhaps also the mantle must have been incorporated in the parent granitic magmas to supply the required calcium, iron, and magnesium, although upper Precambrian and Paleozoic carbonate formations like those exposed in the White and Inyo Mountains and in roof pendants of the eastern Sierra Nevada doubtless supplied some calcium and magnesium. Ultramafic and mafic intrusions in the western metamorphic belt, and basalt flows and hypabyssal intrusives, indicate that mafic material was introduced into the upper crust, and some of this mafic material must have been depressed with the enclosing rocks into the zone of melting; mixing of sialic and femic material could also have occurred at the base of the sial, in the zone of melting. Hurley and others (1963, p. 172) have determined the initial Sr^{87}/Sr^{86} ratio of the granitic rocks of the central Sierra Nevada to have been in the range of 0.7073 ± 0.0010; they deduced from this ratio that if the granitic magmas originated from a mixture of sialic and basaltic materials the ratio was one-third basalt and two-thirds sial.

The fact that the plutonic rocks in the east side of the range are both younger and more felsic than those in the west side seems compatible with differentiation processes within a single parent magma. However, Moore (1959, p. 206) has inferred from systematic difference in K_2O/Na_2O ratios that the rocks on the two sides of his quartz diorite line, which runs through the Sierra Nevada parallel with the long axis of the range, are derived from different parent magmas and are not differentiates of a single parent magma. This interpretation is supported by isotopic dates that suggest gaps of many millions of years between the time of emplacement of some of the largest plutons on the two sides of the range (Kistler and others, 1965). Furthermore, the Mesozoic volcanic rocks also are more felsic toward the east even though some, and perhaps most, of the eastern volcanic rocks are older than the western ones.

Moore (1959, p. 206) suggested that his quartz diorite line "is probably parallel to and not far distant from the edge of the granitic (sialic) layer in the continental crust," and that "granitic rocks emplaced east of the line are generated within a thick sialic layer, whereas those emplaced west of the line are developed within the sima or a thinner sialic layer with great thickness of associated geosynclinal sediments and volcanic rocks." Westward thinning of the sialic layer is in accord with interpretations of Bailey and others (1964, p. 7, p. 143, fig. 35 on p. 164) that the Franciscan Formation was deposited on an oceanic rather than a continental crust.

A reasonable interpretation of the compositional, geographic, and temporal relations of the granitic rocks is that magma was generated several times, each time in a somewhat different area as a result of shift in the locus of downfolding (fig. 2). The isotopic ages indicate three epochs of magmatism but do not preclude other epochs. The oldest epoch is represented by granitic rocks that lie along the east side of the Sierra Nevada and have isotopic ages of 200 ± 20 m.y. (Late Triassic or Early Jurassic). They are chiefly quartz monzonite and granodiorite and are not as mafic as the next younger granitic rocks of the western foothills, which are chiefly granodiorite and quartz

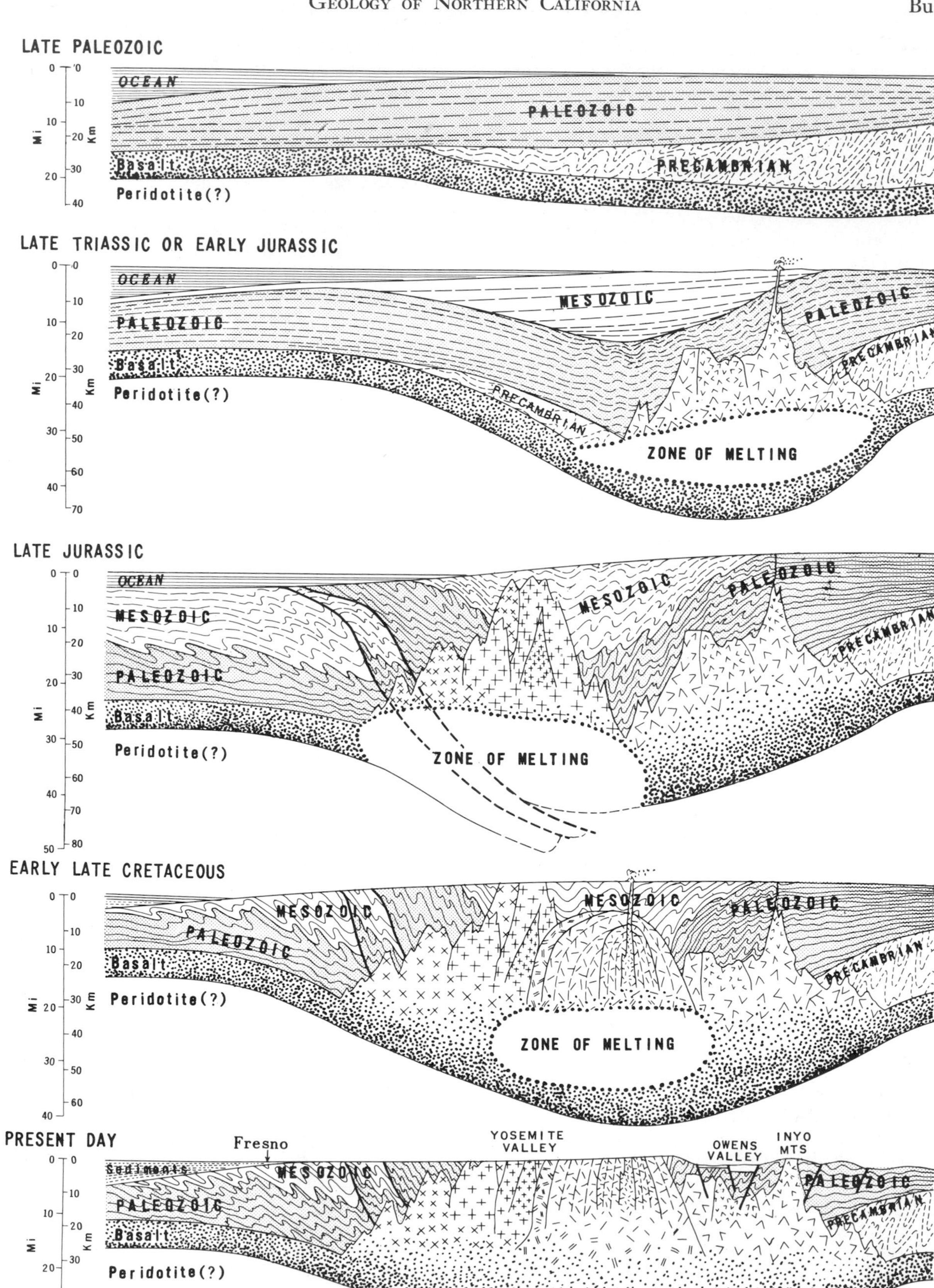
LATE PALEOZOIC
OCEAN
PALEOZOIC
Basalt
PRECAMBRIAN
Peridotite(?)
Mi
Km
LATE TRIASSIC OR EARLY JURASSIC
OCEAN
MESOZOIC
PALEOZOIC
PRECAMBRIAN
Basalt
Peridotite(?)
ZONE OF MELTING
LATE JURASSIC
OCEAN
MESOZOIC
PALEOZOIC
PRECAMBRIAN
Basalt
Peridotite(?)
ZONE OF MELTING
EARLY LATE CRETACEOUS
MESOZOIC
PALEOZOIC
PRECAMBRIAN
Basalt
Peridotite(?)
ZONE OF MELTING
PRESENT DAY
Fresno
YOSEMITE VALLEY
OWENS VALLEY
INYO MTS
Sediments
MESOZOIC
PALEOZOIC
PRECAMBRIAN
Basalt
Peridotite(?)
0 10 20 30 40 50 Mi
0 10 20 30 40 50 60 70 80 Km

diorite and have isotopic ages of 130 ± 10 m.y. (Late Jurassic). The youngest plutonic rocks are those along the crest of the range, which have isotopic ages of 80 to 90 m.y. (early Late Cretaceous), and are more felsic than the rocks to the west. These young rocks also may be more felsic than the Late Triassic or Early Jurassic rocks to the east, but before meaningful comparison can be made of these two groups more analytic data than are now available will be required, and the age assignments of plutons will have to be made more precise.

The picture envisaged is that the sialic upper crust was downfolded and thickened, possibly as the result of convective overturn in the earth's mantle, so that the lower part of the downfold was at or near the melting temperature of sialic rocks. Periodic deformation then caused further downfolding that produced magma in one part or another of the downfold, and the magma rose to form plutons and volcanic rocks.

If this hypothesis is correct, tectonic episodes should have immediately preceded and accompanied epochs of plutonism and volcanism. At the present time the data are permissive only, and the hypothesis cannot be tested until the times of plutonism and of tectonism have been more closely delineated. The only established temporal relation between tectonism and plutonism is that of the well-known Late Jurassic Nevadan orogeny to Late Jurassic plutonism. One of the older periods of deformation that have been recognized in the metamorphic rocks could well be temporally related to the Late Triassic or Early Jurassic plutonism, and deformation in the western metamorphic belt that occurred after the Nevadan orogeny could be an expression of tectonism at the time of the early Late Cretaceous plutonism, but these suggested relations have not been established.

Northwest and west of the Sierra Nevada, in the Klamath Mountains and northern Coast Ranges, Irwin (1964) has recognized two periods of deformation. One of these he identifies as the Late Jurassic Nevadan orogeny, and the other as a Late Cretaceous orogeny, which he designates as the Coast Range orogeny because of its "importance in development of the pre-Tertiary structure of the Coast Ranges." East of the Sierra Nevada, in western and southern Nevada, several periods of compressive deformation since Late Mississippian time are generally recognized, and some of them appear to have occurred at about the same time as the plutonic episodes of the Sierra Nevada.

Temporal correlations between plutonic and volcanic rocks may be possible at some future time, but at present all that can be said is that the volcanic rocks span most and perhaps all of the known epochs of plutonism. Volcanic rocks of Early Jurassic age have been identified in the eastern Sierra Nevada, and ones of Late Jurassic age have been identified in the western metamorphic belt, but most volcanic sequences are unfossiliferous, and their precise ages are unknown.

According to Eaton and Healy (1963) the crust beneath the high central Sierra Nevada is at least 50 kilometers thick, about twice as thick as the crust west of the range and 15 to 20 kilometers thicker than the crust beneath the Basin and Range province east of the range. Not only is this geophysical root centered beneath the highest peaks, at least in the central Sierra Nevada, but it also lies beneath the belt of Cretaceous plutons. These coincidences suggest that the root was formed by downfolding of the crust at the time of the early Late Cretaceous magmatism, and that uplift of the Sierra Nevada during the Late Cretaceous and Cenozoic was caused by a mass deficiency of the root. Negative isostatic anomalies (Oliver, 1960) and analysis of first-order leveling of the U.S. Coast and Geodetic Survey by Oliver (written communication, 1965) that indicates the central Sierran crest has risen during a 60-year period at the rate of about a centimeter per year support the concept of a net mass deficiency extending from the surface downward to some depth of compensation. A serious difficulty with this hypothesis is that an expectable consequence is continuous uplift, though at a steadily diminishing rate, until the root has disappeared. The geologic record indicates, however, that little or no uplift took place during an extended period of 25 to 30 million years that included much of Eocene and Oligocene time. Nevertheless, the Sierra Nevada has certainly been uplifted and deeply eroded, and a better explanation for the uplift than mass deficiency has not been devised.

Figure 2 (opposite). Cross sections illustrating a model for magma generation and emplacement in the Sierra Nevada. The sections are drawn in accordance with the discussion in the text.

DEPTH OF EROSION SINCE MESOZOIC PLUTONISM

In 1963 Bateman and others published a speculation that 11 miles (about 17 km) of rock has been stripped off the Sierra Nevada since the batholith was emplaced. To arrive at this speculation they inferred that the water-vapor pressure (P_{H_2O}) in the most highly fractionated magmas and in the thermally metamorphosed wall rocks was about 5 kilobars, and assumed that $P_{H_2O} = P_{load}$ (pressure equivalent to the weight of the overlying rocks). Since then, Putman and Alfors (1965) have inferred that the P_{H_2O} during crystallization of the Late Jurassic Rocky Hill stock in the western foothills was about 1.5 kilobars, and Sylvester and Nelson (1965) have inferred that the P_{H_2O} during crystallization of the Cretaceous Birch Creek pluton in the White Mountains was 2 to 3 kilobars. In both reports P_{H_2O} was considered to equal P_{load}.

Since Bateman and others' speculations were published much additional information has become available, some of which casts serious doubt on the validity of the assumption that $P_{H_2O} = P_{load}$. In view of this doubt, arguments that require making the assumption that $P_{H_2O} = P_{load}$ are excluded from the following discussion.

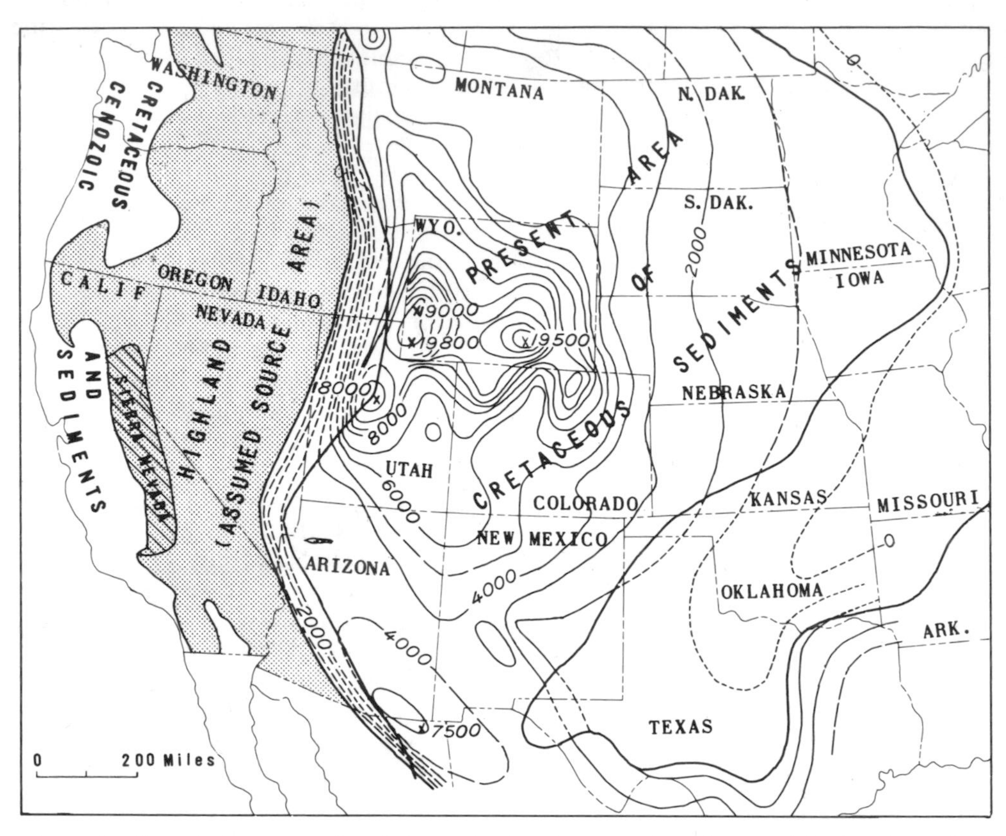

Figure 3. Map of the western United States showing the general distribution of land and sea during the Late Cretaceous. Isopachs show thickness of Cretaceous sediments in the Rocky Mountain geosyncline. Modified from two illustrations by Gilluly (1963).

Unfortunately, there is no simple way to measure the amount of rock that has been stripped away, and the problem can be attacked only indirectly. In the following discussion, two approaches are pursued: One is an evaluation of the volume of sediment of latest Jurassic, Cretaceous, and Cenozoic age that had its source in the Sierra Nevada, and the other is consideration of the significance in terms of load pressure of andalusite and sillimanite in thermally metamorphosed wall and roof rocks.

During the Cretaceous, the Sierra Nevada was part of a north-trending highland that lay between the Rocky Mountain geosyncline on the east and the Pacific coastal region on the west (fig. 3). According to Gilluly (1963, p. 146–147),

> "The Rocky Mountain geosyncline eventually came to hold more than a million cubic miles of dominantly clastic sediment, about five-sixths of it of Cenomanian (early Late Cretaceous) and younger age (Reeside, 1944; Gilluly, 1949). Only a relatively small part of this volume was of juvenile volcanic rocks; the overwhelming bulk was derived from erosion of older rocks. The ostensible source area, that is, a large part of the area between the Rocky Mountain geosyncline and the Pacific geosyncline, was only about 160,000 square miles—at the most generous estimate 200,000 square miles. If this were indeed the whole source, an average denudation of about 5 miles is implied. The bulk involved is tremendous; it is equal to that which would be furnished by slicing 1,600 feet from the entire area of the United States. While this volume was accumulating in the eastern part of the cordilleran region, clastic beds of comparable or perhaps even greater thickness were accumulating in the Pacific geosyncline, west of the Sierra Nevada."

The Cretaceous and Tertiary deposits along the Pacific Coast are chiefly epiclastic and in a large part were deposited in a geosynclinal environment. Unfortunately, discontinuity of exposures and strong deformation prevent calculating their volume from isopachs as Gilluly was able to do for the miogeosynclinal strata of the Rocky Mountain geosyncline. It seems safe to assume, however, that at least as much sediment collected in the Pacific coastal region as in the Rocky Mountain geosyncline.

A few volume estimates of local areas can be cited, but for most parts of the Pacific coastal region the data are inadequate for calculations of sediment volume. The Franciscan Formation of latest Jurassic and Cretaceous age is one of the thickest and most extensive formations. Bailey and others (1964, p. 21) state,

> "By far the most abundant rock of the Franciscan is graywacke, which has a truly astonishing volume. Even if the average thickness is regarded as only 25,000 feet [they estimate the thickness to be 50,000 feet], and the depositional area in California and offshore is about 75,000 square miles, the total volume of the Franciscan graywacke is more than 350,000 cubic miles."

In considering the source of the Franciscan, Bailey and others (1964, p. 146) state,

> "The source of the older, pre-Knoxville Franciscan seems most likely to be the ancestral Klamath Mountains and Sierra Nevada lying east of the depositional area. The source of some of the debris forming the younger Franciscan rocks probably also lay in

the same area, but it seems unlikely that this would have been the source of all the younger Franciscan rocks."

They offer two suggestions for the source of certain younger rocks which are essentially free of K-feldspar, an unknown western source, and cannibalism of uplifted older Franciscan rocks.

Calculations from isopach maps prepared by Repenning (1960) indicate that the volume of shelf and slope facies Cretaceous and Tertiary strata beneath the Great Valley is about 100,000 cubic miles. No estimates are available for the Cretaceous and Tertiary strata of the Coast Ranges exclusive of the Franciscan, but their volume may approach the volume of strata beneath the Great Valley. Thicknesses and volumes of Cretaceous and Tertiary marine strata in western Washington and Oregon are not as well known as in California, but are probably comparable. Thus the volume of sediment of latest Jurassic to Recent age in California is at least 550,000 cubic miles, and a volume of a million cubic miles for the entire Pacific coastal region of the United States does not seem out of line.

The total area of the highland that lay between the Rocky Mountain geosyncline and the Pacific coastal region within the boundaries of the United States was about 400,000 square miles. If the volume of latest Jurassic to Recent rocks along the Pacific Coast of the United States is taken to be equal to volume of sediments that accumulated in the Rocky Mountain geosyncline, and the total is figuratively redistributed over the intervening highland, they would bury it to an average depth of 5 miles. To convert volume of sediment to depth of rock eroded requires an adjustment for differences in the density, but need for this adjustment is more than offset by loss of almost all the very considerable volume of carbonate that was present in the source area, but present in small amounts in the depositional basins (Gilluly, 1963, p. 147). Doubtless much suspended and fine clastic material also was lost.

Undoubtedly some parts of the source area have been more deeply eroded than others. In the Sierra Nevada, isostatic adjustment following deep downfolding probably caused greater uplift and consequently deeper erosion than took place in central and eastern Nevada. If erosion of only the Sierra Nevada is considered, it seems reasonable to look at the epiclastic sedimentary rocks that lie directly to the west. The possibility of long shore drift of sediments and of movement along the San Andreas and other faults introduces very considerable uncertainty into the calculation, but the probability that the volume of sediment has been increased by faulting is less than that it has been reduced, for the San Andreas cuts off the Franciscan Formation on the southwest.

Most of the sediments that underlie the Great Valley undoubtedly were eroded from the Sierra Nevada, either directly or by the reworking of older deposits that were derived from the Sierra Nevada. If to the volume of sedimentary rocks beneath the Great Valley are added half the geosynclinal deposits of the Coast Ranges and half the Franciscan Formation, a conservative total of 325,000 cubic miles of sedimentary rocks are attributed to erosion of the Sierra Nevada. The Sierra Nevada is 400 miles long and averages about 80 miles wide if the downslope continuation of the range beneath the east side of the Great Valley is included, giving an area of about 32,000 square miles. Thus the volume of sediment attributed to erosion of the Sierra Nevada is sufficient to bury the range to a depth of more than 10 miles. This figure can be compared with an estimate by Little (1960, p. 99) that 35,000 feet of rock was eroded from the Nelson batholith of British Columbia during the Portlandian Stage of the Upper Jurassic and the entire Cretaceous; Little suggests that an equal amount was eroded during the Cenozoic.

The other approach to the problem of the amount of stripping is through consideration of the pressures during the thermal metamorphism of the wall and roof rocks implied by recent studies of the Al_2SiO_5 polymorphs contained in these rocks. In 1963, Bell reported the results of experimental studies of the stability of andalusite, sillimanite, and kyanite; and in the same year Khitarov and others published the results of studies of the same minerals and mullite plus quartz. The data contained in these two reports are in good agreement, and Waldbaum (1965) has prepared a composite plot from the tabulated data of Bell and Khitarov and others (fig. 4). The pressure and temperature at the triple point for andalusite, sillimanite, and kyanite are believed to be quite reliable, but the pressure and temperature at the triple point for andalusite, sillimanite, and mullite plus quartz are less well established.

In the Sierra Nevada, andalusite is a common aluminosilicate in the contact metamorphosed wall and roof rocks (Durrell, 1940, p. 44–45; Hietanen, 1951, p. 575; Rose, 1957, p. 642; Bateman, 1965, p. 24; Moore, 1963, p. 9–13), but in many places, especially adjacent to intrusive rocks, andalusite gives way to sillimanite (Knopf, 1917, p. 233–234; Durrell, 1940, p. 46–47;

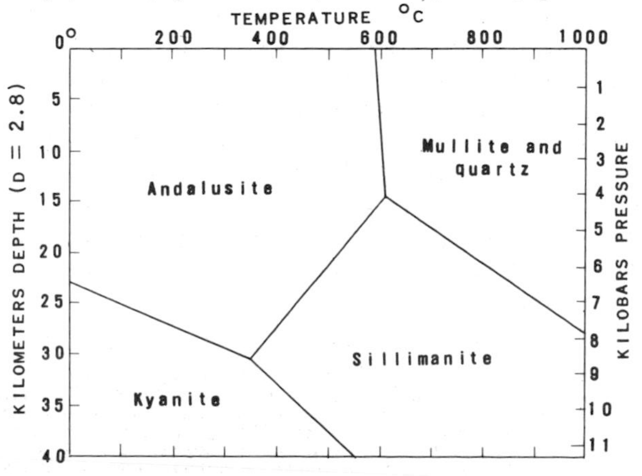

Figure 4. Fields of stability of andalusite and its polymorphs according to Waldbaum (1965). (Modified slightly.)

Rose, 1957, p. 642). These relations show that where andalusite occurs the pressure during metamorphism must not have exceeded the upper limit of its stability, which is about 8.6 kilobars according to the experimental data, and that where sillimanite also occurs the pressure must not have fallen below the lowest pressure limit of its stability, which is about 4 kilobars. The absence of kyanite suggests that the pressure was less than 8.6 kilobars—probably less than 7.5 kilobars.

The pressures involved in the formation of andalusite and sillimanite are total pressures and are not dependent on the presence or absence of water because the two minerals are polymorphs. Tectonic overpressures during metamorphism are unlikely because the metamorphism that produced both minerals was caused by magma, which should have relieved any significant overpressure by upward movement. If the pressures reflect the weight of the overlying rocks, as seems to be required, and if an average density of 2.8 is assumed, the limiting pressures of 4 and 7.6 kilobars correspond to limiting depths of 15 and 27 km (9 and 17 miles, respectively).[1]

Thus both lines of evidence followed here suggest erosion from the Sierra Nevada of the same order of magnitude as was suggested, perhaps fortuitously, by Bateman and others in 1963. The time span of this amount of erosion is the time since the Nevadan orogeny and intrusion of the Late Jurassic granitic rocks. The exposed early Late Cretaceous granitic rocks must have consolidated under less cover than the exposed Late Jurassic granitic rocks, and it may not be accidental that all occurrences of sillimanite thus far reported, with the possible exception of the sillimanite reported by Rose (1957), are along contacts with the older granitic rocks.

THE SUPERJACENT SERIES

On the deeply eroded metamorphic and granitic rocks of the Sierra Nevada rests a nearly flat lying sequence of sedimentary and volcanic rocks of Late Cretaceous and Cenozoic age, which Lindgren, Turner, and Ransome in their geologic folios called the Superjacent series. Where these rocks are found, they were deposited after the great depth of erosion described in the preceding paragraphs was completed. The early geologists believed that the unconformity at the base of these rocks represented a hiatus in the recorded history of the Sierra Nevada, but it now appears that Cretaceous sedimentary rocks were being deposited along the western margin of the range when the granitic rocks we now see along the crest of the range were being intruded.

The Superjacent series is most extensive, and the history it records most complete, in the northern Sierra Nevada north of the Tuolumne River. The most complete sequence is along the western foothills, where there are a few exposures of sandstone, conglomerate, and shale of the Late Cretaceous Chico Formation, a few exposures of early Eocene sandstone and shale, and much more extensive exposures of the middle Eocene Ione Formation, which consists of quartz-anauxite sandstone, kaolin-rich claystone, and coal, deposited during a brief period of almost tropical climate. The equivalent deposits within the range are the prevolcanic auriferous gravels. These indicate that erosion down to the present level of exposure of the granitic rocks was complete throughout the northern Sierra Nevada by middle Eocene time. Overlying the sedimentary formations are two sequences of volcanic rocks: (1) rhyolitic eruptives of Oligocene to middle Miocene age, and (2) andesitic mudflows, lavas, and conglomerate of late Miocene to late Pliocene age.

These formations bury a topography with as much as 3,000 feet of local relief, indicating that the Sierra Nevada was not reduced to a peneplain at the end of the great denudation. Many unconformities occur within the Superjacent series, but the general accordance of stream gradients of Eocene to Pliocene age indicates that during much of the Tertiary the Sierra Nevada was essentially stable. The Superjacent series also indicates that, beginning in the Pliocene, the Sierra Nevada was tilted westward and broken by a complex system of faults along its eastern margin. Uplift along the crest amounted to 4,000–7,000 feet.

The southern part of the range lacks an extensive superjacent cover like that found in the northern Sierra Nevada, but scattered remnants of basaltic flows and a few sedimentary deposits along the western margin record essentially the same story.

The history of the Sierra Nevada in Late Cretaceous and Cenozoic time depends on the interpretation of exposures at a few critical localities, for the superjacent deposits are now fragmentary. The sections that follow contain frequent references to these localities, which are shown on figs. 5 and 6.

Upper Cretaceous Rocks (Chico Formation)

Upper Cretaceous marine sedimentary rocks of the Chico Formation crop out along the west base of the Sierra Nevada in four main areas. In the extreme north, Cretaceous rocks are exposed resting unconformably on metamorphic rocks in the canyons of Big Chico Creek and other streams draining the south end of the Cascade Range just west of the Sierra. The thickest section, about 2,800 feet on Big Chico Creek, is the type locality for the Chico Formation, and consists of about 500 feet of conglomerate at the base, grading upward to arkosic wacke. It ranges in age from Coniacian to middle Campanian (Matsumoto, *in* Rogers, 1962).

---

[1] In early 1966, after this paper was in galley proof, D. F. Weill (Geochim. et Cosmochim. Acta, v. 30, no. 2, p. 223–238) and R. C. Newton (Science, v. 151, no. 3715, p. 1222–1225) published data that suggest the pressure at the andalusite-kyanite-sillimanite triple point is significantly less than is indicated by the data of Bell (1963) and Khitarov and others (1963). According to Newton, andalusite cannot be stable at a pressure greater than 4.2 kilobars, corresponding to a depth of 15 km (9 miles). Until the divergent experimental data have been reconciled, the pressure indicated by the coexistence of andalusite and sillimanite in the same terrane must remain in doubt.

The Chico is also exposed at Pentz, about 8 miles northwest of Oroville. About 5 miles east of the Pentz locality, the lowermost gravels of the Cherokee Hydraulic mine at the north end of Oroville Table Mountain consist largely of boulders and cobbles of greenstone from adjacent bedrock. The upper part of this "greenstone gravel" is a zone of rotted boulders and intercalated red clay, apparently a zone of deep weathering. Typical quartz-pebble auriferous gravel overlies this weathered zone. Allen (1929) and Creeley (1955) suggest that the "greenstone gravel" may correlate with the Chico in the Pentz area.

Two exposures of fossiliferous sandstone and shale of the Chico Formation have been reported by Lindgren (1894; 1911, p. 22) from the vicinity of Folsom. Here a few feet of sedimentary rocks, with a little gold-bearing gravel at their base, rest in depressions in the bedrock surface cut on granodiorite (K-Ar age, 136 m.y., R. W. Kistler, oral communication, 1965) and the Eocene Ione Formation and Pleistocene auriferous gravels overlie them.

About 400 feet of arkosic sandstone containing Cretaceous fossils was intersected in a boring about 5 miles south of Friant on the San Joaquin River (Macdonald, 1941, p. 259). Granitic rocks crop out 1½ miles to the northwest in the south end of Little Table Mountain at altitudes higher than the wellhead, indicating considerable relief on the pre-Cretaceous surface. About 8 miles northwest of the well and about 2 miles west of California Highway 41, a roadcut along the Friant-Madera Road contains an outcrop that may be the feather edge of the Cretaceous beneath the Eocene Ione Formation. In this roadcut, white and light-brown anauxitic sandstone typical of the Ione Formation rests on deeply weathered gabbro and metamorphic rocks. The weathered zone is characterized by thorough decomposition of the original minerals and by mottling in brilliant purple, red, and white—all colors characteristic of the tropical weathering profile at the base of the Ione Formation elsewhere. At the east end of this outcrop, the weathering profile is developed on dense structureless fine-grained material that contains rounded pebbles of quartz, chert, slate, and decomposed granitic and metamorphic rocks. This material is here interpreted as thoroughly decomposed pebbly arkosic beach or stream sand, of possible Late Cretaceous age, weathered before the Ione Formation was deposited.

The Cretaceous exposures described above indicate that the bedrock surface along the western margin of the Sierra Nevada was eroded to its present depth by Maestrichtian time at the latest, approximately 65 to 70 m.y. ago, and in part by Coniacian time, 85 to 90 m.y. ago.

Although biotite dates on the granitic rocks of the western Sierra Nevada range between 124 and 136 m.y., these dates have probably been reduced as a result of reheating by later intrusions, and this belt of granitic rocks was probably emplaced during the Portlandian stage of the Jurassic, 140 to 145 m.y. ago. Consequently between 9 and 17 miles of cover was eroded from the western Sierra Nevada in a time interval of between 55 and 80 m.y., or at a rate of ½ to 1½ feet per thousand years—a rate comparable with the highest rates of denudation measured today.

Lower Eocene Deposits of the Foothills

Allen (1929, p. 368–369) described a sequence of gray shale and biotite-rich sandstone along the banks of Dry Creek and near the west base of Table Mountain, 8 miles north of Oroville, which is about 80 feet thick and contains casts of *Corbicula*. These beds dip about 4° SW. and are overlain, apparently unconformably, by the Ione Formation. They are distinguished from the Ione by an abundance of detrital biotite, hornblende, and feldspar, minerals that are lacking in the Ione and believed to indicate that the climate during early Eocene time probably was not as tropical as during Ione time. Similar material from a shaft about 2 miles north of Oroville contained an early Eocene fauna equivalent to that of the Meganos Formation (Allen, 1929, p. 369).

Gray clay exposed at clay pits near Lincoln, which Allen (1929, p. 363) called the Walkup Clays, may correlate with the beds at Dry Creek. No exposures of these pre-Ione beds have been found farther south, but they have been penetrated in borings beneath the Ione Formation. In Jackson Valley, between Ione and Valley Springs, as much as 65 feet of sandstone similar to that on Dry Creek was encountered in boring into valleys as much as 400 feet deep that are buried by the Ione Formation (Pask and Turner, 1952). Farther west, between Lodi and Oakdale, several hundred feet of dark-gray biotite-bearing feldspathic sandstone and shale, with marine or brackish fossils of Eocene age, were encountered in deep wells (Piper and others, 1939, p. 85–86).

Ione Formation

The Ione Formation is exposed discontinuously along the west base of the Sierra Nevada from Oroville Table Mountain southward to Friant (Allen, 1929). Nearly everywhere it rests on a deeply weathered surface with a local relief of as much as 1,000 feet cut in crystalline basement (Allen, 1929; Pask and Turner, 1952).

Pask and Turner (1952) have shown that the Ione Formation consists of two members, separated by an erosional unconformity with as much as 130 feet of relief. The lower member is chiefly (1) sandstone consisting predominantly of quartz and large flakes of the clay mineral anauxite (kaolinite with excess silica) and with little or no feldspar, biotite, hornblende, or other heavy minerals; (2) clay beds consisting largely of kaolinite or halloysite; and (3) a few lignitic coal beds, ranging from a few inches to 24 feet in thickness. The upper member consists of sandstone with abundant feldspar and common biotite and

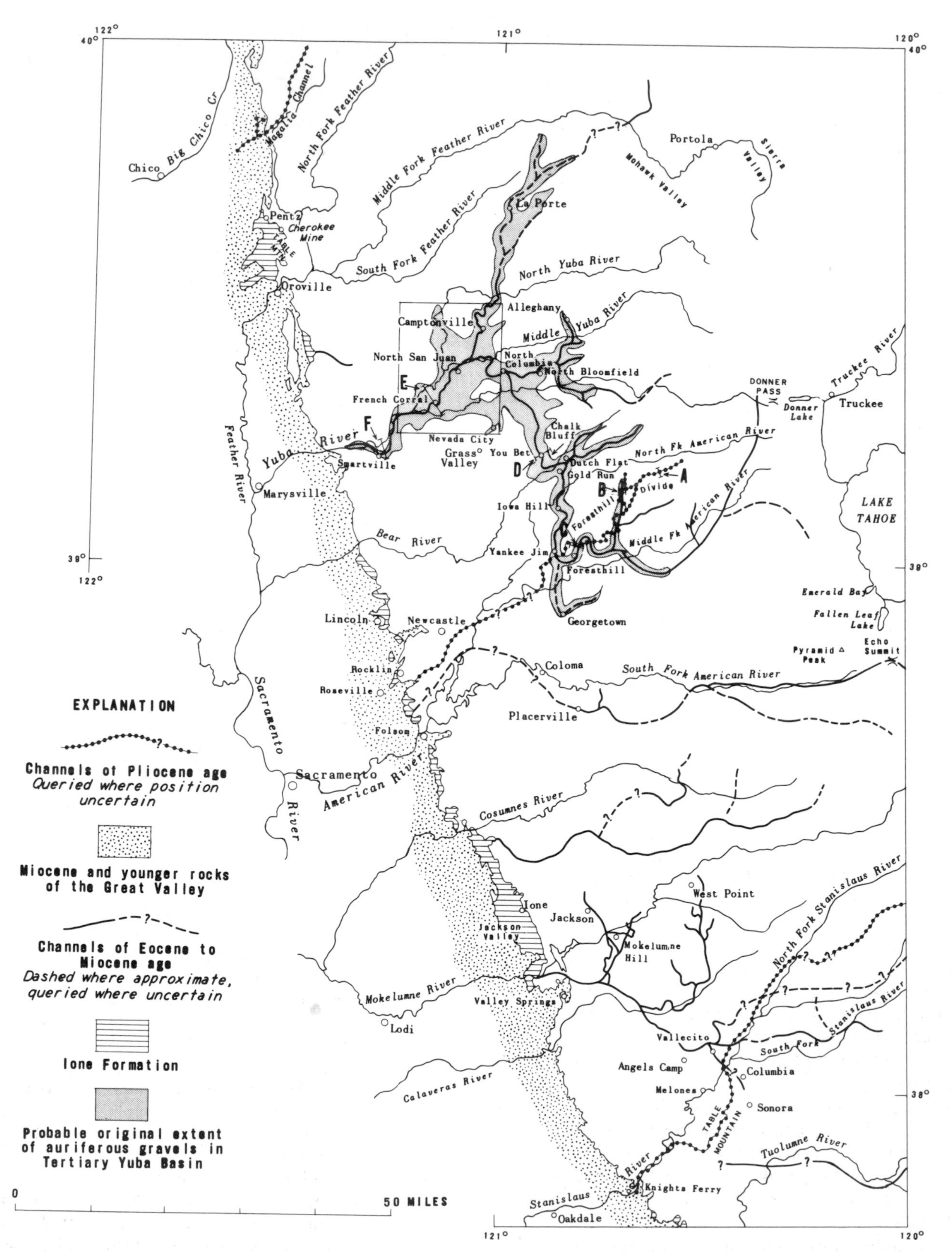

Figure 5. Map showing localities in northern Sierra Nevada mentioned in text, and prevolcanic and intervolcanic channels, Ione Formation, and inferred original distribution of auriferous gravels in the basin of the Tertiary Yuba River. Channels from: Gold Belt Folios; Lindgren, 1911, plate 1; Browne, 1890; Storms, 1894; Clark and others, 1963; Goldman, 1964. Ione Formation from Chico sheet, Sacramento sheet (prelim. comp.), and San Jose sheet (prelim. comp.) of Geologic Map of California, Olaf P. Jenkins edition.

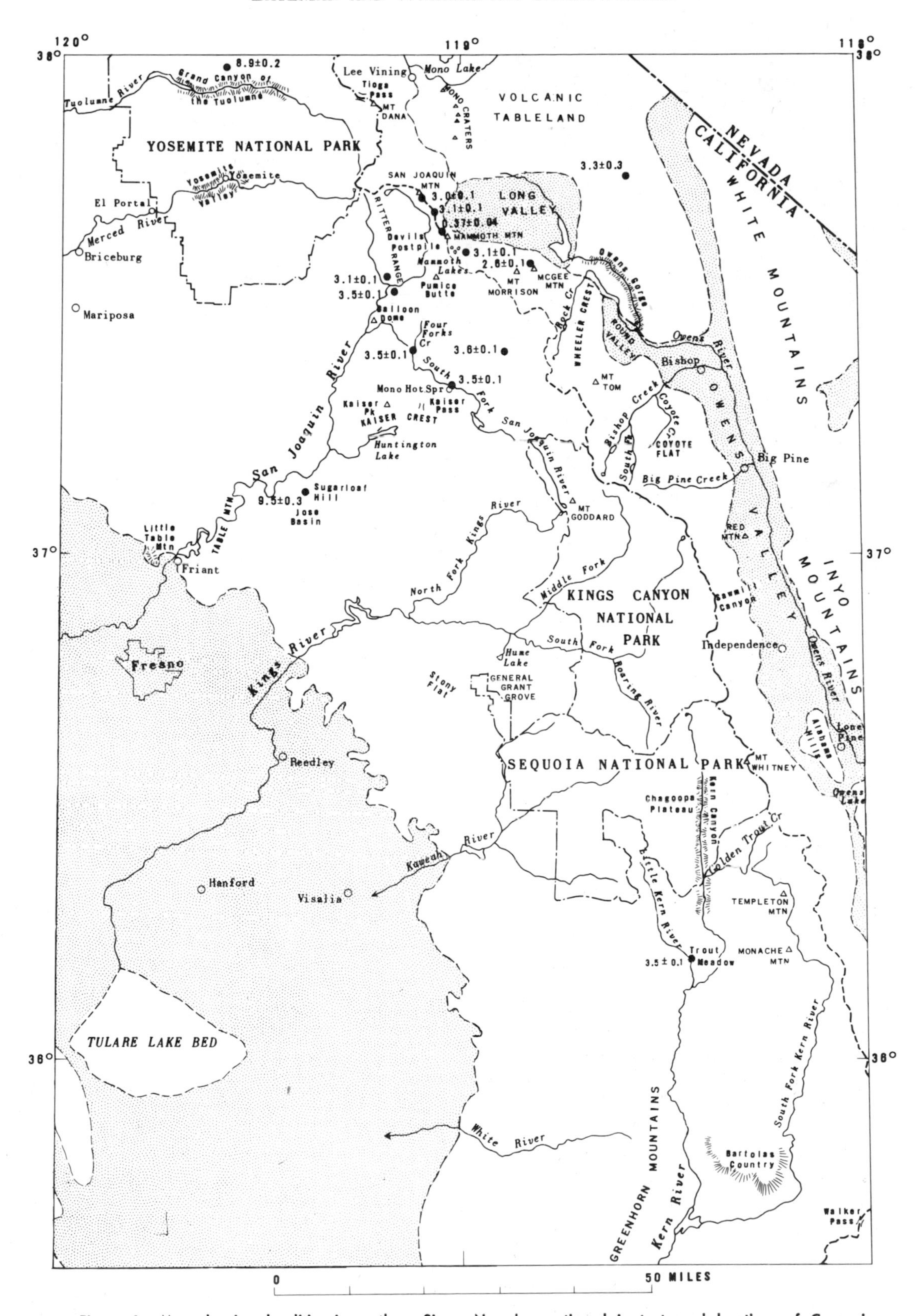

Figure 6. Map showing localities in southern Sierra Nevada mentioned in text, and locations of Cenozoic volcanic rocks in southern Sierra Nevada dated by the potassium-argon method (from Dalrymple, 1963; 1964a, b; Doell, Dalrymple, and Cox, 1966).

Photo 8. Exposure of auriferous gravels in the Malakoff Diggings, North Bloomfield, Nevada County, California. *Photograph by Mary Hill.*

chlorite, interbedded with kaolinitic clay of slightly different composition. The presence of larger amounts of unstable minerals in the upper member than in the lower suggests that either the climate had grown significantly less tropical or accelerated erosion had brought fresher material from the base of the weathering profile to the surface. The Ione Formation generally rests on a lateritic weathering profile. Commonly only the white lithomargic clay of the lower part of the profile is preserved, grading into the underlying weathered bedrock. Locally the iron-rich crust of a typical laterite is preserved, and transported laterite, some containing as much as 44 percent iron, is interbedded in basal beds of the Ione on the flanks of buried highlands.

The Ione Formation shows marked lateral variation in lithology, and interfingering of beds of sand and clay. It is generally thought to have been deposited under deltaic and lagoonal conditions, with coal swamps accumulating in quiet waters behind an outer ridge of islands; channel crossbedding and gravel lenses in much of the coarser part suggest deposition by fluviatile processes. The presence of thin layers with remains and casts of marine shells in the sands indicates periodic incursions by the sea.

The maximum thickness reliably reported is about 450 feet (Piper, Gale, and others, 1939, p. 84), although Turner (1894) reported a thickness of about 1,000 feet. Pask and Turner estimated a maximum thickness of 415 feet for their lower Ione and between 163 and 225 feet for their upper Ione, but the total thickness at any one place is considerably less than the sum of these figures because the upper member overlaps the lower across an erosional unconformity.

A marine mollusk fauna reported by Dickerson (1916) has been placed in the middle Eocene Capay Stage by Merriam and Turner (1937). On plate 16 in Bowen (1962), the Ione Formation is shown as laterally continuous with Kreyenhagen Shale of late Eocene age.

The mineral assemblage of the lower Ione and the thick lateritic soil on which it rests indicate a tropical climate with perhaps alternations of wet and dry seasons for the period of weathering that led to the formation of its sediments (Allen, 1929). The irregular buried topography beneath the formation, and the erosional unconformity within the formation, suggest gradual relative rise in sea level and alluvial ponding of the lower valleys, interrupted by at least one period of relative lowering of base level during the accumulation of the Ione.

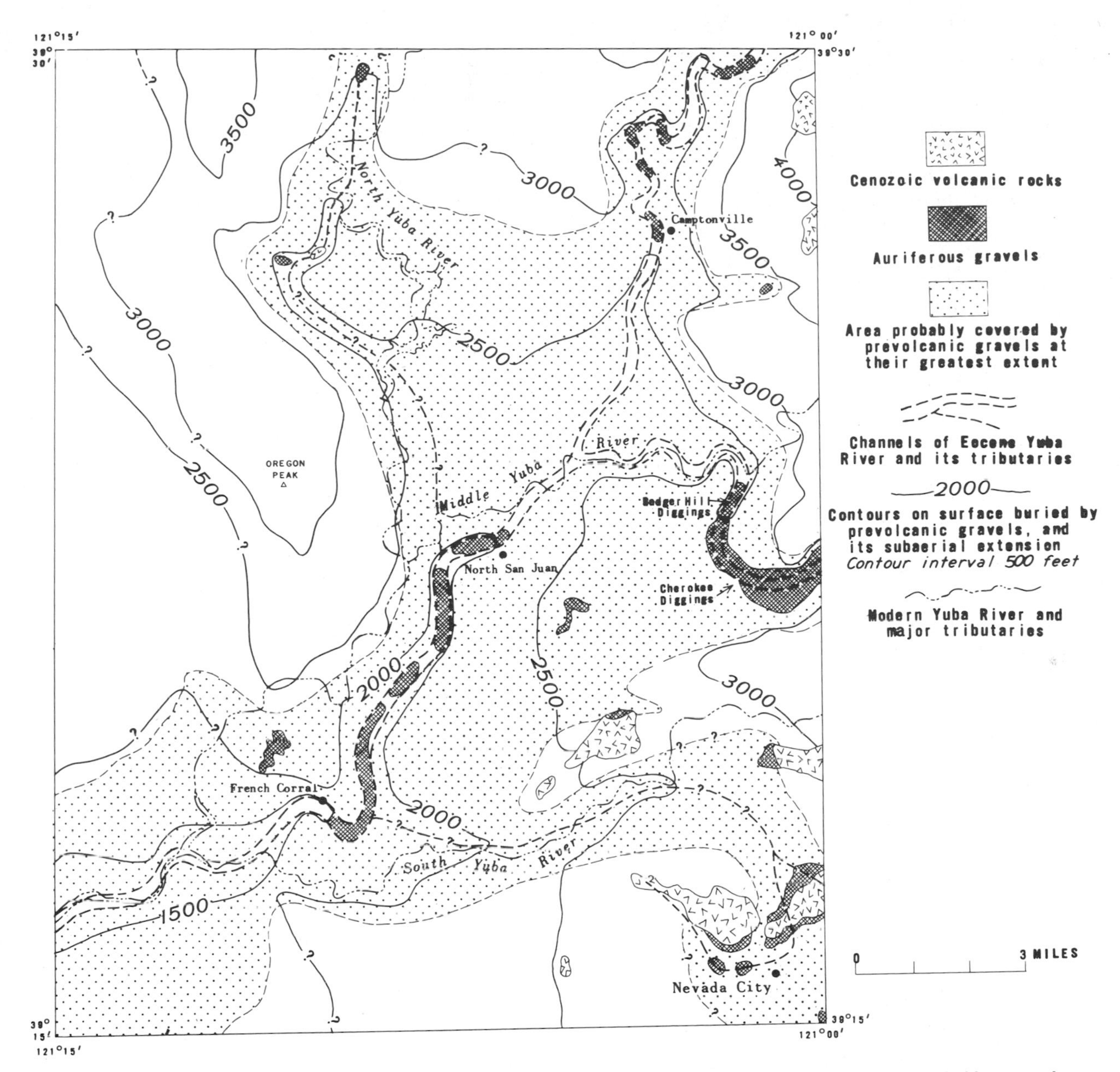

Figure 7. Map of Nevada City quadrangle, showing auriferous gravel deposits, channels of Tertiary Yuba River, probable original extent of gravels, and topography on surface buried by the Cenozoic rocks. Data from Whitney, 1880; Lindgren, 1911, and Smartsville Folio; and original reconnaissance survey. For location of quadrangle see figure 5.

Prevolcanic Gravels

The high-level gold-bearing gravels of the northern Sierra Nevada make possible a rather detailed reconstruction of the early Tertiary topography of the range, as well as an estimate of the amount and character of the late Cenozoic deformation of the range. Magnificent exposures of these gravels, produced through hydraulic mining from 1855 to 1890, have been eroded to fantastic badlands; many segments of the original bedrock channels have been laid bare on the floors of the hydraulic pits.

Most of the auriferous gravels were deposited before the major period of volcanic activity in the Sierra Nevada. These earlier gravels will be called the *prevolcanic* gravels in the pages that follow. Many other gold-bearing gravels, however, were deposited in channels cut during the period of volcanic eruptions or in layers intercalated with the volcanic deposits. In accordance with the usage of Lindgren (1911), these gravels will be called the *intervolcanic* gravels.[1]

The prevolcanic gravels are found as irregular or sinuous patches on the relatively flat interfluves between the deep canyons of the northern Sierra Nevada. Some of the gravel patches clearly define the sinuous

[1] Some volcanic eruptions, notably those recorded by the Wheatland Formation and Reeds Creek Andesite of Clark and Anderson (1938) and some of the eruptions in the extreme northern part of the Sierra (see Durrell, this bulletin) may have taken place before deposition of some of the *prevolcanic* gravels described in this article.

channels of the large rivers that drained the early Tertiary Sierra Nevada—for example, the channel gravels between French Corral and North San Juan (fig. 7). Other gravel patches cap broad areas of ancient valleyside benches, or are found on present-day hilltops, unrelated to any identifiable channel. Many of the gravels crop out discontinuously along the basal contact of the Tertiary volcanic rocks, and have been explored beneath the volcanics by extensive drifts of gold mines.

From a study of the altitude and disposition of the various bodies of prevolcanic gravels, Whitney (1880) and Lindgren (1911) were able to discern on the west slope of the Sierra Nevada a former system of five major rivers with tributary branches and several minor streams. The major streams were named by Lindgren the Tertiary Yuba, American, Mokelumne, Calaveras, and Tuolumne Rivers, after the modern streams which reach the Great Valley at the approximate points where the provolcanic rivers reached the sea. As can be seen in figure 5, the Tertiary Yuba and Calaveras were the major streams which drained the Gold Belt, in contrast to the relatively small streams now bearing those names. The south forks of both of these Tertiary streams flowed for several miles through the foothills in northwestward trending valleys, following a belt of soft slate lying east of ridges of massive greenstone. These northwestward trending courses are critical in evaluating the late Cenozoic tilting of the range.

The piecing together of the courses of the prevolcanic rivers was the work of many years. Early geologists, and most miners, believed that the auriferous gravels were deposited by a series of north-trending streams that flowed approximately perpendicular to the present drainage (cf. Trask, 1854). The great contribution of the Whitney Survey to the study of the auriferous gravels was the demonstration that the gravels were deposited by streams that flowed west and southwest (Whitney, 1880). Lindgren (1911) solved the remaining problem by showing that the northwest-trending belt of gravels between Forest Hill and North Columbia marks the prevolcanic South Fork of the Yuba River. The anomalous slopes of the prevolcanic channel in this belt he explained as the result of subsequent tilting of the range. Chandra (1961) has questioned Lindgren's interpretation of this belt, but imbrication of pebbles and crossbedding in a critical part of the channel, exposed along Highway 40 at Gold Run (Hudson, 1955), confirm that the stream that deposited these gravels flowed north.

The thickness of the prevolcanic gravels is variable, partly because of the irregular topography on which they were deposited and partly because of erosion cutting into them before the deposition of the volcanic formations. The greatest thickness of gravel is in the deposits of the Tertiary Yuba River, and reaches 500 to 600 feet in the diggings between North Columbia and Gold Run. In contrast to the thick gravels deposited along the Tertiary Yuba River, the prevolcanic gravels deposited along the other rivers are only locally more than 50 feet thick.

The prevolcanic gravels consist dominantly of pebble and cobble gravel with interbedded sand and clay. The average size of pebbles in the gravel is between ½ and 1½ inches, and the maximum size in any gravel layer, except near the base of the gravels, is rarely more than 9 inches. Near the base of the gravels, however, the boulders are much larger, with some reported to be 5 to 20 feet across. Most of these boulders are of adjacent bedrock and may have been brought to the channel by tributary torrents or tumbled into it from undercut banks. Even large boulders well above the base of the section could have been incorporated in the gravels in this fashion, and the size of these rare giant boulders is not necessarily a measure of the competence of the Tertiary streams.

In terms of pebble population the prevolcanic gravels are of two contrasting types, although intergradations exist. One type, known to the miners as "blue gravel," consists of a wide variety of pebbles, representing most of the bedrock in the drainage basins of the streams. In this type of gravel, where exposed at Smartsville or North San Juan, for example, the predominant rock types are meta-andesite, schist, and slate; quartz and chert make up 20 to 30 percent at most. Granitic pebbles are rare but persistent components. These "blue gravels" commonly fill the bottoms of the main channels. The other type, known as "white gravel," generally overlies the "blue gravel" in the main channels and rests on bedrock benches. It is made up largely of quartz, chert, and quartzite, which usually constitute 60 to 70 percent of the pebbles, with quartz being the most abundant. The remainder of the pebbles are opaque white pebbles, now consisting largely of clay that can be crushed between the fingers. These may originally have been metamorphic or igneous pebbles, weathered to white clay following deposition.

Practically all the pebbles except those of quartz and chert are weathered. Most nonsiliceous pebbles can be cut with a fingernail or knife, although in many exposures of the "blue gravels," resistant metavolcanic and granitic pebbles are common. The pebbles could not have been transported in this weathered condition, so presumably most were weathered after deposition.

The sands interbedded with the gravels vary in composition with the gravels. Studies by Galen Sturgeon (*in* MacGinitie, 1941) of a cross section of the gravels exposed at You Bet show that the sands associated with the basal blue gravels are arkosic and contain biotite, hornblende, and epidote among the heavy minerals, whereas sands associated with the white quartz-rich gravels consist almost entirely of quartz and anauxite or of quartz with bleached biotite. These latter sands accumulated under climatic conditions

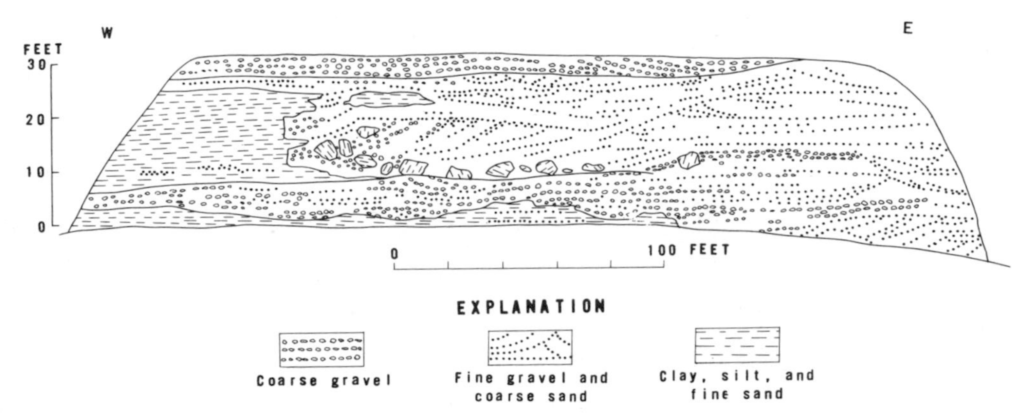

Figure 8. Sketch from photograph of roadcut 1 mile west of North Columbia, Nevada County, California, showing local unconformities probably caused by lateral migration of an aggrading stream into bodies of overbank silt on its floodplain. Vertical exaggeration 2 ×.

comparable to those of the Ione Formation, and are probably to be correlated with the lower member of the Ione (Pask and Turner, 1952). At the top of the auriferous gravels at You Bet are about 150 feet of crossbedded biotite-bearing sand with abundant fresh feldspar, clearly representing conditions of less extreme weathering than the sand below. This upper sand may correlate with the upper Ione of Pask and Turner (1952) or with the Wheatland Formation of Clark and Anderson (1938).

In the thick gravel sections of the Tertiary Yuba River the average pebble size decreases toward the upper part of the section, and the proportion of clay and sand increases. Discontinuous layers of plastic clay are common throughout the upper part of the prevolcanic gravels, but are rare in the deep channel gravels. In many of the drift mines, the top of the section contains 2 or 3 beds 10 to 50 feet thick of dense white "pipe-clay" (cf. Lindgren, 1911, pl. 25). Most of these are apparently floodplain deposits, but some may have been deposited in tributary channels dammed by aggradation along the main channels. Contacts of some of the clay beds with the overlying sand and gravel are local unconformities marked by channels, and angular blocks of clay, apparently torn from the clay beds, are found in the overlying gravels (fig. 8).

The upward decrease in grain size suggests that the river was growing less competent, possibly because of a relative rise in base level or a decrease in overall gradient. The significance of this for the tectonic history of the Sierra Nevada is discussed in a subsequent section.

According to Lindgren (1911, p. 71) fine gold is distributed throughout the entire thickness of the gravels, generally to the value of 2 to 10 cents per cubic yard in the upper gravels, but the bulk of the gold and all the coarse pieces were concentrated within 3 feet of bedrock, where the gravel in the mines ran from 50 cents to $15 per cubic yard (at a price of $21.00 per ounce of gold). Commonly the richest deposits, those justifying drift mining, were in a narrow streak at bedrock along the deepest part of the channel, and the maps of the old drift mines serve therefore to delineate the thalwegs of the ancient rivers. Some of the gold was mined from the upper few feet of weathered bedrock, where it had been forced by the currents or had sunk during weathering.

Allen (1929) showed that the Ione Formation was deposited by the same streams that were depositing the auriferous gravels, and he found the lithology of the Ione to be the same as that in the white quartz gravels, indicating that the prevolcanic gravels are of Eocene age. Paleontologic evidence from the gravels themselves confirms this. The prevolcanic gravels have yielded an extensive fossil flora, which was originally described by Lesquereux (1878) and Knowlton (*in* Lindgren, 1911). The collections studied by Lesquereux and Knowlton were unfortunately mixed with collections from the intervolcanic gravels, and their age assignments are consequently in error. More recently collections from rhyolite tuff immediately overlying the auriferous gravels at La Porte have been studied by Potbury (1937) and collections from clay beds interbedded with the white gravels at Chalk Bluff and the You Bet diggings have been studied by MacGinitie (1941). According to MacGinitie (oral communication, 1965), the Chalk Bluff flora is late early Eocene; the La Porte flora is now regarded as early Oligocene (Wolfe, and others, 1961). A potassium-argon age of 32.4 m.y. has been obtained on the La Porte Tuff (Evernden and James, 1964).

Thus the fossil and stratigraphic evidence indicate that deposition of the prevolcanic gravels took place during much of the Eocene and may have extended into the earliest Oligocene. According to MacGinitie (1941, p. 78), the climate during this time was characterized by an average annual temperature of 65°F, slight seasonal variation in temperature with little or no frost, and an annual rainfall of 60 inches or more with maximum precipitation in the warm season—in other words, a subtropical climate similar to that along the coast of southern Mexico.

Photo 9. West-sloping interfluves and dendritic drainage of northern Sierra Nevada, consequent upon the surface of the andesitic mudflows. In the distance on right can be seen the foothill belt of northwest-trending ridges of Jurassic greenstone. View looking south from over the headwaters of the Cosumnes River with the canyon of the Mokelumne River in the middle distance. U.S. Geological Survey photograph GS-OAH-6-68.

Volcanic Formations and Intervolcanic Gravels of the Northern Sierra Nevada

Inasmuch as the Cenozoic volcanic formations of the northern Sierra Nevada are treated in papers by Durrell and Slemmons in this bulletin, only those aspects of these formations pertinent to the Cenozoic landscapes and subsequent uplift will be treated here.

The rhyolite tuffs, ash flows, and associated clastic rocks of the Valley Springs Formation (Piper and others, 1939), 20 to 30 million years old (Dalrymple, 1964), are in few places more than 800 feet thick (Slemmons, this bulletin). They filled narrow valleys in a landscape whose relief was more than 1,000 feet, and formed a continuous sheet only in the Great Valley. They overtopped a few passes low on the west slope of the Sierra, notably those a few miles east of Nevada City, to effect the first of a series of drainage changes (Lindgren, 1896, 1911). The number of identifiable eruptions during the 14-million-year period of rhyolitic eruptions is small. Contemporaneous streams had ample time to rework the volcanic deposits and to cut through the ash-flow plains to bedrock. The canyons cut through the rhyolitic deposits generally did not coincide with the prevolcanic channels, although they were as deep and in places deeper.

The gravels associated with the Valley Springs Formation consist mostly of quartz and bedrock fragments; recognizable rhyolite pebbles are scarce (Lindgren, 1911; Browne, 1890; Goldman, 1964). They are interbedded with rhyolitic tuffs or fill the bottoms of channels and are overlain by rhyolitic ash flows (called "white cement" by the miners). In part they result from erosion and deposition that took place just before or after the rhyolitic eruptions, and in part they result from later deposition in tributary valleys that were dammed by rhyolite flows. The scarcity of rhyolite pebbles is generally explained as due to the fragile character of the rhyolite tuff. Much of the gold in these gravels may have been reworked from prevolcanic gravels intersected by interrhyolitic channels.

Photo 10. Sinuous flat-topped mountain capped by a latite flow filling an intervolcanic channel: Table Mountain in Tuolumne County, capped by the Table Mountain Latite Member of the Stanislaus Formation, which flowed down the "Cataract Channel", a Pliocene course of the Stanislaus River. The Stanislaus now flows in the deep gorge extending from right to left across the photograph several miles beyond the mountain. The rolling uplands on either side of the mountain are parts of the stripped unconformity at the base of the Superjacent Series. View northeast from between Jamestown and Melones, about three miles west of Sonora. Rawhide Flat in lower left foreground. The town of Columbia in the distance on the extreme right. The northeast-trending light bands on the surface of the flow are unrelated to the course of the flow, and may be the surface expression of northeast-trending regional jointing, propagated upward from the basement into the Superjacent Series. *Aerial photograph by John S. Shelton.*

Most of the auriferous gravels of the Tertiary Calaveras River appear to be assignable to the interrhyolitic gravels (Lindgren, 1911; Storms, 1894; Goldman, 1963). These gravels were rich in gold and locally are 200 feet or more thick.

Extensive andesitic mudflows and conglomerates were deposited during the interval following the deposition of the Valley Springs Formation, from 19 to 5 million years ago (Dalrymple, 1964). They were considerably thicker than the Valley Springs, ranging from more than 3,000 feet thick along the crest of the Sierra to 500 feet in the foothills (Slemmons, this bulletin), and they buried the bedrock topography of the northern Sierra Nevada almost completely. At the close of the andesitic period, the only bedrock highlands rising above the andesitic plains were ridges of resistant greenstone along the western foothills, a few high summits of the middle slopes, and a few ridges along the crest of the range, such as the mountains around Pyramid Peak. As a consequence of this burial, the prevolcanic drainage was entirely obliterated, and a new drainage consequent upon the depositional slopes of the andesitic deposits was developed.

The andesitic deposits along the west foot of the range were named the Mehrten Formation by Piper and others (1939), and Curtis (1951; 1965) applied this name to the andesitic deposits at the crest of the range near Markleeville, which can be traced almost continuously to the western foot of the range. Slemmons, in this bulletin, has split the andesitic deposits into three newly named formations, the Relief Peak (the oldest), Stanislaus, and Disaster Peak Formations. He feels that the Disaster Peak Formation probably correlates with Mehrten of the type locality.

Only in a few places can more than 40 mudflows be identified in a single section of the andesitic deposits, so presumably the 14-million-year period of andesitic eruptions was marked by long intervals without volcanic activity, during which the streams that coursed down the volcanic slopes had time to carve new canyons and valleys. These, in turn, would be filled with the products of new eruptions, and the Stanislaus Formation, defined by Slemmons in this bulletin, occupies just such a valley.

Some of the intervolcanic gravels of this period occupy the bottom of these channels and record stages

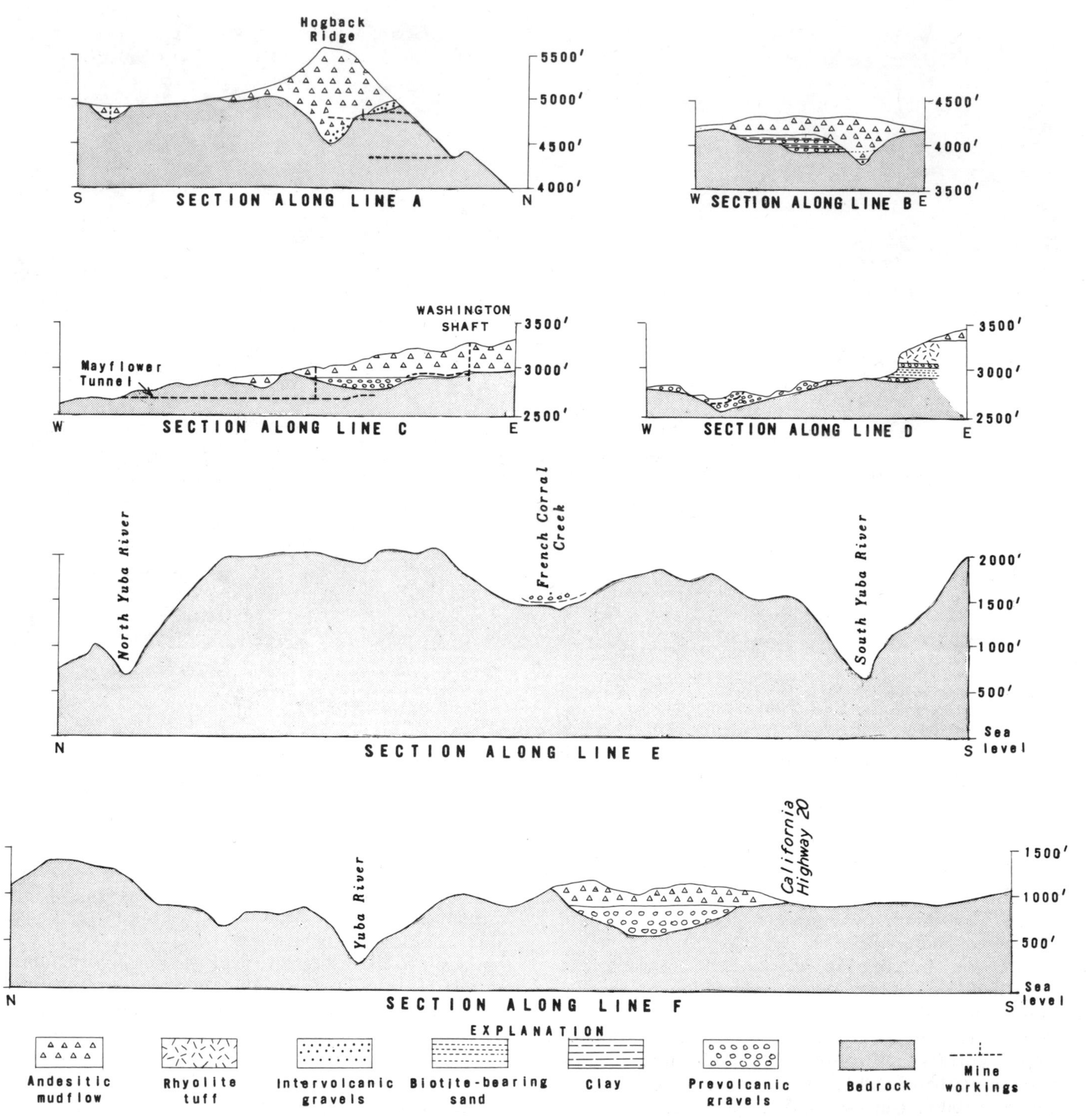

Figure 9. Cross sections of the channel of the Tertiary Yuba River along lines shown on figure 12. Sections A, B, and C from Ross E. Browne, 1890; section D from MacGinitie, 1941, p. 19; sections along E and F constructed from 1:24,000 Smartsville and French Corral quadrangles with geology by Wahrhaftig. Vertical exaggeration 2 ×.

in the development of the present drainage. For example, the intervolcanic channel of the Forest Hill Divide represents the first period of diversion of the South Fork of the Tertiary Yuba River into the drainage of the American River. Similarly the "cataract channel" beneath the Table Mountain Latite Member of the Stanislaus Formation (see Slemmons, this bulletin), records the establishment of the Stanislaus drainage basin at the expense of the South Fork of the Tertiary Calaveras River.

The gravels associated with the andesitic eruptives contain abundant large cobbles of andesite, along with rarer clasts of bedrock and quartz. They only locally contain gold in paying quantities; the gold of the intervolcanic channel of the Forest Hill Divide, which was mined over considerable distances, was probably reworked from prevolcanic channels.

The Tertiary Landscapes of the Northern Sierra Nevada

Remnants of Tertiary landscapes of many different ages are preserved beneath the Tertiary gravels and volcanic deposits. Some notion of the character and minimum relief of the early Tertiary surface can be gained by drawing reconstructed contours on it, using remnants preserved beneath the Tertiary deposits and the surface of the existing pre-Tertiary bedrock in neighboring areas as control. Lindgren (1896) reconstructed the early Tertiary topography of an area around Grass Valley and Nevada City, on the upland between the present Yuba and Bear Rivers, and he showed this area to have had then almost as much relief as it does now. A similar reconstruction of the early Tertiary topography of the 15-minute Nevada City quadrangle is shown in figure 7, which includes the valley of the Tertiary Yuba River around North San Juan. Cross sections of the Tertiary Yuba and modern Yuba are shown in figure 9. From the cross sections, and by comparison of figure 7 to a topographic map of the 15-minute Nevada City quadrangle, it can be seen that local relief on the lower west slope of the Sierra Nevada amounted to as much as 1,000 to 1,500 feet, which is about half of the total relief that exists there today. Other estimates of local relief include a few hundred to 1,800 feet in the lower part of the Tertiary Calaveras River, and as much as 3,000 feet along the present crest of the Sierra, which is the amount that Pyramid Peak rises above the inferred level of the Tertiary American River (Lindgren, 1911) and the amount that Mount Dana in Yosemite Park rises above gravels at its west base which have been correlated with the auriferous gravels (R. W. Kistler, oral communication, 1965). These figures are all minimum figures, for they do not take into account erosion from the highlands during and after the deposition of the auriferous gravels.

The general character of the Tertiary topography was summarized by Lindgren (1911) who recognized three topographic belts: (1) in the western foothills close to the Great Valley a belt of greenstone ridges 1,000 to 1,800 feet high but crossed by the Tertiary rivers in fairly narrow canyons; (2) a lowland eroded on the slates of the Mother Lode belt, in which were cut the valleys of the South Forks of the Tertiary Yuba and Calaveras Rivers; and (3) east of this lowland, a broad plateau, rising rather sharply to altitudes of 1,000 to 2,000 feet above the lowland, and incised to depths of a few hundred to a thousand feet by the valleys of the Tertiary streams. Isolated high mountains surmounted the plateau, notably along the present range crest.

In detail the main valleys seem to have had a central gutter, a few hundred to a few thousand feet wide, underlain generally by fresh bedrock, and with steep and even overhanging fresh bedrock walls as much as 40 feet high. This gutter, which is the main bedrock channel excavated for gold, was the bed or thalweg of the main stream, and is commonly filled with "blue gravel". On either side of the gutter the valley sides rose either as smooth slopes or as a series of benches, on which the quartz gravels rested generally on deeply weathered bedrock or a lateritic soil. The benches on the Yuba were ½ to 1 mile wide, and beyond them the land sloped more steeply to the uplands on either side.

The location of the early Tertiary drainage divide is uncertain. Lindgren placed it at the present crest of the northern Sierra as far south as Lake Tahoe, and somewhat east of the crest south of Lake Tahoe. At least one piece of evidence makes it likely that the divide, in part, lay well to the east of the present crest. In the gravels at the base of the andesites around Ebbetts Pass and a few miles south of Sonora Pass are pebbles of black chert unlike other chert in that part of the Sierra Nevada, and resembling most closely the Paleozoic chert exposed in western Nevada. Also in the Ebbets Pass gravels are pebbles of porphyritic quartz-monzonite that probably came from the Topaz Lake quartz monzonite of Curtis (1951) cropping out east of the present divide.

Cenozoic Volcanic Rocks of the Southern Sierra Nevada

Few Cenozoic deposits are found in the Sierra Nevada south of the Tuolumne River, as erosion has probably been continuous in this southern area since the intrusion of the batholith. The few deposits that exist are chiefly of two kinds: volcanic rocks, which cover less than 1 percent of the surface, and glacial deposits.

The volcanic rocks have an importance far beyond their areal extent, for they provide information on the time and amount of faulting, uplift, and canyon cutting by giving minimum ages for the surfaces and deposits on which they rest. They are chiefly basalt and andesite flows, but include basalt cinder cones, latite domes and volcanoes, and rhyolite tuffs and ash flows. Information on their age is largely from potassium-argon dates on sanidine or plagioclase of the siliceous rocks or on whole-rock basalt (Dalrymple,

Photo 11. View west over the headwaters of the West Walker River and the drainage divide of the Sierra Nevada showing the southern limit of the superjacent series. Base of superjacent series is marked by dashed line. Valley of West Walker River is in the middle distance. Dorothy Lake at the north end of Yosemite Park is in the distance on left, and Relief Peak in center. Sonora Pass lies behind the peaks near the right edge of photograph. Light-colored rock in left half beyond the drainage divide is mainly quartz-monzonite and granodiorite; dark-colored rock with even slopes making up many peaks in right of the picture, including peak in the foreground, is andesite. U.S. Geological Survey photograph GS-OAH-4-144.

1963, 1964a, 1964b; Dalrymple, Cox, and Doell, 1965). The dated volcanic rocks fall into three groups in terms of age: 9 to 10 million years; 2 to 4 million years; and less than 1 million years.

A date of 9.5 ± 0.3 m.y. was obtained from basalt along the San Joaquin River about 20 miles northeast of Friant (Dalrymple, 1963). This occurrence of Pliocene basalt defines the local relief in the southern Sierra Nevada in Pliocene time, and also the amount of deformation since then (Dalrymple, 1963; Christensen, 1966; Wahrhaftig, 1965e). The dated basalt is from Sugarloaf Hill on the floor of Jose Basin, a broad bench about 1,700 feet above the San Joaquin River and surrounded by mountains 2,000 to 3,000 feet higher. Upstream along the San Joaquin River from Friant is a sinuous string of basalt-capped mesas and buttes, whose summits rise evenly eastward from river level at a point about 5 miles south of Friant to about 2,500 feet about 15 miles northeast of Friant, forming a slope of 130 to 140 feet per mile. Beneath the basalt is as much as 320 feet of interbedded gravel and rhyolite tuff (Macdonald, 1941). The basalt-capped mountains define an ancient channel of the San Joaquin River, which when projected eastward upstream coincides in altitude with the basalt of Sugarloaf Hill, and is therefore about 9.5 million years old. The level of this Pliocene stream is marked upstream by a series of benches along the canyon wall, and 10 miles north of Jose Basin, these benches, at an altitude of 4,000 feet, are bordered by mountains 8,000 to 10,000 feet high. Thus during the Pliocene the southern Sierra Nevada had a local relief of 4,000 to 6,000 feet (Dalrymple, 1963).

Basalt from Coyote Flat, about 10 miles southwest of Bishop, dated by Dalrymple at 9.6 ± 0.2 m.y., occupies a shallow north-trending valley which was probably established at the beginning of the warping of the Coyote Flat salient (Bateman, 1965).

A number of undated basalt remnants are probably of early Pliocene or Miocene age, judging from their physiographic relations. A series of remnants along the canyon of the Kings River (Krauskopf, 1953) range in altitude from 3,000 feet at the mouth of the North Fork of the Kings River to about 5,500 feet near Hume Lake, 11 miles east, where they are 3,500 feet above the river. The slope of the channel defined by these basalt patches, if they are all remnants of the same flow, or are nearly contemporaneous flows, is about 140 feet per mile. Other flows that may have formed during this period are the flow on Stony Flat, west of General Grant Grove (Burnett and Matthews, in press), and flows in the Bartolas Country at the forks of the Kern River (Miller and Webb, 1940; Smith, 1965).

Dates in the range from 2 to 4 million years have been obtained for basalt flows in the Kern River Canyon, on the upper San Joaquin River, and along the east side of the Sierra Nevada from the Mammoth Lakes area to the Owens Gorge. All these flows have been extensively eroded, and those on the east side of the range have been deformed. Few eruptive centers can be identified.

At Trout Meadows, at the mouth of the Little Kern River, a basalt flow fills the inner gorge of the Little Kern to within a few hundred feet of the present stream level (Webb, 1953; Dalrymple, 1963). The basalt extends across the trace of the Kern Canyon fault without displacement. The date on the basalt of 3.5 ± 0.1 m.y. shows that the bulk of the cutting of the upper Kern Canyon was completed by that time and that the Kern Canyon fault has been inactive for at least the last 3.5 million years. Evidence presented by Webb (1953) indicates that it has been inactive for a much longer period.

Several flows in the upper San Joaquin basin have been dated at 3.3 to 3.5 m.y. (Dalrymple, 1963, 1964; Doell, Dalrymple, and Cox, 1966). Most of these flows rest on the floor of the broad basin of the South Fork of the San Joaquin River or on mountain slopes graded to that basin. One flow, the basalt at Four Forks Creek, which is 3.5 m.y. old appears to have been dissected in the cutting of the inner gorge of the South Fork; on the other hand, flows dated at 3.5 and 3.3 m.y. appear to have flowed as much as 500 feet down the walls of the inner gorges of the North and Middle Forks of the San Joaquin. Thus the cutting of the inner gorge of the San Joaquin seems to have started before about 3.5 million years ago.

Part of the crest of the Sierra Nevada east of the headwaters of the Middle Fork of the San Joaquin is on basaltic andesite and latite, which fill a canyon cut to within 500 feet of river level—a canyon which drained westward across the present drainage divide (Huber and Rinehart, 1965b). The flows are cut off on the east along the fault scarp that marks this part of the east face of the Sierra Nevada. A date of 3.0 to 3.1 m.y. on these flows (Dalrymple, 1964a) shows that prior to this time the San Joaquin River was receiving drainage from at least part of the Mono Basin, and that much of the range-front faulting on the east side of the Sierra Nevada is less than 3 million years old.

At McGee Mountain, about 15 miles farther southeast along the east front of the Sierra, basalt remnants on the mountain top were dated by Dalrymple (1963) at 2.6 ± 0.1 m.y. This basalt is overlain by the McGee till, which is believed by Putnam (1962) and Rinehart and Ross (1964) to predate several thousand feet of displacement along the eastern fault system of the Sierra Nevada. On the other hand, Lovejoy (1965) regards the basalt and till as post-faulting in age. Christensen (1966) discusses the evidence in this area, and concludes that the estimates of Putnam, and of Ross and Rinehart, are probably correct.

Ten miles east of McGee Mountain, in Owens Gorge, basalt beneath the Sherwin Till has been dated at 3.2 m.y. (Dalrymple, 1963; for description of the locality, see Putnam, 1960; Rinehart and Ross, 1957; and Wahrhaftig, 1965c).

Undated basalt flows on the upland between the San Joaquin and Kings Rivers may belong to the 2- to 4-million-year period of volcanic eruptions.

Quaternary volcanic rocks (those less than a million years old) are predominantly in three volcanic fields that are within or border the southern Sierra Nevada. One field includes Mono Lake, Mammoth Mountain, the Devils Postpile, and the Bishop Tuff. Another extends along the base of the Sierra Nevada between Big Pine and Independence. The third is around the headwaters of the South Fork of the Kern River.

Dated volcanic rocks of the complex Mono Lake-Mammoth field range in age from less than a million years to about 6,000 years. The Bishop Tuff, dated at 700,000 years (Dalrymple, Cox, and Doell, 1965) is a rhyolitic ash flow 400 to 450 feet thick that covers an area of approximately 350 square miles between Mono Lake and Bishop (Gilbert, 1938). It rests on till of the Sherwin Glaciation (Putnam, 1960a; Rinehart and Ross, 1957) and has been faulted and deformed with structural relief of possibly as much as 3,000 feet. It is confined to the valley between the Sierra Nevada and the White Mountains, and indicates that, although much of the range-front faulting took place after 700,000 years, the largest displacements took place before 700,000 years. Tuff identical to that of the Bishop Tuff also occurs in the valley of the Middle Fork of the San Joaquin River. Although geographically separated from the Bishop Tuff by the present Sierra drainage divide, this tuff has tentatively been correlated with it (Huber and Rinehart, 1965a). The basaltic andesite of the Devils Postpile was subse-

Photo 12. Quaternary volcanic field at east base of the Sierra Nevada south of Big Pine, with the east face and crest of the range in the background, as viewed west from Highway 395 about 6 miles south of Big Pine. Headwaters of Big Pine Creek is behind Fish Spring Hill on the right. Taboose Creek canyon on extreme left in background. Birch Mountain is the high white peak on skyline on right; Mount Tinemaha is the high mountain south of it.
In the foreground is a basaltic cinder cone. The rough dark area in the plain at the right foreground is basaltic lava. The dark sharp-pointed hill below and left of Birch Mountain is a perlite dome. *Photograph by Mary Hill.*

quently erupted into the Middle Fork valley, probably during an interglaciation.

Mammoth Mountain is a large quartz-latite volcano on the crest of the Sierra Nevada near the head of the Middle Fork of the San Joaquin River. Dalrymple (1964a) obtained an age of 370,000 years on a sample from the northwest part of the mountain; the mountain still shows signs of thermal activity (Huber and Rinehart, 1965a).

From basaltic cinder cones several miles south of Mammoth Mountain a line of late Pleistocene and Recent eruptive centers extends northward through the Mono Craters to Black Point on the north shore of Mono Lake. Black Point is a basaltic cinder cone that apparently erupted during the last high stand of Mono Lake (Christensen and Gilbert, 1964). Cinder cones and basalt flows, erupted since Mono Lake dropped to its present level, make up parts of Negit and Paoha Islands in the lake.

The Mono Craters are a series of rhyolitic tuff rings and endogeneous domes, some of which have spread as stubby steep-sided flows as much as three-fourths of a mile from the vents, and which continue southward from the main mass for several miles as a series of plug domes. Potassium-argon dates of 6,000 years and 65,000 years have been obtained from the Mono Craters (Evernden, Kistler, and Curtis, 1959). At the southern end of this string of domes are two explosion pits, the Inyo Craters, which radiocarbon data suggest were formed between 500 and 850 years ago (Rinehart and Huber, 1965).

At the south end of the line of eruptive centers lie the Red Cones, of Recent (postglacial) age, and Pumice Butte, of probable late Pleistocene age (Huber and Rinehart, 1965a; 1965b). Pumice from eruptions along this line mantles a large area around the Mono Craters and Mammoth Mountain and extends as far south as Kaiser Summit, east of Huntington Lake.

Numerous basaltic cinder cones and flows lie along the base of the Sierran escarpment between Big Pine and Independence (Bateman, 1965; Moore, 1963). Some flows are interbedded with outwash gravels that may be of Tahoe age, but others are much older, being offset by faults with many tens or even hundreds of feet of displacement. A flow in Sawmill Canyon rests on till of Sherwin(?) age and underlies Tahoe Till; it has a probable age of less than 100,000 years (Dalrymple, 1964b), indicating that the Tahoe Glaciation correlates with the early Wisconsin of the mid-continental United States.

The Toowa Volcanic Field, at the headwaters of the South Fork of the Kern River, includes several well-preserved basaltic cinder cones and flows along Golden Trout Creek, as well as two isolated symmetrical latite(?) domes, Templeton Mountain and Monache Mountain, each about 1,500 feet high (Webb, 1950).

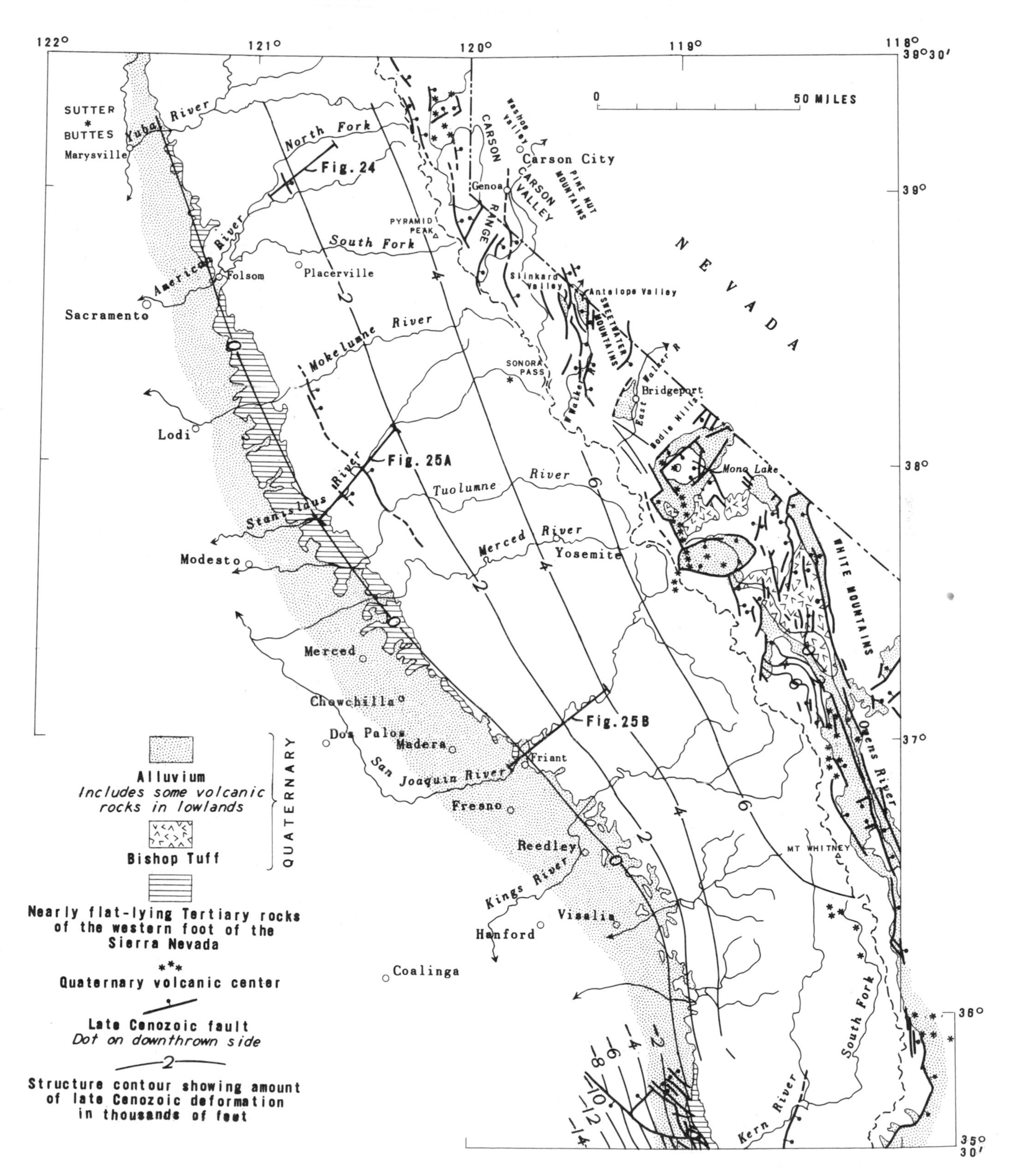

Figure 10. Cenozoic tectonic map of the Sierra Nevada, showing late Cenozoic faults, late Cenozoic deformation by contours, and Quaternary volcanic centers.

Contacts from Chico sheet, Walker Lake sheet, Sacramento sheet (prelim. comp.), San Jose sheet (prelim. comp.), Fresno sheet (prelim. comp.), and Bakersfield sheet, Geologic Map of California, Olaf P. Jenkins edition, and from Bateman and others, 1963; Bateman, 1965; and Pakiser and others, 1964. Contours on west slope of Sierra Nevada after Christensen, in press, 1966; contours and buried faults at south end of San Joaquin Valley on top of Vedder Sand (lowermost Miocene), from Richardson, 1965. Contours on Coyote Flat surface on east side of Sierra Nevada, from Bateman, 1965, and generalized from topography south of Bridgeport; altitudes of these contours reduced by 4,000 feet to agree with deformation datum of contours on west side of Sierra Nevada. Distribution of Bishop Tuff from Gilbert, 1938; and Bateman, 1965.

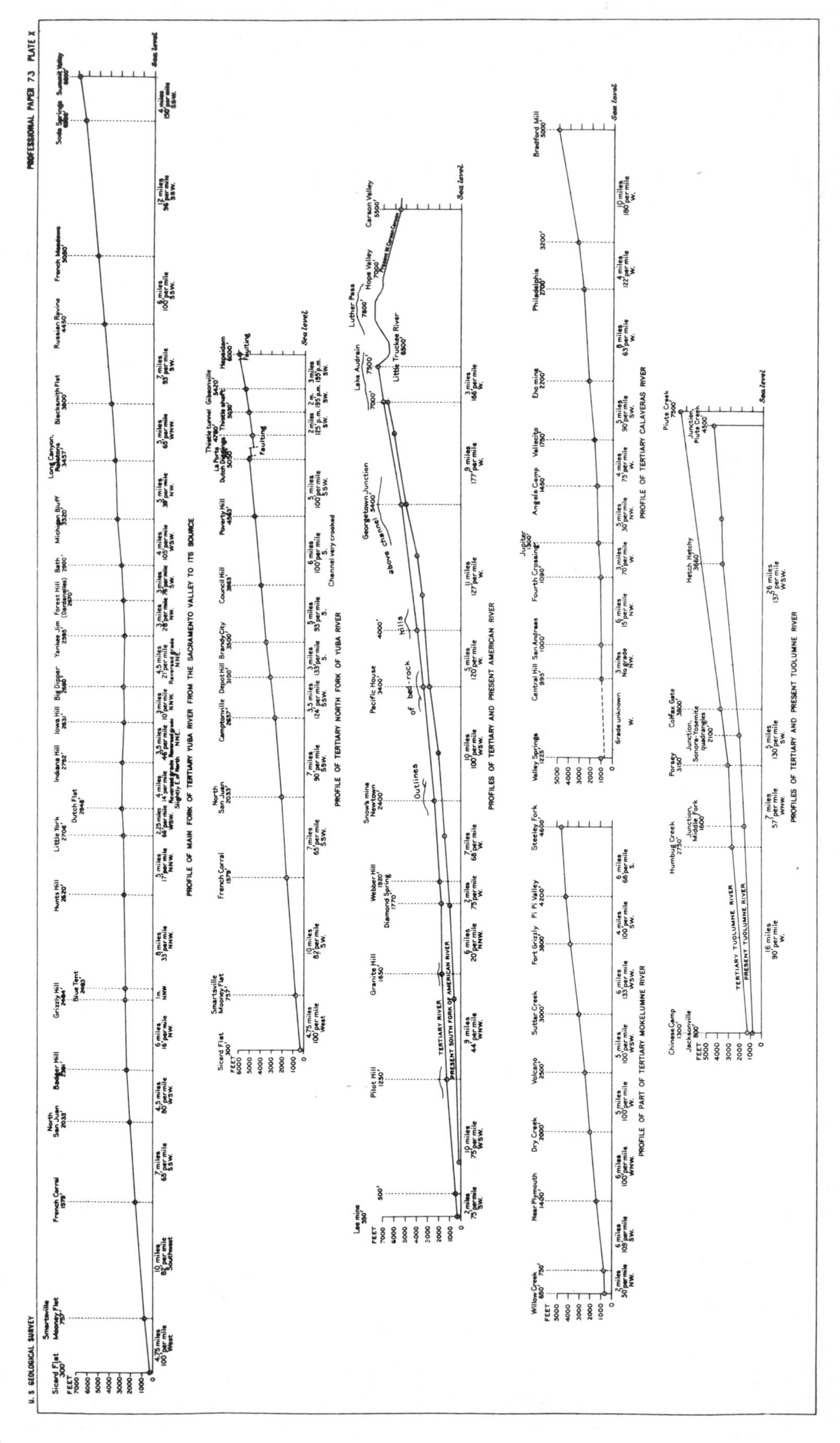

Figure 11. Profiles of the Tertiary channels of the northern Sierra Nevada. From Lindgren, 1911, plate 10.

Flows along Golden Trout Creek extend to the floor of the Kern River Canyon at the south end of Sequoia Park. On their upper surfaces are scattered giant quartz-monzonite boulders which may be glacial erratics and patches of gravel thought to be glacial outwash, both of a pre-Wisconsin glaciation.

LATE CENOZOIC DEFORMATION AND EROSION IN THE NORTHERN SIERRA NEVADA

The evidence for the late Cenozoic deformation of the Sierra Nevada has recently been reviewed by M. N. Christensen (1966) and the discussion that follows draws heavily on his paper.

It is generally agreed that the Sierra Nevada is a great fault block, bounded on the east by a line of faulting and tilted westward more or less as a unit. The eastern boundary is not a single great fault, but a series of *en echelon* and branching faults, interspersed with ramps and arches. There is uncertainty and controversy over the time of uplift and tilting, the total amount of uplift, and the amount of internal deformation, if any. Stratigraphic, structural, physiographic, and paleobotanic evidence has been used to determine the amount and time of deformation. More recently potassium-argon dates on critical volcanic deposits have provided additional information on the time of deformation. As is clear from the preceding pages, the quality of information about the amount and time of uplift and tilting is much better for the northern Sierra Nevada than for that part of the range south of the Tuolumne River. The southern area lacks the extensive superjacent cover of stream gravels and volcanic rocks from which estimates of uplift and tilting can be made, and most conclusions regarding the Cenozoic deformation of the southern part of the range are based on physiographic evidence, such as upland surfaces, valley-side benches, and knickpoints in stream profiles. As will be shown below, these are believed to be unreliable criteria for measuring deformation.

The uplift and erosion of the Sierra Nevada north of the Tuolumne are treated in this section, and that of the Sierra Nevada south of the Tuolumne in the next section.

The best evidence that the Sierra Nevada was tilted as a unit consists of the evenness of the west-sloping interfluves of the northern Sierra Nevada. These broad flat ridgecrests are the surfaces of andesitic mudflows, from which, in some places, overlying gravels and mudflows have been stripped; they show that the Pliocene andesites have suffered very little internal deformation. Demonstrable faults on the west side of the northern Sierra are remarkably few. At La Porte the channel of the Tertiary Yuba River has been offset a total of 550 feet on a northwest-trending fault zone about a mile wide (Lindgren, 1911), the channel of the South Fork of the Tertiary Yuba has been offset at Yankee Jim about 25 feet (Browne, 1890), and the latite of Tuolumne Table Mountain and the andesite at Mokelumne Hill have been offset 100 feet or more on the Mother Lode fault (Eric and others, 1955; Goldman, 1964). All these faults trend northwest and are downthrown on the northeast side.

The classic estimate of the tilting of the Sierra Nevada is that of Lindgren (1911), who compared the slopes of the southwest-flowing segments of the bedrock profiles of the reconstructed Tertiary rivers with the slopes of their northwest-flowing segments. The southwest-flowing segments, he reasoned, would show the maximum increase in gradient, whereas the northwest-flowing segments would parallel the tilt axis and therefore show no increase in gradient. By subtracting the gradients of the latter from those of the former, he could determine the amount of tilting. He found the southwest-directed segments of the lower courses of the Tertiary rivers to have gradients of 70 to 100 feet per mile, and the northwest-directed segments to have gradients of 10 to 30 feet per mile, and by subtraction arrived at an average tilt of about 60 to 70 feet per mile, which gave an uplift along the crest of the range of 3,600 to 4,900 feet between the head of the Yuba and the head of the Mokelumne River. By applying this tilt correction to the north- and northeast-flowing segments of the South Fork of the Tertiary Yuba between Yankee Jim and Dutch Flat, where the direction of flow indicated by sedimentary structures is upslope, he was able to explain the anomalous present slope of these reaches. Lindgren's study of the stream profiles remains a classic in the quantitative application of geomorphology to a tectonic problem.

Hudson (1955) attempted to refine Lindgren's work by using a different method of calculation. He assumed that the bedrock profile of the South Fork of the Tertiary Yuba River was originally smooth, chose triplets of adjacent differently directed segments of the Tertiary bedrock profile, and solved for the direction and amount of tilting that would give the segments of each triplet the same slope. He adjusted his solutions, where necessary, to give a smooth profile and interpolated the slope between sets of triplets. Hudson's results for the Yuba differ considerably from Lindgren's. He concluded that there had been much deformation within the range and that total uplift on the crest amounted to less than 2,000 feet.

Christensen (1966) has reviewed the work of Lindgren and Hudson and concluded that many of the reaches selected by Hudson were so short that irregularities in the river bottom could have seriously affected his results. Christensen determined, from a study of 19 modern alluvial streams of comparable drainage basin area, that the original slope of the alluviated portions of the Tertiary Yuba should be no greater than 30 feet per mile, thus confirming Lindgren's major premise.

In considering the calculations of both Lindgren and Hudson, it is well to recall that the accumulation of 500 feet of prevolcanic gravels in the middle reaches of the Tertiary Yuba River implies either a rise in base level or a backward tilting of the drainage basin, prob-

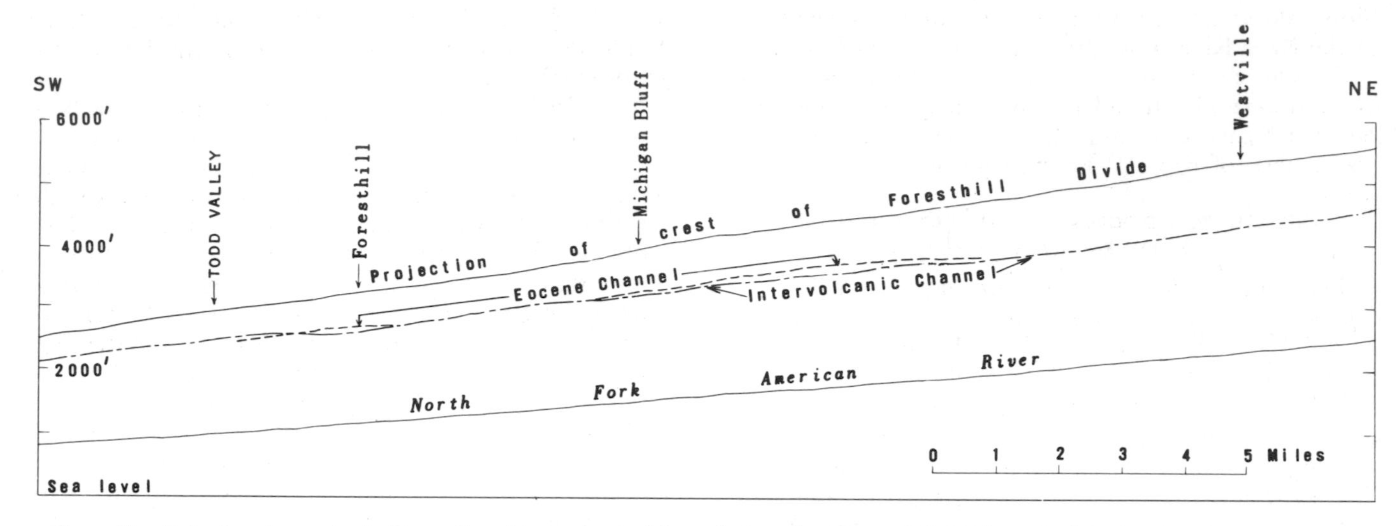

Figure 12. Projection of prevolcanic (Eocene?) and intervolcanic (Pliocene) channels of Forest Hill Divide, and of the North Fork of the American River, onto a vertical plane striking N. 50° E. Data from Ross E. Browne, 1890. For location of projection plane see figure 10. Vertical exaggeration about 10 X.

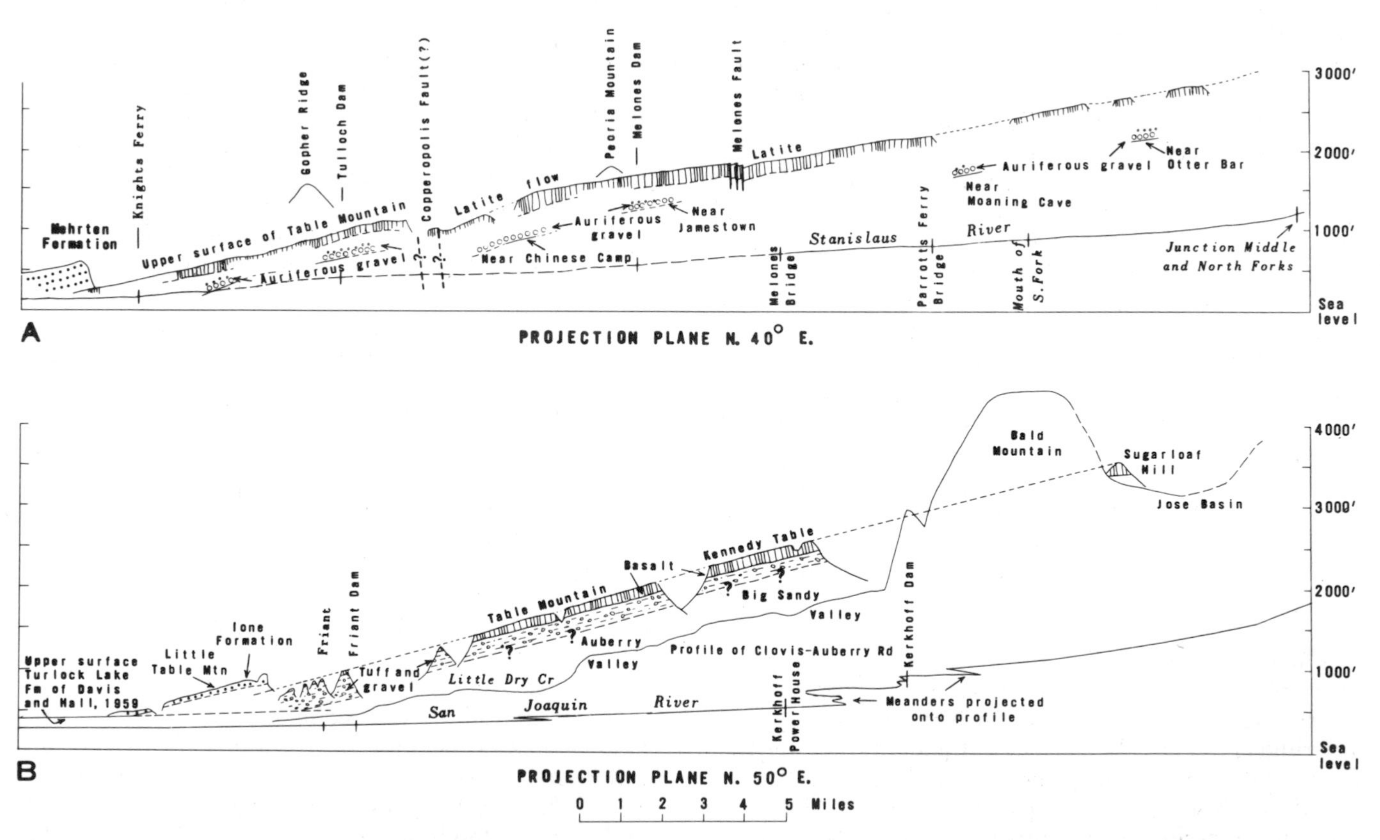

Figure 13. Projections of two volcanic table mountains of the western Sierra Nevada. A. Projection of Tuolumne Table Mountain onto a vertical plane striking N. 40° E. Geology modified from Taliaferro and Solari, 1949; Eric and others, 1955; and Big Trees Folio. B. Projection of Little Table Mountain and the basalt of Table Mountain on the San Joaquin River onto a vertical plane striking N. 50° E. Geology modified from Macdonald, 1941, and original surveys. For location of projection planes see figure 10. Vertical exaggeration about 10 X.

ably both. Lindgren's explanation of the aggradation as due to constriction of the valley at Smartsville seems untenable, for it fails to explain how the valley upstream from Smartsville was cut in the first place. Only the Tertiary Yuba-channel shows this evidence of back tilting or rise in base level—the other streams did not aggrade their beds in prevolcanic times. Hence, in early Tertiary time, there was probably a differential sagging of the crust beneath the Sierra, localized in the Yuba drainage; this sagging may have amounted to 500 feet. The total uplift and tilting after the deposition of the volcanic rocks was the amount calculated by Lindgren, plus whatever downward displacement took place during the accumulation of the gravels. Part of the discrepancy between Hudson's and Lindgren's conclusions may arise from this period of deformation.

The present drainage of the northern Sierra Nevada was undoubtedly consequent upon the surface of the volcanic rocks. The pattern of southwest-flowing streams was developed over a long period, as successive channels were filled and buried by volcanic mudflows and streams were forced to shift to new courses. The present courses are essentially those the streams possessed at the end of the period of volcanic eruptions, modified by changes resulting from superposition onto bedrock structures that were oriented normal to the streams. During uplift and tilting the rejuvenated streams deepened their channels, so they now flow in narrow V-shaped canyons several hundred to as much as 3,000 feet below the floors of the prevolcanic channels. Part of the Tertiary cover was stripped from the relatively flat interfluves, and large areas of the early Cenozoic topography have been exhumed (see fig. 7). Thus the present topography of the northern Sierra Nevada consists of elements of three different ages: prevolcanic topography that was never buried or has been exhumed from beneath the volcanic cover; younger, relatively plane surfaces developed on the volcanic rocks; and steep modern canyons, incised into both volcanic cover and bedrock.

Lindgren (1911) and others have stressed that the tilting was initiated at the beginning of the volcanic eruptions. They base this on the assumed rejuvenation of the streams shown by the steep walls of the intervolcanic channels, and by the coarse andesitic cobbles of the intervolcanic gravels. The steep canyon walls and coarse gravels probably reflect the character of the well-jointed andesitic rocks rather than any change in the gradient of the streams.

Axelrod (1957) has shown that the floras of Miocene age from the Valley Springs Formation and of Pliocene age from the overlying andesites and from their equivalents in west-central Nevada both indicate the same climate, and that they do not indicate the existence of a rain shadow, such as the one now present east of the Sierra Nevada. He estimates from the distribution of floras that in Miocene and early Pliocene time the mountains near Lake Tahoe could not have been higher than 2,000 to 3,000 feet, and therefore that the crest of the range has been subsequently uplifted 5,000 to 6,500 feet.

Reconstruction of the intervolcanic profiles and comparison with the prevolcanic profiles (see fig. 12) shows that at least in the lower and middle reaches of the Sierra Nevada the intervolcanic profiles are essentially parallel to the prevolcanic profiles and at the same altitude. The profiles of the Forest Hill Divide (fig. 12), constructed from data in the map of Ross E. Browne (1890), show the intervolcanic channels to be at most only 100 feet below the prevolcanic channels, in spite of the fact that they were much closer to the mouths of the streams. Similarly, the Cataract Channel of Table Mountain, in Tuolumne and Calaveras Counties, which also has a more direct course to base level than the prevolcanic channel, actually overlies the prevolcanic gravels in the vicinity of Vallecito and Douglas Flat (Turner and Ransome, 1898). There seems to be no reason to infer from the slopes of the intervolcanic channels that the northern Sierra Nevada was tilted before the channels were cut.

Three major *en echelon* zones of complex gravity faults border the Sierra Nevada on the east between Mohawk Valley and Sonora Pass. The northernmost of these extends southeast from Mohawk Valley and the west side of Sierra Valley, through Donner Lake, and along the west side of Lake Tahoe. Its displacement is about 3,000 feet at Mohawk Valley, more than 2,000 feet north of Donner Lake, and is indicated by physiographic evidence to be as much as 5,000 to 6,000 feet west of Lake Tahoe (Birkeland, 1963; Durrell, this bulletin). East of this fault zone and separated by upwarped blocks are the tectonic depressions of Mohawk, Sierra, and Truckee Valleys, and Lake Tahoe (Birkeland, 1963). East of the Tahoe and Truckee depressions lies the north-trending uplift of the Carson Range, which joins the Sierra Nevada south of Lake Tahoe.

The Carson Range is a complex horst, which passes at its northern end into a broad anticlinal arch (Thompson and White, 1964). It faces Washoe and Carson Valleys on the east by magnificent fault scarps that reach a height of 4,000 to 5,000 feet east of the southern part of Lake Tahoe. The total displacement is about 8,000 feet. The line of faults branches southward as it enters California, and the branches continue into the Sierra Nevada and die out near the range crest (Curtis, 1951; 1965).

Carson Valley, to the east, is apparently the depressed side of a tilted fault block whose uplifted eastern part is the Pine Nut Range. This block rises southward, and where it crosses the state line into California it becomes continuously mountainous and merges with the Sierra Nevada. The third zone of complex faults is on the east side of this block, and makes the escarpments on the west side of Antelope

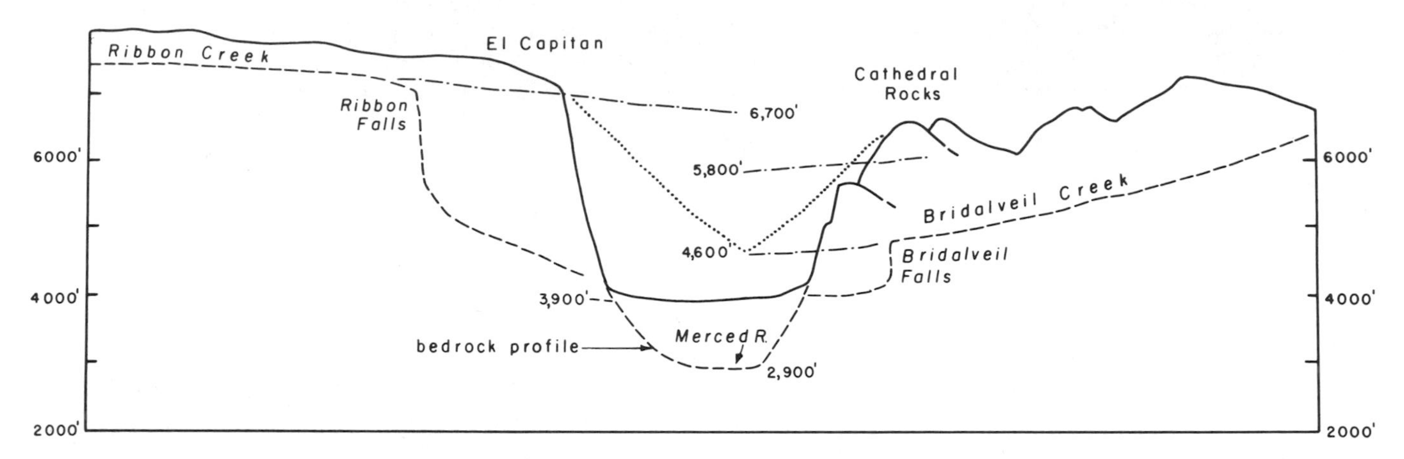

Figure 14. Projection, on a north-south plane, of cross profile of Yosemite Valley between El Capitan and Cathedral Rocks (solid line) and of profiles of Ribbon and Bridalveil Creeks (dashed lines). Elevations of the Merced River of the Broad Valley Stage (6,700 ft), Mountain Valley Stage (5,800 ft), and Canyon Stage (4,800 ft) of downcutting, and the profiles on which they are based (dot-dashed lines), are from Matthes (1930, fig. 27, p. 87). Bedrock surface from Gutenberg, Buwalda, and Sharp (1956, fig. 8, p. 1072). No vertical exaggeration. Reproduced from Wahrhaftig, 1962, p. 38.

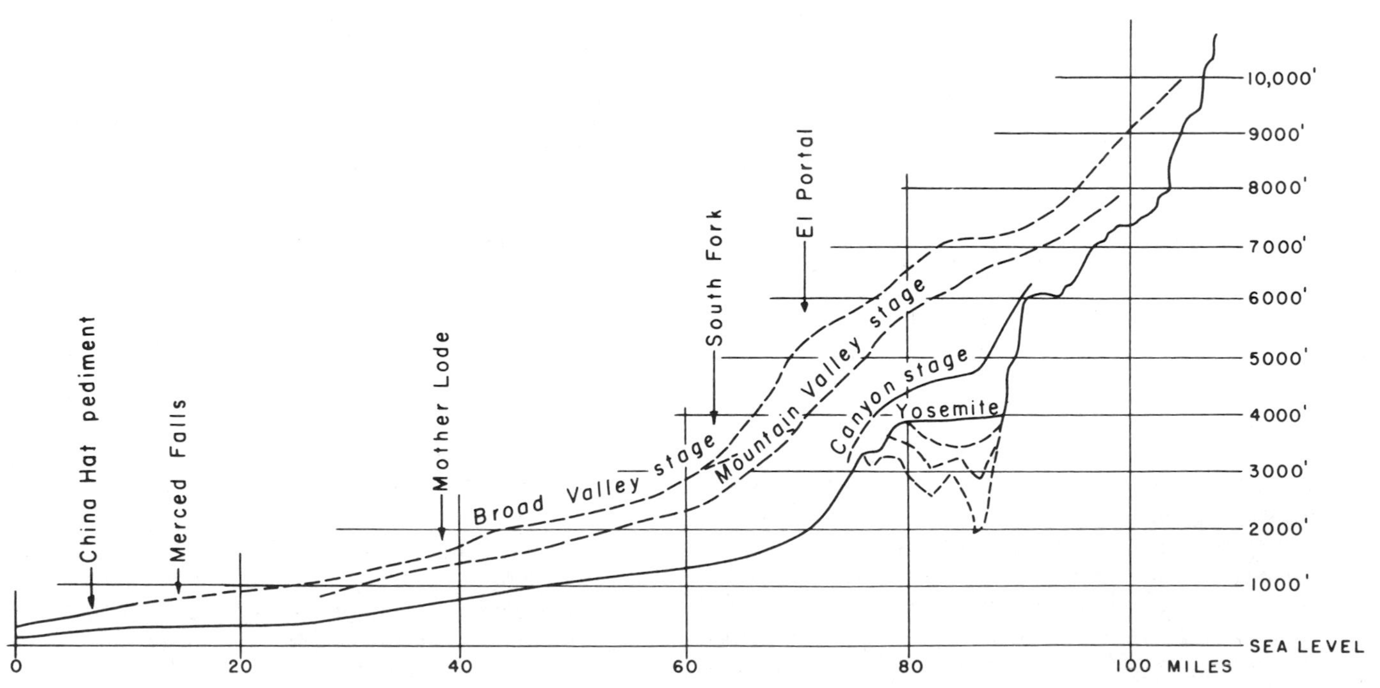

Figure 15. Longitudinal profile of the Merced River (after Hudson, 1960, p. 1551—reproduced from Wahrhaftig, 1962, fig. 3, p. 37).

and Slinkard Valleys. Displacements on the faults on each of these escarpments are 2,000 to 2,500 feet (Curtis, 1965).

Birkeland (1963) and Dalrymple (1964a) have shown that the bulk of the movement along the faults west of Truckee Valley took place after the eruption of an andesite that is 7.4 million years old and before the eruption of the earliest of the flows of the Lousetown Formation that is 2.3 million years old. The oldest of the Lousetown flows is displaced as much as 700 feet along outlying segments of this fault zone, and even the youngest of the Lousetown flows, which is 1.3 million years old, has been offset and tilted.

Deformation of the Carson Range began in middle Pliocene time, during the accumulation of the andesites (Thompson and White, 1964), and no more than 400 feet of deformation and downcutting has occurred since the deposition of the Lousetown flows a little more than a million years ago. That deformation along the major faults is continuing is indicated by fresh slickensided fault scarps exposed at Genoa, in Carson Valley at the east foot of the Carson Range (Lawson, 1912).

According to Curtis (1951; 1965) the fault systems in the headwaters of the Carson River and Antelope Valley had two periods of activity since the eruption of the andesitic mudflows in middle Pliocene time. These were separated by a period of quiescence during which a surface of relatively low relief was carved across the areas.

LATE CENOZOIC DEFORMATION AND EROSION IN THE SOUTHERN SIERRA NEVADA

In the absence of the extensive Tertiary cover that made possible the measurement and dating of uplift in the northern part of the range, geologists working the Sierra Nevada south of the Tuolumne River have had to rely on physiographic criteria of uplift. The physiographic features used are of three kinds: summit uplands and benches, assumed to be remnants of ancient surfaces of low relief formed near base level; profiles of the assumed Tertiary streams, reconstructed from knickpoints on their tributaries; and steep escarpments, assumed to be fault scarps.

In 1904 Lawson described extensive benches and summit uplands on granitic rocks at the head of the Kern River, and he assumed these were remnants of erosion surfaces of low relief formed close to sea level. He named two main surfaces the Subsummit Plateau, 11,000 to 12,500 feet high, and the High Valley, 6,500 to 10,000 feet above sea level. On the basis of the relative amounts of erosion involved, Lawson estimated that the cutting of the Kern Canyon into the High Valley surface took 300 times the length of the post-glacial period (which he estimated to be about 1,000 years long), and the cutting of the High Valley took 2,400 times the length of post-glacial period. Using modern knowledge of the time since the disappearance of the glaciers, these estimates become 3 million and 24 million years respectively.

Knopf (1918) extended the mapping of Lawson's surfaces northward along the east side of the range to the Bishop Creek area. Matthes (1937) refined Lawson's history, and recognized three levels of summit flats and benches, and hence four stages of uplift at the headwaters of the Kern. The two highest surfaces, vertically about 1,000 feet apart and together corresponding to Lawson's Subsummit Plateau, Matthes named the Cirque Peak Surface and the Boreal Plateau Surface. A surface about 2,000 feet lower, corresponding to Lawson's High Valley, he named the Chagoopa Surface; and the final stage of erosion he named the canyon-cutting stage. Matthes' estimates of the duration of these stages were 1 million years for the cutting of the canyon, 10 to 15 million years for the Chagoopa cycle, 20 million years for the Boreal Plateau cycle, and 5 to 10 million years for the Cirque Peak cycle.

More recently, Axelrod (1962; Axelrod and Ting, 1961) has attempted to date the uplift and cutting of the Chagoopa Surface by a study of pollen grains embedded in sediments lying on that surface and in vertebrate-dated sedimentary rocks in the Owens Valley graben east of the Sierra Nevada. He concluded that the Chagoopa Surface is middle Pleistocene (Kansan) in age, and that the bulk of the uplift of the Sierra Nevada took place in Pleistocene time.

Using the second type of physiographic evidence, stream profiles, Matthes (1930) noted that the upper reaches of lateral tributaries of the Merced River flow with gentle gradient in broad shallow valleys to an abrupt knickpoint, from which their lower courses cascade to the Merced River incised in a narrow canyon several hundred to 3,000 feet below (fig. 14). By projecting the gentle gradients downstream to where the tributaries joined the Merced, he defined a series of points marking the bed the river occupied before the uplift and rejuvenation responsible for the knickpoints, and by connecting these points he could reconstruct the present position of the profile of the Tertiary Merced River. Furthermore, Matthes found that many of the streams had two knickpoints, and was able to reconstruct two ancient profiles: the older he called the Broad Valley stage and placed in the Miocene; and the other, the Mountain Valley stage and placed in the Pliocene. He calculated that since the end of the Broad Valley stage the tilting of the Sierra Nevada amounted to about 70 feet per mile and the crest of the range, which formerly was about 4,000 feet high, had been uplifted 9,000 feet. Hudson (1960) extended Matthes' profiles to the San Joaquin Valley (see fig. 15), and from them estimated that the uplift at the crest amounted to only 4,000 feet.

Matthes (1960) later carried this type of analysis into the San Joaquin Basin, where the Miocene and Pliocene profiles of the San Joaquin River were also reconstructed from tributary knickpoints. Here, how-

Photo 13. Distant view of Yosemite Valley, looking east. El Capitan is the white cliff on north side of the valley. Cathedral Rocks are on the south side of valley, opposite El Capitan, with the steep gorge of Bridalveil Creek in front of them. The shadowed face of Half Dome is above and left of El Capitan. The flat light-colored area in lower right is Big Meadow. Bigoak Flat Road, in left foreground, is along a step front; a second and higher step front extends as a series of granite domes and cliffs diagonally to the left from near El Capitan.

On the skyline at left are Tioga Pass and Mount Dana. In front of Mount Dana are sharp peaks of Cathedral Peak Granite on the near side of Tuolumne Meadows. On the central skyline behind Yosemite Valley are the White Mountains, lying east of the Owens Valley Graben. The darker peaks of the Sierra crest between Yosemite Valley and the White Mountains include Mount Lyell and the Ritter Range. On the skyline on right are the mountains around the head of the San Joaquin Basin. U.S. Geological Survey photograph GS-OAH-3-17.

ever, this analysis breaks down, for Matthes' Miocene and Pliocene profiles are not parallel to the ancient stream profile defined by the basaltic lavas of Table Mountain.

The numerous west-facing escarpments in the southern Sierra Nevada were identified by Hake (1928) and Matthes (1950; 1964) as fault scarps. The flat benches and mountain tops behind the scarps were assumed to be offset segments of an originally continuous surface. This explanation was given plausibility by the existence of the famous Kern River fault with its erosional fault-line scarp facing the Great Valley at the south end of the range (Blackwelder, 1928; Gilbert, 1928). Birman (1964), on the other hand, regarded these escarpments as backwasting mountain fronts and the benches between them as *piedmonttreppen*.

The foregoing analyses failed to take into account many of the essential topographic features of the southern Sierra Nevada—features that were not readily apparent until the publication of the U.S. Geological Survey topographic maps at a scale of 1:62,500. The western slope of the Sierra Nevada south of the Tuolumne River gains altitude by a series of giant west-facing steps, which have risers from 100 to several thousand feet high and treads a few hundred feet to several miles across. These steps are irregular in height and map pattern. The risers (or fronts) have abundant outcrops, while most treads are underlain by deep gruss (over 100 feet thick in places) and slope back toward the next higher front (fig. 16), so that minor tributaries commonly flow parallel to the fronts. Most streams cascade down the fronts in short

Figure 16 (opposite). Map of stepped topography of the Sierra Nevada south of Tuolumne River.

Step fronts compiled from 1:62,500 topographic maps. Geology from Burnett and Mathews, 196__; Smith, 1965; Wahrhaftig, 1965e, figure 4; Bateman, 1965a, 1965b, 1965c; Huber and Rinehart, 1965; Peck, 1964; Bateman and others, 1962; and N. King Huber, written communication, 1966.

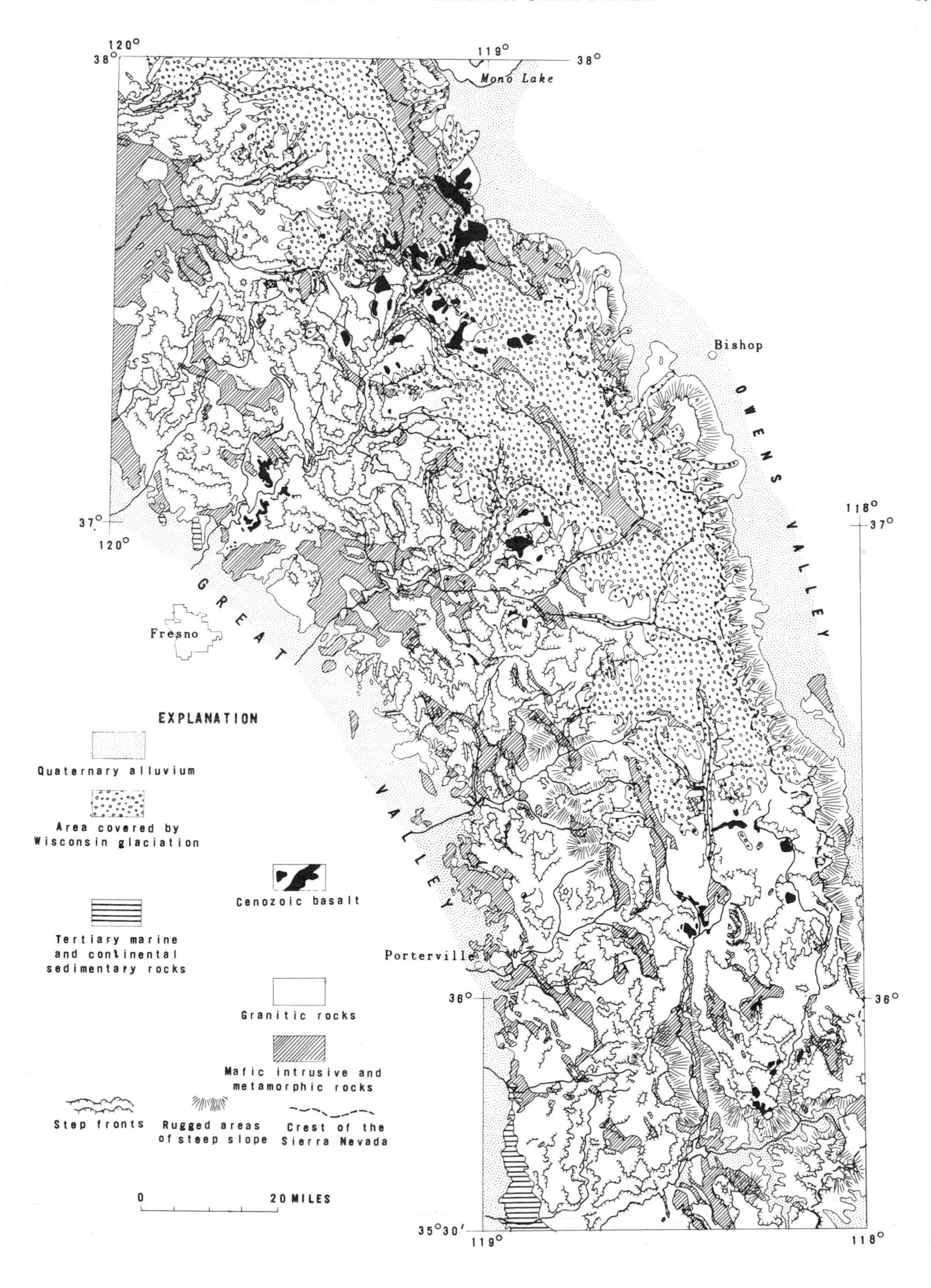
120°
38°
119°
38°
Mono Lake
Bishop
OWENS VALLEY
118°
37°
37°
120°
GREAT
Fresno
VALLEY
EXPLANATION
Quaternary alluvium
Area covered by Wisconsin glaciation
Cenozoic basalt
Tertiary marine and continental sedimentary rocks
Granitic rocks
Mafic intrusive and metamorphic rocks
Step fronts
Rugged areas of steep slope
Crest of the Sierra Nevada
0
20 MILES
Porterville
36°
36°
35°30′
119°
118°

Photo 14 (above). Fuller Buttes in Shuteye Peak quadrangle are fine examples of the many domes in granitic rock in the Sierra Nevada. Bare granite domes such as these weather and erode extremely slowly. Their origin may be due in part to processes similar to those that account for the stepped topography. *Photograph by N. King Huber.*

boulder-choked canyons and cross the treads with graded sandy streambeds. Steps are found not only facing the San Joaquin Valley but also lining the canyons of the San Joaquin, Kings, and Kern Rivers.

According to Wahrhaftig (1965e) these steps are the eventual landform resulting from the fact that soil-covered granite weathers much more rapidly to gruss than does exposed granite, because the buried granite is in contact most of the year with water and organic decay products while the surfaces of the exposed granite dry shortly after each rain. Because granite where widely jointed cannot be eroded until it is weathered to gruss, exposures of solid rock act as local base levels for erosion of the still buried rock upstream or upslope. The exposures grow to lines of outcrops, which grow into escarpments—the step fronts—through lowering of the country downstream from them.

The fixing of streams in bedrock notches from which they cannot migrate, and the establishment of bedrock outcrops at all low points on the crest of a step front, may involve much lateral migration and drainage capture. Once established, however, the growth of the stepped topography is inevitable because the country upstream from each bedrock notch can be flattened to the level of the notch but not below it.

Photo 15. Unloading joints, spaced 2–5 feet apart, exposed by glacial quarrying on the side of a dome in granitic rocks. Northeast side of Chiquito Ridge, Shuteye Peak quadrangle. For an early discussion of their origin see Gilbert, 1904. *Photograph by N. King Huber.*

Photo 16. View south down Kern Canyon from near the mouth of Whitney Creek, Sequoia National Park. The mountain in right foreground is Red Spur, and forested flat area behind it is Chagoopa Plateau, a little over 2,000 feet above the floor of Kern Canyon. The light-colored area in the center of the forest is Sky Parlor Meadow. Behind the Chagoopa Plateau the peaks of the Great Western Divide close southward toward Kern Canyon. The bench above the canyon rim on the left is correlated by Lawson and Matthes with the Chagoopa Plateau. The flat bare area above timberline near the left margin is the Boreal Plateau, with Funston Lake forming a dark area in its center. Beyond the Boreal Plateau is the valley of Golden Trout Creek and the slightly glaciated peaks of the Toowa Range. Mountains on skyline are the southern Sierra Nevada, Tehachapi, and Greenhorn Mountains, and on the extreme right, Mount Pinos and the San Emigdio Mountains lying beyond the south end of the San Joaquin Valley. The remarkable straightness of the Kern Canyon, which is eroded along an inactive fault zone, is evident in this view, as is the fact that the Chagoopa surface is found only at the head of the Kern Canyon. U.S. Geological Survey photograph GS-OAL-1-73.

The characteristics of stepped topography which may be used to identify the process are: (1) the irregular height and map pattern of fronts; (2) the backward slope of the treads (flat mountain-tops that are treads are slightly dished); (3) variation in number and altitude of knickpoints from stream to stream, even on tributaries to the same master stream; and (4) lack of parallelism of summit flats and benches, or of stream profiles reconstructed from knickpoints, with stratigraphically defined surfaces. Broad benches may exist at the headwaters of a stream system and be lacking at the appropriate height downstream.

Most of the benches and escarpments of the granitic terrane of the southern Sierra Nevada have the characteristics enumerated above. In particular, the remnants of the Chagoopa Surface at the head of Kern River do not extend downstream below the mouth of Golden Trout Creek, and as the walls of the Kern Canyon close in for several miles below this creek no equivalent of the Chapooga Surface is possible. Where benches appear along the Kern farther downstream, they are either much lower or much higher than the level defined by the Chagoopa Plateau.

According to the hypothesis of origin presented above, the steps can originate from a variety of causes at any altitude, and the treads therefore probably lack geomorphic significance as remnants of old-age surfaces. Many of the remnants of the supposed Boreal, Chagoopa, Broad Valley, and Mountain Valley surfaces are thought by Wahrhaftig (1965e) to be treads in the stepped topography, and many of the knickpoints used by Matthes in reconstructing his profiles on the Merced and San Joaquin Rivers are thought to be knickpoints in the stepped topography. Thus the Broad Valley and Mountain Valley profiles, if valid, are probably valid only in a general way.

The validity of the strictly physiographic criteria of uplift is therefore in doubt, and they cannot be used alone but must be supplemented with stratigraphic evidence. Some stratigraphic evidence exists within the range, as for example the basalt flows of Table Mountain on the San Joaquin, but most of the available stratigraphic evidence lies buried in the filling of the San Joaquin Valley, and its bearing on uplift within the range is indirect and involves many assumptions. The stratigraphic evidence must be evaluated in the light of the overall shape of the range, which toward the south departs from the simple asymmetric profile with an even westward-slope characteristic of the northern Sierra Nevada. South of Yosemite, subsidiary ridges whose height approaches that of the main crest are found progressively closer to the Great Valley the farther south one proceeds. At the south end of Sequoia Park, crestlines in the eastern half of the range are at about the same altitude over a width of 25 to 30 miles and the western half of the range slopes westward at an angle of about 4° from mountains that are 9,500 feet high, and only 25 miles from the Great Valley floor. This regional change in present overall shape implies a fundamental difference in the pattern of Cenozoic deformation; the northern part is tilted, whereas in the southern part a block, bounded by a flexure that sharpens southward, is bodily uplifted (Christensen, 1966).

The basalt-capped channel of Table Mountain on the San Joaquin River rises toward the northeast at 130 to 140 feet per mile (1°30′); this surface, projected eastward, coincides roughly with broad benches at about 7,000 feet in altitude and 3,000 feet above river level at the forks of the San Joaquin, 45 miles northeast of the Great Valley. Similarly, the basalt remnants along the Kings River rise eastward at about 140 feet per mile. If these streams had gradients of 30 feet per mile, as did the Tertiary streams in the northern Sierra Nevada, tilting of the western part of the range in the last 9.5 million years (the age of a basalt correlated with that on Table Mountain) has amounted to about 110 feet per mile, resulting in about 5,000 feet of uplift at the forks of the San Joaquin.

At the south end of the range, between the Kern and White Rivers, marine and continental sediments of Miocene age along the west base of the Sierra Nevada dip 5° to 6°31′ westward (Pease, 1952; Sperber, 1952). The eastward projection of the base of the Tertiary section at these dips barely clears the tops of the highest peaks for 10 to 15 miles into the range, and then rises above the tops of peaks to be about 2,000 feet above the crest of the Greenhorn Mountains, 25 miles east of the Tertiary outcrops. Farther east, the summit of the Sierra Nevada flattens.

These fragments of data from within the range suggest that the southern Sierra Nevada was tilted along its western margin from 1°30′ to 5° westward during the Pliocene, the dip decreasing eastward into the range and increasing southward along the west flank of the range. In response to this tilting and uplift, the San Joaquin, Kings, Kern, and other rivers deepened their canyons, cutting their inner gorges. The previously cited evidence of the San Joaquin suggests that this deepening affected its upper reaches about 3.5 million years ago. Evidence on the Kern, also cited above, suggests that the canyon of that stream was cut nearly to its present depth by 3.5 million years ago.

The basalt of Table Mountain, and the basalts in the Kings River drainage, impose severe restrictions on the amount of erosion resulting from this uplift, since they define valley-floor profiles only 2,000 to 4,000 feet above the floors of the present narrow canyons. The volume of sediment represented by the post-Pliocene canyons was estimated by filling these parts of relief models of the Fresno and Mariposa (1:250,000) Army Map Service sheets with sand, and measuring the volume of the sand. The total volume eroded from beneath this surface on these two quadrangles was found to be 500 cubic miles, representing an average lowering of the surface of the Sierra Nevada in these two quadrangles of about 300 feet.

The Ione outcrops of Little Table Mountain west of Friant give a measure of the tilting of the Sierra Nevada since Eocene time. Macdonald (1941) shows dips of 3° or about 250 feet per mile on these rocks. Janda (oral communication, 1965) has found, on the other hand, that the upper surface of Little Table Mountain slopes westward at the same angle as the surface of Table Mountain east of Friant, and projected eastward to Big Table Mountain, is about 500 feet higher. He regards the bedding with the steeper dips measured by Macdonald as possibly deltaic foresets. If Janda's interpretation is correct, there was no tilting during the interval between the Eocene and Pliocene, but only relative lowering of base level of about 500 feet.

The slope of stratigraphic surfaces beneath the Great Valley could be projected eastward into the Sierra Nevada to get a measure of tilting and uplift during various intervals within the Cenozoic. The results of a comparison of slopes calculated from well

TABLE 1. Comparison of dip of formations beneath the San Joaquin Valley with the west slope of the Sierra Nevada, in feet per mile.

	Location and reference to cross section		
	Chowchilla-Dos Palos: Union Gamble 7-15 to Pure Oil Chowchilla 1 (Bowen, 1962, pl. 15)	Reedley-Coalinga: Superior White 1 to Amerada Lawton 58-26 (Church, Krammes, and others, 1957b)	Bakersfield: Bald Eagle 74 to Western Gulf, KCL B-45 (Church, Krammes, and others, 1957a)
Base of the Pliocene	--	140	540
Base of the Miocene	103	230	975 (also basement)
Base of the Eocene	119	235	--
Upper surface of basement	336	400	(975)
Slope of Pliocene basalt in Sierra Nevada	140 (San Joaquin)	140 (Kings River)	
Slope of western Sierra Nevada along line east of section	240	270	450

data with the slope of the surface generalized from summit altitudes in the western Sierra Nevada are shown in table 1. From this table it is seen that the slope of the base of the Pliocene agrees reasonably well with the slope of San Joaquin Table Mountain, and that the generalized slope on summit altitudes corresponds to the slope at the base of the Eocene in the central San Joaquin Valley and with the slope of the base of the Pliocene in the southern San Joaquin Valley, and is about ½ to ⅔ the slope of the top of the basement. If the assumption that there is no difference in tilting from the eastern Great Valley to the Sierra Nevada can be made, and if we assume that the depression of the valley was matched by a corresponding rise in the Sierra, then there was little tilting of the Sierra Nevada during Eocene and Oligocene time, about 90 feet per mile of tilting during Miocene time, and about 140 feet per mile of tilting during Pliocene time, in the vicinity of the Kings and San Joaquin Rivers. Farther south, near Bakersfield, the tilting was much greater.

In the southern Sierra Nevada, as in the northern part of the range, the east side is predominantly a zone of gravity faulting. From Antelope Valley southeast to Big Pine the east-facing range-front faults have an *en echelon* pattern, as they do in the north, and alternate with ramps and arches. This pattern is interrupted by two large roughly equidimensional volcano-tectonic depressions—Mono Basin and Long Valley. From Big Pine south to Owens Lake the displacement, totalling 14,000 to 19,000 feet, is along two parallel east-facing faults from 5 to 7 miles apart. Near Owens Lake they converge and continue southward as a single fault zone, which terminates at the Garlock fault near Tehachapi Pass.

Between Antelope Valley and Mono Basin range-front faults are inconspicuous. The triangular Bridgeport Valley, at the east base of the Sierra in this stretch of the front, may be a deep alluvial basin bounded by faults, but elsewhere the range merges with mountains to the east. North of Bridgeport Valley, the Sweetwater Mountains, which are a north-trending range on the east side of Antelope Valley, continue southward along the east side of the West Walker River and merge indistinctly with the Sierra Nevada to the south. Within the Sweetwater Mountains, Cenozoic volcanic rocks are complexly faulted against a granitic and metamorphic basement, but the faults die out southward and none occur at the crest of the Sierra Nevada. Between Bridgeport Valley and the Mono Basin, the east front of the Sierra Nevada, which slopes gently eastward toward the Bodie Hills, is apparently a ramp broken by antithetic faults.

The volcano-tectonic Mono Basin is a roughly triangular depression about 30 miles long in a northeasterly direction and 20 miles wide along its southwest side, which is the eastern escarpment of the Sierra Nevada. Mono Lake lies at the base of the escarpment, and altitudes on late Pleistocene shorelines suggests that the basin floor has recently been titlted down to the west. A pronounced steep-sided gravity low that lies over the central part of the basin is interpreted by Pakiser, Press, and Kane (1960) to represent 18,000 ± 5,000 feet of low-density sedimentary and volcanic deposits of late Cenozoic age.

Long Valley is another volcano-tectonic depression about 15 miles south of Mono Lake (Pakiser, Kane, and Jackson, 1964). It is about 20 miles long east and west, 10 miles wide, and it makes a re-entrant into the east front of the Sierra Nevada. The valley is floored with lake sediments, alluvium, and volcanic deposits of late Cenozoic age (Rinehart and Ross, 1957; 1964; Doell, Dalrymple, and Cox, 1966; Huber and Rinehart, 1965a,b). Its south margin is an east-trending fault scarp in basement rocks nearly 4,000 feet high, and its northeast margin is a fault scarp 2,000 to 4,000 feet high

Photo 17. Eastern escarpment of the Sierra Nevada in the vicinity of Lone Pine and Mount Whitney, seen from over the north end of Owens Lake. Subsidiary fault scarp lies along the east side of the Alabama Hills in the middle distance. Lone Pine is just off the picture on the extreme right, at the point where Lone Pine Creek emerges from the Alabama Hills. Mount Whitney is the high peak at the north end of a serrated ridge at the head of the canyon of Lone Pine Creek. The alluvial and outwash fan apron along the base of the great scarp partly buries the Alabama Hills on the right, and toward the left where the two fault systems merge it is faulted, cut by lakeshores, and dissected. Late 19th century shores of the now dry Owens Lake in the foreground. Owens River on the right. Total relief in this picture, from Owens Lake (3,560 ft) to Mount Whitney (14,496 ft) is nearly 11,000 feet. U.S. Geological Survey photograph GS-OAI-5-18.

exposing late Tertiary volcanic rocks resting on a granitic basement (Gilbert, 1941). To the west and northwest it is overlapped by a volcanic field extending from the Mono Craters through Mammoth Mountain, and to the southeast it is flanked by the Bishop Tuff. A pronounced gravity low underlies the valley and is interpreted by Pakiser, Kane, and Jackson (1964) to represent 18,000 ± 5,000 feet of light late Cenozoic volcanic and sedimentary rocks, in fault contact with basement rocks. The boundary faults are curved, adding weight to the interpretation of volcano-tectonic collapse.

The two volcano-tectonic depressions are closely associated with Quaternary volcanic rocks and subsidence of the depressions with concommitant volcanism and infilling of the basins might have taken as much as 2 to 3 million years. Hot springs and Recent volcanos on the floors and margins of both depressions show that volanic activity has not ceased.

The east-facing Hilton Creek fault extends south from Long Valley for 10 miles into the Sierra Nevada, and has at least 3,500 feet of vertical displacement at McGee Mountain (Rinehart and Ross, 1964). It is the westernmost of three *en echelon* fault zones that make the east face of the Sierra Nevada south of Long Valley.

Six or eight miles to the east, a second fault makes the great east-facing escarpment of Wheeler Crest and Mount Tom. This fault has a displacement at its north end of as much as 7,000 feet, and extends 20 to 25 miles south, with continuously decreasing displacement, to die out in the headwaters of the South Fork of Bishop Creek (Bateman, 1965). The north-facing mountain front between these faults is a steep ramp broken by numerous antithetic faults downthrown to the south (Rinehart and Ross, 1957).

The broad arch of the Coyote Flat warp, east of the Wheeler Crest fault, breaks the continuity of range-front faults between Round Valley and Big Pine (Bateman, 1965). The mountain front here is apparently an erosion surface of relatively low relief, deformed into a broad anticline plunging to the northeast. The north flank of this arch slopes about 1,000 feet per mile northward across Bishop Creek to a shallow east-trending synclinal axis lying between the Tungsten Hills and the Bishop Tuff of the Volcanic Tableland. Its east flank slopes from 1,600 to less than 1,000 feet eastward toward the floor of Owens Valley; gravity studies indicate that the eastward slope of the basement continues at the same gradient beneath the valley floor to the base of a concealed fault along the west flank of the White Mountains. Numerous small antithetic faults break the continuity of this eastward slope.

A few miles north of Big Pine the Coyote Flat arch is broken by an east-facing fault, which passes along the west margin of the alluvial floor of Owens Valley just west of Big Pine and extends farther south, cutting through and offsetting the basaltic volcanoes of Crater Mountain and Red Mountain. The displacement on this fault increases to the south, as indicated by gravity gradients across it (Pakiser, Kane, and Jackson, 1964). South of Red Mountain, it lies at the base of the great alluvial fan apron forming the east front of the Sierra Nevada, and passes along the east flank of the Alabama Hills to the west side of Owens Lake. Its vertical displacement at the Alabama Hills, calculated from gravity anomalies, is about 8,000 feet. The surface breakage of the Lone Pine earthquake of 1870 was concentrated along this fault.

The great escarpment of the Sierra Nevada, lying a half dozen miles west of this fault, probably marks another fault, whose displacement, as indicated by topographic relief, may be 7,000 to 9,000 feet. South of the latitude of Lone Pine the escarpment bends to the east to approach the fault on the east side of the Alabama Hills, and the two faults merge just west of Owens Lake to form a single complex fault system with a total displacement on the order of 15,000 feet (Pakiser, Kane, and Jackson, 1964, fig. 15). This fault zone has been traced southward to its junction with the Garlock fault (Smith, 1965; Jennings and others, 1962).

Deformation along the eastern boundary zone apparently began about 10 million years ago, and has continued to the present. Judging from potassium-argon dates obtained for volcanic rocks associated with the fault scarps and warps, most of the deformation took place in the last 3 million years, and much of it happened in the last 700,000 years. Glacial moraines of Wisconsin age, which are only 10,000 to 100,000 years old, are offset as much as 50 feet by range-front faults.

A basalt dated at 9.6 m.y. fills a valley directed down the north slope of the Coyote Flat warp and indicates that initial deformation to create the warp began before its extrusion. However, patches of ancient till that has been correlated with the Sherwin Till rest on the basalt but are separated from their source by the narrow stream-cut canyon of Coyote Creek, which is more than 1,000 feet deep; presumably much of the warping, and certainly most of the erosion resulting from warping, post-dates the deposition of this till (Bateman, 1965).

As much as 2,500 feet of displacement has taken place on the faults along the north and east sides of McGee Mountain after the deposition of the McGee Till, which sits on a basalt 2.6 m.y. old and presumably predates the Sherwin Till. The 3.0 to 3.1 m.y. andesite and quartz-latite on San Joaquin Mountain (Dalrymple, 1964a), at the head of the Middle Fork of the San Joaquin River, are cut off on the east by the range-front fault along the western margin of Long Valley (Huber and Rinehart, 1965). The volcanic rocks fill a valley through which drainage from Mono Basin appears to have entered the San Joaquin Valley. The McGee and San Joaquin Mountain localities indicate that much of the range-front faulting at Long Valley is less than 3 million years old.

The 700-thousand-year-old Bishop Tuff has possibly as much as 3,000 feet of structural relief, as mentioned in the section on volcanic rocks. Its upper surface has an altitudinal range of as much as 4,300 feet in 25 miles, and much of this altitudinal range may be due to deformation. At least 1,000 feet of warping of the tuff can be demonstrated in the vicinity of Round Valley (Bateman, 1965), and the tuff is offset as much as 500 feet by normal faults (Putnam, 1960a). The fact that it was confined to a valley between the Sierra Nevada and the White Mountains suggests that most of the range-front faulting predates the eruption of the tuff.

According to Sharp (*in* Wahrhaftig and Sharp, 1965), the Sherwin Till on benches along the west side of the Mono Basin predates 1,000 to 2,000 feet of faulting in the basin. As the Sherwin Till at the type locality underlies the Bishop Tuff, 1,000 to 2,000 feet or more of deformation must have taken place within the last 700 thousand years along the east flank of the Sierra Nevada at both the north end of Owens Valley and in the Mono Basin.

In the alluvial floors of Owens Valley as much as 13 feet of net vertical displacement and 9 to 16 feet of right-lateral displacement took place on a fault east of the Alabama Hills during the Lone Pine earthquake of 1870 (Bateman, 1961).

The foregoing evidence indicates that in the southern Sierra Nevada most of the displacement along the eastern fault zone was accomplished within the last 3 million years and much of it occurred within the last 700,000 years; much of it is therefore appreciably younger than any in the northern Sierra Nevada for which there is positive evidence. Most of the erosion in response to the late Cenozoic tilting and uplift of this southern part of the range took place more than 3 million years ago. Thus, the faulting along the east side appears to be later than the tilting of the range, and it is probably due to the collapse of Owens Valley, and other grabens and volcano-tectonic depressions along the crest of the broad arch defined by the Sierra Nevada on the west and the Basin Ranges on the east (Bateman, 1965, pl. 10).

In summary, the available data on deformation on the west side of the southern Sierra Nevada suggest that deformation gradually changed southward from simple westward tilting in the latitude of Yosemite and the San Joaquin River to a flexure along the west margin and vertical uplift of the east half of the range in the latitude of Sequoia Park and farther south. The amount of tilting since the early Pliocene (9.5 m.y. ago) was about 110 feet per mile in the latitude of the San Joaquin and Kings Rivers, and since the Miocene tilting of as much as 5° to 6½° took place along the west margin of the range near Bakersfield. An average of 300 feet of erosion, concentrated in the canyons, has occurred since early Pliocene time, but the canyons had nearly their present depths 3.5 million years ago, suggesting completion of the tilting by then. There is little evidence of tilting in the interval between the early Eocene and the Miocene.

Displacement along the east side northwest of Big Pine was accomplished through a series of *en echelon* faults alternating with arches and ramps, and this part of the front is marked by two large volcano-tectonic depressions with floors possibly as much as 11,000 feet below sea level. Displacement south of Big Pine is distributed along two parallel faults, and totals as much as 19,000 feet. The faults converge to a single complex zone at Owens Lake. Most of the displacement along the eastern front has taken place in the last 3 million years, and displacement has continued to the present. This displacement is apparently later than most of the tilting of the west slope of the range, and may therefore represent collapse of the Owens Valley graben.

GLACIATION

The Sierra Nevada, along with many other high mountains throughout the world, was repeatedly glaciated during the Quaternary. At the height of glaciation it bore a mountain icecap 270 miles long and 20 to 30 miles wide (fig. 17). During the latest glaciations, on the east side of the range valley glaciers descended from this icecap onto the bordering lowlands, and on the west side they extended down canyons to altitudes of 3,000 to 4,000 feet. Some of the earlier glaciations were even more extensive.

The Sierra Nevada now bears about 60 small glaciers at the heads of cirques where they are protected from the summer sun by high north-facing cliffs. These glaciers lie at altitudes ranging from 10,600 feet at the north end of Yosemite Park to 11,500 to 12,000 feet in the vicinity of the Palisades along the east boundary of Kings Canyon National Park. The peaks that shade them range from 11,000 feet in altitude at the north to 14,250 feet in altitude at the south. No peak in Sequoia Park, not even Mount Whitney,

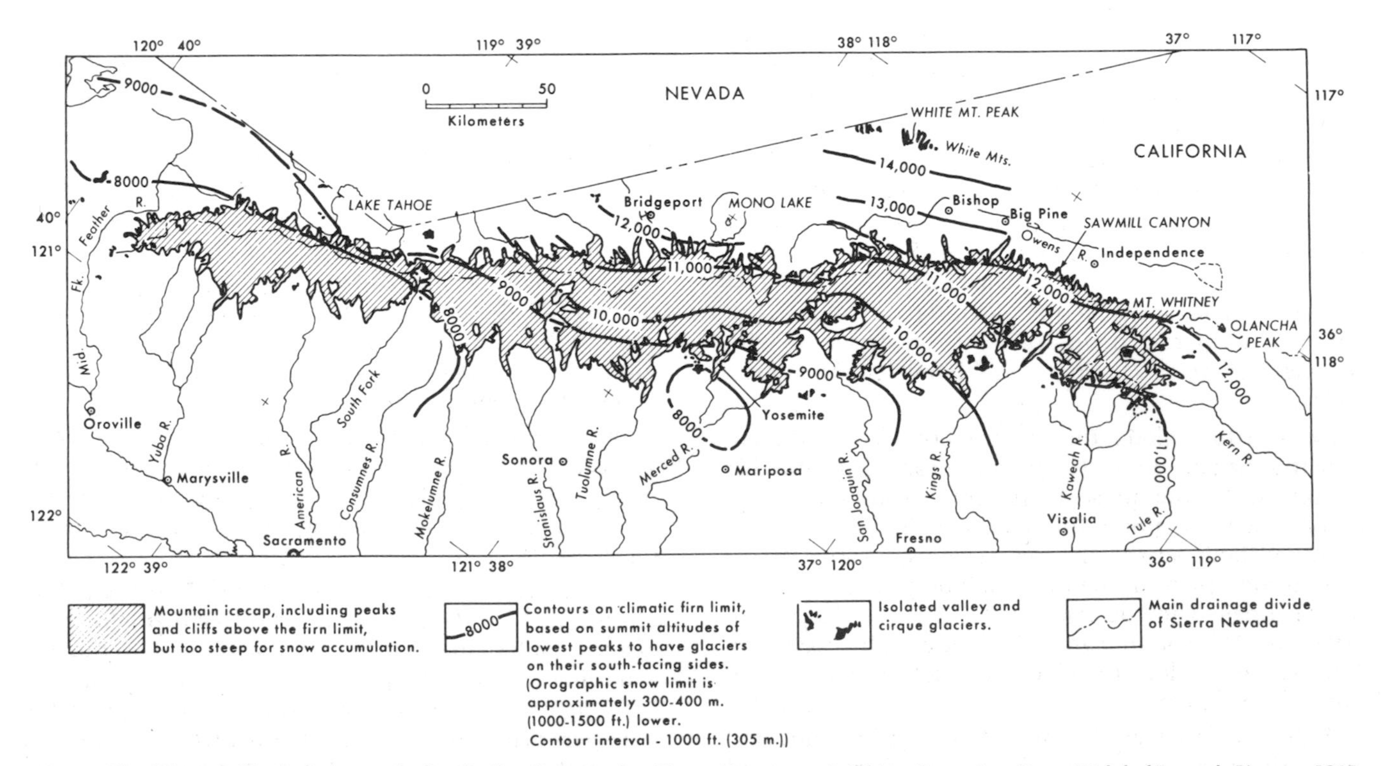

Figure 17. Wisconsin(?) glaciation and climatic firn limit in the Sierra Nevada and White Mountains. From Wahrhaftig and Birman, 1965, figure 2, which should be consulted for sources of information.

Photo 18. Glaciated upland east of Yosemite Valley, with Half Dome in the foreground. Little Yosemite Valley extends east behind Half Dome to headwaters along the west side of the Ritter Range. To the right can be seen the canyon of the Middle Fork of the San Joaquin. Mountains forming the central skyline are the White Mountains. U.S. Geological Survey photograph GS-OAH-3-155.

14,500 feet high, bears any glaciers. The largest glacier, the Palisade Glacier at the head of Big Pine Creek, is about 1 mile long, but the great majority of them are less than ½ mile long. These glaciers, which have formed since the climatic optimum, were twice their present size about 100 years ago, and have been shrinking ever since. Their continued existence, in the face of secular warming, is uncertain.

The climatic firn limit (firn limit on south-facing slopes) at the time of the maximum of the last major glaciation is shown by contours on figure 17. As can be seen from this map, the orographic effect of the Sierra Nevada is much more pronounced than the poleward cooling of world climate, so that the climatic firn limit rose northeastward across the mountains. The lowest cirques, which are less than 8,000 feet in altitude, are found on mountains in the middle slopes of the Sierra Nevada near Yosemite, and mountains 11,000 to 12,000 feet high east of the range bore no glaciers.

At the present time no peak in the Sierra Nevada is above the climatic firn limit. The southernmost peak in the United States to have borne glaciers on its south slopes during historic time is Mount Shasta, 14,161 feet in altitude. Thus, as the climatic firn limit is now above 14,500 feet, and probably above 15,000 feet, in the southern Sierra Nevada, the lowering of the firn limit to bring about the Wisconsin Glaciation was on the order of 3,000 feet or more.

Photo 19. Yosemite Valley, from over El Capitan looking east. The floor of the valley is underlain by nearly 2,000 feet of outwash and lake sediments, resting on the glacier-carved bedrock floor. *Photograph by Mary Hill.*

An orographic firn limit (lower limit of perennial snow on north-facing cirque glaciers) is difficult to define because of the great variation in two factors influencing snow retention: (1) protection from sunlight, and (2) accumulation by avalanches. Thus, although it is not possible to define precisely the orographic firn limit, it can be said in a general way to range now from about 11,700 feet at the north end of Yosemite Park to 11,500 to 13,000 feet in Kings Canyon Park. It appears that during the glacial maximum shown in figure 17 the orographic firn limit was 1,000 to 2,500 feet lower than the climatic firn limit, or at altitudes of 9,500 to 10,500 in the places where the glaciers are today. Southwest of Lake Tahoe, where the lowest glacial cirques are comparable to the glacier-bearing cirques in the Sierra today, the orographic firn limit was as much as 2,500 feet lower than the climatic firn limit.

The mountain icecap indicated on figure 17 was not a continuous ice sheet above which only a few peaks emerged, such as now exist on many ranges of southern Alaska. Rather it represented the filling in a series of separate basins of accumulation, many of which were enclosed on three sides by an almost continuous arête but interconnected to the extent that ice flowed through some passes from one basin to another. The area of almost continuous icecap, where most of the divides were submerged, included the basins of the Tuolumne, Stanislaus, and West Walker Rivers. From the Tuolumne drainage ice also poured through several passes into the headwaters of the Merced River.

At many places along the present drainage divide, glaciers from basins west of the divide spilled over the passes to feed ice tongues in canyons descending the east slope. This ice eroded broad U-shaped passes, which provide many of the routes of access across the range, such as Donner and Tioga Pass.

The ice thickness was generally 1,000 feet or less on the flanks of the arêtes and in the accumulation basins in the headwaters of the main glaciated canyons. The steep glaciers on the east side of the range were also generally about 1,000 feet thick. On the west side of the range, ice flowing into the narrow canyons of the major rivers, such as the Tuolumne, Merced, San Joaquin, and Kings, filled them to great depths. During the last glaciation, the Tuolumne Glacier was 4,000 feet thick in the Grand Canyon of the Tuolumne, where it spilled over the south rim of the canyon. During an earlier glaciation, the Merced Glacier must have had a maximum thickness of nearly 6,000 feet in Yosemite Valley (see fig. 14, photo 19), including 2,000 feet excavated by the ice below the valley's bedrock lip (Gutenberg and others, 1956; Matthes, 1930).

The amount of erosion that the glaciers could accomplish was chiefly controlled by the jointing and weathering of the granitic rocks that floor most of the glaciated areas. Headwater basins were opened to broad cirques; lake basins were carved throughout the glaciated region; and at the glacial termini were formed deep basins, such as hold Donner Lake, Fallen Leaf Lake, and Emerald Bay, and the alluvium-filled rock basin 2,000 feet deep beneath the floor of Yosemite Valley. Many of the valleys were given U-shaped cross-profiles, and a number were deepened considerably. Weathered bedrock was removed from most of the glaciated areas, and trenches were etched along the joints, giving many cirque and basin floors a billowy topography. Frost action sharpened the ridges and peaks to precipitous arêtes and horns. Much of the unusual beauty of the High Sierra is the result of this glacial modification of a previously dissected landscape.

In spite of these spectacular examples of glacial erosion, it is remarkable also what the glaciers did not do. Broad benches that predate glaciation, such as the Chagoopa Plateau and other benches along the Kern River Canyon and the benches along the South Fork of the San Joaquin, were little modified by the ice that poured over them. Many gorges retained a V-shaped profile, in spite of the vigor of the glaciers that poured through them. Examples are the Grand Canyon of the Tuolumne, the canyon of the Merced below Yosemite, and the canyon of the South Fork of the San Joaquin between Mono Hot Springs and Balloon Dome. The V-shaped profiles of these canyons may have been preserved by the presence of large-scale sheeting parallel to the original canyon walls, which controlled the pattern of glacial erosion.

Material eroded by the glaciers was either deposited in the form of moraines or delivered to meltwater streams to be carried out of the glaciated area. The most impressive moraines are at the mouths of canyons along the east side of the Sierra. These moraines project 1 to 3 miles directly away from the mountain front on either side of the glaciated canyons, parallel to the direction of glacier flow, indicating that the glaciers did not spread as piedmont lobes but maintained the widths they had in their mountain canyons by building walls for themselves in the form of sharp-crested embankments a few hundred to a thousand feet high. Many of these morainal ridges have double or triple crests, with narrow trenches running the length of the ridge between the crests, indicating two or three advances of the ice during their construction.

On the forested west slope of the Sierra the moraines are lower and less conspicuous, and are commonly difficult to recognize. They reach their most impressive size along the walls of the broad upper valley of the South Fork of the San Joaquin River (Birman, 1964), north of Kaiser Crest, and along Roaring River, tributary of the South Fork of the Kings. Low terminal moraines cross the floor of Yosemite Valley near Bridalveil Fall.

The bulk of the glacial debris on the west side was probably transported into the Great Valley by swift meltwater streams. Within the range the canyons are so steep and narrow that outwash terraces have not been preserved. Roadcuts in some of the canyons, such as those in Merced Canyon between Briceburg and El Portal, have exposed patches of outwash of several ages and degrees of weathering, preserved beneath mantles of colluvium.

The lithology of the alluvium from the major rivers on the east side of the Great Valley indicates its glacial origin (Janda, 1965b). It contains numerous boulders and pebbles of fresh granitic rocks, rock types that are rare in alluvium from unglaciated basins or in preglacial alluvium. It also contains layers of finely laminated silt and fine sand consisting of unweathered fragments of hornblende, augite, biotite, feldspar, and quartz. Silt of such mineralogy could not have been produced by ordinary weathering processes and must have originated as glacial rock flour.

That the Sierra Nevada was glaciated more than once during the Quaternary was recognized in the late 19th century (Russell, 1889; Turner, 1900; W. D. Johnston, unpublished notes). The classic works on multiple glaciation in the Sierra Nevada are those of Matthes (1930), who established three glacial stages on the west side of the Sierra Nevada around Yosemite Valley, and of Blackwelder (1931), who established four glacial stages on the east side. Blackwelder's terminology of Tioga, Tahoe, Sherwin, and McGee, from youngest to oldest, has been adopted wherever correlations with his type localities were possible. Sharp and Birman (1963) have added two new Pleistocene glaciations to the chronology of Blackwelder: the Tenaya, between the Tioga and the Tahoe; and the Mono Basin, between the Tahoe and the Sherwin. Birman (1964) has, in addition, named three post-Tahoe glaciations, two of which, at least, are post-altithermal.

The difficulty of correlating glaciations along the length of the range has persuaded Birkeland (1964) to adopt local names for the pre-Tahoe glaciations north of Lake Tahoe. Correlation across the range also presents great difficulties; Matthes and Blackwelder, although they were familiar with each other's work, were unable to come up with a mutually satisfactory correlation. Birman (1964), by tracing glacial deposits and landforms across the range between the South Fork of the San Joaquin and Rock Creek, and by statistical study of boulder-weathering ratios, has made a correlation of the younger glaciations across the range,

Photo 20. Roaring River valley in Kings Canyon National Park, seen from the west over Sugarloaf Meadow. In the background are the serrated horns and aretes of the Great Western and Kings-Kern Divides. The prominent morainal ridges that enclose the valley are probably of Tahoe and Tioga age. U.S. Geological Survey photograph GS-OAL-1-211.

although he could distinguish only one pre-Tahoe glaciation on the west side.

Some of the glacial deposits are overlain or underlain by radiometrically dated volcanic deposits (Dalrymple, 1964a; 1964b; Dalrymple, Cox and Doell, 1965); hence, an absolute chronology of some of the glaciations can be approximated. At the moment of writing, the McGee and Sherwin deposits are the oldest Quaternary glacial deposits in the world associated with radiometrically dated rocks.

Tectonics and erosion have considerably obscured the glacial record. Consequently one major concern has been the possibility that there are additional, unrecognized, glaciations, the critical evidence for which is missing through erosion or burial. A more complete record of glaciation is likely to be preserved in the alluvium of the Great Valley than in the mountains themselves. Three and possibly four separate alluvial units of glacial origin, separated by erosional unconformities with well-developed soils, have been recognized along the east side of the valley (Davis and Hall, 1959; Arkley, 1962; Janda, 1965b). Janda has correlated these with glacial deposits in the High Sierra.

The glacial deposits and coeval alluvial deposits can be divided into five groups on the basis of age and degree of preservation; from youngest to oldest these are:

(1) Extremely fresh bouldery moraines deposited by glaciers that advanced only a short distance from the cirque heads. Included are the Matthes and Recess Peak Glaciations of Birman (1964) and neoglacial deposits recognized by Birkeland (1964). These are post-altithermal in age.

(2) Somewhat more extensive and more weathered tills, intermediate in character between the Tioga Tills and the group described above. Included are the deposits of Hilgard Glaciation of Birman (1964) and the Frog Lake Till of Birkeland (1964). These glacial deposits may result from either the latest pulse of the Wisconsin or an early Recent (post-altithermal) advance.

(3) Well-preserved moraines marking a sequence of glaciations, all of which were about as extensive as shown on figure 17. None of the moraines shows any development of a textural B horizon in the soil (Birkeland, 1964). This group includes moraines of the

Tioga, Tenaya, Tahoe, and possibly the Mono Basin Glaciations. Tioga and Tahoe are recognized throughout the length of the glaciated Sierra Nevada. Tenaya and Mono Basin have been recognized in only a few localities south of Sonora Pass. In the walls of excavations, such as roadcuts, the Tioga can be distinguished from the Tahoe, because boulders in the Tioga Till are fresh throughout, whereas many of the granodiorite and quartz-monzonite boulders beneath the surface to depths of 5 to 10 feet in the Tahoe deposits are altered to gruss (Birkeland, 1964; Wahrhaftig, 1965a, 1965e). No roadcut exposures of the Tenaya or Mono Basin Tills are available. In the absence of cuts, distinction and correlation of moraines of this sequence are based on depth of erosion of axial stream channels, sharpness and degree of preservation of the moraines (Blackwelder, 1931), and boulder-weathering ratios and abundance of fine materials in the surface soil (Sharp and Birman, 1963; Birman, 1964; Sharp, 1965a,b; Sharp *in* Wahrhaftig and Sharp, 1965).

The moraines of this group are bracketed by a radiocarbon age of 9,800 ± 800 years (David P. Adam, written communication, 1965) for Tioga Till near Echo Summit; and by potassium-argon dates of 90,000 ± 90,000 and 60,000 ± 50,000 years on basalt beneath Tahoe Till at Sawmill Canyon (Dalrymple, 1964b). Hence the sequence Tioga-Tenaya-Tahoe corresponds to the Wisconsin in the broad sense of midwest chronology. Through study of ice-dammed flood deposits from Lake Tahoe, Birkeland (1965a) has correlated the Tahoe and Tioga with the Eetza and Seehoo Formations, respectively, of Lake Lahontan (Morrison, 1964).

The Modesto Formation of Davis and Hall (1959) in the Eastern San Joaquin Valley has been correlated by Janda (1965b) with the sequence Tioga-Tahoe-Tenaya, on the basis of the lack of a textural B horizon in its soil. According to Janda the formation has three terraces with slightly different weak soil development; these may correlate with the three glaciations recognized by Birman at the head of the San Joaquin drainage.

(4) Poorly preserved moraines and well-preserved outwash terraces, upon which there is a soil with a well-developed B horizon. Till and outwash of the Donner Lake Glaciation (Birkeland, 1964) in the Truckee area is assigned to this group. The glaciation post-dates deformation in the Truckee area. The Riverbank Formation of Davis and Hall (1959) in the eastern San Joaquin Valley, which is slightly dissected and has a well-developed soil with an oxidized clay-rich B horizon or a silica hardpan, or both, is also assigned to this group. With the exception of the deposits of the Truckee area, no extensive glacial deposits have been assigned to this period of glaciation. The excellent soil development indicates that it is much older than Wisconsin. A deposit of weathered gravel, which occurs above the limit of the Tahoe Glaciation just west of Mammoth Mountain, contains quartz-latite derived from Mammoth Mountain, which has been dated at 370,000 years (Janda, 1965a; for discussion of date, see Dalrymple, 1964). If this deposit is a till and is to be correlated with the Donner Lake Glaciation, it is probably younger than 370,000 years and older than the Tahoe Glaciation.

(5) Deposits of till, without morainal topography, buried beneath volcanic deposits, or perched on mountaintops and benches several thousand feet above present-day glaciated canyon floors. The till of this group has customarily been assigned to two glaciations, the Sherwin and the McGee (Blackwelder, 1930; Putnam, 1960a, 1960b, 1962; Rinehart and Ross, 1957, 1964). The type locality of the Sherwin Till is on the Sherwin Grade of U.S. Highway 395, where it is overlain by the Bishop Tuff, dated at 700,000 years (Dalrymple, Cox, and Doell, 1965; Putnam, 1960a; Rinehart and Ross, 1957; Sharp, 1965b). It therefore predates the 1,000–3,000 feet of deformation that affected the Bishop Tuff. The till is deeply weathered and lacks morainal topography. Judging from the even character of the till surface buried beneath the Bishop Tuff, its morainal topography was obliterated before the deposition of the tuff. It may, therefore, be considerably older than the tuff.

Farther north, deposits of till on intercanyon benches on the west side of the Mono Basin are correlated by Sharp (*in* Wahrhaftig and Sharp, 1965) with the Sherwin Glaciation. According to Sharp, these were deposited before the collapse of the Mono Basin, and therefore predate several thousand feet of displacement on the faults enclosing that basin, and according to Pakiser, Press, and Kane (1960), they may predate as much as 18,000 feet of displacement.

The McGee Till rests on a 10,500-foot plateau on the summit of McGee Mountain, about 2,000 feet above the floor of McGee Creek canyon to the south, and more than 3,000 feet above the floor of Long Valley. The most abundant boulders in the till come from granodiorite exposed at the head of McGee Creek, a half-dozen miles to the south. The till rests on basalt with a potassium-argon age of 2.6 m.y. (Dalrymple, 1963). Blackwelder (1931), Putnam (1960, 1962) and Rinehart and Ross (1964) concluded that the till was deposited before several thousand feet of displacement on the range-front faults on the north and east sides of McGee Mountain, and when McGee Creek canyon was much shallower than today. Lovejoy (1964) argued that the till was deposited by a glacier when the topography was essentially as it is today. Christensen (1966) has reviewed the evidence, and presented a justification for the views of Blackwelder, Putnam, and Rinehart and Ross.

Because the Sherwin Till is found at the base of fault scarps like those bordering McGee Mountain, Blackwelder (1931) and all subsequent workers have concluded that the Sherwin and McGee are separate glaciations, and that several thousand feet of displacement occurred on the range-front fault in the interval

Photo 21. The northeast face of the Sierra Nevada in Mount Morrison quadrangle as seen from hills east of Deadman Summit. Mount Morrison is the sharp peak on skyline on the right. The broad flat mountain, on the left, slightly in shadow and in front of snowclad peaks, is McGee Mountain. Deposits of the McGee Till mantle its flat summit, and directly below it is the complex of moraines of the Convict Greek glacier. The plain below the moraines is the floor of Long Valley. The hills from which the photograph was taken are part of the volcanic sequence erupted on the floor of the Long Valley volcano-tectonic depression, and the mountain front here is one wall of that depression. *Photograph by John Burnett.*

between them. Although this is probably so, one cannot really prove that the Sherwin and the McGee are separate glaciations.

In the Truckee area in the northern part of the range, scattered remnants of till and outwash older than the Donner Lake Glaciation are assigned to a glaciation named by Birkeland (1964) the Hobart Glaciation. As the till occurs at the present river level on the Truckee River, the glaciation presumably occurred after the river eroded through the volcanic rocks of the Lousetown Formation to its present position. And because the youngest Lousetown volcanics involved are 1.2 million years old, the Hobart Glaciation took place less than 1.2 million years ago, probably much less. The Hobart may correlate with the Sherwin, but such a correlation cannot be proved.

Alluvium in the San Joaquin Valley that is probably outwash from glaciations that may correlate with the Sherwin or McGee or both, makes up the Turlock Lake Formation of Davis and Hall (1959; see Janda, 1965b). In the Friant area, where the San Joaquin River debouches onto the alluvial plain, this formation consists of two units separated by an erosional unconformity and a well-developed soil. At the base of the upper unit is a pumiceous ash, on which a date of 600,000 years has been obtained (Janda, 1965b). The upper unit of the Turlock Lake Formation is intricately dissected with a relief of about 100 to 200 feet, and on this surface of dissection is a soil with a well-developed textural B horizon. Of the two glaciations represented by the Turlock Lake, one is slightly younger than 600,000 years, and the other much older.

The chronology of glaciations described in the paragraphs above is summarized in table 2.

SUMMARY OF GEOLOGIC HISTORY

During the Paleozoic the Sierra Nevada region was beneath the sea receiving sediments in the east and volcanic and associated sedimentary deposits in the west. Doubtless the Mississippian Antler orogeny of Nevada affected the Sierra Nevada region, and other disturbance may also have occurred during the Paleozoic. In Late Permian or Triassic time a north- to northwest-trending synclinal trough began to subside

TABLE 2. Provisional correlation of glacial and alluvial deposits in the Sierra Nevada.

Age	Mid-continent glaciations	Lake Lahontan (Morrison, 1961, 1964)	Tahoe area (Birkeland, 1964)	Southern Sierra Nevada (Blackwelder, 1931; Sharp and Birman, 1963, Birman, 1964)	Alluvial formations of the San Joaquin Valley (Davis and Hall, 1959; Arkley, 1962; Janda, 1965–b)
Recent		Fallon Formation	Neoglaciation	Matthes Till Recess Peak Till	Alluvium
?	Wisconsin Glaciation	Lahontan Valley Group: Sehoo Formation Eetza Formation	? Frog Lake Till 9,800y.* Tioga Till Tahoe Till	? Hilgard Till Tioga Till Tenaya Till Tahoe Till (60,000–90,000y.*)	Modesto Formation
			?	? Mono Basin Till ?	
			Donner Lake Till	? Till(?) on Mammoth Mountain (Janda, 1965a) (370,000y.*)	Riverbank Formation
Pleistocene	Correlation with mid-continent glaciations uncertain	Two pre-Lake Lahontan units (Morrison, 1965)	Hobart Till 1.2 m.y. (under Hobart)	? Glaciation between tuff of Reds Meadow and andesite of Devils Postpile (Huber, oral comm., 1965) ? (Bishop Tuff, 700,000y.*)	Turlock Lake Formation (upper unit) ? 600,000y.*
				Sherwin Till McGee Till 2.5 m.y. (under McGee)	? Turlock Lake Formation (lower unit)

* For discussion of radiometric dates, see text.

in the area of the Sierra Nevada. This trough was filled during the Late Triassic and Jurassic with great thicknesses of volcanogenic materials. Repeated disturbances are indicated by unconformities and by superimposed minor fold systems. Steep beds, cleavages, and lineations require that the synclinal structure extended downward many miles below the present level of exposure. Faults with stratigraphic separations of many miles cut the west limb of the synclinorium, and serpentine along these faults suggests that they penetrated into the mantle.

Magma of granitic composition was generated in the lower part of this synclinorium during at least three widely separated times—the Late Triassic or Early Jurassic, the Late Jurassic, and early Late Cretaceous—and possibly at other times as well. The generation of magma probably was caused in part by the depression of sialic rocks in the keel of the synclinorium into deep zones of high temperature and in part by thickening of the sial, which contains a greater abundance of the heat-producing radioactive elements than the underlying more femic earth zones. Additional heat might have been supplied by convective overturn in the mantle or by the intrusion of dike swarms into the base of the crust, but no evidence can be cited in support of either process.

Granitic magma is significantly less dense than granitic rock of the same composition and consequently much of it worked its way upward, in much the same manner as salt domes, into the overlying rock. The rising magmas exploited faults and other lines of structural weakness, and crowded the country rocks aside. Most of the magmas rose into the axial region of the synclinorium, but some worked upward along its limbs. As the magmas rose, reactions took place between them and the country rocks, especially between felsic magmas and amphibolitic wall rock. Although convincing evidence of the melting of wall and roof rocks by heat given off by magmas has not been observed, some of the less refractory country rocks, such as shale or graywacke, probably were incorporated in magmas by melting. Differentiation, chiefly through fractional crystallization, took place within the magmas as they rose and produced a diversity of compositions in the rising magmas and in the granitic rocks. In general, the most highly differentiated and most felsic magmas penetrated highest, causing the average composition of the granitic rocks to be more felsic upward. As a consequence of the upward movement and differentiation of magmas, the batholith is composed of a mosaic of plutons of different composition and texture, which are either in sharp contact with one another or are separated from one another by thin septa of metamorphic or older granitic rocks.

The depression of the synclinorium doubtless disturbed the isostatic equilibrium, which required uplift for adjustment. Because of erosion the re-establishment of isostatic equilibrium was a long process that may still be going on today. Considerations of the volume of epiclastic material that was deposited in basins adjacent to a broad north-trending highland that included the Sierra Nevada, and of the significance of andalusite and sillimanite in contact-metamorphic mineral assemblages suggest that at least 9 miles of rock was eroded from the Sierra Nevada since the two earlier periods of plutonism in Late Triassic or Early Jurassic and Late Jurassic time.

This great amount of erosion was probably completed along the west margin of the Sierra Nevada by Coniacian time (about 85 m.y. ago in the Geol. Soc. London time scale, 1964), when the last major granitic plutons were emplaced, and was certainly completed for much of the Sierra Nevada by the end of early Eocene time (about 55 m.y. ago). Consequently between 9 and 17 miles of cover was eroded from the western Sierra Nevada in a time interval of between 55 and 80 m.y., indicating the area was stripped at a rate of ½ to 1½ feet per thousand years.

The timespan from early Eocene to late Oligocene (about 25 to 30 m.y.) was one of virtual standstill in the Sierra. The bulk of the erosion had been completed; river channels whose ages (based on both fossils and radiometric dates) range over this interval are nearly parallel and at the same altitude. Even channels as young as early Pliocene in age show very little difference in slope and altitude from channels of early Eocene age. During the Eocene the Sierra may have been about 3,000 to 5,000 feet high near its crest; along its western margin were mountains of resistant greenstone 1,500 to 2,000 feet high. The still-preserved channel segments are filled with quartz-rich gravels which are 500 feet thick in places and from which many millions of dollars worth of gold was obtained. Along the west margin of the range, the gravels grade into littoral and marine sands and clays of the Ione Formation. The warm-temperate to tropical climate of the early Cenozoic favored deposition of quartz-anauxite sands and halloysitic clays in the Ione Formation, where they rest on lithomargic and lateritic soils. The bulk of the auriferous gravels also date from this interval, although some of the high-level gold-bearing channel gravels (the intervolcanic gravels) are as young as Pliocene.

A period of volcanic activity began in the central Sierra Nevada in middle Oligocene time (about 30 to 33 m.y. ago) with the eruption of predominantly rhyolitic tuffs and ash flows (the Valley Springs Formation). Rhyolitic eruptions lasted until late Miocene time (about 20 m.y. ago) and were followed by eruptions of andesitic mudflows which lasted from late Miocene to late Pliocene time (late Hemphillian—about 5 m.y. ago). The total thickness of the rhyolitic rocks is in few places more than 400 feet, but the andesitic rocks are much thicker and range from a maximum of 3,000 feet along the crest of the range to about 500 feet in the San Joaquin Valley west of the Sierra Nevada. The volcanic rocks are intercalated with gravels, many of which were mined for their gold content. Only locally can more than 30 to 40 flows be observed in a single section a few thousand feet thick, and commonly fewer flows are present. Thus as far as the existing record tells us, volcanic eruptions probably occurred in any one place only a few times every million years. The lavas, tuffs, and mudflows do not suggest an environment any more cataclysmic, on the average, than that prevailing in the Cascade Range today.

The volcanic cover was extensive only north of the Tuolumne River, and even in that region not all of the Sierra Nevada was buried. Groups of granitic mountains near the range crest, such as those around Pyramid Peak, appear to have risen above the volcanic mudflow surface; and along the west front of the range northwest-trending ridges one to two thousand feet high, upheld by resistant greenstone, almost certainly rose above the volcanic plain.

South of the Tuolumne River the Tertiary events in the Sierra Nevada are represented chiefly by scattered volcanic deposits, mainly basaltic flows, whose ages seem to cluster around 9.5 and 2 to 4 m.y. (Dalrymple, 1963), and by the erosion surfaces developed on the volcanic and granitic rocks. The granitic rocks that underlie the bulk of the southern part of the range were subjected to weathering and erosion throughout the Cenozoic, and have evolved a distinctive "stepped" topography that may be peculiar to biotite-bearing crystalline rocks.

At some time in the Pliocene, possibly in middle or late Pliocene time, the northern Sierra Nevada—and probably the southern Sierra Nevada as well—was strongly uplifted and tilted to the west. That uplift of the southern Sierra Nevada began before this in early Miocene time is suggested by evidence in the sedimentary deposits of the San Joaquin Valley. In response to the major uplift, the rivers on the west slope incised their canyons to depths of 2,000 to 4,000 feet below the base of the Tertiary channels, whose remnants are preserved on the flat-topped interstream ridges in the northern part of the range. Basalt flows dated at 3.3 m.y. in the Kern River canyon are evi-

Photo 22. West-facing step fronts and flat to east-sloping plateaus of the southern Sierra Nevada, as seen looking south from over Hume Lake in Fresno County toward the west half of Sequoia Park. Tenmile Creek is in lower right foreground. In the middle distance on left, Big Meadow Creek drains eastward from Big Meadow (the irregular white patch in the forest-covered plateau in the middle distance). The white dome-like mountain on extreme left, just behind Big Meadow Creek, marked by a low cliff along the top of its near face, is Shell Mountain. The Generals Highway follows the ridge that extends diagonally across the picture from the head of Tenmile Creek toward Shell Mountain. The canyon beyond this ridge on the extreme right is Redwood Canyon. High sharp-crested asymmetric ridge left of Redwood Canyon, with bald-rock outcrops on its right side, is Big Baldy Ridge. Rising out of the mist behind Big Baldy Ridge are the Ash Peaks in Sequoia Park. High peaks on the skyline on extreme left are Vandever Mountain and White Chief Peak, south of Mineral King.

The characteristics of the stepped topography are particularly well exemplified by the high east-sloping plateau enclosing Big Meadow, with its westward-facing escarpment. U.S. Geological Survey photograph GS-OAL-1-22.

dence that there the bulk of the downcutting was completed before the end of Pliocene time. Elsewhere most of the canyon cutting appears to have preceded the earliest recognizable glaciation on the west slope.

During the Pliocene, also, the eastern boundary fault system of the Sierra Nevada was active. This activity appears to have begun about 10 m.y. ago or perhaps a little later. In the northern part of the Sierra Nevada, most of the faulting appears to have been completed by 2 million years ago, but in the southern part of the range much of it took place later. Thus faulting along the east side of the Sierra Nevada probably lagged behind the westward tilting of the range. In the Owens Valley segment, at least, the main faulting appears to be much later and may represent collapse of the Owens Valley block. The magnitude of the faulting and uplift are likewise not the same. Uplift in the San Joaquin segments of the Sierra Nevada

Photo 23. The rugged glaciated country of the High Sierra seen looking south toward the Kings-Kern Divide from over Gardiner Basin in Kings Canyon National Park. Mount Gardiner is near the lower right corner, and in the center foreground a rock glacier about ⅓ mile long extends from the base of its east ridge. Charlotte Lake, east base of Mount Bago, is at the east (left) end of the valley directly behind Mount Gardiner Ridge. Deep canyon hidden by Mount Bago is Bubbs Creek canyon, and the lake-dotted canyon directly behind Mount Bago is East Creek canyon, heading in Harrison Pass. Deep canyon in distance beyond Harrison Pass is Kern Canyon. The high peaks on the right are part of the Great Western Divide; those on the left mark the crest of the Sierra Nevada. High asymmetric peak at extreme left is Mount Whitney. The flat mountain tops and plateaus that step downward from Mount Whitney to the Kern Canyon were considered by Matthes to be remnants of the Cirque Peak, Boreal, and Chagoopa surfaces. U.S. Geological Survey Photograph GS-OAL-1-43.

during Pliocene and Pleistocene time probably amounted to no more than 6,000 feet—in the Lake Tahoe region it is only about 4,000 feet. Yet the relief on the basement surface from the range crest to the base of the alluvium in Owens Valley is 14,000 to 19,000 feet.

The Sierra Nevada, in common with all other alpine and arctic regions, was glaciated several times during the Pleistocene. The two earliest glaciations, the Sherwin and McGee, are between 2.5 and 0.7 million years old and are the oldest glaciations stratigraphically related to radiometrically dated materials in the world. Four to six glaciations have been recognized on the east side of the Sierra Nevada, the last two or three corresponding to the Wisconsin; on the west side of the Sierra direct evidence indicates only four glaciations, but indirect evidence in the San Joaquin Valley indicates four major glacial periods, of which the Wisconsin—comprising three glaciations—is the last. Moraines of the two oldest glaciations of the east side, the Sherwin and McGee, have lost their topographic form. These older glaciations seem to have taken place before much of the faulting along the east side of the range, whereas the well-preserved moraines of the younger glaciations (Mono Basin, Tahoe, Tenaya, and Tioga) extend from the existing canyon mouths onto the basin floors. The Wisconsin firn limits were 6,500 to 8,000 feet above sea level in the northern Sierra Nevada and 10,500 to 12,000 feet high in the southern Sierra Nevada, or about 2,500 to 3,000 feet lower than at present. The crest of the range was covered by a mountain icecap which sent tongues 10 to 40 miles long down the canyons on the west side. The glaciation came to an end about 9,500 years ago, and the postglacial climate has been marked by a period of relative warmth, followed by a period in the last 2,000 to 3,000 years during which the climate cooled enough to form small cirque glaciers.

REFERENCES

Allen, V. T., 1929, The Ione formation of California: California Univ. Pubs. Dept. Geol. Sci. Bull., v. 18, no. 14, p. 347–448.

Arkley, R. J., 1962, The geology, geomorphology, and soils of the San Joaquin Valley in the vicinity of the Merced River, California: California Div. Mines and Geology Bull. 182, p. 25–32.

Axelrod, D. I., 1944, The Oakdale flora [California]: Carnegie Inst. Washington Pub. 553, Contr. Paleontology, p. 147–165.

—— 1957, Late Tertiary floras and the Sierra Nevadan uplift [California-Nevada]: Geol. Soc. America Bull., v. 68, no. 1, p. 19–45.

—— 1962, Post-Pliocene uplift of the Sierra Nevada, California: Geol. Soc. America Bull., v. 73, no. 2, p. 183–198.

Axelrod, D. I., and Ting, W. S., 1960, Late Pliocene floras east of the Sierra Nevada: California Univ. Pubs. Geol. Sci., v. 39, no. 1, p. 1–118.

Bailey, E. H., Irwin, W. P., and Jones, D. L., 1965, Franciscan and related rocks, and their significance in the geology of western California: California Div. Mines and Geology Bull. 183, 177 p.

Baird, A. K., 1962, Superposed deformations in the central Sierra Nevada foothills east of the Mother Lode: California Univ. Pubs. Geol. Sci., v. 42, p. 1–70.

Bateman, P. C., 1956, Economic geology of the Bishop tungsten district, California: California Div. Mines Spec. Rept. 47, 87 p.

—— 1961, Willard D. Johnson and the strike-slip component of fault movement in the Owens Valley, California, earthquake of 1872: Seismol. Soc. America Bull., v. 51, no. 4, p. 483–493.

—— 1965a, Geologic map of the Blackcap Mountain quadrangle, Fresno County, California: U.S. Geol. Survey Geol. Quad. Map GQ-428, scale 1:62,500.

—— 1965b, Geologic map of the Mount Goddard quadrangle, Fresno and Inyo Counties, California: U.S. Geol. Survey Geol. Quad. Map GQ-429, scale 1:62,500.

—— 1965c, Geology and tungsten mineralization of the Bishop district, California, *with a section on* Gravity study of Owens Valley, by L. C. Pakiser and M. F. Kane, *and a section on* Seismic profile, by L. C. Pakiser: U.S. Geol. Survey Prof. Paper 470, 208 p.

Bateman, P. C., Clark, L. D., Huber, N. K., Moore, J. G., and Rinehart, C. D., 1963, The Sierra Nevada batholith—a synthesis of recent work across the central part: U.S. Geol. Survey Prof. Paper 414-D, p. D1-D46.

Bell, P. M., 1963, Aluminum silicate system—experimental determination of the triple point: Science, v. 139, no. 3559, p. 1055–1056.

Best, M. G., 1963, Petrology and structural analysis of metamorphic rocks in the southwestern Sierra Nevada foothills, California: California Univ. Pubs. Geol. Sci., v. 42, no. 3, p. 111–158.

Birkeland, P. W., 1963, Pleistocene volcanism and deformation of the Truckee area, north of Lake Tahoe, California: Geol. Soc. America Bull., v. 74, no. 12, p. 1453–1464.

—— 1964, Pleistocene glaciation of the northern Sierra Nevada, north of Lake Tahoe, California: Jour. Geology, v. 72, no. 6, p. 810–825.

—— 1965, The Truckee River canyon between Wadsworth and Vista, Nevada, *in* Guidebook for Field Conference I, Northern Great Basin and California: INQUA (Internat. Assoc. Quaternary Research), 7th Cong., 1965, p. 35.

—— 1965a, Mustang, Nevada, *in* Guidebook for Field Conference I, Northern Great Basin and California: INQUA (Internat. Assoc. Quaternary Research), 7th Cong., 1965, p. 35–38.

—— 1965b, Reno to Mount Rose, Tahoe City, Truckee, and return, *in* Guidebook for Field Conference I, Northern Great Basin and California: INQUA (Internat. Assoc. Quaternary Research), 7th Cong., 1965, p. 48–51.

Birman, J. H., 1964, Glacial geology across the crest of the Sierra Nevada, California: Geol. Soc. America Spec. Paper 75, 80 p.

Blackwelder, Eliot, 1928, The recognition of fault scarps: Jour. Geology, v. 36, no. 4, p. 289–311.

—— 1931, Pleistocene glaciation in the Sierra Nevada and Basin Ranges: Geol. Soc. America Bull., v. 42, no. 4, p. 865–922.

Bowen, O. E., ed., 1962, Geologic guide to the gas and oil fields of northern California: California Div. Mines and Geology Bull. 181, 412 p.

Browne, R. E., 1890, The ancient river beds of the Forest Hill Divide: California Mining Bur. 10th Ann. Rept. State Mineralogist, p. 435–465.

Burnett, J. L., and Matthews, Robert, 196__, Geologic map of California, Olaf P. Jenkins edition, Fresno sheet: California Div. Mines and Geology, scale 1:250,000. (In press)

Byerly, Perry, 1938, The Sierra Nevada in the light of isostasy: Geol. Soc. America Bull., v. 48, Supp., p. 2025–2031.

Calkins, F. C., 1930, The granitic rocks of the Yosemite region, *in* Matthes, F. E., Geologic history of the Yosemite Valley: U.S. Geol. Survey Prof. Paper 160, p. 120–129.

Chandra, D. K., 1961, Geology and mineral deposits of the Colfax and Foresthill quadrangles, California: California Div. Mines and Geology, Spec. Rept. 67, 50 p.

Christensen, M. N., 1963, Structure of metamorphic rocks at Mineral King, California: California Univ. Pubs. Geol. Sci., v. 42, no. 4, p. 159–198.

—— 1966, Late Cenozoic crustal movements in the Sierra Nevada of California: Geol. Soc. America Bull., vol. 77, p. 163–182.

Christensen, M. N., and Gilbert, C. M., 1964, Basaltic cone suggests constructional origin of some Guyots: Science, v. 143, no. 3603, p. 240–242.

Church, H. V., Jr., Krammes, K. F., Chm., and others, 1957a, Cenozoic correlation section across south San Joaquin Valley from San Andreas fault to Sierra Nevada foothills, California: Am. Assoc. Petroleum Geologists, Pacific Sec., Correlation Sec. 8.

—— 1957b, Correlation section across central San Joaquin Valley from San Andreas fault to Sierra Nevada foothills, California: Am. Assoc. Petroleum Geologists, Pacific Sec., Correlation Sec. 9.

Clark, B. L., and Anderson, C. A., 1938, Wheatland formation and its relation to early Tertiary andesites in the Sierra Nevada: Geol. Soc. America Bull., v. 49, no. 6, p. 931–956.

Clark, L. D., 1964, Stratigraphy and structure of part of the western Sierra Nevada metamorphic belt, California: U.S. Geol. Survey Prof. Paper 410, 70 p.

Clark, L. D., Imlay, R. W., McMath, V. E., and Silberling, N. J., 1962, Angular unconformity between Mesozoic and Paleozoic rocks in the northern Sierra Nevada, California: U.S. Geol. Survey Prof. Paper 450-B, art. 6, p. B15–B19.

Clark, L. D., Stromquist, A. A., and Tatlock, D. B., 1963, Geologic map of San Andreas quadrangle, Calaveras County, California: U.S. Geol. Survey Geol. Quad. Map GQ-222, scale 1:62,500.

Cloos, Ernst, 1936, Der Sierra-Nevada-Pluton in Californein: Neues Jahrb., v. 76, no. 3, sec. B, p. 355–450.

Compton, R. R., 1955, Trondhjemite batholith near Bidwell Bar, California: Geol. Soc. America Bull., v. 66, no. 1, p. 9–44.

Condit, Carlton, 1944a, The Remington Hill flora [California]: Carnegie Inst. Washington Pub. 553, Contr. Paleontology, p. 21–55.

—— 1944b, The Table Mountain flora [California]: Carnegie Inst. Washington Pub. 553, Contr. Paleontology, p. 57–90.

Creely, R. S., 1955, Geology of the Oroville quadrangle, California: California Univ., Berkeley, Ph.D. thesis, 269 p.

Crickmay, C. H., 1933, Mount Jura investigation: Geol. Soc. America Bull., v. 44, no. 5, p. 895–926.

Curtis, G. H., 1951, The geology of the Topaz Lake quadrangle and the eastern half of Ebbetts Pass quadrangle: California Univ., Berkeley, Ph.D. thesis, 310 p.

—— 1954, Mode of origin of pyroclastic debris in the Mehrten formation of the Sierra Nevada: California Univ. Pubs. Geol. Sci., v. 29, no. 9, p. 453–502.

—— 1965, Hope Valley to Coleville, *in* Guidebook for Field Conference I, Northern Great Basin and California: INQUA (Internat. Assoc. Quaternary Research), 7th Cong., 1965, p. 63–71.

Curtis, G. H., Evernden, J. F., and Lipson, J. I., 1958, Age determination of some granitic rocks in California by the potassium-argon method: California Div. Mines, Spec. Rept. 54, 16 p.

Dalrymple, G. B., 1963, Potassium-argon dates of some Cenozoic volcanic rocks in the Sierra Nevada, California: Geol. Soc. America Bull., v. 74, no. 4, p. 379–390.

—— 1964a, Cenozoic chronology of the Sierra Nevada, California: California Univ. Pubs. Geol. Sci., v. 47, 41 p.

—— 1964b, Potassium-argon dates of three Pleistocene interglacial basalt flows from the Sierra Nevada, California: Geol. Soc. America Bull., v. 75, no. 8, p. 753–758.

Dalrymple, G. B., Cox, Allan, and Doell, R. R., 1965, Potassium-argon age and paleomagnetism of the Bishop Tuff, California: Geol. Soc. America Bull., v. 76, no. 6, p. 665–674.

Davis, S. N., and Hall, F. R., 1959, Water quality of eastern Stanislaus and northern Merced Counties, California: Stanford Univ. Pubs. Geol. Sci., v. 6, no. 1, 112 p.

Dickerson, R. E., 1916, Stratigraphy and fauna of the Tejon Eocene of California: California Univ. Dept. Geology Bull. 9, p. 363–524.

Diller, J. S., 1908, Geology of the Taylorsville region, California: U.S. Geol. Survey Bull. 353, 128 p.

Doell, R. R., Dalrymple, G. B., and Cox, Allan, 1966, Geomagnetic polarity epochs—Sierra Nevada Data 3: Jour Geophys. Research, v. 71, no. 2, p. 531–541.

Durrell, Cordell, 1940, Metamorphism in the southern Sierra Nevada northeast of Visalia, California: California Univ., Dept. Geol. Sci. Bull., v. 25, no. 1, p. 1–117.

Eaton, J. P., 1963, Crustal structure from San Francisco, California, to Eureka, Nevada, from seismic-refraction measurements: Jour. Geophys. Research, v. 68, no. 20, p. 5789–5806.

Eaton, J. P., and Healy, J. H., 1963, The root of the Sierra Nevada as determined from seismic evidence [abs.]: Internat. Union of Geodesy and Geophysics, 13th General Assembly, Berkeley, Calif., 1963, Abs. Papers, v. 3, art. B28, p. III-46.

Eric, J. H., Stromquist, A. A., and Swinney, C. M., 1955, Geology and mineral deposits of the Angels Camp and Sonora quadrangles, Calaveras and Tuolumne Counties, California: California Div. Mines Spec. Rept. 41, 55 p.

Evernden, J. F., and James, G. T., 1964, Potassium-argon dates and the Tertiary floras of North America: Am. Jour. Sci., v. 262, no. 8, p. 945–974.

Evernden, J. F., Kistler, R. W., and Curtis, G. H., 1959, Cenozoic time scale of the West Coast [abs.]: Geol. Soc. America Bull., v. 70, no. 12, pt. 2, p. 1718.

Evernden, J. F., Savage, D. E., Curtis, G. H., and James, G. T., 1964, Potassium-argon dates and the Cenozoic mammalian chronology of North America: Am. Jour. Sci., v. 262, no. 2, p. 145–198.

Ferguson, H. G., and Gannett, R. W., 1932, Gold quartz veins of the Alleghany district, California: U.S. Geol. Survey Prof. Paper 172, 139 p.

Gilbert, C. M., 1938, Welded tuff in eastern California: Geol. Soc. America Bull., v. 49, no. 12, pt. 1, p. 1829–1862.

—— 1941, Late Tertiary geology southeast of Mono Lake, California: Geol. Soc. America Bull., v. 52, no. 6, p. 781–815.

Gilbert, G. K., 1904, Domes and dome structure of the High Sierra: Geol. Soc. America Bull., v. 15, p. 29–36.

—— 1928, Studies of Basin Range structure: U.S. Geol. Survey Prof. Paper 153, 92 p.

Gilluly, James, 1949, Distribution of mountain building in geologic time: Geol. Soc. America Bull., v. 60, no. 4, p. 561–590.

—— 1963, The tectonic evolution of the western United States: Geol. Soc. London Quart. Jour., no. 474, v. 119, pt. 2, p. 133–174.

Goldman, H. B., 1964, Tertiary fluviatile deposits in the vicinity of Mokelumne Hill, Calaveras County, California: California Univ., Los Angeles, M.A. thesis, 56 p.

Griggs, D. T., 1939, A theory of mountain-building: Am. Jour. Sci., v. 237, no. 9, p. 611–650.

Gutenberg, Beno, Buwalda, J. P., and Sharp, R. P., 1956, Seismic explorations of the floor of Yosemite Valley, California: Geol. Soc. America Bull., v. 67, no. 8, p. 1051–1078.

Hake, B. F., 1928, Scarps of the southwestern Sierra Nevada, California: Geol. Soc. America Bull., v. 39, no. 4, p. 1017–1030.

Hall, W. E., and MacKevett, E. M., Jr., 1962, Geology and ore deposits of the Darwin quadrangle, Inyo County, California: U.S. Geol. Survey Prof. Paper 368, 87 p.

Hamilton, W. B., 1956a, Geology of the Huntington Lake area, Fresno County, California: California Div. Mines Spec. Rept. 46, 25 p.

—— 1956b, Variations in plutons of granitic rocks of the Huntington Lake area of the Sierra Nevada, California: Geol. Soc. America Bull., v. 67, no. 12, pt. 1, p. 1585–1598.

Harte, Bret, 1887, To the Pliocene skull (a geological address), *in* The poetical works including the drama of "The two men of Sandy Bar," 7th ed.: Boston, Mass., Houghton, Mifflin and Co., p. 256–257.

Henderson, J. R., 1953, Preliminary total intensity aeromagnetic maps of the Mother Lode district, California: U.S. Geol. Survey open-file maps, July 23, 1953.

Henderson, J. R., White, B. L., and others, 1963, Aeromagnetic map of Long Valley and Northern Owens Valley, California: U.S. Geol. Survey Geophys. Inv. Map GP-329, scale 1:62,500.

Hietanen, Anna, 1951, Metamorphic and igneous rocks of the Merrimac area, Plumas National Forest, California: Geol. Soc. America Bull., v. 62, no. 6, p. 565–607.

Huber, N. K., and Rinehart, C. D., 1965a, the Devils Postpile National Monument: California Div. Mines and Geology, Mineral Inf. Service, v. 18, no. 6, p. 109–118.

—— 1965b, Geologic map of the Devils Postpile quadrangle, Sierra Nevada, California: U.S. Geol. Survey Quad. Map GQ-437.

Hudson, F. S., 1951, Mount Lincoln-Castle Peak area, Sierra Nevada, California: Geol. Soc. America Bull., v. 62, no. 8, p. 931–952.

—— 1955, Measurement of the deformation of the Sierra Nevada, California, since middle Eocene: Geol. Soc. America Bull., v. 66, no. 7, p. 835–870.

—— 1960, Post-Pliocene uplift of the Sierra Nevada, California: Geol. Soc. America Bull., v. 71, no. 11, p. 1547–1574.

Hurley, P. M., Bateman, P. C., Fairbairn, H. W., and Pinson, W. H., Jr., 1965, Investigtaion of initial Sr^{87}/Sr^{86} ratios in the Sierra Nevada plutonic province: Geol. Soc. America Bull., v. 76, no. 2, p. 165–174.

Irwin, W. P., 1964, Late Mesozoic orogenies in the ultramafic belts of northwestern California and southwestern Oregon: U.S. Geol. Survey Prof. Paper 501-C, p. C1–C9.

Janda, R. J., 1965a, Minaret Summit, *in* Guidebook for Field Conference I, Northern Great Basin and California: INQUA (Internat. Assoc. Quaternary Research), 7th Cong., 1965, p. 89–91.

—— 1965b, Quaternary alluvium near Friant, California, *in* Guidebook for Field Conference I, Northern Great Basin and California: INQUA (Internat. Assoc. Quaternary Research), 7th Cong., 1965, p. 128–133.

Jennings, C. W., Burnett, J. L., and Troxel, B. W., 1962, Geologic map of California, Olaf. P. Jenkins edition, Trona sheet: California Div. Mines and Geology, scale 1:250,000.

Johnston, W. D., Jr., 1940, The gold quartz veins of Grass Valley, California: U.S. Geol. Survey Prof. Paper 194, 101 p.

Khitarov, N. I., and others, 1963, Relations among andalusite, kyanite, and sillimanite under conditions of moderate temperatures and pressures: Geokhimiya, v. 3, no. 3, p. 235–244.

Kistler, R. W., 196_, Structure and metamorphism in the Mono Craters quadrangle, Sierra Nevada, California: U.S. Geol. Survey Bull. 1221-E (In press)

Kistler, R. W., Bateman, P. C., and Brannock, W. W., 1965, Isotopic ages of minerals from granitic rocks of the central Sierra Nevada and Inyo Mountains, California: Geol. Soc. America Bull., v. 76, no. 2, p. 155–164.

Knopf, Adolph, 1917, Tungsten deposits of northwestern Inyo County, California: U.S. Geol. Survey Bull. 640-L, p. 229–255.

—— 1918, A geologic reconnaissance of the Inyo Range and eastern slope of the southern Sierra Nevada, California, with a section on the stratigraphy of the Inyo Range, by Edwin Kirk: U.S. Geol. Survey Prof. Paper 110, 130 p.

—— 1929, The Mother Lode system of California: U.S. Geol. Survey Prof. Paper 157, 88 p.

Krauskopf, K. B., 1953, Tungsten deposits of Madera, Fresno, and Tulare Counties, California: California Div. Mines Spec. Rept. 35, 83 p.

Lawson, A. C., 1904, The geomorphogeny of the upper Kern basin: California Univ. Dept. Geology Bull., v. 3, no. 15, p. 291–376.

—— 1912, The recent fault scarps at Genoa, Nevada: Seismol. Soc. America Bull., v. 2, p. 193–200.

—— 1936, The Sierra Nevada in the light of isostasy: Geol. Soc. America Bull., v. 47, no. 11, p. 1691–1712.

LeConte, Joseph, 1880, The old river-beds of California: Am. Jour. Sci., 3d ser., v. 19, no. 111, p. 176–190.

—— 1886, A post-Tertiary elevation of the Sierra Nevada shown by the river beds: Am. Jour. Sci., 3d ser., v. 32, no. 189, p. 167–181.

—— 1889, On the origin of normal faults and of the structure of the Basin region: Am. Jour. Sci., 3d ser., v. 38, no. 226, p. 257–263.

Lesquereux, Leo, 1878, Report on the fossil plants of the auriferous gravel deposits of the Sierra Nevada: Harvard Coll. Mus. Comp. Zoology Mem. 6, no. 2, 68 p.

Lindgren, Waldemar, 1894, Description of the Sacramento quadrangle, California: U.S. Geol. Survey Geol. Atlas, Folio 5, [3] p.

—— 1896, The gold-quartz veins of Nevada City and Grass Valley districts, California: U.S. Geol. Survey Ann. Rept. 17, pt. 2, p. 13–262.

—— 1911, The Tertiary gravels of the Sierra Nevada of California: U.S. Geol. Survey Prof. Paper 73, 226 p.

Lindgren, Waldemar, Turner, H. W., and Ransome, F. L., (individually and coauthors), 1894–1900, The Gold Belt Folios: U.S. Geol. Survey Atlas Folios 3, 5, 11, 17, 18, 29, 31, 37, 41, 43, 51, 63, 66.

Little, H. W., 1960, Nelson map-area, west half, British Columbia: Canada Geol. Survey Mem. 308, 205 p.

Louderback, G. D., 1924, Period of scarp production in the Great Basin: California Univ. Pubs., Dept. Geol. Sci. Bull., v. 15, no. 1, p. 1–44.

Lovejoy, E. M., 1965, Evidence of Plio-Pleistocene faulting at McGee Mountain, Mono County, California—critical study [abs.]: Geol. Soc. America, Cordilleran Sec., 61st Ann. Mtg., Fresno, Calif., 1915, Program, p. 34.

Macdonald, G. A., 1941, Geology of the western Sierra Nevada between the Kings and San Joaquin Rivers, California: California Univ., Dept. Geol. Sci. Bull., v. 26, no. 2, p. 215–286.

MacGinitie, H. D., 1941, A middle Eocene flora from the central Sierra Nevada: Carnegie Inst. Washington Pub. 534, 178 p.

Matthes, F. E., 1930, Geologic history of the Yosemite Valley: U.S. Geol. Survey Prof. Paper 160, 137 p.

—— 1937, The geologic history of Mount Whitney: Sierra Club Bull., v. 22, no. 1, p. 1–18.

—— (Fryxell, Fritiof, ed.), 1950, Sequoia National Park, a geological album: California Univ. Press, Berkeley, 136 p.

—— 1960, Reconnaissance of the geomorphology and glacial geology of the San Joaquin Basin, Sierra Nevada, California: U.S. Geol. Survey Prof. Paper 329, 62 p.

—— 1965, Glacial reconnaissance of Sequoia National Park, California: U.S. Geol. Survey Prof. Paper 504-A, p. A1–A58.

Mayo, E. B., 1934, Geology and mineral deposits of Laurel and Convict Basins, southwestern Mono County, California: California Jour. Mines and Geology, v. 30, no. 1, p. 79–87.

—— 1937, Sierra Nevada pluton and crustal movement: Jour. Geology, v. 45, no. 2, p. 169–192.

—— 1941, Deformation in the interval Mount Lyell-Mount Whitney, California: Geol. Soc. America Bull., v. 52, no. 7, p. 1001–1084.

—— 1947, Structure plan of the southern Sierra Nevada, California: Geol. Soc. America Bull., v. 58, no. 6, p. 495–504.

Merriam, C. W., 1963, Geology of the Cerro Gordo mining district, Inyo County, California: U.S. Geol. Survey Prof. Paper 408, 83 p.

Merriam, C. W., and Turner, F. E., 1937, The Capay middle Eocene of northern California: California Univ., Dept. Geol. Sci. Bull., v. 24, no. 6, p. 91–113.

Miller, W. J., and Webb, R. W., 1940, Descriptive geology of the Kernville quadrangle, California: California Jour. Mines and Geology, v. 36, no. 4, p. 343–378.

Moore, J. G., 1959, The quartz diorite boundary line in the western United States: Jour. Geology, v. 67, no. 2, p. 198–210.

—— 1963, Geology of the Mount Pinchot quadrangle, southern Sierra Nevada, California: U.S. Geol. Survey Bull. 1130, 152 p.

Morrison, R. B., 1964, Lake Lahontan—geology of the southern Carson Desert, Nevada: U.S. Geol. Survey Prof. Paper 401, 156 p.

—— 1965, General features and stratigraphy of the Lake Lahontan area, *in* Guidebook for Field Conference I, Northern Great Basin and California: INQUA (Internat. Assoc. Quaternary Research), 7th Cong., 1965, p. 18–24.

Oliver, H. W., 1960, Gravity anomalies at Mount Whitney, California: U.S. Geol. Survey Prof. Paper 400-B, art. 146, p. B313–B315.

—— 1965, The U.S. Geological Survey's gravity program in California, Hawaii, Nevada, and Oregon: Am. Geophys. Union Trans., v. 46, no. 1, p. 218–222.

Oliver, H. W., and Mabey, D. R., 1963, Anomalous gravity field in east-central California: Geol. Soc. America Bull., v. 74, no. 10, p. 1293–1298.

Oliver, H. W., Pakiser, L. C., and Kane, M. F., 1961, Gravity anomalies in the central Sierra Nevada, California: Jour. Geophys. Research, v. 66, no. 12, p. 4265–4271.

Pakiser, L. C., Kane, M. F., and Jackson, W. H., 1964, Structural geology and volcanism of Owens Valley region, California—a geophysical study: U.S. Geol. Survey Prof. Paper 438, 68 p.

Pakiser, L. C., Press, Frank, and Kane, M. F., 1960, Geophysical investigation of Mono Basin, California: Geol. Soc. America Bull., v. 71, no. 4, p. 415–447.

Parker, R. B., 1961, Petrology and structural geometry of pre-granitic rocks in the Sierra Nevada, Alpine County, California: Geol. Soc. America Bull., v. 72, no. 12, p. 1789–1805.

Pask, J. A., and Turner, M. D., 1952, Geology and ceramic properties of the Ione formation, Buena Vista area, Amador County, California: California Div. Mines Spec. Rept. 19, 39 p.

Pease, E. W., 1952, Mount Poso Group oil fields, *in* Field trip routes, geology, oil fields: Am. Assoc. Petroleum Geologists-Soc. Econ. Paleontologists and Mineralogists-Soc. Explor. Geophysicists Guidebook, Joint Ann. Mtg., Los Angeles, Calif., 1952, p. 150–151.

Peck, D. L., 1964, Preliminary geologic map of the Merced Peak quadrangle, California: U.S. Geol. Survey Mineral Inv. Field Studies Map MF-281, scale 1:48,000.

Piper, A. M., Gale, H. S., Thomas, H. E., and Robinson, T. W., 1939, Geology and ground-water hydrology of the Mokelumne area, California: U.S. Geol. Survey Water-Supply Paper 780, 230 p.

Potbury, Susan S., 1937, The La Porte flora of Plumas County, California: Carnegie Inst. Washington Pub. No. 465, Contr. Paleontology, p. 29–82.

Putman, G. W., and Alfors, J. T., 1965, Depth of intrusion and age of the Rocky Hill stock, Tulare County, California: Geol. Soc. America Bull., v. 76, no. 3, p. 357–364.

Putnam, W. C., 1960a, Faulting and Pleistocene glaciation in the east-central Sierra Nevada of California, United States of America: Internat. Geol. Cong., 21st, Copenhagen 1960, Rept., pt. 21, p. 270–274.

—— 1960b, Origin of Rock Creek and Owens River gorges, Mono County, California: California Univ. Pub. Geol. Sci., v. 34, no. 5, p. 221–280.

—— 1962, Late Cenozoic geology of McGee Mountain, Mono County, California: California Univ. Pub. Geol. Sci., v. 40, no. 3, p. 181–218.

Ransome, F. L., 1898, Some lava flows of the western slope of the Sierra Nevada, California: U.S. Geol. Survey Bull. 89, 74 p.

Reeside, J. B., Jr., 1944, Thickness and general character of the Cretaceous deposits in the western interior of the United States: U.S. Geol. Survey Oil and Gas Inv. Prelim. Map 10.

Richardson, E. E., 1966, Structure contours on top of the Vedder sand, southeastern San Joaquin Valley, California: U.S. Geol. Survey open-file report Jan. 3, 1966, 15 p., 1 pl., 4 figs.

Rinehart, C. D., and Ross, D. C., 1957, Geology of the Casa Diablo Mountain quadrangle, California: U.S. Geol. Survey Geol. Quad. Map GQ-99, scale 1:62,500.

—— 1964, Geology and mineral deposits of the Mount Morrison quadrangle, Sierra Nevada, California, with a section on a gravity study of Long Valley, by L. C. Pakiser: U.S. Geol. Survey Prof. Paper 385, 106 p.

Rinehart, C. D., and Huber, N. K., 1965, The Inyo Crater Lakes—A blast in the past: California Div. Mines and Geology, Mineral Inf. Service, v. 18, no. 9, p. 169–172.

Rogers, D. A., 1962, Surface geology of the east side of the Sacramento Valley, California: California Div. Mines and Geology Bull. 181, p. 67–68.

Rose, R. L., 1957, Andalusite- and corundum-bearing pegmatites in Yosemite National Park, California: Am. Mineralogist, v. 42, nos. 9–10, p. 635–647.

Ross, D. C., 1958, Igneous and metamorphic rocks of parts of Sequoia and Kings Canyon National Parks, California: California Div. Mines Spec. Rept. 53, 24 p.

—— 1965, Geology of the Independence quadrangle, Inyo County, California: U.S. Geol. Survey Bull. 1181-0, 64 p.

Russell, I. C., 1889, The Quaternary history of Mono Valley, California: U.S. Geol. Survey Ann. Rept., v. 8, p. 261–394.

Safonov, Anatole, 1962, The challenge of the Sacramento Valley, California: California Div. Mines and Geology Bull. 181, p. 77–97.

Sharp, R. P., 1965a, Convict Lake, *in* Guidebook for Field Conference I, Northern Great Basin and California: INQUA (Internat. Assoc. Quaternary Research), 7th Cong., 1965, p. 93–96.

—— 1965b, Rock Creek to Owens Gorge, *in* Guidebook for Field Conference I, Northern Great Basin and California: INQUA (Internat. Assoc. Quaternary Research), 7th Cong., 1965, p. 97–99.

Sharp, R. P., and Birman, J. H., 1963, Additions to classical sequence of Pleistocene glaciations, Sierra Nevada, California: Geol. Soc. America Bull., v. 74, no. 8, p. 1079–1086.

Slemmons, D. B., 1953, Geology of the Sonora Pass region: California Univ., Berkeley, Ph.D. thesis, 201 p.

Smith, A. R., 1965, Geologic map of California, Olaf P. Jenkins edition, Bakersfield sheet: California Div. Mines and Geology, scale 1:250,000.

Sperber, F. H., 1952, Jasmine Field, *in* Field trip routes, geology, oil fields: Am. Assoc. Petroleum Geologists-Soc. Econ. Paleontologists and Mineralogists-Soc. Explor. Geophysicists, Guidebook, Joint Ann. Mtg., Los Angeles, Calif., March 1952, p. 152–155.

Stirton, R. A., and Goeriz, H. F., 1942, Fossil vertebrates from the superjacent deposits near Knights Ferry, California: California Univ. Pubs., Dept. Geol. Sci. Bull., v. 26, no. 5, p. 447–472.

Storms, W. H., 1894, Ancient channel system of Calaveras County: California Mining Bur., 12th Rept. State Mineralogist, p. 482–492.

Sylvester, A. G., and Nelson, C. A., 1965, Petrology of the Birch Creek pluton, White Mountains, California: Geol. Soc. America, Cordilleran Sec., 61st Ann. Mtg., Program, p. 53.

Taliaferro, N. L., 1943, Manganese deposits of the Sierra Nevada, their genesis and metamorphism: California Div. Mines Bull. 125, p. 277–332.

Taliaferro, N. L., and Solari, A. J., 1949, Geology of the Copperopolis quadrangle, California: California Div. Mines Bull. 145 [map only], scale 1:62,500.

Thompson, G. A., and Talwani, Manik, 1964, Geology of the crust and mantle, western United States: Science, v. 146, no. 3651, p. 1539–1549.

—— 1964, Crustal structure from Pacific Basin to central Nevada: Jour. Geophys. Research, v. 69, no. 22, p. 4813–4837.

Thompson, G. A., and White, D. E., 1964, Regional geology of the Steamboat Springs area, Washoe County, Nevada: U.S. Geol. Survey Prof. Paper 458-A, 52 p.

Trask, J. B., [1854], Report on the geology of the coast mountains, and part of the Sierra Nevada—embracing their industrial resources in agriculture and mining: California Geol. Survey, Senate Doc. 9, Sess. 1854, p. 1–88.

Turner, H. W., 1894, Description of the Jackson quadrangle, California: U.S. Geol. Survey Geol. Atlas, Folio 11, [6] p.

—— 1900, The Pleistocene geology of the south central Sierra Nevada with especial reference to the origin of Yosemite Valley: California Acad. Sci. Proc., 3d ser., Geology, v. 1, no. 9, p. 262–321.

Turner, H. W., and Ransome, F. L., 1898, Big Trees, California: U.S. Geol. Survey Geol. Atlas, Folio 51, [8] p.

Tuttle, O. F., and Bowen, N. L., 1958, Origin of granite in the light of experimental studies in the system $NaAlSi_3O_8$-$KAlSi_3O_8$-SiO_2-H_2O: Geol. Soc. America Mem. 74, 153 p.

U.S. Geological Survey, 1964, Geological Survey Research 1964: U.S. Geol. Survey Prof. Paper 501-A, 375 p.

VanderHoof, V. L., 1933, A skull of *Phiohippus tantalus* from the later Tertiary of the Sierran foothills of California: California Univ. Pubs., Dept. Geol. Sci. Bull., v. 23, no. 5, p. 183–194.

Vening Meinesz, F. A., 1934, Report of the gravity expedition in the Atlantic of 1932 and the interpretation of the results: Netherlands Geod. Comm., Gravity Expeditions at Sea, 1923–1932, v. 2, 208 p.

Wahrhaftig, Clyde, 1962, Geomorphology of the Yosemite Valley region, California: California Div. Mines and Geology Bull. 182, p. 33–46.

—— 1965a, Convict Lake to Rock Creek, *in* Guidebook for Field Conference I, Northern Great Basin and California: INQUA (Internat. Assoc. Quaternary Research), 7th Cong., 1965, p. 96–97.

—— 1965b, Owens Gorge overlook, *in* Guidebook for Field Conference I, Northern Great Basin and California: INQUA (Internat. Assoc. Quaternary Research), 7th Cong., 1965, p. 99–101.

—— 1965c, Roadcut at Rock Creek, *in* Guidebook for Field Conference I, Northern Great Basin and California: INQUA (Internat. Assoc. Quaternary Research), 7th Cong., 1965, p. 97.

—— 1965d, Tahoe City to Hope Valley, *in* Guidebook for Field Conference I, Northern Great Basin and California: INQUA (Internat. Assoc. Quaternary Research), 7th Cong., 1965, p. 59–63.

—— 1965e, Stepped topography of the southern Sierra Nevada, California: Geol. Soc. America Bull., v. 76, no. 10, p. 1165–1189.

Wahrhaftig, Clyde, and Birman, J. H., 1965, The Quaternary of the Pacific Mountain system in California, *in* Wright, H. E., Jr., and Frey, D. G., eds., The Quaternary of the United States—A review volume for the VII Congress of the International Association for Quaternary Research: Princeton, N.J., Princeton Univ. Press, p. 299–340.

Wahrhaftig, Clyde, and Sharp, R. P., 1965, Sonora Pass Junction to Bloody Canyon, *in* Guidebook for Field Conference I, Northern Great Basin and California: INQUA (Internat. Assoc. Quaternary Research), 7th Cong., 1965, p. 71–84.

Waldbaum, D. R., 1965, Thermodynamic properties of mullite, andalusite, kyanite, and sillimanite: Am. Mineralogist, v. 50, nos. 1–2, p. 186–195.

Webb, R. W., 1946, Geomorphology of the middle Kern River Basin, southern Sierra Nevada, California: Geol. Soc. America Bull., v. 57, no. 4, p. 355–382.

—— 1950, Volcanic geology of Toowa Valley, southern Sierra Nevada, California: Geol. Soc. America Bull., v. 61, no. 4, p. 349–357.

Whitney, J. D., 1880, The auriferous gravels of the Sierra Nevada of California: Comp. Zoology Mus. Mem., Am. Geology Contr., v. 1, 569 p.

—— 1865, Geological Survey of California, Report of progress and synopsis of the field work from 1860 to 1864: California Geol. Survey, Geology, v. 1, 498 p.

Wolfe, J. A., Gower, H. D., and Vine, J. D., 1961, Age and correlation of the Puget group, King County, Washington: U.S. Geol. Survey Prof. Paper 424-C, p. C230–C232.

Wollenberg, H. A., and Smith, A. R., 1964, Radioactivity and radiogenic heat in Sierra Nevada plutons: Jour. Geophys. Research, v. 69, no. 16, p. 3471–3478.

Wood, H. E., 1960, Eight historic fossil mammal specimens in the Museum of Comparative Zoology: Harvard Coll. Mus. Comp. Zoology Bull., v. 123, no. 3, p. 85–110.

GEOLOGY OF THE TAYLORSVILLE AREA, NORTHERN SIERRA NEVADA

By Vernon E. McMath
Continental Oil Co., Ponca City, Oklahoma

In the northeastern Sierra Nevada, the great batholithic edifice of the High Sierra ignominiously loses its footing amidst terrain dominated by volcanic geosynclinal fill. The eastern marginal fault system of the High Sierra gives way to a series of lesser Basin and Range structures. The degree of metamorphism becomes less. But it is these very diminutions, especially the paucity of plutons, that account for the significance of this relatively small area in the northernmost Sierra Nevada; the geosynclinal record has not been obliterated. The significance of this record was demonstrated by J. S. Diller in a series of papers culminating in U.S. Geological Survey Bull. 353, Geology of the Taylorsville Region (1908). This region, discussed herein, is bounded on the south by the 40th parallel (fig. 1), but much of the Paleozoic section continues beyond the parallel, southward into the adjacent Downieville 30-minute quadrangle (Turner, 1897).

Regionally but lightly metamorphosed Paleozoic, Triassic, and Jurassic marine rocks, all deformed in the Nevadan orogeny, underlie most of the Taylorsville area. The younger granitic plutons and still younger Tertiary volcanic rocks, though locally prominent, are excluded from further consideration here. Because the older stratified rocks are metamorphosed, the prefix "meta" should be attached to the names of all types except those intrinsically connotating metamorphism. For the sake of simplicity, however, the prefix is omitted but is understood to apply to all the pre-Nevadan rocks discussed here.

Regional metamorphism is of the greenschist facies, although locally a prehnite-albite assemblage suggests the lower grade prehnite-pumpellyite metagraywacke facies (Coombs, 1960, 1961). Metamorphic foliation ranges from well developed in phyllites to imperceptible in lava flows, sills, and some tuffs and pyroclastic breccias. It is generally an axial plane cleavage and is more consistent in attitude than bedding. Locally, bedding has been overturned beyond the position of the axial plane so that bedding-cleavage relations indicate an incorrect direction of top. Owing to penetrative deformation, the degree of elongation of originally equidimensional fabric elements may be as much as three- or four-fold but is generally much less. Where original elements have been elongated, they lie in the plane of metamorphic foliation and plunge steeply.

Thickness determinations are only approximate since the strata have been thinned plastically, thickened by minor folds, faulted by numerous indeterminate Cenozoic normal faults, and obscured by extensive forest.

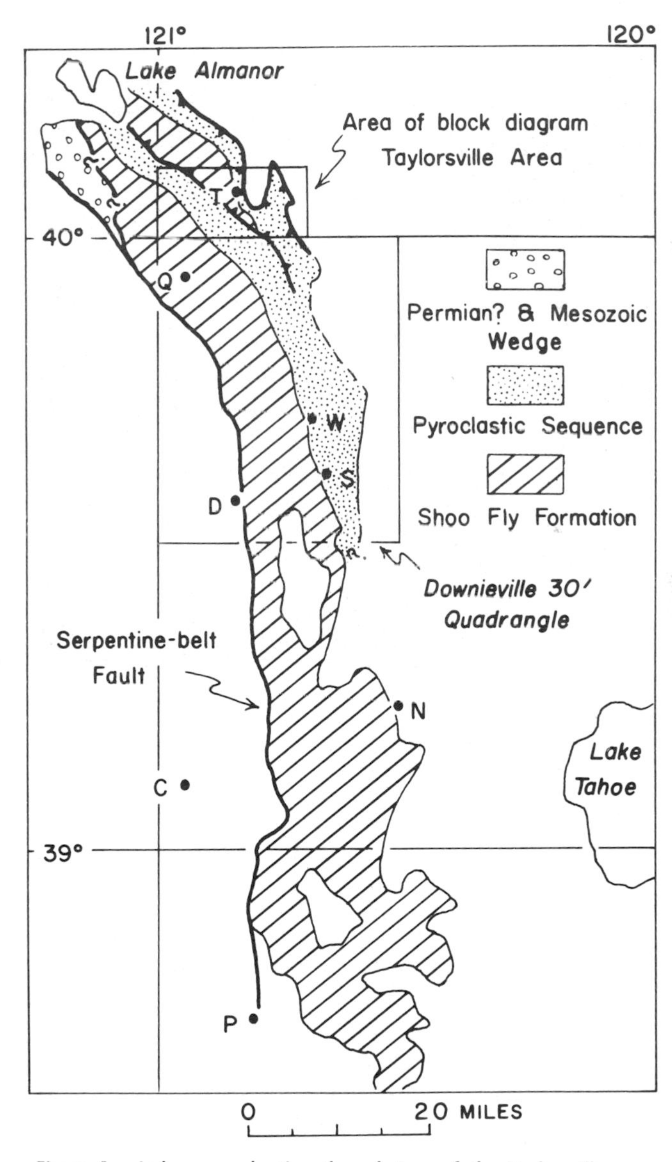

Figure 1. Index map showing the relations of the Taylorsville area to the regional geology. Taylorsville (T), Quincy (Q), Wades Lake (W), Sierra Buttes (S), Downieville (D), North Fork American River where it crosses the top of the Shoo Fly Formation (N), Colfax (C), and Placerville (P) are represented on the map by letters.

Photo 1. View southeast across Indian Valley. Mt. Hough, right skyline, shows exposures of Peale and Arlington Formations of the lower plate of the Taylorsville thrust. Grizzly Peak, left center skyline ridge, shows outcrops of upper plate Shoo Fly (Taylorsville Member), Grizzly, and Sierra Buttes Formations. Mt. Jura, left, exposes Jurassic rocks of the lower plate. Indian Valley is a complex graben. Camera site is underlain by Shoo Fly of the upper plate.

At the present state of understanding of the evolution of the Sierra Nevada, it appears that the Taylorsville area lies athwart the Nevadan structural axis. Farther south in the central Sierra Nevada, this axis is the locus of the batholithic complex. In the north, the axis is that of a major overturned syncline in which the entire known stratigraphic section is involved. The Silurian, Mississippian, Permian, Triassic, and Jurassic and possibly the Devonian systems are represented. That the axis of batholithic activity coincides with a major syncline has been shown by Rinehart and others (1959, p. 941), and they have added the Ordovician and Pennsylvanian to the list of systems represented. All the pre-Nevadan stratified rocks of the Sierra Nevada may be interpreted as defining a faulted synclinorium (Bateman and others, 1963, p. D-6), for which the Nevadan syncline is the axis. That the syncline was continuous involves interpolation of 175 miles, but the large outcrop breadth of 20 to 50 miles combined with the continuity of the west limb in the interval of interpolation permit little room for alternatives. A synclinal axis inferred by Taliaferro (1942, p. 99–100) in Mesozoic rocks west of Lake Tahoe describes an intermediate point.

This Nevadan syncline within the Taylorsville area is overturned to the northeast, and the overturned southwest limb has been thrust northeastward along the Taylorsville thrust onto the synclinal axis (see fig. 2). The upper plate can be traced only 5–10 miles south of the 40th parallel before it is obliterated by granite or covered by Tertiary volcanic rocks. To the east, the moderately dipping normal limb contains only Mesozoic rocks as granite occupies the position where one would expect to find the Paleozoic section. To the

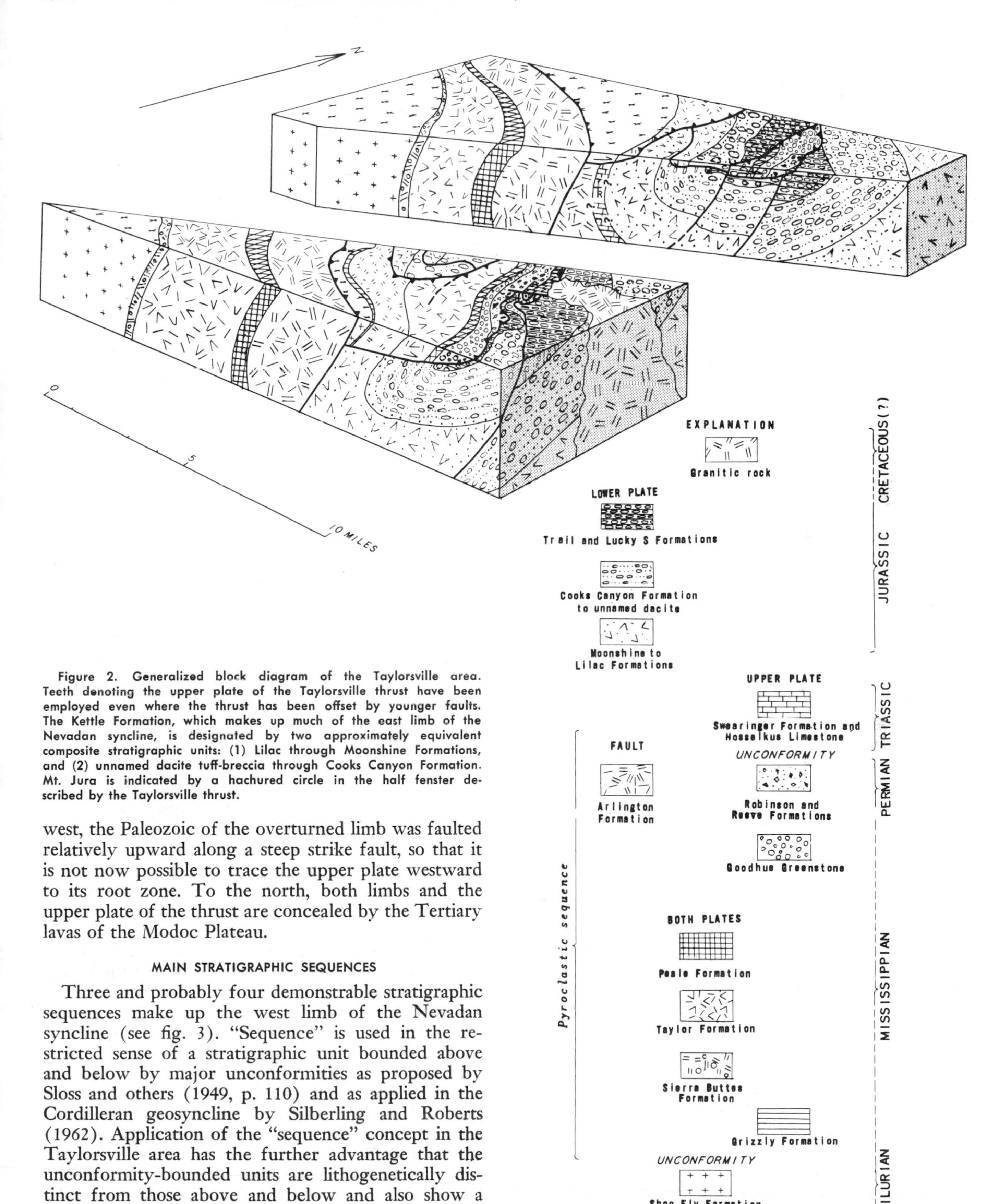

Figure 2. Generalized block diagram of the Taylorsville area. Teeth denoting the upper plate of the Taylorsville thrust have been employed even where the thrust has been offset by younger faults. The Kettle Formation, which makes up much of the east limb of the Nevadan syncline, is designated by two approximately equivalent composite stratigraphic units: (1) Lilac through Moonshine Formations, and (2) unnamed dacite tuff-breccia through Cooks Canyon Formation. Mt. Jura is indicated by a hachured circle in the half fenster described by the Taylorsville thrust.

west, the Paleozoic of the overturned limb was faulted relatively upward along a steep strike fault, so that it is not now possible to trace the upper plate westward to its root zone. To the north, both limbs and the upper plate of the thrust are concealed by the Tertiary lavas of the Modoc Plateau.

MAIN STRATIGRAPHIC SEQUENCES

Three and probably four demonstrable stratigraphic sequences make up the west limb of the Nevadan syncline (see fig. 3). "Sequence" is used in the restricted sense of a stratigraphic unit bounded above and below by major unconformities as proposed by Sloss and others (1949, p. 110) and as applied in the Cordilleran geosyncline by Silberling and Roberts (1962). Application of the "sequence" concept in the Taylorsville area has the further advantage that the unconformity-bounded units are lithogenetically distinct from those above and below and also show a high degree of internal lithologic uniformity.

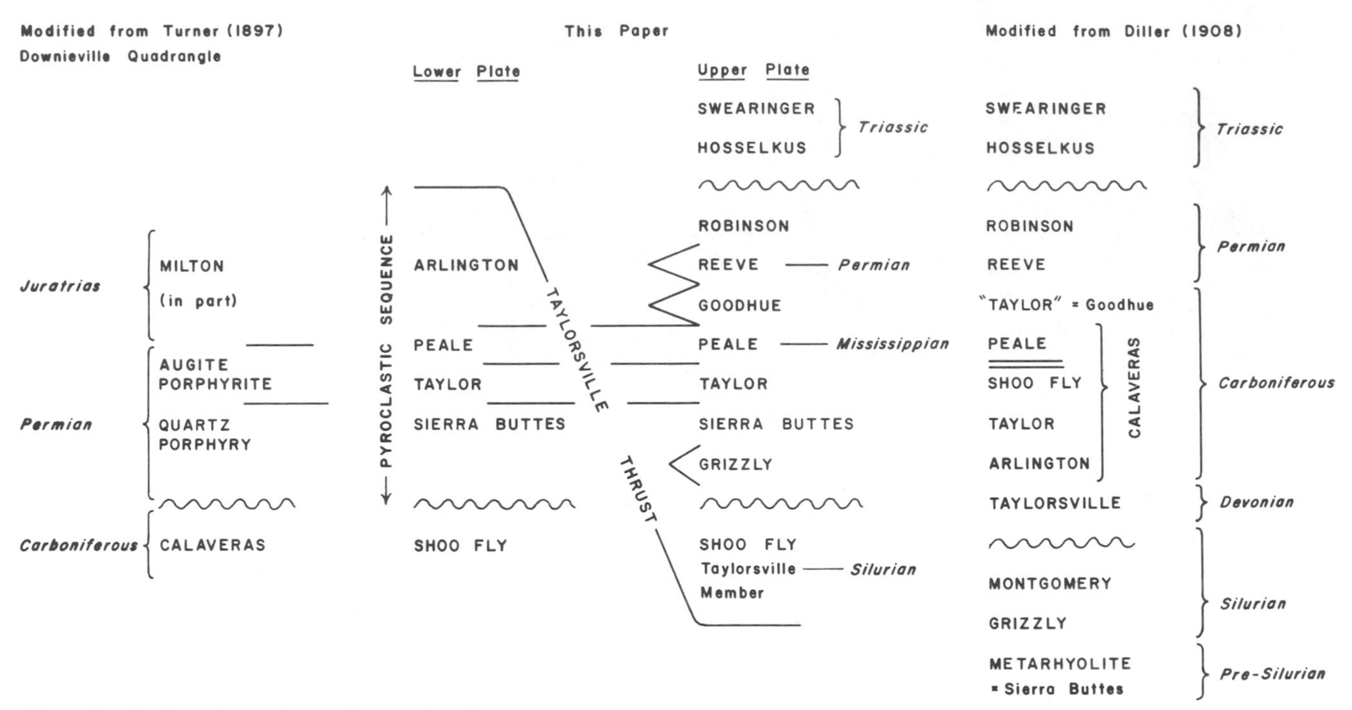

Figure 3. Pre-Jurassic correlation diagram for the Taylorsville area. Diller's column (on right) is modified in that his eastern belt of Taylor Meta-Andesite is inserted between his Peale and Reeve as demanded by his map relations, and his Robinson and Reeve Formations are indicated as Permian as emended by Thompson and others (1946). Turner considered his augite porphyrite and quartz porphyry to be Juratrias in age, but they are shown as Permian as emended by Wheeler (1939).

The lowest sequence consists of only two named formations, the Shoo Fly and the Taylorsville, which as mapped by Diller broadly represent respectively lower and upper plate equivalents. Neither the lower limits nor the stratigraphic makeup of either unit is well known except in local areas. Because the Shoo Fly constitutes a large part of the outcrop belts formerly referred collectively to the Calaveras Group (Clark and others, 1962, p. B-17), has a much greater extent along strike (100 miles or more), and shows promise of a more undisturbed and complete section (possibly 40,000 or 50,000 feet), the name Shoo Fly is provisionally extended to include the upper plate equivalents. Slate or phyllite, chert, and sandstone, the dominant components, contrast markedly with the unconformably overlying pyroclastic sequence. Silurian fossils are present near the top.

The second sequence, here termed the pyroclastic sequence, is found in both the lower and upper plates. It comprises eight formations consisting dominantly (95–98 percent) of coarse water-laid, presumably marine, pyroclastic debris. It is nearly 25,000 feet thick and rests with angular unconformity on the Shoo Fly Formation. Two fossil localities, one near the middle and the other near the top, provide ages of Mississippian and Permian respectively.

Informal reference to the pyroclastic sequence of Plumas County may prove useful; formal designation as the Plumas sequence would be desirable were it not for the possibility that a significant but undetected unconformity may intervene between dated Mississippian and Permian horizons. This sequence provides the key to both the structure and the stratigraphy; hence, it has been the most thoroughly studied and will be the principal subject of this paper.

The third sequence, found only in the upper plate, contains strata of Triassic age only, hence may adequately be referred to as the Triassic sequence. It consists of two fossiliferous shelf-type formations, the Hosselkus Limestone and the Swearinger Formation. The Hosselkus rests with angular unconformity on the pyroclastic sequence. The Triassic sequence is relatively thin, having a preserved thickness of only 1,100 feet. However, its upper boundary is the trace of the Taylorsville thrust and it is locally cut out by a granitic pluton, hence it may well have been thicker. That the sequence probably is separated from the overlying sequence of Jurassic rocks by an unconformity is inferred from relationships demonstrated farther south in the Sierra Nevada, where Clark and others (1962, p. B-19) have shown that the Lower Jurassic apparently oversteps about 400 feet of Upper Triassic(?) limestone within 1 mile.

The fourth and youngest sequence consists only of Jurassic strata, hence again is adequately referred to as the Jurassic sequence. It is about 15,000 feet thick on the east limb and probably a little thinner on the west limb of the Nevadan syncline, and is known only in the lower plate. The widely known sections on Mount Jura have been referred to informally as the Mount Jura sequence for many years, but formal designation is considered neither necessary nor desirable at this time.

The Jurassic sequence is dominated by volcanogenic rocks, although epiclastic or reworked volcanic rubble and possibly nonvolcanic epiclastic material is intercalated here and there in the section. Indeed, orogenic (polymictic) conglomerate is prominent in the upper part of the section, which may well be equivalent to the Mariposa Formation of the foothill belt. Though the thickness of volcanic material suggests a deep trough, the general aspect is one of shoaling compared to that of the pyroclastic sequence. Perhaps this explains why the Mount Jura sequence is unusually fossiliferous for a eugeosynclinal sequence.

Study of this sequence is incomplete; hence this treatment is little more than that of cataloging some of the more significant conclusions.

REVISION OF PALEOZOIC STRATIGRAPHY

The first geologic column of the area was provisionally set up by J. S. Diller (1892, p. 372) in a preliminary account of the earliest systematic study of the Taylorsville area. At the conclusion of intermittent field work, a modified and expanded column was presented in a more complete paper (Diller, 1908, pl. 4) and this is reproduced here as a part of figure 2.

Major discrepancies between Diller's sequence and that of Turner (1897) in the adjacent Downieville 30-minute quadrangle are readily apparent despite the fact that Diller and Turner worked contemporaneously on a project that involved both areas. For example, Turner's east-facing Juratrias sequence of quartz porphyry and augite porphyrite was described by Diller as west-facing Silurian (or pre-Silurian—text and plates are contradictory) metarhyolite and Carboniferous Taylor Meta-andesite, respectively.

It is apparent that a major difficulty facing the early geologists was the lack of paleontologic dating. Only in light of later advances made in stratigraphy could the geology be confidently pieced together without the aid of fossils. These advances consist of the recognition of facies change and of the significance with respect to "top and bottom" of many small-scale (geopetal) structures, of which graded bedding is the most widespread and useful in this area. Drag folds and the angular relationship of cleavage to bedding have been of only secondary usefulness but in some places are misleading.

The discrepancies between the Downieville quadrangle and the Taylorsville area have now been largely reconciled as one result of drastic revision of Diller's structural and stratigraphic interpretation (fig. 2). Turner's east-dipping Juratrias volcanics have proved to be components of the late Paleozoic pyroclastic sequence and are overturned in the north part of the Downieville quadrangle. They continue northward into the Taylorsville area retaining their overturned position and are there repeated by a major low-angle fault, the Taylorsville thrust. The repeated section is now also recognized in the northernmost part of the Downieville quadrangle.

The lower part of Diller's Paleozoic sequence is based on apparent superposition above and below a single dated (fossiliferous) horizon, his Silurian Montgomery Limestone. His four older formations are now recognized to lie in the upper plate, and his three younger formations constitute the lower plate. The uppermost formation of this sequence of seven as established by Diller was the Shoo Fly Formation. Between the Shoo Fly and the upper part of his Paleozoic sequence, Diller indicates a break. Above this break, he placed the three fossiliferous (late Paleozoic and Triassic) formations of the upper plate in their correct relative order. Owing to paleontological control, he correctly recognized that these three formations were overturned, but he could not recognize that the seven below the break were also overturned.

Durrell (*in* Durrell and Proctor 1948, p. 171) described the first irrefutable contact relationship between two of the formations of Diller's Paleozoic succession. Near Wades Lake in the center of the Downieville 30-minute quadrangle, Diller's Shoo Fly Formation (equivalent to and having priority over Turner's Calaveras Formation) is clearly overlain with angular unconformity by the Sierra Buttes Formation (new name for the metarhyolite series of Durrell, quartz porphyry of Turner, and metarhyolite of Diller). Detritus from the Shoo Fly is included in the basal conglomerate of the Sierra Buttes Formation and varies from place to place according to the underlying Shoo Fly rock type. Well exposed in the same area is a gradational contact between the Sierra Buttes and the overlying Taylor Formation, which Turner (1897) called augite porphyrite. Graded bedding in both the Sierra Buttes and the Taylor confirm the succession.

Reconnaissance by Cordell Durrell into the Taylorsville area showed the same succession, but overturned: Shoo Fly, Sierra Buttes, and Taylor. The Sierra Buttes there is thin and was apparently overlooked by Diller. The Arlington Formation of Diller is adjacent to the Taylor and seemed to constitute a fourth and even younger formation of this sequence, for graded bedding indicated that it too is overturned.

Subsequent field studies by the writer showed that Diller also failed to identify his Peale Formation between the Arlington and Taylor. The contact between the Sierra Buttes and the Shoo Fly is clearly an angular unconformity in which a section of the Shoo Fly several thousand feet thick is truncated. No fossils that would permit an age assignment have yet been found. This is the lower plate succession and is tabulated in figure 2 for comparison with Diller's succession.

Another Paleozoic succession, which differs from the lower plate succession owing to facies change, was faulted to the northeast along the Taylorsville thrust. Here again, graded bedding indicates that the succession is generally overturned and that it faces to the northeast as does the lower plate succession.

In the upper plate, the Taylorsville Formation of Diller occupies a stratigraphic position analogous to that held in the lower plate by the Shoo Fly Formation. The type Taylorsville is here provisionally lowered to member status within the Shoo Fly, and the name "Shoo Fly" applied to all upper plate rocks lying unconformably below the pyroclastic sequence. The fossiliferous Silurian Montgomery limestone beds are intercalated near the top of the Taylorsville Member. Diller (1908, p. 18–19) inferred an unconformity between the Montgomery and Taylorsville on rather insecure evidence, and not knowing that the section is overturned, he assigned a probably Devonian age to the Taylorsville.

The next overlying formation in the upper plate is the Grizzly. An angular unconformity, the same as that between the Shoo Fly and Sierra Buttes Formations, separates it from the underlying Taylorsville. The epiclastic Grizzly is interpreted as a basal unit deposited locally on an irregular erosion surface before the beginning of pyroclastic volcanism. It is overlain in turn by the pyroclastic Sierra Buttes Formation (Diller's metarhyolite).

Next in succession, as in the lower plate, are the Taylor and Peale Formations. Diller called the Taylor of this block the Hull Meta-andesite and believed it to consist of Late Jurassic intrusive and volcanic rocks. It is, however, clearly pyroclastic and very much like the type Taylor except that it contains a wider variety of sills and dikes and additional varieties of meta-andesite breccia.

Conformably above the Peale lies the Goodhue Greenstone (new name) which Diller erroneously mapped as Taylor. The type Taylor lies *below* the Peale. Moreover, the rock of the Goodhue is readily distinguished from that of the type Taylor. Although the Goodhue may be synchronous with the lower beds of the lower plate Arlington Formation, the rocks are lithologically dissimilar.

The next two formations are in the same order that Diller placed them: the Reeve Formation, then the Robinson Formation, both of which, however, are herein redefined. Some Reeve rock types are very distinctive, and their presence among the southeastern outcrops of the Arlington Formation strengthens correlation of the upper and lower plates. The Robinson rock type is broadly comparable with that of the bulk of the Arlington Formation of the lower plate.

Diller (1908) included the Peale, Shoo Fly, Taylor, and Arlington Formations in the Calaveras Group of supposed Carboniferous age. Turner (1897) included the direct extension of Diller's Reeve and Robinson in the Calaveras whereas Diller excluded them. Turner excluded the Taylor, and mapped much of the Arlington or Arlington equivalents in his Milton Formation. The Shoo Fly together with its synonym, the Blue Canyon Formation of the Calaveras Group (Lindgren, 1900), have recently been excluded (Clark and others, 1962, p. B-17), in part because rocks of Silurian age were specifically excluded from the Calaveras by Turner (1894, p. 446). Much of the type Calaveras is now known to be Mesozoic in age, and rocks that might be candidates for designation as type Calaveras are structurally very complex (Clark, 1964, p. 8, 12). As at least a temporary expedient, the term "Calaveras" will not be applied to any of the Taylorsville rocks.

DESCRIPTION OF THE SEQUENCES

Shoo Fly Formation

The Shoo Fly Formation underlies nearly the entire area of the largest and most continuous fault-bounded Paleozoic belt on the geologic map of California (in pocket), at least as far south as Placerville (see fig. 1). At the present stage of investigation, the Shoo Fly is formally a formation, but it certainly will eventually be given formal sequence or at least group status. Three lithic units have already been discerned in the upper 10,000 feet of the lower plate.

The uppermost of the three is greenstone, which is 3,000 feet thick and locally truncated by the overlying pyroclastic sequence. Clasts of the greenstone are incorporated in the basal few feet of the pyroclastic sequence.

The middle unit, about 2,000 feet thick, is almost certainly the lithic equivalent of the Taylorsville Member, which is in the upper plate and also about 2,000 feet thick, although its base is faulted out (fig. 2). This unit in both plates underlies the pyroclastic sequence with angular discordance, and it consists principally of laminated slate and phyllite, thin beds of feldspathic, possibly tuffaceous graywacke, and minor intraformational breccia, chert, and limestone.

The lower of the three units is similar to the middle but also contains significant interbedded sandstone, which ranges from feldspathic graywacke to essentially orthoquartzite, and some felsitic tuff or chert. It is 5,000 feet thick.

Below these three units, very thick undifferentiated slate and phyllite, chert, felsitic tuff, graywacke, and greenstone in variable but decreasing proportions in about the order listed comprise the bulk of the Shoo Fly of the lower plate. A few spot observations suggest top is to the northeast for the entire lower plate sequence. If the sequence is homoclinal and unfaulted, it is 40,000 to 50,000 feet thick.

The Shoo Fly of the upper plate includes, in addition to the Taylorsville Member and most of the lithic types found in the lower plate, a wide array of dikes, sills, and small plutons that have hindered further stratigraphic subdivision.

To the southwest, the Shoo Fly is generally bounded by a major serpentine-belt fault (Clark, 1960). However, at the northwest end of the belt, just south of Lake Almanor, a thick east-facing Mesozoic and Permian(?) wedge-shaped unit lies between the sepentine-belt fault and the Shoo Fly, and it must be separated from the Shoo Fly by another fault, probably a thrust (see fig. 1). A fusulinid locality reported by Diller (1908, p. 23) to lie at the west margin of the Shoo

Fly is probably at the base of the Permian(?) and Mesozoic wedge.

No fossils unequivocally collected from the Shoo Fly of the lower plate are diagnostic of its age (see Clark and others, 1962, p. B-17). However, the Middle(?) Silurian Montgomery Limestone of Diller is intercalated in the Taylorsville Member of the upper plate and this in turn is almost certainly equivalent to a unit in the upper part of the Shoo Fly of the lower plate. Thus the Shoo Fly is at least in part Silurian. Owing to its very great apparent thickness, it probably includes rocks as old as Ordovician.

Pyroclastic Sequence

The pyroclastic sequence includes in the lower plate the Sierra Buttes, Taylor, Peale, and Arlington Formations, and in the upper plate the Grizzly, Sierra Buttes, Taylor, Peale, Goodhue, Reeve, and Robinson Formations.

The pyroclastic nature imparts a lithogenetic unity to the sequence and presents a strong contrast with the sequences above and below. A marked and significant feature of the pyroclastic sequence is the relative sharpness and contrast owing to the change of chemical composition from one formation to the next. The gross succession of approximate rock types is dacite, andesite, latite, basalt or andesite, and dacite or silicic andesite. There is remarkably little intergradation between these types.

Contacts between formations of the sequence, however, are generally gradational to some degree. Those that have not been demonstrated to be gradational, hence are conceivably unconformable, are the Taylor-Peale, Peale-Arlington, and Reeve-Robinson. Locally there are breccias at the Goodhue-Reeve contact that are intermediate in chemical composition between the typical Goodhue and Reeve breccias, suggesting a transition from one to the other; however, this is considered only weak evidence for a gradational contact. Clearly, there is a possibility that an unconformity lies undiscovered above the Peale of the lower plate, and above the Goodhue of the upper plate, so that there may be only partial equivalence of the Arlington with the Goodhue, Reeve and Robinson.

Grizzly Formation. Found only on the upper plate, the Grizzly Formation is a thin epiclastic unit probably filling low places on the erosion surface on which it was deposited. It consists principally of black laminated slaty shale and blocky siltstone, and quartz-rich graywacke. It is generally abundantly interlaced with sills so that a true sedimentary thickness is difficult to measure, but the maximum is probably close to 200 or 300 feet. Arkose occurring 20 miles south, where Durrell (Durrell and Proctor, 1948, p. 171) first demonstrated the unconformity, may be nearly correlative.

Sierra Buttes Formation. The name Sierra Buttes Formation is here proposed for Turner's quartz porphyry of the Sierra Buttes (1894, p. 483; 1896, p. 646; 1897, p. 2), Diller's metarhyolite (1908, p. 81) and quartz porphyry (1895), and the metarhyolite series of Durrell and Proctor (1948, p. 171). The Sierra Buttes (fig. 1), the highest and most distinctive peaks composed of the rocks of this formation, are in the south part of the Downieville 30-minute quadrangle. A type section was not designated, but a representative section can be seen in the vicinity of Long Lake and Wades Lakes seven miles northwest of the Sierra Buttes. The thickness of the formation is 4,000 to 5,000 feet but decreases to less than 1,000 feet in the northwest part of the lower plate. Excluding dikes and sills, the formation consists principally of bedded quartz keratophyre breccia, tuff, and perhaps some flows, whose gross chemical composition is probably closer to dacite than to rhyolite. Minor chert, slate, and rare limestone with fragments of marine fossils also are present.

Taylor Formation. The Taylor Meta-andesite of Diller (1908, p. 83), or the augite porphyrite of Turner (1897), is characterized by augite andesite breccia, tuff-breccia, tuff, subordinate flows, minor black tuffaceous slate, and crinoidal limestone. Its thickness is about 8,000 feet. The size of the blocks in the breccia increases to 6 to 8 feet in the Downieville 30-minute quadrangle, hence the source probably lay in that vicinity.

Peale Formation. Dark quartz keratophyre flows and co-magmatic tuff-breccia and tuff, probably marine, characterized by pink alkali feldspar phenocrysts, dominate the lower half of the Peale Formation. The upper half consists principally of varicolored "ribbon" chert, slate, tuffaceous sandstone, and intraformational slump breccia. Maximum thickness approaches 2,500 feet. All known manganese deposits in the northeastern Sierra Nevada are in the middle of the Peale Formation.

Arlington Formation. Countless varieties of andesitic and dacitic tuff and tuff-breccia, water-laid and well graded, and interbedded slate and minor volcanic conglomerate-breccia comprise the Arlington Formation, which is recognized only in the lower plate. Intercalated breccia typical of the Reeve Formation indicates at least broad equivalence of the Arlington with the Goodhue, Reeve, and Robinson succession. The apparent thickness is 8,000 feet.

Goodhue Greenstone. The name Goodhue Greenstone is here applied to a distinctive pyroclastic breccia which Diller (1908, p. 84 and p. 3) called Taylor and referred to as lavas. The Goodhue, restricted to the upper plate, overlies the Peale Formation, whereas the Taylor underlies the Peale. Andesite of the Taylor is characterized by augite phenocrysts, whereas andesite or basalt of the Goodhue contains augite plus a relict second ferromagnesian phenocryst now represented by magnesian chlorite or a serpentine mineral.

Derivation of the name is from the Goodhue homestead on Ward Creek, in the NE¼SW¼SW¼ sec.

14, T. 25 N., R. 11 E. The building is shown on earlier topographic maps, though not on the latest (Kettle Rock, 1950). The type locality includes the east slope of Peale Ridge immediately west of Ward Creek, and the type section is in the NE¼ sec. 22, T. 25 N., R. 11 E. The thickness of the Goodhue Greenstone is 1,500 feet.

Reeve Formation. Keratophyre breccia and tuff, here and there fossiliferous, and minor fusulinid limestone and chert pebble conglomerate comprise the Reeve Formation as redefined here. Diller apparently attempted to map the "sedimentary" tuff and limestone units in his Robinson Formation and the "igneous" breccia in his Reeve. More logical units are obtained by including all rock types intercalated in the breccia as a part of the Reeve, and restricting the Robinson to a distinctly different succession of volcanogenic rocks which Diller also included in his Robinson Formation. The Reeve is characterized by plagioclase phenocrysts having major diameters of 10 to 20 millimeters, whereas those of the Robinson do not exceed 2 millimeters. The maximum apparent thickness is about 2,000 feet.

Robinson Formation. As redefined above, the Robinson consists of andesitic conglomerate-breccia, volcaniclastic calcareous sandstone, slate, and minor limestone. The maximum thickness is 700 feet. Fossils, obtained from conglomeratic beds, are Paleozoic and suggestive of a Permian age.

Age of the Pyroclastic Sequence

Only two horizons are dated by diagnostic faunas. The lower is at about the middle of the Peale Formation, and is at a locality reported by Diller (1908, p. 24). G. A. Cooper kindly studied the brachiopods from a new collection and determined them to be Early Mississippian in age (written communication, 1965).

The upper fossiliferous horizon is broadly in the middle of the Reeve Formation, which as re-defined includes most of the localities Diller (1908, p. 27–28) included in his Robinson Formation. The most diagnostic fossils are large fusulinids, which, however, are too recrystallized to identify specifically. Because of their large size, they are certainly Permian. Thompson and others (1946, p. 11) state that *Fusulina elongata* Shumard listed from the "Robinson locality" by Diller is probably *Parafusulina.*

A Permian age was formerly conceded for the Taylor (specifically for the augite porphyrite of Turner) because a mold of *Helicoprion sierrensis* discovered in Pleistocene till was supposedly derived from Turner's augite porphyrite (Wheeler, 1939, p. 107). However, in the glacial basin from which the till must have been derived, Turner included Peale and probably Arlington rock types in his augite porphyrite. Moreover, a petrographic description of the matrix made for Wheeler compares neither with the Taylor near Peale, but with the Arlington. Thus a Permian age for part of the Arlington is strongly suggested.

Owing to the discovery of probable Devonian fossils in limestone associated with volcanics in the foothill belt (L. D. Clerk, written communication, 1959), a Devonian age for the Sierra Buttes and Taylor is possible.

Regional Relations of the Pyroclastic Sequence

Most units of the pyroclastic sequence continue at least 40 miles southeast along the west limb of the Nevadan syncline to the North Yuba River and Milton Reservoir. In some places all the Milton Formation of Turner (1897) consists of rock types characteristic of the Peale, perhaps the Goodhue, and certainly of the Reeve. Farther south the pyroclastic sequence must be truncated by its bounding unconformity because at North Fork American River, about 50 miles south of the Taylorsville area, Triassic(?) rests directly on the Shoo Fly Formation (Clark and others, 1962, p. B-18). Possibly correlative Pennsylvanian and Permian(?) strata in roof pendants 175 miles south are nonvolcanic (Rinehart and others, 1959); these pendants define the east limb of the Nevadan syncline.

Correlation only on the grounds of lithlogic similarity of the component formations of the pyroclastic sequence with specific formations outside the immediate outcrop belt may well prove impossible. Although the characteristic rock types of the sequence are readily identified for 65 miles along strike, at the northern end of the belt constituent fragments become so fine grained that identification becomes partly subjective. If there has been appreciable telescoping along thrust faults farther west, individual lithic types probably do not persist across faults. However, it may prove feasible to find equivalents of the pyroclastic sequence in a gross manner, assuming that the volcanic episode responsible for the sequence was areally widespread. Perhaps the unfossiliferous Kanaka and Tightner Formations of Ferguson and Gannet (1932) and the Tightner of Chandra (1961, p. 12), which contain abundant volanic material, are broadly equivalents. However, these formations are separated from the outcrop belt of the pyroclastic sequence by a major serpentine-belt fault zone and are 60 miles south of the Taylorsville area. Still farther south, in the Foothill belt, Permian limestones included in the Calaveras Formation are associated with volcanic rocks (Clark, 1964).

Correlation with late Paleozoic rocks outside the Sierra Nevada cannot be attempted even on a gross lithologic basis because of facies changes, and is therefore dependent on paleontologic dating. The nearest correlatives in all directions except to the southeast contain appreciable volcanic constituents and generally are as sparsely fossiliferous as the late Paleozoic of the Taylorsville area. For the interested reader, the more recent pertinent papers are by Coogan (1960),

Albers and Robertson (1961), and Silberling and Roberts (1962).

Triassic Sequence

Rocks of the Triassic System, consisting of the type Hosselkus Limestone and the Swearinger Formation, are exposed in the Taylorsville area only on the frontal margin of the upper plate of the Taylorsville thrust. They are relatively thin, rather abundantly fossiliferous compared to subjacent strata, and in contrast to all other systems in the area, quite free of identified volcanic debris. Their setting was more that of the quiescent shelf than of the mobile eugeosyncline that both preceded and followed their deposition. They rest with angular unconformity on both known and questionable Permian strata, and their upper boundary is the trace of the Taylorsville thrust. Together with the Taylorsville thrust, they are complexly folded, locally involuted, and are thoroughly hornfelsed where an adjacent granitic pluton has intruded them.

Diller (1892) and Hyatt (1892) named the two lithic units the Hosselkus Limestone and the Swearinger Slate, and Hyatt dated them as Late Triassic. The Swearinger dips under the Hosselkus and was therefore presumed to be the older, but Diller (1908, p. 33) subsequently concluded that the Swearinger is the younger and that both are therefore overturned.[1]

On the basis of sedimentary structures indicating the Swearinger is not overturned, and a faulted contact between the Triassic and Permian(?), McMath (*in* Reeside and others, 1957, p. 1470) reversed the sequence to agree with Diller's original interpretation. Subsequent field study showed the sedimentary structures to be contained in involuted beds of the Robinson Formation faulted into juxtaposition with the Swearinger. The faulted contact between the Robinson and the Hosselkus must be an example of an unconformity "unglued" by local flexure folding—an incipient décollement—because a definitive outcrop later discovered outside the zone of intense folding showed a depositional contact. History has repeated itself: the sequence is once again reversed. May this Triassic section forever rest undisturbed upside down!

The contact between the Hosselkus and Swearinger is gradational. Representative thicknesses are about 200 feet for the Hosselkus and perhaps 900 feet for the Swearinger, but flowage during folding, incomplete resolution of structure, and other factors already cited preclude meaningful measurements.

[1] Inversion of the apparent sequence was based on correlation with an Upper Triassic section, also described by Diller (1906), in Shasta County about 100 miles to the northwest. There, two shale formations lithologically comparable to the Swearinger lie both above and below a limestone to which J. P. Smith (1894, p. 604–609) applied the name "Hosselkus." He correlated the limestone and the underlying shale unit—the Pit Formation—with respectively the type Hosselkus and the type Swearinger. The apparent sequence of the two sections is the same. This correlation was discredited when Smith (1898, p. 778) subsequently correlated the shale above the "Hosselkus"—the Brock Shale—with the Swearinger. The faunal tie of the Swearinger with the Brock proved to be closer than with the Pit Formation. But the name Hosselkus was retained for the limestone. And this was done despite the fact that the type Hosselkus was dated so inexactly that Diller subsequently felt free to shift it from above the Swearinger to below. Thus Diller inverted the apparent sequence of the type Hosselkus and Swearinger to make them agree with the supposedly equivalent Shasta County section. He did not question the initial correlation of the type Hosselkus with the Shasta County limestone. Correlation of these two limestones is not established even today according to N. J. Silberling (oral communication, 1965). Nonetheless, Diller was correct in reversing the sequence.

The Hosselkus consists largely of dark gray or black aphanitic limestone which weathers light gray, and is thinly bedded to laminated where bedding is visible. Beds of calcarenite, commonly containing rounded quartz grains, crop out near both margins. Locally abundant white splotches generally represent sheared-out and recrystallized fossils.

Black, calcareous, laminated hornfels having little relict fissility characterizes the Swearinger Formation. Thin black argillaceous limestone, quartzose sandstone beds, two of which are imperfectly graded and indicate top to the east, and a little conglomerate are also present.

Age assignments for the two formations have not changed appreciably from those given by Hyatt (1892, p. 399): Late Triassic and specifically Norian. According to G. E. G. Westermann (1962, p. 753), the age of the beds bearing *Monotis subcircularis* Gabb is probably late Norian. Westermann further postulates that *Monotis* lived in shallow water, perhaps attached to seaweeds.

Correlation of at least the *Monotis* beds of the Swearinger with part of the Brock Shale of Shasta County seems well established (Smith, 1927). Other Late Triassic or supposedly Late Triassic formations that may correlate with either or both the Hosselkus and Swearinger are the Pit Formation and "Hosselkus" Limestone of Shasta County (Diller, 1906; Smith, 1927; Sanborn, 1960; Albers and Robertson, 1961), the Cedar Formation, which is a few miles west of the Taylorsville area (Smith, 1894; Diller, 1895), limestone on the North Fork American River, 50 miles to the south (Clark and others, 1962), and possibly part of the Milton Formation 30 miles south in the Downieville quadrangle (Turner, 1897).

It is conceivable that the boundary between the Triassic and Jurassic sequences is exposed but not yet recognized. The upper part of the Swearinger contains considerable hornfelsed feldspathic sandstone that could readily mark the base of the Jurassic. Alternatively, if the uppermost part of the Triassic sequence were volcanic, it is possible that a horizon in the oldest known Jurassic formation, the Lilac, marks the boundary. A third possibility, at least as likely as the first, is that the Triassic-Jurassic boundary may lie in dark hornfels, which underlies the more obviously volcanic part of the Kettle Formation at its eastern border.

Jurassic Sequence

The marine Jurassic section exposed principally on Mount Jura has long been an outstanding geologic attraction of the Taylorsville region. Like the late Paleozoic sequence, it is volcanogenic and it is structurally and stratigraphically nearly as complex, but on a smaller scale. "It is structurally so complex that a formation placed at its base by one of the two chief authorities is placed by the other authority at its top" (Reed, 1943, p. 106). Owing to the relative abundance of fossils and of distinctive rock types, the principal investigators, J. S. Diller (1892, 1908) aided by Alpheus Hyatt (1892), and C. H. Crickmay (1933) were induced to erect 14 formations; two more are recognized in the present study. One is an unnamed dacite tuff-breccia formerly regarded as intrusive, and the other, the Kettle Formation (Kettle Meta-andesite of Diller), was regarded by Diller (1908, p. 84–85) as Carboniferous.

Crickmay published only a tabular summary of his restudy of the Jurassic sections. In such a brief treatment of his results, he was not able to marshal the evidence for his changes, hence some of them were not readily accepted. Though the present study of the Jurassic is incomplete, and revision will not be documented, an advance summary in support of Crickmay's stratigraphic succession seems warranted.

The Kettle Formation and the overlying Trail Formation of Diller (which is equivalent to Crickmay's Lucky S, Trail, and possibly Combe Formations) constitute the normally dipping east limb of the Nevadan syncline. Although the Kettle is cut out on the northeast by a granitic pluton, the total thickness of the two formations is more than 15,000 feet. The sections on Mount Jura are equivalent to the Kettle in whole or in part, are similarly overlain by Diller's Trail Formation (but mapped by Diller in his Foreman Formation), and constitute the western and overturned limb of the Nevadan syncline. They are repeated by a complicated fault system that appears to be essentially a folded gravity-slide thrust. The upper plate of the Taylorsville thrust largely conceals the synclinal axis, and completely conceals the lower stratigraphic boundary of the Mount Jura sections.

Crickmay (1933, p. 897) stated that his oldest Jurassic formation, the Lilac, rests on Middle Triassic volcanics. Because Upper Triassic rocks were presumably derived by thrusting from the same limb of the Nevadan syncline as the Mount Jura sections, it is suggested that the volcanics in question are even older Jurassic, and that Upper Triassic rocks underlie the volcanics but are concealed by the upper plate of the Taylorsville thrust.

The Mount Jura sequence is outlined in the table below. Thicknesses are generally those listed by Crickmay.

The Combe Formation of Crickmay has not yet been identified. Its age is controversial because Crickmay dated it as younger than the Nevadan orogeny.

The Kettle Formation is equivalent to the Cooks Canyon and earlier formations, and includes the same gross lithic types. A dacite tuff-breccia in the middle of the formation is assumed to be the same as the unnamed dacite tuff-breccia of the Mount Jura section, and the block diagram has been constructed on this assumption. The total thickness of the Kettle is about 10,000 feet, and Callovian (Late Jurassic) ammonites occur about 2,000 feet below the top (Imlay, 1961, p. D-9). It is conceivable that the Kettle extends down to the Triassic or even the Paleozoic.

Jurassic section on Mount Jura		
Trail Formation	Polymictic conglomerate, volcaniclastic sandstone, tuff, and mudstone.	4,000
Lucky S Formation	Black, plant-bearing slate, fine quartz-rich graywacke, and pebble conglomerate.	1,500
Cooks Canyon Formation	Andesitic and dacitic tuff-breccia and tuff, volcanic conglomerate, volcaniclastic sandstone and mudstone.	1,900
Foreman Formation	Dark-gray fossiliferous shale, mudstone, and fine volcaniclastic sandstone.	350
North Ridge Formation	Andesitic tuff-breccia and tuff.	200
Hinchman Formation	Fossiliferous conglomerate-breccia and volcaniclastic sandstone. Includes part of Bicknell Sandstone of Diller.	160
Hull Formation	Andesite tuff-breccia and tuff. Includes part of Bicknell Sandstone of Diller.	700
Unnamed Dacite Tuff-breccia	Biotite-hornblende dacite tuff-breccia and tuff.	600
Moonshine Formation	Volcanic conglomerate, red shale, and tuff. Fossiliferous.	300
Mormon Formation	Volcanic conglomerate, fossiliferous volcaniclastic sandstone, and black *Posidonia* shale.	950
Thompson Formation	Red fossiliferous tuff, limestone, dacite breccia and lava, and volcanic conglomerate.	400
Fant Meta-andesite	Augite andesite flows bearing large feldspar phenocrysts, and minor red tuff.	800
Hardgrave Sandstone	Red volcaniclastic sandstone, highly fossiliferous.	400
Lilac Formation	Dark-gray calcareous sandstone and mudstone, dacite flow-breccia(?) and tuff. Fossiliferous.	725
	Total	13,000

Confirmed or only mildly controversial ages for the Jurassic range from medial Early Jurassic (see Imlay, 1952) for the Hardgrave Sandstone and Lilac Formation to early Late Jurassic (Callovian) for the Foreman Formation (Imlay, 1961, p. D-9).

An interpretive note on the Jurassic conglomerates seems desirable. Several conglomerate beds in the more obviously volcanic section below the Lucky S Formation show features that suggest they are not to be interpreted in terms of subaerial erosion as a result of diastrophic uplift. Such conglomerates are highly lenticular, the rounded clasts are volcanic, and some include angular, penecontemporaneously deformed intraformational blocks as long as 12 feet. Slump structures are locally abundant in associated sandstone beds. These conglomerates are therefore interpreted as representing stream-mouth gravels that accumulated near the shores of volcanic islands, and from time to time slumped farther seaward. Conglomerate beds in the Trail Formation on the other hand are more continuous, associated with cross-bedded sandstone, and contain in addition to volcanic clasts, numerous types of sandstone, tuff, shale, and chert, all rounded. The Trail conglomerates are therefore orogenic in the usually accepted sense.

ACKNOWLEDGMENTS

The author wishes to express deep appreciation for the generous financial aid extended by the Shell Companies Foundation Fellowship Committee, the Geological Society of America (Grant No. 652-54-s56), the University of California at Los Angeles, the University of Oregon, and the National Science Foundation. Among numerous individuals who gave generously of time and advice, Cordell Durrell and John C. Crowell deserve special mention. Part of the paper is condensed from a Ph.D. dissertation submitted to the Graduate Faculty of the University of California, Los Angeles. The Continental Oil Company provided generous aid in the preparation of the manuscript.

REFERENCES

Albers, J. P., and Robertson, J. F., 1961, Geology and ore deposits of east Shasta copper-zinc district, Shasta County, California: U.S. Geol. Survey Prof. Paper 338, 107 p.

Bateman, P. C., Clark, L. D., Huber, N. K., Moore, J. G., and Rinehart, C. D., 1963, The Sierra Nevada batholith—a synthesis of recent work across the central part: U.S. Geol. Survey Prof. Paper 414-D, p. D41–D46.

Chandra, D. K., 1961, Geology and mineral deposits of the Colfax and Foresthill quadrangles, California: California Div. Mines and Geology Spec. Rept. 67, 50 p.

Clark, L. D., 1960, Foothills fault system, western Sierra Nevada, California: Geol. Soc. America Bull., v. 71, no. 4, p. 483–496.

—— 1964, Stratigraphy and structure of part of the western Sierra Nevada metamorphic belt, California: U.S. Geol. Survey Prof. Paper 410, 70 p.

Clark, L. D., Imlay, R. W., McMath, V. E., and Silberling, N. J., 1962, Angular unconformity between Mesozoic and Paleozoic rocks in the northern Sierra Nevada, California: U.S. Geol. Survey Prof. Paper 450-B, art. 6, p. B15–B19.

Coogan, A. H., 1960, Stratigraphy and paleontology of the Permian Nosoni and Dekkas Formations (Bollibokka Group): California Univ. Pubs. Geol. Sci., v. 36, no. 5, p. 243–316.

Coombs, D. S., 1960, Lawsonite metagraywackes in New Zealand: Am. Mineralogist, v. 45, nos. 3–4, p. 454–455.

—— 1961, Some recent work on the lower grades of metamorphism: Australian Jour. Sci. v. 24, no. 5, p. 203–215.

Crickmay, C. H., 1933, Mount Jura investigation: Geol. Soc. America Bull., v. 44, no. 5, p. 895–926.

Diller, J. S., 1892, Geology of the Taylorsville region of California: Geol. Soc. America Bull., v. 3, p. 369–394.

—— 1895, Description of the Lassen Peak quadrangle, California: U.S. Geol. Survey Geol. Atlas, Folio 15.

—— 1906, Description of the Redding quadrangle, California: U.S. Geol. Survey Geol. Atlas, Folio 138.

—— 1908, Geology of the Taylorsville region, California: U.S. Geol. Survey Bull. 353, 128 p.

Durrell, Cordell, and Proctor, P. D., 1948, Iron-ore deposits near Lake Hawley and Spencer Lakes, Sierra County, California: California Div. Mines Bull. 129, pt. L, p. 165–192.

Ferguson, H. G., and Gannett, R. W., 1932, Gold quartz veins of the Alleghany district, California: U.S. Geol. Survey Prof. Paper 172, 139 p.

Hyatt, Alpheus, 1892, Jura and Trias at Taylorsville, California: Geol. Soc. America Bull, v. 3, p. 395–412.

Imlay, R. W., 1952, Correlation of the Jurassic formations of North America, exclusive of Canada: Geol. Soc. America Bull., v. 63, no. 9, p. 953–992.

—— 1961, Late Jurassic ammonites from the western Sierra Nevada, California: U.S. Geol. Survey Prof. Paper 374-D, p. D1–D30.

Lindgren, Waldemar, 1900, Description of the Colfax quadrangle, California: U.S. Geol. Survey Geol. Atlas, Folio 66.

Reed, R. D., 1943, California's record in the geologic history of the world: California Div. Mines Bull. 118, p. 99–118.

Reeside, J. B., Jr., chm., and others, 1957, Correlation of the Triassic formations of North America exclusive of Canada, *with a section on* Correlation of continental Triassic sediments by vertebrate fossils, by E. H. Colbert and J. T. Gregory: Geol. Soc. America Bull., v. 68, p. 1451–1513.

Rinehart, C. D., Ross, D. C., and Huber, N. K., 1959, Paleozoic and Mesozoic fossils in a thick stratigraphic section in the eastern Sierra Nevada, California: Geol. Soc. America Bull., v. 70, no. 7, p. 941–945.

Sanborn, A. F., 1960, Geology and paleontology of the southwest quarter of the Big Bend quadrangle, Shasta County, California: California Div. Mines Spec. Rept. 63, 26 p.

Silberling, N. J., and Roberts, R. J., 1962, Pre-Tertiary stratigraphy and structure of northwestern Nevada: Geol. Soc. America Spec. Paper 72, 58 p.

Sloss, L. L., Krumbein, W. C., and Dapples, E. C., 1949, Integrated facies analysis, *in* Longwell, C. R., chm., Sedimentary facies in geologic history: Geol. Soc. America Mem. 39, p. 91–124.

Smith, J. P., 1894, The metamorphic series of Shasta County, California: Jour. Geology, v. 2, p. 588–612.

—— 1898, Geographic relations of the Trias of California: Jour. Geology, v. 6, p. 776–786.

—— 1927, Upper Triassic marine invertebrate faunas of North America: U.S. Geol. Survey Prof. Paper 141, 262 p.

Taliaferro, N. L., 1942, Geologic history and correlation of the Jurassic of southwestern Oregon and California: Geol. Soc. America Bull., v. 53, no. 1, p. 71–112.

Thompson, M. L., Wheeler, H. E., and Hazzard, J. C., 1946, Permian fusulinids of California: Geol. Soc. America Mem. 17, 77 p.

Turner, H. W., 1894, Rocks of the Sierra Nevada: U.S. Geol. Survey Ann. Rept. 14, p. 435–495.

—— 1896, Further contributions to the geology of the Sierra Nevada: U.S. Geol. Survey Ann. Rept. 17, p. 521–762.

—— 1897, Description of the Downieville quadrangle California: U.S. Geol. Survey Geol. Atlas, Folio 37.

Westermann, G. E. G., 1962, Succession and variation of *Monotis* and the associated fauna in the Norian Pine River Bridge section, British Columbia (Triassic, pelecypoda): Jour. Paleontology, v. 36, no. 4, p. 745–792.

Wheeler, H. E., 1939, *Helicoprion* in the Anthracolithic (late Paleozoic) of Nevada and California, and its stratigraphic significance: Jour. Paleontology, v. 13, no. 1, p. 103–114.

TERTIARY AND QUATERNARY GEOLOGY OF THE NORTHERN SIERRA NEVADA

By Cordell Durrell
University of California, Davis, California

For purposes of this paper the southern limit of the northern Sierra Nevada is arbitrarily taken as the route of U.S. Highway 40, also known as Interstate 80, from Sacramento via Truckee, California, to Reno, Nevada. On the north the limit, equally arbitrary, is set as the line along which the pre-Tertiary metamorphic and plutonic "bedrock series" of the Sierra Nevada disappears beneath volcanic rocks of probable Pliocene age. This is roughly an arc extending from near Oroville in the Sacramento Valley to Susanville (fig. 1). The western limit is, of course, the Sacramento Valley. The eastern limit is the accepted geographic boundary which follows the Honey Lake fault scarp southeastward from Susanville to near Verdi, Nevada, on Highway 40.

Thus defined, the northeastern part includes a portion of the Basin and Range province. The Pacific drainage divide which follows the crest of the Sierra Nevada from its southern end northward along the west side of Lake Tahoe turns sharply east just a few miles north of Truckee on Highway 40. It passes around the south and east sides of Sierra Valley and then follows the crest of the Honey Lake fault scarp to beyond Susanville (fig. 1). The crest of the nearly monolithic fault block which is the Sierra Nevada proper, continues northwestward from Truckee and passes west of Sierra Valley, Mohawk Valley, Spring Garden, American Valley, and continues in the direction of Mount Lassen (fig. 1).

The region between the crest of the Sierra Nevada, as defined above, and the Pacific drainage divide includes the valleys named above, other similar valleys all of which are basins whose origin is due to faulting, and the Grizzly and Diamond Mountains. This region has basin and range structure, but it is not within the Great Basin as it is drained to the Pacific Ocean by the headwaters of the Middle and North forks of the Feather River, both of which cross the Sierra Nevada.

PREVIOUS WORK

The early literature that relates to this area is surprisingly large, but is well summarized in two papers by Henry Turner (1895, 1896). The first important maps are those of Turner and Lindgren of the Downieville, Bidwell Bar, Truckee, Colfax, and Sacramento quadrangles published as folios of the Geologic Atlas of the United States. The monograph on the Tertiary gravels (Lindgren, 1911) was the last general work to be published. Later work was more detailed and confined to small areas. Over most of the area the best information available is still that by Lindgren and Turner. Reconnaissance mapping by the California Division of Mines and Geology has filled in previously unstudied areas for the preparation of the new State geologic map sheets published at a scale of 1:250,000. The reader is referred to the Westwood and Chico sheets of this series for general coverage of the area under discussion.

GEOLOGY

Introduction

The Tertiary and Quaternary rocks of the northern Sierra Nevada include marine and continental sediments of volcanic and nonvolcanic origin, lava flows, and intrusions. Their ages range from middle Eocene to Recent. Marine sediments are confined to a few small areas at the western edge of the range. Continental sediments within the range are fluviatile, lacustrine, glacial, and volcanic. The volcanic sediments are volcanic fanglomerate, conglomerate, sandstone, and mudstone; tuff, tuff breccia, mudflow breccia, and ignimbrite. Lavas are olivine basalt and andesite, as are also plugs and dikes. Lava flows are far less abundant than clastic volcanic rocks so that stratigraphic problems are as important as petrologic problems.

STRATIGRAPHY

Cretaceous

Just north of the area under discussion and near the margin of the Sacramento Valley are marine Upper Cretaceous sandstones, shales, and conglomerates. The type section of the Chico formation on Chico Creek ranges in age from probable late Coniacian to middle Campanian (Popenoe, 1960). The section is 4,000 feet thick, dips gently westward, and rests on the "bedrock series" of the Sierra Nevada. Beds of Upper Cretaceous age also occur at Pentz in Butte County, and at Folsom, just south of the limit of the area (fig. 1). This distribution suggests that the edge of Cretaceous beds beneath the Sacramento Valley is not far from the edge of the mountain range. The Upper Cretaceous shoreline paralleled the trend of the range and was for a time at the present limit of outcrop, but there is no information as to how far east younger Cretaceous beds may have lapped on to the "bedrock series."

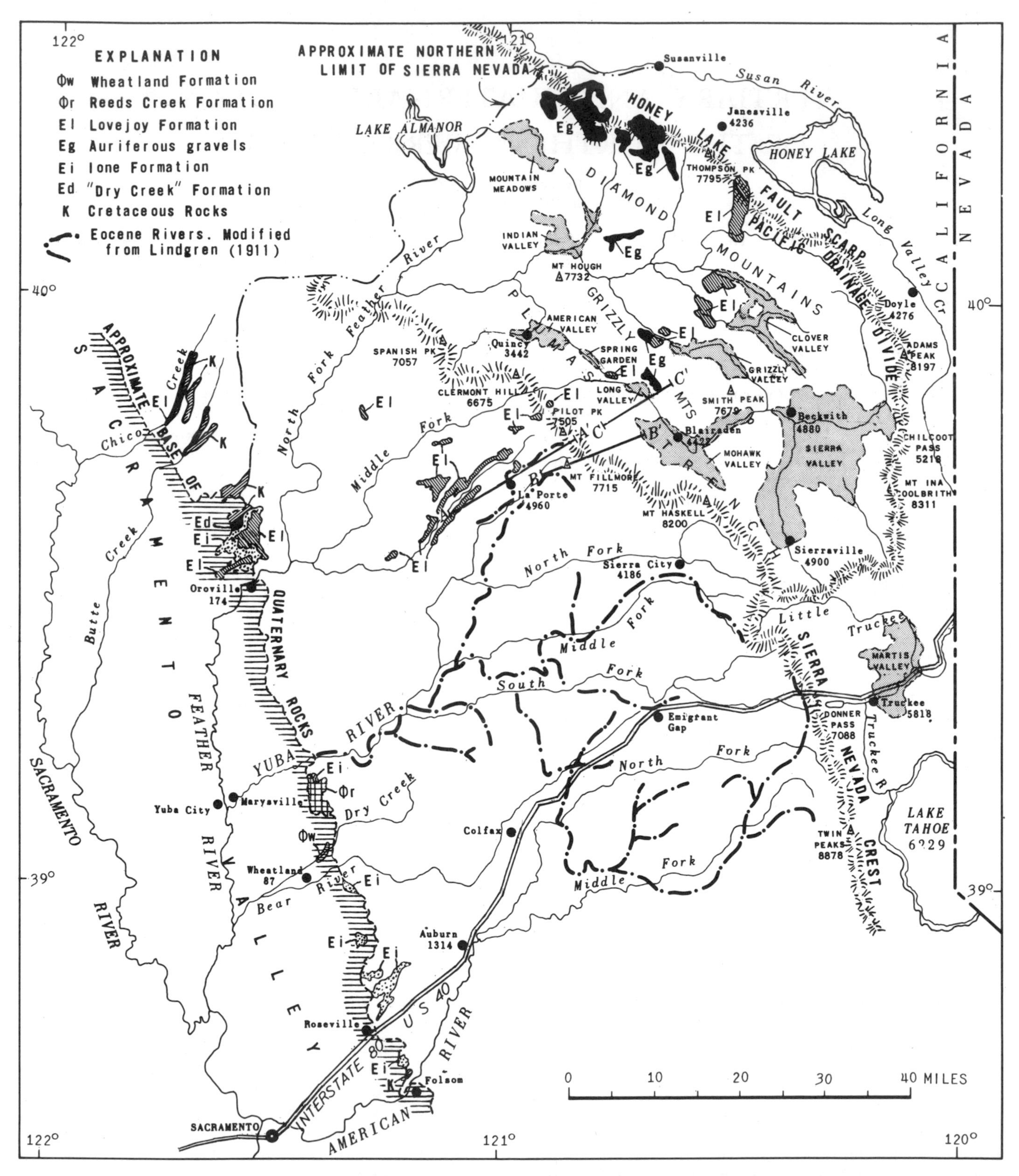

Figure 1. Map of the northern Sierra Nevada, showing geographic features, distribution of Cretaceous and older Tertiary rocks, and the Eocene River system. Lines A-A′, B-B′, and C-C′ show positions of cross sections shown on figure 3.

The nature of the Cretaceous beds indicates that during their deposition the Sierra Nevada was a low-lying land contributing mud, sand, and pebbles to the adjacent sea. Presumably this was the condition at the beginning of the Tertiary, but there is no record during the long time span of Paleocene and lower Eocene.

Eocene

"Dry Creek" Formation

The Upper Cretaceous beds at Pentz are overlain by gray shale and sandstone rich in biotite. The shale contains a marine fauna of middle Eocene age (Allen, 1929, p. 367–369). Allen named the Eocene beds "Dry Creek"; that name was preempted but no new name has been assigned. According to Creely (1955) who reviewed the problem, the "Dry Creek" is 80 feet thick at the type locality. The area of exposure is quite small (fig. 1).

Ione Formation

The Ione Formation, which rests without angular discordance on the "Dry Creek" Formation at Pentz and elsewhere on the "bedrock series," is a group of continental sediments that crops out at intervals along the west base of the range as far south as Fresno County. It grades eastward into Eocene river gravels and sands. Westward it extends into the Sacramento Valley subsurface where it rests on the marine lower Eocene Capay Shale. It is considered equivalent to the marine middle Eocene Domengine Formation, and is overlain by the marine Markley Formation of upper Eocene age.

The Ione consists of claystone of various colors, mostly light shades, and of kaolinitic sandstones in which the sand grains are predominantly angular quartz. Much of the sandstone contains pearly flakes of kaolin, which Allen (1929) called anauxite. These flakes are to a considerable extent obviously pseudomorphs of biotite, although biotite itself is rare. The sandstones are white, red, orange, or mottled. They are usually not cemented, but are bonded with clay. Some glauconite is present. In places there are lenses of quartz-rich gravel, and coal and lignite beds that are present have been mined locally.

At Oroville Table Mountain the Ione is 600 feet thick (Creely, 1955, p. 140), and at Ione it is about 1,000 feet thick (Allen, 1929).

The Ione is evidently a littoral-continental deposit that comprises a strip parallel to the length of the range. At South Oroville Table Mountain, just north of the city of Oroville (fig. 1), the Ione on the west side is believed to grade into fluviatile "auriferous gravels" on the east side, a relationship agreed to by everyone who has studied the area. Allen (1929) cites abundant evidence from other areas to show the equivalence of the Ione and the "auriferous gravels." At Oroville Table Mountain both units contain cobbles of hornblende andesite.

Because the Ione Formation rests in many places on the "bedrock series" deeply weathered to lithomarge, and because the Ione itself is composed principally of quartz and clay, Allen believed that the Ione sediments were derived under tropical or subtropical weathering conditions.

"Auriferous gravels"

The term "auriferous gravels" has been applied since early times to the ancient quartz-rich, gold-bearing stream deposits of the Sierra Nevada, once thought to be Miocene, but later recognized to be Eocene. Besides their physical equivalence to the Ione, and of that to the Domengine Formation, they are independently dated paleobotanically (MacGinitie, 1941). Younger gold-bearing gravels are, of course, excluded from this category. Although the name is inappropriate because gold occurs in gravels of younger age, including the Recent, no one has yet suggested a better name.

The "auriferous gravels" are in ancient river valleys and the river systems have been reconstructed in part (Lindgren, 1911) as shown on figure 1. The channels, in the valley bottoms, can be examined in places where the gravel has been removed by hydraulic mining. Elsewhere the channels were explored by underground mining, and there is scarcely any portion of them that is unexploited.

Most of the gold occurred in the lowest part of a channel where the gravel was generally bouldery, and composed mostly of local rock types. Above the gold-bearing sections the gravel is quartz rich, but not composed entirely of vein quartz, for chert and other quartz-rich rocks are abundant. At La Porte, for example, black, gray, white, and variegated chert unlike any yet discovered in the "bedrock series" of the Sierra Nevada is common, and it indicates a source east of the present limits of the range. Quartz-rich sand is abundant, and claystone and carbonaceous clays, no doubt deposited in ponds on flood plains, are present at La Porte.

Lindgren (1911) believed that the rivers had their headwaters in the present Sierra Nevada, and he thought that he knew where the divide was between the coastal and the interior drainage as far back as the Cretaceous. His conclusion requires that all of the channel filling, including the gold, originated within the range as we now know it. However, the size of the channels in the present summit region and the occurrence of cobbles of rocks foreign to the Sierra Nevada indicate that the streams headed far to the east. Thus the Jura River that was supposed to flow northwestward across Sierra and Plumas Counties in the summit region could not have existed. Furthermore, its course was drawn by linking occurrences of gravel of different ages and quite different petrologic characteristics.

The plant remains contained in the "auriferous gravels" not only date them as Eocene or early Oligocene, but indicate that the climate of the region at that time was near-tropical, thus confirming the opinion of Allen (1929) with respect to the Ione Formation. Potbury (1935) concluded that: "The distribution of the modern relatives [of the fossil plants found at La Porte] indicates that the climate at La Porte during early Tertiary was intermediate between the tropical climate of the windward side of southern Mexico and Central America and the warm temperate climate of the leeward side." And, "An analysis of the leaf characters suggests that the flora occupied a position intermediate between a strictly temperate and tropical environment."

Gravels, composed mostly of metavolcanic rocks and chert, and younger than the quartz-rich gravels also occur in Plumas County. Many of the pebbles and cobbles are like Sierra Nevada rocks and were no doubt of local origin, but many are not, and these must have been brought in from the east. These younger gravels occupy different channels than the quartz-rich gravels, although they overlap the latter in places. Mostly they are beneath the lavas of the Lovejoy Formation. They are unconformable on the older gravels and the "bedrock series."

The headward extensions of these ancient rivers are either lost by erosion or concealed beneath younger rocks.

Lovejoy Formation

The Lovejoy Formation (Durrell, 1959b) is restricted to the northernmost Sierra Nevada (fig. 1). It consists of a series of black olivine basalt lava flows that comprise a chain of outcrops extending across the region from the Honey Lake fault scarp above Honey Lake to Oroville Table Mountain. The same basalts are present in the Sacramento Valley subsurface, and they crop out on the west side of the valley at Orland Buttes. The Putnam Peak Basalt near Vacaville is probably the same series of flows.

The several areas of occurrence across the Sierra Nevada are isolated from each other as a result of faulting and erosion, but there can be little doubt that they are remnants of a once continuous body. The occurrences are limited to a narrow belt across the region, and probably their original distribution was restricted in a similar way, as by confinement to a broad shallow valley.

The lavas of the Lovejoy Formation form flat-topped table lands with stepped sides. The cliffs usually extend through a single flow and benches mark the interflow contacts. As many as ten flows can be recognized in some sections. The maximum thickness is about 600 feet. The ground over the flows is stony, even in forest. Vegetation is usually sparse, and the poor soil is typically chocolate colored. The rocks weather brown or dark gray and are dull black on fresh surfaces. A poorly defined columnar structure is present in most places and joints are closely spaced. Vesicles, sparse in most flows but abundant in a few, usually show no flattening due to flow. An orientation of feldspar microlites is present in some flows and is evidenced by a sheen on the surface. Scoria zones are absent between flows, and even in good exposures the interflow contacts are difficult to locate. Sand and gravel in small amounts occur locally between flows.

The unusual microscopic textures of the lavas have been discussed in detail by Durrell (1959b), and are the principal basis for correlation of the many isolated occurrences of the lavas.

The Lovejoy Formation rests unconformably on either the "auriferous gravels," the Ione Formation, or the "bedrock series."

No local sources of the basalts have been identified; hence they are believed to have originated east of the Honey Lake fault scarp. Pebbles and cobbles between flows include hornblende andesite, and granitoid rocks unlike those of the northern Sierra Nevada, which, therefore, indicate an eastern source.

The Lovejoy Formation has been dated by Durrell (1959b) from relationships at La Porte, where in the Upper Ditch Diggings of the La Porte hydraulic pit there are two immense boulders of Lovejoy Basalt and numerous smaller pieces. Small pieces are also present in lacustrine clays that overlie the gold-bearing gravels. Above the clays is the La Porte tuff which contains a flora dated as latest Eocene or early Oligocene (Potbury, 1935). Thus the Lovejoy is older than the La Porte flora and could be latest Eocene or early Oligocene also. The Lovejoy lies unconformably below the Ingalls Formation, which is believed to be Oligocene, and that in turn is unconformably below the Delleker Formation which is probably lower Miocene.

On the other hand, Dalrymple (1964) considers the Lovejoy to be early Miocene by radiometric methods. Whole rock determinations of Lovejoy basalts give dates of not more than 13.6 million years which are considered invalid. A date of 23.8 million years obtained on plagioclase from a tuff bed below the Lovejoy at Oroville Table Mountain is considered valid. For this reason Dalrymple believes the Lovejoy to be younger than that, in spite of the fact that this date is also younger than some he obtained from the Delleker Formation (20.5 to 26.1 million years) which rests unconformably on both the Lovejoy and Ingalls Formations. Dalrymple explains away the relations at La Porte on grounds that he was unable to find the clasts of Lovejoy basalt in place in the clays below the La Porte tuff.

Oligocene

Wheatland Formation

The Wheatland Formation (Clark and Anderson, 1938) crops out in a small area along Dry Creek 6 miles northwest of the town of Wheatland at the west base of the mountains (fig. 1). The occurrence is surrounded by alluvium. The beds are about 300 feet thick and dip 3° to 5° to the southwest. They consist of shale, sandstone, and conglomerate containing pebbles of granitoid and metamorphic rock, hornblende andesite, and olivine basalt. A marine invertebrate fauna described by Clark (Clark and Anderson, 1938) is determined to be lowest Oligocene or upper Eocene, and is considered by Weaver *et al.* (1944) to be lowest Oligocene. A radiometric age by Dalrymple (1964) of andesite pebbles from the Wheatland is 53.5 million years.

Reeds Creek Andesite

A few miles north of the Wheatland Formation along Reeds Creek there crops out a series of andesite mudflow breccias and conglomerates that rests on the Ione Formation and overlaps the "bedrock series", named the Reeds Creek Andesite by Clark and Anderson (1938). This is in turn overlain by rhyolite tuff, which is probably a correlative of either the Delleker Formation or the Valley Springs Formation of the central Sierra Nevada, but the contact between the two is concealed by a strip of alluvium three-fourths of a mile wide. Clark and Anderson suggest that the Reeds Creek might be the source of the hornblende andesite pebbles in the Wheatland Formation, and that it might, therefore, be Eocene. It is not really certain whether the Reeds Creek is older or younger than the Wheatland for no fossils have been found in it.

Ingalls Formation

The Ingalls Formation (Durrell, 1959a) consists of andesite mudflow breccia, which is virtually unbedded except locally at the base where conglomerate occurs. The mudflows and the clasts in them are dark colored, and mostly of pyroxene andesite, but with some hornblende andesite in which the hornblende phenocrysts are large in size but small in amount. Quartz diorite blocks of local origin are present in the lower part, and clasts of the Lovejoy Formation basalts have been found in the breccia. The Ingalls rocks characteristically form prominent black craggy outcrops.

The Ingalls is separated from both older and younger rocks by unconformities. It rests variously on "auriferous gravels," the Lovejoy Formation, and on the "bedrock series." It lies across fault contacts between older rocks, hence is separated from them by an episode of faulting and erosion. Because its upper surface is also an unconformity, its original thickness is unknown. The present maximum thickness is 550 feet.

The Ingalls is present in the Diamond and Grizzly Mountains and in the Plumas Trench between the Grizzly Mountains and the Sierra Nevada. It has not been identified in the Sierra Nevada proper.

The age of the Ingalls has not been closely established. It is younger than the Lovejoy Formation, but is older than the superimposed Delleker Formation which appears to be early Miocene. The Ingalls is possibly correlative with the Alta Andesite at Virginia City, Nevada, which contains the Oligocene Sutro Tuff Member (Gianella, 1936), and with the Wheatland Formation, also Oligocene.

Miocene

The Miocene Delleker and Bonta Formations and their equivalents together with the Pliocene Penman Formation and the Warner Basalt and their equivalents are shown as a single unit in figure 2. West of the crest of the Sierra Nevada these rocks are confined to the interstream ridges, and the irregular pattern of occurrence is owing to erosion. The rocks are more extensively preserved east of the crest owing to their structurally lower position.

Delleker Formation and Its Probable Equivalents

Rhyolite tuff is widely distributed in the northern Sierra Nevada but has been assigned a formation name only in Plumas County where it was named Delleker by Durrell (1959a). It is not clear whether the Delleker and the Valley Springs Formation of the central Sierra Nevada, also rhyolite tuff, are equivalent.

The rhyolitic deposits consist of welded tuff, or ignimbrite, especially in the east, water-lain ash and volcanic mud, and quartz-sand and gravel. Most of the tuff is white or cream colored, but some of the ignimbrite is tan, brown, and pink. Quartz, sanidine, and biotite are usually conspicuous.

Sand and gravel beds are common especially at or near the base, but in many places pebbles and cobbles are found distributed through the tuff. In Placer County, along Highway 40 (Interstate 80) the quartz-sand and gravel is undoubtedly reworked from the older "auriferous gravels." In Plumas County, gravels at the base of the Delleker are auriferous and contain granophyric granite and metaquartzite that are foreign to the Sierra Nevada and indicate an eastern source.

The rhyolite tuff was no doubt deposited as a sheet over the region, but it is now discontinuous and present often in only very small areas. This distribution is owing both to erosion alone, which isolated the lowest parts of the formation, and to faulting and erosion as is clearly the case in the Grizzly and Diamond Mountains.

The rhyolite tuff beds are usually less than 400 feet thick, but equivalent beds farther east are very much thicker, as for example, in the Virginia Range west of Pyramid Lake, Nevada, where they are 3,500 feet thick (McJannet, 1957).

No sources of rhyolite tuff are known in the northern Sierra Nevada, and they undoubtedly lie farther east. Tuff flows hot enough to weld reached the eastern part of the range, but only water-lain tuff is present farther west.

The age of the Delleker Formation in Plumas County is established only indirectly by paleontologic means. In the Virginia Range, west of Pyramid Lake, Nevada, the equivalent of the Delleker is overlain by a diatomite that contains fossil leaves dated as middle Miocene (D. I. Axelrod in McJannet, 1957). Hence the Delleker is probably middle or lower Miocene, or possibly even Oligocene. Radiometric ages on samples from Plumas County (Dalrymple, 1964) range from

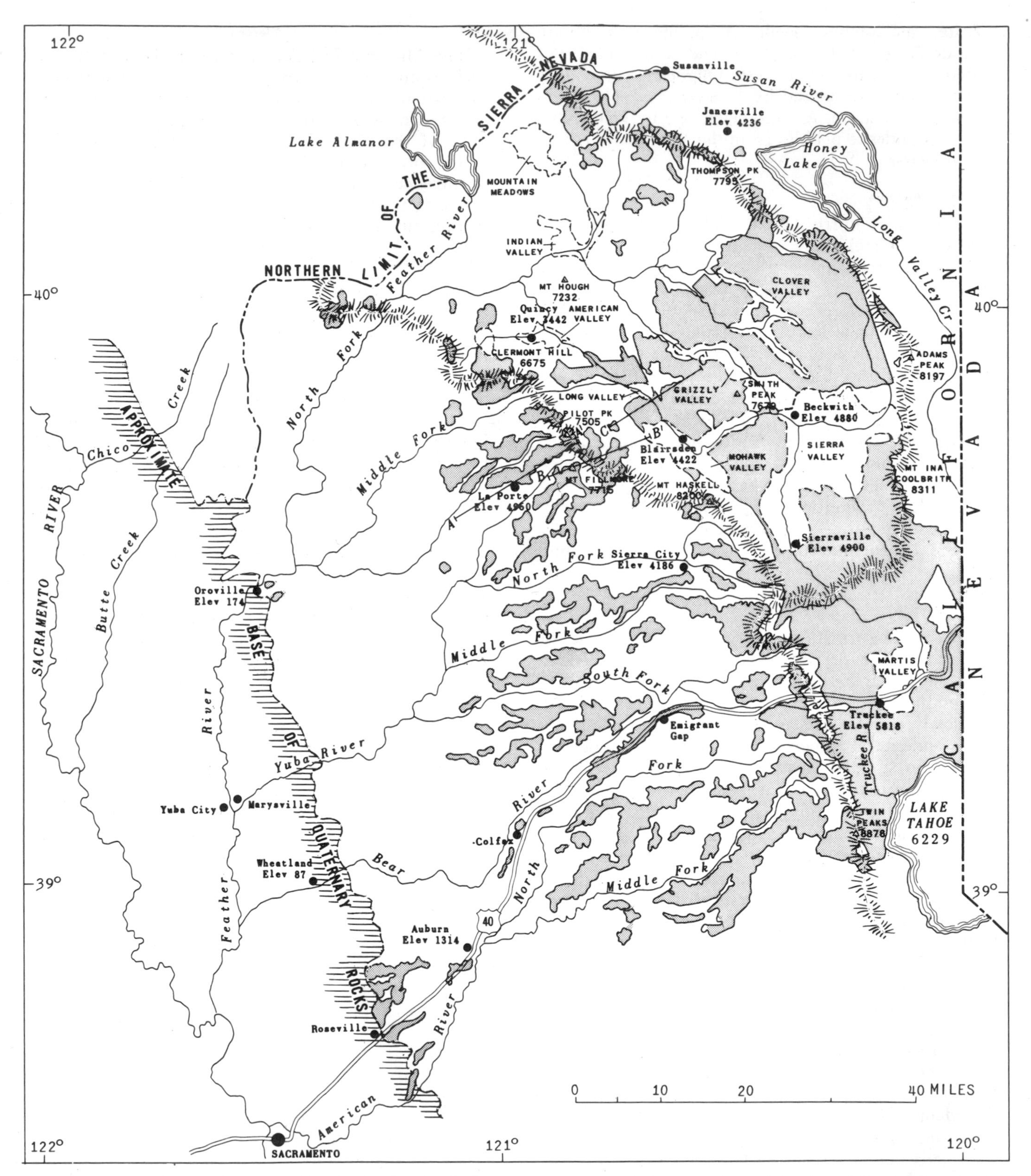

Figure 2. Map of the northern Sierra Nevada, showing the distribution of Miocene and Pliocene rocks, and location of lines of cross sections shown in figure 3.

20.5 to 29.9 million years, based on potassium-argon ratios in sanidine and biotite. Because of possible contamination of the biotite with biotite reworked from Mesozoic plutonic rocks, the older dates are considered unreliable. The ages based on sanidine range from 20.5 to 26.1 million years, or early Miocene, according to Dalrymple (1964). Determinations on sanidine from the ignimbrites at Donner Pass on Highway 40 give values of 33.2 and 26.0 million years, which Dalrymple assigns to late Oligocene and early Miocene, being roughly in agreement with the radiometric age of the Delleker Formation in Plumas County.

Bonta Formation

The Bonta Formation is widespread in eastern Plumas County in the Grizzly and Diamond Mountains and in the Mohawk Valley. So far it has been recognized in the Sierra Nevada proper only at Gold Lake in Sierra County, where recent road construction exposed a thin fossiliferous section previously entirely concealed by glacial deposits.

The Bonta consists mostly of volcanic conglomerate but includes some mudflow breccia. The conglomerate is mostly of pyroxene and hornblende andesite blocks, cobbles, and boulders, some of which are surely reworked from the Ingalls Formation. Rhyolitic debris reworked from the Delleker Formation ranging from single clear crystals of quartz and sanidine to blocks and boulders of ignimbrite 4 feet in diameter are widely present. Phases of the Delleker not known to occur any place farther west than Red Rock Canyon on the California-Nevada boundary are found in the Bonta 30 miles west of there.

Boulders of quartz diorite of local origin, some as much as 20 feet in diameter are common and conspicuous, and are found many hundreds of feet above the base of the formation. Consideration of the geology of the "bedrock series" indicates transportation in a westerly or southwesterly direction. In the Diamond Mountains the Bonta Formation contains granitic debris and feldspar fragments, probably from pegmatites, that are not known any place west of the Honey Lake fault scarp. Grains of quartz, biotite, and feldspar from granitoid sources are present everywhere in the Bonta. The mudflow breccias are of hornblende andesite in which the hornblende phenocrysts are rather large and few in number. The rock fragments are predominantly dark colored. These features serve to distinguish the Bonta from the younger Penman Formation.

The Bonta rests unconformably on the Delleker, the Ingalls, the Lovejoy, and the "bedrock series." Faulting preceded the episode of erosion expressed by the unconformity. The maximum known thickness of the Bonta is about 1,000 feet.

The age of the Bonta is established as upper Miocene by the fossil leaves of the so-called Mohawk flora found at its base near Clio, California. The flora was first described by Knowlton (Turner, 1891, 1895) and assigned to the Miocene. Axelrod (1957) referred the age to upper Miocene. The recently discovered flora at Gold Lake is the same age (D.I. Axelrod personal communication).

The well-exposed section of andesite mudflow breccia and conglomerate 1 mile east of Emigrant Gap on Highway 40, is very much like the Bonta Formation, but it is not dated.

The source of much of the material comprising the Bonta Formation is known, but much, especially the mudflow breccia, has unknown sources. Hornblende andesite intrusions in the Sierra Nevada, Grizzly, and Diamond Mountains resemble more the younger Penman Formation; none are considered to be sources of the Bonta.

Pliocene

Penman Formation and Its Probable Equivalents

The Penman Formation (Durrell, 1959a) consists of volcanic mudflow breccia, with lesser amounts of conglomerate, fanglomerate, mudstone, sandstone, tuff, and lavas, dominantly of hornblende andesite, and with relatively little nonvolcanic material.

The andesites are light colored, with very abundant, small phenocrysts of hornblende. The induration of the clastic rocks is much less than that of older units.

In the Grizzly Mountains, which contain the type area, and in the Diamond Mountains the deposition of the Penman was preceded by an episode of faulting and erosion. The Penman consequently rests on all of the older rocks in one place or another. It extends into the Sierra Nevada proper, and, with minor exceptions already noted, all of the hornblende andesite north of the North Fork of the Yuba River that has been recently examined is Penman Formation. Andesitic rocks south of the North Fork of the Yuba have not been studied in recent years.

The Penman Formation as established in the Grizzly Mountains cannot be closely dated. It is unconformable on the Bonta, which is upper Miocene at its base. It is older than the Warner Basalt which is believed to be middle or upper Pliocene. Hence, the Penman is probably lower or middle Pliocene or both.

At Remington Hill, in the Yuba River basin, andessitic rocks contain fossil leaves which have been assigned to the Mio-Pliocene by Condit (1944), and correlated with the Mio-Pliocene Mehrten Formation of the central Sierra Nevada.

The relationship of the Penman to the Mehrten Formation of the central Sierra Nevada is not clear, but it is possible that the Mehrten is equivalent to the Penman and Bonta together.

The maximum thickness of the Penman in the Grizzly Mountains is 1,350 feet, which is less than the original thickness by an unknown amount because of erosion. In the Sierra Nevada proper, the Penman and its probable equivalents farther south are about a thousand feet thick in the summit region, and 200 to 400 feet thick at the edge of the Great Valley. There is a rough gradation from coarse to fine toward the west. In Plumas County there is some evidence of westerly transport across the present summit region of the Sierra Nevada.

The Penman is presumed to have had many local sources both in the summit region of the Sierra Nevada and farther east. Plugs of hornblende andesite as much as a mile in diameter and many lesser intrusions are abundant. The problem of the origin of the breccia structures is discussed more fully in a later section of this report.

Warner Basalt

The Warner Basalt consists of lava flows of predominatly light-gray olivine basalt with conspicuous, abundant, small phenocrysts of yellow or golden olivine. Green augite phenocrysts are present in some rocks. Diktytaxitic texture is characteristic but is not present in all flows. Where the "bedrock series" is granitoid the basalt is often contaminated. Such rocks commonly lack olivine, and usually contain obvious xenocrysts from the granitoid rocks.

Platy jointing is pronounced and columnar jointing is uncommon. Individual flows are usually thin, vesicular structure is common, and scoriaceous zones occur.

The thickness of the Warner varies depending on the amount of erosion that it has suffered. It is 1,000 feet thick at Thompson Peak in the Diamond Mountains, 350 feet thick in the Grizzly Mountains, and less than that in the Sierra Nevada in Sierra County. No clastic material and no fossils are known to be associated with these rocks.

The Warner was deposited as a sheet over the region of the Diamond Mountains and Grizzly Mountains, and a part of the northern Sierra Nevada proper, with flows undoubtedly originating locally from the numerous plugs of the same rock scattered over the area. No traces of volcanoes remain in this region except possibly for Mount Ingalls in the Diamond Mountains.

The flows were extruded onto an erosional surface that cut deeply into all the older formations so that in various places it rests upon Penman, Bonta, Ingalls, Lovejoy, and the "bedrock series."

The name Warner was first applied by R. J. Russell (1928) in the Warner Range of far northeastern California, and was extended by Durrell (1959a) to the Sierran region. The age is considered provisionally to be upper Pliocene because of its apparent relation to the Tuscan Formation of the region just north of the Sierra Nevada (Durrell, 1959a).

Similar rocks near Lake Tahoe and Truckee are associated with cinder cones and are believed younger than the Warner farther north (Birkeland, 1963).

The Warner Basalt was the last unit to be deposited across the northeastern part of this region, and its deposition was followed by the episode of faulting that lifted the Sierra Nevada to its present height, produced the Grizzly and Diamond Mountain blocks, and finally terminated drainage across the Sierra Nevada from what is now the Great Basin.

Plio-Pleistocene Lacustrine Deposits

The episode of post-Warner faulting mentioned above created a number of basins that held lakes, all of which became filled with sediments, or had their waters drained, before modern times. Lakes existed in Martis, Sierra, Mohawk, Long, Spring Garden, American Grizzly, Clover, and Indian Valleys, and in the basins now occupied by the reservoirs of Lake Almanor and Mountain Meadows (figs. 1 and 2).

Of all these basins only Martis Valley and Mohawk Valley have been dissected, and they alone have received recent study.

The Mohawk Lake beds are localized in a T-shaped basin with the 14-mile-long head at the base of the Sierra Nevada, and the 7-mile-long stem extending northeastward. The lacustrine sediments are boulder and pebble conglomerate, sandstone, shale, and lignite. The carbonaceous sediments are localized in the central part of the basin. All sedimentary materials are of local origin. The exposed thickness of beds is 400 feet, and another unexposed 400 feet is known because of wells in the center of the basin. The total thickness is unknown.

The lake floor terrace is well preserved in many places, and the shoreline lay between 5,000 and 5,050 feet elevation. The basin probably still contained water to a depth of 200 feet when it was drained by capture. Small faults cut the lake beds, but there has been no large-scale deformation.

A till sheet is interbedded with the lake sediments along part of the south side of the basin, and great moraines rest on the lake terrace; hence most of the basin fill is preglacial. A pollen flora from carbonaceous beds at the lowest exposed level shows a forest like that present in the region today (D. I. Axelrod, oral communication).

Pleistocene and Recent

Glacial Deposits

Four glaciations have recently been recognized in the region between the north end of Lake Tahoe and Truckee and extending north of Highway 40 for some distance (Birkeland, 1964). The corresponding deposits are described in the same work.

At least four stages of glaciation are visible on casual examination of the divide between the North Fork of the Yuba River and the Middle Fork of the Feather, but no detailed studies have been made. The earliest is represented by the till sheet in the Mohawk Lake beds south of Blairsden. Lateral moraines as much as 3 miles long extend out onto the Mohawk Lake terrace along Jamison, Gray Eagle, and Frazier Creeks. Lesser glacial stages are represented at higher levels. Glacial lake basins resulted both from deposition and erosion, and some of them later became filled with sediment. The town of Johnsville is situated on a terrace resulting from the filling of a moraine-dammed lake that has been dissected consequent on the drainage of the slightly lower Mohawk Lake.

Minor glacial deposits occur elsewhere in the higher parts of the region including the Grizzly Mountains and Mount Ingalls.

Terrace Deposits

Terrace deposits are minor but occur sparingly along the southwest-flowing streams. All were mined for gold in the early days of the gold rush. Terraces occur in Mohawk Valley and seem to have been caused by a short-lived landslide dam on the Middle Fork of the Feather River.

Alluvium

The Region is undergoing erosion so that, with the exception of the lacustrine deposits already described, alluvial deposits are only narrow strips of coarse clastic sediments along the stream courses.

GEOLOGIC STRUCTURE

The Sierra Nevada proper is a nearly monolithic block tilted westward by uplift along a fault system at its eastern limit. The simple fault block concept must be qualified, however, because faults that cut rocks as young as Pliocene are present within the block, although most have small displacements. Their presence was early recognized by Whitney (1880) in the La Porte-Gibsonville area. Because of their small displacement, and because they were observed during underground mining of the "auriferous gravels" and their location is therefore now uncertain, they are not shown on section A-A′ of figure 3.

Faults within the range are apparently more closely spaced near the crest (sec. B-B′, fig. 3). Not all faults affect the youngest rocks, and such is the case on Boreal Ridge, a mile northwest of Donner Pass (Hudson, 1951), where basalts dated as Pliocene (7.4 million years) by Dalrymple (1964) are not cut by faults that cut older Tertiary. No one has yet detected within the range Eocene to Miocene episodes of faulting, yet it is clear that deformation did occur for the several stratigraphic units of that age are separated by unconformities.

In contrast to the apparently simple structural history of this block, the region immediately to the east has had a long and complex history. The east front of the Sierra Nevada northwestward from Donner Pass is a complex zone of faulting. It has not been studied in detail except at Donner Pass (Hudson, 1948, 1955) and in the Blairsden quadrangle and vicinity in Plumas County (Durrell, 1959a, 1965). Northeast of the Sierra Nevada proper, in the Grizzly and Diamond Mountains, the Lovejoy, Ingalls, Delleker, Bonta, and Penman Formations, and the Warner Basalt and Mohawk Lake beds are each separated from the previous unit by a period of faulting and erosion. All beds are still essentially horizontal. The pattern of faulting and erosion was such that each unit rests at one place or another on each older unit including the "bedrock series." This is illustrated in part in section C-C′ of figure 3. There it is seen that the "auriferous gravels," Lovejoy, Bonta, and Penman Formations rest on the "bedrock series," and the Bonta rests also on "auriferous gravels" and on the Lovejoy Formation. Nearby, though not on the line of section, the Bonta occurs in its normal position on the Delleker Formation. The Penman rests also on the Bonta Formation in section C-C′ and elsewhere, but nearby it rests on Delleker and Ingalls. The Warner is present in section C-C′ only in its normal position above Penman, but at Gold Lake in the Sierra Nevada it rests on the "bedrock series"; about a mile southeast of the midpoint of section C-C′ it rests on Bonta, and 5 miles north of the northeast end of the section it rests on both Ingalls and Lovejoy.

Most faults are apparently normal, but not all can be so categorized since a good many show reversal of movement (fig. 4). The fault surfaces generally dip steeply, and no doubt some are vertical or nearly so.

Between the Sierra Nevada and the Grizzly Mountains is a graben comprising a lowland called the Plumas Trench which contains Mohawk, Long, Spring Garden, and American Valleys (fig. 1 and 2). The boundary faults are normal, that is, they dip toward the graben at 55° to 75°. However, the major fault on the southwest side of the graben has a left-lateral separation of 3½ miles (Durrell, 1950, 1965). There is evidence that suggests left-lateral separation of as much as 8 to 9 miles on the northeast boundary fault. The date of the lateral components of motion on these faults is uncertain.

A pronounced change in the Tertiary stratigraphic section takes place along the northeast side of the graben—that is to say, the section in the graben is more like that of the Sierra Nevada proper than that of the Grizzly Mountains. The Ingalls Formation is absent, the Bonta is scarcely represented, and the other units are generally thinner on the southwest. Thus it is evident that the Sierra Nevada block tended to be high relative to the land to the northeast, and this was evidently accomplished by slip on the northeast side of the present graben. If the uplift occurred on the fault or faults that now bound the graben on its northeast margin, then the movement was reverse and the forces were probably compressional. In late Pliocene or early Pleistocene when the Sierra Nevada was elevated and drainage systems from the interior were finally disconnected, the movement on the previously active reverse fault was reversed and ultimately became larger in amount so that present stratigraphic separations indicate only normal faulting.

The more recent fault movements produced the existing major landscape features: the Sierra Nevada; the adjacent lowlands such as Martis Valley, Sierra Valley, and the Plumas Trench; the Grizzly Moun-

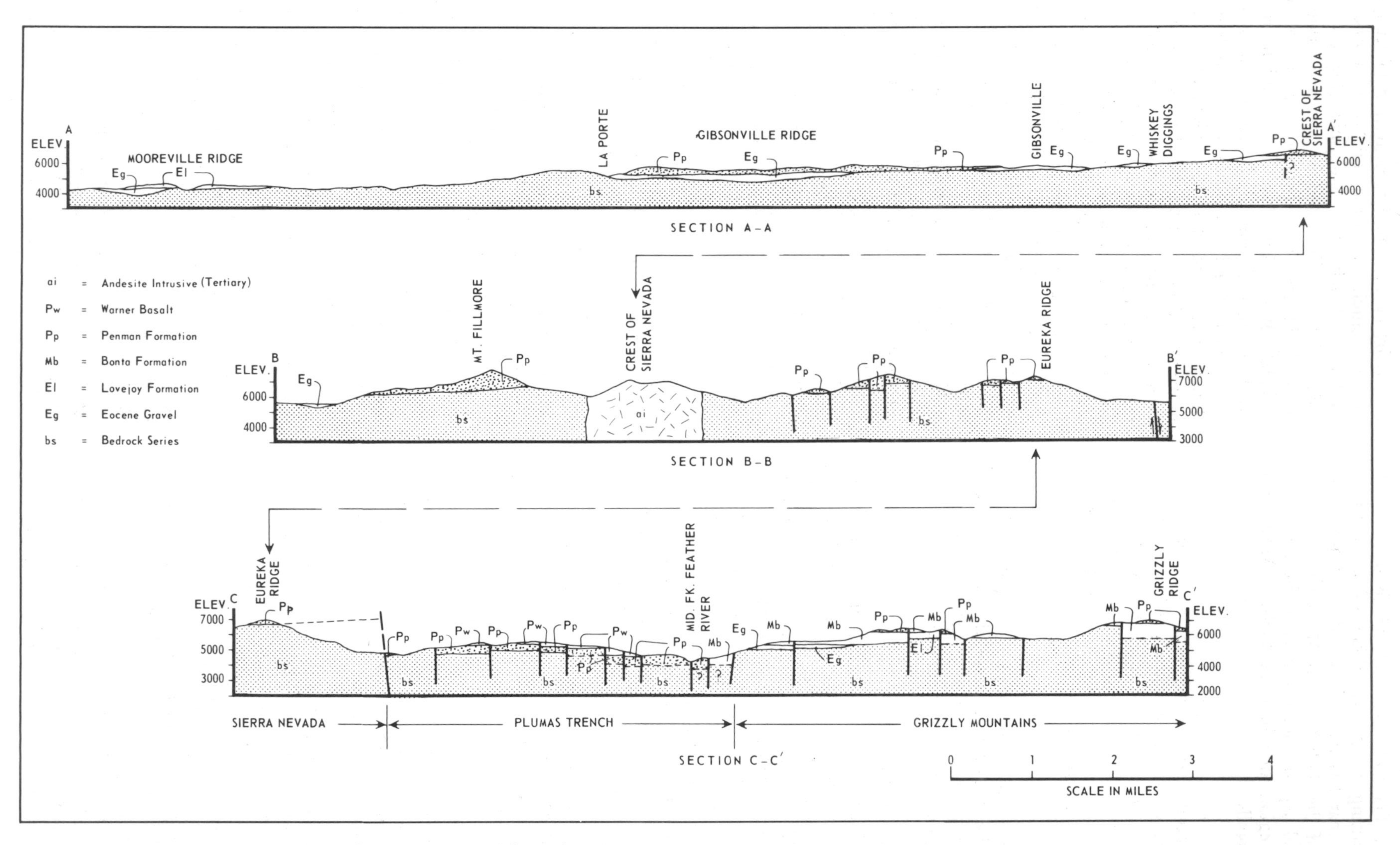

Figure 3. Geologic cross sections of the northern Sierra Nevada, La Porte to the summit of Grizzly Ridge, Plumas County, California.

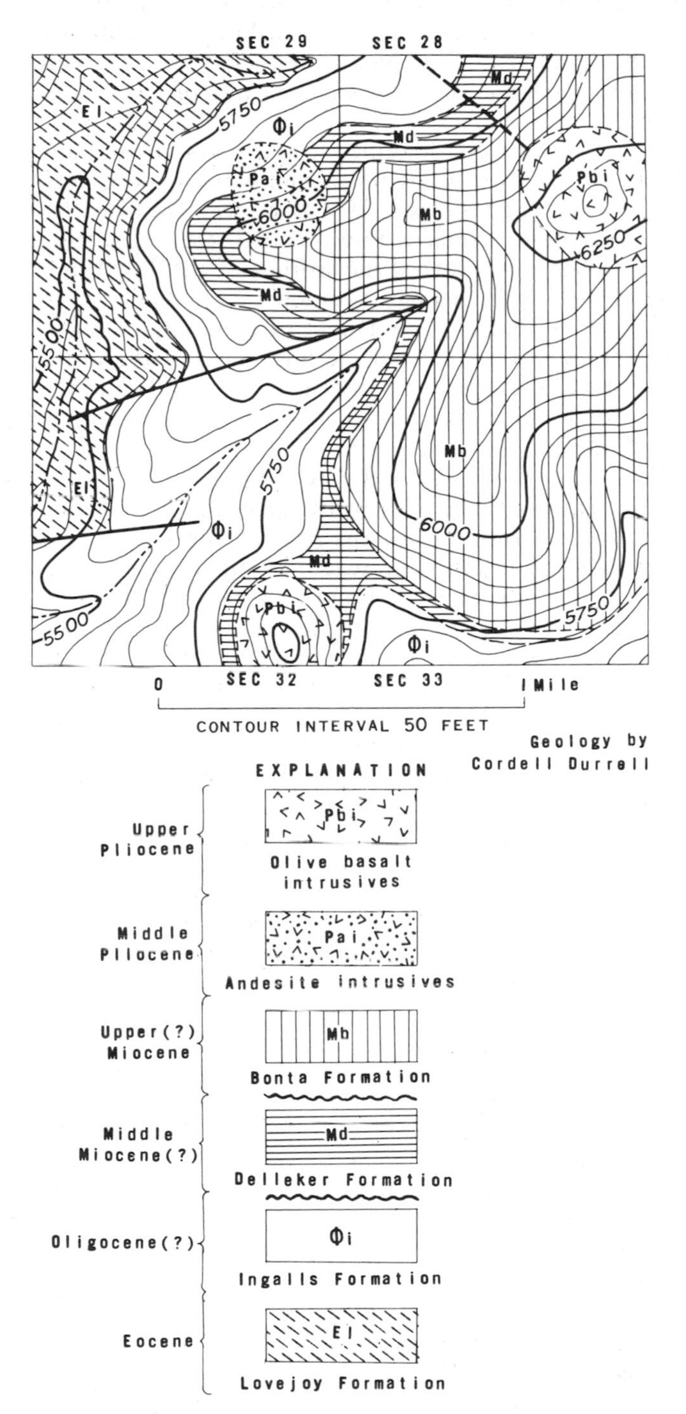

Figure 4. Geologic map of a small portion of the Blairsden quadrangle, Plumas County, California, showing reversal of fault movement.

tains, Grizzly Valley, the Diamond Mountains, and the Honey Lake Basin.

Fault displacements at this time within these major structural units were probably small, but erosion has cut so deeply that the Warner Basalt, the youngest unit affected, has been largely removed, making it difficult to determine the amount of movement.

The magnitudes of net separations vary greatly. In the Sierra Nevada proper, as between La Porte and Gibsonville, they range from a few feet to a few tens of feet. Toward the eastern limit of the Sierra Nevada proper as shown in Section B-B′ of figure 3, vertical separations are as much as 300 feet. The main fault between the Sierra Nevada and the Plumas Trench has a vertical separation at the base of the Penman Formation of 2,500 to 3,000 feet in the vicinity of Section C-C′ of figure 3. Farther southeast where the Penman is concealed beneath the Mohawk Lake beds, the vertical separation could be more than 4,000 feet. Vertical separations along the northeast side of the Plumas Trench are more difficult to determine, but they exceed 1,000 feet in many places and probably exceed 2,000 feet in others.

In the Grizzly and Diamond Mountains the pattern of faulting is exceedingly complex with many instances of reversal of movement (fig. 4). Most vertical separations are of the order of a few hundred feet. It would be good to know the absolute elevation changes connected with faulting, but this has not yet been determined by physical methods in spite of some valiant attempts by Lindgren and Hudson (1955, 1960). The best information is paleobotanical in nature and the best data are contained in the writings of D. I. Axelrod.

Clearly, from middle Eocene through early Oligocene the region had a near-tropical climate (Allen, 1929; Potbury, 1935), and was probably not far above sea level. By upper Miocene, when the lower part of the Bonta Formation was deposited the land was still low, but the climate was much more temperate. The fossil flora (Mohawk flora) at Clio in the Mohawk Valley, at an elevation of 4,450, is the same as that at Gold Lake at an elevation of 6,600 feet. Both were deposited at an elevation of not more than 2,000 feet above sea level (Axelrod, 1962). Since the Mohawk Lake beds of latest Pliocene or early Pleistocene contain a pollen flora like that of the present forest, it appears that the net uplift of the northern Sierra Nevada between upper Miocene and early Pleistocene was more than 4,000 feet. This must have occurred entirely in post-Penman time, and possibly entirely in post-Warner time.

The elevation of the Sierra Nevada culminated in glaciation, already described. Sufficient elevation occurred to permit minor glaciation on the north slopes of the highest parts of the Grizzly and Diamond Mountains.

PETROLOGY

Many problems in sedimentary and in igneous petrology, and many that are combinations of the two, await study.

It is now 35 years since Allen (1929) published his superb monograph on the Ione Formation and the weathered zone that underlies it, and although his main conclusions are not likely to be changed it is possible that refined interpretations could come from a study based on the newer techniques of petrology.

The "auriferous gravels" have never been studied petrographically except by students whose dissertations remain unpublished. In order to understand the sources of mineral and rock constituents, we must have a much better knowledge of the petrography of the "bedrock series" than we have at present. Some slight progress has been made in Plumas County as is indicated above. The courses of the streams that deposited the gravels are subject to reinterpretation through modern approaches to petrology, stratigraphy, and structure.

The Lovejoy Formation presents a puzzling problem in regard to the source of lava. No sources have been recognized anywhere, yet if the source lies concealed east of the Honey Lake fault scarp, the required distance of flow seems unreasonably long. No attempt has yet been made to correlate individual flows from outcrop to outcrop. If this could be accomplished it would certainly shed light on the source problem.

Although some intrusions of rhyolite have been described from the summit region of the central Sierra Nevada (Curtis, 1954), the rhyolite tuffs and ignimbrites mostly had sources east of the Sierra Nevada. They are a part of the enormous mass of rhyolitic eruptive material of mid-Tertiary age that extends throughout the Great Basin. Correlation of tuff beds and ignimbrites from one area of ocurrence to another is a difficult problem in the absence of fossils; the radiometric data seems yet to be insufficiently sensitive, hence the uncertainty about the relation of the Delleker to the Valley Springs Formation. It is not clear how many episodes of rhyolitic eruption occurred.

The Warner Basalt presents some interesting problems resulting from its contamination by silicic material that are awaiting study. The Warner is also part of a large problem, for that part in the northern Sierra Nevada is but the southernmost portion of a flood of olivine basalt that covers an enormous area in northeastern California, northwestern Nevada, and Oregon.

Perhaps the most fascinating petrologic problem concerns the origin of the andesite intrusive breccias and the andesite mudflow breccias that comprise by far the greater part of all the Tertiary deposits of the region. The mudflow breccias puzzled the older workers, and they remain a puzzle. Turner (1895, 1896) was probably the first person to consider their origin. He pointed out that they are in fact mudflow deposits and not ordinary pyroclastic rocks. Lindgren (1897) also described them and noted that they originated from sources along the crest of the range.

Anderson (1933) thoroughly reviewed the mudflow problem in connection with his study of the Tuscan Formation, which is widespread immediately adjacent to this region on the north. He concluded that mudflows could travel far enough to account for the distribution of the Tuscan Formation—about 50 miles (a comparable distance would apply to the Sierra Nevada)—and that they could move on slopes such as seem to have existed when the Tuscan was deposited. He thought that melting snow and ice could provide the water, and he discussed the capability of mudflows to transport very large blocks of rock. However, it is not clear what he thought was the cause of the brecciation.

In 1944 Durrell described eight dikes of andesite breccia that intrude andesite mudflow breccia, tuff, and a brecciated andesite lava flow near Blairsden. In this lava flow, which is flow banded, the brecciation process has not disturbed the attitude of the flow banding, which is in parallel position in all blocks even where separated by several feet of comminuted andesite indistinguishable from the finer parts of the intrusive breccias. Durrell concluded that the dikes and the lava flows were brecciated by the same process, which he thought due to increasing vapor pressure of water dissolved in the glass of the cooling rock.

He expressed the view that generally brecciation took place before the magma reached the surface, but that in some instances it was delayed until after extrusion; that the water vapor that caused the brecciation altered the glass to clay; that the water then condensed to form a mud matrix; and that the extruded product was a breccia with a mud matrix. Motion due to the intrusive impulse or due to gravity seemed unnecessary to account for the brecciation.

In 1954, G. H. Curtis published an important paper on the origin of the andesite breccias of the Sierra Nevada; he expressed a different interpretation based on observations on the mudflow breccias and on many intrusive breccias and brecciated lava flows like those previously described by Durrell. Notable new observations were that some of the dikes have massive unbrecciated selvages and that some of the brecciated lava flows are massive at the base.

Curtis again reviewed the problem of the origin of volcanic mudflows. In his view the andesite magmas have a low water content; the initial stages of brecciation of both the lava flows and the dikes is due to the escape of the small amount of fluids, and the major part of the brecciation is due to motion of the nearly congealed magma, although he recognized that some of the breccias give evidence of only very slight motion.

In Curtis' opinion, mudflows resulted from the mixing of the water of rivers, lakes, and rain with the extruded breccia. He had nothing to say about the formation of clay or its role as a lubricant in the extrusion process, or on the matter of the slopes necessary to initiate flows of volcanic breccia that have traveled more than 50 miles.

Clearly the problem of the brecciated lava flows, dikes, and mudflow breccias is not yet solved. Some salient facts that must be accounted for are the following: The amount of extrusive breccia is very large. Durrell once estimated it to be between 1,100 and 1,300 cubic miles, and Curtis (1954) estimated it to be 2,000 cubic miles. Lava flows including brecciated flows comprise a minute proportion of the total. The slope over which the mudflows traveled was very gentle, as paleobotanic evidence indicates that the elevation of the present summit region was not more than 2,000 feet. Since the western edge could not have been lower than at present, the slope averaged 1:130. Certainly portions of the summit regions may have exceeded 2,000 feet in height, but no great chain of high volcanoes like those of the Cascade Mountains existed here in late Miocene or Pliocene time. Although most of the breccia is late Miocene and Pliocene in age, there are similar rocks of Oligocene age, so that the process of mudflow formation extended through a major portion of the Tertiary. The brecciated lava flows and some of the breccia dikes and plugs give evidence that brecciation can occur without a significant amount of motion, that is, without translation or rotation of blocks from the prebrecciation position. Clay is a significant part of the brecciated lavas and intrusions, and is also the binder of the mudflow breccias. These facts indicate that the cause or causes of brecciation are not surficial accidents but are in some way related to the nature of the magma.

REFERENCES

Allen, V. T., 1929, The Ione formation of California: California Univ., Dept. Geol. Sci. Bull., v. 18, no. 14, p. 347–448.

Anderson, C. A., 1933, The Tuscan formation of northern California, with a discussion concerning the origin of volcanic breccias: California Univ., Dept. Geol. Sci. Bull., v. 23, no. 7, p. 215–276.

Axelrod, D. I., 1957, Late Tertiary floras and the Sierra Nevada uplift [California-Nevada]: Geol. Soc. America Bull., v. 68, no. 1, p. 19–45.

—— 1962, Post-Pliocene uplift of the Sierra Nevada, California: Geol. Soc. America Bull., v. 73, no. 2, p. 183–198.

Birkeland, P. W., 1963, Pleistocene volcanism and deformation of the Truckee area, north of Lake Tahoe, California: Geol. Soc. America Bull., v. 74, no. 12, p. 1453–1464.

—— 1964, Pleistocene glaciation of the northern Sierra Nevada, north of Lake Tahoe, California: Jour. Geology, v. 72, no. 6, p. 810–824.

Clark, B. L., and Anderson, C. A., 1938, Wheatland formation and its relation to early Tertiary andesites in the Sierra Nevada: Geol. Soc. America Bull., v. 49, no. 6, p. 931–956.

Condit, Carlton, 1944, The Remington Hill flora [California], Chap. 2 of Chaney, R. W., ed., Pliocene floras of California and Oregon: Carnegie Inst. Washington Pub. 553, Contr. Paleontology, p. 21–55.

Creely, R. S., 1955, Geology of the Oroville quadrangle, California: California Univ., Berkeley, Ph.D. thesis.

Curtis, G. H., 1954, Mode of origin of the pyroclastic debris in the Mehrten formation of the Sierra Nevada: California Univ., Dept. Geol. Sci. Bull., v. 29, no. 9, p. 453–502.

Dalrymple, G. B., 1964, Cenozoic chronology of the Sierra Nevada, California: California Univ., Dept. Geol. Sci. Bull., v. 47, 41 p.

Durrell, Cordell, 1944, Andesite breccia dikes near Blairsden, California: Geol. Soc. America Bull., v. 55, no. 3, p. 255–272.

—— 1950, Strike-slip faulting in the eastern Sierra Nevada near Blairsden, California [abs.]: Geol. Soc. America Bull., v. 61, no. 12, pt. 2, p. 1522.

—— 1959a, Tertiary stratigraphy of the Blairsden quadrangle, Plumas County, California: California Univ., Dept. Geol. Sci. Bull., v. 34, no. 3, p. 161–192.

—— 1959b, The Lovejoy formation of northern California: California Univ., Dept. Geol. Sci. Bull., v. 34, no. 4, p. 193–220.

—— 1965, La Porte to the summit of the Grizzly Mountains, Plumas County, California: Sacramento Geol. Soc., Ann. Field Trip, 1965, Guidebook, 22 p.

Gianella, V. P., 1936, Geology of the Silver City district and the southern portion of the Comstock Lode, Nevada: Nevada Univ. Bull., v. 30, no. 9, 105 p.

Hudson, F. S., 1951, Mount Lincoln-Castle Peak area, Sierra Nevada, California: Geol. Soc. America Bull., v. 62, no. 8, p. 931–952.

—— 1955, Measurement of the deformation of the Sierra Nevada, California, since middle Eocene: Geol. Soc. America Bull., v. 66, no. 7, p. 835–870.

—— 1960, Post-Pliocene uplift of the Sierra Nevada, California: Geol. Soc. America Bull., v. 71, no. 11, p. 1547–1573.

Lindgren, Waldemar, 1897, Description of the Truckee quadrangle, California: U.S. Geol. Survey Geol. Atlas, Folio 39.

—— 1900, Description of the Colfax quadrangle, California: U.S. Geol. Survey Geol. Atlas, Folio 66.

—— 1911, The Tertiary gravels of the Sierra Nevada of California: U.S. Geol. Survey Prof. Paper 73, 226 p.

MacGinitie, H. D., 1941, A middle Eocene flora from the central Sierra Nevada: Carnegie Inst. Washington Pub. 534, 178 p.

McJannet, G. S., 1957, Geology of the Pyramid Lake-Red Rock canyon area, Washoe County, Nevada: California Univ., Los Angeles, M.A. thesis.

Popenoe, W. P., Imlay, R. W., and Murphy, M. A., 1960, Correlation of the Cretaceous formations of the Pacific Coast (United States and northwestern Mexico): Geol. Soc. America Bull., v. 71, no. 10, p. 1491–1540.

Potbury, S. S., 1935, The La Porte flora of Plumas County, California: Carnegie Inst. Washington Pub. 465, p. 29–81.

Russell, R. J., 1928, Basin Range structure and stratigraphy of the Warner Range, northeastern California: California Univ., Dept. Geol. Sci. Bull., v. 17, no. 11, p. 387–496.

Turner, H. W., 1891, Mohawk lake beds [Plumas County, California]: Philos. Soc. Washington Bull., v. 11, p. 385–409.

—— 1894, The rocks of the Sierra Nevada: U.S. Geol. Survey, 14th Ann. Rept., pt. 2, p. 435–495.

—— 1896, Further contributions to the geology of the Sierra Nevada: U.S. Geol. Survey 17th Ann. Rept., pt. 1, p. 521–762.

—— 1897, Description of the Downieville quadrangle [California]: U.S. Geol. Survey Geol. Atlas, Folio 37.

—— 1898, Description of the Bidwell Bar quadrangle [California]: U.S. Geol. Survey Geol. Atlas, Folio 43.

Weaver, C. E., and others, 1944, Correlation of the marine Cenozoic formations of western North America [Chart 11]: Geol. Soc. America Bull., v. 55, no. 5, p. 569–598.

Whitney, J. D., 1880, The auriferous gravels of the Sierra Nevada of California: Harvard Coll., Museum Comp. Zoology, Mem., v. 6, no. 1, 569 p.

CENOZOIC VOLCANISM OF THE CENTRAL SIERRA NEVADA, CALIFORNIA

By David B. Slemmons
Mackay School of Mines, University of Nevada,
Reno, Nevada

The purpose of this article is to review the Cenozoic volcanic activity of the central Sierra Nevada and, more briefly, the volcanism in the southern part of the range. In a companion article in this bulletin, Dr. Cordell Durrell reviews the Cenozoic volcanic activity of the northern Sierra Nevada.

Although nearly all of the central Sierra Nevada has been mapped by reconnaissance methods, the exact age of the volcanic units has been a matter of broad generalization, due to sparse preservation of fossil faunas and floras and general lack of published detailed mapping. Because sophisticated methods for dating volcanic rocks by potassium-argon isotope analysis have recently been developed, it is now possible to subdivide more accurately the volcanic sequences and to correlate between widely separated, nonfossiliferous units. The present paper, therefore, will utilize the recent age dates of Dalrymple (1963, 1964a, 1964b), Evernden and James (1964), and Evernden, Savage, Curtis, and James (1964) as summarized in figure 1.

The problem of describing the volcanic activity of this region is further confused by the general lack of formational assignment of many of the volcanic units and by the absence of data regarding detailed field relations of those formations now recognized. Although most of the major rock units were recognized by Ransome and Turner in the late 1800's, no formal formational names were proposed by them. The description of map units in the foothill region was assisted by Piper and others (1939) who proposed the formational names, "Valley Springs Formation" for the early rhyolites, and "Mehrten Formation" for younger andesites of the foothill area. Near the summit areas of the range, however, the volcanic section is much more diverse and additional formational assignments were found to be necessary during thesis studies by Curtis (1951), Halsey (1953), and Slemmons (1953). Although the results of these studies are available, none of the new formational names included have been formally proposed. This summary article will utilize their data in subdividing the volcanic stratigraphy into formations that are consistent with this more recent research.

Some of the research which contributed to this paper was developed during a study of the Sonora Pass Remote Sensing Test Site, under NASA Research Grant NGR-29-001-015, and also during studies of active tectonism in the Basin and Range province under NSF Grant GP-5034.

I wish also to express my gratitude to Gary Ballew, Peter Chapman, Jim Sjoberg, David Sterling, and William Tafuri for assistance in compiling isopach maps included with this article. The editorial and technical assistance of Harold Bonham, Ira Lutsey, Dick Paul, and Ron Gunderson, of the Nevada Bureau of Mines, is also gratefully acknowledged. The quality of the detail supporting the distribution of the various volcanic units was greatly improved by the preliminary release of data by John Burnett, Robert Matthews, and Rudolph Strand of the California Division of Mines and Geology.

RÉSUMÉ OF THE CENOZOIC HISTORY OF THE SIERRA NEVADA

The Cenozoic volcanic history can be divided into four major episodes: (1) an Oligocene to Miocene period of eruption and deposition of the Valley Springs rhyolite tuffs, (2) a late Miocene or early Pliocene period of andesite eruptions resulting in the accumulation of the mudflows and volcanic sediments of the Relief Peak Formation (new), (3) an early Pliocene period of eruption of latite and quartz latite flows and tuffs of the Stanislaus Formation (new), and (4) later eruptions of Pliocene andesites of the Disaster Peak Formation (new) and late Pliocene to Quaternary andesites, basalts, and rhyolites.

The earliest activity in the central Sierra Nevada is much younger than that of the northern Sierra Nevada where andesites were erupted as early as 53.5 m. y. ago (Dalrymple, 1964a), that is, in the late Paleocene or early Eocene. The initial activity of the central Sierra Nevada consisted mainly of deposition of rhyolitic tuffs, which are widely distributed in the range north of the Madera-Mariposa County line. These rhyolitic eruptions were of nuée ardente type, and the sporadic eruptions, which commenced about 33 m. y. ago, spread a succession of welded tuffs that blanketed most of the northern and central parts of the range. The thickness of rhyolite that has escaped erosion decreases from a maximum of more than 4,000 feet near Pyramid Lake and in the Virginia Range of Nevada, to about 420 feet near Valley Springs in the western foothills of the range. The eruptive centers were both along and east of the Sierran divide. Many sources lay to the east, for the northeast-trending belts

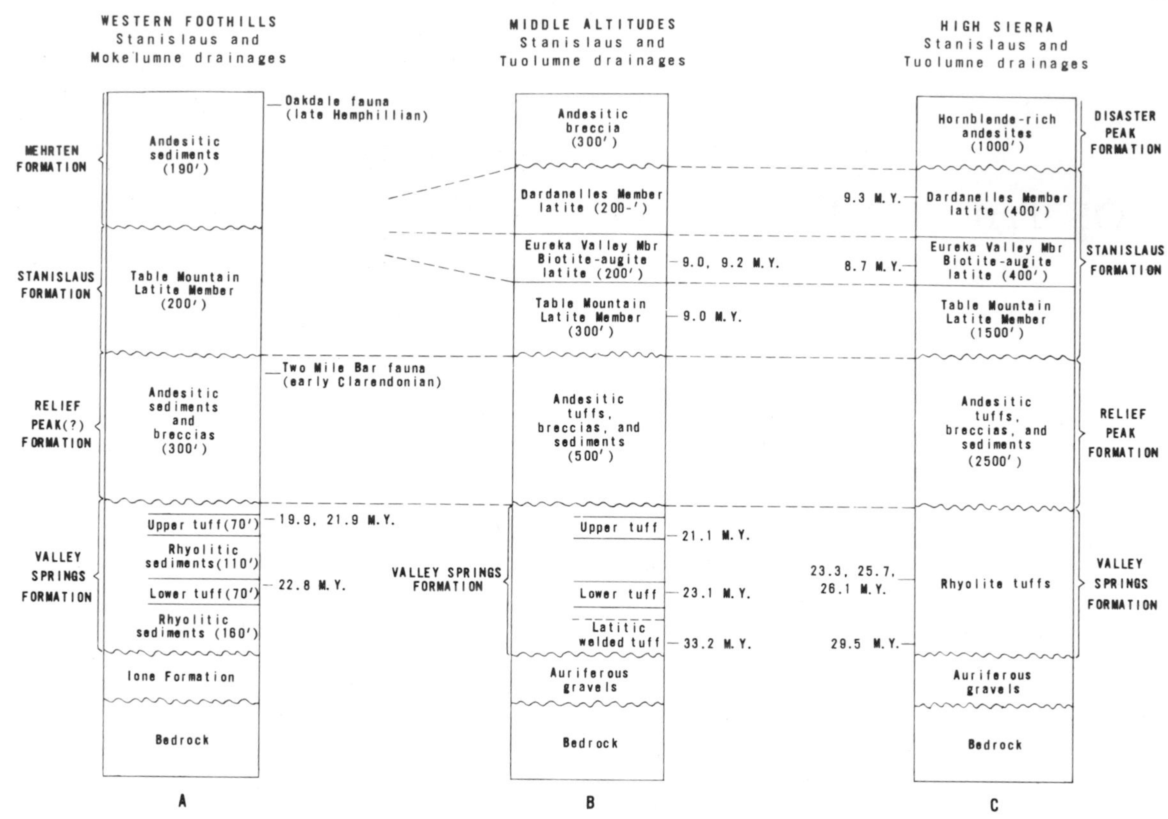

Figure 1. Correlation and summary diagram of Tertiary rocks of the central Sierra Nevada (after Dalrymple, 1964): A, Composite section from Valley Springs Formation type section and Knights Ferry area; B, Composite section from Ponderosa Way, Rattlesnake Hill, McKay, and Jawbone Ridge; C, Composite section from Sonora Pass and Rancheria Mountain.

of rhyolite increase in thickness to the northeast, and some rhyolite intrusions have been recognized near the summit of the range. In the central Sierra Nevada, the rhyolites are generally called the "Valley Springs Formation," but ranges in actual age dates (16.1 to 33.4 m. y.) indicate that activity was sporadic during an extended period. Slemmons (1953) and Dalrymple (1964a) have recognized more than one member both in the summit region and at the type locality in the foothills (fig. 1). This further confirms the intermittent character of the eruptions. In the foothill region the basal unconformity generally has low relief, with broad floored valleys and narrow inner gorges, suggesting that some uplift and rejuvenation preceded the eruptions. The basal unconformity commonly is above rocks that are weathered to a hematite-red color and, locally, overlies lateritic soils. This ancient weathering probably developed during a subtropical climatic phase of the Eocene.

The rhyolitic extrusives were sufficiently extensive to force the establishment of new drainage systems that no longer followed the former trellis pattern of longitudinal valleys and ridges, but generally drained directly southwestward across the general structural grain of the basement rocks.

The andesitic deposits forming the main postrhyolite volcanic accumulations of the range have been grouped together and loosely referred to as the "Mehrten Formation." The Mehrten Formation was the name applied by Piper and others (1939) to a sequence of predominantly andesitic clays, sandstones, and breccias exposed in a belt in the Sierra Foothills extending from Bellota on the Calaveras River to Cosumnes on the Cosumnes River. The type locality is near the Mehrten damsite on the Mokelumne River. Although it was recognized that other andesitic rocks elsewhere in the Sierra Nevada were correlative, Piper and others (1939, p. 69) clearly did not include the rocks east of the Foothill belt in their Mehrten Formation. Detailed mapping by Slemmons (1953) and recent age dates by Dalrymple (1964a), by Evernden and James (1964), and by Evernden and others (1964), however, indicate that in the Sonora Pass area (fig. 1), there are three main postrhyolite petrographic sequences, two of which are older than the Mehrten Formation at its type locality.

The lowermost of the three postrhyolite units consists of the andesites of the Relief Peak Formation that are probably mainly lower Pliocene. These overlie the Valley Springs rhyolites unconformably on a surface exhibiting a youthful stage of erosion. This surface has a relief of about 1,500 feet near the summit of the range, where great thicknesses of andesitic mudflows (lahars) predominate. In going westward from the crest, the mudflows gradually thin, and near the western edge of the range they grade into andesitic sands and gravels. The age of the andesites is more than the 9-m.y.-old latites of the Sonora Pass area.

Unconformably on the Relief Peak Formation are the latites of the Stanislaus Formation (new), which occur in a belt up to 20 miles in width. These latites and quartz latites were erupted from sources near Dardanelles Cone, Lighting Ridge near Sonora Pass, Sonora Pass, and from important but as yet undiscovered sources east of Sonora Pass. At least one flow extended westward 60 miles or more to Knights Ferry on the Stanislaus River, and for several tens of miles eastward into Nevada. Although there is some evidence that uplift of the range had already begun (Slemmons, 1953), and that Basin and Range faulting had possibly begun, the uplift could not have amounted to more than a third of the total Late Cenozoic uplift and tilt of the range, since there is no abrupt change in the thickness of the latites as the westernmost Basin and Range faults are crossed. Pre-latite faulting is believed to be relatively minor, although near Sonora Pass the unconformity between the latites and the underlying andesites had up to 1,500 feet of relief.

Andesitic and basaltic lavas were deposited on the Stanislaus latite, and as only a weakly defined unconformity separates the two units the erosional interval between the eruption of the latites and the extrusion of andesites and basalts was brief. Relatively few dates are available for the andesitic and basaltic section, but the Oakdale flora in the youngest andesitic sediments in the Sierran foothills has been dated middle Pliocene (Hemphillian) by Axelrod (1958)—supported by a recent potassium-argon date of 5.7 m.y. (Dalrymple, 1964a). Dalrymple (1964a; 1964b) has also suggested that the most recent vigorous uplift and tilting of the Sierra Nevada was initiated during the middle to late Pliocene (between 3.5 and 9 m.y. ago). Typical Basin and Range faulting may be somewhat younger; it probably began in the Mono Lake area, less than 2.6 and 3.2 m.y. ago, and in the Truckee area near the end of the interval between 7.4 m.y. and 2.2 to 2.3 m.y. ago. Thus there seems to be a time lag between the tilting of the Sierra Nevada and the beginning of the present Basin and Range faulting.

Following the deposition of these young andesites in the Sierra Nevada, uplift and tilting of the Sierran block has caused erosion to cut deeply into the range. Downcutting by extensive glaciers and streams has incised the canyons far below the gently inclined surface at the top of the volcanic section, and the erosion cycle is still in a youthful stage with a consequent stream pattern.

EARLY RHYOLITIC ACTIVITY

Extensive remnants of rhyolite welded tuff, water-sorted tuffs, and rhyolite-bearing gravels commonly form the basal unit of the Cenozoic section in the central Sierra Nevada (fig. 1). The deposits generally grade from tuffs near the eastern part of the range into types that show more extensive sedimentary reworking toward the western edge of the range. The basal rhyolites were named "Valley Springs Formation" by Piper and others (1939, p. 72–73), for the foothill town of Valley Springs where two welded tuffs were described. The section there includes the two rhyolitic tuffs, and also clays, sandstones, and conglomerates, lying unconformably on the Ione Formation (Eocene), on auriferous gravels, or locally on pre-Tertiary basement rocks.

The Valley Springs rhyolites are widely distributed from the northern end of the range to about 37° lat. near the western foot of the range. On the western slope the rhyolite occupies narrow belts, 10 miles or so in width, extending from the summit westward to the foothills, where the rhyolite disappears underneath the younger sedimentary and volcanic rocks that form the uppermost part of the filling in the Great Valley. Few outcrops of rhyolite are present in the main Sierran slopes south of the 38° lat., near the north end of Yosemite National Park, although a narrow belt of rhyolites extends along the edge of the Great Valley at least as far southward as Friant (Macdonald, 1941).

The thickness of the rhyolites is highly variable, owing not only to vagaries of initial distribution from various vents east of the Sierra Nevada causing the pyroclastic materials to be channeled down different westward-trending valleys, but also to extensive erosion that occurred during different intervals after their deposition. The thicknesses generally decrease southwestward from maximum values of 1,200 feet near Sonora Pass and more than 1,000 feet near Riverton, to 450 feet at the type locality near Valley Springs and 270 feet at La Grange near the Merced River. The rhyolite of the Hartford Hill Formation in the Virginia Range is of comparable geologic age (Schilling, 1965), and similar rhyolite that is widely distributed in western Nevada has thicknesses of over 3,000 feet (figs. 1 and 2).

The rhyolites unconformably overlie either older Tertiary gravels and sands or the Ione Formation. The rhyolites were sufficiently thick to block the valleys in which they flowed, requiring the establishment of new drainage patterns during the subsequent erosion cycle. The surface developed on the rhyolite was one of moderate relief, with up to 1,000 feet of local relief toward the source areas. The extensive erosion which followed both the rhyolitic and andesitic eruptions stripped much of the rhyolite from valley walls, but small bands of protected portions of rhyolites still remained sporadically below the very irregular base of overlying andesites or latites.

The Valley Springs Formation was assigned a late Miocene age on the basis of a small flora (Axelrod, 1944, p. 217). Recently, more than 25 potassium-argon dates have become available for early Sierran rhyolites, (Evernden and others, 1962; Evernden and James, 1964; and Dalrymple, 1964a). These dates show a broad range in time, from as much as 33.4 m.y. (late Oligocene) to as little as 16.1 m.y. (middle Miocene). According to Dalrymple (1964a, p. 21), part of this disparity of ages is due to discordance in dates from various minerals in the same rock, probably as a result

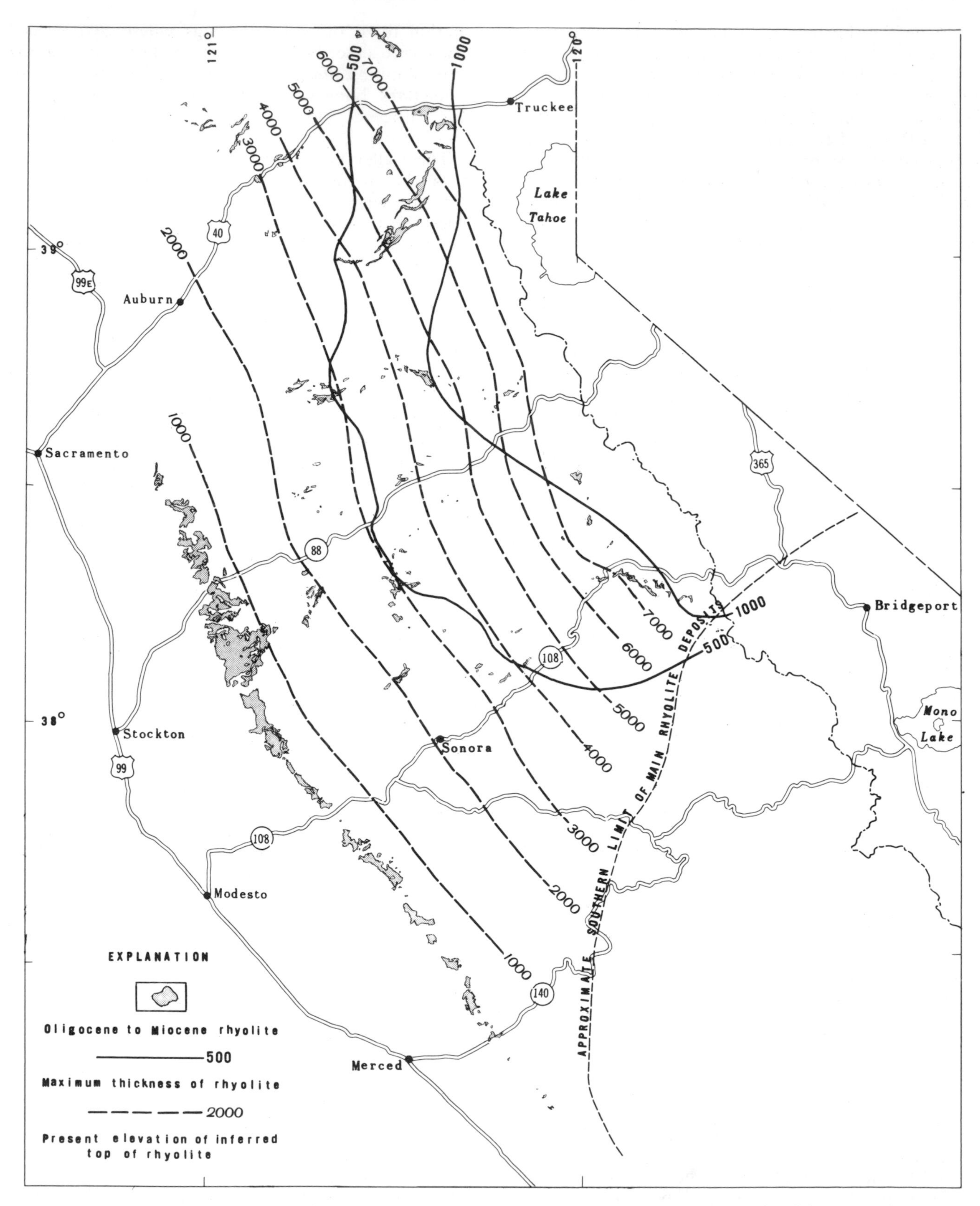

Figure 2. Map showing distribution of Oligocene to Miocene rhyolites of the central Sierra Nevada, with solid contours denoting their approximate maximum original thickness. The dashed contours indicate the approximate elevation of the inferred top of the rhyolites. The deep and repeated dissection of the rhyolites makes the indicated isopachs minimal values for the thickness in deeper valleys. Although there may have been several areas of nondeposition between some of the southwest-trending channels of maximal thickness, the isopachs and contours of elevation are projected between the main channels.

of contamination by older bedrock minerals. Most of the variation, however, is believed to indicate a prolonged, but intermittent, period of rhyolitic activity, with the main eruptions occurring in the early Miocene.

Most, if not all, the rhyolites had a northeasterly source. This is indicated by the progressive increase in thickness of the rhyolites in a northeast, upslope direction, the presence of some Tertiary rhyolite intrusions toward the eastern edge of the range, and the progressive change from rhyolitic sediments in the southwest, to massive tuffs and welded tuffs toward the northeast.

EARLIER ANDESITIC ACTIVITY

Postrhyolite flows, mudflows, gravels, and sands, derived mainly from centers of basic andesite eruptions in the central Sierra Nevada, extend in a continuous zone from at least as far east as Ebbetts Pass and Sonora Pass to the western foothills at Knights Ferry. This sequence of andesites and associated rocks is herein named the Relief Peak Formation. It unconformably overlies the Valley Springs Formation, and is unconformably overlain by the Stanislaus Formation. The thickness of the Relief Peak Formation decreases from the crest of the range toward the western foothills, where it contains a Mio-Pliocene flora and underlies latites with ages of about 9 m.y.

The Relief Peak Formation crops out on the slopes of Relief Peak, designated herein as the type area, in a sequence that is not only of the unusually great thickness of about 3,000 feet, but also is of varied lithology. The sequence includes on the north flank of the mountain, in secs. 18, 19, and 20, T. 5 N., R. 21 E., about 20 feet of gravel with abundant granitic and metamorphic rocks of the Emigrant Basin type, andesitic sands, and, near the base, much reworked rhyolitic material, including cobbles and sands from the underlying Valley Springs Formation. Above these volcanic sediments, the section is composed mainly of mudflow breccias and autobrecciated andesitic flows.

The thickness of the Relief Peak Formation varies from 3,000 feet near the source at Relief Peak, and at Mount Emma near Sonora Pass, to about 300 feet near the Jamestown-Knights Ferry area shown on figure 1a, where the formation disappears under younger deposits of the Great Valley of California.

This unconformity, between the early andesites of the Relief Peak Formation and underlying basement rocks or Cenozoic rhyolites and sediments, is generally one of moderate relief in the foothills, but to the east the relief increases to about 2,000 feet and provides a buried youthful erosion surface with slopes of over 25°, which is as steep as the present mountain slopes. The unconformity preserves dendritic channels in the underlying rhyolites that followed paths which led more or less directly downslope to the southwest. The erosional interlude between the deposition of the 20- to 33-m.y. old rhyolites and the Relief Peak andesites was sufficiently long to create new, youthful valleys with a relief as great as that on the prerhyolite terrain. In the old valleys at the base of the andesites in places are included sands and gravels, generally contaminated both with basement rocks and easily eroded Cenozoic rhyolites.

From andesites underlying the Table Mountain Latite Member of the Stanislaus Formation near Jamestown that are herein assigned to the Relief Peak Formation, Condit (1944) has described a Mio-Pliocene flora, the Table Mountain flora. Stirton and Goeriz (1942) assign an early Clarendonian age to the same rocks on the basis of a small fauna. The potassium-argon dates for the overlying Stanislaus Formation ranges between 8.8 and 9.3 m.y., and the underlying rhyolites are probably older than 19.9 m.y., which is the age of the youngest of the underlying Valley Springs rhyolites.

On the basis of a flora found on Niagara Creek, the basal sediments of the andesites of the Relief Peak Formation higher in the range appear to have a late Miocene age (D. I. Axelrod, oral communication, 1965). In this area the underlying rhyolite yields a potassium-argon date of 23.3 m.y. on sanidine and 25.7 and 26.1 m.y. on biotite samples; of the three dates, Dalrymple (1964a, p. 22) considers the sanidine date as the most reliable. In either case, the lower Miocene age of the rhyolite is well established. The Stanislaus Formation, which unconformably overlies the Relief Peak, is Hemphillian, with potassium-argon ages of about 9 m.y. The weakly eroded nature of the unconformity at the base of the latites in this area suggests that the youngest of the Relief Peak andesites may be lower Pliocene, and these early andesites may have been erupted at various stages during late Miocene to lower Pliocene.

Dikes and plugs of andesite are abundant in the area from Sonora Pass and Relief Peak to Mount Emma, and this must have been at least one of the major source areas for the Relief Peak mudflow breccias, tuffs, and flows. Extensive andesitic volcanic activity in nearby parts of Nevada could have provided additional sources for some of the mudflows, sands, and gravels of the Relief Peak Formation.

STANISLAUS FORMATION

Latites erupted after the Relief Peak andesitic activity, and herein named the Stanislaus Formation, may prove to be of singular importance in deciphering the structural and geomorphological development of the central Sierra Nevada, for they seem to form the only well-defined stratigraphic and time marker that extends from under the Great Valley of California, across the range, and into the eastern portion of the Basin and Range province. Because the Stanislaus Formation predates by a short interval most of the Sierra Nevada uplift and the development of the present Basin and Range topography by faulting, it not only provides a measure of fault displacements but also a means of correlating between the two provinces.

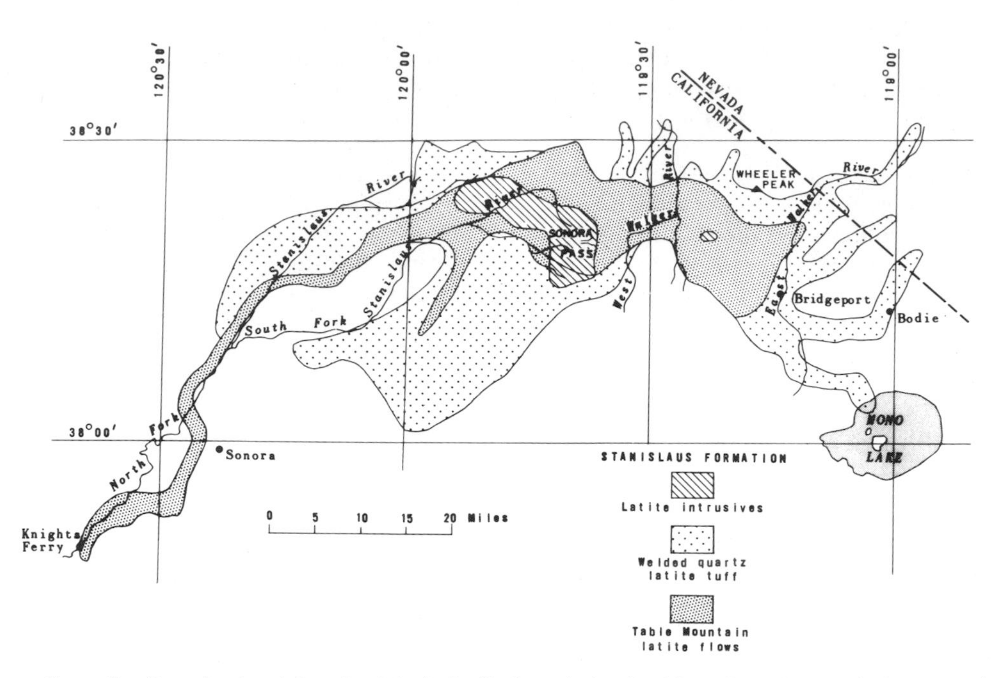

Figure 3. Map showing inferred original distribution of the Stanislaus Formation, and the original distribution of the Table Mountain Latite Member and the welded biotite-quartz latite tuffs of the Eureka Valley Member. The volcanic centers for the Table Mountain Member are in the area indicated by the diagonal pattern near Sonora Pass, and a possible intrusive source for the Eureka Valley Member is similarly indicated about 15 miles east of Sonora Pass.

The latites now assigned to the Stanislaus Formation were divided into three units by Ransome (1898) and Slemmons (1953). The three units, now considered to be members, are herein defined from oldest to youngest as: (1) Table Mountain Latite Member, mostly olivine-augite latite flows including the type locality for latites, (2) Eureka Valley Member, consisting of several latite flows with interbedded welded biotite-augite quartz-latite tuff, probably the type "quartz latites," and (3) Dardanelles Member, containing flows ranging from latitic to basaltic in composition.

The Stanislaus Formation is named for its conspicuous development along the various tributaries of the Stanislaus River of California, and the type locality is designated as the Bald Peak-Red Peak ridge which separates the Clarks Fork and Deadman Creek branches of the Middle Fork of the Stanislaus River. The three formally named members are defined on the basis of the three most characteristic localities for each of the members, and with an attempt to fit the terminology as closely as possible to the nomenclature proposed informally in the classic description of type latites and, probably, quartz latites, by Ransome (1898).

The lowermost unit is here designated the Table Mountain Latite Member, in conformity with Ransome's (1898, p. 14–27) references to the "Table Mountain facies" of the latites, and to the "Table Mountain flow." This member is, accordingly, named for "Tuolumne Table Mountain," half a mile west of Shaws Flat in the Columbia (1:24,000) quadrangle, California, where it is almost 200 feet thick. The Table Mountain Latite Member has been traced from its type locality at Table Mountain almost continuously (Ransome, 1898; Slemmons, 1953) to its source area near Sonora Pass, where at Sonora Peak and Leavitt Peak there are as many as 40 flows of this same type of latite lava comprising a thickness of 1,500 feet.

The middle member, the "biotite-augite-latite" of Ransome (1898, p. 37–46), is here named the Eureka Valley Member for Eureka Valley in the Dardanelles quadrangle (1:62,500). The type locality is the ridge between Bald Peak and Red Mountain where the section shows great diversity of lithology and a thickness of 200 feet (Slemmons, 1953, p. 67–71). This member conformably overlies the Table Mountain Latite Member.

The uppermost member of the Stanislaus Formation is here named the Dardanelles Member (as currently spelled) after the "Dardanelle flow" of Ransome (1898, p. 46–52) for the West Dardanelle of the Dardanelles Cone quadrangle. At the West Dardanelle, which is designated as the type locality, the flows are similar to the augite latites of the Table Mountain Member, but plagioclase phenocrysts in them are smaller and more sparse. Eastward from West Dardanelle, the Dardanelles Member includes a number of basalt and olivine basalt flows. This member conformably overlies the Eureka Valley Member.

The Stanislaus Formation attains a maximum thickness of more than 1,500 feet near Sonora Pass, but it thins southwestward to where, in the Table Mountain area near Sonora, it consists of a single augite latite flow only 200 feet thick. It is unfossiliferous, but Dalrymple has dated six samples by the potassium-argon method and obtained dates of from 8.8 to 9.3 m.y., indicating a lower Pliocene (Hemphillian) age. Some of the latite lava erupted from dikes and fissures between Dardanelles Cone and Sonora Pass, and other flows may have erupted east of the present divide (Halsey, 1953).

The great areal extent of the Stanislaus Formation is shown by figure 3. The lower unit, the Table Mountain Latite Member, extends eastward from near Knights Ferry, where it emerges from beneath younger volcanics and sediments that mantle the Great Valley. It attains a maximum width near Sonora Pass in the source area and fans out east of the summit area. Still farther east it narrows and becomes sporadically distributed as it approaches its eastern limit near the Nevada-California boundary. The overlying welded augite-biotite quartz latite tuffs do not extend as far westward as the flows of Table Mountain augite latite, but their total area is greater. The quartz latite outcrop width increases greatly as the summit of the range is approached, its limits extending farther north, east, and south than the flows of the Table Mountain Latite Member. The basalts and latites of the uppermost unit, the Dardanelles Member, are believed to be more limited in areal extent, having a known distribution from Big Trees on the west to the Nevada-California boundary on the east (Ransome, 1898; Slemmons, 1953; and Halsey, 1953). Future detailed mapping, however, will probably extend the limits as indicated in figure 3.

The thickness of the Stanislaus Formation varies greatly because of the irregular unconformity at the base of the formation, the irregular initial deposition, and because of subsequent deep dissection. The Table Mountain Latite Member at Knights Ferry has a thickness of 200 feet, and near the source at Sonora Pass has its maximum thickness of 1,500 feet. It thins out to the east at Fales Hot Springs, but a small auxiliary field of similar augite latites is developed near Bridgeport, California. The Eureka Valley Member varies in thickness from a few tens of feet near Big Trees to 400 feet in the Sonora Pass area and Bell Meadows, 3 miles southeast of Pinecrest Reservoir. The overlying latites and basalts of the Dardanelles Member are developed mainly between the Dardanelles, where they are 200 feet thick, and the eastern edge of the Fales Hot Springs quadrangle.

The unconformity which separates the latites of the Stanislaus Formation from the underlying Relief Peak andesites is generally one of low relief, and may indicate only a short hiatus in deposition. No lateral equivalents to the latites are known.

The age of the Stanislaus Formation can be placed rather closely in spite of the absence of fossil localities in it because the consistency of the several available potassium-argon dates restricts the latitic activities to a brief period. The date for the Table Mountain Member is 9 m.y., the four values for the biotite-augite quartz latite welded tuffs of the Eureka Valley Member are 9.2 m.y. at Big Trees, 8.8 and 8.9 m.y. for the summit region, and 9.0 m.y. for the Jawbone Ridge area. The Dardanelles Member, the uppermost unit, is represented by a 9.3 m.y. date (Dalrymple, 1964a). The only other potassium-argon age date similar to those of the latites is from the Table Mountain basalt (Sugar Loaf Hill) of the Friant area (Dalrymple, 1963; Wahrhaftig, 1965) and Coyote Flat. This unit is probably an olivine basalt (Macdonald, 1941; Dalrymple, 1963; and Wahrhaftig, 1965), although Dalrymple's whole-rock analyses indicate a potassium content of 2.01 percent at Sugar Loaf Hill and 1.82 percent at Coyote Flat, suggestive of alkaline-potassium affinities. Their potassium-argon ages are 9.5 m.y. and 9.6 m.y., respectively.

The source of at least part of the Stanislaus Formation is indicated by the occurrence of more than 20 augite latite dikes recognized between Dardanelles Cone and Sonora Pass. Halsey (1953) also has noted the possibility of quartz latitic centers of eruption near Fales Hot Springs. The thickest sections are between Sonora Pass and Pinecrest, which suggests that there may be other sources to the west of the present divide.

POSTLATITE VOLCANIC ROCKS

Postlatite lavas, mostly andesites and basalts, form a thick succession near Sonora Pass, and extend across the entire width of the range to the Great Valley of California, where they form the type locality for the Mehrten Formation (Piper and others, 1938). These lavas probably extend northward to, or beyond, Donner Pass, but the lack of adequate potassium-argon dates or paleontological control, and the absence of latitic lavas, have made it difficult to distinguish them from the older andesites of the central Sierra Nevada. In addition to this thick sequence of lavas, there are in the Sierra a number of isolated outcrops of flows of basalt, andesite, and rhyolite that are mainly younger than this thick sequence. As many of these postlatite rocks occupy especially significant positions on erosion surfaces of varying geomorphological age, they have received special attention (Axelrod and Ting, 1960, 1961; Dalrymple, 1963a, 1963b, 1964; Wahrhaftig, 1965).

The thickest and most widespread of the post-Stanislaus Formation lavas of the Sonora Pass area are hornblende-rich andesites herein designated as the Disaster Peak Formation (fig. 1c). They are very well exposed in a section preserved on the slopes of Disaster Peak, Sonora Pass quadrangle, which is designated as the type locality. This formation can be recognized in the source area between Ebbetts Pass and Relief Peak by the presence in it of large cobbles and breccia clasts of hornblende andesites, generally with abundant hornblende phenocrysts up to 1 inch in length. The hornblendes are sufficiently large to "twinkle" in the sunlight as the outcrops are crossed, even when one is

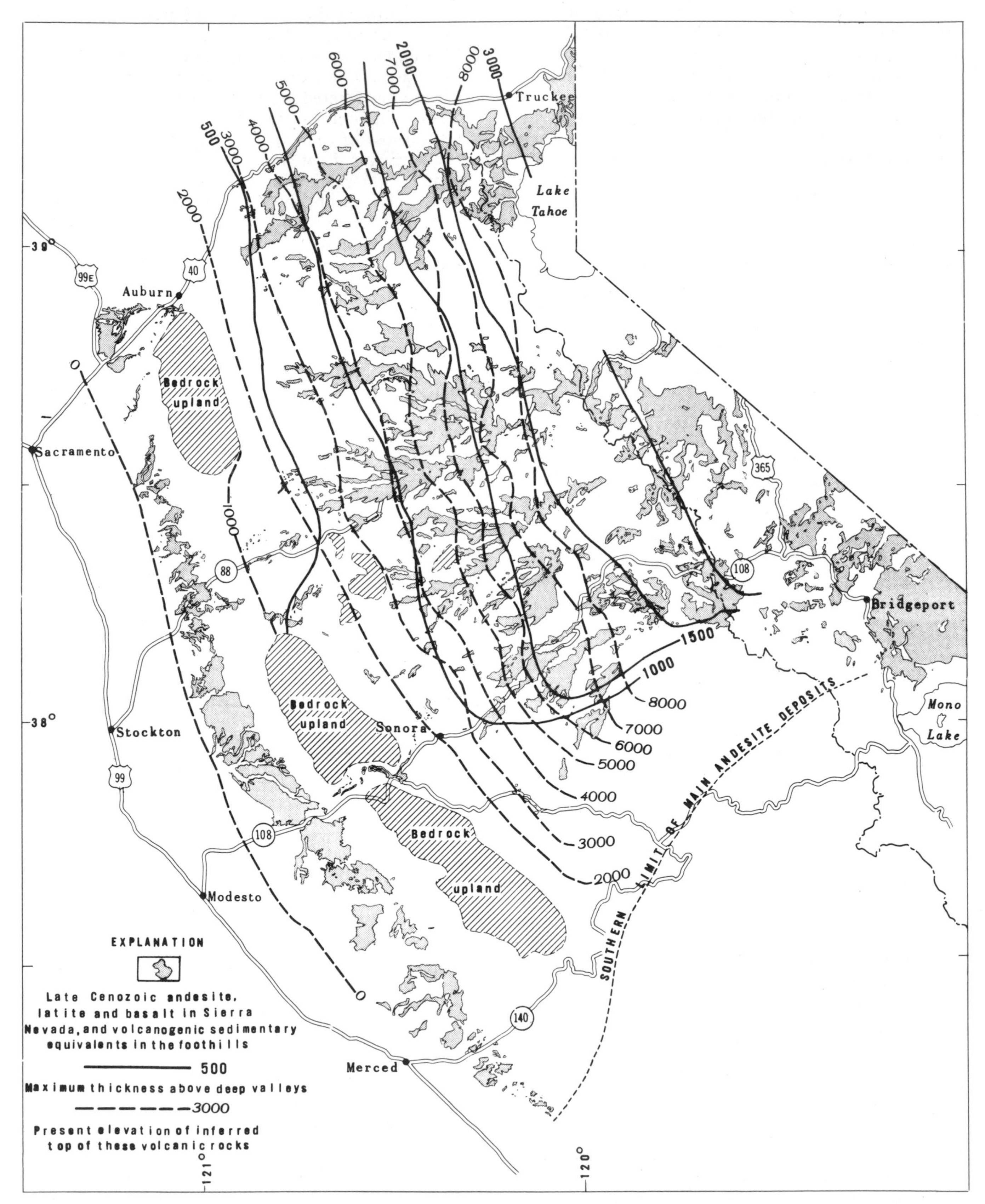

Figure 4. Map showing distribution of late Cenozoic andesite, latite, basalt, and Pliocene rhyolite. The approximate maximum original thickness above the deeper pre-andesite valleys is indicated by the solid isopachs. The dashed contours denote the approximate present elevation of the inferred top of these volcanic rocks. In addition to the main bedrock uplands of the foothill belt, there were probably other areas at higher elevations on which little or no volcanic rock was deposited.

crossing rapidly in a car. The deposits are mainly mudflow breccias, autobrecciated flows, and subordinate volcanic sediments. The section is approximately 1,000 feet thick, both near Disaster Peak and also farther south near Castle Rock and East Flange Rock where the Disaster Peak andesites lie on latite. The Disaster Peak Formation may prove to be the equivalent of the Mehrten Formation in the type area, but owing to large gaps in the mapping it seems best to apply a new name rather than guess at the correlation.

The composition of the younger volcanic rocks varies from dominantly hornblendic andesites, which contrast with the pyroxene-bearing types that predominate in the older andesitic volcanics of the central Sierra Nevada (Curtis, 1951), to rhyolite and basalt. South of the Sonora Pass area, the volcanic rocks are limited in extent and are mainly basalts, rhyolite in domes, and pyroclastic beds. The deposits attain maximum thicknesses in excess of 1,500 feet between the Sonora Pass area (fig. 1c) and the south end of Lake Tahoe. East of the Sierra Nevada, volcanics of similar age are even thicker, suggesting that many of the volcanics present in the Sierra Nevada may have had an eastern source. That the latest volcanic activity is more diversified than in earlier parts of the Cenozoic is shown in figure 1.

The thickness of the young volcanic rocks is highly variable, for much of the southern part of the range is either unaffected by volcanic activity, or contains only sporadic flows, mainly of basalt. There is a general increase in thickness of the Disaster Peak Formation to the east in the central part of the range, with a variation of from several hundred feet near the type locality of the Mehrten Formation at the edge of the Great Valley to over 3,000 feet near Sonora Pass and Lake Tahoe.

The Disaster Peak Formation unconformably overlies either the Stanislaus Formation, usually with an erosion surface of low relief, or the early andesites and Valley Springs rhyolites with a deeply dissected surface of moderate relief.

The postlatite lavas vary widely in age, and include andesites only slightly younger than the 9-m.y.-old latites of the Stanislaus Formation, as well as andesitic material from the Verdi area in adjoining Nevada that has been dated at 5.7 m.y. (Evernden and James, 1964), and the Oakdale flora and faunas of the foothill region (Axelrod, 1944; Stirton and Goeriz, 1942). The younger basalts include a wide range of dates from scattered sources in the summit region.

The source of these young volcanic rocks of the Sierra Nevada lies mainly in many separate vents, most of which are near the crest of the range or east of the range.

PETROCHEMISTRY

The petrochemical character of the Sierra Nevada volcanic activity is different for each of the separate and independent periods of eruption. Activity during Mesozoic appears to be distinct in character from that

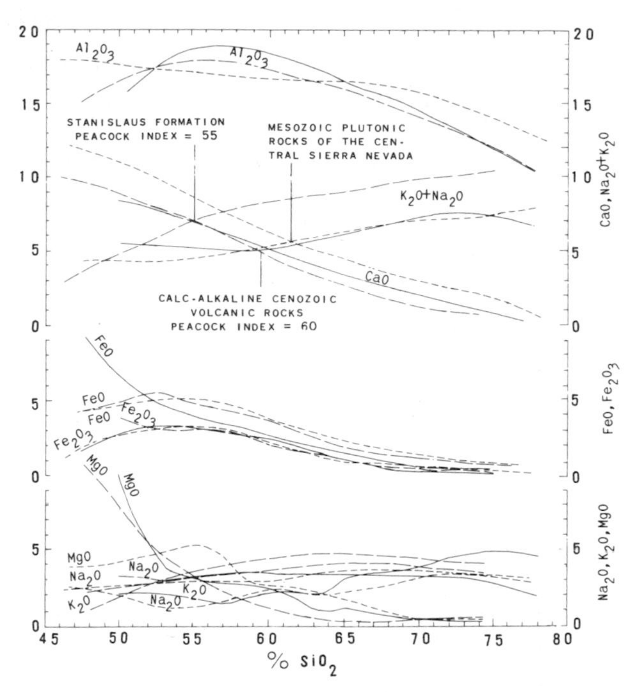

Figure 5. Silica variation diagram for Cenozoic volcanic rocks of the alkalic Stanislaus Formation (solid lines), the calc-alkaline volcanic rocks of the Mehrten Formation (dashed lines), and calc-alkaline Mesozoic plutonic rocks of the central Sierra Nevada (dotted lines). The principal sources of analytical data are from Curtis (1951), Halsey (1953), Slemmons (1953), and Washington (1917).

of the three main periods of the Cenozoic (fig. 1), although the small number of analyses of Mesozoic intrusive rocks prevents a good comparison.

The Oligocene and Miocene magmas of the Valley Spring Formation were dominantly rhyolitic. The overlying Relief Peak andesites, though not represented by many chemical analyses, were mainly basaltic, and basic to intermediate, andesites. The latites of the Stanislaus Formation are much different from both younger and older volcanic rocks because they are alkalic, and potassium predominates over sodium in most of them (fig. 5). Their alkaline character is indicated by the Peacock calc-alkali index being lower for these rocks than for most Sierra Nevada volcanic rocks. Postlatitic activity has, except for the major period of eruption of the Disaster Peak hornblendic andesites, been marked by diverse activity in which extreme chemical types seem to be dominant. Rhyolites and basalts were erupted intermittently during the last part of the Pliocene and the Quaternary. This activity is well marked east of the range both at Mono Lake and in Owens Valley, as well as within the main Sierran block.

The eruptive record provides sharp contrasts in chemical character, from the mainly rhyolitic character of the early activity in the Oligocene and Miocene, to the andesitic character of the Mio-Pliocene or early Pliocene, to latites and quartz latites with highly alkaline and strongly potassic affinities, to the youngest periods of andesitic, rhyolitic, and basaltic activity with a calc-alkaline character.

REFERENCES

Axelrod, D. I., 1944, The Oakdale flora [California]: Carnegie Inst. Washington Pub. 553, Contr. Paleontology, p. 147–165.

—— 1957, Late Tertiary floras and the Sierra Nevada uplift [California-Nevada]: Geol. Soc. America Bull., v. 68, no. 1, p. 19–45.

—— 1958, The Pliocene Verdi flora of western Nevada: California Univ. Pub. Geol. Sci., v. 34, no. 2, p. 91–159.

—— 1962, Post-Pliocene uplift of the Sierra Nevada, California: Geol. Soc. America Bull., v. 73, no. 2, p. 183–198.

Axelrod, D. I., and Ting, W. S., 1960, Late Pliocene floras east of the Sierra Nevada, California: California Univ. Pub. Geol. Sci., v. 39, no. 1, p. 1–118.

—— 1961, Early Pleistocene floras from the Chagoopa surface, southern Sierra Nevada: California Univ. Pub. Geol. Sci., v. 39, no. 2, p. 119–194.

Burnett, J. L., and Jennings, C. W., 1962, Geologic map of California, Olaf P. Jenkins edition, Chico sheet: California Div. Mines and Geology, scale 1:250,000.

Burnett, J. L., and Matthews, R. A., 196__, Geologic map of California, Olaf P. Jenkins edition, Fresno sheet: California Div. Mines and Geology, scale 1:250,000. (In press 1965)

Condit, Carlton, 1944, The Table Mountain flora [California]: Carnegie Inst. Washington Pub. 553, Contr. Paleontology, p. 57–90.

Curtis, G. H., 1951, Geology of the Topaz Lake quadrangle and the eastern half of the Ebbetts Pass quadrangle: California Univ., Berkeley, Ph.D. thesis, 310 p.

Dalrymple, G. B., 1963, Potassium-argon dates of some Cenozoic volcanic rocks of the Sierra Nevada, California: Geol. Soc. America Bull., v. 74, no. 4, p. 379–390.

—— 1964a, Cenozoic chronology of the Sierra Nevada, California: California Univ. Pub. Geol. Sci., v. 47, 41 p.

—— 1964b, Potassium-argon dates of three Pleistocene interglacial basalt flows from the Sierra Nevada, California: Geol. Soc. America Bull., v. 75, no. 8, p. 753–758.

Evernden, J. F., and James, G. T., 1964, Potassium-argon dates and the Tertiary floras of North America: Am. Jour. Sci., v. 262, no. 8, p. 945–974.

Evernden, J. F., Savage, D. E., Curtis, G. H., and James, G. T., 1964, Potassium-argon dates and the Cenozoic mammalian chronology of North America: Am. Jour. Sci., v. 262, no. 2, p. 145–198.

Halsey, J. G., 1953, Geology of parts of the Bridgeport, California, and Wellington, Nevada quadrangles: California Univ., Berkeley, Ph.D. thesis.

Koenig, J. B., 1963, Geologic map of California, Olaf P. Jenkins edition, Walker Lake sheet: California Div. Mines and Geology, scale 1:250,000.

Lindgren, Waldemar, 1894, Description of the Sacramento quadrangle, California: U.S. Geol. Survey Geol. Atlas, Folio 5, [3] p.

—— 1897, Description of the Truckee quadrangle, California: U.S. Geol. Survey Geol. Atlas, Folio 39, [8] p.

—— 1900, Description of the Colfax quadrangle, California: U.S. Geol. Survey Geol. Atlas, Folio 66, 10 p.

Lindgren, Waldemar, and Turner, H. W., 1894, Description of the Placerville quadrangle, California: U.S. Geol. Survey Geol. Atlas, Folio 3, 9 p.

—— 1895, Description of the Smartsville quadrangle, California: U.S. Geol. Survey Geol. Atlas, Folio 18, [6] p.

Lindgren, Waldemar, and Hoover, H. C., 1896, Description of the Pyramid Peak quadrangle, California: U.S. Geol. Survey Geol. Atlas, Folio 31.

Macdonald, G. A., 1941, Geology of the western Sierra Nevada between the Kings and San Joaquin Rivers, California: California Univ., Dept. Geol. Sci. Bull., v. 26, no. 2, p. 215–286.

Piper, A. M., Gale, H. S., Thomas, H. E., and Robinson, T. W., 1939, Geology and ground-water hydrology of the Mokelumne area, California: U.S. Geol. Survey Water-Supply Paper 780, 230 p.

Ransome, F. L., 1898, Some lava flows of the western slope of the Sierra Nevada, California: U.S. Geol. Survey Bull. 89, 74 p.

Rogers, T. H., 196__, Geologic map of California, Olaf P. Jenkins edition, San Jose sheet: California Div. Mines and Geology, scale 1:250,000. (In press 1965)

Schilling, J. H., 1965, Isotopic age determinations of Nevada rocks: Nevada Bur. Mines Rept. 10.

Slemmons, D. B., 1953, Geology of the Sonora Pass region: California Univ., Berkeley, Ph.D. thesis, 201 p.

Stirton, R. A., and Goeriz, H. F., 1942, Fossil vertebrates from Superjacent deposits near Knights Ferry, California: California Univ., Dept. Geol. Sci. Bull., v. 26, no. 5, p. 447–472.

Strand, R. G., 196__, Geologic map of California, Olaf P. Jenkins edition, Mariposa sheet: California Div. Mines and Geology, scale 1:250,000. (In press 1965)

Turner, H. W., 1894, Description of the Jackson quadrangle, California: U.S. Geol. Survey Geol. Atlas, Folio 11, [6] p.

Turner, H. W., and Ransome, F. L., 1897, Description of the Sonora quadrangle, California: U.S. Geol. Survey Geol. Atlas, Folio 41, [7] p.

—— 1898, Description of the Big Trees quadrangle, California: U.S. Geol. Survey Geol. Atlas, Folio 51.

Wahrhaftig, Clyde, 1963, Origin of stepped topography of the west-central Sierra Nevada, California [abs.]: Geol. Soc. America Spec. Paper 73, p. 71.

—— 1965, Stepped topography of the Sierra Nevada (Stop 11-4 to Stop 11-6), *in* Guidebook for Field Conference I, Northern Great Basin and California: INQUA (Internat. Assoc. Quarternary Research), 7th Cong. 1965, p. 123–128.

Washington, H. S., 1917, Chemical analyses of igneous rocks: U.S. Geol. Survey Prof. Paper 99, 1201 p.

ECONOMIC MINERAL DEPOSITS OF THE SIERRA NEVADA

By William B. Clark
California Division of Mines and Geology

The Sierra Nevada province has been a major source of minerals since Marshall's historic gold discovery at Sutter's mill in 1848. At the present time this region is the source of large quantities of sand and gravel, crushed and broken stone, tungsten, limestone, and limestone products which include cement, lime, and rock used in sugar refining. In addition, substantial amounts of asbestos, barite, dimension stone, mineral filler, rhyolitic ash, soapstone, and uranium are being produced; and smaller amounts of gold, silver, copper, zinc, molybdenum, silica, gem and ornamental minerals, and wollastonite are also recovered. Unfortunately, complete production statistics for many of these mineral commodities are not available.

The output of gold, which was once the principal commodity, has a cumulative value of more than $2 billion. However, gold mining has decreased greatly in recent years. Other commodities formerly produced in large amounts are copper, zinc, magnesite, chromite, dimension granite and marble, slate squares, and sulfur. Also found in the Sierra Nevada, though little exploited, are deposits containing arsenic, antimony, andalusite, clay, garnet, cobalt, lead, nickel, platinum, feldspar, pyrite, manganese, mercury, quartz crystal, tellurium, thorium, and zirconium. Much of the mineral wealth exploited in the past or available for the future is in the western foothills, especially in the central and northern portions of the range (see fig. 2). Fewer deposits are found in the southern end of the range and along the eastern flank, although even here there are scattered deposits of major importance; for example that of the Pine Creek tungsten mine.

In the western foothills there are primary gold, copper, and zinc deposits believed to be genetically related to the intrusions of the Sierran granitic batholith but occurring largely in the belt of metamorphic rocks. Slate, greenstone, and amphibolite are the principal host rocks. In some districts, such as Grass Valley, Ophir, West Point, and Soulsbyville, the gold-quartz veins are in or around small granitic intrusions that are branches of the main batholith. In other districts, such as those at Alleghany, Washington, and Forest Hill, the gold-quartz veins are adjacent to serpentine bodies. Although this entire foothill region is often referred to as the Mother Lode, technically the Lode is a system of linked or *en echelon* gold-quartz veins and intervening mineralized schist and greenstone that extends from Georgetown and Greenwood southeast to Mariposa, a distance of 120 miles. The most productive portions of this belt have been the Jackson, Carson Hill, Angels Camp, and Jamestown districts.

The placer deposits of the Sierra Nevada have yielded vast amounts of gold; some estimates have placed its total value at nearly $1 billion. There are two main types of placer deposits, the older or Tertiary deposits which are on the interstream ridges, and the younger or Recent ones in and adjacent to the present stream channels. The Tertiary deposits consist predominantly of quartzitic gravels deposited in the channels that existed many million years ago and were capped by thick beds of andesite. They have been worked mainly by hydraulic and drift mining. The Recent gravels have been worked by dredging, river mining, and small-scale methods, and were the source of the tremendous yields of gold in the days of "49." The gravel tailings from these old placer mines are now important sources of aggregate.

A discontinuous belt of copper and zinc mineralization extends along the lower western foothills. Here lenticular sulfide bodies that occur in zones of alteration in greenstones, amphibolites, and chlorite schists have yielded more than 200 million pounds of copper and 50 million pounds of zinc. The most productive mines have been at Campo Seco and Copperopolis in western Calaveras County. Remote from the foothill belt, in northeastern Plumas County are the famous Walker, Engels, and Superior copper mines which have yielded more than 300 million pounds of copper. At the Walker mine the ore bodies are chalcopyrite-bearing quartz veins in schist and hornfels near granitic rocks, while those at the Engels and Superior mines are bands of chalcopyrite and bornite in granitic rocks. Some by-product copper is recovered from the Pine Creek tungsten mine near Bishop.

The serpentine belts of the western Sierra Nevada contain or are associated with a variety of mineral deposits. These include chromite, asbestos, nickel, gem minerals, ornamental stones, magnesite, and soapstone. The Pillikin mine in El Dorado County has been the chief source of chromite, which occurs disseminated in serpentinized dunite. At present substantial amounts of chrysotile asbestos are mined and milled a few miles south of Copperopolis, where the chrysotile occurs as stockworks of cross fiber veins in massive serpentine. Gem minerals also are associated with serpentine. Included are jade in Mariposa County, chrysoprase in Amador, Mariposa, and Tulare Counties, and idocrase in Butte and Tulare Counties. Mariposite-bearing rock

Photo 1. Diamond Springs limestone quarry, El Dorado County. *Photo by Mary Hill.*

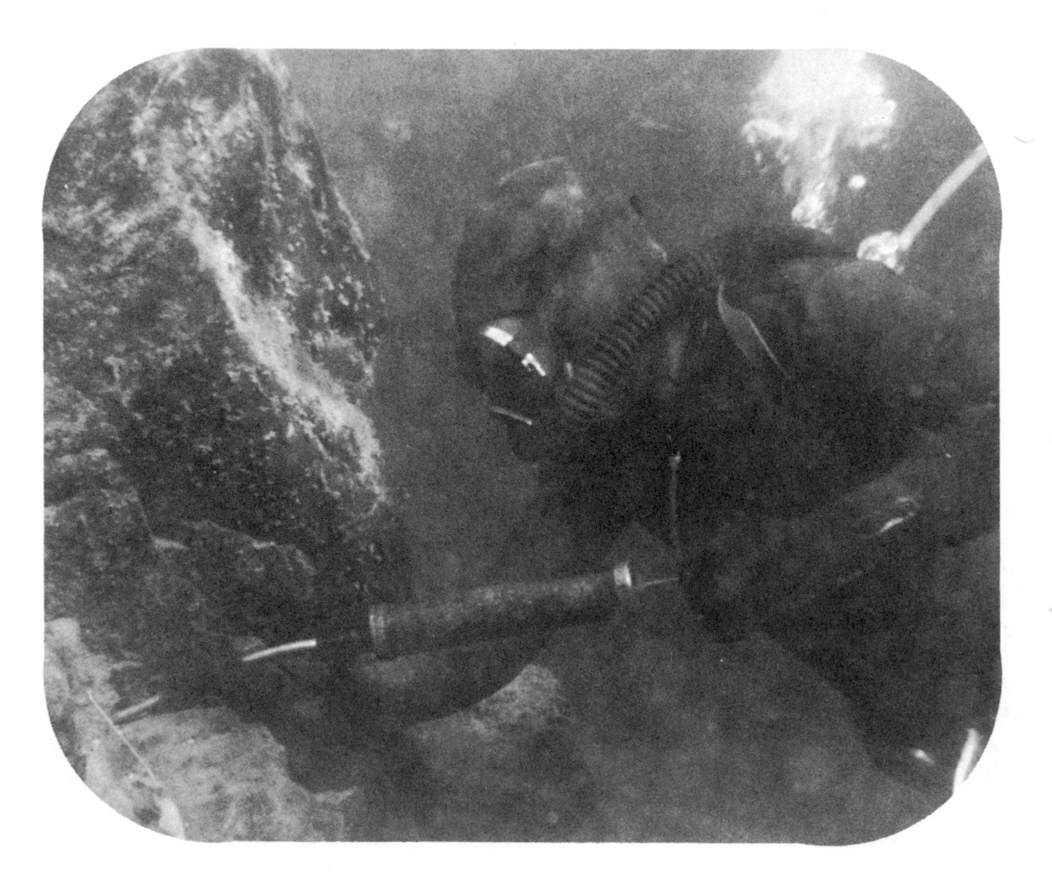

Photo 2. Diving for gold in the American River. *Photo courtesy Underwater Enterprises.*

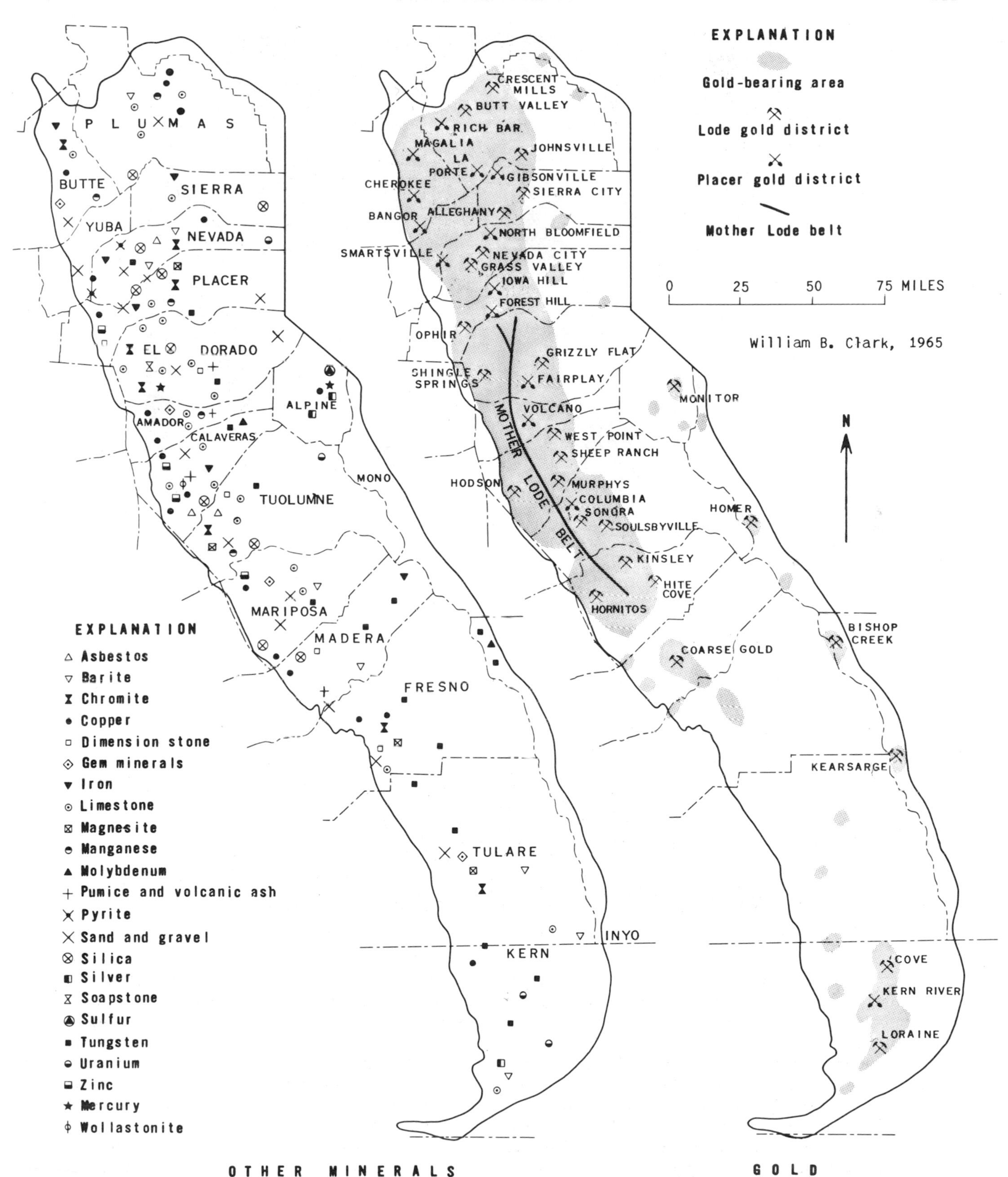

Figure 1. Location of economic deposits of the Sierra Nevada province.

Photo 3. Pine Creek tungsten mine and mill, Inyo County. *Photo courtesy Curtis Phillips, Bishop.*

associated with serpentine is a popular ornamental stone, and large quantities have been trucked to the metropolitan areas of the State. At one time considerable magnesite was mined in Fresno County, and smaller amounts were also extracted in Tuolumne, Tulare, and Nevada Counties. Soapstone has been mined near Shingle Springs, El Dorado County, for many years from lenses of talc schist with serpentine. Nickel has been found to be concentrated in laterites that overlie serpentine in several places, though no deposits have yet been exploited.

The production of limestone and limestone products is now the largest segment of the mineral industry in the Sierra Nevada, amounting to 10's of millions of dollars a year. Crystalline limestone and dolomite, the basic source rocks, occur as lenses in various types of metamorphic rocks and granitic rock. Although the age of most of the limestone deposits is not known, a few of them have yielded fossils ranging from Mississippian to Permian in age. The limestone usually is white to blue-gray in color, and fairly pure. The largest masses are in the Sonora-Columbia area of Tuolumne County, but extensive deposits are in Plumas, El Dorado, Amador, Calaveras, Mariposa, Kern, and Tulare Counties. The principal districts producing commercial limestone at present are at Cool, Shingle Springs, and Diamond Springs, El Dorado County, where most of it is used in beet sugar refining

Photo 4. Argonaut gold mine at Jackson, Amador County. *Photo by Mary Hill.*

or the manufacture of lime; San Andreas, Calaveras County, where it is quarried for cement by the Calaveras Cement Co.; Columbia and Sonora, Tuolumne County, where terrazzo stone and lime are made; and Tehachapi, Kern County, the site of the Monolith Cement Co. operation. At one time limestone was quarried near Briceburg, Mariposa County, for use in a cement plant in Merced County. Wollastonite occurs with limestone at San Andreas and is used in cement.

One of the largest sources of tungsten in the world is the Bishop district in northwestern Inyo County on the steep east Sierran flank. The Pine Creek mine, the principal property, has yielded about 1.5 million units of WO_3. The ore bodies here are in a roof pendant of schist, hornfels, quartzite, and marble surrounded by granitic rocks. Disseminated scheelite and molybdenite occur in garnetiferous tactite bodies, along with some copper minerals and gold, which are recovered as by-products. Other important contact-metamorphic tungsten deposits are at the Tungstar and Tulare mines, Tulare County; Garnet Dike mine, Fresno County; and the Strawberry mine, Madera County. Substantial amounts of tungsten also have been recovered from the Idaho-Maryland and Union Hill gold mines at Grass Valley, Nevada County, from scheelite-rich quartz veins in amphibolite.

Barite has been mined in the Sierra Nevada, the chief source having been the El Portal district in Mariposa County where nearly $3 million of barite have been recovered. The deposits are veinlike bodies of barite and witherite that have replaced limestone in slate and schist. Barite has also been recovered from limestone-replacement deposits near Alta and Graniteville, Nevada County, and Greenville in Plumas County. Many years ago iron was mined near Auburn in Placer County, where magnetite and hematite occur at the contact of greenstone, slate, and limestone with granodiorite. The undeveloped though sizable Minarets deposits in eastern Madera County are flat-lying magnetite-rich lenses in a sequence of metamorphosed volcanic rocks. In northern Sierra County there are magnetite replacements of clastic sediments, tuffs, and dikes.

Large quantities of sulfur were produced recently from the Leviathan mine in Alpine County and sent to Nevada for use in copper milling. This deposit consists of masses and veins of native sulfur in altered andesite.

Uranium is found in a number of places, but the principal deposits are in the high Sierra Nevada in eastern Tuolumne County and upper Kern River area in Kern County. In eastern Tuolumne County the uranium occurs in black shale in a fault zone; in the upper Kern River region it occurs in fractures in granitic and metamorphic rocks, and also in Recent bogs. Elsewhere uranium has been found in a few gold and copper quartz veins, though apparently not in commercial amounts.

Other important mineral commodities of the Sierra Nevada are lead and silver, virtually all of which have been recovered as a by-product of gold and copper-zinc mining. Manganese is widespread and has been mined, but it is mostly found in small deposits in chert. Minor amounts of platinum occur as small grains in placer gold deposits. Although platinum minerals have not been found in place, the grains found in placers are believed to have been derived from the serpentinized ultrabasic rocks. Garnet, ilmenite, and zircon are found in black sands throughout the region. Small diamonds once were recovered at the Cherokee hydraulic mine in Butte County. Minor amounts of mercury have been recovered west of Nashville, in El Dorado County, and north of Monitor, in Alpine County, where cinnabar is in silicified breccia in andesite. During the early days of the gold rush the tellurium minerals, petzite, calaverite, hessite, sylvanite, and melonite, were recovered in quantity at Carson Hill on the Mother Lode.

The sand and gravel and stone industry has grown greatly in recent years in California as a whole and in the Sierra Nevada. Both Recent and Tertiary gravels contain large reserves. At present the principal operations are along the Bear and Yuba Rivers and near Lake Tahoe. Crushed and broken stone of various types are obtained in a number of places. Rocks that are or have been quarried include rhyolite tuff, marble, andesite, serpentine, granitic rocks, slate, and greenstone. Limestone, slate, and rhyolite tuff are quarried in El Dorado County for use as roofing granules. Quartz cobbles and massive quartz veins in the Mother Lode area have been mined as a source of silica. Some years ago quartz crystals of piezo-electric grade were recovered near Mokelumne Hill in Calaveras County.

At one time the quarrying and shaping of dimension stone was a major industry. The principal sources were the granite quarries of Rocklin and Penryn in Placer County, Raymond in Madera County, and Academy in Fresno County, and the marble quarries at Columbia, Tuolumne County. The State capitol is built of Rocklin granite, while a number of public buildings in San Francisco and the University of California at Berkeley are of Raymond granite. Large bodies of andalusite-rich mica schist of potential value are in western Mariposa and Madera Counties.

REFERENCES

Averill, C. V., 1937, Mineral resources of Plumas County: California Jour. Mines and Geology, v. 33, p. 79–143.

Bateman, P. C., 1965, Geology and tungsten mineralization of the Bishop district: U.S. Geol. Survey Prof. Paper 470, 208 p.

Bowen, O. E., Jr., and Gray, C. H. Jr., 1957, Mines and mineral deposits of Mariposa County, California: California Jour. Mines and Geology, v. 53, p. 34–343.

Clark, W. B., and Carlson, D. W., 1956, Mines and mineral resources of El Dorado County, California: California Jour. Mines and Geology, v. 52, p. 369–591.

Clark, W. B., and Lydon, P. A., 1962, Mines and mineral resources of Calaveras County, California: California Div. Mines and Geology County Rept. 2, 217 p.

Ferguson, H. G., and Gannett, R. W., 1932, Gold quartz veins of the Alleghany district, California: U.S. Geol. Survey Prof. Paper 172, 139 p.

Jenkins, O. P., and others, 1948, Geologic guidebook along Highway 49—Sierran gold belt—The Mother Lode Country: California Div. Mines Bull. 141, 164 p.

Johnston, W. D., Jr., 1940, The gold quartz veins at Grass Valley, California: U.S. Geol. Survey Prof. Paper 194, 101 p.

Knopf, Adolph, 1929, The Mother Lode system of California: U.S. Geol. Survey Prof. Paper 157, 88 p.

Lindgren, Waldemar, 1911, The Tertiary gravels of the Sierra Nevada: U.S. Geol. Survey Prof. Paper 73, 226 p.

Logan, C. A., 1935, Mother Lode gold belt of California: California Div. Mines Bull. 108, 240 p.

Ransome, F. L., 1900, Mother Lode district, California: U.S. Geol. Survey Geol. Atlas, Folio 63, 11 p.

Troxel, B. W., and Morton, P. K., 1962, Mines and mineral resources of Kern County: California Div. Mines and Geology County Rept. 1, 370 p.

CHAPTER V
GREAT VALLEY PROVINCE

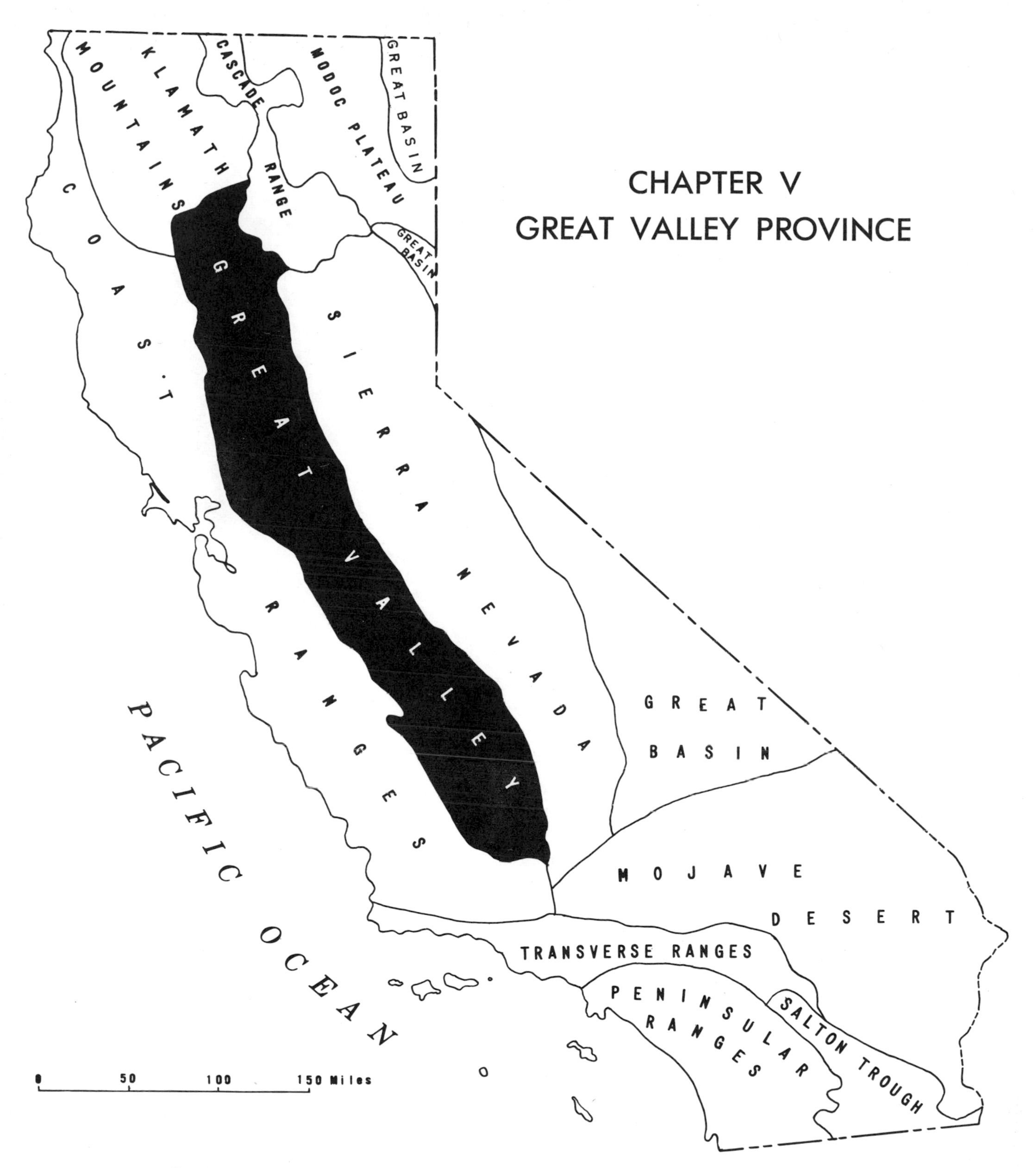

Marysville (Sutter) Buttes.

Sketched by Howel Williams.

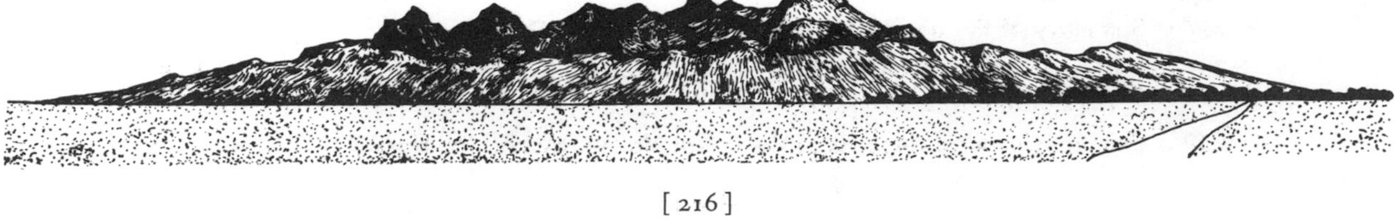

SUMMARY OF THE GEOLOGY OF THE GREAT VALLEY

By Otto Hackel
Buttes Gas and Oil Co., Oakland

A close association exists between physiography and geology in many parts of California, and although details may vary, large contiguous areas of the State have distinctive features not shared by the adjacent terrane. These large physiographic-geologic provinces have been designated "geomorphic provinces" to indicate that the division has been made subject to the rock fabric. One of the largest and most obvious of these provinces in California is the Great Valley—the topic of the following geologic summary.

The Great Valley of California, also called the Central Valley of California or the San Joaquin-Sacramento Valley, is a nearly flat alluvial plain extending from the Tehachapi Mountains on the south to the Klamath Mountains on the north, and from the Sierra Nevada on the east to the Coast Ranges on the west. The valley is about 450 miles long and has an average width of about 50 miles. Elevations of the alluvial plain are generally just a few hundred feet above sea level, with extremes ranging from a few feet below sea level to about 1,000 feet above. The only prominent topographic eminence within the central part of the valley is Marysville (Sutter) Buttes, a Pliocene volcanic plug which rises abruptly 2,000 feet above the surrounding valley floor.

The northern portion of the valley is called the Sacramento Valley and the southern portion the San Joaquin Valley. Each of these segments is drained by the river after which the valley has been named, and these, after joining about 30 miles east of San Francisco, empty into San Francisco Bay. The southern extremity of the San Joaquin Valley, however, has interior drainage via the Kings and Kern Rivers into the depressions that in the past supported Tulare and Buena Vista Lakes.

The Great Valley has been the source of about $10 billion worth of crude oil, $2 billion worth of natural gas, and $1 billion worth of natural gas liquids. The Sacramento Valley part has yielded tremendous amounts of gas but almost no oil, whereas the San Joaquin Valley has yielded both oil and gas. Because of the differences between the two main parts of the Great Valley, and to some extent because of its size, geologists, particularly petroleum geologists, have generally studied intensively either the Sacramento or the San Joaquin Valley, but not both. As a result, relatively few reports on the geology of the combined Sacramento-San Joaquin Valley have been published. In the preparation of this article a little-known comprehensive report on the entire Great Valley by C. A. Repenning (1960) has been of great value, and almost all of the paleolithologic maps used herein are direct reproductions from his excellent report.

Geologically, the Great Valley is a large elongate northwest-trending asymmetric structural trough that has been filled with a tremendously thick sequence of sediments ranging in age from Jurassic to Recent. This asymmetric geosyncline has a long stable eastern shelf supported by the subsurface continuation of the granitic Sierran slope and a short western flank expressed by the upturned edges of the basin sediments. The basin has a regional southward tilt, which is interrupted by two significant cross-valley faults. The northernmost fault, the Stockton fault, is the boundary used by most geologists to separate the Great Valley Basin into two sub-basins, the Sacramento and San Joaquin. The other great cross-fault lies near the southern extremity of the basin and has been named the White Wolf fault.

STRATIGRAPHY

The Great Valley has been filled with a thick sequence of sedimentary rocks of Jurassic to Recent age, but the locale of the thickest accumulation of sediments varied throughout geologic time. In the Tertiary the thickest accumulation was along the western edge of the southern portion of the San Joaquin basin, about at the present position of the structural low. Mesozoic rocks, however, are thickest along the west side of the Sacramento basin, indicating that their greatest deposition was probably west of the western edge of the present valley structural trough. It appears likely that a minimum of 60,000 feet of Mesozoic sediments were laid down in the area just west of the present margin of the Sacramento Valley.

The sedimentary sequence rests on a basement floor of metamorphic and igneous rocks in the eastern half of the valley. These basement rocks, which are exposed in the Sierra Nevada foothills, are composed of Paleozoic and Mesozoic metasediments and volcanics as well as Jurassic and Cretaceous granites. Along the west margin of the valley, where the very thick Mesozoic strata are present, basement has not been observed, either in outcrop or in well bores. Recent studies indicate that the terrane lying between the central part of the valley and the San Andreas fault and containing Franciscan rocks is probably underlain by a basaltic or ultramafic basement (Bailey, et al, 1964).

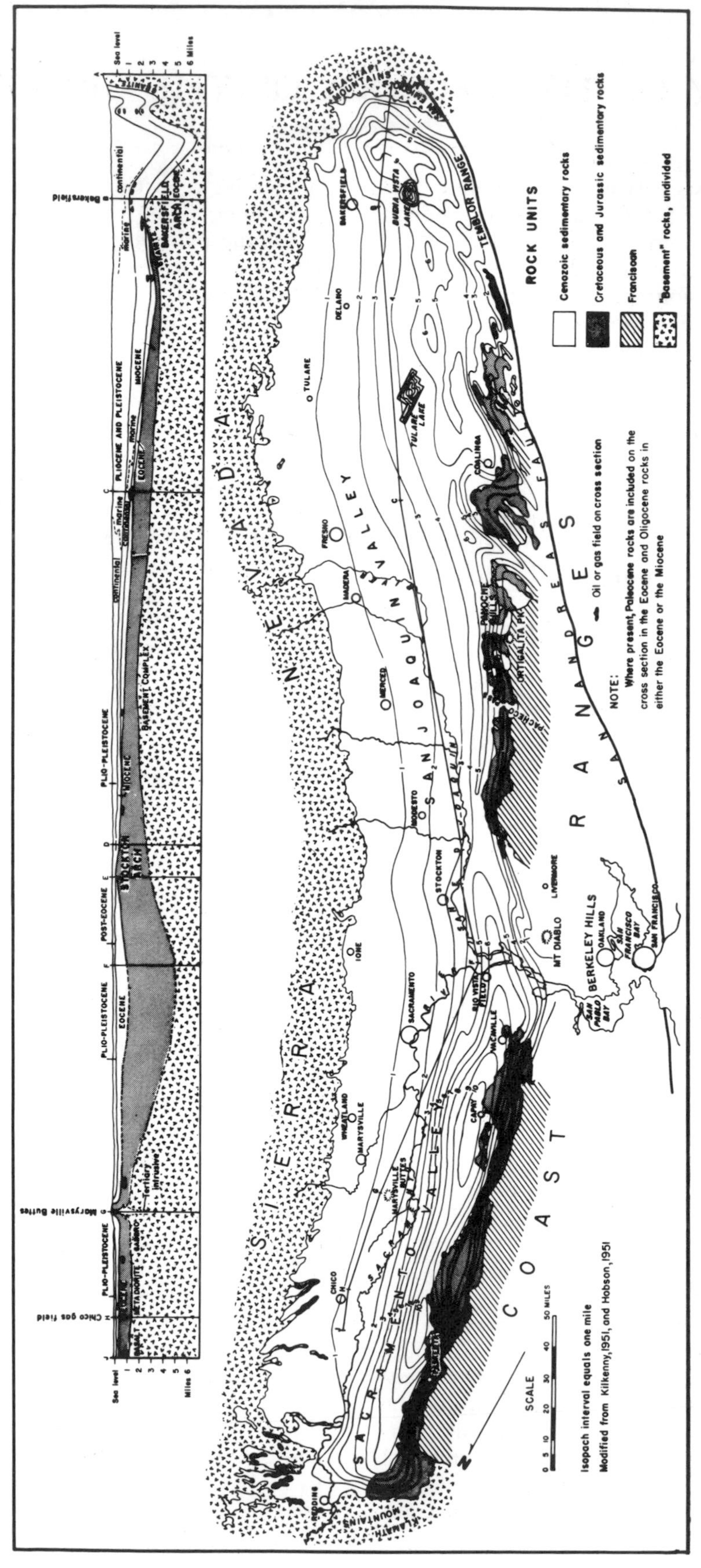

Figure 1. Map of central California showing thickness of sedimentary rocks in the Great Valley. After Repenning (1960, fig. 2).

The Jurassic, Cretaceous, and Tertiary rocks are, for the most part, of marine origin, though significant thicknesses of continental rocks are present in the Tertiary section. Through the entire sequence the rocks are almost entirely clastic, with siltstone, claystone, and sandstone, in that order, the dominant lithologic types. Except for rare occurrences, carbonate rocks are virtually absent. Volcanic rocks compose about 10 percent of the Franciscan Formation and are present in minor, though important, amounts in the Tertiary.

Cretaceous deposits make up the predominant formations in the Sacramento Valley, while Tertiary strata attain the greatest thickness in the San Joaquin Valley. The Cretaceous section is characterized by general lithologic similarities over great distances throughout the Great Valley. It is not unusual for one to be able to recognize at a glance Cretaceous sediments at localities several hundred miles apart. On the other hand, the Tertiary strata are extremely variable and rock units may change facies over very short distances.

The sediments that form the thick valley section were largely derived by erosion of land areas located to the east of the depositional trough. For the major portion of the Jurassic and Cretaceous sediments of the valley, the source area seems most likely to have been the batholiths of the Klamath Mountains and the Sierra Nevada. This hypothesis is based on the several percent of K-feldspar found in these rocks and presumed to have been derived from the granitic rocks of these northern and eastern highlands (Bailey and Irwin, 1959). The lack of K-feldspar in the valley (east of the San Andreas fault) Franciscan Formation either indicates a different source area or that most of this formation predates the unroofing of the batholiths (Bailey and others, 1964). There is evidence to indicate that the Diablo Range was a periodically emergent land mass during later parts of the Late Cretaceous and that this area contributed sediments to the Late Cretaceous sea. The arkosic nature of the Tertiary sediments seems to indicate the principal source area was probably the elevated granitic batholiths of the Sierra Nevada and Tehachapi Mountains. Coarse arkosic sediments in the upper Miocene of the western San Joaquin basin, however, may indicate a granitic source area then existed west of the town of Fellows. Other localized areas in the Coast Ranges probably contributed debris into the Tertiary seas.

The Mesozoic basin of deposition covered a greater area than just the Great Valley trough, as Jurassic and Cretaceous rocks are either exposed in or underlie large portions of the region between the valley and the Pacific Ocean. In contrast, the Tertiary basins were much more restricted and distinct; they had relatively narrow and limited connections to the open western sea.

Pre-Uppermost Jurassic Rocks

Except along the west side, Paleozoic and other pre-uppermost Jurassic (pre-Tithonian) rocks are exposed on the highlands along the edges of the Great Valley. These rocks appear to have been uplifted and regionally metamorphosed near the close of the Jurassic with accompanying intrusion of granitic batholiths. Such rocks have been described from outcrops north of the Great Valley in the Redding and Taylorsville area, as well as all along the Sierra Nevada. Exotic blocks of marble and other metamorphic rocks of undetermined age in the San Emigdio Mountains, and in the Temblor Range west of Fellows, may indicate such rocks were formerly also exposed south and southwest of the valley.

Uppermost Jurassic Rocks

Recent geologic studies of the Upper Jurassic and Cretaceous rocks of the Great Valley and environs has led to the conclusion that two entirely different suites of rocks were deposited at the same time in closely adjoining areas (Irwin, 1957). These two units are the Franciscan assemblage and the thick sequence of equivalent clastic rocks that are best exposed along the western edge of the Great Valley. Both the Franciscan and the Great Valley sequence have been proven through fossil evidence to range from Late Jurassic to Late Cretaceous. Consequently, it now appears that any discussion of the stratigraphy of the Great Valley must include the Franciscan not as "basement," but as a eugeosynclinal facies of the miogeosynclinal Great Valley sequence.

Franciscan Formation

The assemblage of rocks generally referred to as Franciscan is widely scattered throughout the west side of the Great Valley from Paskenta south to Parkfield. Isolated intrusions of ultrabasic rocks carrying Franciscan inclusions are present as far south as Cedar Canyon at the S¼ cor. T. 27 S., R. 18 E. This is the southernmost occurrence of Franciscan east of the San Andreas fault, and it is interesting that this locale is nearly as far south as the southward extent of the Great Valley sequence on the west side of the San Joaquin Valley. The two sequences seem to go hand in hand.

The Franciscan comprises a thick sequence of graywacke, dark shale, volcanic rocks of submarine origin (pillow lavas), chert, limestone, and some metamorphic rocks containing minerals of the glaucophane or blueschist facies. Serpentinites are commonly associated with the Franciscan rocks but are excluded from the formation because they appear to be intrusions. The above may appear from the description to be a heterogeneous assemblage, but it is so typical and distinct that most of the Franciscan outcrops are readily recognizable as such.

The base of the Franciscan has never been seen, but it has been inferred that the formation lies on an ultramafic (peridotite) basement. The top of the formation is also subject to question and has not been adequately defined. The contact between the Franciscan and the Great Valley sequence, where exposed, is always a fault so that the relationship between these major units is also difficult to deduce.

The thickness of the Franciscan cannot be calculated by any conventional stratigraphic means owing to its great deformation as well as to the lack of a known base or top. Adding thicknesses of sections that are thought to have been deposited at different times leads one to conclude that a minimum thickness of about 50,000 feet was deposited (Bailey and others, 1964).

The fossils that have been found in the Franciscan give a range in age of from Late Jurassic to Late Cretaceous. Megafossils are very rare, but Foraminifera in limestone and Radiolaria in chert are locally abundant. It is unfortunate that the limestones with their diagnostic microfossils are so small a part of the Franciscan that a great deal of the formation cannot be dated by this means.

The source of most of the Franciscan along the west side of the Great Valley appears not to have been the same (Klamath Mountains and Sierra Nevada) as that of the Great Valley sequence because of the lack of K-feldspar and lithologic dissimilarity of the rocks. It appears likely that, except for older pre-Knoxville Franciscan rocks, the source area was to the west or even from cannibalism of older Franciscan exposures. This latter source area during the Late Upper Cretaceous may have been the emergent central part of the Diablo Range, as shown by a stratigraphic hiatus in the Great Valley sequence in this area.

Knoxville Formation

The oldest known unit that can be considered to be a part of the Great Valley sedimentary sequence is the Knoxville Formation of the Late Jurassic age. The Knoxville, as a formational unit, is based mainly on faunal rather than lithic criteria and most commonly refers to the beds containing the Late Jurassic *Buchia piochii* (White, 1885, p. 19).

The Knoxville crops out along the west side of the Sacramento Valley from just north of Mount Diablo northward to beyond Paskenta to the Elder Creek fault zone. Its eastern limit is buried in the Valley beneath younger rocks. On the west side of the San Joaquin Valley several areas contain limited outcrops of rocks that have been assigned to the Knoxville because of their fossil content. Such areas are found in the Tesla, Pacheco Pass, Priest Valley, and Panoche quadrangles, in the Orchard Peak area, and southward along the crest of the Temblor Range between Bitterwater and Salt Creeks. In these latter areas, however, the Jurassic fossils are either mixed with Cretaceous assemblages or the rocks have been so inadequately studied that stratigraphic conclusions are not certain.

Lithologically, the Knoxville includes all varieties of clastic rocks ranging from shale to conglomerate, but dark-gray to black hackly fracturing shale or mudstone predominates. Massive lenticular conglomerates up to several thousand feet thick are erratically distributed in the mudstone. The sandstones are dark gray and of the graywacke type. The lower part of the section in some places contains volcanic flows, tuff beds, and chert.

The thickest sections of the Knoxville are in the Sacramento Valley, where south of Paskenta it is about 20,000 feet thick. In other places the preserved Knoxville section is less, but as the basal contacts are usually faults it is difficult to determine whether there was actually reduced sedimentation in a southward direction.

The basal contact of the Knoxville is invariably faulted against Franciscan or associated rocks. In most areas the upper contact with overlying Cretaceous rocks is gradational with similar lithologies above and below. At the north end of the Sacramento Valley, however, buried Knoxville rocks are presumed to be overlapped by Lower Cretaceous strata that in outcrop rest on basement.

The depositional environment of the Upper Jurassic rocks was marine but of fairly shallow water, and the limited faunas suggest a turbid, brackish or very cold water ecologic condition. The source of the sediments was apparently from the Klamath Mountains to the north and the Sierra Nevada to the east.

The Knoxville fauna includes common *Buchias* (= *Aucella*), scattered belemnites and ammonites, and rare Foraminifera. The index fossil is *Buchia piochii*.

Cretaceous Rocks

Miogeosynclinal Cretaceous rocks are present throughout the Great Valley as far south as western Kern County. The Early Cretaceous sediments have commonly been assigned to the Shasta Series and Late Cretaceous rocks to the Chico Group. As a rule, lithologic similarities throughout the section have made division into formations difficult so that the separation of the Cretaceous rocks into the Shasta Series and Chico Group has been based mainly on faunal rather than lithologic criteria. Except for areas of limited extent, the most commonly used subdivisions in the subsurface are also based on faunal content.

Lower Cretaceous (Shasta) Rocks

Lower Cretaceous rocks are widely exposed along the western margin of the Great Valley, but they do not extend to the eastern side. The distribution of these rocks in the Sacramento Valley is fairly well documented but in the San Joaquin Valley they have not been as thoroughly studied. The apparent absence, near the base, of faunal zones found elsewhere in this interval, has led some geologists to place an unconformity at the lower boundary of the series, but the generally unfossiliferous character of the lower hundreds of feet of strata could account for this discrep-

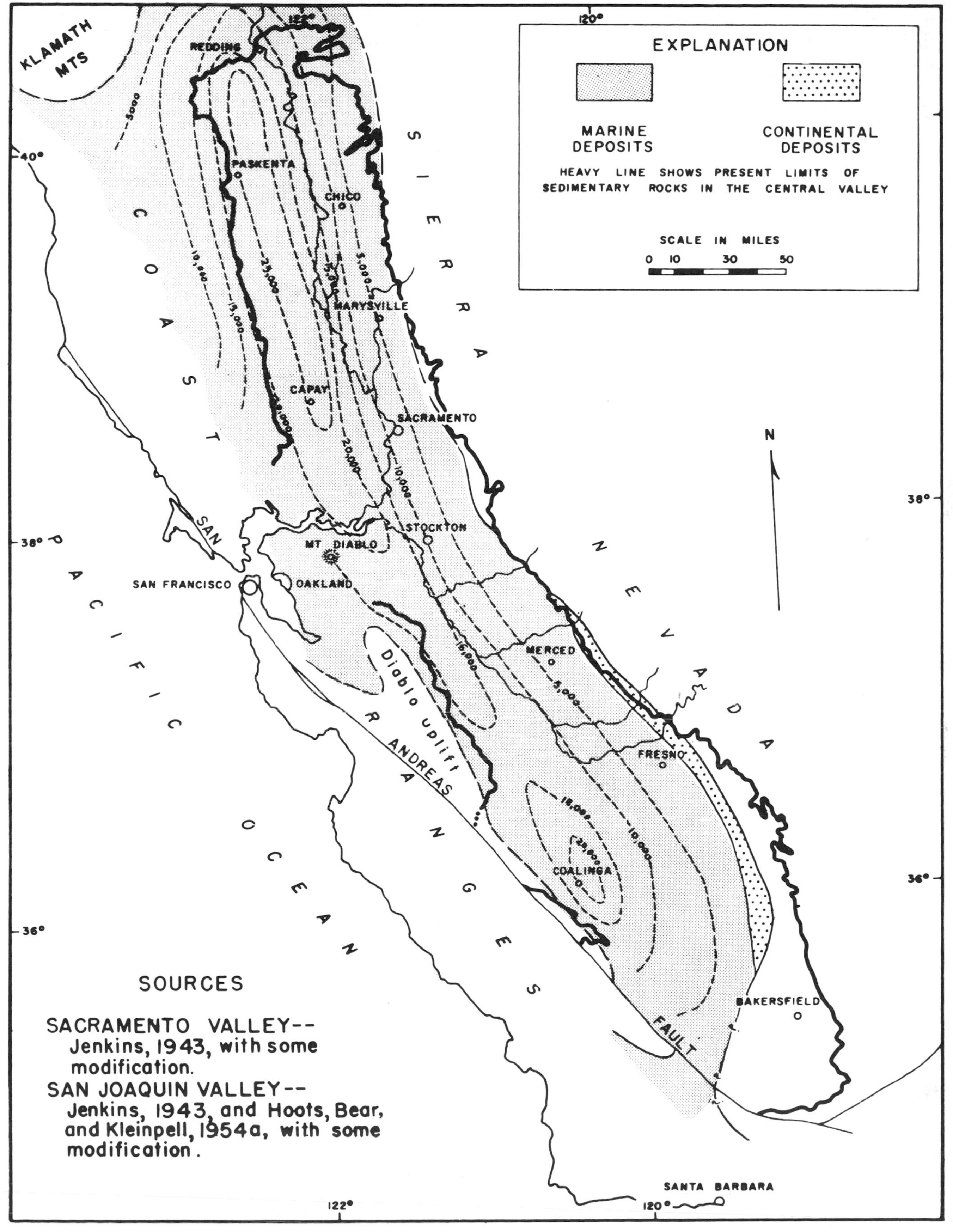

Figure 2. Distribution and thickness of Cretaceous sediments in the Great Valley at the beginning of Tertiary time. After Repenning (1960, fig. 4).

ancy equally well. The consensus of geologists now is that the Lower Cretaceous rocks are conformable at their base with the Knoxville and also at their upper contact with the Chico, except locally at the margins of the depositional basin where Upper Cretaceous rocks overlap the older units.

The Lower Cretaceous Shasta Series consists of over 20,000 feet of mudstone, siltstone, conglomerate, graywacke, and minor limestone. The mudstones cover large areas and are the dominant rock type. The graywacke sandstones occur in limited amounts, whereas the conglomerates attain great thicknesses but are very lenticular. In parts of the section the mudstones and sandstones are rhythmically interbedded, and the sandstones exhibit graded bedding indicative of deposition by turbidity currents.

The Lower Cretaceous sediments locally contain a moderately abundant and diversified megafossil fauna. Although ammonites are generally uncommon, with the help of pelecypods every stage of the Lower Cretaceous has been identified. Foraminifera occur throughout the section but are most numerous in the upper portion where some attempts to use them for zoning have been made.

The distribution of the megafossils, with many more in the northern area, indicates that the depositional environment for the Lower Cretaceous rocks was shallower in the north portion of the Great Valley than in other areas of outcrop. Farther south the predominant fine clastic lithology and the abundance of turbidities points to deposition below wave base for most of the section. One exception to this is the unusually great areal extent of the *Buchia crassicollis* fauna, which is ubiquitous in coarse sandstones or massive conglomerates near the base of the Lower Cretaceous. In the Sacramento Valley the coarser clastics to the north have been cited as an indication that the sediments were derived from a source area to the north or the northeast.

Upper Cretaceous (Chico) Rocks

Upper Cretaceous rocks are much more widespread than the previously described older Mesozoic units. They crop out throughout the west side of the Sacramento Valley and extend eastward beneath younger rocks in the valley to exposures in the eastern foothills where they are much thinner. The type Chico area on the east side of the Sacramento Valley represents only a small part of the Upper Cretaceous exposed on the west side. In the San Joaquin Valley, the Upper Cretaceous rocks crop out through the length of the Diablo Range and extend southward into the northern Temblor Range.

The Upper Cretaceous rocks have been studied in many areas in recent years, and many formations, members, and faunal zones have been described and named. In the Sacramento Valley, Kirby (1943) divided the upper part of the Upper Cretaceous strata exposed on the west side from Putah Creek in Yolo County to Logan Creek in Glenn County into six formations. At the northwest end of the Sacramento Valley, Murphy and Rodda (1960) described the Bald Hills Formation. In the northern San Joaquin Valley, from Mount Diablo southward to Coalinga, the Upper Cretaceous rocks have been subdivided into the Panoche and Moreno Formations. Further subdivision is made in the Coalinga area where two prominent sandstone members separated by a shale in the Panoche have been named in descending order the Brown Mountain Sandstone, Ragged Valley Shale, and Joaquin Ridge Sandstone.

Goudkoff (1945) subdivided the Upper Cretaceous rocks into several microfaunal zones lettered from A to H. These zones have been widely accepted as working units by most geologists dealing with the Cretaceous of the Great Valley, and they provide the basis for most subsurface correlations. Other Upper Cretaceous units, however, have been informally named by geologists working with well bore information in particular areas, and several of these units that are now widely known and used should be formally described and named. These units have such names as Dobbins Shale, Sacramento Shale, Lathrop Sand, Winters Sand, Tracy Sand, Starkey Sand, Delta Shale, Garzas Sand, Kione Sand and others.

The most distinct lithologic break present in rocks exposed along the west side of the Sacramento Valley separates the lower and upper portions of the Upper Cretaceous strata rather than the Lower and Upper Cretaceous beds. The sediments of the lower Upper Cretaceous are lithologically more like the Lower Cretaceous than the overlying Upper Cretaceous beds. Beds that represent the lower part of the Upper Cretaceous can be readily separated and mapped as a unit throughout Colusa, Glenn, Tehama, and Shasta Counties, but south of Colusa County there is no apparent distinction between beds assigned to the lower part of the Upper Cretaceous and those belonging to the Lower Cretaceous. In southern Colusa County, the lower Upper Cretaceous is thickest (about 6,500 feet) and it thins northward. Northeast of Ono in Shasta County it is completely overlapped by the upper Upper Cretaceous strata. As is the case in the Lower Cretaceous, sandstones and conglomerates are important components in the north and shale is predominant to the south. However, in Colusa County, a persistent conglomerate, the "Salt Creek" Conglomerate (Dennings, 1954), marks the base of the lower Upper Cretaceous. Similar though discontinuous conglomerates are found more or less at the same stratigraphic level at the north end of the valley. These conglomerates carry reworked Lower Cretaceous clasts, which is interpreted by some geologists as indicating a period of uplift and erosion in local marginal areas at the end of the Lower Cretaceous.

An upper, major, part of the Upper Cretaceous on the west side of the Sacramento Valley has been well described by Kirby, whose formation—the Venado, Yolo, Sites, Funks, Guinda and Forbes—were deposited during this period. Alternations of sandstone with siltstone and shale comprise these formations, with the finer clastics being slightly predominant. Conglomerates are much less abundant than in the underlying older Cretaceous sequence, and most of those present are in the lowermost unit, the Venado Formation. Eastward across the Sacramento Valley equivalents of the Venado, Yolo, and Sites Formations are overlapped by the younger formations. No rocks older than Venado have been penetrated by wells in the alluviated portion of the Sacramento Valley, and no beds younger than Forbes crop out, except at the extreme southern end. The thickest section of strata assigned to the upper part of the Upper Cretaceous is along Putah Creek, on the Solano-Yolo County line, where 15,000 feet are present. Most of the gas produced in the fields recently discovered in the central and west side of the Sacramento Valley comes from lenticular sands equivalent in part to the Forbes Formation.

In the San Joaquin Valley, the Panoche Formation of the type locality (Panoche Hills-Fresno County) has been subdivided into six formations by Payne (1962). His subdivisions in ascending order are the Redil, Benito, Ciervo, Marlife, Television, and Uhalde Formations. They are composed of shale, sandstone, and conglomerate, with shale predominating, and they attain an aggregate thickness of over 22,000 feet. The overlying Moreno Formation consists of about 3,000 feet of interbedded organic shale and fine-grained sandstone, with a sand-shale ratio about 0.12. The contact between the Cretaceous and Tertiary rocks is gradational and has been placed within the Moreno.

The southernmost occurrence of Upper Cretaceous rocks in the Great Valley is at the headwaters of Salt Creek in the SE¼ of T. 29 S., R. 20 E., in western Kern County, where there are exposed interbedded shale and sandstone strata assigned by Dibblee (1962a) to the Panoche. At this point the Panoche is overlapped from the south by Tertiary beds, and its southward subsurface continuation is not known.

Source areas for the Upper Cretaceous rocks in the northern Sacramento Valley have not been positively identified, but the Klamath Mountains and Sierra Nevada are the most likely sources. Undoubtedly the Sierra Nevada also contributed substantially to the sediments deposited during Late Cretaceous time in the southern Sacramento Valley and the northern San Joaquin Valley, but studies of sand distribution in the subsurface of these areas indicate that a western source also existed during certain periods (Callaway, 1964; Hoffman, 1964). The strongest evidence for a western source is the fact that thick sand bodies appear to change facies to shale in an eastward direction. Parallel studies of the clasts and detritus in the west side outcrops have not been definitive enough to establish either a western or eastern source.

Tertiary Rocks

Development of the general form of the Tertiary basins began with tectonic movements near the close of the Late Cretaceous Period. These movements elevated many Coast Range areas, including the Diablo Range adjacent to the northern San Joaquin Valley and the larger regional uplift along the entire west side of the Sacramento Valley. The ancestral Tertiary San Joaquin and Sacramento Basins were thereby brought into being as restricted troughs of deposition lying between the uplifted western Coast Ranges and the eastern Sierra Nevada landmass. In these troughs marine and continental deposition took place throughout the Tertiary Period.

Tertiary rocks, ranging in age from Paleocene to Pliocene and of both marine and continental origin, were continuously deposited at one place or another in the Great Valley. The greatest accumulation of these strata is in the southern San Joaquin Valley, where they are more than 35,000 feet thick. In the Sacramento Valley at least 12,000 feet of Tertiary rocks occur in the southern part, or Delta area. These points of greatest accumulation, and their relationships, indicate that the Tertiary marine rocks were laid down in two separate basins. These basins, the San Joaquin and the Sacramento, were separated by a faulted trans-valley Cretaceous high called the Stockton Arch (Hoots and others, 1954). Northward toward this Stockton Arch the lower Tertiary marine sediments of the San Joaquin Basin appear to thin and in the vicinity of Modesto they are truncated by overlying continental sediments. Because of this truncation one cannot determine whether lower Tertiary sediments were deposited and later eroded from the Stockton Arch or were never deposited there. On the north side of the arch a thick section of marine Tertiary sediments abuts the large fault which marks the north edge of the arch (Am. Assoc. Pet. Geologists, 1958, no. 10), indicating its crest during the lower Tertiary deposition was not in its present position near Stockton but farther south in the vicinity of Modesto. In the Sacramento Basin the Tertiary marine section also thins northward and is overlapped by Pliocene continental sediments north of Chico.

The depositional history in the Great Valley during the Tertiary was very complex. Rapid lateral changes in thickness and lithology are common, and as a result a large number of units have been named, both formally and informally.

Paleocene Rocks

Rocks of Paleocene age are present in both the northern San Joaquin Valley and in the southern Sacramento Valley. In both areas deposition appears to have been continuous from Cretaceous into Paleocene time, and time boundaries do not necessarily coincide with lithologic boundaries.

Formations in the San Joaquin Valley which have been assigned to the Paleocene include the upper part

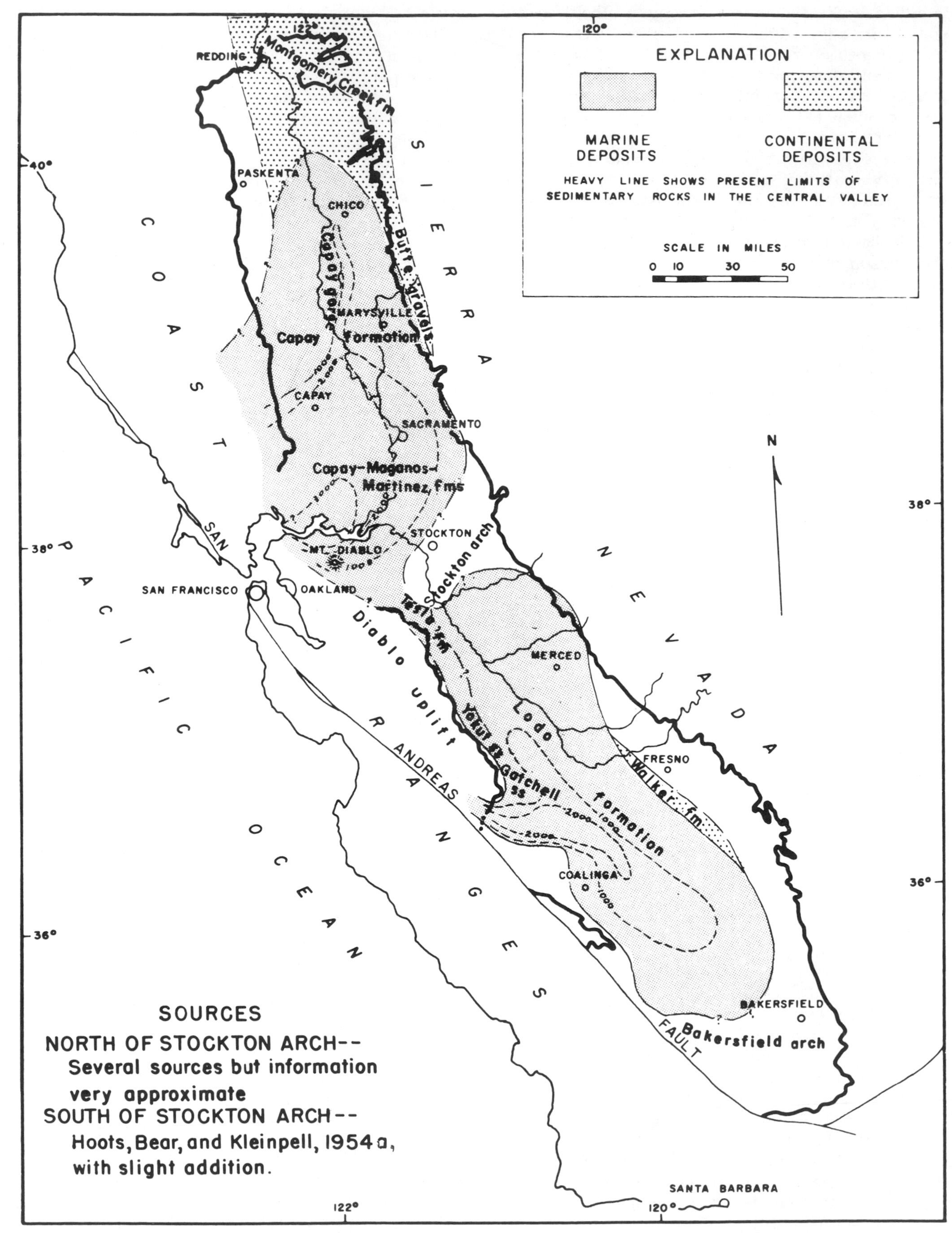

Figure 3. Distribution and thickness of Paleocene and lower Eocene sediments in the Great Valley at the beginning of late Eocene time. After Repenning (1960, fig. 5).

of the Moreno, the Laguna Seca, the lower portion of the Lodo, the Dos Palos, and the Weyant sand of the Helm oil field. They are best developed along the west side of the Valley north of Coalinga. However, in the southern San Joaquin Valley, Paleocene rocks seem to be absent and probably they do not extend south of a line drawn between Coalinga and Hanford. Toward the Stockton Arch in the vicinity of Modesto, Paleocene rocks are truncated by the overlying Miocene-Pliocene continental beds (Hoffmann, 1964). Eastward from the central part of the valley the Paleocene units are truncated by the significant unconformity at the base of upper Eocene.

In the southern Sacramento Valley the Paleocene is represented by the Martinez Formation and the lower portion of the Meganos Formation. The type Martinez contains rocks younger than those considered to be of Paleocene age, but in outcrop in other areas and in the subsurface it has been restricted to the Paleocene. The Martinez pinches out in exposures south of Mount Diablo, but is present in the subsurface to the east and north. At the type section it consists of 2,000 feet of silty claystone with thin interbeds of sandstone and conglomerate. The younger Paleocene rocks generally are assigned to the lower part of the Meganos Formation, which is dominantly sand with shale interbeds. Meganos sediments fill a meandering channel or gorge several hundred feet deep, which has been found by drilling and other methods to extend from the vicinity of the Thornton gas field (Silcox, 1962) westward through the Brentwood oil field.

Recognition of Paleocene strata in many places depends solely on faunal content. In some areas of outcrop megafossils have been used, but in the subsurface Foraminifera are most useful. Laiming (1943) subdivided the Eocene (including the Paleocene) into faunal zones lettered A through E, with the Paleocene section forming his D and E zones.

Eocene Rocks

Eocene rocks of both marine and continental facies are widespread throughout the Great Valley. The thickest deposition took place along the western margin of the basin with greatest accumulation in the Delta area of the Sacramento Valley and at Devils Den in the San Joaquin Valley. Sand distribution patterns suggest that source areas for the Eocene sediments were highlands lying on all sides of the basin.

Lower Eocene Rocks. Lower Eocene rocks in the Sacramento Valley are assigned to the Capay Formation and the upper part of the Meganos Formation; in the San Joaquin Valley they are assigned to the upper part of the Lodo Formation and to the Yokut Sandstone. South of Mount Diablo, Huey (1948) has described the Tesla Formation and assigned it to the lower Eocene. As is the case with the Paleocene, no lower Eocene rocks are present in the southern San Joaquin Valley.

In the Sacramento Valley lower Eocene rocks are exposed along the west side as far north as Chico. In the central Sacramento Valley the lower Eocene is buried, but is known to be largely confined to a deep narrow subsurface gorge which has been named the "Capay Gorge" (Repenning, 1960) or "Princeton Gorge" (Am. Assoc. Pet. Geologists, 1960, no. 13; Safonov, 1962). Although most of the lower Eocene rocks of the Sacramento Valley are referred to the Capay Formation, some in the Mount Diablo area and in the nearby subsurface are assigned to the upper part of the Meganos. The Capay Formation, and the portion of the Meganos assigned to the lower Eocene, is composed of dark shale, which appears to have been deposited in a basin with stagnant bottom conditions. In general, the Capay thickens westward, but throughout most of the southern Sacramento Valley it has a rather uniform thickness of 300 to 400 feet. At the type locality, however, it is about 2,500 feet thick, and it fills the "Capay Gorge" to depths of 2,000 feet.

Lower Eocene strata are discontinuous across the Stockton Arch, but south of it lies the Lodo Formation that is similar lithologically to the Capay but with a much larger content of sand and fewer features suggesting stagnant marine conditions. These differences suggest that the Stockton Arch acted as a barrier between two basins of deposition during the early Eocene.

In the San Joaquin Valley the lower Eocene was deposited as far south as the Bakersfield Arch, but is not found south of it (Hoots and others, 1954). Deposition began with the Lodo Formation, which has been subdivided into the lower Cerros Shale, the intermediate Cantua Sandstone, and the upper Arroyo Hondo Shale. The Lodo has a maximum thickness of 5,000 feet in the west side outcrops but in many areas is less than 1,000 feet thick. In going eastward the Lodo Formation pinches out by thinning from the bottom and truncation at the top. The Yokut Sandstone overlies the Lodo Formation along the western side of the San Joaquin Valley between Coalinga and the Panoche Hills. In outcrop it is usually about 200 feet thick, but it is thicker to the east and south where in the subsurface it is known as the Gatchell Sand.

The Tesla Formation where exposed along the western edge of the northern San Joaquin Valley attains a thickness of 2,000 feet. It is predominantly a sandstone unit and contains megafossils indicating it is equivalent in age to the Lodo and Yokut. Just south of Mount Diablo it is overlapped by Miocene units.

Minor amounts of continental sediments may have been deposited at this time in the eastern San Joaquin Valley forming the lower part of the Walker Formation, and in the northern Sacramento Valley forming the Montgomery Creek Formation.

The early Eocene closed with a marked regression of the sea that resulted from uplifts along the margins of the Great Valley and from elevation and folding

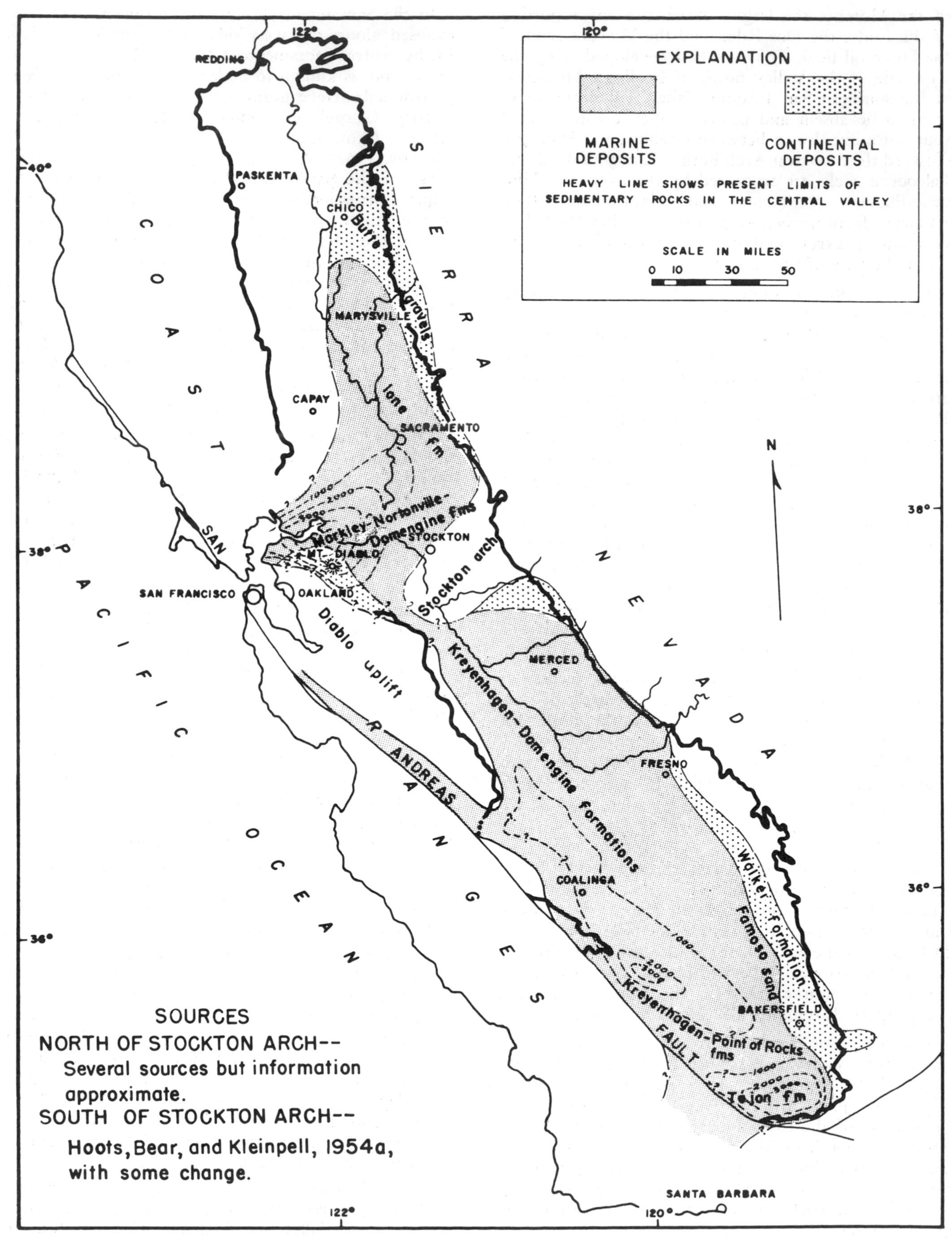

Figure 4. Distribution and thickness of upper Eocene sediments in the Great Valley at the beginning of Oligocene time. After Repenning (1960, fig. 6).

of some previously submerged basin areas in the valley.

Upper Eocene Rocks. Regional subsidence at the beginning of late Eocene time brought about an extensive marine transgression in the San Joaquin Valley and to a lesser extent in the Sacramento Valley, forming a significant unconformity between the lower and upper Eocene. In the San Joaquin Valley, this unconformity is at the base of the Domengine Sandstone, or beneath younger units that overlap the Domengine at the margin of the basin. In the Sacramento Valley, the unconformity is also present at the base of Domengine in the Delta area and is at the base of the Ione Formation to the north and east.

In the San Joaquin Valley the upper Eocene rocks comprise a fairly complete cycle of basin deposition, and the different cycles and lithologic facies in different areas have received numerous names. The earliest transgression of the late Eocene sea deposited in the northern San Joaquin Valley a gritty or conglomeratic sandstone called the Domengine Formation, and at about the same time in the area south of Bakersfield the Uvas Conglomerate Member of the Tejon Formation was deposited. Well bore data suggest that the Domengine and the older portion of the Tejon were separated in the vicinity of Bakersfield by a barrier—the Bakersfield Arch (Hoots and others, 1954). Subsequent Eocene deposition covered the Bakersfield Arch, but differences between the Tejon fauna and the Kreyenhagen fauna in rocks farther north indicate that the depositional environment north and south of the Arch was not the same. The Tejon Formation at the south end of the valley consists of 2,500 to 4,000 feet of sandstone, siltstone, and clay shale believed to have been derived from the nearby San Emigdio and Tehachapi Mountains still farther south. At the same time farther north and west in the San Joaquin Valley the Domengine, Canoas, Point of Rocks and Kreyenhagen Formations were deposited. The Domengine is quite variable in thickness, ranging from a few feet of "grit zone" to 1,000 feet of strata in the Mount Diablo area. An equivalent of the Domengine found in the Kettleman Hills area is the thick (1,000± feet) Avenal Sandstone. The Canoas consists predominantly of clay shale and in certain areas, such as Devils Den, it contains sand lenses of significant thickness. Overlying the Canoas is the Point of Rocks Sand, which has a maximum of several thousand feet. The Kreyenhagen Formation consists of a thick and widespread sequence of shale which crops out along the western side of the San Joaquin Valley from south of Pacheco Pass to the vicinity of Devils Den. It extends in the subsurface southward and eastward towards the central part of the basin. The Kreyenhagen, Point of Rocks, and Canoas, are in reality depositional facies of one another laid down in different environments during the upper Eocene. Farther east these marine units change facies to a near-shore deposit known as the Famosa Sand, which, in turn, grades still farther eastward into nonmarine clays and sands that have been included in the Walker Formation. The Walker, however, encompasses more than just Eocene sediments, as the term has been used to include nonmarine sediments of Eocene to early Miocene age along the east side of the southern San Joaquin Basin (Rudel, 1965). The Kreyenhagen becomes sandier to the north and is correlative with the Nortonville and Markley Formations of the Mount Diablo area.

In the Sacramento Valley the oldest upper Eocene rocks are represented by the Ione Formation, which is present throughout the central part of the valley. In most places the Ione is an unusual nearly massive quartzose sand with a high percentage of interstitial clay, but a shale which overlies the sand in the center of the basin is generally also assigned to the Ione. The formation throughout most of the area is about 200 feet thick, although near Mount Diablo an Ione equivalent, which lies in the Domengine, is about 500 feet thick. The Ione grades northeastward into the Butte Gravels, which overlie the granitic basement along the eastern edge of the valley. Throughout the central and northern part of the Sacramento Valley the Ione represents the last marine invasion, and it is unconformably overlain by Oligocene or Miocene volcanic rocks or nonmarine Pliocene sediments. In the southern part of the Sacramento Valley, however, younger Eocene rocks are marine and include, in ascending order, the Domengine, Nortonville, and Markley Formation. The Domengine Formation in outcrop along the north side of Mount Diablo is about 1,000 feet thick and consists of a lower shale and coal unit, 500 feet of sandstone called "Ione," and 800 feet of upper shaly brown sandstone. In the subsurface of the Delta area, in the southern Sacramento Valley, the lower unit varies in thickness and character but the typical white of the "Ione" sand and brown (greenish in subsurface) of the upper sandstone are prominent. Towards the eastern margin of the basin the Domengine thins and the units lose their individual character. The younger Markley Formation on the north flank of Mount Diablo is composed of a lower 2,000-foot sandstone member, a 700-foot shale unit, and an upper 500-foot sandstone. The intermediate shale unit has been correlated with the Kreyenhagen Shale of the San Joaquin Valley. The basal unit of the Markley has been called the Nortonville Formation, and in the subsurface of the southern Sacramento Valley this is a relatively widespread unit of marine shale locally containing thin sandy beds. A well-documented buried channel—the Markley Gorge —filled with upper Eocene and Oligocene sediments extends in the subsurface from southeast of Marysville beneath Sacramento and continues to the south towards the Rio Vista Gas Field. (Almgren and Schlax, 1957; Safonov, 1962). To the north up the regional gradient of the Sacramento Valley, the channel cuts down into the Upper Cretaceous Starkey Sand but in

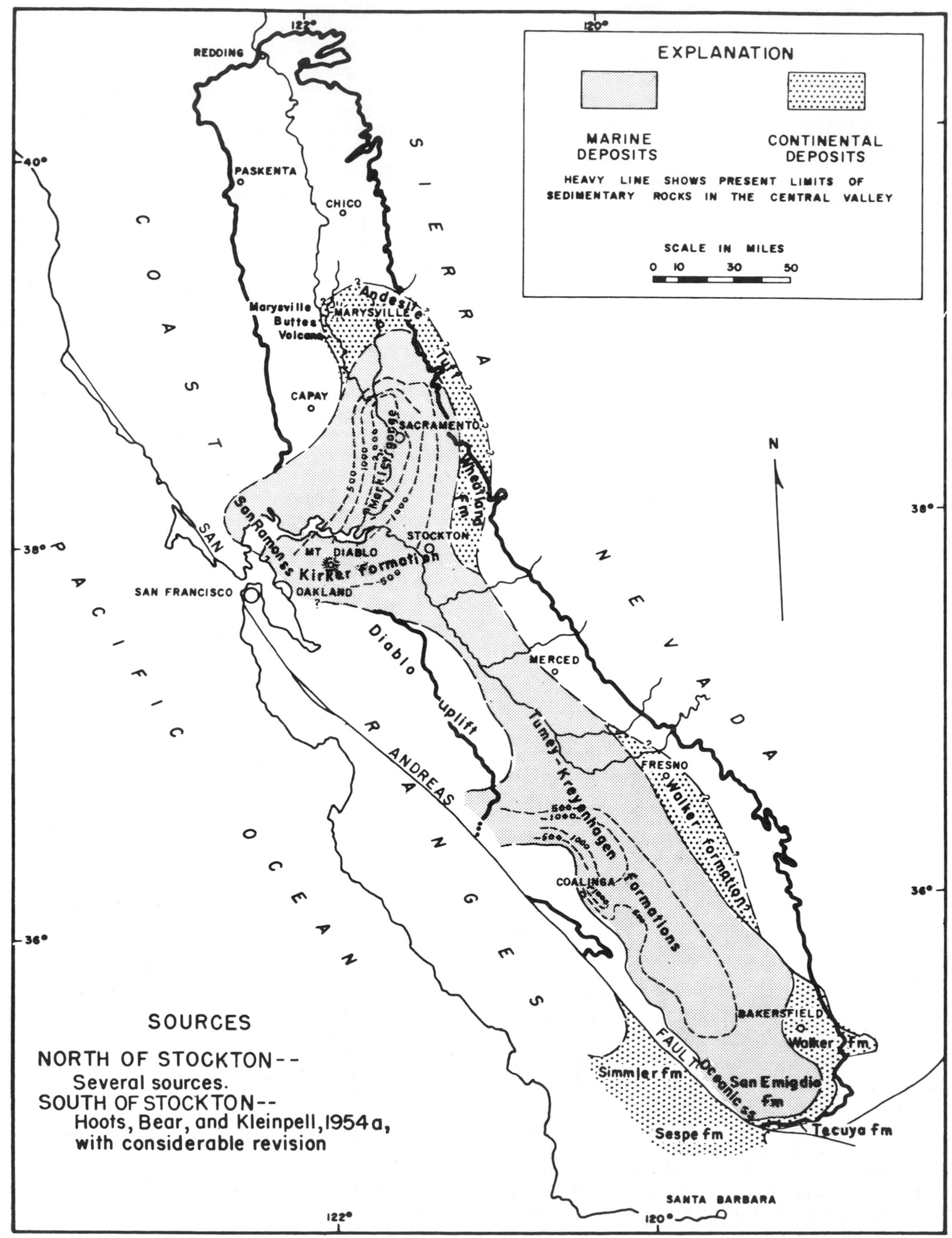

Figure 5. Distribution and thickness of Oligocene sediments in the Great Valley at the beginning of Miocene time. After Repenning (1960, fig. 7).

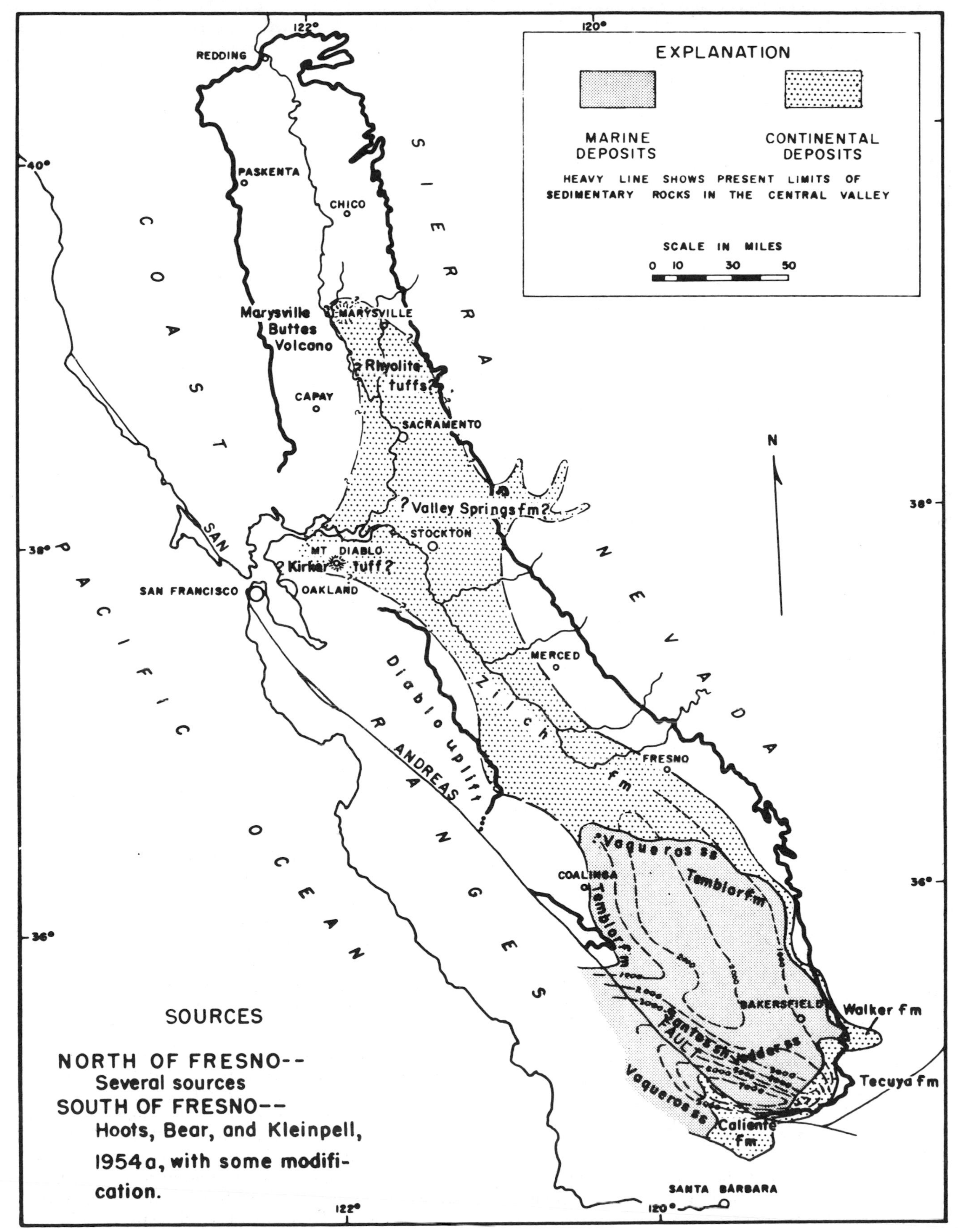

Figure 6. Distribution and thickness of lower Miocene sediments in the Great Valley at the beginning of middle Miocene time. After Repenning (1960, fig. 8).

the vicinity of Rio Vista it only breaches the Capay Shale.

Oligocene Rocks

Regional uplift at the close of Eocene time affected the basin areas of the Great Valley, with the result that Oligocene marine deposits are thinner and more restricted in extent than the Eocene marine rocks.

Oligocene rocks in the San Joaquin Valley includes such marine units as the Tumey Shale (including in certain areas the upper part of the Kreyenhagen Shale) the Oceanic Sand, the San Emigdio Formation and a portion of the Pleito Formation. Continental deposits are represented by the Tecuya and the Walker Formations. The Tumey Shale is present along the western and central parts of the San Joaquin Valley from the Panoche Hills southward to the Bakersfield Arch, and along the west side it includes a basal sandstone which crops out north of Coalinga. Farther south, in the subsurface between Devils Den and McKittrick, a basal sand that has been termed the Oceanic Sand is present. South of the Bakersfield Arch the predominantly marine sandstone and siltstone of the San Emigdio Formation and the lower part of the Pleito Formation were deposited near the present base of the San Emigdio Mountains. At the southeastern extremity of the Valley a series of continental deposits was laid down in late Oligocene and early Miocene time—these rocks have been named the Tecuya Formation. Similar continental rocks, known as the Walker Formation, were deposited farther north along the east side of the San Joaquin Valley.

In the Sacramento Valley, Oligocene rocks are represented by the Kirker Formation along the western margin, and possibly by the Wheatland Formation along the southeastern margin. The San Ramon Sandstone of the Berkeley Hills is of the same age. The Kirker Formation, which was described in the area north of Mount Diablo, consists of 400 feet of sandstone and tuff resting unconformably on underlying rocks. Very little is known of the subsurface distribution as the available information is inadequate to separate it from younger continental sediments lying on it. The Markley Gorge in the subsurface of the Sacramento Valley has been reported to contain marine Oligocene sediments as well as upper Eocene strata.

In nearly all parts of the Great Valley an erosional unconformity separates Oligocene or older units from the overlying Miocene rocks. In the southern San Joaquin Valley, especially in the basinal portions, the discordance is well developed, with marked angularity and truncation of beds north of the Panoche Hills, and on the Stockton Arch pre-Miocene rocks are truncated across the whole width of the valley.

Miocene Rocks

The Miocene rocks of the Great Valley have very complex facies variations, and the stratigraphic nomenclature, both formal and informal, reflects the many lithologic dissimilarities of the different depositional environments. In general, the basin contains nonmarine clays, sands, and conglomerates along its margins, marine near-shore sandstones in the intermediate areas, and marine, deep-water, shales and sandstones in the center.

The seas were confined to the southern San Joaquin Basin during the early Miocene but gradually, probably with some recessions, spread northward so that by late Miocene time marine sediments were being deposited along most of the western side of the Great Valley at least as far north as Vacaville.

The Miocene rocks were derived from the granitic highlands on the east and south and from the Franciscan terranes exposed on the west along the rising Diablo uplift between Coalinga and Mount Diablo. Along the southwest margin of the basin, granitic source areas also appear at times to have been present, perhaps as a result of uplifts in the area west of the San Andreas fault.

Lower Miocene Rocks. Marine sediments of early Miocene age are restricted to the southern San Joaquin Valley where they have been segregated into numerous units. On the west side of the basin these units have been named, in ascending order, Salt Creek Shale, Phacoides Sand, Lower Santos Shale, Agua Sand, Upper Santos Shale, Carneros Sand, and Media Shale. The east side equivalents are the Vedder Formation, Pyramid Hill Sand, Jewett Silt, Freeman Silt, and the lower portion of the Olcese Sand. In the Coalinga-Kettleman Hills area the lower Miocene marine rocks have been subdivided more loosely into the "Vaqueros" and lower "Temblor."

Nonmarine lower Miocene rocks are represented along the south and southeast margin of the San Joaquin basin by the upper part of the Tecuya and Walker Formations, and north of Coalinga continental deposits that have been named the Zilch Formation, or simply "continental Miocene," probably include some lower Miocene rocks. In the southern Sacramento Valley such units as the Valley Springs Formation and the Kirker Tuff may include deposits of early Miocene age.

Uplift of the Tehachapi-San Emigdio area in early Miocene was accompanied by volcanism that laid down basalt and dacite flows at the south end of the valley. Ash beds and bentonites in the Freeman Silt and at the top of the Vedder also reflect volcanism in the lower Miocene.

Unless one calls upon large lateral displacement along the San Andreas fault, it is difficult to determine through what inlet the seas entered the San Joaquin Basin during lower Miocene time. No marine lower Miocene rocks occur anywhere immediately west of the San Andreas fault opposite the San Joaquin marine basin. This relationship of a thick marine section of rocks east of the San Andreas fault adjacent to a nonmarine section west of the fault continues to

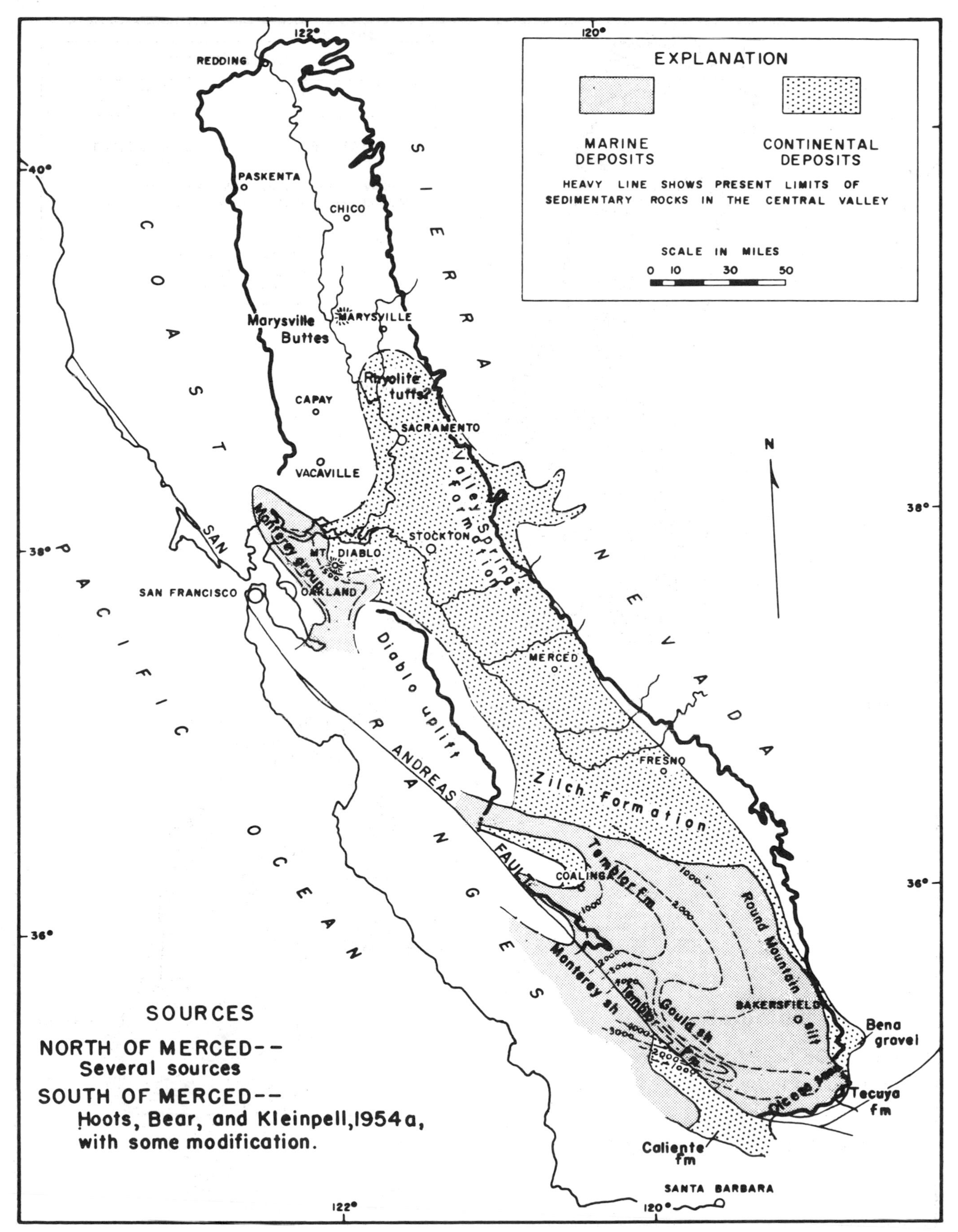

Figure 7. Distribution and thickness of middle Miocene sediments in the Great Valley at the beginning of late Miocene time. After Repenning (1960, fig. 9).

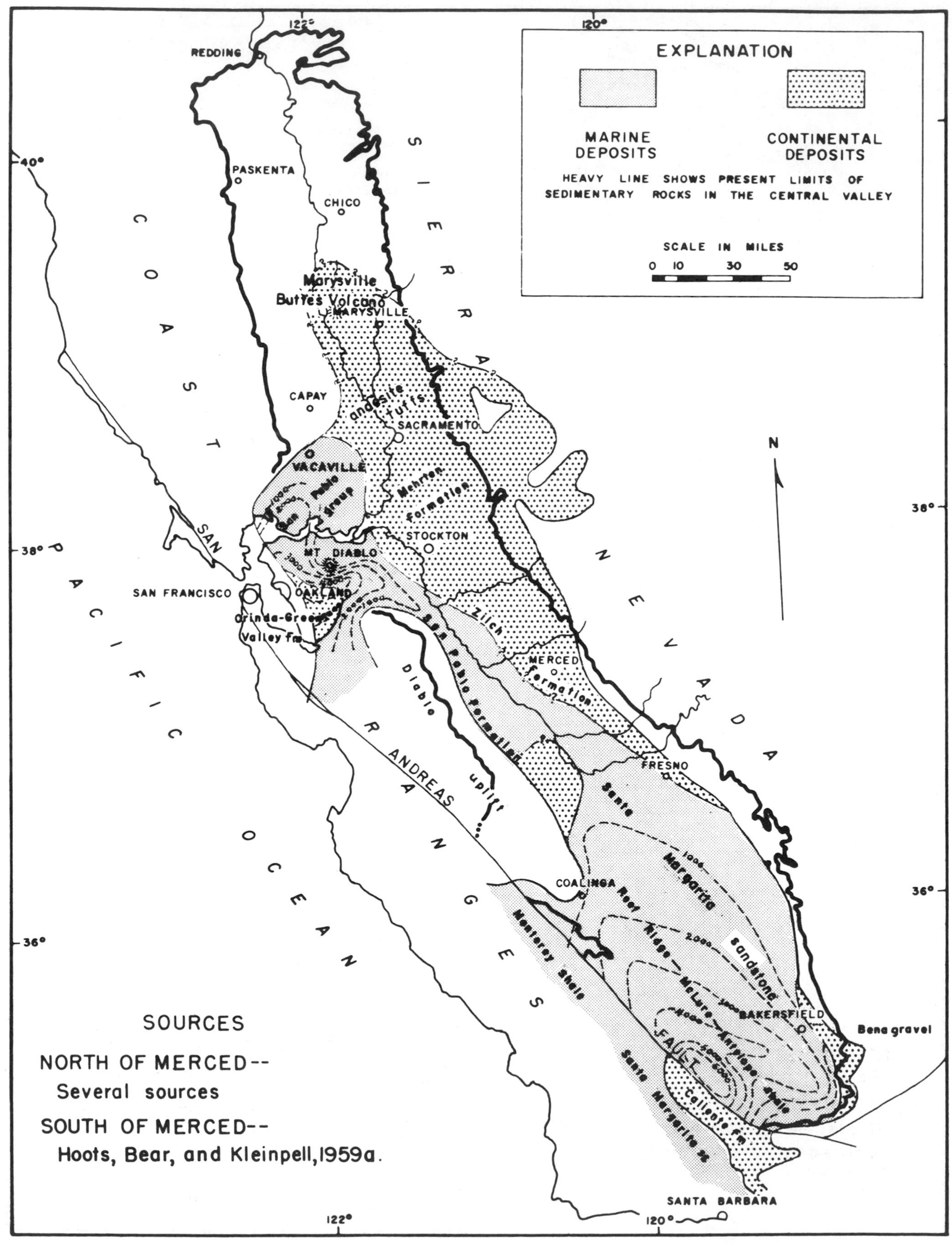

Figure 8. Distribution and thickness of upper Miocene sediments in the Great Valley at the beginning of Pliocene time. After Repenning (1960, fig. 10).

show up on paleogeographic maps drawn to represent various intervals throughout the remainder of the Miocene.

The thickest sequence of lower Miocene rocks in the Great Valley lies in the southwest portion of the basin where several thousand feet of marine sediments were deposited. Pulsating movements of the sea in the area of the San Joaquin Basin during lower Miocene time are suggested by basal conglomerates (or "grits") at the base of the Salt Creek Shale (base of Miocene), at the base of the Phacoides Sand, and at the base of several units of the Vedder Sand.

Middle Miocene Rocks. Deposition of marine rocks in the Great Valley in the middle Miocene, as in lower Miocene time, was limited to the southern half of the San Joaquin Basin. On the west side of the Valley, these rocks have been assigned in ascending order to the Button Bed Sand, Gould Shale, and Devilwater Silt. On the east side, equivalent marine rocks are encompassed in the Olcese Sand and Round Mountain Silt. In the Coalinga-Kettleman Hills area the middle Miocene is represented by the upper part of the Temblor Formation. To subdivide the marine middle Miocene rocks into more discreet and local units, especially in the subsurface, many informal names are commonly used by petroleum geologists. In this category fall such names as Kettleman sand, Belridge sand, Nozu sand, Reserve sand, Upper and Lower Variegated, Big Blue, and lower Maricopa shale.

A long, narrow trough which was the site of deposition of the marine Temblor Formation occupied the area of the present Vallecitos syncline northwest of Coalinga (Flynn, 1963). This trough may have provided the outlet from the San Joaquin Basin to the western sea.

Nonmarine sediments of considerable thickness were also deposited in the Great Valley during middle Miocene time. Areas of extensive nonmarine deposition occur throughout the basin north of Coalinga and along its eastern and southeastern margins. These central valley terrestrial beds have been called the Zilch Formation or "continental Miocene". At the southern extremity of the valley terrestrial deposits of middle Miocene age have been assigned to the upper portion of the Tecuya Formation, and north of the White Wolf fault and south of the Kern River similar rocks comprise the Bena Gravels.

Middle Miocene was a time of local uplifts along the margins of the San Joaquin Basin. Evidence for this is found in the coarse Franciscan detritus found in the Big Blue and Upper and Lower Variegated Members of the Temblor Formation in the Coalinga area, and in the presence of nonmarine or very coarse deposits in the middle Olcese Sand and Round Mountain Siltstone (Bena fanglomerate lenses).

As the middle Miocene seas were restricted to the southern end of the Great Valley only nonmarine deposits, assigned to the Valley Springs Formation, are present in the Sacramento Valley. West of Mount Diablo there are marine sands and shales of the Monterey group but they are not Great Valley deposits.

The thickness of middle Miocene rocks varies to a great degree, depending on their position in the basin. The greatest accumulation appears to be in the northern Temblor Range, where the marine sediments are more than 4,000 feet thick (Seiden, 1964).

Upper Miocene Rocks. Deposition of marine rocks was more widespread during late Miocene time than earlier in the Miocene, though the distribution and persistency of the sea still favored the southern San Joaquin Valley, where more than 6,000 feet of strata were deposited.

On the west side of the basin, the marine units of the upper Miocene are primarily shale and have been called the Reef Ridge, McLure, and Antelope Shales. Locally on the west side very contrasting facies of shale, diatomite, chert, and even conglomerate were deposited adjacent to, and interspersed with, each other. Toward the east a great portion of the marine upper Miocene is taken up by a subsurface wedge of sand, which has been termed the Stevens Sand. Sands are also present in local channels in the subsurface near the west side of the basin, and have received such local names as Leuthholtz, "555", and Asphalto Sands. A similar environment appears to be present along the eastern limit of the Stevens Sand deposition, which was perhaps at the hinge line of the basin, where sands at the Rosedale and Bellevue oil fields have long, narrow trends. East of the deep-water Stevens Sand province, marine rocks are represented by the widespread Santa Margarita sand of shallow marine origin. Other local marine upper Miocene units in the subsurface on the east side of the San Joaquin Basin have been named Fruitvale Shale and Wicker Sand.

Towards the eastern margin of the San Joaquin Basin, the Santa Margarita sand grades into the upper portion of the nonmarine Bena Gravels. Northward it appears to interfinger with the nonmarine Zilch Formation. Farther north, on the west side of the San Joaquin Valley and in the southwestern Sacramento Valley, the marine San Pablo Group appears to be the equivalent of the Santa Margarita. Whether or not continuous upper Miocene marine sediments exist in the subsurface from Mount Diablo to Fresno is not yet determined.

Nonmarine rocks of probable late Miocene age are extensive on the east side of the northern San Joaquin Valley and in the Sacramento Valley as far north as Marysville. In this area they have been assigned to the Mehrten and Zilch Formations, but commonly they are simply referred to as "continental Miocene" by petroleum geologists. Other thick nonmarine deposits of coarse detritus are exposed in the Caliente Creek drainage of the southeastern San Joaquin Valley and have been described and named the Bena Gravels.

A substantial part of the eastern and southern San Joaquin Valley received an accumulation of nonmarine clay and sand during the late Miocene; these rocks comprise the lower part of the Chanac Formation. This formation is one manifestation of the orogeny that elevated the east side of the San Joaquin Valley near the end of Miocene time. By means of the uplifts that came into being during this time, the present general structural configuration of the Great Valley Basin was formed.

Pliocene Rocks

The tectonic movements which began in the upper Miocene continued into the Pliocene and resulted in considerable erosion, particularly along the edges of the San Joaquin Valley. As a result, Pliocene deposits of continental origin are found in all parts of the Valley. Regional uplifting in most of the Valley continued throughout Pliocene time, and marine waters were able to invade only the southern and western portions of the San Joaquin Basin.

Marine rocks of the lower and middle Pliocene have been assigned to the Etchegoin Formation, although in the vicinity of Coalinga the lower portion of the undifferentiated Etchegoin is called the Jacalitos Formation. The most extensive marine member of the Etchegoin is the Macoma Claystone, a subsurface unit. The Macoma Claystone extends well east of the main mass of the Etchegoin, and it separates the nonmarine Chanac Formation from the overlying terrestrial Kern River Formation (Am. Assoc. Pet. Geologists, 1957, No. 8).

The upper portion of the marine Pliocene strata has been named the San Joaquin Formation, which is best developed in the deepest portion of the San Joaquin embayment. The San Joaquin Formation represents the last stand of marine waters in the Great Valley.

Marine Pliocene rocks attain a gross thickness of somewhat over 5,000 feet and are composed of claystone, sandstone, and conglomerates.

The extensive continental deposits of the Pliocene on the east side of the San Joaquin Valley have been assigned to the Chanac and Kern River Formations and those in the western San Joaquin Valley are called the Tulare Formation. In the northern San Joaquin Valley the Pliocene rocks include parts of the Mehrten and Laguna Formations. Farther north, in the Sacramento Valley, the nonmarine Pliocene rocks have been assigned to the Tehama Formation. In the western part of the Sacramento Valley, north of Mount Diablo, continental beds equivalent to the Laguna Formation have been called the Wolfskill Formation. The Wolfskill overlies a lower Pliocene tuff called the Pinole or Lawlor Tuff. Further north, a similar tuff called the Nomlaki Tuff occurs near the base of the Tehama Formation.

The nonmarine Pliocene rocks vary considerably in lithology, depending on the local source area. As an example, beds equivalent to the Tehama have been called the Tuscan Formation where they are largely derived from a volcanic terrain. In general the lithology of these continental deposits consist of claystones, sandstones, and conglomerates, with the coarser units becoming more common as source areas are approached. The greatest thickness of nonmarine Pliocene occurs in the Tehama where a thickness of about 2,000 feet is present.

Pleistocene and Recent Rocks

Rocks of Pleistocene and Recent age occur throughout the Great Valley. They are all continental in origin and generally grade downward into similar Pliocene units. They are discussed in greater detail in this bulletin in the following article by J. F. Poland and R. E. Evenson.

At the northern extremity of the valley a coarse fluvial unit of predominant red color, called the Red Bluff Formation, attains a thickness of about 100 feet. In the southern part of the valley the nonmarine Pleistocene sediments have been assigned to either the Tulare Formation on the west side or to the Kern River Formation on the east. Both the Tulare and Kern River Formations have lithologies indicating local sources. It is common for the Tulare to be composed of shale-pebble conglomerates derived from the uplifted Temblor Range, and the equivalent Kern River Formation is generally formed of granitic sands and conglomerates derived from erosion of the Sierra Nevada. The Tulare and Kern River Formations attain thicknesses of several thousand feet, with the maximum being about 5,000 feet on the downthrown side of the White Wolf fault south of the Bakersfield Arch.

Recent alluvium and lake deposits cover most of the central lower parts of the present Great Valley.

IGNEOUS ACTIVITY

The areas of igneous activity in the Great Valley of California are, curiously enough, at its two extremities. In the northern Sacramento Valley, volcanic rocks are present at the surface and in the subsurface from south of the Marysville Buttes north to the latitude of Chico. At the south end of the San Joaquin Valley, volcanic flows are found in surface and subsurface of the Tejon embayment, and in the outcrop north of the White Wolf fault in the vicinity of Bena.

The Marysville Buttes, which form an isolated topographic prominence about 2,000 feet high northeast of the town of Marysville, are the most prominent igneous feature in the Great Valley. The Buttes are circular in shape, about 10 miles in diameter, and their topography reflects their geology. They consist of a central core of andesite porphyry and tuff surrounded by a ring of sediments, and these sediments are embraced in turn by a ring of andesite tuff and breccia which extends to the Valley alluvium. Intrusions of rhyolite porphyry are scattered through the sediments and in the central core. The porphyries were the first volcanic rocks emplaced and appear to have been injected at a slow rate; the final igneous activity, however, was an explosive phase forming a

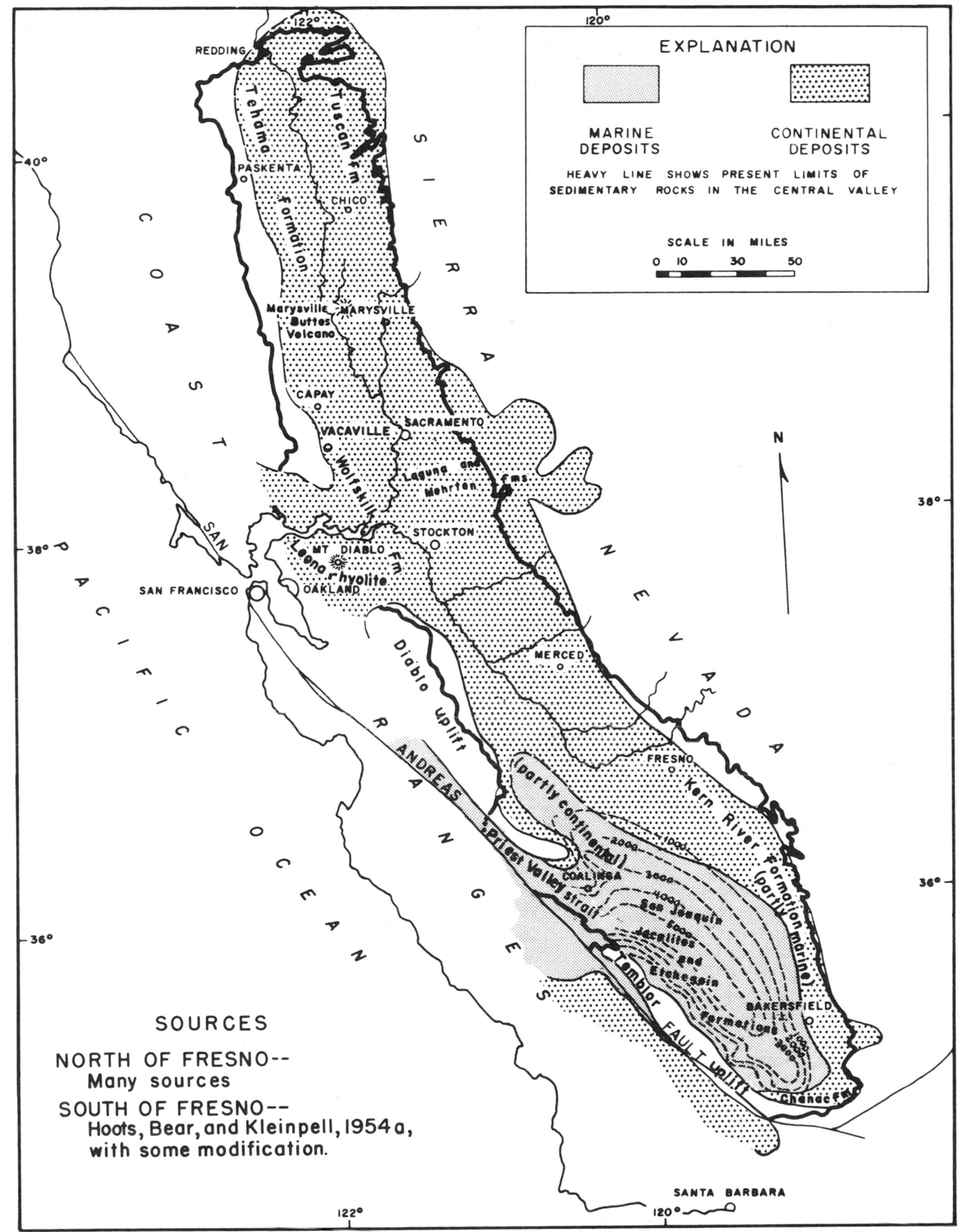

Figure 9. Distribution and thickness of Pliocene sediments in the Great Valley at the beginning of Pleistocene time. After Repenning (1960, fig. 11).

volcano one mile in diameter which ejected fragments of andesite varying in size from boulders to fine-grained tuff. Subsurface information shows that the volcanic rocks have been intruded into Upper Cretaceous and Eocene sediments as well as into the lower part of the Tehama Formation, thus fixing the time of the intrusion.

North of the Marysville Buttes, volcanic flows of basalt are common, and they generally occur near or at the base of the Tehama Formation.

The volcanic rocks at the south end of the San Joaquin Valley consist of basalt and dacite flows. These rocks are enclosed within lower Miocene sediments and most appear to have been submarine flows.

STRUCTURE

Structurally, the Great Valley of California is a large, elongate, northwest trending, asymmetric trough. This trough has a long stable eastern shelf, which is supported by the buried west-dipping Sierran slope, and it has a short western flank, which is formed by the steep upturned edges of the basin sediments.

Four major periods of tectonism are recorded in the sedimentary section of the Great Valley. These are the post-Moreno, the pre-Domengine, the pre-Pliocene, and the mid-Pleistocene. These periods of maximum structural activity are responsible for the major changes in the configuration of the basin throughout geologic time. The most severe period of deformation was in the mid-Pleistocene, and it brought to a climax the structural evolution of the basin.

The Great Valley geosyncline with its pronounced regional southward tilt is significantly interrupted by two cross-valley faults. These major structures, the Stockton fault and the White Wolf fault, are associated with the cross-valley structural highs known as the Stockton Arch and the Bakersfield Arch.

The Stockton Arch, located in the central portion of the basin, extends from the Sierran slope across to the Diablo uplift of the western flank. The high appears to have been formed by Eocene time, though uplift may have continued into the Miocene. Most of the present elevation of the arch appears to be due to upward movements on the south side of the Stockton fault, though stratigraphic evidence suggests that, when the arch first began, its axis lay further south in the vicinity of Modesto.

The Bakersfield Arch, in the southern end of the basin, also extends from the Sierran slope westward, but appears to terminate near the axis of the geosyncline instead of continuing on to the western flank. This arch apparently formed the southern edge of the valley depositional basin until middle Eocene time. The barrier was then overwhelmed and the Eocene seas spilled into the sub-basin that is sometimes called the Tejon embayment south of the White Wolf fault.

The Tejon embayment south of the Bakersfield Arch, and in particular south of the White Wolf fault, has been a somewhat distinct structural unit through geologic time and has been thought by some geologists to be more closely related to a group of intermontane basins formed during the lower Tertiary to the west in the adjacent Coast Ranges. Evidence for this is found in the similarity of sections in the Oligocene and Miocene, for example, in the red bed sequences in the Tecuya Formation of the valley and the Sespe Formation of the Coast Ranges. The Coast Range basins, west of the San Andreas fault, are thought to have been offset northward along the fault so far that they are no longer adjacent to the valley basin. More detailed structural and stratigraphic studies are needed, however, before such a hypothesis can be regarded as proven.

Other subsidiary basins along the Great Valley trough also complicate the concept of a simple southerly tilted basin. In the Sacramento part of the trough, for example, such basins are in the vicinity of Colusa and between Rio Vista and the Kirby Hills.

The mid-Pleistocene orogeny formed many flexures throughout the Great Valley, and it also rejuvenated many of the folds that had formed during previous orogenic periods. Much of the disturbance took place along the short mobile western flank, where numerous folds and faults are now particularly evident. Many of these flexures are asymmetric and associated with compressional faults of the reverse type. The magnitude of the folds decreased eastward but was still strong enough to cause the formation of lines of folding out to, and even beyond, the basin axis. The eastern shelf is relatively free of folds, and faulting in this region is of the normal tensional type.

The western mobile flank flexures are too numerous to enumerate, but because of their economic importance those of the Central Valley will be summarized. Many of these folds are evident at the surface, but because of the extensive alluvium cover, many other flexures are known only from seismic data and well bore information. In the Sacramento Valley significant anticlinal trends are found at Corning, Willows-Beehive Bend, Sites, Rumsey Hills, Wilbur Springs, Dunnigan Hills, Lodi-Thornton, Rio Vista, and McDonald-Roberts Island. In the San Joaquin Valley, most of the large anticlines are in the southern portion; among these are the Coalinga Nose-Kettleman Hills-Lost Hills Trend, North and South Belridge, Salt Creek-Cymric-McKittrick Front Trend, Elk Hills, Buena Vista Hills, Wheeler Ridge, Coles Levee, Ten Sections, and Greeley-Rio Bravo.

Faults are numerous in the Great Valley. In the Sacramento Valley the most prominent faults are those (1) associated with the Willows-Beehive Bend trend, (2) reverse faults at the north flank of Dunnigan Hills, (3) faults north of Mount Diablo near Willow Pass, and (4) the Midland fault which traverses the Rio Vista gas field. This latter fault was active during Eocene time as demonstrated by the different thickness of equivalent rock units on each side of it. In the San

Photo 1. Natural gas well being drilled at Marysville Buttes. *Photo by Edmund W. Kiessling.*

Joaquin Valley, faults with considerable displacement are common. The Stockton and White Wolf faults have already been mentioned. In the reverse or thrust category are such faults as (1) the McKittrick thrust in western Kern County, (2) the Pleito thrust in the Tejon embayment, and (3) the Edison fault in the outcrop southeast of Bakersfield. Large normal faults which bear mentioning are the Kern Gorge fault and its associated echelon members the Round Mountain and Mount Poso faults; also deserving mention are the group of faults in the Edison and Mountain View oil fields, some of which appear to cut only middle Miocene and older sediments while others are present only in the Pliocene and upper Miocene.

Tectonic activity, though reaching its climax in the mid-Pleistocene, is still continuing in the Great Valley as borne out by seismic disturbances, the most recent of which was the destructive earthquake of 1952 that originated along the White Wolf fault.

ECONOMIC GEOLOGY

The mineral economic resources of the Great Valley are summarized in this bulletin in an article prepared by Earl W. Hart and will be only commented upon here. Briefly the highlands on each side of the basin have yielded millions of dollars from the metallic minerals recovered; prime examples, of course, are the gold of the Sierra Nevada and the mercury associated with the Franciscan in the Coast Ranges. In the Great Valley itself, although these minerals are also found, the mineral commodities of greatest value are oil and gas, water, and gravel deposits.

The sedimentary section of the Great Valley has been found to be an enormous storehouse for oil and gas. The Sacramento Valley has been found lacking in any important oil resources, but gas in economic quantities has been produced from at least 25 fields. Much of this gas has been reservoired in rocks of Eocene and Late Cretaceous age. In the San Joaquin Valley, both oil and gas are prevalent, though the oil resources are concentrated in the central and southern part. Oil has been found, in significant amounts, as far north as the latitude of Fresno; north of there the hydrocarbon accumulations are gas. The billions of barrels of oil found in the San Joaquin Valley have been reservoired in sediments ranging in age from Late Cretaceous to Pleistocene; however, the majority have been produced from Miocene and Pilocene rocks. Of the dry gas produced in the San Joaquin Valley most in the southern end comes from Pliocene rocks and in the northern portion most is from Upper Cretaceous rocks. Several theories have been advanced to explain why oil is found chiefly in the San Joaquin Valley and dry gas occurs largely in the Sacramento Valley. It is likely that the distribution is related to the source material in the sediments; certainly, the organic content of the Eocene and Cretaceous shales of the Sacramento is very different from the Miocene and Pliocene shales of the San Joaquin.

The water resources of the Great Valley are becoming more and more important as the population increases at an accelerated rate. The available waters of the valley come from two main sources: (1) the numerous streams flowing westward from the Sierra Nevada, and (2) the ground-water reservoirs. Most of the ground-water resources exist in the younger portion of the sedimentary column—the Pliocene, Pleistocene, and Recent alluvium. The following article in this bulletin by Poland and Evenson presents a more thorough treatment of this subject.

Again, chiefly as a result of the increase in population, the sand and gravel deposits suitable for road building and construction are becoming more and more important. The broad expanses of stream gravels along the major streams flowing from both sides of the valley offer an almost unlimited source. Their economic utilization usually is dependent only on the distance to the market.

REFERENCES

Almgren, A. A., and Schlax, W. N., Jr., 1957, Post-Eocene age of "Markley Gorge" fill, Sacramento Valley, California: Am. Assoc. Petroleum Geologists Bull., v. 41, no. 2, p. 326–330.

American Association of Petroleum Geologists, 1951–1960, Correlation sections * * * [San Joaquin Valley and Sacramento Valley] California: Am. Assoc. Petroleum Geologists, Pacific Sec., nos. 1, 6, 8, 9, 10, 11, and 13.

Bailey, E. H., and Irwin, W. P., 1959, K-feldspar content of Jurassic and Cretaceous graywackes of the northern Coast Ranges and Sacramento Valley, California: Am. Assoc. Petroleum Geologists Bull., v. 43, no. 12, p. 2797–2809.

Bailey, E. H., Irwin, W. P., and Jones, D. L., 1964, Franciscan and related rocks and their significance in the geology of western California: California Div. Mines and Geology Bull. 183, 177 p.

Callaway, D. C., 1964, Distribution of uppermost Cretaceous sands in the Sacramento-northern San Joaquin Basin of California: San Joaquin Geol. Soc., Selected Papers, v. 2, p. 5–18.

Chuber, Stewart, 1962, Late Mesozoic stratigraphy of the Sacramento Valley [California]: San Joaquin Geol. Soc., Selected Papers, v. 1, p. 3–16.

Cross, R. K., 1962, Geology of the Carrizo-Cuyama basin, *in* Guidebook, Geology of Carrizo Plains and San Andreas fault: San Joaquin Geol. Soc. and Am. Assoc. Petroleum Geologists-Soc. Econ. Paleontologists and Mineralogists, Pacific Sec. [field trip], 1962, p. 27–35.

Dibblee, T. W., Jr., 1961a, Geologic structure of the San Emigdio Mountains, Kern County, California: Soc. Econ. Paleontologists and Mineralogists-Soc. Econ. Geologists-Am. Assoc. Petroleum Geologists, Pacific Sec., and San Joaquin Geol. Soc., Guidebook, Spring field trip, 1961, p. 2–5.

—— 1961b, Geologic map, San Emigdio Mountains [California]: Soc. Econ. Paleontologists and Mineralogists-Soc. Econ. Geologists-Am. Assoc. Petroleum Geologists, Pacific Sec., and San Joaquin Geol. Soc., Guidebook, Spring field trip, 1961, in pocket.

—— 1962a, Displacements on the San Andreas rift zone and related structures in Carrizo Plain and vicinity [California], *in* Guidebook, Geology of Carrizo Plains and San Andreas fault: San Joaquin Geol. Soc. and Am. Assoc. Petroleum Geologists-Soc. Econ. Paleontologists and Mineralogists, Pacific Sec. [field trip], 1962, p. 5–12.

—— 1962b, Geologic map of Caliente and Temblor Ranges, San Luis Obispo and Kern Counties, California, *in* Guidebook, Geology of Carrizo Plains and San Andreas fault: San Joaquin Geol. Soc. and Am. Assoc. Petroleum Geologists-Soc. Econ. Paleontologists and Mineralogists, Pacific Sec. [field trip], 1962, in pocket.

Dibblee, T. W., Jr., Bruer, W. G., Hackel, O., and Warne, W. H., 1965, Geologic map of the southeastern San Joaquin Valley-Kern River to Grapevine Canyon, *in* Geology of southeastern San Joaquin Valley, California: Am. Assoc. Petroleum Geologists-Soc. Econ. Geologists-Soc. Econ. Paleontologists and Mineralogists, Pacific Sec., Guidebook, p. 7.

Durham, J. W., 1962, The late Mesozoic of central California: California Div. Mines and Geology Bull. 181, p. 31–38.

Flynn, D. B., 1963, The San Benito-Waltham Canyon trough—possible oil province?, *in* Guidebook to the geology of Salinas Valley and the San Andreas fault: Am. Assoc. Petroleum Geologists-Soc. Econ. Paleontologists and Mineralogists, Pacific Sec., Ann. Spring field trip, 1963, p. 27–33.

Goudkoff, P. P., 1945, Stratigraphic relations of Upper Cretaceous in Great Valley, California: Am. Assoc. Petroleum Geologists Bull., v. 29, no. 7, p. 956–1007.

Gribi, E. A., Jr., 1963, The Salinas basin oil province, *in* Guidebook to the geology of Salinas Valley and the San Andreas fault: Am. Assoc. Petroleum Geologists-Soc. Econ. Paleontologists and Mineralogists, Pacific Sec., Ann. Spring field trip, 1963, p. 16–27.

Hoffman, R. D., 1964, Geology of the northern San Joaquin Valley [California]: San Joaquin Geol. Soc., Selected Papers, v. 2, p. 30–45.

Hoots, H. W., Bear, T. L., and Kleinpell, W. D., 1954, Geologic summary of the San Joaquin Valley, California, [pt.] 8 *in* Chap. 2 of Jahns, R. H., ed., Geology of southern California: California Div. Mines Bull. 170, p. 113–129.

Huey, A. S., 1948, Geology of the Tesla quadrangle, California: California Div. Mines Bull. 140, 75 p.

Irwin, W. P., 1957, Franciscan group in Coast Ranges and its equivalents in Sacramento Valley, California: Am. Assoc. Petroleum Geologists Bull., v. 4, no. 10, p. 2284–2297.

Kirby, J. M., 1943, Upper Cretaceous stratigraphy of the west side of Sacramento Valley south of Willows, Glenn County, California: Am. Assoc. Petroleum Geologists Bull., v. 27, no. 3, p. 270–305.

Lachenbruch, M. C., 1962, Geology of the west side of the Sacramento Valley, California: California Div. Mines and Geology Bull. 181, p. 53–66.

Laiming, Boris, 1943, Eocene foraminiferal correlations in California: California Div. Mines Bull. 118, p. 193–198.

Murphy, M. A., and Rodda, P. V., 1960, Mollusca of the Cretaceous Bald Hills Formation of California: Jour. Paleontology, v. 34, no. 5, p. 835–858.

Owens, L. D., 1963, Regional geology of the central portion of the Great Valley of California, *in* Central portion of Great Valley of California, San Juan Bautista to Yosemite Valley: Geol. Soc. Sacramento Guidebook, Ann. field trip, 1963, p. 88–97.

Payne, M. B., 1962, Type Panoche group (Upper Cretaceous) and overlying Moreno and Tertiary strata on the west side of the San Joaquin Valley: California Div. Mines and Geology Bull. 181, p. 165–175.

Repenning, C. A., 1960, Geologic summary of the Central Valley of California with reference to disposal of liquid radioactive waste: U.S. Geol. Survey TEI Rept. 769, 69 p.

Rudel, C. H., 1965, Rock units of the general east side area Cottonwood Creek to Tejon Hills, *in* Geology of southeastern San Joaquin Valley, California: Am. Assoc. Petroleum Geologists-Soc. Econ. Geologists-Soc. Econ. Paleontologists and Mineralogists, Pacific Sec., Guidebook, p. 7.

Safonov, Anatole, 1962, The challenge of the Sacramento Valley, California: California Div. Mines and Geology Bull. 181, p. 77–100.

Seiden, Hy, 1964, Kettleman Hills area [California]: San Joaquin Geol. Soc., Selected Papers, v. 2, p. 46–53.

Silcox, J. H., 1962, West Thornton and Walnut Grove gas fields, California: California Div. Mines and Geology Bull. 181, p. 140–148.

Teitsworth, R. A., 1964, Geology and development of the Lathrop gas field, San Joaquin County, California: San Joaquin Geol. Soc., Selected Papers, v. 2, p. 19–29.

Walrond, Henry, and Gribi, E. A., Jr., 1963, Geologic map of part of the Salinas Valley-San Andreas fault area, *in* Guidebook to the geology of Salinas Valley and the San Andreas fault: Am. Assoc. Petroleum Geologists-Soc. Econ. Paleontologists and Mineralogists, Pacific Sec., Ann. Spring field trip, 1963, in pocket.

Warne, W. H., 1965, The White Wolf fault, *in* Geology of southeastern San Joaquin Valley, California: Am. Assoc. Petroleum Geologists-Soc. Econ. Geologists-Soc. Econ. Paleontologists and Mineralogists, Pacific Sec., Guidebook, p. 8–9.

White, C. A., 1885, On the Mesozoic and Cenozoic paleontology of California: U.S. Geol. Survey Bull. 15, 33 p.

HYDROGEOLOGY AND LAND SUBSIDENCE, GREAT CENTRAL VALLEY, CALIFORNIA *

By J. F. Poland and R. E. Evenson
U.S. Geological Survey, Sacramento, California

The first part of this paper describes the significant geomorphic features, presents a tentative correlation of the geologic units that constitute significant elements of the tremendous ground-water reservoir in the Great Central Valley, summarizes the post-Miocene geologic history, and describes briefly the ground-water conditions of the valley. It is a supplement to the more comprehensive companion paper by Otto Hackel on the geology of the valley from Late Jurassic time to the end of Pliocene marine deposition.

The second part of the paper describes the extent and magnitude of the land subsidence that is taking place in the San Joaquin Valley, caused chiefly by intensive pumping of ground water and the resulting decline in artesian head. Subsidence of the land surface is a critical aspect of the hydrogeology because it poses serious problems in construction and maintenance of engineering structures for water transport, especially large canals or aqueducts.

The first part of this paper is based largely on U.S. Geological Survey studies in the Sacramento Valley by Olmsted and Davis (1961), and in the San Joaquin Valley by Davis and others (1959 and 1964). The authors are also indebted to representatives of the Pacific Gas and Electric Company and the Sacramento Municipal Utility District for providing background data that facilitated estimates of ground-water withdrawal for irrigation use in 1964.

HYDROGEOLOGY

Geomorphology

The Central Valley constitutes a structural downwarp extending more than 400 miles from Redding on the north to the Tehachapi Mountains on the south; it has an average width of about 40 miles, and spans 15,000 sq. mi. or about one-tenth of the State. About the northern third of the valley is known as the Sacramento Valley and the southern two-thirds as the San Joaquin Valley. Drainage from the Sacramento Valley is southward through the Sacramento River to its confluence with the San Joaquin River, near Suisun Bay, and then westward through San Francisco Bay to the Pacific Ocean. The northern part of the San Joaquin Valley drains northward through the San Joaquin River but the southern part of the valley is a basin of interior drainage tributary to ephemeral lakes in the trough of the valley. These often nearly dry lake areas are known as Kern, Buena Vista, and Tulare Lake Beds.

The valley floor is divided, as shown on figure 1, into four geomorphic units: (1) dissected uplands, (2) low alluvial plains and fans, (3) river flood plains and channels, and (4) overflow lands and lake bottoms.

Dissected uplands fringe the valley along its mountain borders and are underlain principally by unconsolidated to semiconsolidated continental deposits of Pliocene and Pleistocene age which have been structurally deformed. Topographic expression of these uplands ranges from dissected hills with relief of several hundred feet to gently rolling lands where relief is only a few feet.

Low alluvial plains and fans that border the dissected uplands along their valleyward margins are generally flat to gently undulant and are underlain by undeformed to slightly deformed alluvial deposits of Pleistocene and Recent age.

The river flood plains and channels lie along the Sacramento, San Joaquin, and Kings Rivers in the axial parts of the valley and along the major streams on the eastern side of the valley. Those rivers that are incised below the general land surface have well-defined flood plains; but in the axial trough of the valley, the rivers are flanked by low-lying overflow lands and there the flood-plain and channel deposits are confined to the stream channel and to the natural levees that slope away from the river.

Overflow lands and lake bottoms include the historic beds of Kern, Buena Vista, and Tulare Lakes in the southern part of the valley, and also the lowlands adjacent to the natural levees of the major rivers. They are almost level and are underlain by lake and swamp deposits of Recent age.

Geologic Units

The deposits containing fresh ground water are principally unconsolidated continental deposits of Pliocene to Recent age that extend to depths ranging from less than a hundred to more than 3,500 feet. Locally, marine sediments contain fresh water and in other areas continental deposits contain saline water, but such conditions are of minor extent. Table 1 shows a tentative correlation of geologic units of hydrologic significance in the ground-water reservoir of the Central Valley and table 2 is a résumé of the post-Miocene

* Publication authorized by the Director, U. S. Geological Survey.

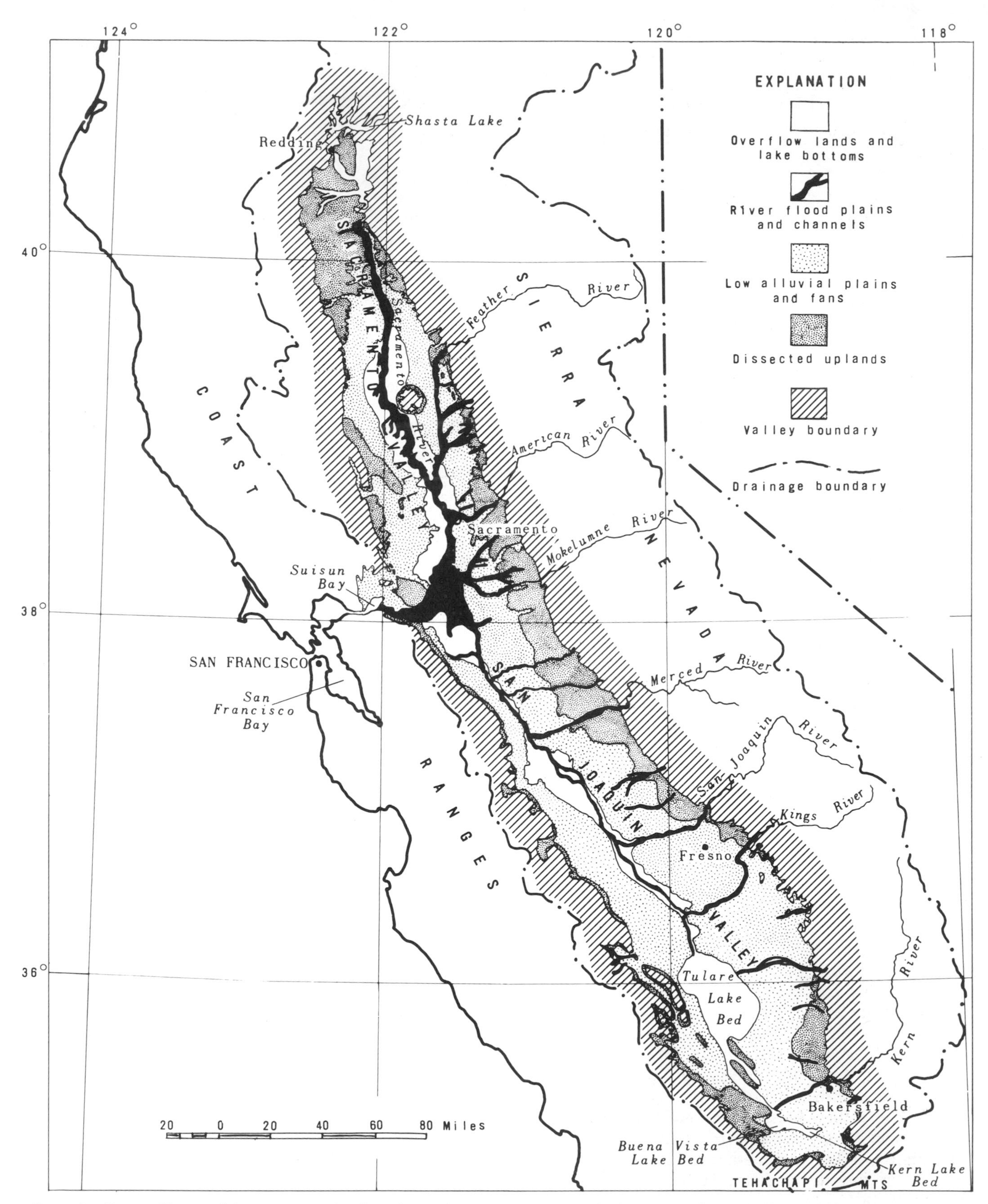

Figure 1. Geomorphic map of the Great Central Valley. Geomorphic units after Davis and others (1959, pl. 1) and Olmsted and Davis (1961, pl. 1).

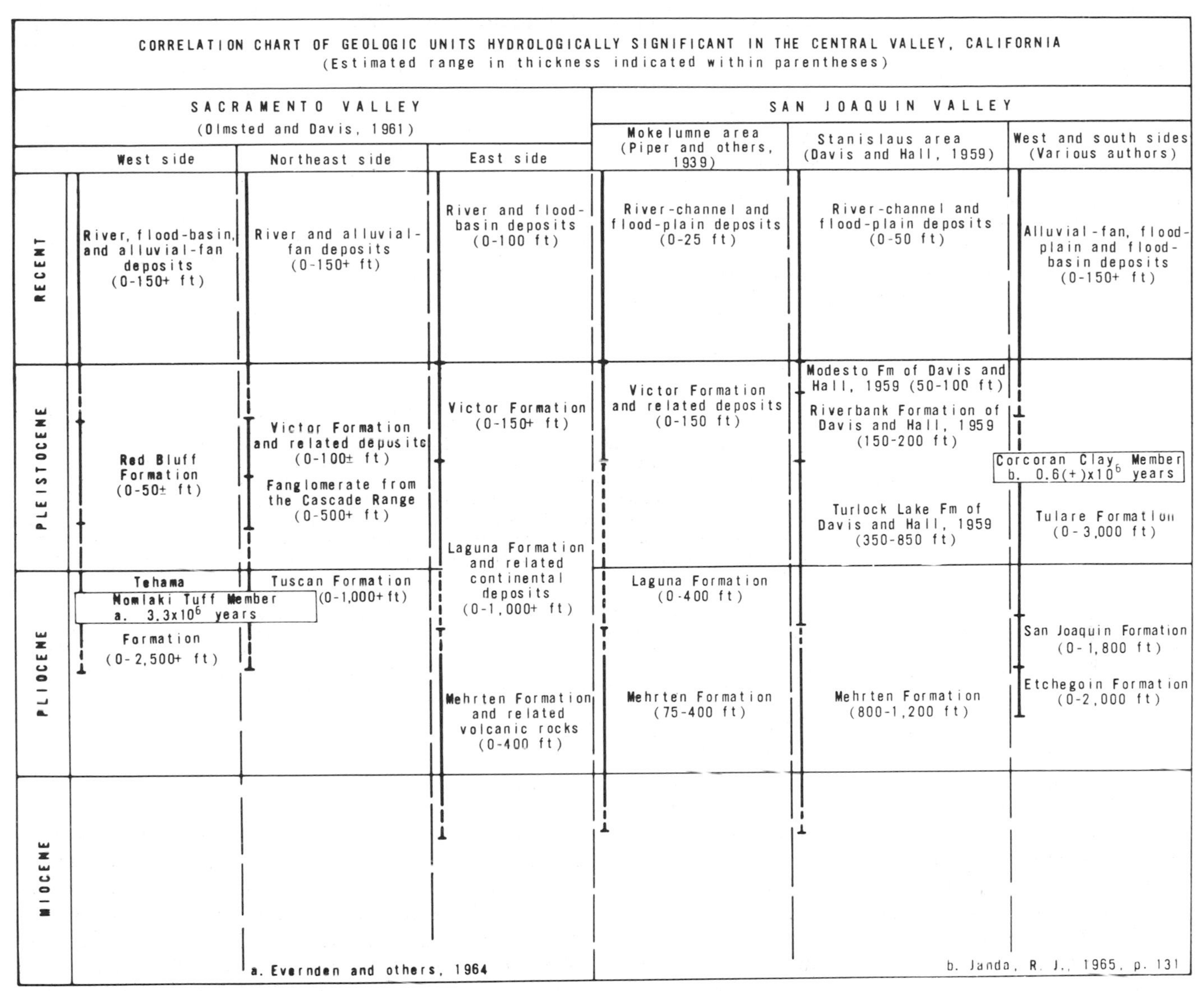

CORRELATION CHART OF GEOLOGIC UNITS HYDROLOGICALLY SIGNIFICANT IN THE CENTRAL VALLEY, CALIFORNIA
(Estimated range in thickness indicated within parentheses)

	SACRAMENTO VALLEY (Olmsted and Davis, 1961)			SAN JOAQUIN VALLEY		
	West side	Northeast side	East side	Mokelumne area (Piper and others, 1939)	Stanislaus area (Davis and Hall, 1959)	West and south sides (Various authors)
RECENT	River, flood-basin, and alluvial-fan deposits (0-150+ ft)	River and alluvial-fan deposits (0-150+ ft)	River and flood-basin deposits (0-100 ft)	River-channel and flood-plain deposits (0-25 ft)	River-channel and flood-plain deposits (0-50 ft)	Alluvial-fan, flood-plain and flood-basin deposits (0-150+ ft)
PLEISTOCENE	Red Bluff Formation (0-50± ft)	Victor Formation and related deposits (0-100± ft) Fanglomerate from the Cascade Range (0-500+ ft)	Victor Formation (0-150+ ft) Laguna Formation and related continental deposits (0-1,000+ ft)	Victor Formation and related deposits (0-150 ft)	Modesto Fm of Davis and Hall, 1959 (50-100 ft) Riverbank Formation of Davis and Hall, 1959 (150-200 ft) Turlock Lake Fm of Davis and Hall, 1959 (350-850 ft)	Corcoran Clay Member b. 0.6(+)x10⁶ years Tulare Formation (0-3,000 ft)
PLIOCENE	Tehama Formation (0-2,500+ ft) Nomlaki Tuff Member a. 3.3x10⁶ years	Tuscan Formation (0-1,000+ ft)	Mehrten Formation and related volcanic rocks (0-400 ft)	Laguna Formation (0-400 ft) Mehrten Formation (75-400 ft)	Mehrten Formation (800-1,200 ft)	San Joaquin Formation (0-1,800 ft) Etchegoin Formation (0-2,000 ft)
MIOCENE						

a. Evernden and others, 1964
b. Janda, R. J., 1965, p. 131

Table 1.

geologic history. Because of space limitations, the reader is referred to the cited references for information on the physical and water-bearing character of the individual geologic units listed in table 1.

The unconsolidated continental deposits consist chiefly of alluvium but in some areas include widespread lacustrine and marsh or estuarine sediments. These deposits constitute late Cenozoic fill in the structural trough, whose axis in the San Joaquin Valley lies west of the present topographic axis of the valley. Appreciable folding and minor faulting also has occurred; however, these structural features have had no significant barrier effect on ground-water movement.

Consolidated rocks form the boundaries beneath and on the flanks of the productive ground-water reservoir in the unconsolidated deposits. Only minor quantities of water occur in joints or fractures in the consolidated rocks in the Sierra Nevada, and the principal water supply to the valley—the stream runoff—passes over them.

Ground-Water Occurrence and Use

Ground water occurs under both confined (artesian) and unconfined (water table) conditions in the Central Valley. The degree of confinement varies widely because of the heterogeneity of the continental deposits. In the big alluvial fans on the east side of the San Joaquin Valley, the ground water is unconfined. The most extensive confined aquifer is the major aquifer system overlain by the Corcoran Clay Member of the Tulare Formation (table 1), which covers more than 5,000 square miles in the San Joaquin Valley.

Recharge to the ground-water reservoir is by infiltration of rainfall, infiltration from streams, canals, and ditches, by infiltration of excess irrigation water, and by underflow entering the valley from tributary stream canyons.

TABLE 2.—RESUME OF POST-MIOCENE GEOLOGIC HISTORY.

Epoch	Coast Ranges	Central Valley	Sierra Nevada
Pliocene	Folding and faulting on regional scale in late Pliocene time outlines present form of ranges. Northern part of central Coast Ranges undergoing subaerial erosion, concurrently with deposition of marine sediments in local basins in southern part of ranges during early and middle Pliocene time.	Deposition of marine sediments in southwestern part of valley during early and middle Pliocene time. Streams from Sierra Nevada depositing generally fine-grained alluvium on east side, including much coarse-grained volcanic detritus in early Pliocene time. All the valley was above sea level in late Pliocene time. Great thicknesses of continental deposits accumulating in downwarping basins along western and southern margins of valley. Extensive lake occupies western part of valley and present foothill area in late Pliocene time. Igneous activity pushed up an andesitic plug through Sacramento Valley sediments shattering or deforming them and forming the Sutter Buttes. Later rhyolitic domes and necks intruded the plug and around its periphery.	Relative structural stability, only minor crustal movement. Great volcanic activity; consequent streams erode volcanic deposits and move them toward the Central Valley.
Pleistocene	Major faulting and folding accentuates existing structures. Erosion of mountains with deposition in intermontane valleys.	Deposition of coarse alluvial deposits by streams draining Sierra Nevada contemporaneous with dissection of tilted older alluvial-fan deposits. Extensive lake in San Joaquin Valley deposits diatomaceous clay. Lowering of sea level and climatic changes during Pleistocene glaciations cause major rivers and tributaries to excavate trenches graded to lower base level or to mountain valley downcutting. Alluvial fans on east side tilted with Sierra Nevada block. Coast Range streams continue to build alluvial fans in downwarping area on west side of valley. Several lake clays of variable extent deposited in late Pleistocene time.	Several stages of glaciation in higher parts of range. Glacial scouring locally important in modifying land forms. Last major uplift of range along faults on eastern margin with additional westward tilting.
Recent	Subaerial erosion forms present topography. Minor structural movements continuing to present; many faults and folds still active; earthquakes frequent.	Deposition of stream-channel, alluvial-fan, overflow, and lacustrine deposits contemporaneous with mild dissection of tilted alluvial fans on east side of valley. Deposition of broad coalescing alluvial fans on west side and south end of valley. Sediments generally finer grained than Pleistocene deposits. Trenches of major rivers and tributaries back-filled as sea level rises with retreat of continental glaciers.	Subaerial erosion. Glacially scoured features being modified by weathering, erosion, and deposition.

In the Sacramento Valley, water for irrigation, public supply, and industry is obtained primarily from surface-water sources, but in part from wells. These wells, in general, range in depth from 100 to about 500 feet, although some wells are as much as 1,000 feet deep. Most wells of large capacity are used for irrigation or for public supply; their yields range from 200 to 2,000 gpm (gallons per minute). Estimated withdrawal of ground water for irrigation in the Sacramento Valley during 1964 was on the order of 2,400,000 acre-feet. This represents an increase of 85 percent from the estimated withdrawal of about 1,300,000 acre-feet in 1950 (Olmsted and Davis, 1961, p. 8). The estimated total storage capacity of the deposits in the 20- to 200-foot depth range is about 33½ million acre-feet. However, the flood-basin deposits are fine-grained silt and clay, and thus are not usable for cyclic storage. Therefore, the total rechargeable storage capacity to a depth of 200 feet is about 28 million acre-feet.

Water levels in the Sacramento Valley have not been drawn down excessively by pumping. In most of the valley water levels have not declined as much as 100 feet, and in some areas levels have been raised by seepage from surface-water irrigation.

In the San Joaquin Valley, water for irrigation is supplied both from surface-water sources and from wells, but probably about 60 percent is from wells. Well water is the sole supply for half the irrigated land and a supplemental supply for another quarter. Furthermore, ground water supplies nearly all the municipal, industrial, and domestic needs.

Depths of water wells range widely, from 100 feet to 3,500 feet, depending either on the permeability of the deposits or on water-quality controls. For example, wells tapping the highly permeable alluvial-fan deposits derived from the Sierra Nevada granitic complex are relatively shallow. Accordingly, on the east side of the valley, from the Mokelumne River to the south edge of the Kings River fan, and within the Kern River fan, well depths range from 100 to 500 feet and the average depth is only about 250 feet. In contrast, on the central west side in western Fresno County, where the alluvial deposits of the Tulare Formation are derived chiefly from sandstone and shale detritus of Coast Range origin, and the shallower ground water is of poor quality, wells range in depth from 500 to 3,500 feet with the average depth being about 1,500 feet. At the south end of the valley, south of the Kern River fan, well depths range from 600 to 2,000 feet; the average is about 1,000 feet.

Yields of irrigation wells in the San Joaquin Valley also vary widely, ranging from 100 to more than 3,000 gpm, but most wells yield 500–1,500 gpm. Estimated storage capacity of the deposits in the depth interval from 10 to 200 feet is 93 million acre-feet. Locally the reservoir has been dewatered to a depth in excess of 350 feet.

Estimated withdrawal of ground water for irrigation in the San Joaquin Valley during 1964 was on the

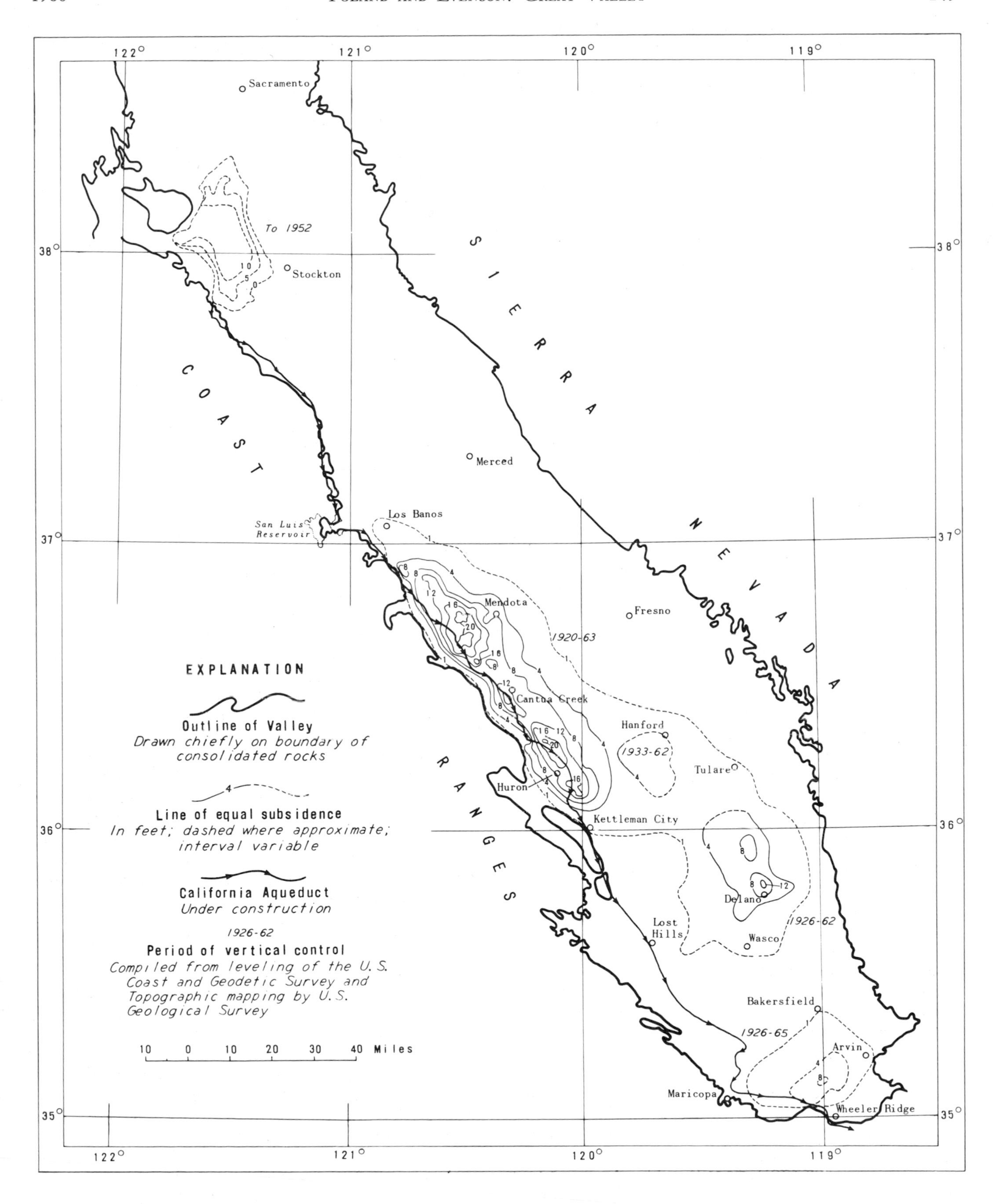

Figure 2. Areas of major land subsidence in the Great Central Valley.

order of 10,700,000 acre-feet, representing more than a threefold increase since 1940 when the draft was about 3 million acre-feet. This large withdrawal has caused substantial overdraft on the central west side and in much of the southern part of the Valley, where replenishment is small compared to withdrawal. As a result, water levels have declined 100 to more than 400 feet in the confined aquifer system in the Tulare Formation in western Fresno County and more than 300 feet in the same formation in Kern County south of the Kern River fan.

LAND SUBSIDENCE

In the great agricultural development of the Central Valley, man has caused major subsidence of the land surface in three extensive areas between Sacramento and the south end of the Valley. (See figure 2.) These three areas aggregate about 4,000 square miles, or roughly one-third of the valley lands south of Sacramento. Maximum subsidence ranges from 8 feet south of Bakersfield to 23 feet southeast of Los Banos. Nowhere else in the world has man produced such extensive subsidence of this magnitude.

The subsidence is of three types. In the lowlands of the Delta at the confluence of the Sacramento and San Joaquin Rivers, subsidence has been caused chiefly by the oxidation of peat lands accompanying drainage and cultivation. In the largest area, between Los Banos and Wasco, and at the south end of the valley between Arvin and Maricopa, most of the subsidence has been caused by lowering of the artesian head in confined aquifer systems, due to the intensive pumping of ground water. Locally, on the west and south flanks of the valley, a third type of subsidence has been caused by near-surface compaction of moisture-deficient alluvial-fan deposits above the water table, after initial wetting by percolating irrigation water. This third type of subsidence is of such local extent that it cannot be shown on figure 2.

Subsidence of the Delta

The organic soils or peat lands at the confluence of the Sacramento and San Joaquin River systems are highly productive agricultural lands. Drainage for cultivation began in 1850 and development continued for the next 70 years. The Delta is now a complex system of islands and channels, and prior to reclamation the islands were approximately at mean sea level. Levees were constructed around the islands at the time of their reclamation, and as the islands have subsided farther and farther below sea level the maintenance of levees and channels has been an increasingly difficult job.

The generalized lines of equal subsidence shown on figure 2 were constructed from topographic maps of the Geological Survey based on field surveys in 1952. The subsiding area covers about 450 square miles and more than one-third of the island area was 10 to 15 feet below sea level in 1952. The peat ranges in thickness from near zero to more than 40 feet.

Weir (1950) studied the subsidence in the Delta area for about 35 years, beginning in 1922. He found that subsidence on one island (Mildred Island) was 9.29 feet from 1922 to 1955, and was relatively uniform, averaging 0.28 foot per year. He concluded that the causes of the subsidence were: oxidation, compaction by tillage machinery, shrinkage by drying, burning, and wind erosion. Stephens and Johnson (1951) studied a similar peat subsidence in the Florida Everglades and concluded that the principal cause was oxidation due to action of aerobic bacteria above the water table. Hence, the primary cause of the Delta subsidence is the lowering of the water table by drainage in order to grow crops.

The sediments beneath the peat also have subsided to a much lesser degree, possibly because of extraction of gas and water from major local gas fields.

Near-Surface Subsidence

Locally on the west and south flanks of the San Joaquin Valley, near-surface alluvial-fan deposits above the water table have subsided in response to the first irrigation of the land. In the Los Banos-Kettleman City area, this near-surface subsidence or hydrocompaction encompasses two areas 4 to 6 miles wide and aggregating 22 miles in length along the west edge of the valley. Along the southwest flank of the valley between Lost Hills, Maricopa, and Wheeler Ridge, are four areas susceptible to near-surface subsidence; these aggregate at least 40 miles in length.

The deposits susceptible to hydrocompaction have been moisture deficient ever since their deposition. When water is applied to them the clay bond is weakened and the deposits compact (Bull, 1964). Subsidence of 5 to 10 feet is common and locally as much as 15 feet has been observed. This type of subsidence poses a serious problem in the construction and maintenance of large canals, irrigation distribution systems, pipelines, powerlines, highways, and buildings. The California Aqueduct (fig. 2), now under construction, passes through about 60 miles of these deposits between Los Banos and Wheeler Ridge. As a preventative measure the susceptible deposits along the Aqueduct alignment are being precompacted by prolonged basin-type wetting prior to the placing of the concrete lining.

Subsidence Due to Water-Level Lowering

The areas of significant land subsidence related to water-level lowering are in the San Joaquin Valley. The two areas of major extent are outlined on figure 2. The larger area extends about 145 miles southeast from Los Banos to Wasco, and includes about 3,300 square miles within the 1-foot subsidence line. The smaller area south of Bakersfield includes about 450 square miles. Together these areas cover about one-third of the San Joaquin Valley. The subsidence has been greatest at three centers. The center of maximum subsidence is 7 miles west of Mendota where 23 feet of subsidence has occurred (1963); the maximum rate of subsidence from 1959 to 1963 was about 1.5 feet per year. A second center is 2 miles north of Delano where 12 feet of subsidence has occurred, but subsidence has almost ceased there because of recovery of water levels. The third center, 18 miles south of Bakersfield, has subsided 8 feet.

These areas of land subsidence overlie confined aquifer systems, in which the artesian head has been drawn down everywhere more than 100 feet and as much as 400 feet locally north of Kettleman City. The area between Los Banos and Wasco is almost wholly underlain by the Corcoran Clay Member of the Tulare Formation which confines the underlying productive aquifer system that is also in the Tulare Formation.

The relationship of subsidence to head decline near the three centers of subsidence is illustrated by figures 3, 4, and 5. Figure 3 shows the nearly parallel trends

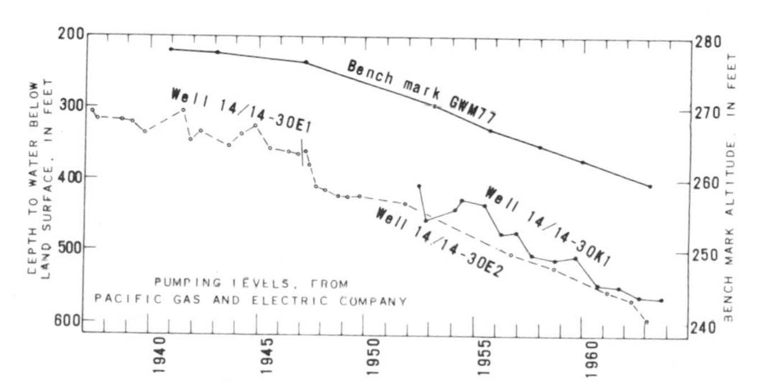

Figure 3. Subsidence and change in artesian head in an area 8 miles southwest of Mendota, Fresno County.

of bench-mark subsidence and artesian-head decline from 1940 to 1963 at a site 8 miles southwest of Mendota. In this 22-year period, the bench mark subsided about 18.5 feet and the artesian head in nearby wells tapping the confined aquifer system decreased about 260 feet. The ratio of subsidence to head decline was approximately 1:20 from 1940 to 1950 and 1:10 from 1950 to 1963. This increase in the ratio with increasing drawdown of artesian head is characteristic of much of the subsiding area. It suggests a cumulative increase in delayed compaction of the fine-grained interbeds as head declines, due to slow adjustment of pore pressure.

Five miles northeast of Delano, artesian head declined continuously from 1930 to 1951 (fig. 4) and then recovered rapidly as a result of delivery of surface water for irrigation from the Friant-Kern Canal, which brings water south from the San Joaquin River. Nearby bench marks showed a parallel subsidence into the early 1950's, after which the rate of subsidence decreased in response to the recovery of artesian head.

The relation of subsidence to artesian-head decline 21 miles south of Bakersfield (about 5 miles northwest of the town of Wheeler Ridge) is shown on figure 5. The water level declined from about 130 feet below the land surface in 1946 to 415 feet below in 1962, at

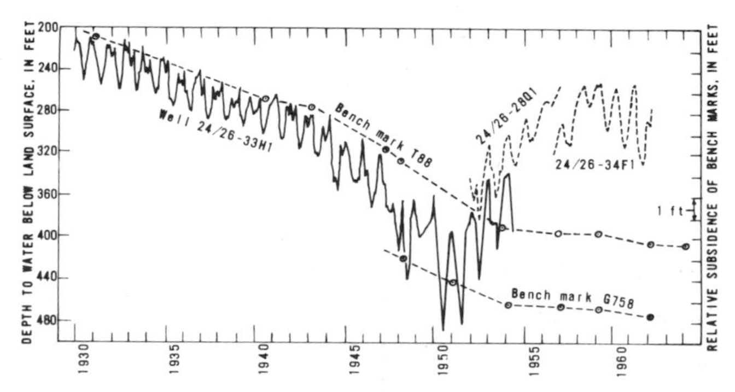

Figure 4. Subsidence and change in artesian head near Delano, Kern County.

an average rate of 18 feet per year. From 1947 to 1953 the rate of subsidence of nearby bench mark A-303 was 0.16 foot per year and during 1959–62 was 0.30 foot per year. At this site, therefore, the ratio of subsidence to artesian-head decline increased from 1:112 (1947–53) to 1:60 (1959–62).

To determine how much of the subsidence is caused by compaction of the deposits tapped by water wells, and to investigate the character of the response of the sediments to increasing effective stress (decreasing artesian head), the U.S. Geological Survey has established depth bench marks and operated compaction recorders in about 30 unused wells or cased core holes. The compaction-recorder installation (fig. 6) furnishes

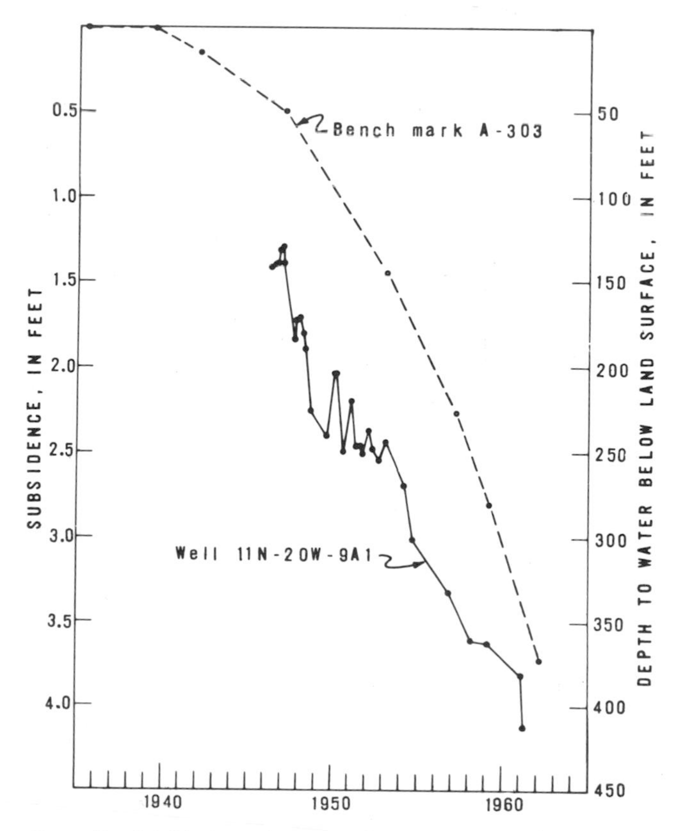

Figure 5. Subsidence and artesian-head decline, south of Bakersfield. After Lofgren (1963, fig. 47.3).

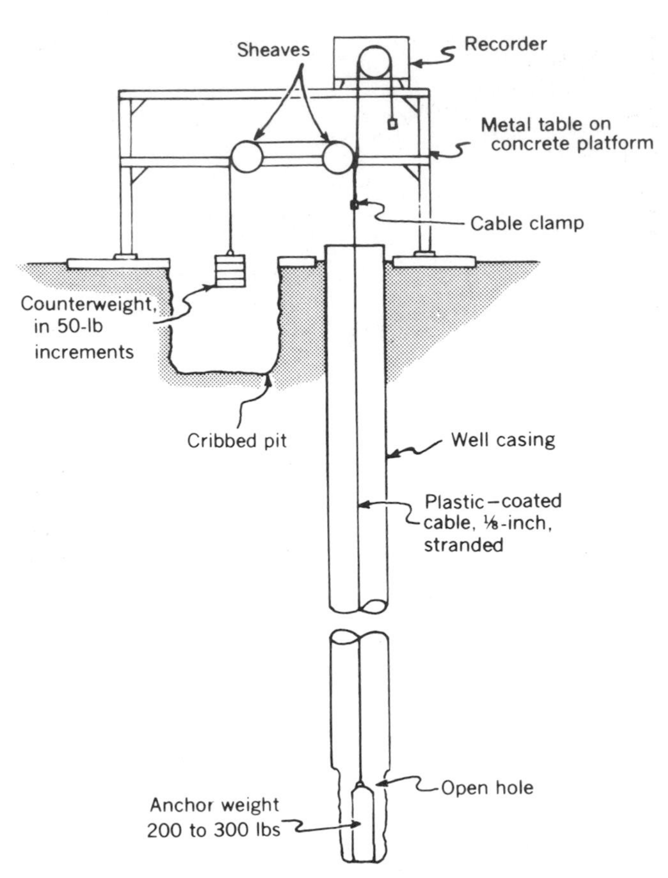

Figure 6. Diagram of typical compaction-recorder installation.

continuous measurement of compaction occurring between the land surface and the depth bench mark at the well bottom.

The first compaction recorder of this type was installed in a well 2,030 feet deep near Huron in 1955. Figure 7 shows the record of compaction from 1956 into 1960, the subsidence of nearby surface bench mark B 889 as determined by precise leveling of the U.S. Coast and Geodetic Survey, and the fluctuation of artesian head in a nearby well. During the 4.8 years of record shown, measured compaction of the aquifer system to a depth of 2,030 feet was 3.8 feet, the land subsided 4.6 feet, and artesian head declined about 40 feet. Thus, the measured compaction was 82 percent of the subsidence, indicating that 0.8 foot of compaction occurred below 2,030 feet, which is reasonable because nearby wells withdraw water from greater depths. The rate of compaction is variable, being greatest during periods of rapid decline in artesian head; recovery of head results in decrease or cessation of compaction. Such evidence, obtained here and at many other sites, indicates that the aquifer system is extremely sensitive to change in effective stress as defined by change in artesian head. At one site, increase of about 1 percent in effective stress (a 5-foot lowering of artesian head) caused noticeable compaction.

At a site near the town of Cantua Creek, a compaction recorder installed in a 2,000-foot well (N1) in 1958 recorded 7.43 feet of compaction by the end of 1964 (fig. 8). Two shallower installations registered

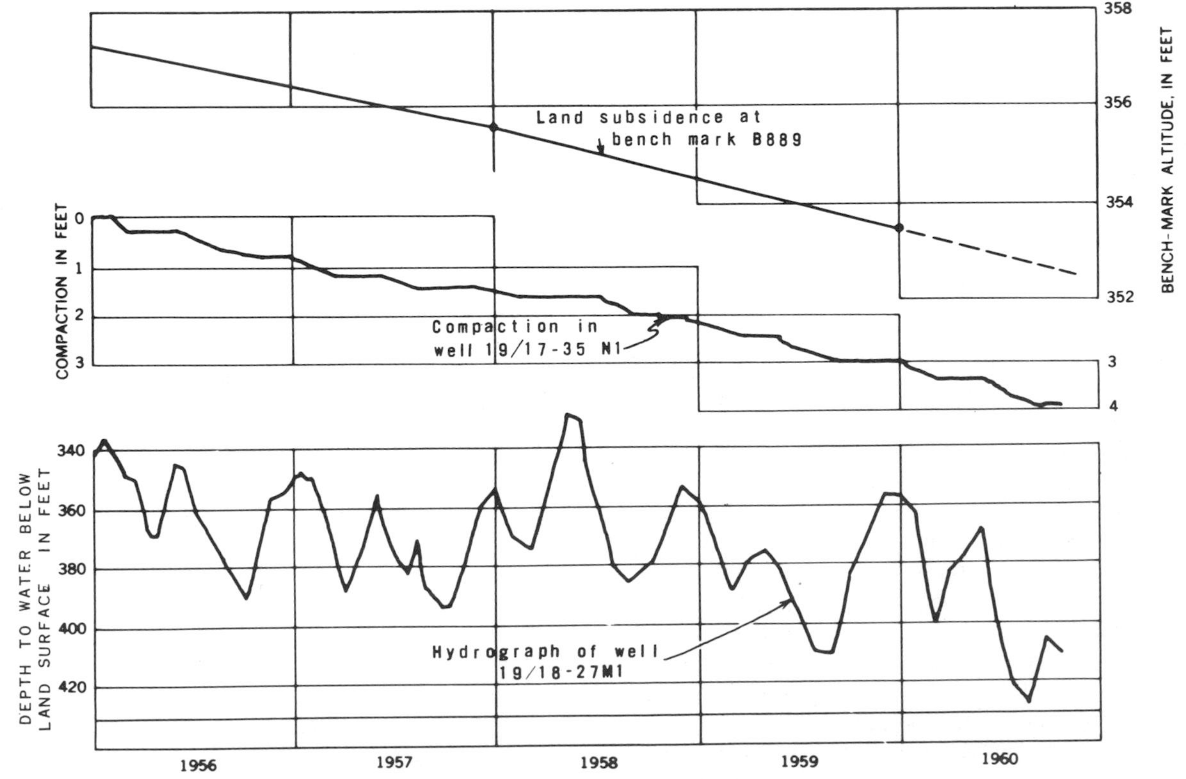

Figure 7. Measured subsidence, compaction, and water-level change, near Huron, Fresno County. After Lofgren (1961, fig. 24.2).

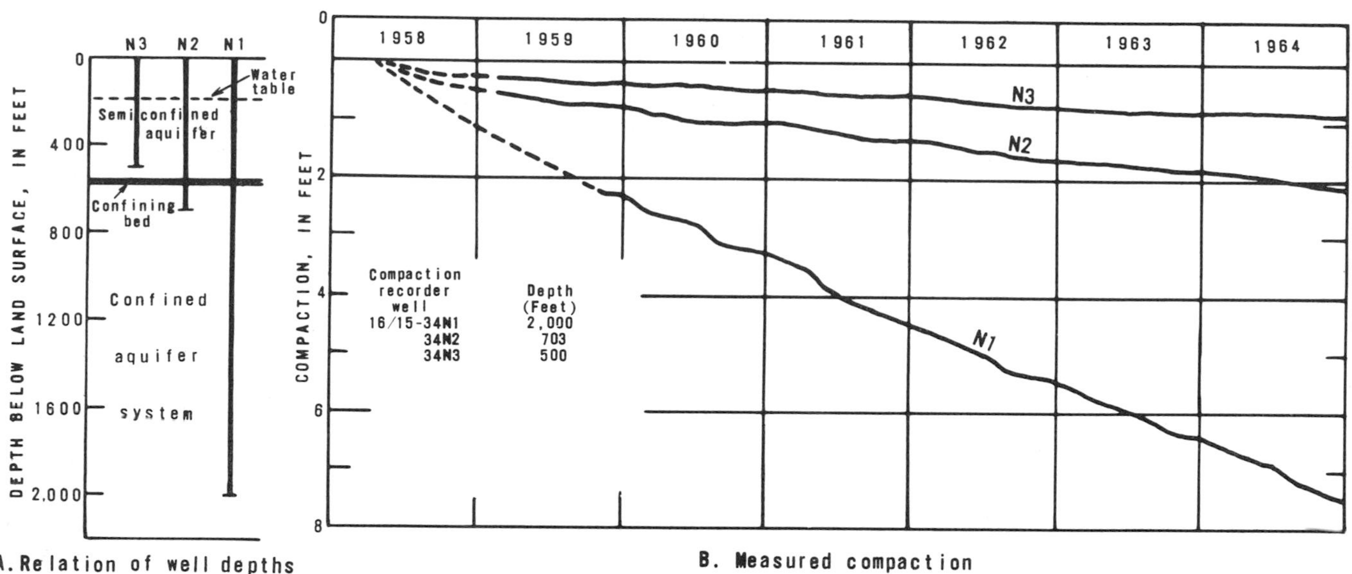

Figure 8. Compaction in three wells near Cantua Creek, Fresno County, during 1958–64.

0.89 foot (N3; 500 feet deep) and 2.10 feet (N2; 703 feet deep) of compaction during the same period. If the distribution of compaction in the interval between the bottoms of wells N3 and N2 was uniform, about 17 percent of the measured compaction occurred above the principal confining bed and 83 percent in the confined aquifer system. The measured compaction to 2,000 feet (well N1) from February 1960 to March 1963 was 3.37 feet; subsidence measured by leveling to surface bench marks in the same period was 3.45 feet. Thus, the measured compaction to this depth accounted for about 98 percent of total subsidence. It is noteworthy that the rate of compaction has been about constant throughout the year, even though the artesian head in an adjacent well fluctuates 60 feet or more seasonally. This suggests that at this site the residual excess pore pressure in the fine-grained interbeds is much greater than the annual fluctuation of head.

In conclusion, decrease in artesian head in compressible confined aquifer systems results in increased effective stress (grain-to-grain load) on the confined sediments and they compact, causing land subsidence. The magnitude of the subsidence is dependent on the magnitude of change in head and on the compaction characteristics and thickness of the sediments. The greater the number of clayey interbeds in the system, the greater is the compaction. Continuous measurements of compaction indicate rapid response to head change at most places in these subsiding areas. Subsidence can be slowed down or stopped by a rise in the artesian head sufficient to eliminate residual excess pore pressures. However, the compaction is almost entirely permanent. Recovery of water levels has not caused appreciable recovery of the land surface in any of the areas studied. This has been demonstrated on a broad scale in the Delano area.

REFERENCES

Bull, W. B., 1964, Alluvial fans and near-surface subsidence in western Fresno County, Calif.: U.S. Geol. Survey Prof. Paper 437-A, p. A1–A71.

Davis, G. H., Green, J. H., Olmsted, F. H., and Brown, D. W., 1959, Ground-water conditions and storage capacity in the San Joaquin Valley, California: U.S. Geol. Survey Water-Supply Paper 1469, 287 p.

Davis, G. H., Lofgren, B. E., and Mack, Seymour, 1964, Use of ground-water reservoirs for storage of surface water in the San Joaquin Valley, California: U.S. Geol. Survey Water-Supply Paper 1618, 125 p.

Davis, S. N., and Hall, F. R., 1959, Water quality of eastern Stanislaus and northern Merced Counties, California: Stanford Univ. Pub. Geol. Sci., v. 6, no. 1, p. 1–112.

Evernden, J. F., Savage, D. E., Curtis, G. H., and James, G. T., 1964, Potassium-argon dates and the Cenozoic mammalian chronology of North America: Am. Jour. Sci., v. 262, p. 145–198.

Janda, R. J., 1965, Quaternary alluvium near Friant, California, *in* Internat. Assoc. for Quaternary research, VIIth Congress, Guidebook for field conference I, Northern Great Basin and California, p. 128–133.

Lofgren, B. E., 1961, Measurement of compaction of aquifer systems in areas of land subsidence: Art. 24 in U.S. Geol. Survey Prof. Paper 424-B, p. B49–B52.

—— 1963, Land subsidence in the Arvin-Maricopa area, Calif.: Art. 47 *in* U.S. Geol. Survey Prof. Paper 475-B, p. B171–B175.

Olmsted, F. H., and Davis, G. H., 1961, Geologic features and ground-water storage capacity of the Sacramento Valley, California: U.S. Geol. Survey Water-Supply Paper 1497, 241 p.

Piper, A. M., Gale, H. S., Thomas, H. E., and Robinson, T. W., 1939, Geology and ground-water hydrology of the Mokelumne area, California: U.S. Geol. Survey Water-Supply Paper 780, 230 p.

Stephens, J. C., and Johnson, Lamar, 1951, Subsidence of organic soils in the Upper Everglades region of Florida: U.S. Dept. Agr., Soil Cons. Service, 16 p., 25 figs.

Weir, W. W., 1950, Subsidence of peat lands of the Sacramento-San Joaquin Delta, California: California Univ. Agr. Exp. Station, Hilgardia, v. 20, no. 3, p. 37–56.

Pioneer conditions at Midway. Rush of teams with material for rigs on claims located under placer law. Photograph by R. B. Moran.

ECONOMIC MINERAL DEPOSITS OF THE GREAT VALLEY

By Earl W. Hart
California Division of Mines and Geology

Of more than 50 different mineral commodities produced in California, only 15 are currently exploited in the Great Valley, and the valley is generally thought of in terms of its agricultural rather than mineral wealth. Nevertheless, the province yielded $489,250,000 worth of minerals in 1964, which was 31 percent of the State's total mineral production. Table 1 shows that petroleum fuels—petroleum, natural gas, and natural-gas liquids—constitute 90 percent of the mineral production of the province. Sand and gravel make up nearly 9 percent of the total and the 11 other commodities account for the rest.

The economic importance and geologic occurrence of the various mineral commodities are discussed briefly below. The oil and gas fields and the more significant mineral deposits, which are mainly those that are being utilized, are shown on the map (fig. 1). For more detailed data on the mineral deposits, the reader is referred to U.S. Geological Survey (in press), Wright (1957), and many other publications of the California Division of Mines and Geology, California Division of Oil and Gas, U.S. Geological Survey, and U.S. Bureau of Mines.

Table 1.—*Mineral production in the Great Valley in 1964.*

Rank	Mineral	Production[1]	
		Quantity	Value
1	Petroleum__________bbls	123,683,000	$299,981,000
2	Natural gas ____1,000 cu ft	414,296,000	123,876,000
3	Sand and gravel short tons	27,830,000	34,131,000
4	Natural-gas liquids 1,000 gals	401,291	26,020,000
5	Gold	*	*
6	Gypsum________short tons	838,000	1,472,000
7	Clay__________short tons	447,000	1,289,000
	Unapportioned† (gold, peat, coal, pumicite, carbon dioxide, stone, platinum, silver, gemstones)		2,481,000
	Total__Great Valley		$489,250,000
	Total_____California		$1,560,510,000

[1] Based on data collected by the U. S. Bur. Mines.
* Concealed under unapportioned to avoid revealing the production of individuals.
† Listed in approximate order of decreasing value.

PETROLEUM

Virtually all of the petroleum (or crude oil) is produced from fields of the San Joaquin Valley, which comprises the southern half of the Great Valley. The so-called San Joaquin basin yields 335,000 barrels of oil per day, or 41 percent of California's production. Most of the oil comes from sand and, to a lesser extent, fractured shale reservoirs of Cenozoic (mainly Miocene and Pliocene) formations. A substantial amount of oil also is obtained from fractured schist of pre-Cretaceous age. Upper Cretaceous sands yield very little oil. Comulative oil production to January 1, 1965, is more than 5½ billion barrels, and proven oil reserves are about 2 billion barrels. "Giant" oil fields, with more than 100 million barrels of cumulative production, are listed in table 2.

Table 2.—*Oil fields of the Great Valley with cumulative production greater than 100 million barrels of oil.*

Fields	Cumulative oil production, in barrels, through 1964
Midway-Sunset	947,891,000
Coalinga	549,931,000
Buena Vista	524,291,000
Kettleman North Dome	440,395,000
Coalinga East Extension	408,523,000
Kern River	393,479,000
Elk Hills	271,471,000
Mount Poso	149,464,000
Coles Levee North	124,270,000
McKittrick	112,566,000
Belridge South	109,402,000
Kern Front	105,937,000
Rio Bravo	105,096,000

NATURAL GAS

A large quantity of "wet" natural gas is produced from oil reservoirs in the San Joaquin Valley. More than half of this wet gas, after extraction of natural-gas liquids, is returned to the oil fields to maintain reservoir pressures; the balance is marketed or otherwise used. "Dry" natural gas, on the other hand, is obtained from gas reservoirs in which oil is not present. Such gas occurs mainly in the Sacramento Valley and northern San Joaquin Valley, but a few important gas fields lie close to the oil fields of southern San Joaquin Valley. The dry gas comes from sands of Late Cretaceous and Tertiary age. In 1964, net production of dry and wet natural gases respectively amounted to 166 and 248 billion cubic feet for the Great Valley. Combined, this is 62 percent of the State's gas production. Natural gas reserves as of December 31, 1964 are estimated at nearly 7.5 trillion cubic feet, about 55 percent of which is wet gas. Only six dry gas fields

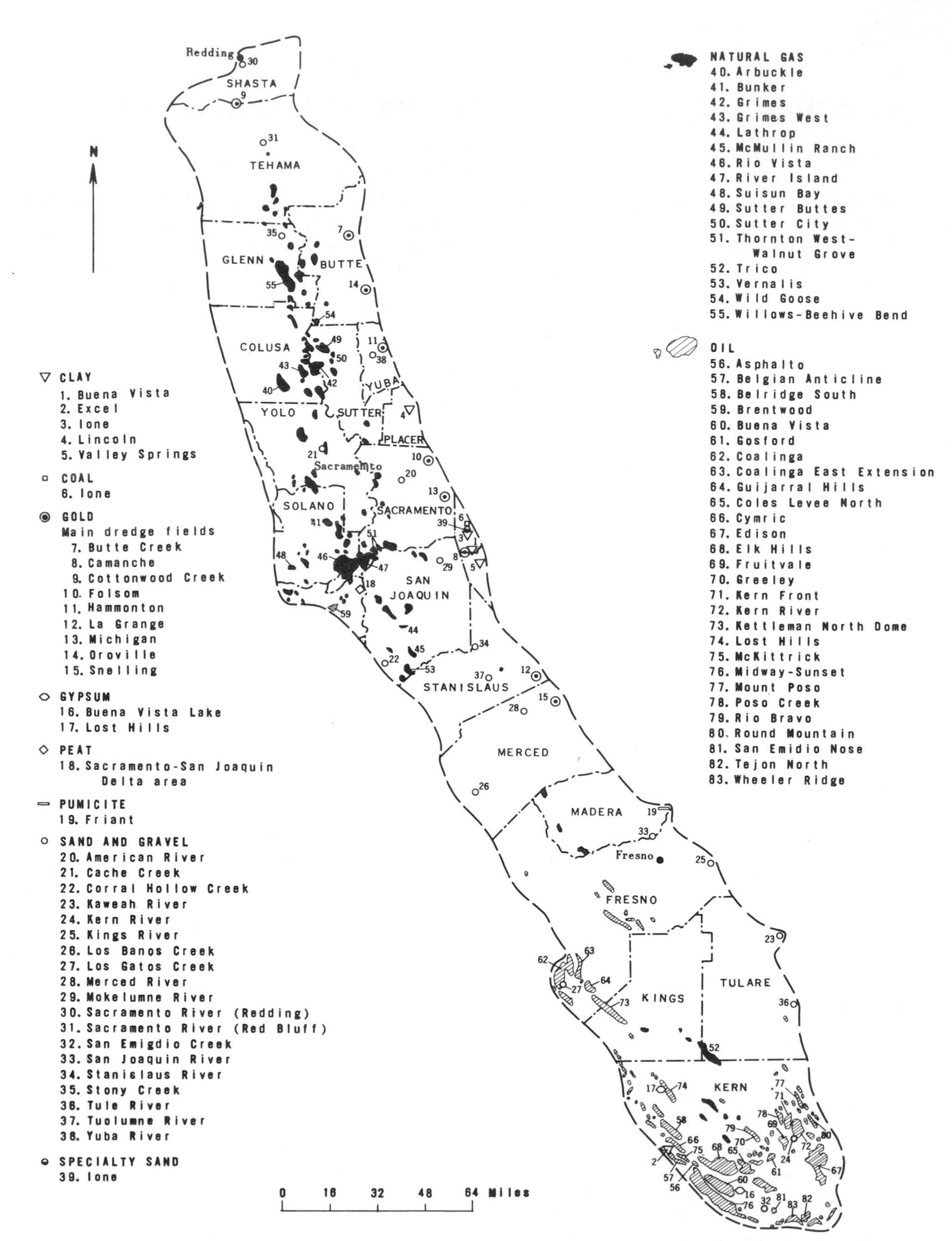

Figure 1. Map of the Great Valley, showing the location of the principal economic mineral deposits.

have yielded more than 100 billion cubic feet of gas; these are listed below:

Fields	Cumulative gas production, in 1,000's of cu ft, through 1964
Rio Vista	2,264,283,942
Willows-Beehive Bend	179,059,716
Trico	168,080,550
McDonald Island	151,402,407
Buena Vista	129,258,333
Elk Hills	100,213,017

NATURAL-GAS LIQUIDS

Natural-gas liquids are obtained from "wet" natural gas produced from oil and condensate zones. Nearly all of the wet gas withdrawn from formations is processed. Natural-gas liquid extraction takes place in or close to the fields at 16 natural gasoline plants and 2 cycle plants. Production in 1964 included 232,574,000 gallons of natural gasoline and cycle condensate, and 168,717,000 gallons of liquefied petroleum gases (propane, butane, and isobutane). These products constitute 37 percent of the natural-gas liquids produced in California.

CARBON DIOXIDE

A small yearly production of carbon dioxide is made at a natural gasoline plant near Taft, Kern County. The carbon dioxide is extracted from natural gas produced at a nearby oil field.

GOLD, SILVER, AND PLATINUM

As a result of Quaternary erosion of the various placer and lode gold deposits of the Sierra Nevada and Klamath Mountains, a considerable amount of gold was transported from the mountains and deposited in the lower reaches of streams in the Great Valley. Such placer gold has been recovered mainly by dredging the extensive stream and adjacent flood-plain deposits formed where the major streams enter the Great Valley. The principal gold-dredging areas in terms of estimated total production are Hammonton ($130,000,000); Folsom ($125,000,000); Oroville ($50,000,000–$55,000,000); Snelling ($17,000,000); La Grange ($13,000,000); Camanche ($10,000,000); and Butte Creek, Cottonwood Creek, and Michigan Bar (several million dollars each). Most of these areas are still more or less active.

Gold dredging has diminished sharply in recent years, and only one major company is now active. This is Yuba Consolidated Industries which works the Yuba River gravels by means of two bucket-line dredges. Relatively small amounts of gold also are recovered as a byproduct of 12 sand and gravel operations along the American, Feather, Stanislaus, Tuolumne, Merced, and San Joaquin Rivers. Minor quantities of placer gold also are obtained by prospectors, snipers, etc. Silver, which is alloyed with all native gold, is recovered as a minor byproduct of gold. A small quantity of native platinum and related metals is also produced as a byproduct of gold dredging by Yuba Consolidated.

SAND AND GRAVEL

Nearly 28 million tons, or 25 percent of the sand and gravel produced in California in 1964, came from the Great Valley. Most of this was used as aggregate in portland cement and bituminous concretes, as base materials, and as imported fill. A small but significant amount, however, was used for glass manufacture and as molding sand.

Much of the sand and gravel used in construction comes from young stream deposits (including gold dredge tailings) associated with the present rivers and creeks. These deposits are found not only in the modern stream channels, but also along the banks and adjacent flood plains and in alluvial fans formed from former channel deposits. Somewhat older (Pliocene and Pleistocene) flood-plain, fan, and terrace deposits also are used to some extent. In addition, a small production of Recent dune sand for construction use comes from Antioch, Contra Costa County. More detailed data on sand and gravel are given by Goldman (1961 and 1964).

Since 1955, sand from the Ione Formation (Eocene), which is discontinuously exposed along the east side of Sacramento and northern San Joaquin Valleys, has been excavated and processed on a large scale for use in glass manufacture. Some also has been used for molding sand, and for refractory and other industrial purposes. Where worked southwest of Ione, Amador County, the Ione Formation contains a weakly consolidated, massive bed 70 feet thick, consisting of 60 percent quartz sand, 35 percent clay, and 5 percent heavy minerals. The quartz sand produced is a coproduct of fire clay and is of flint-glass quality. In 1964, at least three Ione sand deposits were being worked in Amador County.

Specialty sands produced from the Eocene Domengine and Tesla Formations exposed in the hills along the west side of the valley in Contra Costa and Alameda Counties are described in the article on the economic deposits of the Coast Ranges province in this bulletin.

CLAY

The Ione Formation (Eocene), previously mentioned as a source of glass sand, has yielded most of the clay produced in the Great Valley. The formation contains not only sand but also clay-sand mixtures, with local lenses of clay, shale, gravel, and lignite deposited in a lagoon environment (Cleveland *in* Wright, 1957, p. 135–136). Ione clay is produced from numerous pits, mainly near Lincoln in Placer County, Ione and Buena Vista in Amador County, and Valley Springs in Calaveras County. Smaller deposits are worked near Wheatland in Yuba County, Michigan Bar in Sacramento County, and Knights Ferry and La Grange in Stanislaus County. Clay from the Ione consists mainly of kaolin minerals and is used as fire clay (refractory, structural, and whiteware), although the Stanislaus County deposits are used as ball clay and probably contain some montmorillonite. In 1964, about 70 percent of the clay produced in the Great Valley came from the Ione Formation, both as a principal product and as a coproduct of glass sand.

With one exception, the rest of the clay is obtained from Quaternary alluvial deposits which are present in most parts of the valley. About 10 deposits were worked in 1964 to obtain clay for the manufacture of common and adobe brick and various heavy clay products, as well as for drilling mud.

Perhaps the most unusual deposit is the Excel Mineral Co. deposit in Kern County, where massive, moderately hard, blocky, altered, tuffaceous shale of the Maricopa Formation (Miocene) is quarried for its absorbent properties and sold for cat litter and floor sweepings. The quarried material is largely composed of sericite, and it appears to be similar to, if not typical of, much of the Maricopa Formation, which is probably several thousand feet thick. This formation may well be the largest source of absorbent cat litter in California.

GYPSUM

Quaternary deposits of impure gypsum, or gypsite, occur in several places along the southwest margin of the San Joaquin Valley, where little rain falls and evaporation is rapid. According to Ver Planck (1952, p. 49), three types of gypsite deposits are recognized: (1) "Cap gypsum" that forms secondarily on the upturned edges of older gypsiferous rocks; (2) efflorescent deposits that occur around the margins of periodic lakes; and (3) "channel gypsite" that forms along the beds of dry washes. Perhaps the cap gypsum deposits are most numerous, but the largest deposit (Holloway) at Lost Hills consists of the second and third types of gypsum. In 1964, there were two active producers in the Lost Hills and another at Buena Vista Lake in Kern County. Minor production also was recorded near Los Banos in Merced County. All this gypsite was used for agricultural purposes.

PEAT

Approximately 400 square miles of the Sacramento-San Joaquin River delta area is underlain by peat and peaty muck deposits, which may be more than 40 feet thick. The peat is a reed-sedge type and probably formed during the Recent Epoch. Modest production is obtained by two operators at Frank's Tract, Contra Costa County. The peat is used for soil improvement.

COAL

Modest amounts of coal for fuel have been mined sporadically from thin lignite seams in the Ione area of Amador County from 1888 to 1947. Since 1948, American Lignite Products Co. has worked a 12-foot seam of lignite from which montan wax is extracted. The wax, used in the carbon paper, polish, and rubber industries, is mined nowhere else in the United States.

PUMICITE

Small amounts of pumicite are obtained from two places along the east side of the Great Valley—near Friant, in Madera County, and Buena Vista in Amador County. The Friant deposits are currently and historically the most significant, having been worked since the early 1900's. The pumicite occurs in the Friant Formation (Pleistocene) generally as thin beds, but locally as beds 150 feet thick (Chesterman, 1956, p. 34). More recently developed is the pumicite deposit near Buena Vista. This deposit is part of the Valley Springs Formation (upper Miocene) and is said to be relatively large, although the production to date has been small. Most of the pumicite is used as an insecticide carrier, but some is used as lightweight aggregate.

STONE

Crushed and broken stone are produced intermittently for a variety of purposes from a few places along the perimeter of the Great Valley and from Sutter Buttes, near its center. Some Cretaceous dimension sandstone from the Sites quarry (Colusa County) was used years ago to construct many buildings in the San Francisco area. The most important stone deposit was at Cement Hill, Solano County, where Quaternary travertine was used to manufacture portland cement in 1902–1910 and for lime, flux, and dimension stone at other times. The travertine reserves are now largely depleted. Another nearby travertine deposit at Tolenas Springs is currently supplying small amounts of travertine and calcareous onyx for terrazzo and other decorative stone uses.

GEMSTONES

Minor amounts of semi-gem and mineral materials are obtained by mineral dealers, lapidarists, mineral societies, and amateur collectors from various parts of the valley. The precise localities of production are undetermined.

OTHER MINERAL DEPOSITS

A few other deposits—such as asphalt seeps and veins, marl, and salt springs—were productive of minerals in the past but no longer appear to be of significant economic interest.

REFERENCES

Chesterman, C. W., 1956, Pumice, pumicite, and volcanic cinders in California: California Div. Mines Bull. 174, 119 p.

Goldman, H. B., 1961, Sand and gravel in California, an inventory of deposits, Part A—Northern California: California Div. Mines and Geology Bull. 180-A, 38 p.

—— 1964, Sand and gravel in California, an inventory of deposits, Part B—Central California: California Div. Mines and Geology Bull. 180-B, 58 p.

U. S. Geological Survey in cooperation with the California Division of Mines and Geology (in press), Mineral and water resources of California.

Ver Planck, W. E., 1952, Gypsum in California: California Div. Mines and Geology Bull. 163, 151 p.

Wright, L. A., ed., 1957, Mineral commodities of California: California Div. Mines Bull. 176, 736 p.

CHAPTER VI
COAST RANGES PROVINCE

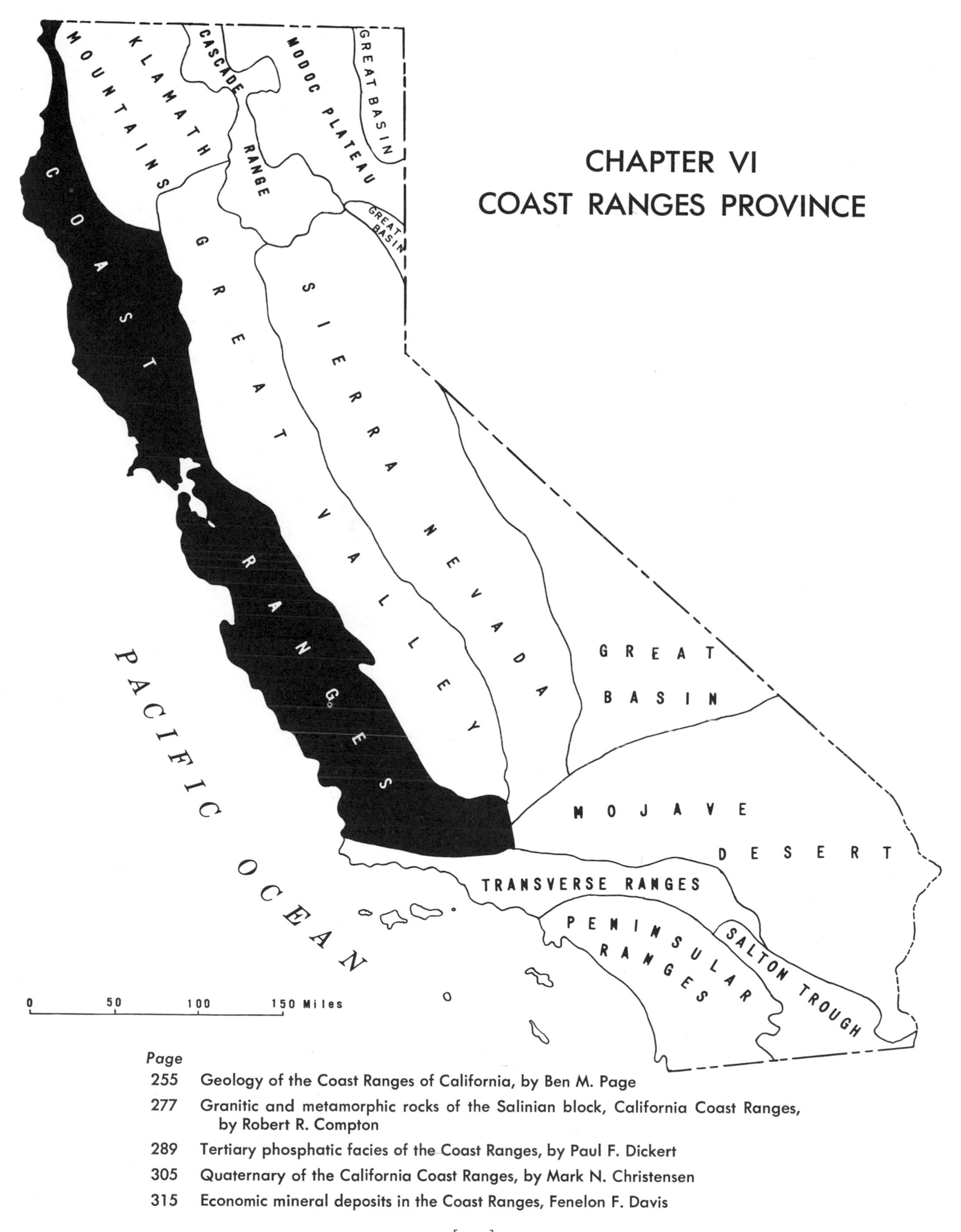

Page

Quicksilver mines at New Almaden. From J. M. Hutchings, *Scenes of wonder and Curiosity in California,* 1861.

GEOLOGY OF THE COAST RANGES OF CALIFORNIA

By Ben M. Page
Stanford University, Stanford, California

The Coast Ranges are plural. The province includes many separate ranges, coalescing mountain masses, and several major structural valleys. Typical tectonic, sedimentary, and igneous processes of the Circum-Pacific orogenic belt have been involved in the evolution of the Coast Ranges, and the geological problems are correspondingly interesting and challenging.

Many geologists have contributed to a better understanding of the province, but only a few can be listed here. A. C. Lawson, an early professor at the University of California, Berkeley, stands out eminently for his studies in the San Francisco Bay region (see, for example, Lawson, 1895 and 1914). Ralph Arnold and Robert Anderson (for example, 1910) typify a scholarly group of petroleum geologists who did pioneer work in the central and southern Coast Ranges. R. D. Reed, a man of extraordinary perception, wrote the first comprehensive volume on the geology of California (Reed, 1933) while employed by an oil company. N. L. Taliaferro and his students at the University of California, Berkeley, accomplished a large amount of fieldwork and interpretation (for example, Taliaferro, 1943). T. W. Dibblee, Jr., formerly a petroleum geologist and currently a member of the U.S. Geological Survey, has mapped and deciphered more Coast Range geology than any other individual. Much work by Taliaferro and Dibblee is incorporated in the Geologic Map of California. E. H. Bailey, W. P. Irwin, and D. L. Jones of the U.S. Geological Survey deserve to be included among principal contributors because of their elucidation of the Franciscan rocks in the northern and central Coast Ranges, and because of their discernment of the structural significance of the relations between these rocks and "normal" rocks. Scores of other persons whose work is outstanding must be left unnamed here, but a few are cited farther on in the text. Readers who desire more references should consult the following: Reed, 1933; Taliaferro, 1943; Bowen, 1962; and Bailey, Irwin, and Jones, 1964.

Among the most valuable aids to the advancement of knowledge of the Coast Ranges are the publications of the California Division of Mines and Geology. Particularly noteworthy is the Olaf P. Jenkins edition of the Geologic Map of California, compiled by C. W. Jennings and others. The reader of this summary will profit by referring to the San Luis Obispo, Bakersfield,[1] Santa Cruz, San Francisco, San Jose, Santa Rosa, Ukiah, and Redding map sheets.

[1] In press, 1966.

OVERVIEW

The California Coast Range province is characterized by particular kinds of rocks and structures. A peculiar distinction is the presence of two entirely different core complexes, one being a Jurassic-Cretaceous eugeosynclinal assemblage—the Franciscan rocks—and the other consisting of Early (?) Cretaceous granitic intrusives and older metamorphic rocks. The two unrelated, incompatible core complexes lie side by side, separated from each other by faults of impressive magnitude. A thick blanket of latest Cretaceous and Cenozoic clastic sedimentary rocks covers large parts of the province, tending to conceal the inner schisms. A record of intermittent but persistent crustal unrest is written in the sediments and intervening unconformities. Folds, thrust faults, steep reverse faults, and strike-slip faults developed as a consequence of Cenozoic deformation, some of which is continuing today.

Although it is hazardous to rank the numerous orogenic events, perhaps four may be singled out as particularly important. They are: (1) The Early(?) Cretaceous orogeny recorded in the Salinian block, marked by intrusion of the plutons of the granitic-metamorphic core complex. (2) Presumed early Tertiary thrusting which, over very large areas, brought "normal" uppermost Jurassic and Cretaceous sedimentary rocks into juxtaposition with quasi-contemporary eugeosynclinal Franciscan rocks. (3) Prolonged Cenozoic strike-slip faulting of great accrued displacement along the San Andreas fault system. (4) Late Pliocene and Pleistocene folding and faulting.

DUAL CORE COMPLEXES (PRE-LATEST CRETACEOUS)

The presence of two types of "basement" in the Coast Ranges was emphasized by R. D. Reed (1933, p. 27–31, and following). Observing that the two types are mutually exclusive in their respective areas of outcrop, he perceived structural and chronologic enigmas which are still only partially solved. Reed's "basement" rocks will here be called "core complexes." One of these is a granitic-metamorphic complex, and the other is the Franciscan assemblage of eugeosynclinal rocks.

Granitic-Metamorphic Core Complex

A complex comprising regionally metamorphosed rocks and granitic plutons is exposed in various places throughout a tract extending several hundred miles northwest from the Transverse Ranges. The northernmost part is largely under the sea, extending to the

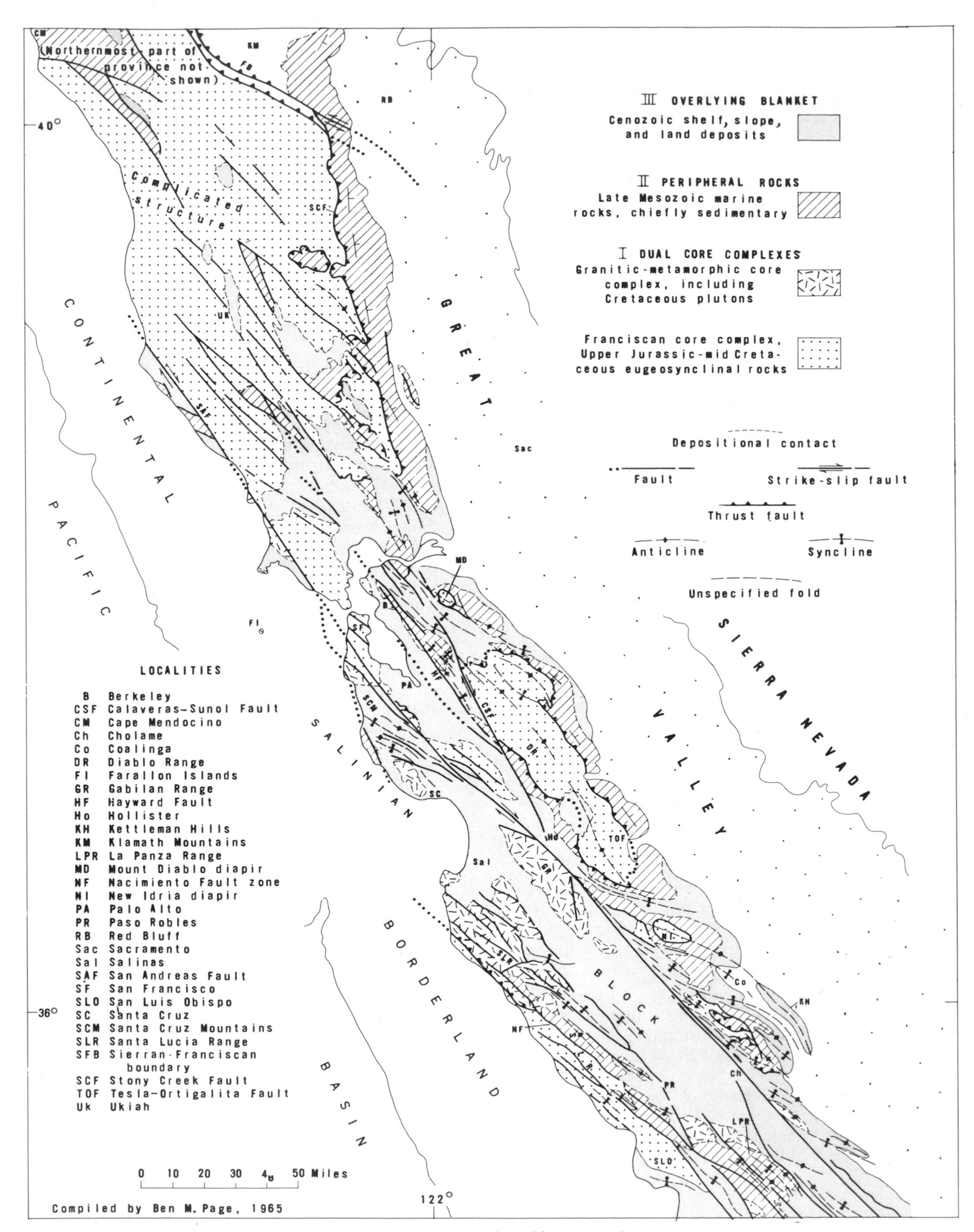

Figure 1. Tectonic map of the California Coast Ranges.

edge of the continental shelf. This tract is bounded on its two sides by the Nacimiento and San Andreas fault zones, and among its prominent topographic features is the Salinas Valley. The name "Salinia" was applied to the area by Reed (1933, p. 12, 73, 314), with paleogeographic implications. For present purposes, the tract will be called the "Salinian Block," following R. R. Compton. The granitic-metamorphic core complex of this block is discussed by Compton in the next section of this bulletin, so the following summary is a mere introduction.

Metamorphic rocks. The earliest available history of any part of the Coast Ranges province is contained in the metamorphic rocks of the Salinian block. These rocks are most extensively exposed and best known in the Santa Lucia Range, where they were named the Sur Series by Trask (1926, p. 134). The rocks of the Sur Series include gneisses, schists, quartzites, marbles, and granulites, which are believed to be chiefly high-grade metamorphic equivalents of shelf or miogeosynclinal sandstone, shale, and carbonate rocks. They have been investigated petrologically and structurally by Compton (1960a, 1966, and this bulletin). A smaller terrane of metamorphic rocks north of Santa Cruz around Ben Lomond Mountain has been studied by Leo (1961). Leo describes marbles, calc-silicate rocks, granitic orthogneiss, quartzites, sillimanite-garnet-mica schists, cordieriate-bearing schists, and migmatitic gneisses. Comparable rocks occur as roof pendants in plutons of other ranges; for example, in the Gabilan Range (Bowen and Gray, 1959; Compton, this bulletin), and in the La Panza Range (Compton, this bulletin).

The ages of the metamorphic rocks are unknown, except that poorly preserved corals and crinoid fragments in marble of the Gabilan Range vaguely suggest a Paleozoic age. Quite possibly several systems are represented by the various rock units.

Granitic plutons. Granitic rocks are extensive in the La Panza, Santa Lucia, Gabilan, and Santa Cruz Ranges (fig. 1). Small exposures occur in intervening

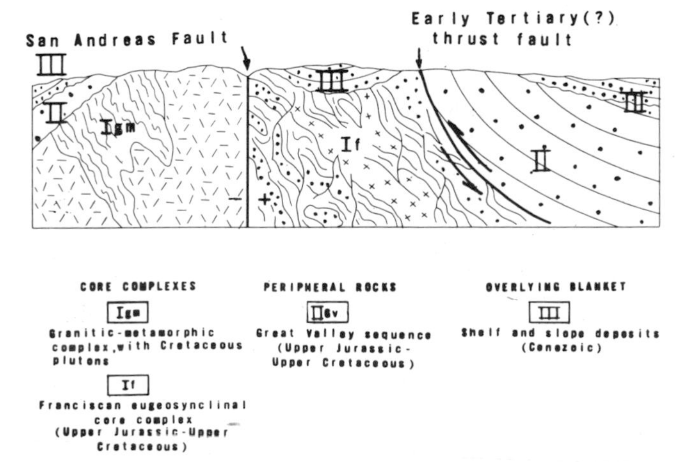

Figure 2. Schematic section across Coast Ranges, not drawn to scale, showing the relations of the principal rock assemblages.

areas, supporting the conclusion that "granite" probably underlies much of the Cenozoic cover in the Salinian block. Granitic rocks are known in such unlikely places as Carmel Submarine Canyon, the Farallon Islands and Cordell Bank at the outer edge of the continental shelf, and Bodega Head 42 miles north of San Francisco. Compton has examined all the main areas of granitic outcrop on land, and has made particularly detailed studies in the Santa Lucia Range. References to other workers will be found in Compton's article, following this one.

Some of the granitic terranes consist of numerous plutons. Quartz diorite, granodiorite, and adamellite predominate, but potassic granite and other varieties also occur. The granitic plutons are commonly accompanied by small ultramafic and gabbroic bodies, some of which appear to be earlier than the more silicic intrusions. According to Spotts (1958), the plutonic rocks of Ben Lomond Mountain, Montara Mountain, Farallon Islands, Point Reyes, and Bodega Head all show almost identical heavy minerals within each particular rock type (such as quartz diorite or granodiorite), as though the geographically separated intrusives might have had similar origins.

Age determinations for the granitic rocks have led to far-reaching hypotheses and to substantial progress in understanding the magnitude and rate of crustal events in the Coast Ranges. Curtis, Evernden, and Lipson (1958) published a paper of great impact in which they reported potassium-argon ages of 81–92 m.y. from six widely separated granitic masses in the Coast Ranges. They concluded that the "granites" are Late Cretaceous, and therefore younger than some Franciscan rocks, a possibility that previously was not widely admitted. They pointed to the incongruous lack of granitic intrusions and appropriate metamorphism in Franciscan rocks where they lie alongside granitic massifs, and argued convincingly for a large displacement on the San Andreas fault. C. O. Hutton (1952, p. 52; 1959, p. 20) had independently deduced an age of 106 m.y. (late Early Cretaceous) for part of the Santa Lucia granitic massifs, based upon (U+Th) : Pb ratios in detrital monazite "clearly derived from the granitic rocks at Monterey."

Cretaceous orogenies. The various "absolute" age determinations indicate that granitic plutons either formed throughout the latter two-thirds of the Cretaceous Period, or that they formed in the Early Cretaceous and were later affected by other disturbances, as favored by Compton (this bulletin).

The Early Cretaceous is presumed to have been a time of heating of sialic material, folding, regional metamorphism, local melting, and emplacement of granitic plutons. Doubtless uplift and erosion accompanied these events. Direct evidence of the metamorphism and plutonism is entirely restricted to the Salinian block, although these actions must have been much more extensive laterally than the present width of the block. The petrologic and structural effects are sharply terminated at the San Andreas and Nacimiento faults.

The Late Cretaceous probably witnessed deformation and elevation of the previously formed granitic-metamorphic complex, which was then further exposed by erosion before subsiding beneath the sea in, or just before, Campanian time. The granitic-metamorphic complex is locally overlain unconformably by Upper Cretaceous strata (Campanian or Maestrichtian). The Late Cretaceous uplift may correspond to the "Santa Lucian orogeny" of Taliaferro (1943, p. 130–132; 1944, p. 484–486), although some of Taliaferro's stratigraphic evidence does not apply to the events envisioned here.

Franciscan Eugeosynclinal Core Complex

In contrast to the rocks described above, a second type of core material in the Coast Ranges is a vast, diverse assemblage of eugeosynclinal rocks with unsystematic structure and without the regional metamorphism and granitic plutons of the other complex. Typical rocks of this assemblage in the vicinity of San Francisco were called the Franciscan Series by Lawson (1895), and the name "Franciscan," with various modifications, has since been used for similar material throughout the province. The areal extent of the assemblage is much greater than that of the granitic-metamorphic core complex, and much of the northern Coast Range region consists of Franciscan rocks with limited remnants of superposed formations. Bailey, Irwin, and Jones (1964) have admirably described and interpreted the Franciscan and associated rocks in a recent important work.

The Franciscan should not be visualized as a formation or sequence with ordinary physical, spatial, and temporal coherence, but rather as a disorderly assemblage of various characteristic rocks that have undergone unsystematic disturbance. The rocks include deep-water sediments and mafic marine volcanic material, all of which are locally accompanied by masses of serpentine.

Sandstone. The prevalent rock type in the Franciscan assemblage is sandstone—chiefly graywacke. The beds are generally 1 to 10 feet thick, and although separated by shale intercalations, as a rule they are not internally layered. In certain areas, for example near Mount Hamilton, some graywacke beds show sole marks, graded texture, and laminated upper parts, but these features are not widespread. Slump structures occur locally. The sand grains of the graywacke are angular and dominantly medium in size. Sorting is poor, and normally more than 10 percent of the rock by volume is a fine matrix of chlorite and mica. The majority of sand grains are plagioclase, quartz, and lithic particles such as greenstone, chert, shale, and schist. Some of the lithic detritus appears to be of intraformational origin. Soliman (1958) made point counts of 80 specimens, mostly from the Mount Hamilton region. He reports quartz, chert, and quartzite collectively ranging from 23 to 62 percent, feldspar 9 to 46 percent, and less stable grains about 9 to 45 percent. Bailey, Irwin, and Jones (1964, p. 30) find that the average of published estimates and measurements of the proportion of feldspar in Franciscan graywackes is about 35 percent.

The K-feldspar content of Franciscan and quasi-contemporary non-Franciscan graywackes was studied by Bailey and Irwin (1959). These authors reported that the median K-feldspar content of graywacke in very typical Franciscan areas is virtually 0. On the other hand, the K-feldspar content of non-Franciscan graywacke of the west side of the Sacramento Valley is approximately 0.5 percent for the uppermost Jurassic rocks, 2.8 percent for the Lower Cretaceous, and 10.6 percent for the Upper Cretaceous. An intermediate content (about 4.5 percent) was found in a large atypical Franciscan terrane in the western Coast Ranges well north of San Francisco. This terrane lacks the greenstone and chert which characterize much of the Franciscan, and is believed to be a different facies.

The graywacke sediments are very immature, were derived by rapid erosion, and were deposited swiftly without normal wave action, probably in part by mass flows and turbidity currents. The source areas are believed to have been metamorphic terranes, and only in the case of the sediments containing K-feldspar was granite present. Soliman (1958, p. 122–127) believes that the graywackes he studied were deposited in a north-south trough, and that the sediment was mainly carried lengthwise along the trough from a source to the north, with minor additions from the sides.

Shale and conglomerate. Shale may amount to 10 percent of the Franciscan sedimentary rocks, but it has not been extensively studied. It occurs as intercalations between graywacke beds and as thicker units which locally predominate over the other rock types. Most of the shale is gray to black, silty, brittle, and somewhat fissile. According to Bailey, Irwin, and Jones (1964, p. 38–39), the shales that have been studied contain only a small percentage of clay minerals and are mineralogically somewhat similar to the graywackes.

Conglomerate is uncommon but informative. It occurs in small, lenticular bodies in graywacke sequences and in tectonically deformed shale. The clasts include quartzite, black chert, and siliceous porphyritic-aphanitic rocks. Granitic cobbles are well known but scarce. Significantly, some conglomerates contain, among other constituents, rounded clasts of graywacke, red and green chert, greenstone, and rocks containing jadeite or glaucophane. This might indicate destruction and re-deposition of earlier parts of the Franciscan assemblage. If the jadeite- and glaucophane-bearing pebbles were derived from previously metamorphosed Franciscan rocks, the implication would be that deep burial, uplift, and profound erosion occurred between periods of Franciscan deposition. However, a conglomerate with jadeite- and glaucophane-bearing pebbles has been shown by Fyfe, Turner, and Zardini (1965) to be a metaconglomerate; jadeite and glaucophane replaced parts of the matrix as well as the pebbles, and these minerals also formed in adjacent graywackes. It is uncertain whether or not these findings apply to most of the conglomerates which appear to contain pebbles of Franciscan metamorphic rocks.

Volcanic rocks. The Franciscan volcanic rocks are described as follows in the abstract of the comprehensive paper by Bailey, Irwin, and Jones (1964, p. 6):

"Altered mafic volcanic rocks, termed greenstones, comprise about a tenth of the assemblage and are widespread. Most consist of pillows, tuffs, or breccias resulting from submarine eruptions, but some massive units may be intrusive. The volcanic accumulations range in size from a few feet to many thousands of feet in thickness and 20 miles in extent. Plagioclase and augite are the chief minerals, and olivine is rare. Altered mafic glass is a nearly ubiquitous component. Plagioclase ranges from bytownite or labradorite to albite * * * . The least hydrous massive varieties, which are the least altered, are chemically similar to tholeiitic basalt, but with soda intermediate between spilite and tholeiite. However, most greenstones are abnormally hydrous, and their composition has been altered through reaction with sea water. As pillows and matrices provide samples of a single magma that have had different opportunities for sea water reaction, analyses of the core, rim, and matrix for two pillows were obtained. If magnesia is regarded as a constant, these analyses show from the center outward large losses in silica, alumina, lime, and soda, and smaller losses of iron; only potash was enriched in the shell or matrix."

Chert and limestone. Franciscan cherts are distinctive, thin-bedded, green or red, closely jointed rocks commonly associated with the greenstones. The packets of beds form discontinuous lenses generally less than a mile in length. Individual beds appear to be uniform when seen in small exposures, but they are actually inconsistent and some have original blunt terminations. The chert is composed of chalcedonic quartz with scattered tests of Radiolaria but with virtually no clastic grains. Commonly, but not invariably, volcanic rocks are found near the chert. This is well illustrated around San Francisco Bay—for example, on the north side of the Golden Gate, at Candlestick Park, and Coyote Hills. Bailey, Irwin, and Jones (1964, p. 65–68) propose that the cherts are chemical precipitates formed by reaction of lava with sea water. These authors demonstrate loss of silica in pillow lavas, based on analyses of parts that were varyingly exposed to sea water. They cite data on solution and dissolution of silica, and conclude that Franciscan lava contributed silica to the ocean at depths of 13,000 feet or more, where the water could attain a high temperature (about 350°C) without boiling, and thereby dissolve large quantities of silica. The silica could have precipitated as a gel when the water cooled.

Limestone occurs in some Franciscan terranes, generally as small, discontinuous bodies. One variety—the Calera Limestone—locally occurs in larger masses and is well known. It is commonly light colored or white and includes a thin-bedded variety with lenses of gray chert. It is extremely fine grained and shows little clastic detritus, but contains tests of pelagic Foraminifera. An associated type is bioclastic and is partly composed of bits of calcareous algae, corals, and pelecypods which are not specifically identifiable. Bailey, Irwin, and Jones (1964, p. 72–77) have described oolitic, pelletal, and other types of limestone. G. A. Thompson (oral communication, 1960) noted the position of Franciscan limestones on thick submarine basalts, and suggested that they represent reef and lagoonal deposits on volcanic piles. The relationship to volcanic rocks is well shown on a map of the New Almaden district (Bailey and Everhart, 1964, pl. 1). Bailey and associates postulate that much of the Franciscan limestone originated by chemical precipitation induced by hot subaqueous lava. Lava may have contributed lime to the water, and the heat may have induced precipitation by driving off CO_2.

Metamorphic rocks. Ordinary kinds of metamorphic rocks are rare in the Franciscan, but some uncommon kinds are characteristic. Notable are the sporadically distributed lenses and masses of glaucophane-bearing rocks, jadeitized graywacke, and eclogite. The glaucophane-bearing materials have attracted much study, as summarized by Bailey, Irwin, and Jones (1964, p. 93–112). Glaucophane, a dark-blue amphibole of composition $Na_2Mg_3Al_2Si_8O_{22}(OH)_2$, occurs in a variety of rocks including blueschist, often with lawsonite, $CaAl_2Si_2O_7(OH)_2 \cdot H_2O$. Glaucophane-bearing rocks appear to have formed isochemically from basalts and (less commonly) from graywackes (Ernst, 1965). Jadeite, a pyroxene of composition $NaAlSi_2O_6$, was discovered as a replacement of graywacke by Maddock (1955) and Bloxam (1956), and was soon recognized in many localities. Near Pacheco Pass, E. B. McKee (1958, 1962) mapped an area of 50 square miles in which graywacke has been jadeitized without noticeable change in outward appearance. Subsequently, suspiciously high densities have been noted in widely distributed Franciscan graywackes (Bailey, Irwin, and Jones, 1964, p. 92).

Theory, experiments, and petrographic observations bearing on the stability of mineral assemblages in the glaucophane-, lawsonite-, and jadeite-bearing rocks point to a widely accepted conclusion: In most instances, these rocks were formed under high confining pressure (say 5.5–7.5 kb), but relatively moderate temperature (say 200° to 300°C). Sufficient lithostatic pressure would prevail at depths of 22 to 30 km, but ordinarily the temperature at such depths would probably be too high to allow this type of metamorphism. One hypothesis to explain the paradox presumes rapid burial to depths of 20 to 30 km, and prompt uplift and unloading by erosion before the normal temperature gradient becomes established. This explanation seems applicable to jadeitized nonschistose graywacke and some glaucophane-lawsonite rocks (McKee, 1962). A second hypothesis, for certain other cases, calls upon tectonic stresses to account for high pressures without excessive temperatures. Coleman and Lee (1963) ascribed such an origin to progressively metamorphosed Franciscan basalt exposed along Ward Creek in Sonoma County. Where tectonic stresses are important, one might expect regional schistosity. This indeed is the case in a large blueschist and phyllite belt along the fault zone forming the east boundary of the Franciscan in the northern Coast Ranges (Blake and Ghent, 1965).

Eclogite has long been known as one of the curious lithologic components of the Franciscan. It generally occurs as lumps or masses tectonically enveloped in other rocks, thus arousing doubts as to its source (crust, or mantle?) and its implications with regard to the tectonic history of the Franciscan assemblage. Coleman, Lee, Beatty, and Brannock (1965) point out mineralogical differences between Coast Range eclogites and those elsewhere which are more reliably associated with the mantle. They believe that various types of eclogite may originate under different pressure-temperature conditions. They give reasons for doubting that Coast Range eclogites originated in the mantle, and suggest formation in the crust under tectonically imposed pressure.

Ultramafic bodies. Serpentine and other ultramafic rocks are common associates of the Franciscan assemblage. In a few localities, partly serpentinized dunite or peridotite dikes, sills, and plugs appear to have been introduced as molten or "crystal mush" intrusions. In other instances, serpentine has been emplaced cold as sill-like bodies along faults, or as diapiric masses. Cold intrusion is indicated by lack of contact metamorphism and typical igneous contacts, and by the sheared, slickensided structure of the masses. The ultimate source of the ultramafic masses is probably the mantle, which may immediately underlie the Franciscan.

Structure of Franciscan terranes. The structure of the Franciscan is as characteristic as the petrology. Rock types such as graywacke and greenstone form outcrop belts with a rough overall preferred trend (generally NW-SE to E-W), but individual beds and layers are discontinuous and erratic. In few places is there an intact succession of strata of large vertical or lateral extent. Many of the contacts between superposed units are tectonic, and structural pinching-out along the strike is typical. Anticlines and synclines with ordinary continuity are uncommon. More commonly, unsystematic strikes and dips are observed. In areas of abundant shale, tectonic pods of graywacke, greenstone, and chert may be found dispersed in the shale matrix. Some of the confusion may be primary, as suggested by slump structures occasionally observed in graywacke and shale. Perhaps large-scale submarine sliding occurred; certainly some Franciscan terranes resemble the *argille scagliose* of Italy.

The Franciscan assemblage has apparently undergone early tectonic events, few of which have been sorted out. At least locally, erosion and redeposition of older Franciscan materials occurred. McKee (1958) describes partly jadeitized mylonite, signifying intense shearing prior to the development of high pressure minerals which he ascribes to load metamorphism.

Following possible depositional disturbances and early tectonic events, the Franciscan was subjected to repeated faulting and folding or quasi-plastic deformation. In some areas, mappable fault zones thousands of feet wide are composed of sheared, squeezed, and strewn-out fragments (see, for example, Bailey and Everhart, 1964, pl. 1). In other cases, structural confusion is not confined to linear belts. Viewed in broad perspective, the entire Franciscan might be regarded as a gigantic tectonic zone at the fringe of the continent.

Age and stratigraphic limits. The age of the Franciscan has been extremely difficult to determine because of the scarcity of fossils and because of uncertain relations with well-dated formations. Some Franciscan rocks are latest Jurassic (Tithonian), as inferred from rare specimens of *Buchia piochii*. However, much of the Franciscan is Cretaceous. A few occurrences of *Buchia crassicollis* indicate Early Cretaceous (Valanginian) age. Thalmann (1942) showed that the Calera Limestone contains *Globotruncana* species of mid-Cretaceous age. An ammonite, *Douvilleiceras* cf. *D. mammillatum* (Schlotheim), discovered in graywacke near the Golden Gate, denotes a late Early Cretaceous (Albian) age, as reported by Schlocker, Bonilla, and Imlay (1954). The youngest fossils found to date in rocks that are definitely Franciscan indicate early Late Cretaceous age (Cenomanian and Turonian). The existing paleontological data are summarized by Bailey, Irwin, and Jones (1964, p. 115–122). One may conclude that the rocks of the assemblage range at least from uppermost Jurassic to lower Upper Cretaceous.

Neither the original top nor the base of the Franciscan assemblage has been recognized. Although there have been reports of upward gradation into the Knoxville Formation (Upper Jurassic), the field relations are invariably dubious. Failure to find the base of the assemblage is particularly significant. It is a striking fact that, despite the innumerable tectonic displacements within the Franciscan terranes, no older materials have been brought into view. This is all the more remarkable when contrasted with occurrences of Precambrian, Paleozoic, Triassic, and Lower Jurassic rocks in adjacent provinces. Some geologists have surmised that the Franciscan assemblage was deposited directly upon the mantle or upon an oceanic crust. The serpentine masses and some of the basaltic rocks which are incorporated in the assemblage may have been dislodged from the substratum.

PERIPHERAL ROCKS OF LATE MESOZOIC AGE

Clastic sedimentary rocks, some of which are about the same age as the Franciscan assemblage but of a different character, are disposed around the Franciscan core complex and are separated from it by fault contacts. Some of these peripheral rocks belong to orderly stratigraphic columns extending unbroken from Upper Jurassic (Tithonian) into the Upper Cretaceous.

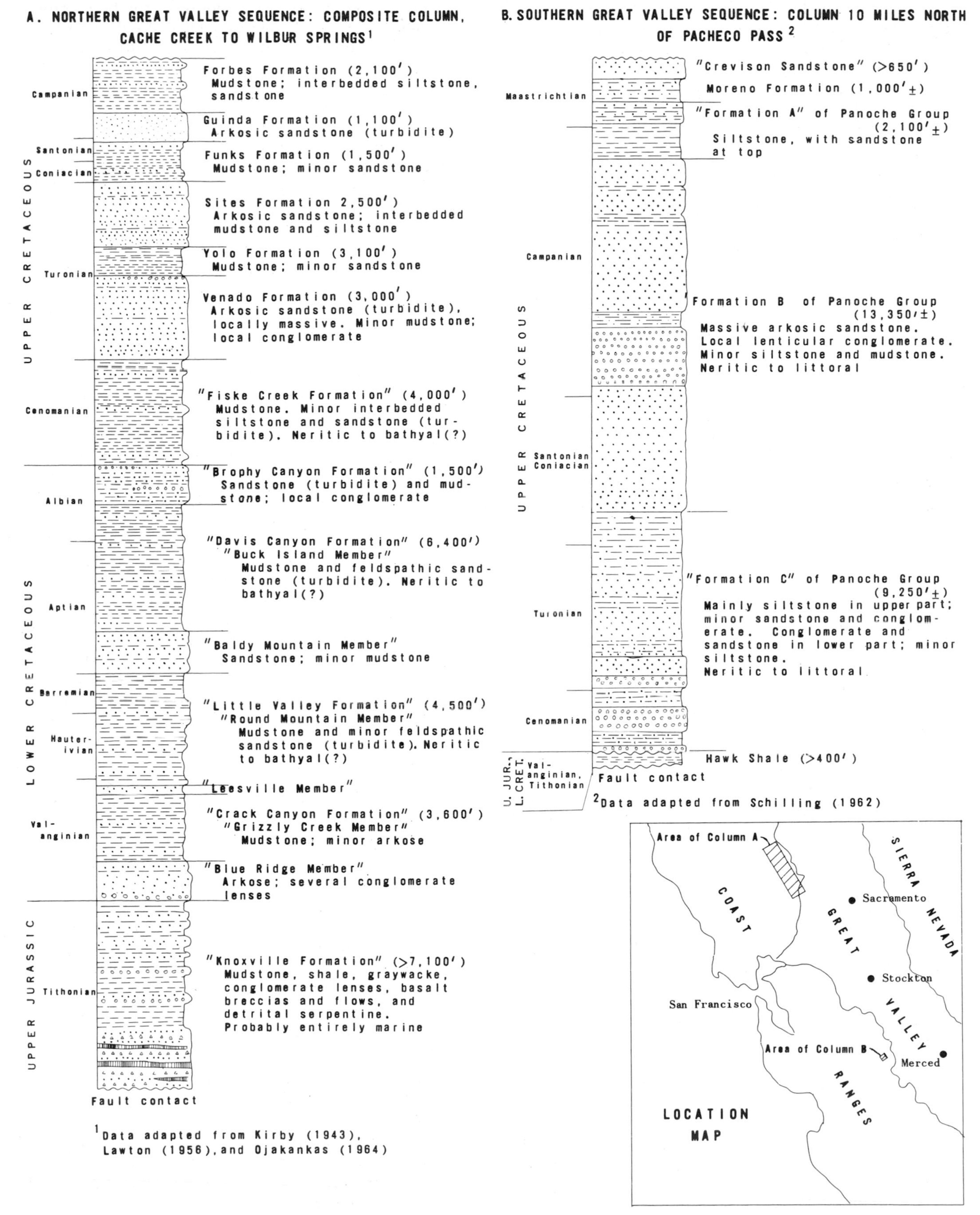

Figure 3. Representative columnar sections of "peripheral rocks" of late Mesozoic age.

In the Salinian block, uppermost Cretaceous strata rest unconformably upon the granitic-metamorphic core complex, whereas contemporary strata to the east seem to be a continuation of a little interrupted sedimentary sequence.

The non-Franciscan sedimentary rocks of Late Jurassic to latest Cretaceous age are here called, for brevity, "Late Mesozoic peripheral rocks," although they occur upon, as well as around, the core complexes. They are interesting on their own merits, but they are also interesting for what they tell of tectonic events.

Great Valley Sequence, Flanking the Franciscan Core

The Great Valley sequence extends along the east flank of the Coast Ranges near the margin of the Sacramento and San Joaquin Valleys. It comprises an imposing volume of marine sandstone, shale or mudstone, and conglomerate. This orderly, little-interrupted sequence, because of its relatively simple petrology and structure, contrasts strikingly with the Franciscan assemblage. Yet today it lies alongside the partly contemporary Franciscan rocks with their eugeosynclinal features and tumultuous structure. The juxtaposition of the two different facies is forceful evidence for large-scale tectonic movement.

Northern part of the Great Valley sequence.—The Jurassic and Cretaceous rocks of non-Franciscan facies along the west side of the Sacramento Valley have been the subject of modern studies by Kirby (1943), Murphy (1956), Lawton (1956), Chuber (1961), Brown and Rich (1961), Ojakangas (1964), and others. References to older work will be found in the foregoing papers.

Upper Jurassic rocks, often called "Knoxville" (White, 1885, p. 19), occur in a north-south belt more than 110 miles long. The section attains a thickness of 16,000 feet, and the upper few thousands of feet contains *Buchia piochii* (Gabb), indicating Tithonian (latest Jurassic) age. Dark shale generally predominates, but it is rhythmically interrupted by thin graywacke beds. In some intervals graywacke is as abundant as shale. In several areas the lower part of the section contains basaltic pillow lava, breccia, and basaltic sandstone, suggesting an affinity with the Franciscan, but the rest of the column differs markedly from the Franciscan assemblage. Great bodies of conglomerate are common, and a few pebbly mudstones have been described (Crowell, 1957, p. 995–998). Pebbles and cobbles are well rounded and include basic igneous rocks, aphanitic-porphyritic dacites or rhyolites, quartzite, chert (gray, black, red, and green), and rare granitic material. Few, if any, of these clasts have been matched with formations *in situ*, and the source areas of the sediment are unknown except for the clues offered by paleocurrent indications (see below). It would be of interest to compare the clasts of the "Knoxville" conglomerates with those of the rarer, quasi-contemporaneous Franciscan conglomerates.

A magnificent Cretaceous section is the best known feature of the Great Valley sequence. Neglecting local folds, the strata tend to lie homoclinally along the entire west side of the Sacramento Valley, generally dipping eastward. There is no physical break at the Jurassic-Cretaceous time boundary, so the lowest Cretaceous (Valanginian) beds are only distinguished from the "Knoxville" by fossils such as *Buchia crassicollis* (Keyserling). In some areas the stratigraphic column extends upward from the Upper Jurassic "Knoxville" through the Lower Cretaceous and well up toward the top of the Upper Cretaceous, apparently representing continuous marine deposition. The Cretaceous rocks are sandstone, shale or mudstone, and conglomerate; these are collectively 34,000 feet thick in places. The sandstone varies from graywacke to arkosic sandstone. Conglomerate occurs at many horizons in lenticular units up to 500 feet or more in thickness, some extending along the strike for miles. The pebbles are said to be lithologically similar to those in the "Knoxville" conglomerates.

Sedimentary structures of Cretaceous and uppermost Jurassic sandstones of the west side of the Sacramento Valley were studied by Ojakangas (1964). He concludes that the sediments were derived from the north and east, and were deposited by turbidity currents in an outer-neritic, upper bathyal environment, presumably in a wide, north-south trough with no land to the west. His measurements of 900 paleocurrent directions show prevailing movement from north to south except at particular horizons. Probably detritus entered the trough along the east side, and was then swept southward parallel with the axis. Ojakangas notes the advent of quartz-plagioclase plutonic debris in rocks of the upper Tithonian or lower Valanginian Stage, perhaps denoting unroofing of Nevadan (Kimmeridgian?) batholiths. A sudden flood of K-feldspar in rocks of the upper Albian Stage is believed to signal deroofing of Cretaceous granitic rocks. It may be relevant that local submarine slump deposits containing Albian fossils and granodiorite blocks have been found at the top of the Cenomanian part of the column by Brown and Rich (1960). Chuber (1961, p. 88) finds an exceptional abundance of conglomerate in the early Cenomanian part of the Cretaceous section, and relates this to orogeny accompanying emplacement of plutons somewhere in the source area, although granitic clasts are not abundant in the conglomerates he examined.

Southern part of the Great Valley sequence.—The stratigraphy of the Great Valley sequence has been studied in various more southerly areas along the west side of the San Joaquin Valley by Briggs (1953), Payne (1951, 1962), Schilling (1962), Marsh (1960), and others.

Along the edge of the San Joaquin Valley, Upper Jurassic "Knoxville"-type shale and Lower Cretaceous strata appear only at intervals, but Upper Cretaceous rocks form a more nearly continuous belt southward all the way to Kern County. Although the Upper Cretaceous deposits are largely sandstone, shale, and conglomerate like their northern counterparts, turbidites are not so omnipresent and depositional conditions seem to have varied. Most of the Upper Cretaceous is included in the Panoche Group (Anderson and Pack, 1915, p. 38–39; Payne, 1962, p. 165–175). The Moreno Shale (Maestrichtian-Danian), overlying the Panoche Group, differs greatly from the older rocks. It is largely composed of brown, somewhat siliceous mudstone rich in organic matter, Foraminifera, diatoms, Radiolaria, and silicoflagellates. Comparable siliceous mudstones appear at intervals in Eocene, Miocene, and Pliocene sections of various parts of the Coast Ranges.

In a recent study of an area east of Pacheco Pass, Schilling (1962) describes an unbroken 28,000-foot Upper Cretaceous section including both the Panoche Group and the Moreno Shale, collectively ranging in age from Cenomanian through Maestrichtian. This section rests unconformably upon Valanginian rocks (lower Lower Cretaceous). Perhaps the late Albian-early Cenomanian uplift and erosion which is indicated by the unconformity is related to the orogeny (in the Sierra region?) that is marked in the northern Great Valley sequence by changes in sediment. The lower half of the Upper Cretaceous section examined by Schilling contains lenticular conglomerates. As pointed out by earlier workers, the pebbles include granitic rocks but virtually no distinctive Franciscan clasts. The majority of pebbles are dark aphanitic porphyritic rocks which are not known *in situ.* Schilling believes the detritus came from the east, perhaps in part from surficial volcanic rocks in a terrain now covered by sediments of the San Joaquin Valley. He believes that the debris was deposited in mid-neritic to littoral environments and that during the early Late Cretaceous, repeated orogeny occurred immediately to the east. In the late Late Cretaceous, the shoreline moved east to the area of the present Sierra Nevada. Evidently the deep Cretaceous trough envisaged by Ojakangas along the site of the Sacramento Valley area swerved to the west or became shallower before reaching the region studied by Schilling.

In the general latitude of the Bay area, Upper Jurassic and Lower Cretaceous rocks of the Great Valley type are found as far west as the Hayward fault and locally, perhaps, as far as the San Andreas fault. To date, there is no convincing evidence that sediment derived from the Salinian block was deposited on the east side of the San Andreas fault. Salinia was involved in Late Cretaceous uplift and was deeply eroded. If no sediment from that orogenic area is included in the Great Valley sequence, the Salinian block could hardly have been in its present position during the Late Cretaceous. This is a strong argument for the hypothesis of large displacement on the San Andreas fault, as pointed out by Curtis, Evernden, and Lipson (1958, p. 14–15) and Bailey, Irwin, and Jones (1964, p. 139).

Upper Cretaceous Cover on Granitic-Metamorphic Core

No autochthonous Upper Jurassic or Lower Cretaceous sedimentary rocks are known in the tract underlain by granitic-metamorphic basement west of the San Andreas fault—the Salinian block. This is consistent with the Cretaceous dates which have been deduced for important orogenies recorded in the block. If indigenous Upper Jurassic or Lower Cretaceous strata ever existed in the Salinian block, they are now part of the metamorphic complex invaded by granitic plutons. However, uppermost Cretaceous sediments are well known. The Asuncion Group (Taliaferro, 1943, p. 132; 1944, p. 486–512), which is believed to be more than 6,000 feet thick, consists of biotitic feldspathic sandstone and smaller amounts of shale and conglomerate. It is partly composed of detritus from the granitic-metamorphic complex. Sandstones which are probably correlative with part of the Asuncion group unconformably lap over the Sur Series and granitic plutons. Some of these sandstones contain late Late Cretaceous fossils such as the rudistid *Coralliochama orcutti* White (Campanian or Maestrichtian).

OVERLYING BLANKET: CENOZOIC SHELF AND SLOPE DEPOSITS

For decades the Coast Ranges have been known as a province of thick, well-folded Cenozoic sedimentary rocks. These are described in a voluminous literature and in even more voluminous files of petroleum companies. Convenient summaries include Reed (1933) and Taliaferro (1943), but these are somewhat out of date. Relatively recent local studies have been made by Cummings, Touring, and Brabb (1962) in the Santa Cruz Mountains; J. C. Clark (1966) farther south in the same range; Colburn (1961) in the Mount Diablo region; Case (1963) in the Berkeley Hills; Hall (1958) in the Niles-Pleasanton area; and a number of others.

Marine sedimentary formations are known for virtually every epoch and stage from early Paleocene to Pleistocene, but no single locality possesses a complete column. This is a consequence of orogenic interruptions which were not everywhere simultaneous. The sediments are predominantly nondistinctive sandstone and shale or mudstone, many of the formations are of restricted areal extent, and marked changes in lithofacies occur within short distances. Accordingly, correlation and interpretation are not easy, particularly where the structure is complex. The use of megafossils, chiefly molluscan, in determining geologic ages and correlations was introduced in the Coast Ranges before the present century, and is continuing today. The study of heavy detrital mineral grains was introduced in the 1920's. The use of Foraminifera, beginning in earnest in the 1930's, proved to be extremely effective. Faunal stages for the Miocene were established on the basis of Foraminifera by Kleinpell (1938), and comparable stages were set up for the Paleocene and Eocene by Mallory (1959). More recently, efforts have been made to date and to correlate by means of palynomorphs, but so far few results applicable to the

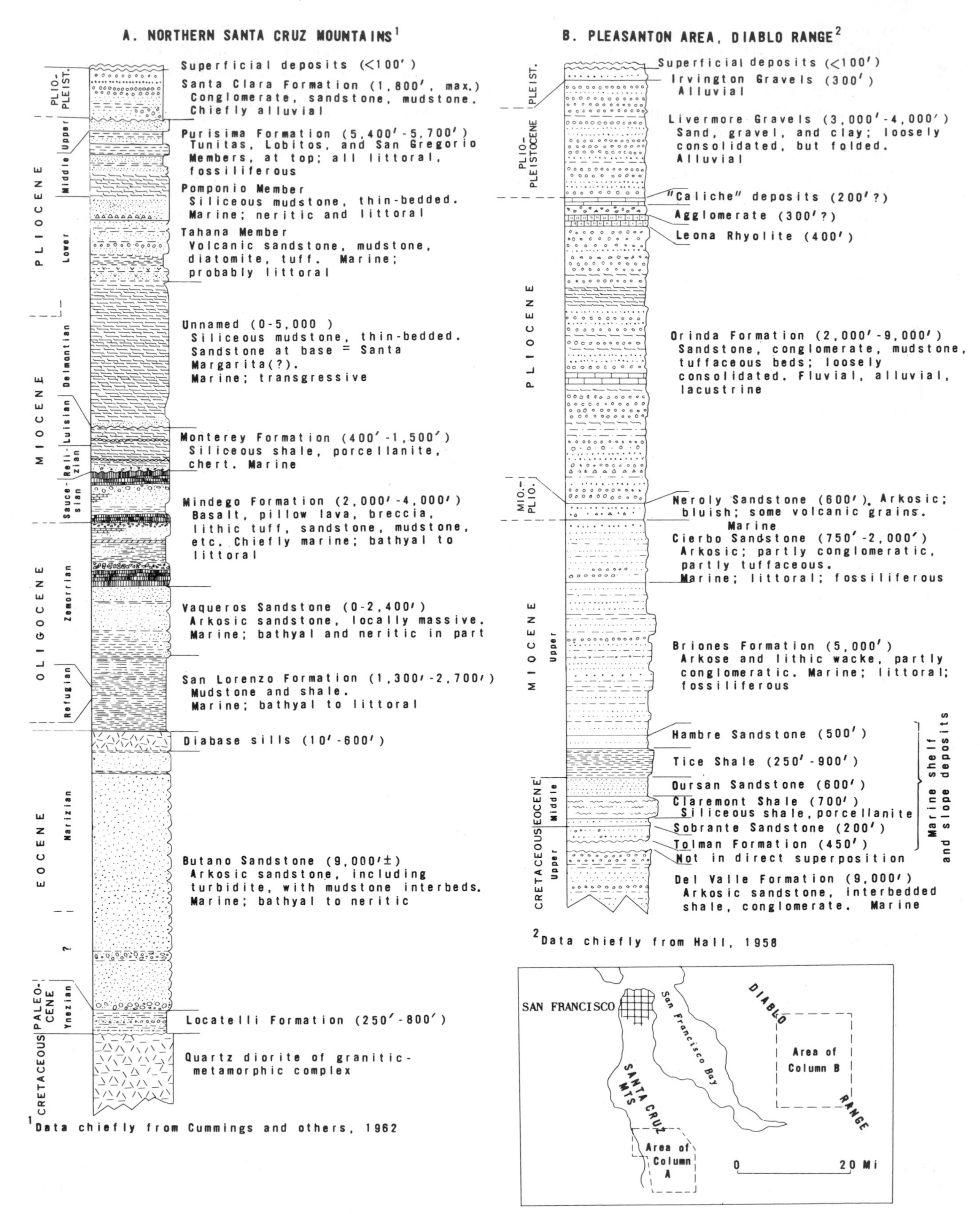

Figure 4. Representative columnar sections of "overlying blanket" of Cenozoic deposits.

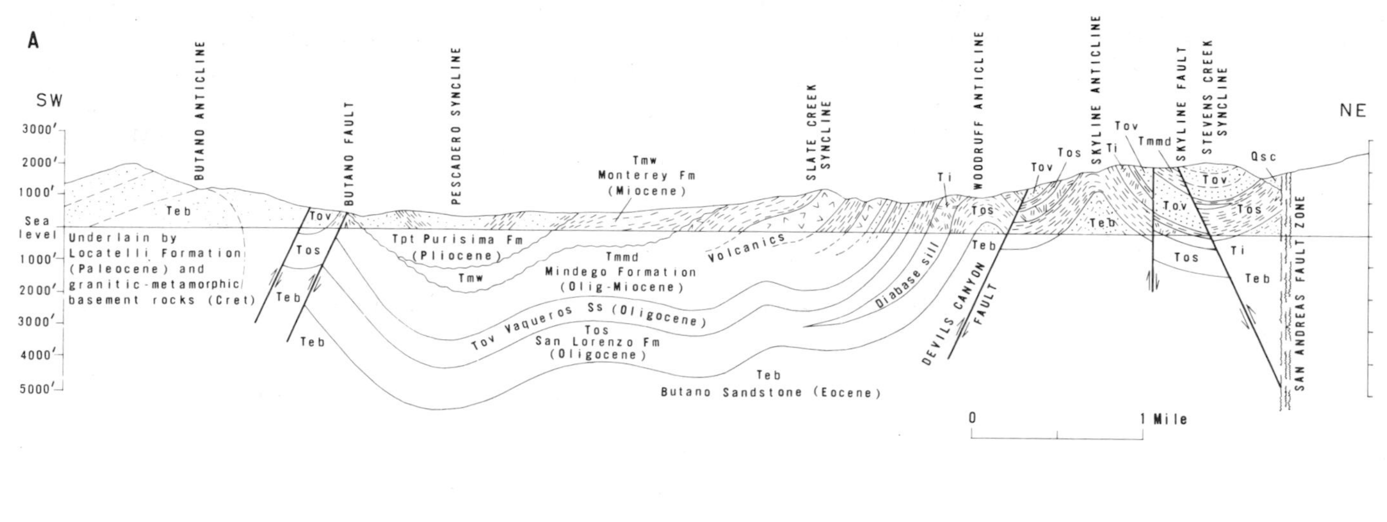

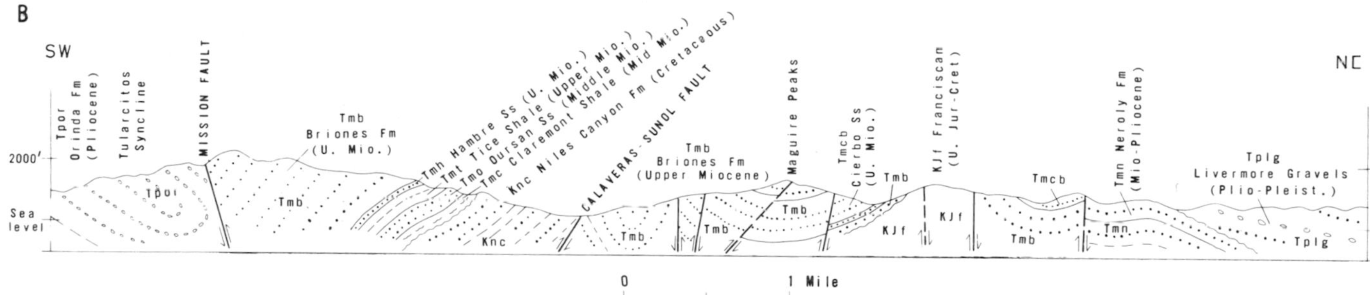

Figure 5. Typical cross sections. Cross section A is modified from Cummings, Touring, and Brabb, 1962 and is in area of column A, figure 4. Cross section B is modified from Hall, 1958, and is in area of column B, figure 4.

Cenozoic rocks of the Coast Ranges have been published. In the meantime, a most important endeavor has been made by Evernden and associates (1964) to relate critical faunas and floras to ages obtained by the potassium-argon method. This promises to reduce the confusion caused by conflicting geologic age assignments by specialists in different branches of paleontology—a confusion compounded by the occurrence of various biofacies at a particular time horizon.

Paleocene rocks. For present purposes, "Paleocene" refers to rocks representing the Ynezian and Bulitian foraminiferal stages (Mallory, 1959, p. 74–75). Rocks of this age are not broadly distributed, but are nonetheless interesting for paleogeologic information. West of the San Andreas fault, marine Paleocene clastic sections generally begin with shore deposits unconformably resting on Cretaceous rocks—for example, at Point Reyes, Point San Pedro, Ben Lomond Mountain, Point Lobos, and the Santa Lucia Mountains. In some cases the underlying rocks are granitic plutons, and in other cases they are Upper Cretaceous sedimentary rocks. It appears that Paleocene marine transgression followed widespread erosion in what is now coastal California, but the unroofing of Cretaceous plutons had already taken place prior to the deposition of latest Cretaceous sediments, and the pre-Ynezian erosion may not have accomplished much beyond the stripping of postplutonic sediments.

Paleocene strata near Clear Lake and Mount Diablo also rest unconformably on older rocks. Surprisingly, despite the proximity of Franciscan rocks in these areas, the Paleocene sediments contain little or no Franciscan detritus. The basal conglomerates hold a story which has not yet been worked out although Reed (1933, p. 125 and following) long ago recognized the probable importance of this record.

Along the west side of the San Joaquin Valley marine deposition may have been locally continuous from Late Cretaceous into early Paleocene time, judging from published data, but eastward under the valley the Paleocene sandstones overlap successively older formations.

Eocene rocks. Eocene marine arkosic sandstone and mudstone formations are well known and locally prominent. In the Santa Cruz Mountains, the Butano Sandstone (more than 6,000 feet thick) includes turbidite sediments chiefly derived from the Salinian block and deposited in a bathyal environment (Cummings, Touring, and Brabb, 1962, p. 184–186). This formation probably represents part of the Penutian, all of the Ulatisian, and much of the Narizian, as judged from Foraminifera. In the Santa Lucia Range, the same stages are also represented by massive arkose and smaller amounts of mudstone. The environment of deposition is thought to have varied from littoral to bathyal.

On the east flank of the Coast Ranges, Eocene deposits also record extremely variable conditions. The Lodo Formation, consisting of mudstone and sandstone, is said to yield Foraminifera indicating neritic or deeper zones, but the middle part (Penutian) locally contains thin calcareous layers with orbitoidal foraminifers and corals denoting clear, shallow, warm water (Mallory, 1959, p. 35–36). The stratigraphically higher Kreyenhagen Formation (mostly Narizian) is mainly organic-rich, somewhat siliceous mudstone. In the very fine clastic matrix there are abundant Foraminifera and diatoms, including species believed to indicate neritic to bathyal conditions, and in some beds there are mud pectens. The Kreyenhagen Formation also contains many thin, bentonitic, tuffaceous beds resulting from explosive volcanism in or near the Narizian sea.

Middle Eocene formations east of Mount Diablo and southeast of Livermore are distinctive for the sporadic occurrence of white quartz-rich sands, thin beds of sub-bituminous coal, and local clays of economic interest. These sediments collectively indicate littoral and swamp deposition in a tropical or subtropical climate.

In summary, although at first acquaintance the Eocene rocks may seem like a monotonous repetition of sandstones and mudstones, they range from bathyal turbidites to swamp deposits. An exact time correlation between various facies is lacking, but certainly there is marked variability both laterally and vertically. The Kreyenhagen mudstones, like the older (Cretaceous) Moreno Shale and some younger formations, reflect a distinctive type of sedimentation in which nondetrital silica plays a part. Moreover, the Kreyenhagen contains subtle evidence of volcanism. Finally, the climate of the Eocene was warmer and moister than the rest of the Tertiary epochs, judging from the floras, faunas, and physical features of shallow marine and swamp deposits.

Oligocene rocks. For present purposes, the Oligocene is assumed to be represented by the Refugian and Zemorrian foraminiferal stages. Oligocene rocks in the western part of the province show some interesting vertical and lateral changes. For example, in the Santa Lucia Range, near San Juan Bautista, and in the southern Santa Cruz Mountains, nonmarine Oligocene beds are overlain by, or interfinger with, marine Vaqueros Sandstone of Zemorrian-Saucesian age. In the Santa Cruz Mountains, shale and mudstone of the San Lorenzo Formation extend from the upper Narizian through the Refugian and part of the Zemorrian stage, and represent slow deposition at bathyal depths, changing to rapid deposition in a restricted basin (Brabb, 1964). The San Lorenzo grades upward into the Zemorrian part of the Vaqueros Sandstone, which interfingers laterally with submarine basalt flows and tuffs (Cummings, Touring, and Brabb, 1962, p. 188–193). These volcanic rocks are probably the earliest post-Franciscan basalts in the Coast Ranges.

Nonmarine Oligocene deposits are found not only in the localities mentioned above, but are also reported west of Paso Robles and between Santa Maria and Carrizo Plain. Some Oligocene nonmarine sediments are closer to the present shoreline than any other pre-Pliocene nonmarine deposits, and they show that land (or islands) occupied the present coastal area for considerable lengths of time. However, along the west side of the San Joaquin Valley, the upper part of the Kreyenhagen Formation represents Oligocene (Refugian) marine deposition continuing from the Eocene. Near Mount Diablo, the Kirker Formation, which is also marine, contains nearly 100 feet of rhyolitic ash.

Although the Oligocene rocks show an interesting range of depositional conditions, the record is very imperfect because of difficulties in correlation and loss by erosion of most of the sedimentary record.

Miocene rocks. The rocks of Miocene age are more widely preserved than those of the earlier Tertiary. They are varied, but taken as a whole they differ from most of the older formations by the presence of more organic material, more megafossils, and more prevalent siliceous mudstone units. To be sure, these features also obtain in a few exceptional older formations such as the Moreno Shale and Kreyenhagen Formation.

Local orogenic events, typical of the Cenozoic history of the Coast Ranges, are well documented by the Miocene deposits. Sediments were deposited in open shelf seas and embayments, and in many areas the stratigraphic succession rests discordantly on older rocks, contains angular unconformities, or loses lower members toward the edges of the depositional basin. For example, in part of the Santa Lucia Range west of King City, the Miocene column of marine sediments is continuous from the Vaqueros Sandstone (Zemorrian-Saucesian), Sandholdt Formation (a somewhat siliceous, organic mudstone of Saucesian-Relizian-Luisian age), Monterey Formation (siliceous shale, porcelanite, and chert, of largely Luisian and Mohnian age), and Santa Margarita Formation (white, quartzose arenite, of Delmontian age). About 15 miles to the west and south in the same range, the Monterey Formation rests directly on the basement complex. This paradox could be explained in various ways, as follows: (1) The basin or embayment was fully formed and static during deposition, so that the older sediments were only laid down in the middle as the water level rose. This seems unlikely, as the rim of the basin would have been more than 8,000 feet above the floor (judging from the thickness of the deposits), and the sediments should be correspondingly coarse grained. (2) There was no basin as presently delimited; instead, the older strata were widely distributed, and were later eroded from an uplifted peripheral area; deposition continued in the central part and spread laterally in the Luisian stage when the uplift of the periphery had ceased. In this case, the central sediments might be expected to contain a record of the peripheral uplift; however, such a record has not been discerned. (3) The basin formed gradually by tectonic deformation, and was concurrently submerged. This third hypothesis seems more realistic than the other two.

A double cycle of Miocene-Pliocene sedimentation is evident in the Santa Cruz Mountains. According to J. C. Clark (oral communication, 1963), a transgressive upper Relizian sandstone, locally resting on the granitic basement, is overlain by lower Luisian siliceous organic mudstone equivalent to the Monterey Formation. These units are in turn transgressed, with an intervening angular unconformity, by another sandstone—the Santa Margarita, of Mohnian-Delmontian age—which is followed by slightly siliceous mudstone, as in the first cycle. Orogenic disturbance prior to each period of deposition is clearly evident. It is equally clear in other localities that disturbances did not take place everywhere in coastal California at these particular times, but that various areas underwent comparable movements at different times in the Miocene and Pliocene.

Opaline silica, organic matter (or derived hydrocarbons), and phosphate are notable features of some of the Miocene marine sediments. The occurrence and significance of the phosphate is treated in this bulletin by Paul Dickert. Siliceous sediments include abundant siliceous mudstone and porcelanite, less plentiful chert, and local diatomite. The siliceous sediments of the Monterey Formation are believed by Bramlette (1946) to have involved accumulation of silica in diatom tests and redistribution of the silica during diagenesis. Either the influx of normal clastic detritus was reduced (perhaps because of low topographic relief adjacent to the area of deposition) or the accumulation of silica was relatively rapid. Some geologists (for example, Taliaferro, 1933) have maintained that the abundance of silica is ultimately related to volcanism. Volcanic ash is often reported in the siliceous sediments, but the latter are very fine grained, and much of the fine material is difficult to identify. The dissolution of silica from vitric ash, if such was present, would have been relatively easy, and this may have encouraged the growth of diatoms or perhaps the direct accumulation of silica gel. However, the role of ocean currents, as suggested by the presence of phosphatic precipitates, may have been more important than volcanism.

Regardless of the question of origin of siliceous sediments, the fact remains that the Miocene rocks contain more evidence of volcanism than most of the preceding Tertiary sequences. At intervals in the Monterey Formation, there are layers of bentonitic clay an inch or less thick. Actual flows and tuffs of Miocene age occur in several areas. These volcanic rocks, which include rhyolites, dacites, andesites, and basalts, are discussed by Taliaferro (1943, p. 142–144). Intermittent volcanism persisted into the Pliocene.

Mio-Pliocene and Pliocene rocks. Volcanic clastic detritus and ash are quite obvious in several marine sandstones which are either uppermost Miocene or Lower Pliocene—for example, the lower part of the Purisima Formation, the Neroly and Cierbo Formations, and the Jacalitos Formation. In the order named, these formations occur from the present coast to the west edge of the San Joaquin Valley. They are upper Delmontian or younger. These sandstones contain grains of andesite, and some of the grains have a bluish coating. Lerbekmo (1956) concluded that most of the andesitic detritus came from the Mehrten Formation, a widespread volcanic blanket covering parts of the Sierra Nevada, and he showed that the bluish coating on the grains is a film of montmorillonoid mineral derived from andesitic material.

The variety of sediments in the Pliocene rocks is well illustrated by the Purisima Formation of the Santa Cruz Mountains (Cummings, Touring, and Brabb, 1962, p. 197–212). The lowest member contains volcanic sandstones, diatomite, and a vitric tuff bed as well as normal mudstones. The succeeding member, more than 2,000 feet thick, comprises lower and middle Pliocene siliceous mudstone and porcelanite and resembles the Miocene Monterey Formation. This is followed by sandstone and mudstone members of middle and upper Pliocene age. Along the edge of the San Joaquin Valley, marine and brackish water Pliocene formations of the Jacalitos-Etchegoin sequence differ from the foregoing in their preponderance of silt and sand. A thickness on the order of 6,500 feet is attained just west of Coalinga. Nonmarine sediments compose the Upper Pliocene rocks in a number of areas in the Coast Ranges.

Volcanic material is not only represented by clastic detritus and fine ash in certain Pliocene sediments, but also appears as flows and coarse fragmental extrusives in some localities—most notably in a 700 square mile area north of San Francisco Bay. Here the Sonoma Volcanics consist mainly of andesitic flows, breccias, and tuffs which are locally separated by thin nonmarine sediments.

Plio-Pleistocene deposits. One of the most characteristic types of deposit in the southern and middle Coast Ranges is coarse, poorly sorted, rudely stratified, alluvial sediment of Plio-Pleistocene age. These deposits rest unconformably on folded Tertiary rocks, and obviously postdate an important amount of deformation, but are probably syn-orogenic in the sense that local uplift in the source areas continued to provide swiftly deposited sediment. Moreover, the alluvial strata themselves were folded in zones of resumed deformation in middle and late Quaternary time. The distribution, petrology, and structure of deposits such as the Santa Clara Formation, Livermore Gravels, Packwood Gravels, San Benito Gravels, Paso Robles Formation, and Tulare Formation hold the key to interpretation of the late Cenozoic orogenic history of the Coast Ranges, as discussed by M. N. Christensen in a subsequent part of this bulletin.

MAJOR STRUCTURAL BOUNDARIES

If we peel the Late Mesozoic and the Cenozoic deposits from western California, exposing the dual core complexes, four major structural boundaries stand out starkly (fig. 6). Three of the boundaries separate the granitic-metamorphic complex from the Franciscan rocks. The fourth, at the margin of the deep ocean floor, appears to truncate the continental rocks and structures abruptly. Although it is tectonically relevant to the Coast Ranges, it will not be discussed here. These major structural features have been insufficiently studied, and are not well understood. Of the four, only the San Andreas fault is being intensively investigated.

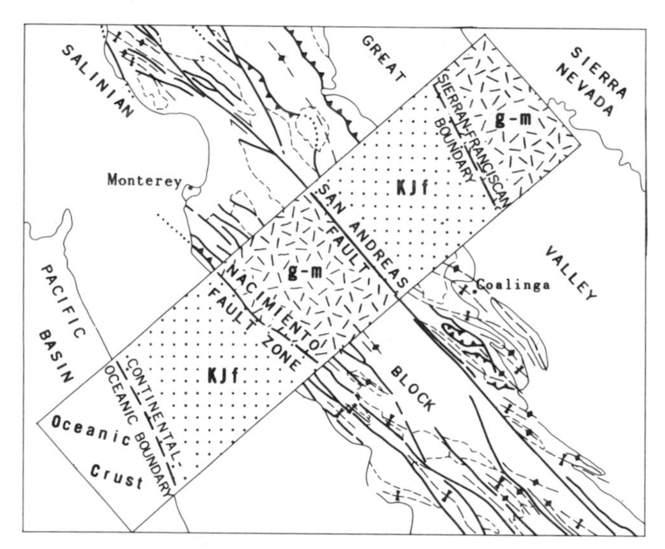

Figure 6. Major structural boundaries of the Coast Ranges, shown by a part of figure 1 redrawn with younger rocks "peeled" from transverse rectangular area to reveal underlying rocks and principal contacts.

Sierran-Franciscan boundary. The granitic-metamorphic basement of the Sierra Nevada passes beneath the sediments of the Great Valley, and there presumably meets (or approaches) the Franciscan rocks. The zone of contact (or proximity) is nowhere recognized except in the north part of the State, where it emerges from the Great Valley and passes northwestward toward the Pacific, forming the juncture between the Klamath Mountains and the Coast Ranges. Here it appears to be a thrust fault zone dipping east and northeast (Irwin, 1960, 1964, and this bulletin). This zone is locally bordered on the southwest by a belt of phyllitic metasediments considered by some to be metamorphosed Franciscan rocks. The total amount of displacement is entirely unknown, but it is sufficient to bring the older rocks of the Klamath Mountains against the somewhat younger Franciscan rocks of the Coast Ranges throughout a distance of 260 miles in Oregon and northern California alone, to say nothing of the inferred southward continuation of the zone beneath the Great Valley.

Near the edge of the Sacramento Valley west of Red Bluff, the Sierran-Franciscan boundary behaves peculiarly, judging from available maps and reports. (For example, see Geologic Map of California, Redding Sheet, 1962, and Ukiah Sheet, 1960.) A tentative explanation is shown in figure 7. The boundary appears to have been overlapped depositionally by Lower Cretaceous strata of the Great Valley sequence, including Hauterivian beds. This is difficult to explain, because the fault which constitutes the exposed part of the boundary truncates Franciscan rocks and accordingly is most likely post-mid-Cretaceous. The Great Valley strata are offset, showing several northwest to southeast separations collectively amounting to 15 miles, but this can hardly represent the total displacement along the Sierran-Franciscan boundary. Rather, it probably indicates left-lateral slip, like that of a tear fault, associated with westward thrusting of the Sierran complex. South of the postulated tear fault, the margin of the Sierran complex presumably lies deep beneath the Sacramento Valley, and extends southward under a thick cover of Tithonian, Cretaceous, and Cenozoic strata. However, west of Red Bluff the surficial aspect of the principal fault abruptly changes in character. As it passes southward from the tear fault, the main fault trace abandons the Sierra-Franciscan boundary, and becomes the tectonic contact (known as the Stony Creek fault) between the Franciscan assemblage and the Great Valley sequence. Probably the Stony Creek fault is a thrust which flattens at depth and passes under the margin of the Sierran complex beneath the Sacramento Valley.

Nacimiento fault zone. The Nacimiento fault and its relatives form a northwest-trending zone which passes out to sea near Point Sur. This structural zone is analogous to the Sierran-Franciscan boundary, inasmuch as it separates granitic-metamorphic basement rocks on the northeast from Franciscan rocks on the southwest. It appears to be a northeast-dipping thrust zone where it is best exposed along the coast. The similarities between this and the Sierran-Franciscan boundary have led Hill and Dibblee (1953) and others (for example, King, 1959) to imply that the two boundaries may be one and the same, the San Andreas fault having produced an apparent duplication. This is an appealing hypothesis. If it is valid, the Nacimiento fault zone and the Sierran-Franciscan boundary should be the same age. This seems entirely possible, but is unproved. The Sierran-Franciscan boundary fault west of Red Bluff is presumably latest Cretaceous or Tertiary. The Nacimiento fault zone did not exist at the time of the Early(?) Cretaceous plutonism, but was active during some interval in or after the latest Cretaceous, as it cuts strata of Campanian or Maestrichtian age. The Nacimiento fault zone is not now active, but the time of cessation of its activity has never been

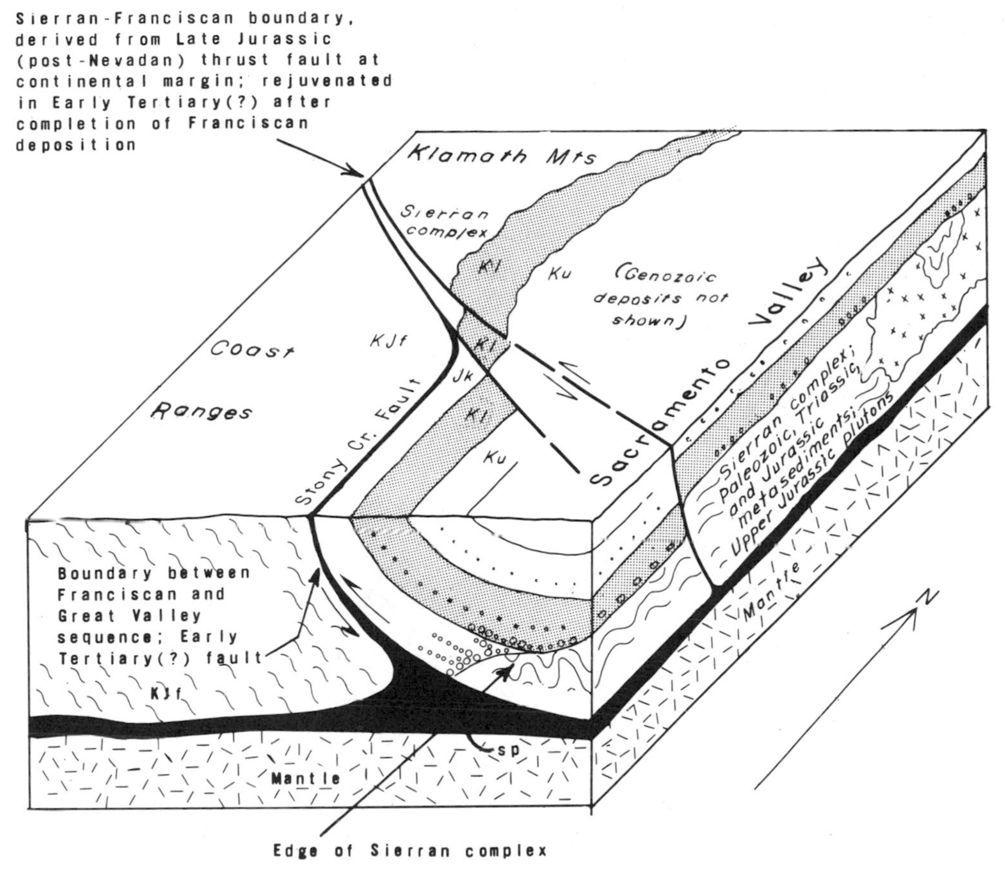

Figure 7. Block diagram showing tentative schematic interpretation of the structural relations in an area west of Red Bluff.

determined. Taliaferro (1944, p. 470) published a map showing the Asuncion Formation (Upper Cretaceous) on both sides of the Nacimiento fault zone which, however, was not depicted. He described (1944, p. 488) certain western patches of "Asuncion" conglomerate containing clasts of both Franciscan and granitic-metamorphic types, but he did not pursue the tectonic implications. If the conglomerate is really correlative with the Asuncion (say Campanian or Maestrichtian in age), the Nacimiento fault zone underwent most of its activity in an earlier part of the Late Cretaceous, bringing both types of core complex into proximity in time to provide detritus for the conglomerate. The dating of the conglomerate should be reexamined.

Recently Hsu (1965) proposed that the Franciscan rocks of the Santa Lucia Range comprise a klippe of material which moved west from the site of the Great Valley. If tenable, this hypothesis would have a bearing on the interpretation of the Nacimiento fault zone.

Both the Sierran-Franciscan boundary and the Nacimiento fault zone separate typical sialic rocks from oceanic deposits, and may have originated at the former continental margin. It has occurred to some that the present continental margin is just such a tectonic zone, having been affected by differential movement between the continental plate and oceanic crust. Such movement is implicit in theories of "sea floor spreading" (Dietz, 1964) and various corollaries of continental drift and convection currents in the mantle.

San Andreas fault. The great San Andreas fault is treated by other authors in a separate section of this bulletin. Clearly, the fault cannot be understood unless one recognizes it as the demarcation between the granitic metamorphic core complex and the Franciscan rocks. One must then either accept a total strike slip of several hundred miles, or resort to some other radical explanation, because the two mutually incompatible core complexes lie adjacent to each other on either side of the fault for at least 260 miles. The fault displacement may not be exclusively the result of strike slip, and various alternatives are being considered (for example, Bailey, Irwin, and Jones, 1964, p. 158–165).

The San Andreas fault north of the Transverse Ranges separates sialic rocks from oceanic rocks. However, the eugeosynclinal deposits lie on the northeast (continental) side, and the sialic rocks lie on the southwest (oceanward) side. Therefore, one cannot regard the fault as the former margin of the continent, as has been proposed for the Sierran-Franciscan boundary and the Nacimiento fault zone.

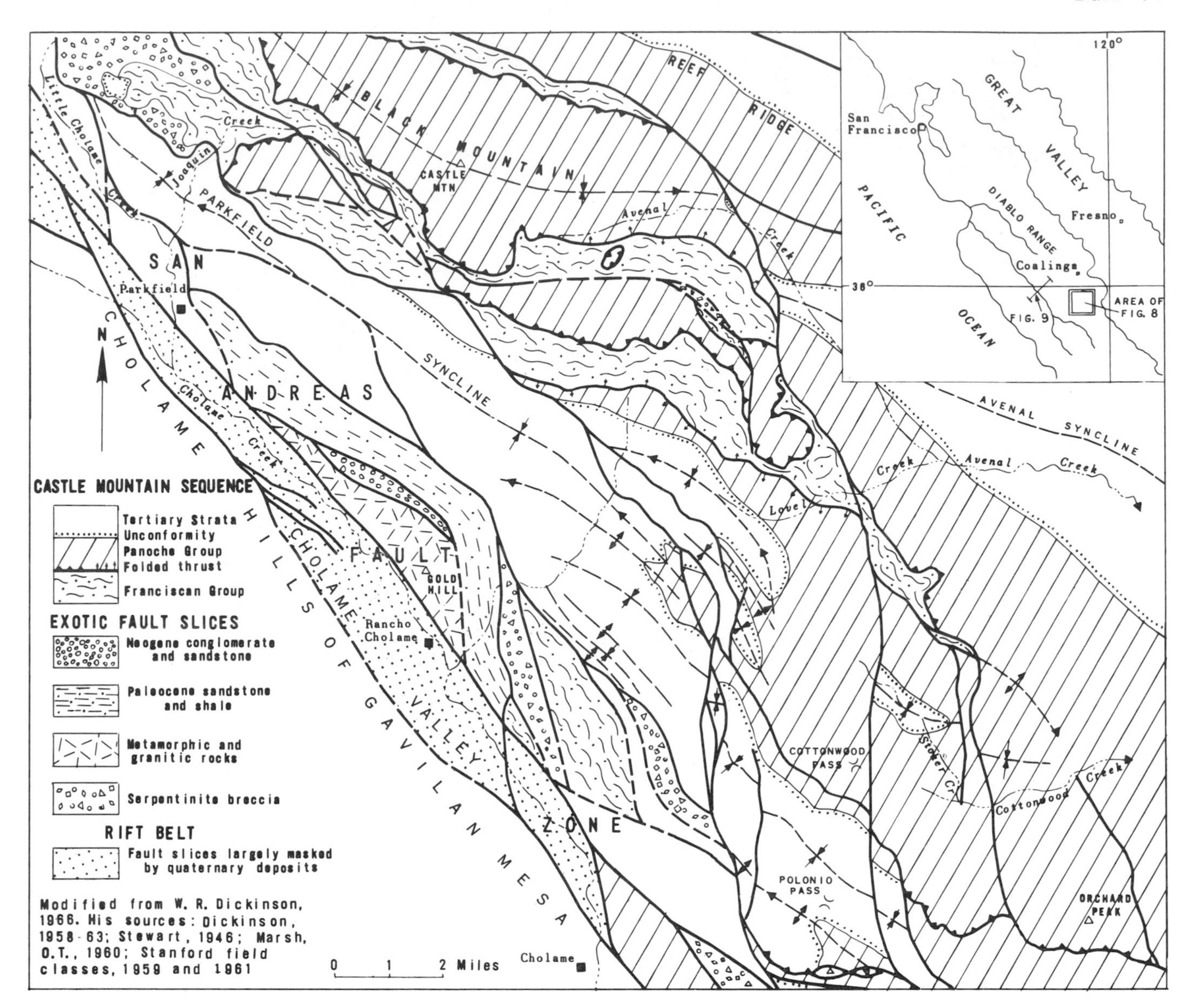

Fgiure 8. Geologic map of an area east of Cholame Valley in the southern part of the Coast Ranges (after W. R. Dickinson).

PROBABLE EARLY TERTIARY THRUST FAULTING

Stony Creek fault. Faulting of large magnitude is evident along most zones of contact between eugeosynclinal Franciscan rocks and quasi-contemporary Jurassic-Cretaceous deposits of the Great Valley type. A conspicuous example is the Stony Creek fault (Kirby, 1943, p. 607; Irwin, 1960; Brown and Rich, 1961). This important feature extends north-south along the east flank of the Coast Ranges near the west side of the Sacramento Valley, and it forms here the eastern limit of exposed Franciscan rocks. The Stony Creek fault is probably steeply dipping for many miles, as its trace is straight. Chuber (1961, pl. 4) represents it as vertical, and McKee (1965) describes it as "high-angle." However, it has brought together quasi-contemporary rocks of strikingly different facies, and this cannot be explained by steeply inclined dip slip alone. Local areal vagaries of the fault seem to rule out strike slip as the principal motion. The only remaining possibility appears to be thrusting, which would require the fault to flatten at depth in order to permit the miles of displacement necessary to account for juxtaposition of different Jurassic-Cretaceous facies. Nevertheless, the fault probably extends deep into, or through, the crust, as shown in figure 5 of Irwin (1964) and figure 8 of this article. The zone of movement is occupied by serpentine, which presumably came from the upper mantle. The serpentine, together with greenstone, comprises a belt 0.5 to 2 miles wide and more than 70 miles long. Much of the serpentine is subdivided into slickensided lenses separated by highly sheared material, and it appears to have been introduced into the fault zone as a cold intrusion or thick plastic smear. The serpentine is bordered on the west by phyllitic and schistose clastic metasediments with lesser amounts of basic volcanic rocks, presumably of the Franciscan assemblage. These have been metamorphosed to rocks of the blueschist facies, and comprise one of the largest known terranes of this facies (Blake and Ghent, 1964). The blueschist type of metamorphism results from high pressure and relatively low temperature. In the area under discussion, the metamorphism is said to be locally more pronounced in topographically high places than in valleys (Kilmer, 1961), so it may have been caused by the pressure of an overriding thrust sheet—the westward extension of the hanging wall of the Stony Creek fault.

A probable thrust forming a klippe of Jurassic(?) basaltic volcanic rocks west of Stonyford is described by Brown (1964). The klippelike mass rests upon Franciscan(?) phyllonite and semischist with minor amounts of basaltic rocks, and is locally separated from these by serpentine. Brown suggests that the inferred thrust is part of the Stony Creek fault, which must have been folded if this interpretation is correct. Farther north, McKee (1965), working near Paskenta, reports intrusive basaltic material (greenstone) in the "Knoxville" rocks near the Stony Creek fault, and states that basaltic material as well as serpentine has been introduced into the fault zone. The latter has been "wedged open" as much as 3 miles.

The age of the Stony Creek fault is post-Franciscan, hence presumably post-Turonian, but the upper age limit is difficult to establish. The sedimentary column which is (now) adjacent on the east apparently shows continuous marine sedimentation from the uppermost Jurassic through the Campanian (upper Upper Cretaceous). Subsurface sections in the western part of the Sacramento Valley show no angular unconformities in the Upper Cretaceous except locally within the Maestrichtian Stage. Above this, the section is severely interrupted at several horizons—notably at the base of the Capay Formation (Lower Eocene). The Oligocene and most of the Miocene are not represented. Therefore, the Stony Creek fault was probably active in the early Tertiary. However, the evidence is conflicting near Wilbur Springs, where strata in the lower part of the Great Valley sequence near the Stony Creek fault contain huge lenses of detrital serpentine (Lawton, 1956). This suggests that the serpentine mass which occupies the fault, and which is believed to have been the source of the detrital serpentine, was already emplaced in the latest Jurassic or Early Cretaceous—an unsolved paradox.

Tesla-Ortigalita fault. A major structure, sometimes called the Telsa-Ortigalita fault, lies along and within the east flank of the Diablo Range. Like the Stony Creek fault, it separates Franciscan rocks in the core of the mountains from the Great Valley sequence. Again like the Stony Creek fault, it is probably a large-scale thrust, judging from the disparity between the quasi-contemporary rocks on either side. This cannot be explained by steep dip slip, and the sharp curves in the fault trace preclude strike slip. Various segments of the Tesla-Ortigalita fault have been mapped by Huey (1948), Leith (1949), Briggs (1953), Maddock (1955), Schilling (1962), and others. The maps and reports all indicate variable dips, mostly nearly vertical or steep southwestward, but a few dips as low as 30° are shown. Even where the fault is steep, adjacent beds of the Great Valley sequence are, in places, overturned as though by northeastward movement of the Franciscan rocks. However, this may be illusory, because the fault has been folded, as is especially apparent in the area mapped by Maddock. Folding probably explains the fact that the Tesla-Ortigalita fault does not continue southeast across the Vallecitos syncline, which lies athwart its projected path. It evidently turns and encircles the main Franciscan terrane of the Diablo Range, describing an elliptical trace. If so, it must be involved in an elongate structural dome or antiform (see fig. 1), as pointed out by Bailey, Irwin, and Jones (oral communication, 1963). This means that a fault mapped by Enos (1963) west of Panoche Valley, on the south side of the Franciscan terrane, is a continuation of the Tesla-Ortigalita fault; Enos found that the fault locally dips north, south, and vertically, which might be explained by folding. If the Tesla-Ortigalita fault does indeed encircle the core of the Diablo Range, and if it is indeed a thrust fault, a bare minimum figure for its displacement is 15 miles, which is the width of the elliptical exposure of Franciscan rocks.

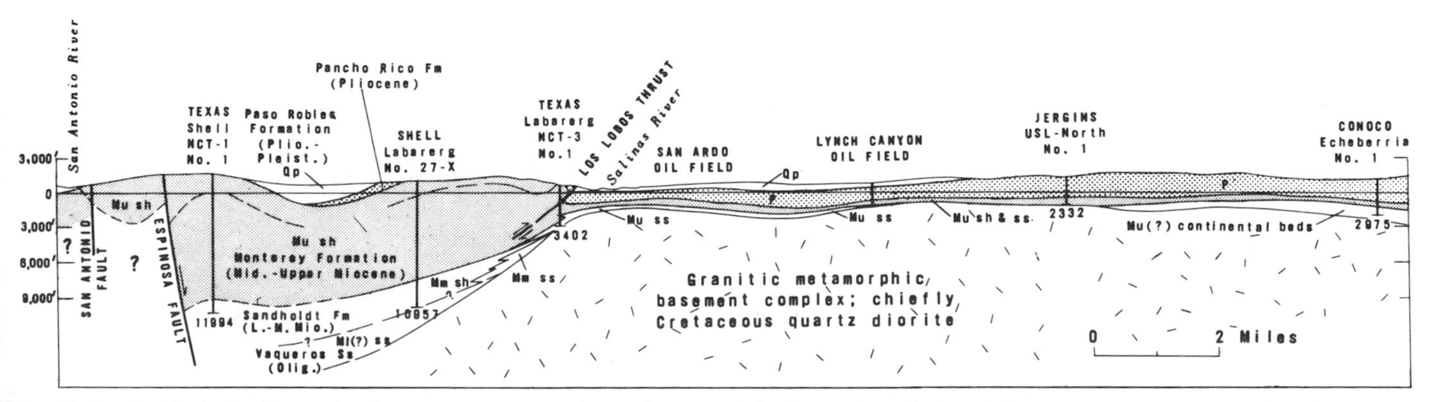

Figure 9. Geologic cross section through an area near San Ardo, west of the San Andreas fault and the area shown in figure 8. Modified from Plate 2 of A.A.P.G.—S.E.P.M., Guidebook to the Geology of Salinas Valley and the San Andreas fault, 1963, by H. Waldron and E. A. Gribi.

The Tesla-Ortigalita fault probably achieved most of its displacement in the Paleocene or Early Eocene, according to the following reasoning: If the Franciscan assemblage, which is cut by the fault, is correctly dated as Tithonian-Turonian, the fault is post-Turonian. The adjacent Panoche strata and Moreno Shale show unbroken marine deposition from the Cenomanian through the Maestrichtian, precluding thrusting in the Late Cretaceous. Middle Eocene sediments which unconformably overlie the Upper Cretaceous rocks are said to contain Franciscan detritus, suggesting that the displacement had been accomplished by the time of this sedimentation. The fault is covered, in places, by Pleistocene red gravel deposits which are not dislocated (Briggs, 1953, pl. 1).

Folded thrust near Cholame Valley. W. R. Dickinson (1965) describes a folded thrust fault east of Cholame Valley. It occurs between Franciscan rocks and an overriding mass of non-Franciscan "normal" Cretaceous strata of the Great Valley sequence. The strongly folded thrust is shown in figure 9, which is taken from a part of Dickinson's map.

Conclusions regarding early Tertiary thrusting. It is a striking fact that the Stony Creek fault, the Tesla-Ortigalita fault, and the folded thrust mapped by Dickinson near Cholame all show the same relation of the Great Valley sequence vis-à-vis the Franciscan. It is increasingly doubtful that the Great Valley sequence has ever been observed in depositional contact on the Franciscan. Moreover, it is increasingly doubtful that the base of the Jurassic part of the Great Valley sequence has ever been seen. One might conjecture that wherever the Great Valley sequence and the Franciscan rocks are in contact, a fault intervenes.

It is probable that a great thrust or series of thrusts carried rocks of the Great Valley sequence over the Franciscan assemblage for a distance of tens of miles, as suggested by Irwin (1964), Bailey, Irwin, and Jones (1964, p. 163–165), and Dickinson (1965). The Stony Creek fault, Tesla-Ortigalita fault, and the fault described by Dickinson appear to be parts of this gigantic thrust or system of thrusts. The overriding sheet is believed to have moved from east to west relative to the underlying Franciscan rocks. The total displacement exceeds 50 miles, judging from the position of probable outliers. The major part of the movement seems to have taken place in the Paleocene or Early Eocene. The thrust sheet was subsequently folded, particularly in the Pliocene and Plio-Pleistocene.

If the foregoing hypothesis is correct, the Paleocene or Early Eocene was one of the important times of orogeny in the Coast Ranges.

LATE CENOZOIC FOLDS AND FAULTS

Ordinary Folds

General character. The Cenozoic and uppermost Cretaceous sedimentary rocks of the Coast Ranges are generally folded, so that moderate to steep dips are commonplace, even in young strata. Neglecting minor crumples in incompetent rocks, the ordinary anticlines and synclines generally have wavelengths of 3,000 to 15,000 feet. Flexural slip has prevailed as a mechanism in the predominant sandstone-shale sequences of the province. (This does not necessarily apply to Franciscan rocks, however.) Folding is locally acute, and overturned limbs are common, but the sense of overturning is not everywhere the same. For example, near Mount Diablo most of the overturning is toward the southwest; that is, the uppermost parts of the folds appear to have moved southwest with respect to underling parts. It the Santa Cruz Mountains, on the other hand, most overturning is toward the northeast. Fold axes in the Coast Ranges vary in trend from east-west to north-south, but the majority lie between N. 40° W. and N. 60° F. (fig. 1), making an appreciable angle with the coastline and the axis of the Great Valley.

Plio-Pleistocene beds are involved in many folds, indicating the recency of deformation. However, older formations are folded more strongly beneath successive unconformities. Some anticlines and synclines began to form in the early Tertiary or before, and were subsequently revived several times. The episodes of revival were sometimes separated by erosion and prolonged submergence, as illustrated by the Pescadero syncline in the Santa Cruz Mountains (fig. 5).

The folding described above not only involves near-surface deposits, but probably maintains its character to a depth of 3 to 5 miles. For example, in the Santa Cruz Mountains, Plio-Pleistocene (renewed) folding involved Pliocene, Miocene, Oligocene, Eocene, and Paleocene formations. If these were all present in any one fold, they would comprise more than 30,000 feet of strata. Actually, parts of the section were lost during three previous episodes of folding and erosion. Nevertheless, some of the Eocene rocks that have been reached in drill holes in the axial regions of anticlines must have been under a 15,000-foot cover at the time of latest folding. In them no obvious changes in fabric or minerals have been reported, and the style of folding is presumed to be similar to that which is observed at the surface.

Role of core complexes. Reed (1933, p. 29) implied that the difference in strength of the Franciscan rocks, as compared with that of the granitic-metamorphic complex, is reflected in the structural behavior of overlying strata. Certainly any Tertiary strata resting upon the Franciscan core complex are almost invariably folded. Similar strata resting upon the granitic-metamorphic core complex may or may not be folded. In some, but not all, cases granitic basement rocks have defied stresses which affected nearby terrains, and the overlying strata are still relatively flat lying. The best-known example is the Gabilan Range. More commonly, the granitic-metamorphic complex has failed and has participated in the folding. This behavior has been little studied except by Compton (1966, and in this bulletin), who has made an outstanding analysis.

High-Angle Reverse Faults

Steep reverse faults are probably more common than normal faults in the Coast Ranges, judging from published data. They are particularly well known in the Santa Lucia Range of the Salinian block (Dickinson, 1959; Compton, 1966), where they form a northwest-southeast system which originated in the Pliocene or early Pleistocene. Several of the faults in this system have brought basement rock on the northeast (hanging-wall) side up against Tertiary rocks on the southwest (footwall) side. Dickinson showed that one such fault terminates against an east-west fault which had been active in the early Eocene, and which was adapted as an oblique-slip tear fault during the Plio-Pleistocene. The Santa Cruz Range exhibits high-angle reverse faults comparable with those of the Santa Lucia Range. Dip separations are on the order of 1,000 to 10,000 feet, and because contemporaneous folds lie parallel with the faults the movement is apparently dip slip rather than strike slip.

High-angle reverse faults do not exactly correspond to the shear fractures that would be expected if the maximum principal stress were horizontal. Principal stresses are supposed to be normally parallel with, and perpendicular to, the earth's surface, because horizontal shear stress is effectively zero at the interface between the atmosphere and the solid earth. Assuming a reasonable angle of internal friction for rock, and assuming that the Mohr-Coulomb theory applies, a horizontal maximum principal (compressive) stress should produce thrust faults dipping 25° to 35°. In the case of the steep reverse faults of the Santa Lucia Range, perhaps the maximum principal stress was not horizontal—a possibility favored by Compton (1966). Or, perhaps the rocks are insufficiently homogeneous or brittle to respond like ideal media. There is reason to believe that some steep reverse faults of the Coast Ranges may become less steep at depth, acquiring the character of conventional thrust faults (for example, the Los Lobos thrust, fig. 9).

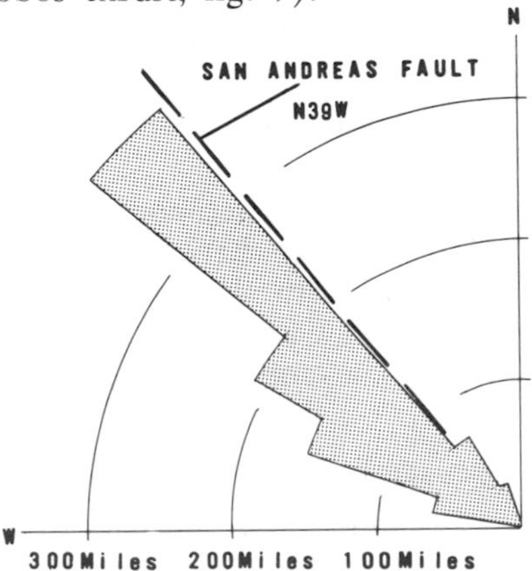

Figure 10. Diagram showing relation of fold trends to strike of San Andreas fault in area between Santa Maria and Coalinga. Predominant trend is N. 40°–50° W., making only a small angle with the San Andreas fault. Based on cumulative lengths of fold axes lying within 10-degree intervals of azimuth; measurements from part of tectonic map by Reed and Hollister, 1936.

Late Cenozoic Thrust Faults

Low-angle thrust faults are being more frequently recognized in the Coast Ranges, and some are much younger than the probable Paleocene or Early Eocene thrust described in preceding pages. An excellent example is given by Marsh (1960), who studied an area east of Paso Robles near the edge of the San Joaquin Valley. A thick sequence of Cretaceous formations has been thrust south or southwest over Miocene rocks. The thrust plate is subdivided by subsidiary thrusts, one above another, and the collective displacement apparently exceeds 9 miles. The thrusts are supplemented by north-south tear faults in the various imbricate sheets. Most of the tear faults show a right-lateral strike slip, which is consistent with a general northeast-southwest crustal shortening. One of the lower thrust faults is partly occupied by tectonically emplaced serpentine which crops out discontinuously along the fault (Marsh, 1960, fig. 14, pl. 1, and pl. 2).

In the Palo Alto quadrangle, Dibblee (in press) and others have mapped a gently dipping thrust fault between Franciscan rocks (Jurassic-Cretaceous) and Cenozoic sediments. The latter include the Santa Clara Formation (Plio-Pleistocene), which is locally vertical to overturned near the thrust. In the same quadrangle, slippage of décollement type is thought to have occurred between two unconformable Tertiary formations (Page and Tabor, in press).

Studies of California quicksilver mines, most of which are in Franciscan rocks, have disclosed a number of thrust faults where the Franciscan has overridden Tertiary or peripheral Upper Cretaceous strata. Instances are cited by Bailey, Irwin, and Jones (1964, p. 157–158).

Where late Cenozoic thrusts have been carefully examined, the inferred direction of thrusting generally ranges from northeast-southwest to nearly north-south. The upper plate has moved in either sense with respect to the underlying rocks. To the extent of present knowledge, the direction of maximum shortening seems consistent with Coast Range folding, which was approximately concurrent with thrusting during the Pliocene and Pleistocene.

Franciscan-Cored Antiforms and Diapirs

Franciscan-cored antiforms. The exposed Franciscan core of the Diablo Range between the Vallecitos syncline and Livermore Valley is flanked by rocks which are more or less outward dipping, thus delineating an antiform more than 90 miles long. The inferred thrust fault between core and flanks must be folded anticlinally, and it seems to be locally overturned. To the southeast, Franciscan rocks are exposed in the piercement core of New Idria, and still farther southeast, they again appear in an area described by Bailey (1942) and by Dickinson (1959, and fig. 9 of this paper). These several Franciscan exposures are cores of *en echelon* antiforms separated by synclinal tracts of younger rocks. The *en echelon* structures trend N. 55° to 70° W., whereas the broad zone which contains them trends about N. 35° W. To the north, the pattern continues at least to the piercement core of the Mount Diablo anticline—a structure trending N. 40° to 70° W. Bailey, Irwin, and Jones (1964, p. 154–155 and fig. 29) call the entire zone the "Diablo antiform," and extend it from near Parkfield on the south to Clear Lake on the north, a distance of approximately 250 miles. Some of the individual *en echelon* folds of this zone were largely formed in the Pliocene and were partly denuded prior to the deposition of Plio-Pleistocene nonmarine sediments, but were subsequently rejuvenated.

Piercement structures. Franciscan rocks and serpentine have locally pushed up through the overlying arched strata of the Diablo antiform. One of the prime examples is at New Idria (Eckel and Myers, 1946). The crest of an anticline in Upper Cretaceous sandstone and shale of the Great Valley sequence is occupied discordantly by a 5- by 13-mile elliptical mass of serpentine and lesser amounts of sedimentary Franciscan rocks. A steeply dipping faultlike boundary encircles the discordant mass. Contact-metamorphic effects are lacking. The core was exposed at the surface early in the Late Cretaceous(?), middle Miocene, and Pliocene, as shown by floods of serpentine detritus in sedimentary rocks a few miles to the east and south, and it may actually have extruded (Eckel and Myers, 1946, p. 94).

Another famous diapir is at Mount Diablo, where various Franciscan sedimentary and volcanic rocks, plus serpentine, form a pluglike mass 4 by 6 miles in plan. Structurally, this mass is a sharp protuberance rising from the general subsurface level of the Franciscan in the axial region of an overturned anticline (Taff, 1935). The anticline includes uppermost Jurassic and Cretaceous strata of the Great Valley sequence, and numerous Tertiary formations. The piercement core has been studied by Pampeyan (1963), and the rest of the structure and stratigraphy have been examined in detail by Colburn (1961). The stratigraphic record of the flanks shows that the core was probably not exposed at any time until the late Pliocene or Pleistocene, as Franciscan detritus is lacking in the section up to, and through, the Orinda Formation of middle Pliocene age (Colburn, 1961). However, successive crustal disturbances are indicated by unconformities below the Paleocene, middle Eocene, middle Pliocene, and possibly other horizons.

It should be pointed out that diapirism alone does not fully account for the anomalous relations between the Franciscan and rocks of the Great Valley sequence in the Diablo Range. The Great Valley sequence must first have been thrust over the Franciscan assemblage before the latter could be squeezed up into the superincumbent strata. By the same token, dating of the diapirism (for example, pre-middle Miocene at New Idria) places a limit on the time of thrusting.

Strike-Slip Faults

The geologic aspects of the great San Andreas fault are discussed in this bulletin by Oakeshott and Dibblee, and role of the fault as a boundary between dual core complexes has been mentioned, so they will not be treated further here.

The Hayward fault supposedly branches from the San Andreas fault near Hollister and extends northwest along the foot of the mountains east of the Santa Clara Valley and east of San Francisco Bay. Like the San Andreas fault, it is currently active and shows right-lateral displacement. The Calaveras-Sunol fault branches from the Hayward fault or directly from the San Andreas fault, and extends north-northwest obliquely across the low mountains near San Jose, continuing toward Walnut Creek west of Mount Diablo. It shows less obvious signs of strike slip and is not known to be active, but it cuts Plio-Pleistocene deposits and might be considered to be only dormant. The stratigraphic column differs somewhat on the two sides of the Calaveras fault, and apparently differs greatly on the two sides of the Hayward fault, probably indicating a long history of activity. Case (1963, p. 81) shows that the rocks of the Monterey Group in the Berkeley Hills were deposited in greatest thickness within a structural basin between the Hayward fault and the Calaveras-Sunol fault. Therefore the faults are presumed to have existed in the Miocene.

Other relatively straight northwest-trending faults occur here and there—for example, in the predominantly Franciscan areas of the northern Coast Ranges. Some of these may be strike-slip faults, but the disorderly rocks hardly lend themselves to the diagnosis of faults. McNitt (1961) shows a number of northwest-southeast faults near Kelseyville, west of Clear Lake. He interprets some as right-lateral strike-slip faults and some as normal and reverse faults.

It would not be surprising if right-lateral strike-slip had occurred fairly commonly on northwest-trending faults of diverse origins in the Coast Ranges. This type of motion has been observed in historical times in a number of localities between the Coast and central Nevada, sometimes taking advantage of preexisting dip-slip faults.

North-south right-lateral strike-slip faults of small to moderate displacement have already been mentioned in connection with thrust faulting. They are compatible with the Coast Range folds and thrusts, but would seem to be unrelated to the San Andreas type of motion.

OVERALL CRUSTAL DEFORMATION

A problem is posed by the fact that folding, high-angle reverse faulting, thrusting, and strike-slip faulting in the Coast Ranges have been more or less simultaneous. All of these types of disturbances have affected Plio-Pleistocene deposits in one area or another, so all have been active in the Quaternary, at least locally.

Clearly, some of the structures were initiated before the Quaternary, and features such as the San Andreas fault have endured for several epochs. Nevertheless, different kinds of structures, old and new, have responded to various stresses more or less concurrently.

What overall strain is consistent with movements indicated by the individual structures? It seems to the writer that folds, rather than the more spectacular San Andreas fault, are the key. The predominant trend of fold axes in the Coast Ranges between the latitudes of Santa Maria and Coalinga is N. 40° to 50° W., as shown in figure 10. Accordingly, the direction of maximum shortening accomplished by folding is about N. 40° to 50° E. This is in harmony with the direction of maximum shortening indicated by high-angle reverse faults such as those in the Santa Lucia Range, and is not in serious conflict with less reliable deductions based upon Plio-Pleistocene thrust faults.

A quantitative determination of present-day crustal strain in parts of the Coast Range province has been carried out by Burford (1965), using U.S. Coast and Geodetic Survey data on the apparent relative movement of triangulation stations. Burford studied areas extending east from Monterey Bay and northeast from Estero Bay. Applying infinitesimal strain theory in a simplified two-dimensional analysis, he concludes that the crust today is undergoing strain consistent with folding of the recent past. The deduced direction of maximum shortening is about N. 35° E., and the rate of shortening is on the order of 1 to 5 cm per kilometer for a period of 19 to 21 years. Locally superimposed upon this general strain is the effect of strike slip in the immediate vicinity of the San Andreas and related faults, where simple shear allows north-south shortening and east-west extension.

One may conjecture that the long-established San Andreas fault could not have originated as a shear fracture in response to compression in a N. 35° E. direction, as the angle between this direction and the strike of the fault is about 74°. The angle deduced from fold axes is even greater. However, regardless of the mode of origin, once formed, the fault might respond to influences in the upper mantle that would produce northeast-southwest compression in the crust.

REFERENCES

Anderson, Robert, and Pack, R. W., 1915, Geology and oil resources of the west border of the San Joaquin Valley north of Coalinga, California: U.S. Geol. Survey Bull. 603, 220 p.

Arnold, Ralph, and Anderson, Robert, 1910, Geology and oil resources of the Coalinga district, California: U.S. Geol. Survey Bull. 398, 354 p.

Bailey, E. H., 1942, Quicksilver deposits of the Parkfield district, California: U.S. Geol. Survey Bull. 936-F, p. 143–169.

Bailey, E. H., and Everhart, D. L., 1964, Geology and quicksilver deposits of the New Almaden district, Santa Clara County, California: U.S. Geol. Survey Prof. Paper 360, 206 p.

Bailey, E. H., and Irwin, W. P., 1959, K-feldspar content of Jurassic and Cretaceous graywackes of the northern Coast Ranges and Sacramento Valley, California: Am. Assoc. Petroleum Geologists Bull., v. 43, no. 12, p. 2797–2809.

Bailey, E. H., Irwin, W. P., and Jones, D. L., 1964, Franciscan and related rocks, and their significance in the geology of western California: California Div. Mines and Geology Bull. 183, 177 p.

Blake, M. C., Jr., and Ghent, E. D., 1965, Regional glaucophane-schist-facies metamorphism in the northern Coast Ranges of California [abs.]: Geol. Soc. America Spec. Paper 82, p. 241.

Bloxam, T. W., 1956, Jadeite-bearing metagraywackes in California: Am. Mineralogist, v. 41, nos. 5–6, p. 488–496.

Bowen, O. E., Jr., ed., 1962, Geologic guide to the oil and gas fields of northern California: California Div. Mines and Geology Bull. 181, 412 p.

Bowen, O. E., Jr., and Gray, C. H., Jr., 1959, Geology and economic possibilities of the limestone and dolomite deposits of the northern Gabilan Range, California: California Div. Mines Spec. Rept. 56, 40 p.

Brabb, E. E., 1964, Subdivision of San Lorenzo Formation (Eocene-Oligocene) west-central California: Am. Assoc. Petroleum Geologists Bull., v. 48, no. 5, p. 670–679.

Bramlette, M. N., 1946, The Monterey formation of California and the origin of its siliceous rocks: U.S. Geol. Survey Prof. Paper 212, 57 p.

Briggs, L. I., Jr., 1953, Geology of the Ortigalita Peak quadrangle, California: California Div. Mines Bull. 167, 61 p.

Brown, R. D., Jr., 1964, Thrust-fault relations in the northern Coast Ranges, California: U.S. Geol. Survey Prof. Paper 475-D, art. 123, p. D7–D13.

Brown, R. D., Jr., and Rich, E. I., 1960, Early Cretaceous fossils in submarine slump deposits of Late Cretaceous age, northern Sacramento Valley, California: U.S. Geol. Survey Prof. Paper 400-B, art. 149, p. B318–B320.

—— 1961, Geologic map of the Lodoga quadrangle, Glenn and Colusa Counties, California: U.S. Geol. Survey Oil and Gas Inv. Map OM-210, scale 1:48,000.

Burford, R. O., 1965, Strain analysis across the San Andreas fault and Coast Ranges of California: Paper presented at Second Symposium, Commission on Recent Crustal Movements, Aulanko, Finland, August 1965.

Case, J. E., 1963, Geology of a portion of the Berkeley and San Leandro Hills, California: California Univ., Berkeley, Ph.D. thesis, 319 p.

Chuber, Stewart, 1961, Late Mesozoic stratigraphy of the Elk Creek-Fruto area, Glenn County, California: Stanford Univ., Stanford, Calif., Ph.D. thesis, 173 p.

Clark, J. C., 1966, Tertiary stratigraphy of the Felton-Santa Cruz area, Santa Cruz Mountains, California: Stanford Univ., Stanford, Calif., Ph.D. thesis.

Colburn, Ivan, 1961, The tectonic history of Mt. Diablo, California: Stanford Univ., Stanford, Calif., Ph.D. thesis, 276 p.

Coleman, R. G., and Lee, D. E., 1963, Glaucophane-bearing metamorphic rock types of the Cazadero area, California: Jour. Petrology [Oxford], v. 4, no. 2, p. 260–301.

Coleman, R. G., Lee, D. E., Beatty, L. B., and Brannock, W. W., 1965, Eclogites and eclogites—their differences and similarities: Geol. Soc. America Bull., v. 76, no. 5, p. 483–508.

Compton, R. R., 1960a, Charnockitic rocks of the Santa Lucia Range, California: Am. Jour. Sci., v. 258, no. 9, p. 609–636.

—— 1960b, Relations of major folds and reverse faults in Santa Lucia Range, California [abs.]: Geol. Soc. America Bull., v. 71, p. 2054.

—— 1966, Analysis of Plio-Pleistocene deformation and stresses in northern Santa Lucia Range, California: Geol. Soc. America Bull., (in press).

Crowell, J. C., 1957, Origin of pebbly mudstones: Geol. Soc. America Bull., v. 68, no. 8, p. 993–1010.

Cummings, J. C., Touring, R. M., and Brabb, E. E., 1962, Geology of the northern Santa Cruz Mountains, California: California Div. Mines and Geology Bull., 181, p. 179–220.

Curtis, G. H., Evernden, J. F., and Lipson, J. I., 1958, Age determination of some granitic rocks in California by the potassium-argon method: Califronia Div. Mines Spec. Rept. 54, 16 p.

Dibblee, T. W., 1966, Geology of the Palo Alto quadrangle Santa Clara and San Mateo Counties, California: Calif. Div. Mines and Geology, Map Sheet 8.

Dickinson, W. R., 1959, Structural relationships of Church Creek and Willow Creek faults, Santa Lucia Range, California [abs.]: Geol. Soc. America Bull., v. 70, no. 12, pt. 2, p. 1715.

—— 1965, Folded thrust contact between Franciscan rocks and Panoche Group in the Diablo Range of central California [abs.]: Geol. Soc. America Spec. Paper 82, p. 248–249.

—— 1966, Geologic relations of Table Mountain serpentinite extrusion in California Coast Ranges: Geol. Soc. America Bull. (In press)

Dietz, R. S., 1964, Origin of continental slopes: Am. Scientist, v. 52, no. 1, p. 50–69.

Eckel, E. B., and Myers, W. B., 1946, Quicksilver deposits of the New Idria district, San Benito and Fresno Counties, California: California Jour. Mines and Geology, v. 42, no. 2, p. 81–124.

Enos, Paul, 1963, Jurassic age of Franciscan Formation south of Panoche Pass, California: Am. Assoc. Petroleum Geologists Bull., v. 47, no. 1, p. 158–163.

Ernst, W. G., 1965, Mineral paragenesis in Franciscan metamorphic rocks, Panoche Pass, California: Geol. Soc. America Bull., v. 76, p. 879–914.

Evernden, J. F., Savage, D. E., Curtis, G. H., and James, G. T., 1964, Potassium-argon dates and the Cenozoic mammalian chronology of North America: Am. Jour. Sci., v. 262, no. 2, p. 145–198.

Fyfe, W. S., Turner, F. J., and Zardini, R. A., 1966, Franciscan metaconglomerates [abst.]: Geol. Soc. America Spec. Paper, Abstracts for 1965.

Hall, C. A., Jr., 1958, Geology and paleontology of the Pleasanton area, Alameda and Contra Costa Counties, California: California Univ. Pubs. Geol. Sci., v. 34, no. 1, p. 1–89.

Hill, M. L., and Dibblee, T. W., Jr., 1953, San Andreas, Garlock, and Big Pine faults, California—a study of the character, history, and tectonic significance of their displacements: Geol. Soc. America Bull., v. 64, no. 4, p. 443–458.

Hsu, K. J., 1966, On the klippe origin of the Franciscan rocks of the Santa Lucia Range, California—a working hypothesis [abs.]: Geol. Soc. America Spec. Paper, Abstracts for 1965.

Huey, A. S., 1948, Geology of the Tesla quadrangle, California: California Div. Mines Bull. 140, 75 p.

Hutton, C. O., 1952, Accessory mineral studies of some California beach sands: U.S. Atomic Energy Comm., RMO-981.

—— 1959, Mineralogy of beach sands between Halfmoon and Monterey Bays, California: California Div. Mines Spec. Rept. 59, 32 p.

Irwin, W. P., 1960, Geologic reconnaissance of the northern Coast Ranges and Klamath Mountains, California, with a summary of the mineral resources: California Div. Mines Bull. 179, 80 p.

—— 1964, Late Mesozoic orogenies in the ultramafic belts of northwestern California and southwestern Oregon: U. S. Geol. Survey Prof. Paper 501-C, p. C1–C9.

Kilmer, F. H., 1961, Anomalous relationship between the Franciscan formation and metamorphic rocks, northern Coast Ranges, California [abs.]: Geol. Soc. America Spec. Paper 68, p. 210.

King, P. B., 1959, The evolution of North America: Princeton, N. J., Princeton Univ. Press, 190 p.

Kirby, J. M., 1943, Upper Cretaceous stratigraphy of the west side of Sacramento Valley south of Willows, Glenn County, California: Am. Assoc. Petroleum Geologists Bull., v. 27, no. 3, p. 270–305.

Kleinpell, R. M., 1938, Miocene stratigraphy of California: Tulsa, Okla., Am. Assoc. Petroleum Geologists, 450 p.

Lawson, A. C., 1895, Sketch of the geology of the San Francisco Peninsula [California]: U.S. Geol. Survey 15th Ann. Rept., p. 349–476.

—— 1914, Description of the San Francisco district; Tamalpais, San Francisco, Concord, San Mateo, and Hayward quadrangles: U.S. Geol. Survey Geol. Atlas, Folio 193, 24 p.

Lawton, J. E., 1956, Geology of the north half of the Morgan Valley quadrangle and the south half of the Wilbur Springs quadrangle [California]: Stanford Univ., Stanford, Calif., Ph.D. thesis.

Leith, C. J., 1949, Geology of the Quien Sabe quadrangle, California: California Div. Mines Bull. 147, p. 7–35.

Leo, G. W., 1961, The plutonic and metamorphic rocks of Ben Lomond Mountain, Santa Cruz County, California: Stanford Univ., Stanford, Calif., Ph.D. thesis, 194 p.

Lerbekmo, J. F., 1956, The character and origin of Late Tertiary blue sandstones in central California: California Univ., Berkeley, Ph.D. thesis.

Maddock, M. E., 1955, Geology of the Mt. Boardman quadrangle: California Univ., Berkeley, Ph.D. thesis.

—— 1964, Geology of the Mt. Boardman quadrangle: California Div. Mines and Geology Map Sheet 3.

Mallory, V. S., 1959, Lower Tertiary biostratigraphy of the California coast ranges: Tulsa, Okla., Am. Assoc. Petroleum Geologists, 416 p.

Marsh, O. T., 1960, Geology of the Orchard Peak area, California: California Div. Mines Spec. Rept. 62, 42 p.

McKee, E. B., Jr., 1958, The geology of the Pacheco Pass area, California: Stanford Univ., Stanford, Calif., Ph.D. thesis, 88 p.

—— 1962, Widespread occurrence of jadeite, lawsonite, and glaucophane in central California: Am. Jour. Sci., v. 260, no. 8, p. 596–610.

—— 1966, Knoxville-Franciscan contact near Paskenta, western Sacramento Valley, California [abs.]: Geol. Soc. America Spec. Paper, Abstracts for 1965.

McNitt, J. R., 1961, Geology and mineral deposits of the Kelseyville SE. quadrangle, Sonoma County, California: California Univ., Berkeley, Ph.D. thesis.

Murphy, M. A., 1956, Lower Cretaceous stratigraphic units of northern California: Am. Assoc. Petroleum Geologists Bull., v. 40, no. 9, p. 2098–2119.

Ojakangas, R. W., 1964, Petrology and sedimentation of the Cretaceous Sacramento Valley sequence, Cache Creek, California: Stanford Univ., Stanford, Calif., Ph.D. thesis, 190 p.

Page, B. M., and Tabor, L. L., 1966, Chaotic structure and décollement in Cenozoic rocks near Stanford University, California: Geol. Soc. America Bull., (in press).

Pampeyan, E. H., 1963, Geology and mineral deposits of Mount Diablo, Contra Costa County, California: California Div. Mines and Geology Spec. Rept. 80, 31 p.

Payne, M. B., 1951, Type Moreno formation and overlying Eocene strata on the west side of the San Joaquin Valley, Fresno and Merced Counties, California: California Div. Mines Spec. Rept. 9, 29 p.

—— 1962, Type Panoche group (Upper Cretaceous) and overlying Moreno and Tertiary strata on the west side of the San Joaquin Valley: California Div. Mines and Geology Bull. 181, p. 165–175.

Reed, R. D., 1933, Geology of California: Tulsa, Okla., Am. Assoc. Petroleum Geologists, 355 p.

Schilling, F. A., Jr., 1962, The Upper Cretaceous stratigraphy of the Pacheco Pass quadrangle, California: Stanford Univ., Stanford, Calif., Ph.D. thesis, 253 p.

Schlocker, Julius, Bonilla, M. G., and Imlay, R. W., 1954, Ammonite indicates Cretaceous age for part of the Franciscan group in the San Francisco Bay area, California: Am. Assoc. Petroleum Geologists Bull., v. 38, no. 11, p. 2372–2381.

Soliman, S. M., 1958, General geology of the Isabel-Eylar area, California, and petrology of the Franciscan sandstones: Stanford Univ., Stanford, Calif., Ph.D. thesis.

—— 1965, Geology of the east half of the Mount Hamilton quadrangle, California: California Div. Mines and Geology Bull. 185.

Spotts, J. H., 1958, Heavy minerals of some granitic rocks of central California: Stanford Univ., Stanford, Calif., Ph.D. thesis, 80 p.

Taff, J. A., 1935, Geology of Mount Diablo and vicinity: Geol. Soc. America Bull., v. 46, no. 7, p. 1079–1100.

Taliaferro, N. L., 1933, The relation of volcanism to diatomaceous and associated siliceous sediments: California Univ., Dept. Geol. Sci. Bull., v. 23, no. 1, p. 48–49.

—— 1943, Geologic history and structure of the central Coast Ranges of California: California Div. Mines Bull. 118, p. 119–163.

—— 1944, Cretaceous and Paleocene of Santa Lucia Range, California: Am. Assoc. Petroleum Geologists Bull., v. 28, no. 4, p. 449–521.

Thalmann, H. E., 1942, *Globotruncana* in the Franciscan limestone, Santa Clara County, California [abs.]: Geol. Soc. America Bull., v. 53, no. 12, pt. 2, p. 1838.

Trask, P. D., 1926, Geology of the Point Sur quadrangle, California: California Univ., Dept. Geol. Sci. Bull., v. 16, no. 6, p. 119–186.

White, C. A., 1885, On the Mesozoic and Cenozoic paleontology of California: U.S. Geol. Survey Bull. 15, 33 p.

GRANITIC AND METAMORPHIC ROCKS OF THE SALINIAN BLOCK, CALIFORNIA COAST RANGES

By Robert R. Compton
Stanford University, Stanford, California

The Salinian block is an elongate segment of the Coast Ranges, characterized by a basement of granitic and high-grade metamorphic rocks. The granitic rocks have been dated as Cretaceous in a number of places (fig. 1), yet they nowhere intrude nor metamorphose older Franciscan rocks that lie against the block along

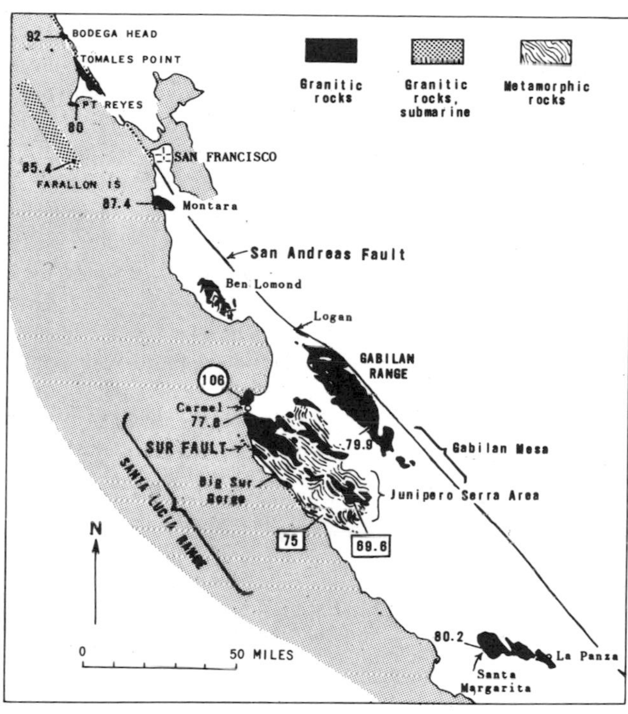

Figure 1. Index map of a central part of the Coast Ranges showing principal exposures of Salinian granitic and metamorphic rocks. Numbers are absolute ages in millions of years; those unmarked are from Curtis, Evernden, and Lipson (1958) recalculated to 1965 values of decay rates; the circled 106 is a nonisotopic Th-Pb age for monazite from Pacific Grove (Hutton, 1959, p. 20); the numbers in rectangles are unpublished K-Ar ages determined by John Obradovich (see table 1), and the underlined 92 is an unpublished K-Ar age determined by R. W. Kistler (see table 1). Submarine outcrop from Uchupi and Emery, 1963.

the San Andreas and Sur faults. This interesting situation has led to several important hypotheses involving large-scale displacements on the east side of the block (Curtis, Evernden, and Lipson, 1958; Bailey, Irwin, and Jones, 1964). The west side, however, has remained a puzzle. Moreover, almost nothing has been written about the overall nature and history of the Salinian rocks themselves. Do the scattered basement exposures constitute one closely related suite of rocks? What tectonic histories do their structures suggest? How do the various absolute ages fit into this history? This paper presents a brief summary of data and ideas pertaining to these and related questions.

The writer's knowledge of the region is based on a fairly thorough study of the Junipero Serra area of the Santa Lucia Range, on far briefer studies in the Lucia quadrangle, the Santa Margarita-La Panza area, the north end of Gabilan Range, and the Ben Lomond area, and on reconnaissance of the other major exposures. Several geologists have kindly discussed areas and contributed data and thin sections from work in progress: Fred Berry and Edward Gribi (Gabilan Mesa), Oliver Bowen (Monterey quadrangle and northern Gabilan Range), Allan Galloway (Point Reyes-Tomales Bay area), Olaf Jenkins (Monterey-Gabilan Range area), G. W. Leo (Ben Lomond), Julius Schlocker (Bodega Head), and Robert Wiebe (northern Santa Lucia Range). John Obradovich, then at the University of California at Berkeley K-Ar laboratory, generously determined the ages of two biotites from the Junipero Serra area, and Garniss Curtis was helpful in providing these data for publication. Julius Schlocker also contributed a K-Ar age determined for him by R. W. Kistler of the U.S. Geological Survey. John Spotts' thin sections in the Stanford Mineralogy Collection proved invaluable, as did a number of thin sections borrowed from the collections of the University of California at Berkeley. The U.S. Forest Service and many private land owners were helpful with the field studies, and funds from the Shell Grant for Fundamental Research financed part of the field work as well as six new chemical analyses.

SANTA MARGARITA TO LA PANZA AREA

The most southerly major exposure of Salinian basement consists of adamellite that probably extends considerably beyond the 10- by 30-mile exposed tract. Samples from ten widely separated localities, studied in thin section and on large, stained slabs, have compositions close to: quartz, 30 percent; K-feldspar, 25 percent; calcic oligoclase, 35 percent; and biotite, 10 percent. K-feldspar phenocrysts are generally present and commonly are zoned and elongate parallel to the *a*-axis like those described by Lawson (1893) from the Carmel area. Small inclusions of fine-grained diorite occur widely, and in a few places adamellite

Table 1. Data for unpublished K-Ar age determinations on Salinian rocks.

Lab number	Field number	Mineral	Weight in grams	Percent K	Radiogenic Ar^{40} moles $\times 10^{-11}$	Percent atmospheric Ar^{40}	Age* (10^6 yr)
KA-585-I[1]	58-7[3]	biotite	0.5355	7.30	49.70	27	70.2
KA-585-II[1]	" [3]	biotite	0.4934	7.30	45.01	17	69.0
KA-586[1]	Cone Pk[4]	biotite	0.5754	7.14	55.90	21	75.0
KA-399[2]	JS-145BD[5]	hornblende	2.1515	0.83	30.30	13	92

* The constants used in calculations: $\lambda\xi = 0.584 \times 10^{-10}yr^{-1}$; $\lambda\beta = 4.72 \times 10^{-9}yr^{-1}$; moles K^{40}/moles K = 1.19×10^{-4}.
[1] Analyses by John Obradovich at University of California, Berkeley.
[2] Analysis by R. W. Kistler, U. S. Geological Survey.
[3] Quartz diorite near south border Junipero Serra pluton; Cone Peak quadrangle, T. 21 S., R. 5 E., 2,500 ft north and 400 ft east of SW corner sec. 12.
[4] Pyroxene-biotite-plagioclase granofels; summit of Cone Peak; for description and rock analysis see Compton (1960).
[5] Granodiorite collected by Julius Schlocker, U. S. Geological Survey, at Pacific Gas and Electric Co. atomic reactor site, Bodega Head, Sonoma County.

grades to quartz diorite around large gabbroic inclusions. Marbles, diaphthoritic schists, and biotite-orthoclase-andesine quartzites closely similar to Sur series relics in the Gabilan Range form inclusions as much as a mile long in the northeast part of the area. The inclusions have vague early lineations and distinct later folds that plunge at low angles to the northwest in some places and to the south or southeast in others. In the adamellite, these same trends are defined by complexly folded fabrics and by folded swarms of diorite inclusions which are themselves locally elongated parallel to the fold axes. Some granitic dikes have been recrystallized to give the same tectonite pattern (fig. 2).

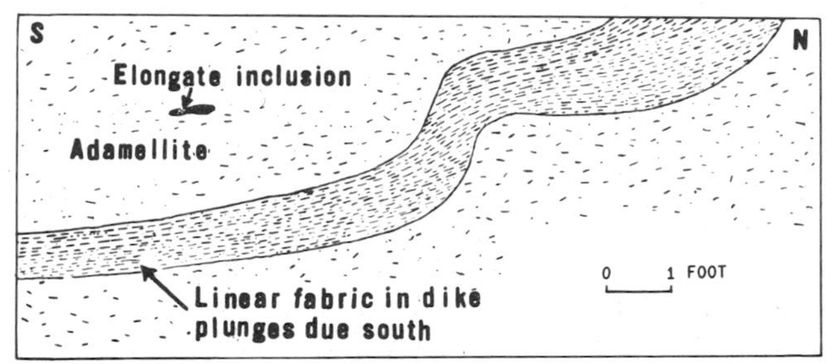

Figure 2. Granitic dike with strongly linear fabric as exposed in vertical cut on Black Mountain road, 1½ miles northwest of Navajo Road summit. The dike strikes due west.

Petrofabric diagrams of biotite from two localities in adamellite show two fabric axes: One parallel to the northwest-plunging fold axes and an earlier one at about right angles to them (fig. 3). Under the microscope, the biotites form complex groups, some of which are folded; yet textures are not protoclastic and plagioclase grains are subhedral and show oscillatory zoning. These various relationships suggest the adamellite was deformed at a very late magmatic stage but under highly insulated conditions. If it was deformed in two episodes, they must have succeeded each other closely, or else the rock body remained hot for a long time.

JUNIPERO SERRA AREA

This sector of Santa Lucia Range is underlain largely by high-grade metamorphic rocks that can be traced northwest to the type area of the Sur series designated by Trask (1926). In the area the writer has mapped in detail (fig. 4) they are mainly biotite-feldspar quartzites and quartzo-feldspathic granofelses and gneisses, with many layers of calc-silicate granofelses, amphibolites, aluminous schists, calcite marbles, and metadolomites. Judged from their present associations and bulk compositions, roughly 70 percent of the original sedimentary rocks were feldspathic or argillaceous sandstones and siltstones; 10 percent were silty, argillaceous limestones and dolomites; 10 percent were Ca-poor claystones; 5 percent were nearly pure limestones and dolomites, and 5 percent were very quartzose sandstones. That many of the quartzo-feldspathic rocks were originally calcareous or dolomitic is indicated by their abundant calcic to intermediate plagioclase, as well as by the intricately interlayered calc-silicate rocks. Some associations of the quartzites and

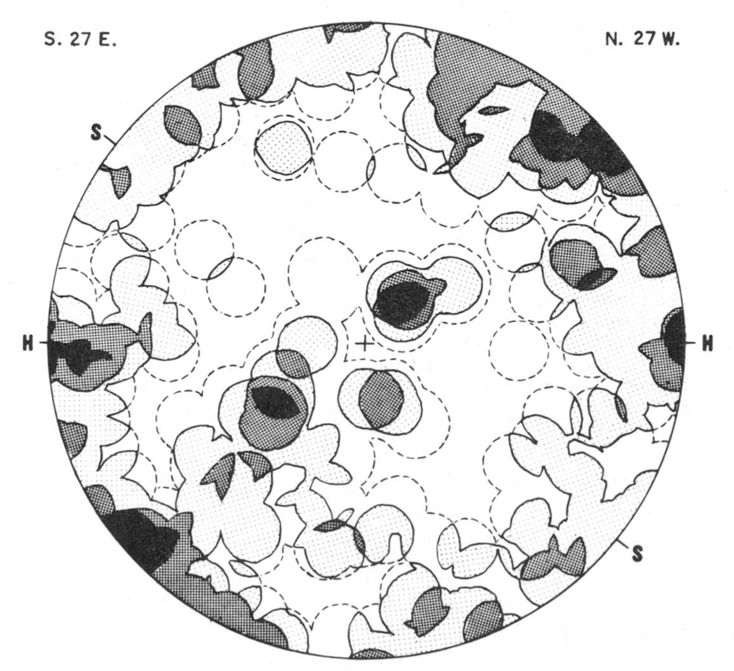

Figure 3. Petrofabric diagram of poles to cleavage in 200 biotite grains, corrected for *Schnitteffekt*. Contours at 3, 2, 1, and 0.5 percent per 1 percent of area. Thin section cut perpendicular to one lineation and parallel to second. *HH*, horizontal; *SS*, principal foliation. Adamellite on Highway 178, ½ mile west of La Panza.

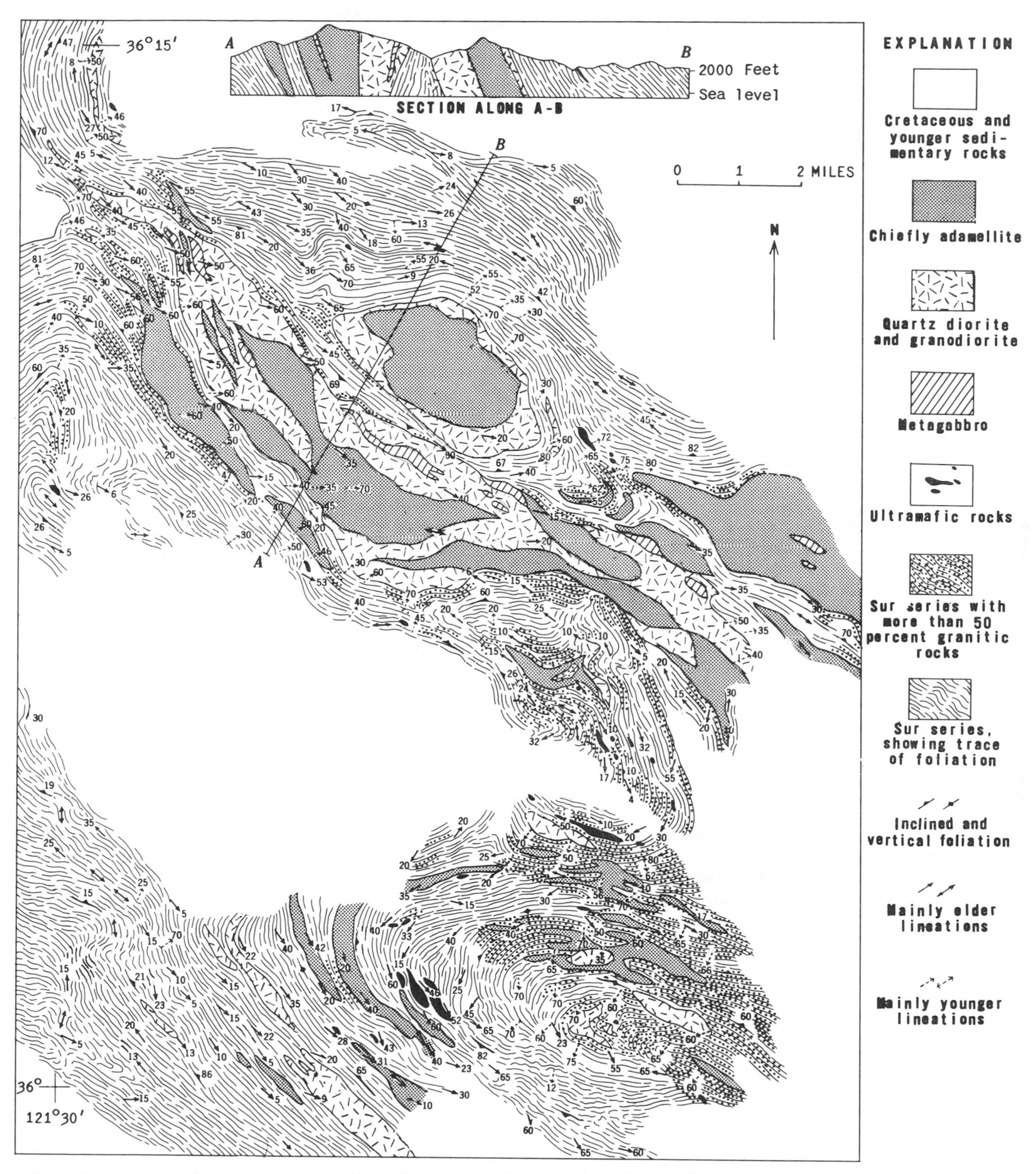

Figure 4. Basement rocks and structures of the Junipero Serra 15′ quadrangle and surroundings. The main figure is a horizontal section at 2,000 feet altitude.

Table 2. Chemical analyses of Salinian plutonic rocks.

	1 Pyroxe-nite	2 Horn-blendite	3 Quartz diorite	4 Grano-diorite	5 Adamel-lite	6 Granite	7 Gabbro	8 Gabbro	9 Biotite diorite	10 Quartz diorite
SiO_2	47.82	53.04	55.85	71.74	71.90	73.65	46.23	49.26	58.44	63.12
TiO_2	0.56	0.61	1.19	0.42	0.45	0.16	tr	tr	0.15	tr
Al_2O_3	5.10	9.98	19.64	13.46	14.76	13.86	18.29	16.88	17.06	16.13
Fe_2O_3	1.03	1.20	1.70	1.52	0.06	0.35	6.55	6.49	1.36	3.53
FeO	8.45	7.30	5.59	2.03	1.55	0.79	7.07	6.94	5.06	3.65
MnO	n.d.	n.d.	n.d.	n.d.	n.d.	n.d.	0.12	0.61	0.50	0.38
MgO	20.43	13.58	2.38	0.94	0.63	0.43	7.04	4.80	2.96	1.86
CaO	14.57	10.53	6.29	2.22	2.11	0.82	9.99	7.58	5.82	5.04
BaO	n.d.	n.d.	0.026	0.016	0.053	0.10	n.d.	0	n.d.	n.d.
Na_2O	0.53	1.08	4.64	3.35	3.10	1.92	3.07	3.41	3.40	2.78
K_2O	0.11	0.36	1.32	3.30	4.50	6.79	0.79	0.72	2.84	1.08
H_2O^+	1.12	1.04	1.01	0.69	0.43	0.26	1.02	2.90	2.12	0.93
H_2O^-	0.26	0.46	0.31	0.33	0.16	0.25	0.05	0.41	0.38	0.97
Cr_2O_3	0.22	0.19	n.d.	n.d.	n.d.	n.d.	n.d.	n.d.	n.d.	n.d.
NiO+CoO	n.d.	n.d.	n.d.	n.d.	n.d.	n.d.	tr	0.05	n.d.	n.d.
SrO	n.d.	n.d.	n.d.	n.d.	n.d.	n.d.	tr	tr	n.d.	0.03
P_2O_5	n.d.	n.d.	n.d.	n.d.	n.d.	n.d.	0.21	0.34	1.41	0.39
S	0.11	0.32	n.d.	n.d.	n.d.	n.d.	tr	tr	n.d.	n.d.
F	tr	0.050	n.d.	n.d.	n.d.	n.d.	n.d.	n.d.	n.d.	n.d.
Cl	0.007	0.007	n.d.	n.d.	n.d.	n.d.	n.d.	n.d.	n.d.	n.d.
Total	100.317	99.747	99.946	100.016	99.703	99.38	100.43	100.39	101.50	99.89

1. Olivine-hornblende pyroxenite (CP-8-68A). Cone Peak quadrangle; T. 22 S., R. 5 E.; 930 ft south and 1,920 ft east of NE cor. sec. 14. Analysis by Morito Chiba. Mode, in percent by volume: augite, 45; hornblende, 21; olivine, 15; hypersthene, 14.5; plagioclase, 4; calcite, 0.2.
2. Plagioclase-pyroxene-hornblende rock (BC-3-32B). Bear Canyon quadrangle; T. 21 S., R. 6 E., 3,600 ft north and 1,930 ft east of SW cor. sec. 32. Analysis by Morito Chiba. Mode, in percent by volume: hornblende, 51; plagioclase, 15.5; augite, 11.5; quartz, 8.5; hypersthene, 6; biotite, 6; pyrrhotite, 1; apatite, 0.3; rutile, 0.1.
3. Quartz diorite (CP-2-1). Cone Peak quadrangle; T. 21 S., R. 5 E., 3,900 ft north and 600 ft west of SE cor. sec. 11. Analysis by Morito Chiba. Mode, in percent by volume: plagioclase, 64; biotite, 16; quartz, 10; hornblende, 9; sphene, 0.5; apatite, 0.3; pyrite, 0.2.
4. Granodiorite (JSP-6-2). Junipero Serra Peak quadrangle; 700 ft south and 860 ft west of NE cor. sec. 11. Analysis by Morito Chiba. Mode, in percent by volume: plagioclase, 42.5; quartz, 29.2; K-feldspar, 19.2; biotite, 9.
5. Adamellite (JS-1). Junipero Serra Peak quadrangle; T. 20 S., R. 5 E., 950 ft north and 1,580 ft east of SE cor. sec. 34. Analysis by Morito Chiba. Mode, in percent by volume: K-feldspar, 38; plagioclase, 31; quartz, 26; biotite, 4; ilmenite, 1.
6. Granite (BC-1-4C). Bear Canyon quadrangle; T. 21 S., R. 6 E.; 3,320 ft south and 320 ft east of NE cor. sec. 16. Analysis by Morito Chiba. Mode, in percent by volume: K-feldspar, 49; quartz, 28.5; plagioclase, 17; biotite, 5.4.
7. Hornblende gabbro ("diorite") occurring as fine-grained inclusions in coarser quartz-bearing rocks, Pajaro (Logan) quarry. Analysis by J. A. Reid. Mode: roughly equal amounts of labradorite and hornblende, with accessory opaques and apatite (Reid, 1902).
8. Hornblende gabbro ("diorite"); same locality and analyst as 7. Mode: chiefly labradorite and hornblende, with accessory opaques, apatite, biotite, and quartz (Reid, 1902).
9. Biotite diorite from south end of Bodega peninsula. Analysis by V. C. Osmont. Mode: roughly equal amounts of biotite and andesine, with accessory apatite, opaques, sphene, and appreciable "decomposition products" (Osmont, 1905).
10. Quartz-biotite diorite; same locality and analyst as 9. Mode: chiefly andesine and biotite, with quartz, hornblende, and orthoclase, and accessory apatite and sphene (plus "decomposition products") (Osmont, 1905).

marbles suggest metamorphosed platform-type sediments, for the marbles are locally phosphatic, the quartzites contain abundant rounded zircon grains, and the contacts between quartzites and marbles are sharp. The bulk compositions of the quartzo-feldspathic rocks, and their large detrital zircons, suggest a granitic source for a large share of the sediments.

Only one marble and one quartzite unit proved thick and distinctive enough to be mapped readily across the brushy terrain; they are shown by sets of parallel lines in the northern part of figure 4. In all distinctly layered rocks, metamorphic foliations are generally parallel to compositional layers that may be relict sedimentary beds. Outside of the rounded zircon grains, however, there are no convincing relics of sedimentary grains or structures, so that stratigraphic sequence is as yet undetermined.

Grain sizes average 1–2 mm in quartzo-feldspathic rocks and 4–8 mm in marbles (except for those affected by late granulation and recrystallization). Locally, quartzites have grains 1–2 cm in diameter and marbles are as coarse as 4–8 cm—attesting to prolonged crystallization or to unusually mobile conditions of crystallization.

The abundant biotitic quartzites and gneisses give a misleading impression of moderate metamorphic grade, but aluminous rocks are sillimanite-garnet-cordierite-orthoclase schists and gneisses; basic rocks are hornblende-andesine granofelses, locally with clinopyroxene and hypersthene; most calc-silicate rocks contain abundant clinopyroxene and meionitic scapolite as well as accessory orthoclase, and wollastonitic schists occur in several places. These mineral assemblages are of highest grade amphibolite facies and locally granulite facies. The granulite facies rocks define a broad, crude metamorphic zoning: they are most abundant in the southwest part of the area, occur here and there in the central part, and are wholly missing in the northern part. The granulite facies rocks commonly form irregular to tabular, coarse veins cutting through amphibolite facies rocks—suggesting they formed where water was lost along fracture systems (Compton,

1960). In the southwest part of the area, the rather common occurrence of dolomitic marbles without periclase and of meionitic scapolite rather than calcic plagioclase indicate that pressures outside of the fracture systems were so high as to inhibit reactions producing free CO_2.

Granitic veins and dikes make up 5 to 15 percent of most outcrops and average over 50 percent throughout large areas. The granitic bodies range from nebulous spots to dikes and lenses 100 ft thick. Their compositions are closely correlative with the rocks in which they occur. Diorite veins and dikes occur only in mafic metagabbro and ultramafic bodies, while quartz diorite and calcic granodiorite veins occur only in quartzo-feldspathic rocks containing little if any K-feldspar. Small adamellite bodies occur in rocks containing both feldspars, but coarse-grained dikes and dilative lenses of adamellite may cut through all kinds of metamorphic rocks. Potassic granite veins and dikes, some coarse-grained and intrusive, occur only in and near Ca-poor schists (no. 6, table 2). Significantly, the specific gravities of ten samples of schists associated with these granites range from 2.81 to 3.16 and average 2.95. In three samples, spinel or corundum grains lie only a few millimeters from granitic veins. Considered along with the correlation of vein and host-rock compositions, these data indicate the various veins were segregated from their hosts. The intrusive adamellite and granite dikes are probably partial melts from the Sur series, for they may occur far from any of the major intrusive bodies and are texturally and mineralogically different from rocks of these major bodies.

The rocks were folded strongly twice. The earlier folds generally have subhorizontal axes and are commonly isoclinal (fig. 5). Coarse adamellite and granite were locally emplaced during the folding (fig. 6), and high-temperature minerals such as sillimanite lie roughly parallel to fold axes. Lineations tend to steepen near the main granitic bodies, for example in the northwest part of figure 4. Possibly this resulted from solid flowage consequent on intrusion of the plutonic bodies.

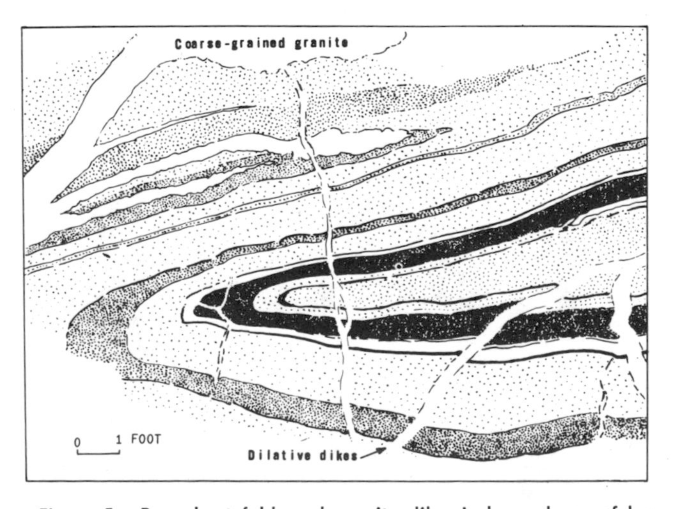

Figure 5. Recumbent folds and granite dikes in layered granofelses consisting of various proportions of hornblende, plagioclase, and clinopyroxene. Sketched from exposure in vertical roadcut near Escondido Camp, 5 miles west of Junipero Serra Peak.

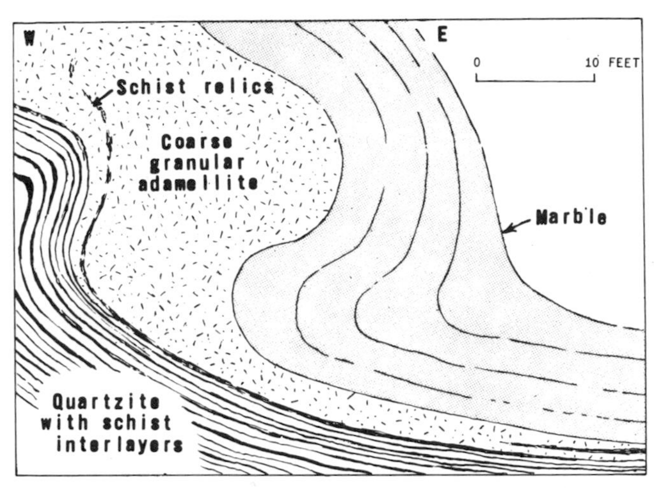

Figure 6. Coarse-grained adamellite intruded between marble and quartzite layers during first folding of Sur series. View is approximately along fold axes. Sketched from exposure on vertical canyon wall, 5½ miles west-northwest of Junipero Serra Peak.

The second folding repeated the stratiform rocks across the southern part of the area in a series of broad loops which have steeply plunging axes. The earlier lineations were rotated around these folds. New mineral lineations were formed but are restricted to sectors near plutonic bodies, indicating that the plutons supplied the heat required for pronounced recrystallization during this folding. Because lineations of the first folding are imprinted in several of the plutonic bodies, the two deformations were closely spaced in time or else the plutons were emplaced and crystallized over a long period.

The plutonic bodies themselves are three-fourths granitic rocks but may include rocks ranging from peridotite to granite. The largest and most complexly composite is 2½ miles wide and more than 16 miles long. All the bodies have curving contacts that tend to parallel the second folds in the Sur series, and many of the quartz diorites are lineated parallel to the earlier lineations in adjoining metamorphic rocks. Where distinct, the lineations consist of elongate biotite flakes and linear clusters of biotite grains. Petrofabric diagrams show parallel plagioclase lineations (fig. 7). Because these fabrics are far more distinct in the outer parts of the plutons, they are judged to have formed when the plutons were still partly molten. Even the last emplaced and most massive of the plutonic units, the adamellite that forms the central part of the main pluton, has vague elongate biotite clusters with tectonite fabrics.

The numerous ultramafic bodies are especially interesting because they were emplaced at various times during plutonism. Those with granoblastic textures, granulite facies mineral assemblages, and lineations parallel to the older fold axes are judged to be the oldest plutonic rocks in the area. At the other extreme,

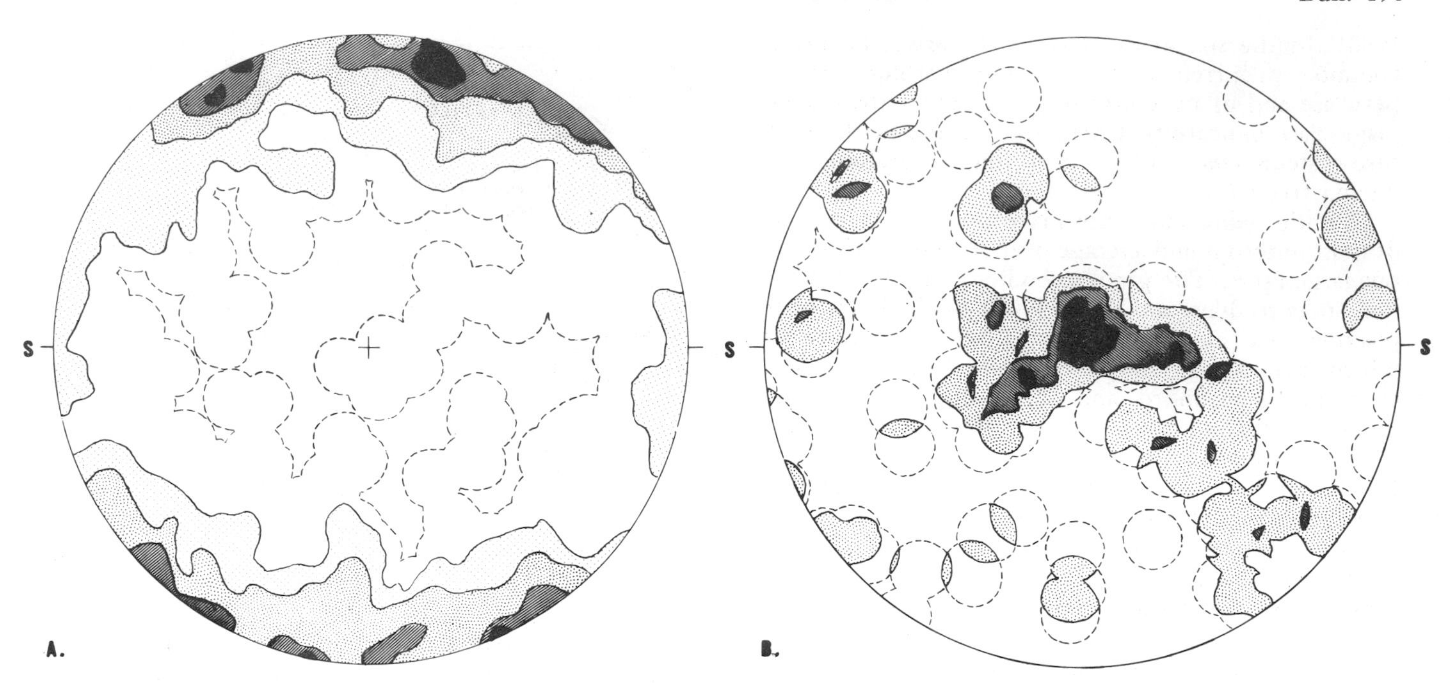

Figure 7. Petrofabric diagrams of quartz diorite sectioned approximately at right angles to megascopic lineation that is parallel to first fold axes of Sur series. A, Poles to cleavage in 500 biotite grains, corrected for *Schnitteffekt;* contours at 4, 3, 2, 1, and 0.2 percent per 1 percent of area. B, X optic axes (approximately parallel to *a* crystallographic axes) of 100 andesine grains in same thin section as A; contours at 6, 4, 2, and 1 percent per 1 percent of area. SS, biotite foliation. Sample from San Antonio River narrows, 7½ miles southeast of Junipero Serra Peak.

several bodies in the northeast part of the area are serpentinized peridotites similar to other Coast Range serpentinites except for containing appreciable amphiboles, chlorite, and talc. These bodies were presumably emplaced during the waning stages of the metamorphism. Bodies of intermediate age are most abundant and consist of coarse to very coarse inner zones of olivine-hornblende-pyroxene rocks (no. 1, table 2) and outer zones of amphibolites or pyroxene-hornblende rocks bearing appreciable plagioclase, biotite, and quartz (no. 2, table 2). The zonal arrangements, the unusual compositions, and the appreciable content of Cr_2O_3 indicate the bodies originated by mixing of peridotite with materials from the metamorphic rocks, possibly anatectic magma.

Gabbros, recrystallized almost totally to plagioclase-hornblende rocks, probably once formed sizable bodies but are now reduced to a few large relics and to hosts of dark inclusions in subsequent quartz diorite intrusions. The earlier granitic rocks are typically heterogeneous and range from rather basic quartz diorite (no. 3, table 2) to granodiorite with only 10 percent of biotite. All are allotriomorphic, have plagioclase (andesine) that is unzoned and commonly antiperthitic, and carry mafic minerals in clusters rather than simple grains (photo 1). A complex history of recrystallization is further indicated by the tectonite fabrics already mentioned and by a small relic of charnockitic (hypersthene-garnet) quartz diorite in normal quartz diorite near the southern contact of the main pluton.

Most of the adamellite was intruded subsequently, for it forms dilative dikes in the more basic rocks in many places. The youngest and most massive of the adamellites is rather fine-grained and porphyritic (no. 5, table 2). Heterogeneous gneissoid adamellites, locally garnetiferous, occur in mixed zones with granodiorite near the borders of the main pluton (no. 4, table 2).

That the larger plutons are intrusive is indicated by the diking effects of their constituent rocks and by their fairly distinct outer contacts. The northeast and southwest contacts of the main pluton dip distinctly toward one another (sec. A-B, fig. 4), and the con-

Photo 1. Photomicrograph of typical allotriomorphic quartz diorite of Junipero Serra area, showing clustered biotite grains. View is 12 mm across. Plane polarized light.

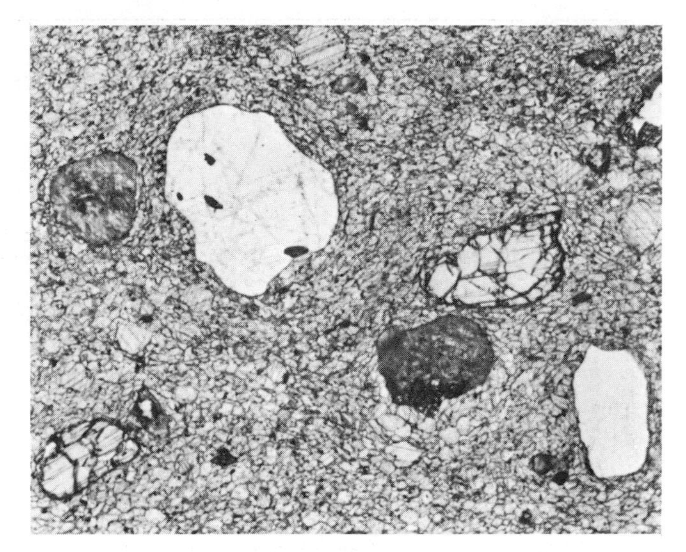

Photo 2. Photomicrographs of Sur marble. *Left,* strongly twinned calcite grains with black graphite tablets and equidimensional, white grains of apatite and K-feldspar. *Right,* recrystallized fine-grained calcite with large relics of K-feldspar (white), clinopyroxene (lined), and altered meionitic scapolite (dark gray). Views are 6 mm across. Plane polarized light.

tacts of the other mapped bodies either converge downward or are parallel. This geometric relationship suggests the exposed level was once in the deep root-zone of one or more plutons—a view supported by the high-grade metamorphism of the Sur series and the abundance of segregated granitic dikes and veins. Possibly, the plutons themselves arose in part as melts from underlying metamorphic rocks.

Following the second folding and the last of the plutonic intrusions, the rocks were uplifted and eroded, and by Late Cretaceous (Campanian) time fossiliferous marine strata were deposited on them. Considering the magnitude of this uplift, post-granite deformational structures are surprizingly localized. The marbles appear to have taken up most of the movement within the rock mass, for they are rather commonly crushed or recrystallized, with abundant {01$\bar{1}$2} twin lamellae (photo 2). Stress analyses of strongly twinned calcite grains, based on methods described by Turner and Weiss (1963), suggest that maximum compressive stresses were aligned so as to plunge steeply to moderately toward the southwest quadrant. Quartz deformation lamellae in a quartzo-feldspathic blastomylonite indicate a similar stress orientation. Minor folds in this blastomylonite are subhorizontal and trend northwest.

NORTHERN SANTA LUCIA RANGE

The Sur series metamorphic rocks that occur widely in the northern part of Santa Lucia Range show a fairly pronounced geographic variation from the coast inland. Marbles and calc-silicate rocks are abundant along the coastal ridge but fall off toward the east, so that the northeast ridge of the range consists almost entirely of quartz-rich metasediments (Fiedler, 1944, p. 182). The scarce marble lenses in the northeast half of the range are relatively pure and in sharp contact with quartzose rocks, much as in the Junipero Serra area. Graphitic quartzites and schists, which occur only locally in the Junipero Serra area, are more common in the northern part of the range (Trask, 1926; Reiche, 1937).

Metamorphic mineral assemblages of the coastal ridge as far north as Big Sur gorge are of highest grade amphibolite facies and locally of granulite facies. To the north and northeast, the rocks tend to be finer grained and are probably entirely of amphibolite facies. The distribution of veins and dikes emphasizes this pattern: to the west, minor granitic bodies are abundant and are much like those of the Junipero Serra area (Trask, 1926, p. 129), whereas the northeast ridge of the range exposes few of them (Fiedler, 1944, p. 185).

All earlier workers noted folds in the Sur series but apparently considered them unimportant. The writer has observed northwest-trending minor folds and mineral lineations along the coastal ridge as far north as Big Sur gorge, and Robert Wiebe (oral communication, 1965) has mapped well-developed subhorizontal lineations that have been refolded in the area northeast of Big Sur gorge. Judged from Wiebe's work and rather scant data on published maps, metamorphic foliations generally strike northwest, parallel to the range, but are folded sharply around some plutons. Major steep-axis convolutions like those of the Junipero Serra area are apparently absent, except possibly at the north end of the range, where Bowen (oral communication, 1965) has mapped a broad northeast trend in the Sur rocks.

Granitic rocks form about half the basement in the north part of the Santa Lucia Range. The individual bodies continue elongate and narrow for 10 to 15 miles north of the Junipero Serra area but then gradually merge so as to form a single mass at least 10 miles wide at the north end of the range. Textures change

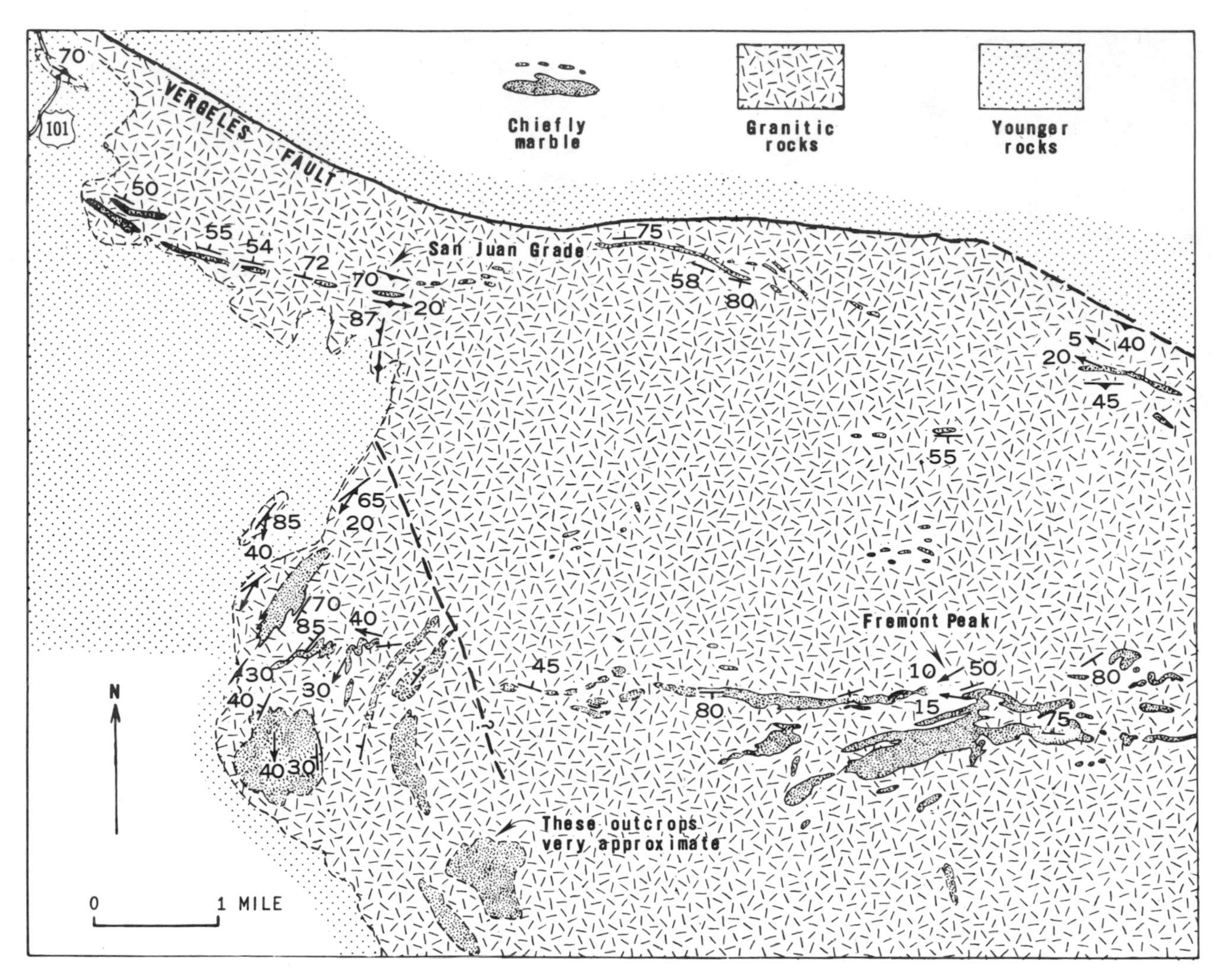

Figure 8. Map of north end of Gabilan Range, with marble relics suggesting a large fold around which earlier lineations have been rotated. Chiefly from maps of Allen (1946), Bowen and Gray (1959), and Santa Cruz sheet of the Geologic Map of California (Jennings and Strand, 1958), with additions by the writer.

significantly toward the north and east. Along the coastal ridge south of Big Sur gorge, quartz diorites are allotriomorphic and locally charnockitic (Compton, 1960). North and east of these bodies, granitic rocks become increasingly hypidiomorphic granular, with plagioclase subhedra showing oscillatory zoning. Ultramafic rocks form numerous small bodies for 15 miles northwest of the Junipero Serra area and then fall off markedly. Most of them are like the least metamorphosed peridotites of the Junipero Serro area rather than the strongly metamorphosed hybrid types. Finally, the number of metamorphosed basic intrusions (amphibolites) decreases toward the northeast side of the range (Fiedler, 1944, p. 183).

GABILAN RANGE

Basement rocks are not well exposed in this range but appear to form a broad granitic complex enclosing numerous large metamorphic relics. The metamorphic rocks are marbles, quartzites, schists, and calc-silicate rocks, many originally dolomitic and graphitic. Their gross interlayering and petrographic features suggest a direct correlation with the Sur series of the adjoining northern Santa Lucia Range. The correlation is important because Bowen and Gray (1959) noted occurrences of possible crinoid and cup coral remains in marbles on Fremont Peak. These are the only known fossils from the Salinian basement.

Except for the medium- to coarse-grained calcite and dolomite marbles, the rocks are rather fine-grained schists and quartzites, some of which are nearly black because of their large graphite content. Metamorphic minerals reported by Bowen and Gray (1959), and those studied by the writer, are mainly indicative of amphibolite facies, but transitions to lower grade rocks are suggested by widespread occurrences of tremolite-actinolite and muscovite. Local occurrences of sillimanite and wollastonite may reflect contact metamorphism, though the syntectonic nature of some of the granitic bodies makes it difficult to distinguish between pregranitic and contact-metamorphic effects.

Dikes from the plutonic bodies cut the metamorphic rocks in many places, but intricately veined rocks like those of the Junipero Serra area occur only locally near pluton contacts.

Folds in the Sur series were examined only in the northern part of the range, where structurally aligned marble relics that trend east-west through Fremont Peak swing N. 60° E. to N. 30° W. near the west side of the range—thereby defining a large steeply plunging fold (fig. 8). Subhorizontal mineral lineations and axes of small-scale folds trend around this major fold form, and subhorizontal lineations have clearly been refolded on steeply plunging small-scale folds. A third deformation is recorded by zones of fine-grained porphyroclastic marble that cut through coarser rock here and there. The sequence of structures is thus the same as that in the Junipero Serra area.

Granitic rocks form the great bulk of the range, and drill-hole data compiled by Fred Berry and Edward Gribi (oral communication, 1965) suggest that granitic rocks and gneisses underlie much of the Gabilan Mesa—the upland extending southeast from the Gabilan Range. The exposed plutonic rocks are dominantly silicic, ranging from biotite granodiorite to adamellite and granite (Wilson, 1943; Bowen, oral communication, 1965). Quartz diorite forms a considerable body extending from the south end of the range southeast under the Gabilan Mesa (Andrews, 1936). Quartz diorites and hornblende-biotite granodiorites examined by the writer at the north end of the range are lineated in parallel with subhorizontal folds in nearby marbles (fig. 8).

Quartz diorite is the principal rock in scattered outcrops extending for 10 miles northwest of the range. Metagabbro inclusions are locally abundant in these quartz diorites, which grade to more basic rocks in some places (nos. 7 and 8, table 2). Basic rocks also intruded the quartz diorites, and half a mile south of where U.S. Highway 101 crosses the San Andreas fault an irregular dike of amphibole-bearing peridotite cuts quartz diorite and metagabbro (Olaf Jenkins, oral communication, 1965). This rock is petrographically identical to some of the younger peridotites of Santa Lucia Range and is the most northerly ultramafic Salinian rock known to the writer.

BEN LOMOND AREA

Basement outcrops extending for 15 miles northwest of Santa Cruz have been studied extensively by Leo (1961) and locally by the writer. Leo estimated that the metamorphic rocks are 90 percent pelitic schists, quartzites, and gneisses, and 10 percent marbles and calc-silicate rocks. The marbles form thick lenses and layers in quartzose metasediments. Locally, as at Spring Street quarry in Santa Cruz, the writer found them interlayered with graphitic schists, exactly as in the Gabilan, La Panza, and northern Santa Lucia areas.

The mica-quartz schists and granofelses are rather fine grained and are only very locally injected by small granitic dikes. Muscovite is a common constituent of the schists, and tremolite is widespread in the marbles and calc-silicate rocks. Locally near intrusions, Leo found wollastonite in calc-silicate rocks and K-feldspar, cordierite, and sillimanite in coarse-grained schists, suggesting high-temperature metamorphism by the granitic bodies.

Foliations in the metamorphic rocks strike east-west on the average, and distinct mineral lineations and small-scale folds plunge at low angles, generally to the east-southeast in the eastern part of the area and to the west-southwest in the western part. Foliations and lineations swing concordantly with the contacts of the larger (quartz diorite) plutonic bodies, indicating they were refolded on steep axes before or during emplacement of the intrusions.

Apparently, the oldest of the plutonic rocks is a granodiorite that is distinctly gneissose parallel to the schistosity of adjoining schists but oblique to the granodiorite-schist contact. Another rock that appears to have been emplaced at an early tectonic stage is a garnetiferous biotite adamellite (Leo's Smith Grade pluton) which has vaguely to distinctly lineated biotite clusters that are subhorizontal and trend N. 70° E. to east-west, parallel to mineral and fold lineations in nearby schists and quartzites. Plagioclase in this rock is subhedral and zoned, suggesting a crystallization relationship very much as in the lineated adamellites of La Panza Range.

Small bodies of hornblende-cummingtonite gabbro, studied in detail by Leo, were emplaced before voluminous quartz diorite which crops out over areas as large as 6 by 10 miles. The quartz diorite is typically heterogeneous, orthoclase-bearing, and carries about 10 percent biotite and 5 percent hornblende; locally, it grades to more basic rocks as well as to granodiorite. Textures are consistently medium-grained hypidiomorphic granular and plagioclase is commonly zoned. Tectonic lineations like those of the Junipero Serra quartz diorites appear to be absent. Spotts (1962) reported that accessory epidote, chlorite, and sphene are common and that magnetite is scarce. Fine-grained mafic inclusions are widespread, some apparently having formed by disruption of mafic dikes emplaced into the granitic rocks at a late magmatic stage.

MONTARA MOUNTAIN AND THE FARALLON ISLANDS

As nearly as the writer could determine, granitic rocks form the entire exposures of these two areas. The Montara exposure, measuring about 4 by 10 miles, is mainly coarse-grained quartz diorite mineralogically like that of Ben Lomond. Quartz-bearing diorite inclusions are common and are locally associated with markedly mafic granitic rock. Along the sea cliff and Highway 1 (the only exposures the writer could examine in detail) strikingly planar inclusions lie parallel to a crudely gneissoid fabric that strikes N. 70° W. to E-W and dips steeply. The inclusions are locally elongate, but the writer could detect no consistent linear pattern nor any linear fabric in the granitic rocks themselves. In the southeast part of the area, quartz diorite appears to grade to ferrohastingsite-biotite granodiorite. Textures of all the granitic rocks range from allotriomorphic to hypidiomorphic, with plagioclase commonly showing oscillatory zoning. The accessory minerals are closely similar to those of the Ben Lomond rocks (Spotts, 1962).

The rocks of the Farallon Islands apparently range from quartz diorite to granodiorite which contains only a few percent of biotite and ferrohastingsite. Texturally and mineralogically they are closely similar to the rocks of Ben Lomond and Montara. Dredged samples indicate the same body of quartz diorite forms a 6-mile wide strip along the edge of the continental shelf, extending for 30 miles northwest of the islands (Uchupi and Emery, 1963). Samples described by Chesterman (1952) from the same submarine outcrop are like quartz diorites from Montara and Ben Lomond.

BODEGA HEAD, TOMALES-INVERNESS RIDGE, AND POINT REYES

The granitic rocks of these areas apparently represent a closely related group of intrusions, each bearing evidence of a complex emplacement history. The rocks on Bodega Head are mainly hornblende-biotite quartz diorite (no. 10, table 2) and somewhat less mafic granodiorite, grading locally to schlieren and large inclusions of mafic biotite diorite (no. 9, table 2) and also to schlieren of adamellite. Dikes of adamellite and potassic granite pegmatite locally cut the other rocks. Texturally and mineralogically, the quartz diorites and granodiorites are nearly identical to those of Montara Mountain; even their accessories are similar (Spotts, 1962). The schlieren and crudely gneissoid fabrics, which are generally steeply inclined and strike due north to N. 20° W., are locally folded on steeply plunging axes. Some granite pegmatites are folded on moderately inclined axes. Lineate biotite fabrics, however, were not noted by the writer.

The plutonic body underlying Tomales Point and Inverness Ridge is at least 18 miles long and consists of granodiorite and adamellite, with quartz diorite occurring locally at its north end. Large relics of metamorphic rocks are abundant along the northeast (Tomales Bay) side of the body and occur here and there elsewhere. They are mainly biotitic quartzites, calc-silicate rocks, and aluminous schists. Graphitic marbles, which form several small bodies 3 miles southeast of Inverness, carry orthoclase and meionitic scapolite, and are cut by foliated porphyroclastic bands like those occurring elsewhere in the Salinian block. The various rocks are rather fine grained, but sillimanite occurs in schists at several outcrops.

All of the Tomales Point outcrops examined show at least minor lineations, and several of the larger ones display tight folds formed during metamorphism. An excellent exposure at the south end of McClures Beach, on the west side of Tomales Point, shows thin-layered metamorphic rocks folded on nearly vertical axes. An adamellite on the south side of these rocks has strongly lineated biotite clusters oriented parallel to the metamorphic fold axes, indicating that at least this part of the plutonic body was emplaced before or during folding. Granodiorite and quartz diorite just north of the metamorphic outcrop appear to be younger for they are massive and contain unusually large, undeformed biotite subhedra. Half a mile to the north, however, these large biotites are crenulated, and rock foliations are locally folded on subhorizontal axes. Other granitic outcrops on the Tomales-Inverness Ridge show no compelling evidence of paracrystalline deformation, but few are suitable for detailed structural study.

Complex age relationships are also indicated by the excellent outcrops at the east end of Point Reyes. The silicic granodiorite and adamellite that extend for half a mile east and west of the Coast Guard lifeboat station range from massive to gneissoid and from fine gained to coarse grained. Some contacts between textural varieties are sharp and some are gradational, yet steeply dipping foliations swing gradually from northeast to northwest as one proceeds east from the lifeboat station to the point, suggesting that the entire mass was deformed after its emplacement. Unfortunately, the writer could not observe the relationships between these adamellites and the rocks exposed at the west end of the point. These appear to be mainly hornblende-biotite granodiorite and quartz diorite, locally with mafic inclusions and schlieren.

INTERPRETATION

This survey of the principal basement exposures indicates a complex but reasonably consistent plutonic history for the Salinian rocks. The metamorphic rocks apparently represent one heterogeneous sedimentary assemblage of Paleozoic or Mesozoic age. Their platform-type sandstones and limestones and the abundance of dolomitic rocks prove they are not metamorphosed Franciscan rocks. All were folded and metamorphosed more than once; in most areas, folding on subhorizontal axes was followed by folding on steeply inclined axes. Plutonic rocks ranging from peridotite to potassic granite were emplaced before or during the first folding as well as later. The granitic textures and the distribution of the second mineral lineations indicate these events constitute one prolonged period of plutonism. Local recrystallization and cataclasis recorded a final tectonic episode that may well have been synchronous with uplift of the entire Salinian mass.

Increase in metamorphic grade and increasing abundance of granitic veins and dikes toward the southwest edge of the block indicate this part of the terrain was most heated and probably most deeply buried. The narrow, lens-shaped granitic bodies of this sector appear to represent the lower (catazonal) parts of one or more plutons, while the broad granitic bodies exposed to the north and east represent higher (mesozonal) sections through related plutons. This geometric scheme is based mainly on geographic variations in the shapes of granitic bodies in Santa Lucia Range; it is supported by regional variations in granitic textures and mineralogy as well as by the degree to which the terrain yielded during the second folding. If the scheme is correct, the plutonic suite could not have originated by gravitative differentiation in place, for the lower parts of the plutons are at least as silicic as the higher parts. The heterogeneity of the quartz diorites and granodiorites suggests they might have arisen by mixing of gabbroic melt with anatectic materials from underlying metamorphic rocks. The numerous zoned ultramafic bodies are almost certainly hybrid.

In spite of the excellent K-Ar determinations available, it is difficult to assign dates to the various plutonic events. The difficulty is epitomized by the Junipero Serra rocks, which have given the youngest ages (69.6 and 75 m.y.) yet are overlain by Upper Cretaceous beds containing Campanian fossils. This relationship suggests that the K-Ar ages represent a postgranite event, for example the deformation that produced the fine-grained recrystallized marbles. In this light, it is interesting to note that the other K-Ar ages tend to increase away from the Junipero Serra area, in a rough correlation with the broad depth zoning just described. It is thereby suggested that the higher parts of the plutons crystallized during mid-Cretaceous time, yielding the oldest K-Ar ages (around 90 m.y.). The more deeply buried rocks continued to recrystallize during this time and began to accumulate argon only when lifted and cooled as the Salinian block was uplifted and eroded. The possibility that the plutonic suite is much older than Cretaceous tends to be disallowed by Hutton's Th-Pb determination (fig. 1) and by Pb isotope ratios (of rocks 5 and 6, table 1) which are closely similar to ratios of Cretaceous to Recent silicic igneous rocks from other parts of the western United States (Doe, in press).

If the granulite facies rocks were in fact generated during the Cretaceous, the Salinian block was uplifted many miles during Late Cretaceous time. The metamorphic zoning indicates the west side was uplifted farther than the east. A suggestion of early movement with a strike-slip sense (such as might be related to an ancestral San Andreas fault) is found in the steep-axis folds in the Sur rocks; however, not enough folds have been mapped to test for sense of shear or asymmetry. The latest set of metamorphic structures (those of the fine-grained recrystallized marbles) suggests maximum compressive stresses aligned roughly normal to the length of the block.

Not the least perplexing problem is the apparent disappearance of the great mass of sediments eroded from the rising block. Because the Cretaceous sediments east of the block were likely derived from the east (Bailey, Irwin, and Jones, 1964), the Salinian detritus was presumably carried west into the Pacific Ocean. From here, it was conceivably thrust or dragged eastward under the continental edge, generating the deep root required for the continued rise of the Salinian block. This sense of movement is suitable to the youngest metamorphic structures in the Junipero Serra area and also to the general northeastward dip of foliations and axial planes of folds in the Sur series and in the Franciscan rocks of the adjoining coastal strip. Otherwise, the model must be pure conjecture until the ages of the plutonic rocks are fixed more firmly.

REFERENCES

Allen, J. E., 1946, Geology of the San Juan Bautista quadrangle, California: California Div. Mines Bull. 133, p. 9–75.

Andrews, Philip, 1936, Geology of the Pinnacles National Monument: California Univ., Dept. Geol. Sci. Bull., v. 24, no. 1, p. 1–38.

Bailey, E. H., Irwin, W. P., and Jones, D. L., 1964, Franciscan and related rocks, and their significance in the geology of western California: California Div. Mines and Geology Bull. 183, 177 p.

Bowen, O. E., Jr., and Gray, C. H., Jr., 1959, Geology and economic possibilities of the limestone and dolomite deposits of the northern Gabilan Range, California: California Div. Mines Spec. Rept. 56, 40 p.

Chesterman, C. W., 1952, Descriptive petrography of rocks dredged off the coast of central California: California Acad. Sci. Proc., 4th ser., v. 27, p. 359–374.

Compton, R. R., 1960, Charnockitic rocks of Santa Lucia Range, California: Am. Jour. Sci., v. 258, no. 9, p. 609–636.

Curtis, G. H., Evernden, J. F., and Lipson, J., 1958, Age determination of some granitic rocks in California by the potassium-argon method: California Div. Mines Spec. Rept. 54, 16 p.

Doe, B. R., 196..., The bearing of lead isotopes on the source of granitic magmas: (In press)

Fiedler, W. M., 1944, Geology of the Jamesburg quadrangle, Monterey County, California: California Jour. Mines and Geology, v. 40, p. 177–250.

Hutton, C. O., 1959, Mineralogy of beach sands between Halfmoon and Monterey Bays, California: California Div. Mines Spec. Rept. 59, 32 p.

Jennings, C. W., and Strand, R. G., 1959, Geologic map of California, Olaf P. Jenkins edition, Santa Cruz sheet: California Div. Mines, scale 1:250,000.

Lawson, A. C., 1893, The geology of Carmelo Bay [California]: California Univ., Dept. Geology Bull., v. 1, no. 1, p. 1–59.

Leo, G. W., 1961, The plutonic and metamorphic rocks of Ben Lomond Mountain, Santa Cruz County, California: Stanford Univ., Stanford, Calif., Ph.D. thesis, 169 p.

Osmont, V. C., 1905, A geological section of the Coast Ranges north of the Bay of San Francisco: California Univ., Dept. Geology Bull., v. 4, p. 39–87.

Reiche, Parry, 1937, Geology of the Lucia quadrangle, California: California Univ., Dept. Geol. Sci. Bull., v. 24, no. 7, p. 115–168.

Reid, J. A., 1902, The igneous rocks near Pajaro: California Univ., Dept. Geology Bull., v. 3, p. 173–190.

Spotts, J. H., 1962, Zircon and other accessory minerals, Coast Range batholith, California: Geol. Soc. America Bull., v. 73, no. 10, p. 1221–1240.

Trask, P. D., 1926, Geology of the Point Sur quadrangle, California: California Univ., Dept. Geol. Sci. Bull., v. 16, no. 6, p. 119–186.

Turner, F. J., and Weiss, L. E., 1963, Structural analysis of metamorphic tectonites: New York, McGraw-Hill Book Co., 545 p.

Uchupi, Elazar, and Emery, K. O., 1963, The continental slope between San Francisco, California, and Cedros Island, Mexico: Deep-Sea Research, v. 10, no. 4, p. 397–447.

Wilson, I. F., 1943, Geology of the San Benito quadrangle, California: California Jour. Mines and Geology, v. 39, no. 2, p. 183–270.

The Geysers area, Sonoma County. After J. M. Hutchings, *Scenes of wonder and curiosity in California,* 1861.

TERTIARY PHOSPHATIC FACIES OF THE COAST RANGES

By Paul F. Dickert
San Jose State College, San Jose, California

The mid-Tertiary marginal seas which crossed central and southern California contained luxuriant growths of phytoplankton. Massive evidence from modern seas shows that a complex circulation of currents lay behind these plant concentrations. The phytoplankton were nourished by sustained turbulent upwelling of cold phosphorus-rich water from deep-sea reservoirs, the blooms multiplying in swift and close relation to the phosphorus supply (Redfield and others, 1963). The upwelling and the productivity were focused in large stable eddies which accompanied prevailing southerly coastal currents (Currie, 1953; Emery, 1960). These slowly rotating swirls, extending for as much as 200 miles, further concentrated the phytoplankton in vividly colored patches of surface water and channeled their remains into thick accumulations on the shelving sea floor.

Photo 1A. Phosphatic shale consisting of light laminae, ½ cm thick, of carbonate fluorapatite in dark organic silt shale. Monterey Formation. Naples.

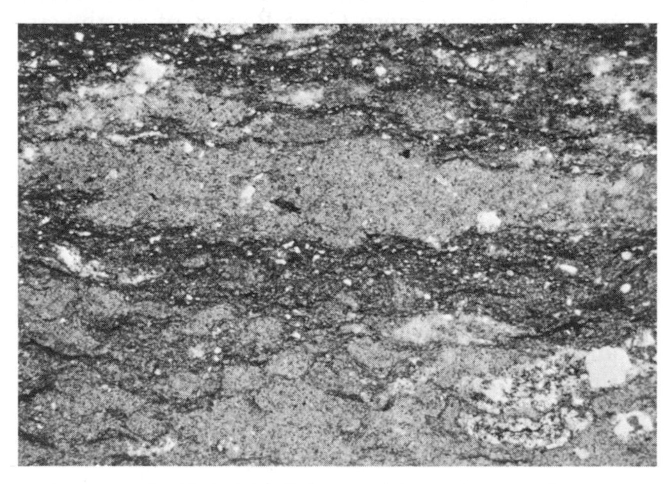

Photo 1B. Photomicrograph showing billowy phosphate laminae and organic interlayers. Field of view is 1 cm.

In a temperate, slowly oxidizing environment, phosphorus was regenerated from this organic debris and formed colloidal aggregates that were eventually incorporated in two principal rock types, depending on the depth of the shelf and the mechanical energy of the bottom water. One type, phosphatic shale (photo 1A, B), consisting of billowy blebs, lenses, and laminae of carbonate fluorapatite, a centimeter or less thick, typically, in organic argillaceous to sandy silt shale, originated in the outer deeper portions of the shelf, where relatively quiescent bottom water permitted mass flocculation of the apatite colloids.* A second type formed in the shallower, more agitated water of the inner shelf, where intensified particle contact, cluster formation, and agglomeration pelletized the apatite colloids in sand-sized grains, and with increased energy shoreward created oölitic structures. Mechanical concentration of pellets and oölites by tidal currents and other near-bottom turbulence resulted in the formation of pelletal phosphorite or pelletite (photo 2A, B). The transition from phosphatic shale to pelletal phosphate occurred where the shoreward movement of apatite clusters was balanced by the tractive forces that carried sand relatively seaward. By analogy with the existing shelf, a transition zone at 100 to 130 m may be conjectured.

These phosphatic rock types, varying laterally and vertically with respect to each other and to their position within the enveloping formation or formations, comprise the phosphatic facies whose distribution and stratigraphic relations in the central and southern Coast ranges are summarized in the following pages and shown in figures 1 and 2. Localities are numbered in the text and in these figures.

Two features of the California setting make these facies worth study: The phosphate occurrences were sediments of marginal seas of a greater range of depths and phosphate sediment types than their more abundant counterparts from epeiric environments whose deposits have received the most attention, and the California terrestrial occurrences are adjacent to marine basins that contain existing phosphate sediments.

* The modes of formation of the phosphatic rock types are treated in a California Division of Mines Bulletin in preparation.

Photo 2A. Washed concentrate of pelletal phosphate. Long diameters are ½ to 1 mm. Monterey Formation. Carmel Valley.

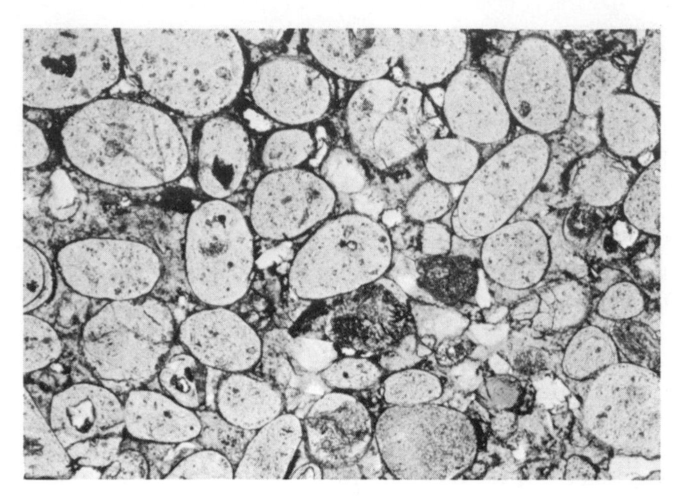

Photo 2B. Photomicrograph of pelletal phosphate. Most such pelletites have been mechanically concentrated. Note broken pellet, upper center, elongation of some pellets by accretion, and partial solution of phosphate at boundaries of some adjoining pellets.

GENERAL FEATURES OF DISTRIBUTION

The phosphatic facies are thickest and richest in southern and central California. From peak concentrations in the Ventura and Los Angeles basins, the phosphate-bearing rocks diminish in thickness and in phosphorus content northward through the Coast Ranges, with the major facies, which is of middle Miocene age, pinching out somewhere in the vicinity of the 38th parallel north of San Francisco Bay (fig. 1). Only a few scattered occurrences of phosphate rock are known north of this latitude within the Coast Ranges, in spite of northern occurrences of rock types and microfossil assemblages with which the 400-mile-wide Miocene facies is associated in the central and southern areas.

Although Paleozoic and Mesozoic rocks comprise approximately as much of the present California land surface as the Tertiary rocks outlined in figure 1, nearly all the phosphate-bearing strata shown are in Miocene or younger rocks. A few known occurrences of phosphate pellets and nodules of Late Jurassic to Early Cretaceous age are widely separated in the northern and central Coast Ranges. A nodular facies of Late Cretaceous age may underlie the western Sacramento Valley. Late Eocene pelletal mudstone crops out in the Panoche Hills along the western edge of the San Joaquin Valley. An Eocene and Oligocene phosphatic shale-pellet facies appears in the Santa Cruz Mountains, and a ferruginous phosphatic unit of comparable age is known in the northern Santa Lucia Range. However, none of these thinly scattered pre-Miocene occurrences is known to extend more than a few tens of miles.

In contrast, the Miocene series, and especially the middle Miocene, hosts abundant and extensive deposits. Phosphatic shales and pelletal sandstones and mudstones are seen in Zemorrian and lower Saucesian strata in the Temblor Range along the southwestern border of the San Joaquin Basin, and in uppermost Zemorrian and Saucesian strata in scattered localities from the Santa Cruz Basin to the eastern Ventura Basin. Instances of phosphate deposition become more numerous in rocks of Relizian age, the phosphate-bearing rocks become more extensive, more clearly correlative with each other, and in general continue into younger strata. The mounting incidence of phosphate accumulation culminates in a widespread facies of Luisian age in which phosphate, in one discrete form or another, was deposited within shales and contiguous sandstones almost continuously from the vicinity of the site of San Francisco Bay to the northern Santa Ana Mountains, and from Point Conception to the Sierra Nevada foothills east of Bakersfield. In southern California, and locally in central California, deposition continued into early Mohnian time.

Though lacking the continuity of the middle Miocene phosphatic facies, early or early middle Pliocene deposits—in the northern Coast Ranges of northwestern Sonoma County, on Gabilan Mesa, in the east-central Diablo Range, and in the northern Purissima Hills—are thought to be correlative.

This nonuniform distribution of phosphates in time reflects, in part, a greater abundance of data for the younger rocks, as a result of the focusing of oil exploration in the middle and upper Tertiary. Nonetheless, the paucity of phosphate concentrations in pre-Tertiary strata in California is thought to be real, and a result of differences in sedimentary and tectonic environments of deposition—in the turbulent deposition of the eugeosynclinal Franciscan sediments, for instance—as compared with the more stable shelf setting of the mid-Tertiary marginal seas.

PRE-TERTIARY PHOSPHATIC ROCKS

The few known instances of phosphate deposition in the lower two-thirds of the stratigraphic record in

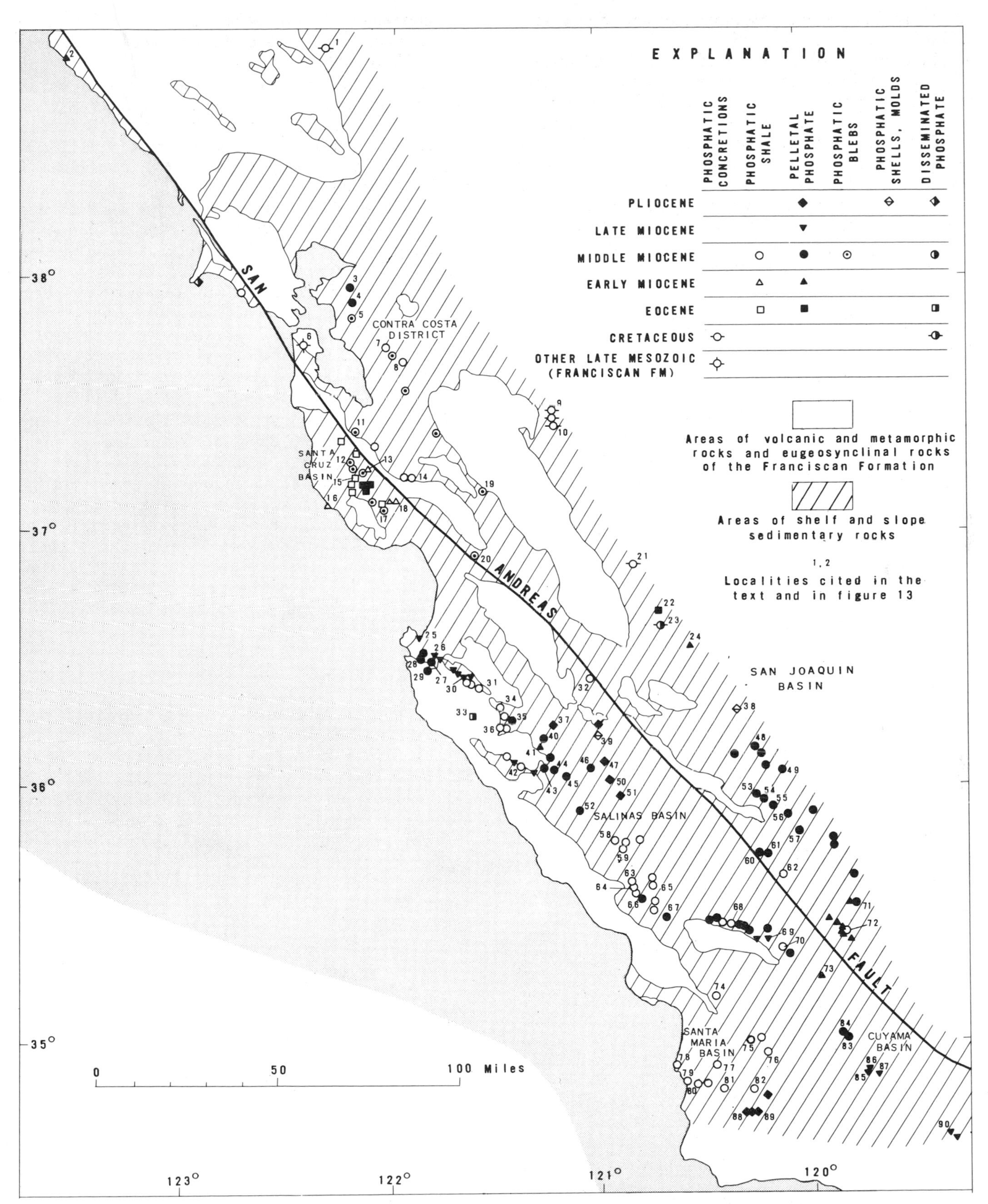

Figure 1. Map of phosphate-bearing localities in the central and southern Coast Ranges of California.

the Coast Ranges are geographically and stratigraphically isolated.

The only phosphates reported in the 15,000-square-mile area of Franciscan outcrop are nodular concretions, containing about 10 percent P_2O_5, taken from a shear zone within greywackes and shales near Laguna Honda in San Francisco (J. Schlocker, oral communication, 1965). These concretions contain what appear to be *Marthasterites tritrachiatus*, a calcareous nannofossil that is abundant in the California Eocene but rare in Cretaceous or in older rocks (W. R. Evitt, oral communication, 1965), so that even this rare instance of phosphate deposition in the Franciscan may be based on a displaced specimen.

Near the apparent boundary between the Lower and Upper Cretaceous in uppermost sandy mudstone beds of the Brophy Canyon Formation near Cache Creek, Yolo County (1), coarse phosphate pellets are found within concretions, and smaller (2 to 3 cm) pods of pelletal phosphate appear in the subjacent Buck Island Member of the Davis Canyon Formation (R. W. Ojakangas, oral communication, 1964).

At several localities along the western margin of the Sacramento Valley, phosphate concretions to lengths of 5 cm are distributed in the organic mudstone of the Upper Cretaceous Moreno Formation (10, C. E. Bishop, oral communication, 1965; 9, 21, C. A. McLeroy, oral communication, 1965). In Escarpado Canyon, Fresno County, this unit includes mudstone in which phosphate is so finely disseminated that its presence is known only by chemical test (Gulbrandsen and others, 1963), and locally it also contains apatized wood with small nodules of leucophosphite. Although these small nodules resemble pelletal apatite, the leucophosphite is a secondary mineral concentrated near fractures and toward the outer surfaces of the phosphatized specimens—a rare form of marine phosphate which, in deposits all over the world, tends to assume the composition and structure of carbonate fluorapatite.

EOCENE AND OLIGOCENE * PHOSPHATIC FACIES

The oldest phosphatic facies of significant areal extent recognized in California consists of Eocene and Oligocene(?) phosphatic shales in the Big Basin area of the central Santa Cruz Mountains (15, Brabb, 1960). These are olive-black carbonaceous phosphatic shales, interlayered to thicknesses of 50 m in massive arkosic late Eocene sandstones of the upper Butano Sandstone and lower San Lorenzo Formation over an area of at least 200 square miles. The phosphate beds are cut to the east by the San Andreas fault. They are distinguished from their thicker, more extensive mid-Miocene counterparts by the presence of thin, sharply outlined, pizza-shaped † laminae and local, very thin, weakly phosphatic sandstones which are cross bedded and convoluted. Brabb has assigned a late Narizian age to the shales on the basis of faunal reports by the staff of the Union Oil Co.

South of the Ben Lomond-Gabilan pluton, in the northeastern Santa Lucia Range, a ferruginous phosphatic mudstone appears in Oligocene (Refugian) remnants which parallel Church Creek (33, W. R. Dickinson, oral communication, 1963). Continuity of the San Lorenzo Formation of Narizian and Refugian age with the Church Creek Formation has been suggested by Dickinson (1956), who notes similarities of stratigraphic succession, lithology, and fauna. A correlation of the phosphatic horizons, and continuity of the Narizian and Refugian basin from the Santa Cruz Mountains across the Ben Lomond pluton into the Santa Lucia Range, may eventually be established if the phosphatic facies of the San Lorenzo can be traced southward into the Refugian San Juan Bautista Formation at the northern edge of the Gabilan Range.

The top of the phosphatic shales in the San Lorenzo Formation in the Big Basin area is marked by half a meter of glauconite in which phosphate is finely disseminated. In massive mudstone of the upper San Lorenzo Formation an apparent break in deposition is characterized by a glauconite and phosphate pellet and pebble bed to 3 m in thickness. The latter unit can be recognized as a marker bed over a distance of 12 miles. These strata have been identified with the bottom of the Refugian and Zemorrian Stages, respectively, by Brabb (1960).

North of the mouth of Skooner Gulch near Point Arena (2), about 150 miles north of the San Lorenzo glauconite, there is a somewhat similar unit. It consists of 3 m of glauconitic sandy siltstone with 1 or 2 percent of phosphate pebbles 2 to 3 cm long, marking the base of the Gallaway Beds of C. E. Weaver (1943). Below the phosphate pebble bed, the glauconitic beds coarsen to gritty sandstones of Weaver's Skooner Gulch Formation; 25 m above the pebble zone, thin (0.8 m) lenses of similarly sized phosphate pebbles appear where the glauconitic sandy siltstones are succeeded by finer clastics. Foraminifera identified by Kleinpell (1938, table 16) from approximately the same stratigraphic level as the phosphate pebble zone indicate an early Zemorrian age.

East of the San Andreas fault, in the Panoche Hills at the western edge of the San Joaquin Valley, phosphate pellets are scattered in a half-meter thick mudstone unit that intervenes between basal sandstone and glauconite pebble beds and shale units of the Kreyenhagen Formation of Eocene and Oligocene(?) age (22, Payne, 1951).

The thin occurrences of pelletal phosphate near Point Arena and in the Panoche Hills illustrate, on a small scale, a phenomenon that is more apparent in the younger, more extensive phosphatic rocks—a concentration of phosphate pellets at transitions from fine to coarse clastic deposition or the reverse. As a result of major transitions in sedimentation, pellet beds will

* The boundaries of the European-based epochs of the Tertiary are assigned here according to the recent usage of Mitchell and Repenning (1963, table 1), which places the California equivalent of the Aquitanian Stage (Zemorrian Stage) within the Miocene.

† A thickening of the rims of the laminae is thought to be a diagenetic modification.

Photo 3. Distorted phosphatic shale of the Lambert Formation at the core of a small anticline at Año Nuevo Point. Field of view is 1.8 m.

commonly coincide with the base or top of a formation, but phosphate pellets may also appear where irregularities in basin topography or shifts of climate have brought about minor variations in sediment types within major lithologic units. Consequently, phosphate pellet beds are less reliable as marker horizons than the phosphate-laminated shales, which tend to be more uniform and more persistent because they form in a deeper and more stable shelf environment.

Photo 4. Graded phosphatic laminae. Light collophane particles coarsen and grade downward into dark organic silt interlayers. About 1½ cm thickness shown. Lambert Formation. Zayante Canyon.

LOWER MIOCENE PHOSPHATIC FACIES

Conspicuous phosphatic strata were laid down in the early Miocene at an uppermost Zemorrian or lower Saucesian horizon at two widely separated localities in the central and southern Coast Ranges on opposite sides of the San Andreas fault.

In the central Santa Cruz Mountains (18, J. C. Clark, oral communication, 1964), the Lambert Formation (Dibblee, 1965) includes up to 75 m of dark-gray phosphatic shales closely resembling the Eocene and Oligocene phosphatic shales in the Big Basin area. A coastal exposure near Año Nuevo Point (16, J. C. Clark, oral communication, 1964) (photo 3), and several exposures 20 miles inland near the San Andreas fault (13), indicate that the Lambert phosphatic facies once occupied much of the same area as the older phosphatic shales, though it is separated from them near the fault by as much as 1,500 m of mudstone and sandstone. Like the Butano and San Lorenzo Formations, these strata show bedding features uncommon to the younger phosphatic shales—thin graded sandstone interbeds and sharply graded phosphatic laminae (photo 4), implying a deeper and quieter bottom environment than that of the locally current-bedded Eocene shales. Small phosphatic blebs,* which are interspersed in all the phosphatic shales in California, continue for several meters above and below the phosphatic laminae in the eastern exposures of the shale. Foraminifera from the phosphatic facies are predominantly of the lower Saucesian *Siphogenerina transversa* zone.

South of the Ben Lomond-Gabilan pluton, in the western Santa Lucia Range near King City, small phosphate pellets comprise up to 10 percent of a mudstone member of the Vaqueros sandstone. In Reliz Canyon (41), the mudstone is judged to be of probable middle or late Zemorrian age, on the basis of a lower Saucesian fauna identified by R. M. Thorup (1942) in the superjacent Sandholdt Formation. A southward extension of the Lambert phosphatic facies along a former narrow seaway across the Gabilan uplift is more conjectural than for the Eocene-Oligocene phosphatic facies, because the rocks of the Vaqueros group (of Allen, 1946) in isolated exposures south of San Juan Bautista are interbedded and overlain by continental breccias and conglomerates composed largely of limestone and granite derived from the emerging Gabilan Range. On the other hand, some intermittent shallow inundation during Zemorrian, and possibly into Saucesian, time is indicated by sandy marine beds within and below the Vaqueros continental debris, and in overlying volcanic agglomerates.

Scattered instances of earliest Miocene phosphate deposition, south of the phosphatic shale of the Santa Cruz Mountains and Vaqueros beds and west of the San Andreas fault, are not known to fit regional facies

* Small (to 5 cm) lenticular segregations of phosphorus about which laminae or other bedding features form a swirl pattern. The blebs formed—presumably from phosphate in interstitial water, which by analogy with modern sediments was an adequate source—after the sediments were deposited, but before they were compacted (see photo 7A, B).

Photo 5. Steeply dipping pellet-bearing Upper Santos Shale in Chico Martinez Creek canyon. Sandstone interbed in upper left has slumped into poorly consolidated pelletal shale. Field view, 2.2 m.

patterns. Collophane pellets in siliceous clay shale in the upper part of the Zemorrian Soda Lake Formation in the Carrizo-Cuyama basin (73, R. K. Cross, 1962), and thin pellet-bearing upper Zemorrian beds in the lower Rincon Formation in the western Transverse Ranges, may be synchronous, in part, with the phosphate deposition to the north. However, the distribution of the Soda Lake pellets is not known, and the usually sparse, irregularly distributed pellets in the lower Rincon and subjacent Vaqueros Formation of the Ventura basin do not comprise a traceable zone of well-defined vertical range.

East of the San Andreas fault, and 175 miles south of the Santa Cruz Basin, a well-known Miocene section exposed along Chico Martinez and Zemorra Creeks (72), on the southwestern margin of the San Joaquin Basin, contains a pelletal phosphate facies correlative with the Lambert phosphatic shales of the Santa Cruz Mountains. Phosphate pellets appear at intervals throughout a sandy lower and lower middle Miocene section in the western San Joaquin Basin. Discrete concentrations (17 to 20 percent pellets over one 10-m section) at the base of the brownish-gray finely fractured upper Santos Shale (photo 5) and within a lower part of the Santos Shale are a recognizable facies over 8 miles of outcrops between Salt Creek and Media Agua Creek. They also extend subsurface for at least 10 miles to the Belridge oil field. The pellet beds are characterized by abundant glauconite, by oölites of alternating glauconite and collophane shells around glauconite and/or collophane cores (photo 6), and, locally, by crusts of gypsum. The pellet beds of the upper Santos Shale lie directly above the top of Kleinpell's Zemorrian Stage at his type locality.

Data from wells in several localities in the western San Joaquin Basin record collophane or pyritized collophane pellets at scattered intervals within the lower Miocene of the Temblor Formation, but few of the occurrences have been correlated with the phosphate beds in Santos Shale outcrops, or with each other (71, Wharton, 1943; Woodring and others, 1940; 57, Curtin, 1955; 24, Garrison, 1955).

THE MIDDLE MIOCENE PHOSPHATIC FACIES

A north to south traverse of the phosphate-bearing strata in the California middle Miocene bypasses the northern third of the State to the 38th parallel. Although the Eel River Basin, in Humboldt County, and the Gualala Block, near Point Arena, both contain diatomaceous mudstone and shale-bearing Luisian and Mohnian Foraminifera, which is an auspicious rock-time association to the south, phosphate has not been recognized in these northern units. Chemical tests made on samples from Miocene sections along the Eel River, along Salmon Creek to the west of Fortuna, and along the Point Arena coast have been generally negative.

Contra Costa Basin

The northernmost exposures of the middle Miocene phosphatic facies in the Contra Costa and Santa Cruz Basins are only meagerly phosphatic. However, minor phosphate components can be traced throughout the lateral extent of the middle Miocene Monterey Group of the Contra Costa Basin. Small pellets are disseminated in the lower part of the upper Luisian Oursan Sandstone of Pinole Ridge (3) and other localities to the south; pellet beds lie in silty shale near the top of the lower Luisian Claremont Shale along Oursan Ridge near Bear Creek (4); pellets and pebbles increasing in coarseness and concentration are found toward the top of an 8-m-thick zone in the Claremont Shale [1] south of Dublin (8); 20 m of phosphatic shale with discontinuous nodular laminae occur within an isolated fault-bound siliceous shale sequence of the Monterey Formation of early Luisian age east of Los Gatos (14); and weakly phosphatic shale has been found in the

[1] These phosphate pebble beds, which bear little resemblance to the typical Claremont Shale, are shown in the most recent literature of the area as Cretaceous.

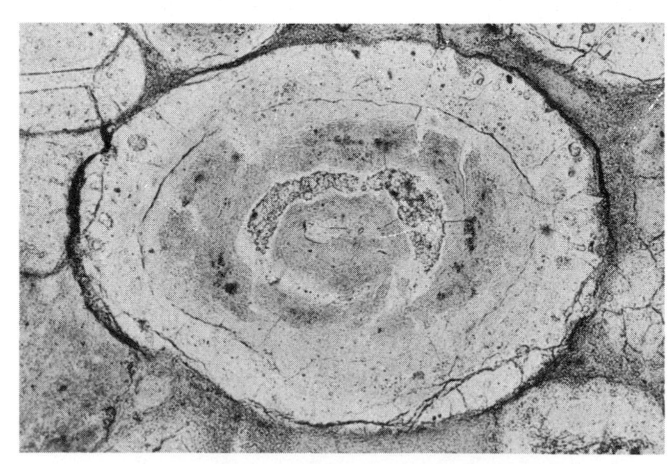

Photo 6. Core and shell of glauconite (dark) alternating with shells of collophane (light). Pellet is ½ mm long. Santos Shale. Chico Martinez Creek.

Photo 7A. Phosphate blebs, indicated by arrows, in Claremont Shale at Mission Pass. Field of view is .5 m.

Photo 7B. Photomicrograph of phosphate bleb. Displaced laminae and platy flecks of organic material form flow patterns around these blebs.

Monterey Formation of Allen (1946) near the faulted western basin margin north of San Juan Bautista (20).

These occurrences share a relatively narrow time range within the Luisian Stage, but they are discontinuous and do not of themselves form a traceable phosphatic horizon. Continuity is supplied, however, by small white phosphate blebs, from 1 to 2 cm long, sparsely distributed within the finely laminated siliceous Claremont Shale (photo 7A, B). The blebs are identical with those which extend above and below the lower Saucesian phosphatic shale facies in the Santa Cruz Mountains. In the Claremont Shale, phosphate blebs are dispersed over a strike length of 60 miles, from the western Berkeley Hills southeast to the northwestern flanks of the Diablo Range east of Morgan Hill (19) (see fig. 1).

In Crow Canyon at the southern end of Las Trampas Ridge (7), a phosphate pellet and pebble zone 2 m thick in olive-gray sandstone, has been assigned to the Sobrante Formation by Aarons (1958), which is subjacent to the Claremont Shale. The phosphate outcrops are part of a complex fold pattern in which sandstone and shale are encountered successively down section. Both the shales, which are of similar lithology to some that have been assigned to the Claremont in this area, and these pelletal sandstones may be interbedded within the Claremont Shale and part of the Luisian facies as are the pebble beds south of Dublin.

To the west of the Stanford University campus, sparse collophane pellets occur in an unnamed dark-gray silty sandstone of probable Luisian age penetrated by boreholes drilled for the Stanford linear accelerator (11).

Santa Cruz Basin

In the neighboring Santa Cruz Basin, west of the San Andreas fault, the Woodhams Shale Member of the Monterey Formation (Cummings and others, 1962) over a strike length of at least 15 miles is characterized by light-pinkish-gray phosphatic blebs, to 5 cm in length. The blebs are most abundant in northern exposures near Peters Creek (12) and are sparser to the south. Although they differ in color and size, their distribution is similar to that of the blebs in the Claremont Shale. Phosphate blebs in the Monterey Formation north of Felton (17) are of early Luisian age (J. C. Clark, oral communication, 1963), and correlation with the Claremont Shale east of the San Andreas fault is probable.

Salinas Basin

The phosphate beds increase markedly in concentration and in chronologic range south of the Ben Lomond-Gabilan-Monterey massif, which separated deeper portions of the Santa Cruz and Salinas basins during the middle and early late Miocene. A near-continuous phosphatic shale and pellet facies cuts through the Sandholdt, Monterey, and Santa Margarita Formations, where these units and their southern correlatives comprise the Relizian, Luisian, and lower Mohnian Stages, from Carmel Valley to the Cuyama and Santa Maria basins and beyond into the Transverse and Peninsular Ranges provinces. In general, the phosphatic sequences in the foraminiferal clay shale of the Sandholdt Formation are characterized by dispersions of phosphatic blebs and by phosphatic laminae; the phosphate beds in the opaline and diatomaceous shales of the Monterey Formation in the Salinas Basin consist mostly of discrete layers of pellets and phosphatized organic remains.

In the northwestern Salinas Basin where the phosphatic strata abut the Monterey granodiorite pluton, they grade northward from phosphatic shales of the Sandholdt Formation occupying deeper portions of the basin in the Paloma Valley lowland to a consistent pellet facies within the transgressive Monterey Formation overlying the Monterey massif in the vicinity of Carmel Valley. These beds include phosphatized fish and invertebrate remains and collophane pellets which appear near the top of the basal sandstone of the Monterey in exposures in Potrero (28) and Robinson (27, O. E. Bowen, oral communication, 1963) canyons and in the vicinity of San Jose Creek (29). In younger, thick, otherwise barren sequences of opaline shales interlayers of flood pellets 5 to 50 cm thick appear in many exposures over a distance of more than 20 miles from Canyon del Rey north of Monterey (25, R. R. Compton, oral communication, 1963) through Carmel and Tularcitos valleys (26, 30) and along Tularcitos Ridge as far south as Cachagua Conejo Creek (31, Weidman, 1964). Although most pelletal phosphate in California is little altered by weathering, some sandy porous ridge-top exposures in the Tularcitos area have been leached of most of their phosphate, leaving only cavities, or kernels of phosphate within cavities, remaining in the siltstone matrix.

The phosphatic basal sandstone in Robinson Canyon contains Luisian Foraminifera. The pellet beds within the superjacent Monterey shales extend into the lower Mohnian Stage north of Monterey (Brabb and others, 1962), and near Juan de Matte Canyon in Carmel Valley they lie 20 m above the granodiorite base (O. E. Bowen, oral communication, 1963). East of Chupines Creek in Tularcitos Valley they are upper Luisian or lower Mohnian.

The calcareous phosphatic shales and mudstones of the Sandholdt Formation, containing phosphates in the form of grayish-pink blebs and a few thin phosphatic laminae, outcrop 16 miles southeast of Tularcitos Ridge in Paloma Valley (34). Here the Sandholdt wedges between Monterey and the conformably underlying Vaqueros Formation, and the foraminiferal ages for the phosphatic beds in different exposures range from lower Luisian to upper Luisian. Phosphate elements become more prominent within the Sandholdt as the unit thickens toward the Arroyo Seco. A transitional contact with underlying Vaqueros Formation is marked by abundant phosphate blebs and locally by 10 to 15 cm of pebble phosphorite, and the phosphate grades upward from thin lenses in sandy siltstones to near-continuous laminae and abundant blebs in silty shale. About 30 m of this phosphatic shale, containing Luisian Foraminifera, are well exposed west of Rocky Creek (36).

A few pelletite interlayers and the familiar phosphate blebs mark the apparent top of the facies in the Paloma Creek-Arroyo Seco basin. In an exposure south of Sand Creek (35), for instance, a single interlayer of coarse pellets, phosphate pebble fragments, and very fine grained sand occur in porcelaneous shale in which phosphate blebs to 4 cm in length are dispersed over a 30-m thickness. On either side of Reliz Canyon (40), a few hard dolomitized beds 5 to 60 cm thick of pellets and phosphatized organic debris are interlayered in porcelaneous shale and bituminous limestone. These occur near the base of the Mohnian Stage, as established by R. M. Kleinpell (1938) in his detailed section in this area. Similar pellet beds at the same approximate horizon in Vaqueros Creek were mentioned by R. D. Reed in 1927, and this is believed to be the first published reference to phosphate of the California middle Miocene facies.

The lateral facies change from phosphatic shale to pelletal phosphorite observed toward the northwestern margin of the basin is also seen in central portions of the basin, where the phosphatic facies pinches and swells above undulations in the former basin topography. Thus, the Sandholdt Formation and its phosphatic shale interbeds thin toward the San Antonio River, and the entire unit condenses from nearly 100 m at its faulted margin west of Arroyo Seco to a sandy phosphate pellet zone, 25 m thick, near Mission Creek (43) in the northern part of the Hunter Liggett military reservation (Stanford Univ. Summer Field Classes, 1952, 1953).

Similar, less-conspicuous changes in form are observed in phosphatic interlayers within younger siliceous shales deposited on this irregular mid-Miocene basin floor. Along the North Fork of the San Antonio River (42), phosphatic blebs, comparable to those in the subjacent Sandholdt in size (to 4 cm) and abundance (500 or more per cu m *), are seen in thinly laminated opaline shales of the Monterey Formation. South of Cosio Knob, east of Quemado Canyon (44, 45, R. W. Weidman, 1958), and along the eastern border of the Santa Lucia Range in the vicinity of Espinosa Canyon (46, D. L. Durham, 1964), light-brown well-polished collophane oölites comprising up to 25 percent of thin sandy silt interlayers within the siliceous beds. Farther east, at the head of Topo Valley (32) where a depression of the Gabilan shelf adjoins the San Andreas fault, Luisian calcareous and siliceous shales and earthy mudstones of the Monterey Group of I. Wilson contain finely disseminated phosphate which does not appear to have been pelletized.

Except for a few thin beds of small pill-shaped pellets in diatomaceous (Monterey) shale in Lockwood Valley (52, D. L. Durham, oral communication, 1965), the phosphate exposures along the southern course of the San Antonio River, in Bee Rock Canyon (58) and in the vicinity of Nacimiento Dam (59), consist mostly of weakly phosphatic shales whose pale laminae and blebs are commonly almost imperceptible against a background of silt interlayers of the same color.

The middle Miocene phosphatic facies extends southward as a richly foraminiferal phosphatic silt rock and shale sequence that is well exposed in the Adelaida area west of Paso Robles (63, 64). An abundant microfauna in Peachy Canyon (65) includes usually diagnostic forms of both lower Relizian and upper Relizian Stages. An apparently older isolated occurrence of flood pellets (0.6 m thick) is exposed on Willow Road southeast of Adelaida (66) in uncertain stratigraphic relationship to phosphatic shales which crop out within a mile. Its generally Saucesian fauna is the age equivalent of an extensive pellet facies of the western Ventura basin, but broken collophane grains and similar sorting of pellets, associated clasts, and Foraminifera suggest that the fauna is displaced. None-

* A plane surface does not give the impression of such an abundance of phosphate blebs; a cu m of rock containing 500 blebs will show on a plane surface an average of only 9 per sq m.

Photo 8. (A, top) Pelletal phosphate interbedded with porcelaneous shale of the Monterey Formation in roadcut near Indian Creek. (B, bottom) Pelletal phosphate beds 10 and 25 cm thick separated by fractured porcelanite.

theless, the lower range of the middle Miocene facies, which does not appear until the middle Relizian in most localities where its age is definitely known, may be less distinct, and in this area the facies may merge with older phosphatic rocks.

The middle Miocene phosphatic strata diverge around granodiorite and Mesozoic rocks of the La Panza Range eastward into the Carrizo-Cuyama Basin and southeast through the Arroyo Grande-Huasna trough into the Santa Maria Basin. Near the point of divergence north of Atascadero (67), a few thin beds of small black collophane pellets are interspersed within large thicknesses of porcelanite. This is the westernmost of a series of exposures of pelletal phosphate, within porcelaneous and diatomaceous shale, which can be traced for 65 miles along the eastern flank of La Panza Range into the Cuyama Basin. In exposures in Quailwater and Indian Creeks (68), these beds are part of an uninterrupted succession of phosphatic clay shale, pelletal phosphorite interlayered with phosphatic shale, and flood concentrations of pellets to 60-cm thickness in porcelaneous shale. Overlying these are ash beds and sandstones of the Santa Margarita Formation. In Hay Canyon (70), pellets also appear in sandy siltstones within the Monterey-Santa Margarita transition.

The porcelanite tends to mark the highest appearance of shale in the Indian-Quailwater Creek section. Its ratio to interlayered pellets is locally as low as 2.5 to 1. The beds average 20 to 25 percent pellets over thicknesses of 4 m or less, but over larger thicknesses the porcelanite-pellet ratio expands to 10 to 1 or more (photo 7A, B).

At the type locality, 3 miles west of Quailwater Creek, the top of the Luisian Stage has been designated by Kleinpell as the horizon between diatomaceous and cherty organic shale and overlying pellet-bearing sandstone and siltstone. In the Quailwater Creek exposures, the lower soft organic phosphatic shale portion of the facies may extend through the Luisian Stage. Upper Relizian or lower Luisian assemblages were obtained in this locality both near and 20 m below the lowest porcelanite bed which marks the top of the Sandholdt Shale (Saltos Shale Member of Monterey Formation of Hill and others, 1958). The phosphatic sandy siltstones in Hay Canyon are of latest Luisian or early Mohnian age.

These exposures illustrate the typical shoreward facies progression of phosphate deposition in the marginal seas of the California middle Tertiary. The sequence is the vertical equivalent of the lateral transition from phosphatic shale, to phosphate pellets, to sandstones observed toward Carmel Valley. The order contrasts with a transition in the eastern Santa Monica Mountains of the Los Angeles Basin where mid-Miocene submergence resulted in a reverse vertical sequence—an erosional unconformity overlain by successive deposits of sandy conglomerate, phosphate pellets and pebbles, and bituminous phosphatic shale with interbedded limestone.

Within the lower Santa Margarita Formation northeast of the La Panza Range is found a sequence of interlayered porcelaneous shale, siltstone, and pelletite nearly identical to the older Monterey occurrences, in lithology, except for an admixture of sand. These younger beds, which are 10 m thick in exposures on the west side of Windmill Creek (69), may be condensed equivalents of much larger thicknesses of late Miocene diatomaceous siltstone and shale which have been measured by Richard (1933) within his Santa Margarita Formation to the north and west. If so, these pelletal shales may constitute a separate younger facies despite their appearance as transitional beds of the older Monterey Formation. A pattern of occurrence of pelletal phosphate, both at the base of the Santa Margarita Formation and in a shale unit within the sandstones, is also observed in the Cuyama Basin 50 miles southeast.

In the southern Santa Lucia Range southwest of the La Panza Range, the middle Miocene facies continues into the Santa Maria Basin via the Arroyo Grande-Huasna Valley.

Santa Maria Basin

The consistent succession from organic clay shale to siliceous shale that distinguishes the Sandholdt from the Monterey Formation in the Salinas Basin is not everywhere in evidence in middle Miocene shale farther south, and most workers in the Santa Maria Basin combine the two lithologies as the Monterey Formation. In the northern Huasna Valley east of Arroyo Grande (74), for instance, phosphatic blebs and laminae appear in siliceous silt shales which lie between Santa Margarita sandstone and a subjacent unit of porcelaneous mudstone. This phosphate-bearing shale is Luisian on the basis of microfossil dating by Kleinpell, and partly Mohnian on the basis of a megafossil assemblage studied by C. A. Hall.

South of Huasna, on the northern side of Cuyama Valley (75), the following 30-m succession is exposed —arkosic silty sandstone with sparse phosphate pellets, a few glauconite-bearing phosphate pellet interlayers in silty shale, organic silt shale with thin poorly defined phosphatic laminae, and thinly laminated cherty shale containing a few phosphate blebs. Locally, the thicker pellet interlayers within the silty shale are sites of large carbonate concretions which have formed around and through the phosphatic interlayers without having replaced them (photo 9). Here, the relative stratigraphic position of phosphatic pellets and laminae reverses that north to the La Panza Range. A few species of poorly preserved Foraminifera recovered from these rocks are probably Relizian.

Phosphatic shales continue south of Cuyama Valley through scattered exposures in the western San Rafael Mountains (76); they disappear beneath the basin cover south of Santa Maria and crop out farther west near Casmalia and in sea cliffs north and south of Point Sal (80, 78, 79). Woodring and Bramlette (1950) assign a late Relizian and Luisian age to this phosphate horizon in the western Santa Maria Basin. Numerous oil well logs (77, 81) indicate that these phosphate-bearing shales occur through a 210-m total thickness in the East Cat Canyon field (82, R. K. Cross, 1943) and extend throughout the subsurface Monterey Formation in the Santa Maria Basin.

In the adjoining Transverse Range province, the middle Miocene phosphatic shales crop out east of Point Conception along the southern flank of the Santa Ynez Mountains and extend another 160 miles eastward, almost without interruption, to the Peninsular Ranges east of Los Angeles (photo 10A, B).

Cuyama Basin

In the southeastern prong of the Salinas Basin, the pelletal facies within the Monterey, which can be traced along the northeastern La Panza Range for 25

Photo 9. Thin beds of pelletal phosphate distended by a carbonate concretion. Monterey Formation. Cuyama Valley.

miles, is concealed beneath the northern edge of the alluvial Carrizo Plain, and is inconspicuous through the Caliente Range to Cuyama Valley. Only a few thin layers of pellets in sandy gypsiferous diatomaceous shale have been observed near the top of the Monterey Formation in Morales Canyon (83) and to the west (84, Gower and Madsen, 1964). However, south of Cuyama Valley between the Monterey Formation (here called the Branch Canyon Formation by Hill and others, 1958) and the Santa Margarita Formation, a transitional zone includes at least 10 m of thinly interlayered pelletite, pelletal sandy siltstone, and porcelaneous shale. This interval is prominently exposed east of Branch Canyon (85). The lower beds of the Branch Canyon Formation contain Relizian Foraminifera, according to Hill and others who project a Luisian age for the rest of the unit, but megafossils suggest a Mohnian-equivalent age for the pellet beds within the transition zone, according to J. G. Vedder.

The phosphate-pellet zone in a fine-grained sequence of the Santa Margarita Formation of the northeast La Panza Range is matched by similarly placed pellet beds within the Santa Margarita of the Cuyama Basin. Abundant late Miocene oyster shells enveloped in collophane pellets underlie 30 m of pelletites and pelletal

Photo 10. Middle Miocene phosphatic shale facies exposed (A, left) in sea cliffs east of Naples in the Ventura Basin, (field of view, .7 m) and (B, right) in the Los Angeles Basin, at Malaga Cove (field of view, 1.8 m).

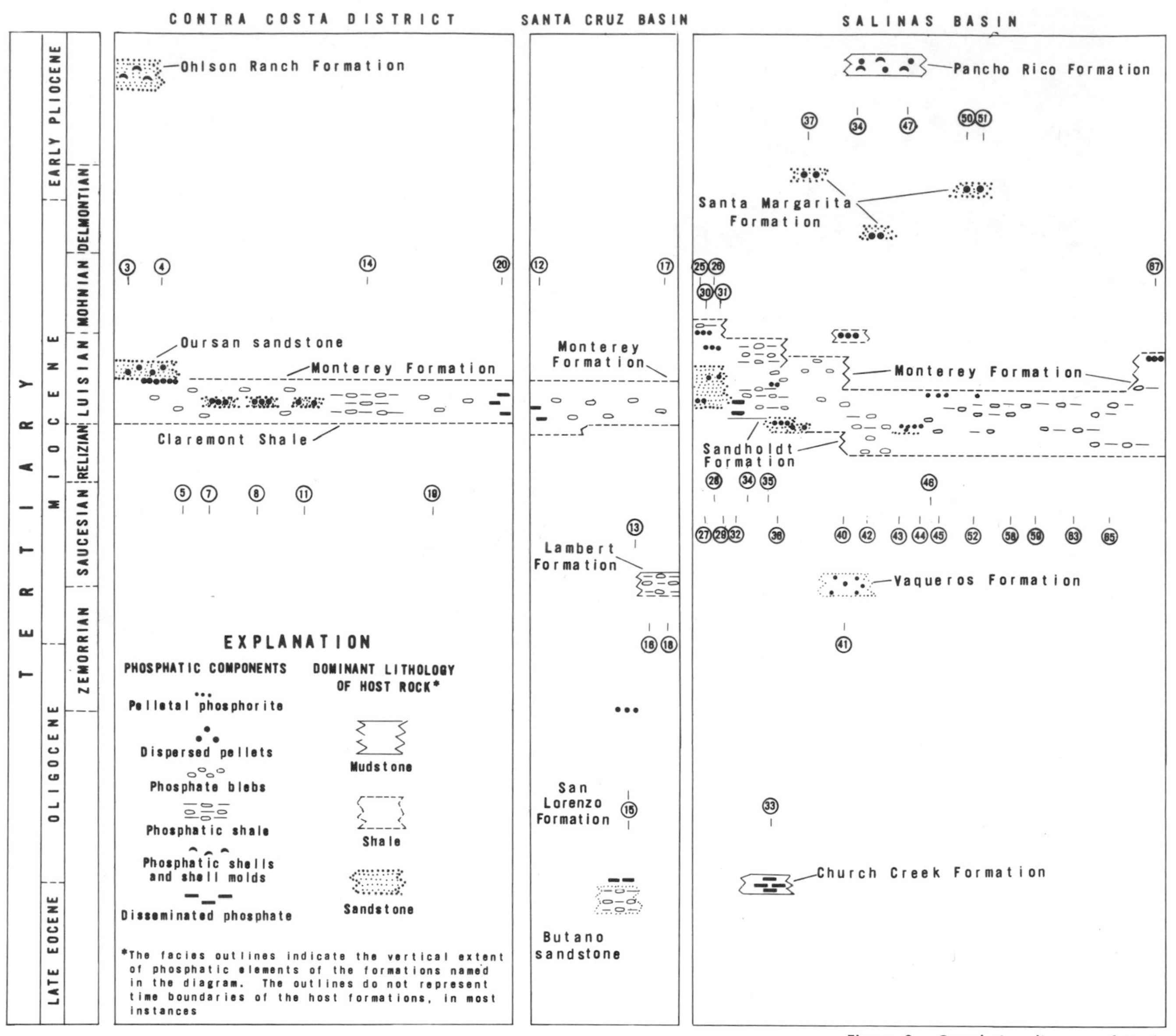

Figure 2. Correlation diagram of Tertiary

sandstones and siltstones in exposures in the southeast Cuyama oil field (86). A 24-m thickness is reported for this zone east of Newsome Canyon (87, Gower and Madsen, 1964).

A large erosion remnant exposed 25 miles southeast of Branch Canyon near Sespe Creek includes thick sandstones of the Santa Margarita Formation in which a zone of pellet-bearing fine clastics locally exceeds 80-m thickness. It crops out for 6 miles to a fault boundary. Pellets comprise more than 70 percent of beds that are as much as 0.75 m thick, and over one 32-m measured section (90) the average pellet concentration is 16.5 percent. Massive gypsum beds occur a few tens of meters higher in the sandstone. These pellet deposits, which were discovered by the Stanford University Summer Field Class of 1963 led by W. R. Dickinson, may become the first commercial source of phosphate developed in California.

Despite a resemblance in lithology to the younger Santa Margarita pellet zone in Cuyama Valley, and apparently similar stratigraphic positions within their respective sandstone units, the Sespe Creek pelletites are believed, on the basis of a similar succession of megafossils at the two localities (J. G. Vedder, oral communication, 1964), to correlate with the older pellet zone at the base of the Santa Margarita Formation to the north.

Any formerly existing lateral merging of the lower Cuyama-Sespe Creek pellet facies with the phosphatic shale facies lying relatively seaward in coastal exposures of the Ventura Basin has been removed by erosion, but continuity of these two prominent phosphatic horizons may be reasonably inferred on the basis of the well-established lateral and vertical relations of the facies elsewhere. The time for mechanical accumulation of the thick pellet zone near Sespe Creek

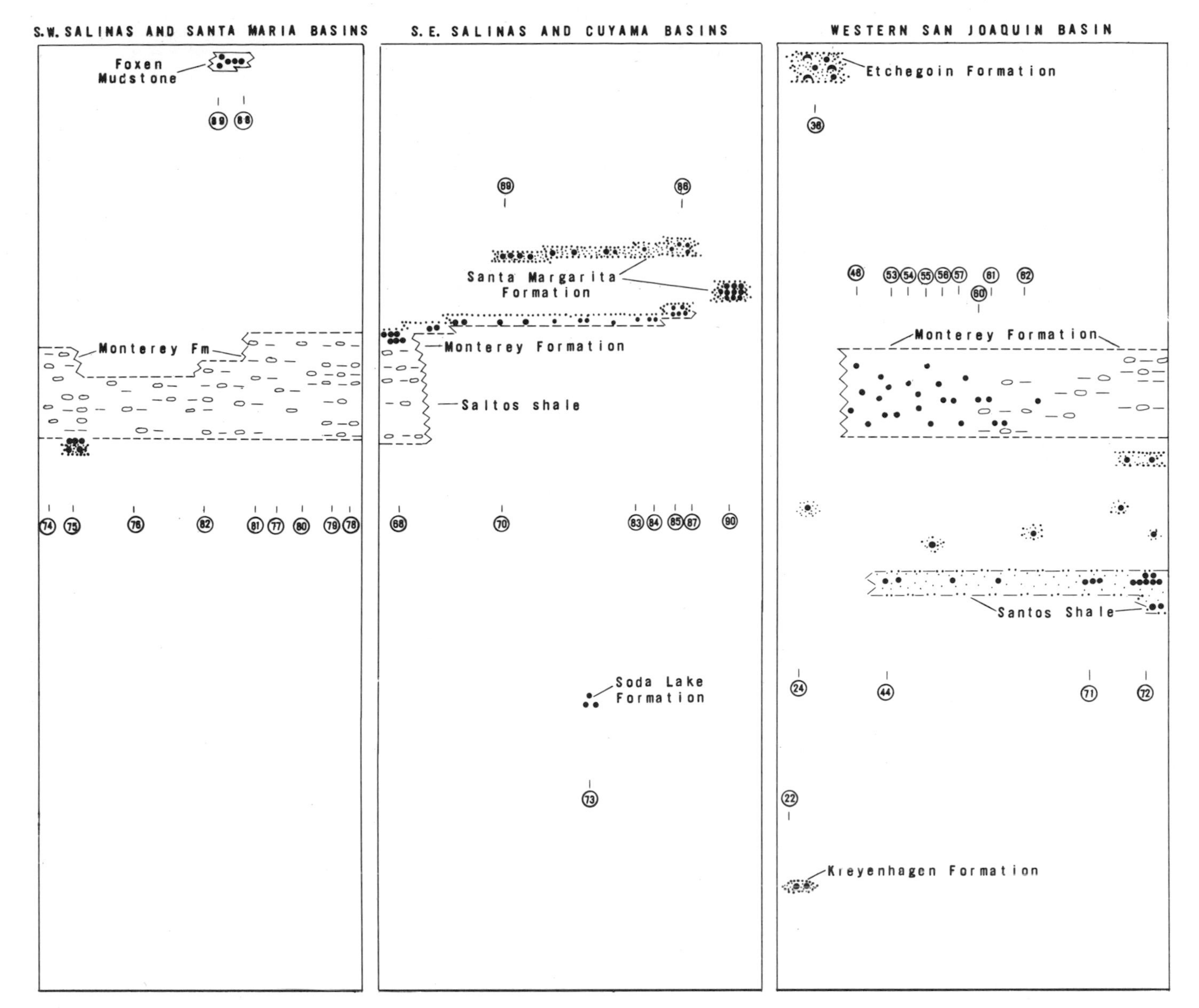

phosphatic facies in the Coast Ranges.

would be expected to extend somewhat beyond the cessation of deposition of phosphate farther south in the early Mohnian.

Western San Joaquin Basin

The pelletal phosphorites of the Cuyama Basin grade northeast into gypsiferous continental deposits, negating any correlation of phosphatic facies across the San Andreas fault into the southwest San Joaquin Basin. The point to the north where the phosphatic facies abuts the fault, and could continue eastward, is concealed beneath the Carrizo Plain.

The phosphatic shales which characterize the Monterey Formation of the coastal basins are known only in the southern San Joaquin Valley; to the north, the middle Miocene facies is represented by a pellet-bearing brown shale which has long served oil geologists as a marker horizon.

Phosphatic blebs and laminae are dispersed within 75 m (M. N. Bramlette, 1946) of an upper Luisian soft foraminiferal clay shale (Devilwater Silt Member) in the Monterey Formation along Chico Martinez Creek (72). On the eastern side of the San Joaquin Basin, phosphatic streaks are reported in well cuttings from the Fruitvale Shale at substantially the same horizon.

The phosphatic character of these units changes northward to a mixed pellet and shale zone near Still Canyon, and to a dispersed pellet zone in the vicinity of Polonio Pass. Calcareous shales in Still Canyon (62) containing upper Relizian to Luisian Foraminifera include at intervals several meters of phosphate blebs and laminae, nodules, a few thin compact beds of poorly sorted pellets, and lenses of hard yellow weakly phosphatic limestone. Ten miles northwest the phosphate zone is well exposed over more than 100-m thickness, and consists only of pellets dispersed in glauconitic clayey mudstone and a thin phosphate pebble bed (60 and 61, Gower and Madsen, 1964).

On the north slope of Reef Ridge, this unit is from 10 to 60 m thick. It includes phosphate pebble conglomerates to the south near Sulphur Springs Canyon (56), but only sparse pellets northward in Canoas and Baby King Creeks (53, 54) and in Garza Creek (55, Woodring and others, 1940). Numerous well logs show that this "brown shale" thickens eastward to nearly 300 m in the Middle Dome of the Kettleman Hills (49), extends at least 60 miles southward to the Belridge field (71), and reduces to 15 m in the Guijarral Hills east of Coalinga (48). Seven or more discrete layers of these pellets, typically pyritized and referred to locally as "sporbo," an acrostic term, from *s*mooth, *po*lished, *r*ound, *b*lack, *o*bjects (photo 11), are stratigraphically persistent in the Kettleman Hills area (Goudkoff, 1934). The subsurface brown "sporbo shale" is equated with the Luisian *Valvulineria californica* zone by most oil geologists.

The pellet facies wedges out against the southern edge of the Diablo Range, and any northern extension into the Contra Costa Basin is interrupted by erosion.

Summary

Contemporaneous or correlative deposition of phosphate on a regional scale spanning several marine basins began in Relizian time, and in most areas in late Relizian time, and extended into the Luisian. Deposition continued into the early Mohnian south of Monterey and probably took place somewhat later in the inland Cuyama Basin and its southeast extension, but the horizon of most widespread and continuous deposition is of Luisian age. All of 40 sections that summarize the distribution of phosphate in the several basins and extend through the middle Miocene show phosphate-bearing rock within the Luisian Stage (Dickert, 1965). Within the perimeter of the area in which this facies is distributed, each stratigraphic sequence which could be dated as Luisian—through direct microfossil evidence, inference from faunas in contiguous strata, or through extensions of dated beds—includes phosphatic components, or, as in a few instances, the sequence consists of coarse sandstones or graywackes that doubtless inhibited the deposition of phosphate. The weight of this evidence then is that in the middle Miocene, and in particular in early Luisian time, a near-continuous phosphatic facies existed over an area of some 20,000 square miles in central and southern California.

PLIOCENE PHOSPHATIC ROCKS

At the approximate time that sandy diatomaceous sediments with pelletal phosphate were beginning to form on granodiorite in the vicinity of Monterey, a thick accumulation of Monterey-type pellet-bearing sediments was being covered by sand 120 miles to the southeast near the present site of Santa Margarita. This shale-sandstone transition can be traced northwestward

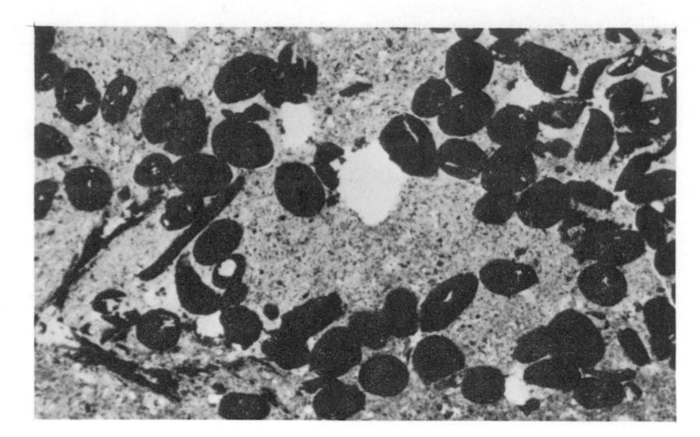

Photo 11. Pyritized pellets. A bone fragment in lower left is partially replaced by pyrite. Field of view 3 mm. Monterey Formation. Kettleman Hills.

back over the traverse of the Salinas Basin previously described; and, as the contact becomes progressively younger, the pelletal phosphate shrinks in thickness and in concentration, although some pellets and phosphatized organic debris appear in basal Santa Margarita beds that may be Delmontian or younger in the northern Salinas Basin (50, 51; 37, R. M. Weidman, 1958).

In Sonoma County, basal sandstones of the late early or early middle Pliocene Ohlson Ranch Formation locally exhibit coarse, dark pelletal phosphate and phosphatized shell fragments (Higgins, 1960). Over the northern half of the Gabilan Mesa of the Salinas Basin, the Pancho Rico Formation of similar age includes a thin extensive blanket of pellets and phosphatized organic debris (47, T. W. Dibblee, oral communication, 1965; 39, D. L. Durham, oral communication, 1965).

The Pliocene Sisquoc Formation of the Santa Maria Basin is marked locally at its base by a few phosphate nodules and pellets, and a few interlayers of collophane pellets and phosphatic fossil molds occur at intervals throughout the overlying diatomite (Woodring and Bramlette, 1950). Similar stringers of phosphate nodules and pebbles were observed within the superjacent Foxen Mudstone, which thins eastward from about 250 m in the western Purisima Hills to less than 15 m where it disappears in the central Purisima Hills. This condensation (88, 89) is represented chiefly by pelletites and pellet-bearing sandy siltstone, with the pellets extending up into the lower part of the overlying Careaga Sandstone and down into the uppermost Sisquoc diatomite. Pellets comprise 20 percent of a 16-m section, which includes near its base layers 20 cm to 1.5 m thick containing 60 percent or more well-sorted pellets.

In the San Joaquin Basin south of Anticline Ridge (38), basal beds of the Pliocene Etchegoin Formation of sandy siltstones contain lustrous dark phosphate pellets and phosphatic organic debris in concentrations to 20 percent. Phosphatic pellets and nodules at the base of this unit are recorded in two subsurface sections in the southeastern sector.

The Ohlson Ranch, Pancho Rico, and Foxen Formations have been correlated with the Etchegoin of the San Joaquin Basin on both microfossil and megafossil evidence by several workers. Further reconnaissance of Pliocene units in California may reveal the existence of a lower Pliocene phosphatic facies almost as extensive as that of the middle Miocene. However, in the absence of thick deposits of phosphatic shale, such a facies will probably lack the continuity found in the older beds and will consist largely of disconnected aggregates of granular phosphate.

SOME IMPLICATIONS OF THE PHOSPHATIC FACIES

With their lateral continuity and vertical limitations established in part, the phosphatic facies may be used to shed light on some cloudy areas in the stratigraphy of the Coast Ranges. Two illustrations follow.

The Monterey Formation in the Light of its Phosphatic Facies

Most of the extensive middle Miocene phosphate beds are usually assigned to the Monterey Formation, a unit much better known for its siliceous rocks. Moreover, the siliceous and phosphatic facies tend to be exclusive of each other. Littoral pelletite beds commonly interlayer with thick siliceous sequences, but the more synchronous phosphatic shales consistently formed earlier than the siliceous strata.

The transition from a predominantly calcareous phosphatic facies to a siliceous facies is thought to relate to lowered water temperatures in early Mohnian time. The latitudinal and bathymetric distribution of marine phosphate implies the existence of a depth-temperature fence, colder but analogous to that restricting the distribution of authigenic calcium carbonate, known authigenic carbonate-fluorapatite as rare in cold abyssal waters * at low and intermediate latitudes as in shallower waters at high latitudes. The supply of carbonate ion which diminishes with the increased capacity of colder water to retain carbon dioxide is a possible limiting factor.

On the other hand, colder temperatures tend to enhance the production of diatoms and the persistence of their remains, the probable sedimentary source of silica in the Monterey Formation (Bramlette, 1946). Experiments cited by Conger (1942) show that the attendant increase in dissolved oxygen and carbon dioxide markedly favor diatom growth; the cold-water inhibition of phosphate deposition increases the supply of this nutrient for diatom production; and the lowered temperatures tend to diminish solution of their remains. The extraordinary concentration of diatoms in the Monterey sediments presumably required a significant ultimate source of silica such as water-deposited vitric pyroclastics, and the emergence of protected basin-receptacles to concentrate the diatomaceous deposits, as suggested by Bramlette. However, lowered temperature is the common environmental modification which both inhibited the retention of phosphate in sediments and favored the production and retention of diatoms. The reappearance of an extensive phosphatic facies in the late early Pliocene appears to coincide with the warmer temperatures inferred by Ingle (1963) for that period.

Only diatomaceous sediments, with interlayered phosphate pellets and basal phosphatic sands, were deposited on the submarine prominence at the Monterey type locality. However, both the siliceous and subjacent calcareous phosphatic shale facies appear in deeper portions of the Salinas Basin. Here, the calcareous unit is distinguished by most workers as the Sandholdt Formation, or the Sandholdt or Saltos Shale Member of the Monterey Formation. Elsewhere, as in parts of the Ventura and Los Angeles basins, both facies are combined in the Monterey Formation.

In those basins where continuity with the type locality is broken by the San Andreas fault or by a submarine barrier, the presence or absence of the middle Miocene phosphatic facies has been helpful in discriminating between units which have been referred to the Monterey chiefly on the basis of apparently abnormally siliceous strata. For example, in the Santa Cruz Basin, though separated by a sandstone unit and by an unconformity, both the Woodhams Shale Member, containing phosphate inclusions, and a younger diatomaceous mudstone have been assigned to the Monterey Formation for many years. The latter unit is non-phosphatic even at its lower sandstone contact, in contrast to the Monterey Formation at the type locality 25 miles to the south, and these strata have recently been designated a separate formation by J. C. Clark (1966). The older phosphatic Woodhams Shale Member is the age equivalent of basal phosphatic sandstones at the Monterey type locality, and is also equivalent in age and lithology to the Claremont Shale, which contains similar phosphate inclusions, east of the San Andreas fault.

The latter correlation inevitably suggests another stratigraphic puzzler.

Phosphate Beds across the San Andreas Fault

Much of the data cited to support small cumulative offset on the San Andreas fault expectably centers on the matching of rock units directly across the fault zone. The existing evidence of the phosphatic facies may be summarized as follows. While distinctive time-restricted phosphate-bearing units may be traced with confidence from northwest to southeast over very large distances on either side of the fault, these beds have not been traceable directly across the fault zone, so far.

One notable exception is the probable continuity of the Woodhams Shale Member in the Santa Cruz Basin with the Claremont Shale of the Contra Costa district. However, since their cumulative exposures are about 100 miles long and the units are separated by the 25 mile-wide San Francisco Bay block, their original relationship is obscure.

Tertiary strata of the central Santa Cruz Basin and time-related rocks adjacent to the east of the San

* The very few known abyssal occurrences show evidence either of transport or of a previously shallower environment.

Andreas fault comprise one of several comparative sections analyzed by B. Oakeshott (this bulletin) as evidence of small cumulative displacement along the fault, and the distinctively laminated phosphatic shales of Narizian and of late Zemorrian or early Saucesian age should furnish a check on this continuity. Both of these facies outcrop within a mile of the western border of the San Andreas fault trace through the Santa Cruz Mountains, but have not been observed directly to the east in the rocks thought to be of similar age.

Some of the more distant possible continuities are amenable to similar tests. The conspicuous phosphatic laminates which characterize the lower part of the San Lorenzo Formation of the Santa Cruz Mountains should be sought in the San Emigdio Formation, the eastern counterpart to the San Lorenzo in the southern San Joaquin Basin Suggested by T. W. Dibblee (this bulletin).

Studies of interceptions of the phospatic facies by the San Andreas fault will be most useful if linear elements, such as phosphatic shale-pelletite transition or a depositional boundary, can be identified. For example, along the faulted eastern margin of the San Joaquin Basin, Luisian pellet-bearing Monterey "sporbo" shale gives way to a sandstone barrier to the blebby Claremont Shale of the Contra Costa district at some point north of the presently known northernmost pelletal shale exposure in Polonio Pass. In the Salinas Basin just west of the fault, Luisian phosphate-bearing shales are similarly barred from the phosphatic Monterey shale of the Santa Cruz Basin, with the northernmost exposure encountered so far 65 miles north of Polonio Pass. Continuity of a boundary of non-deposition north of these localities has not yet been investigated but close study of points of interception by the San Andreas fault of such explicit lithologic features as the phosphatic facies may be fruitful.

REFERENCES

Aarons, B. L., 1958, Geology of the Las Trampas Ridge and Hayward quadrangles, California: California Univ., Berkeley, M.S. thesis.

Allen, J. E., 1946, Geology of the San Juan Bautista quadrangle, California: California Div. Mines Bull. 133, p. 9–75.

Brabb, E. E., 1960, Geology of the Big Basin area, Santa Cruz Mountains, California: Stanford Univ., Stanford, Calif., Ph.D. thesis.

Brabb, E. E., Bowen, O. E., Jr., and Hart, E. W., 1962, Field trip No. 2—San Francisco to Monterey via California Highways 1, 5, 17, and connecting routes, March 26, 1962: California Div. Mines Bull. 181, p. 381–390.

Bramlette, M. N., 1946, The Monterey formation of California and the origin of its siliceous rocks: U.S. Geol. Survey, Prof. Paper 212, 57 p.

Clark, J. C., 1966, Tertiary stratigraphy of the Felton-Santa Cruz area, Santa Cruz Mountains, California: Stanford Univ., Stanford, Calif., Ph.D. thesis.

Conger, Paul S., 1942, Accumulation of diatomaceous deposits: Jour. Sed. Petrology, v. 12, no. 2, p. 55–65.

Cross, R. K., 1943, East Cat Canyon area of the Cat Canyon oil field [California]: California Div. Mines Bull. 118, p. 435–437.

—— 1962, Geology of the Carriso-Cuyama basin, *in* Guidebook, Geology of Carrizo Plains and San Andreas fault: San Joaquin Geol. Soc. and Am. Assoc. Petroleum Geologists-Soc. Econ. Paleontologists and Mineralogists Pac. Sec. [field trip], 1962, p. 27–35.

Currie, Ronald, 1953, Upwelling in the Benguela current: Nature, v. 171, no. 4351, p. 497–500.

Curtin, George, 1955, Pyramid Hills oil field [California]: California Oil Fields, v. 41, no. 2, p. 25–33.

Dibblee, T. W., Jr., 1966, Geology of the Palo Alto quadrangle, Santa Clara and San Mateo Counties, California: California Div. Mines Map Sheet 8.

Dickert, Paul F., 1966, Neogene phosphatic facies in California: Stanford Univ., Stanford, Calif., Ph.D. thesis.

Dickinson, W. R., 1956, Tertitary stratigraphy and structure west of the Arroyo Seco, Monterey County, California: Stanford Univ., Stanford, Calif., M.S. thesis.

Durham, D. L., 1964, Geology of the Cosio Knob and Espinosa Canyon quadrangles, Monterey County, California: U.S. Geol. Survey Bull. 1161-H, p. H1–H29.

Emery, K. O., 1960, The sea off southern California, a modern habitat of petroleum: New York, John Wiley and Sons, Inc., 366 p.

Garrison, L. E., 1959, Miocene Foraminifera from the Temblor formation north of Coalinga, California: Jour. Paleontology, v. 33, no. 4, p. 662–669.

Goudkoff, P. P., 1934, Subsurface stratigraphy of Kettleman Hills oil field, California: Am. Assoc. Petroleum Geologists Bull., v. 18, no. 4, p. 435–475.

Gower, H. D., and Madsen, B. M., 1964, The occurrence of phosphate rock in California: U.S. Geol. Survey Prof. Paper 501-D, p. D79–D85.

Gulbrandsen, R. A., Jones, D. L., Tagg, K. M., and Reeser, D. W., 1963, Apatitized wood and leucophosphite in nodules in the Moreno Formation, California: U.S. Geol. Survey Prof. Paper 475-C, art. 85, p. C100–C104.

Higgins, C. G., 1960, Ohlson Ranch formation, Pliocene, northwestern Sonoma County, California: California Univ. Pubs. Geol. Sci., v. 36, no. 3, p. 199–231.

Ingle, J. C., Jr., Miocene-Pliocene paleoecology of the San Fernando Basin, California [abst.]: Am. Assoc. Petroleum Geologists Bull., v. 47, no. 9, p. 1771.

Kleinpell, R. M., 1938, Miocene stratigraphy of California: Tulsa, Okla., Am. Assoc. Petroleum Geologists, 450 p.

Mitchell, E. D., Jr., and Repenning, C. A., 1963, The chronologic and geographic range of desmostylians: Los Angeles County Mus. Contr. Sci., v. 78, p. 1–20.

Payne, M. B., 1951, Type Moreno formation and overlying Eocene strata on the west side of the San Joaquin Valley, Fresno and Merced Counties, California: California Div. Mines Spec. Rept. 9, 29 p.

Redfield, A. C., Ketchum, B. H., and Richard, F. A., 1963, The influence of organisms on the composition of sea-water, *in* Hill, M. N., ed., The sea: New York, Interscience Publishers, p. 26–77.

Reed, R. D., 1927, Phosphate beds in the Monterey shales [abs.]: Geol. Soc. America Bull., v. 38, no. 1, p. 195–196.

Richards, G. L., 1933, Geology of the Santa Margarita Formation, San Luis Obispo County, California: Stanford Univ., Stanford, Calif., M.A. thesis.

Rogers, A. F., 1944, Pellet phosphorite from Carmel Valley, Monterey County, California: California Div. Mines and Geology, v. 40, no. 4, p. 411–421.

Thorup, R. R., 1942, The stratigraphy of the Vaqueros Formation at its type locality, Monterey County, California: Stanford Univ., Stanford, Calif., M.A. thesis

Weaver, C. E., 1943, Point Arena-Fort Ross region [California]: California Div. Mines Bull. 118, p. 628–632.

Weidman, R. M., 1959, Geology of the King City quadrangle, California: California Univ., Berkeley, Ph.D. thesis.

Wharton, J. B., 1943, Belridge oil field [California]: California Div. Mines Bull. 118, p. 502–504.

Woodring, W. P., and Bramlette, M. N., 1950, Geology and paleontology of the Santa Maria district, California: U.S. Geol. Survey Prof. Paper 222, 185 p.

Woodring, W. P., Stewart, R. B., and Richards, R. W., 1940, Geology of the Kettleman Hills oil field, California; stratigraphy, paleontology, and structure: U.S. Geol. Survey Prof. Paper 195, 170 p.

QUATERNARY OF THE CALIFORNIA COAST RANGES

By Mark N. Christensen
University of California, Berkeley

Movements of the earth's crust have dominated the Quaternary history of the California Coast Ranges, and warping, faulting, and vulcanism have produced the topographic patterns that today characterize this province. Along the coast, marine terraces record the interplay between orogenic processes and climatically induced fluctuations of sea level.

The Coast Ranges southward from San Francisco Bay consist of a series of parallel, linear ranges, up to 40 miles wide and 5,800 feet high, separated by structural depressions from 1 to 10 miles wide, lying at elevations near sea level. Northward from San Francisco Bay the several ranges merge into a broad, nearly continuous highland with elevations up to 8,000 feet, but a number of equidimensional to elliptical structural basins occur within this highland. Linear structural elements within the Coast Ranges trend obliquely to the trend of the Coast Ranges as a whole (pl. 1).

The principal elements of the Quaternary history of these ranges are recorded by sedimentary strata, marine terraces, and drainage anomalies. The history of the southern ranges is documented by rather extensive sedimentary deposits of Pliocene and Pleistocene age. In the northern ranges, the stratigraphic record is less complete, but anomalous drainage patterns are much more conspicuous. Glacial effects are recorded only on a few isolated peaks in the northern Coast Ranges.

STRATIGRAPHY

Deposits of late Pliocene and Pleistocene age are mainly slightly consolidated gravels, sands, and silts of local derivation with some interbedded clays, marls, and freshwater limestones. Most of the strata are of continental origin, except for those adjacent to the present coast. Fossils are sparse in the continental strata, and the ages of many of the continental deposits are known only from their relations to older rocks. Radiometric dates obtained from volcanic rocks intercalated with the sediments are beginning to fill in some blank places. Locations, distributions, and ages of units referred to in the following discussions, together with selected references are provided in figure 1 and table 1. Deposits discussed in this article are referred to provincial ages, wherever possible, rather than to European epochs, because any given fossil assemblage can be referred much more precisely to provincial ages or stages than to classic European ages. Further, the absolute ages of provincial land mammal ages are known much more precisely than are those of the European epochs (see fig. 2). Where primary sources have referred fossil assemblages to European ages, I have followed the original usage, even though this procedure introduces an unnecessary uncertainty into the age assignment.

The widely accepted notion of a major mid-Pleistocene orogeny in the California Coast Ranges that stemmed from study of the Tulare and Paso Robles Formations in major oil fields seems to be overemphasized. These units are conformable on older strata in the structural depressions of the San Joaquin and Salinas Valleys, where the major oil fields occur. On the flanks of the ranges, however, these strata overlap older Tertiary units with profound angular unconformity and rest on Mesozoic rocks. The pattern of unconformities (see fig. 1) indicates that the "mid-Pleistocene orogeny" was but one unexceptional pulse in an orogeny that began in Miocene time; subsequently, the ranges have risen repeatedly while the basins have rather steadily subsided.

Deformed strata of Blancan and Irvingtonian age occur in the vicinity of the structural depression of San Francisco Bay and its extension southeastward along the San Andreas fault (fig. 1 and table 1, localities 2, 3, 5, 6, 9, 10, and 12). The Irvington Gravels (no. 3) are the type locality for the Irvingtonian land mammal age (Savage, 1951). The Merced Formation (no. 5) is marine through its lower 4,500 feet, and predominantly nonmarine through its upper 500 feet. The heavy minerals of the lower, marine section are characteristic of local source rocks. About 100 feet above the marine-nonmarine transition the heavy minerals abruptly change to a suite like that now carried by the Sacramento-San Joaquin River system which drains the Sierra Nevada. Hall (1965) interprets this change to represent the inception of drainage from the Central Valley through San Francisco Bay. Marine megafossils below this change in the heavy minerals correlate with the San Joaquin Formation, which is at least in part of Blancan age. About 300 feet above the mineral change occur teeth of *Mammuthus*, of Irvingtonian age. A few tens of feet above the *Mammuthus* locality occurs a hornblende-bearing tuff which has been dated at 1.5 m.y. by the K-Ar method.

The Clear Lake Volcanic Series consists of basalt, dacite, and obsidian. The older eruptives include deformed basalt that is interbedded with the upper Cache Beds of lower Pleistocene age. The youngest features include undissected flows, domes, and cinder cones.

Photo 1. View east across a section of the central Coast Ranges, climaxing in Mount Diablo. *Photo by Commercial Photo and View Company, courtesy East Bay Municipal Utility District.*

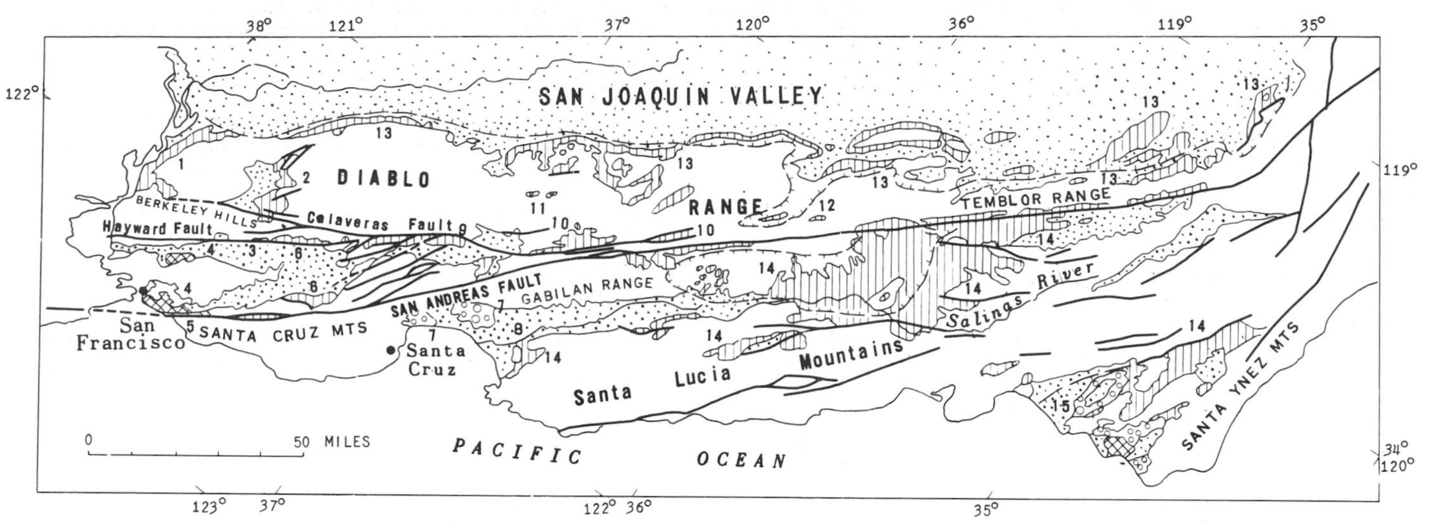

COAST RANGES SOUTH OF SAN FRANCISCO BAY

EXPLANATION FOR BOTH MAPS

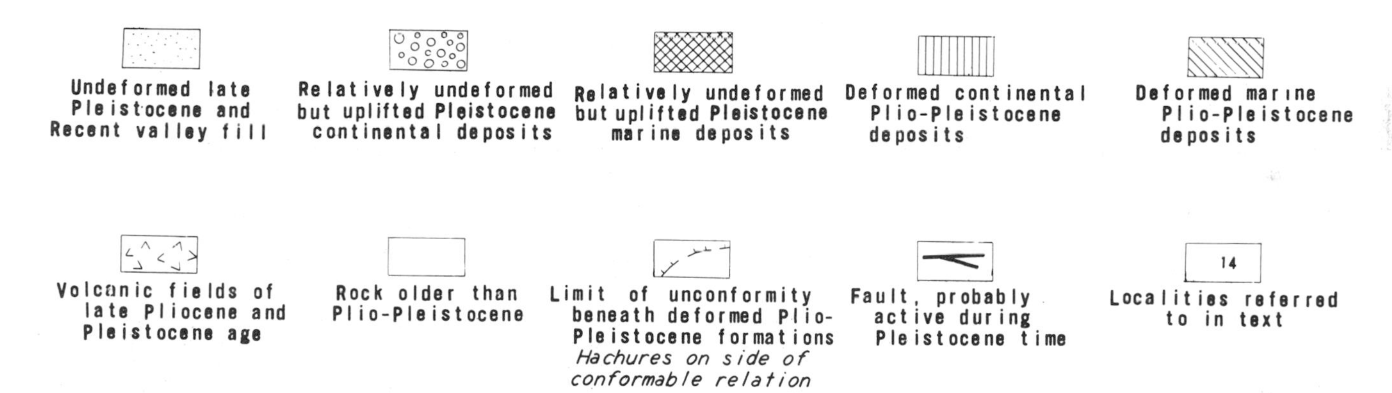

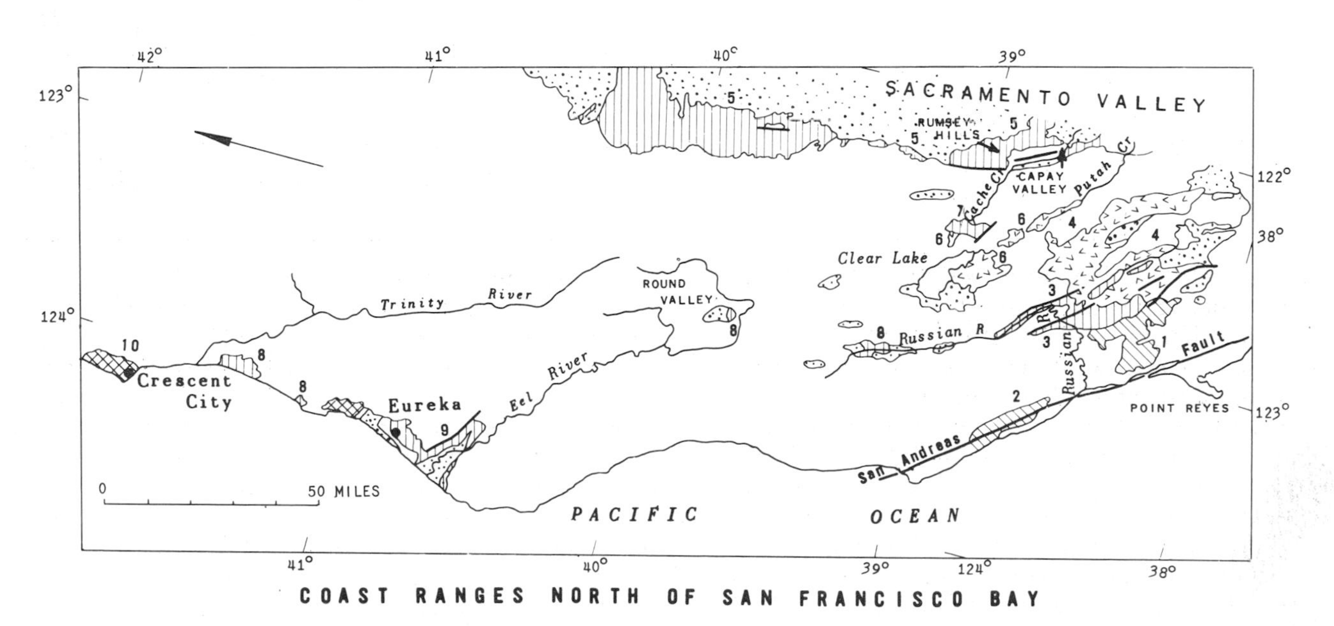

COAST RANGES NORTH OF SAN FRANCISCO BAY

Figure 1. Geologic maps of the Coast Ranges north and south of San Francisco, showing late Pliocene and younger rocks, surfaces on which they were deposited, and faults believed to have been active during the Pleistocene. Maps also show localities referred to by numbers in the text.

Table 1, Part A—Table of Late Cenozoic formations in the Coast Ranges south of San Francisco Bay

Locality	Formation	Age from fossil or physical evidence	Relation to older rocks	Reference
1	Wolfskill (Tehama)	Blancan	Unconformable on Pliocene	Weaver, 1949; Savage, 1951, p. 217; Taliaferro, 1951
2	Livermore Gravels	Late Pliocene to Irvingtonian	Unconformable on middle Pliocene	Savage 1951, p. 284; Hall, 1959, p. 32
3	Irvington Gravels	Irvingtonian	Unconformable on upper Miocene	Savage, 1951, p. 276; Hall, 1959, p. 32
4	Various formations in San Francisco Bay area	Rancholabrean and younger	Conformable(?) on lower Pleistocene. Unconformable on Tertiary and older	Lawson, 1914; Louderback, 1951; Trask and Rolston, 1951; Radbruch, 1957; Schlocker and others, 1958
5	Merced	Late Pliocene and Pleistocene; Irvingtonian near the top	Unconformable on Mesozoic	Glen, 1959; Hall, 1965
6	Santa Clara Gravels	----	Unconformable on lower Pliocene	Branner and others, 1909; Lawson, 1914; Cummings, Touring, and Brabb, 1962, p. 213
7	Aromas Red Sands	----	Unconformable on upper Pliocene	Allen, 1946, p. 43
8	Alluvium of Salinas Valley	----	Conformable(?) on lower Pleistocene	Woodford, 1951
9	Packwood Gravels	----	Faulted against Mesozoic	Crittenden, 1951, pl. 1
10	San Benito Gravels	Blancan(?)	Unconformable on upper Pliocene	Wilson, 1943, p. 245
11	Peckham	----	Unconformable on Miocene(?)	Leith, 1949
12	Hans Grieve	Late Pliocene and Pleistocene	Unconformable on middle Pliocene	Rose and Colburn, 1963, p. 44
13	Tulare	Blancan, Irvingtonian, early Rancholabrean(?); 600,000 yrs. at base of upper third	Conformable on Pliocene in San Joaquin Valley; unconformable on Tertiary and Mesozoic on east flank of the Diablo Range	Woodring and others, 1940, p. 14; Taliaferro, 1943a, p. 147; Huey, 1948, p. 49; Long and Carpenter, 1963; Carpenter, 1965
14	Paso Robles	----	Conformable on lower Pliocene in Salinas Valley; unconformable on Miocene to middle Pliocene in the ranges	Schombel, 1940, p. 33; Taliaferro, 1943a, p. 147; 1943b, p. 460; Durham, 1963, p. Q21; Gribi, 1963a, p. 16; Jennings, 1958; Jennings and Strand, 1958
15	Orcutt Sand	----	Unconformable on Paso Robles Formation	Woodring and Bramlette, 1950, p. 51; Dibblee, 1950, p. 50; Upson and Thomasson, 1951, p. 39

Mount Konocti is an almost perfectly preserved dacitic strato-volcano, about 2,700 feet high. Numerous hot springs and solfataras are still active.

Deformed continental strata occur around the flanks of eight small structural basins in the central part of the northern Coast Ranges. These deposits are unfossiliferous, but their stratigraphic and structural relations, and degrees of consolidation and deformation are similar to those of the Cache Beds and of continental sediments associated with the Sonoma Volcanics of Blancan age. That these valleys are downwarped structures is clearly shown by the fact that alluvial fills extend as much as 1,000 feet below the lowest part of the bedrock rims.

Late Quaternary deposits that fill the centers of many of the structural valleys are essentially undeformed. Although in the centers of the valleys they may be conformable on older Pleistocene strata, around the margins they lie unconformably on lower Pleistocene or yet older strata. These deposits are best known in the San Francisco Bay area, where they are important for engineering purposes, and in Salinas Valley, where they are important aquifers. In both places marine strata alternate with nonmarine strata, probably representing fluctuations of sea level corresponding to glacial and interglacial periods. The structural depression at San Francisco Bay existed before these late Pleistocene fluctuations; the present flooding

Table 1, Part B—Table of Late Cenozoic formations in the Coast Ranges north of San Francisco Bay

Locality	Formation	Age from fossil or physical evidence	Relation to older rocks	Reference
1	Merced	Late Pliocene	Unconformable on Mesozoic	Johnson, 1943; Weaver, 1949; Travis, 1952; Gealey, 1951; Higgins, 1952; Stirton, 1952
2	Ohlson Ranch	Middle and late(?) Pliocene	Unconformable on Mesozoic	Higgins, 1960; Peck, 1960
3	Glen Ellen and Huichica	----	Unconformable on Sonoma Volcanics	Weaver, 1949
4	Sonoma Volcanics	Blancan, 3.4 m.y.	Unconformable on middle Pliocene and older	Axelrod, 1944, 1957; Weaver, 1949; Travis, 1952; Cardwell, 1958; Kunkel and Upson, 1960; Koenig, 1963; Evernden and James, 1964
5	Tehama	Blancan, 3.3 m.y.	Unconformable on Cretaceous	VanderHoof, 1933; Stirton, 1936; Anderson and Russell, 1939; Evernden and others, 1964
6	Clear Lake Volcanic Series	Pleistocene and Recent	Unconformable(?) on Sonoma Volcanics	Anderson, 1936; Brice, 1953
7	Cache Beds	Pleistocene in part	Unconformable on Eocene	Anderson, 1936; Brice 1953; Upson and Kunkel, 1955
8	Deformed unfossiliferous continental deposits	----	Consolidation and stratigraphic relations similar to Cache, Glen Ellen, and Huichica Formations	California Div. Water Resources, 1958
9	Carlotta	Early Pleistocene(?)	Conformable on upper Pliocene	Lawson, 1894; Ogle, 1953
10	St. George	Early Pleistocene	Unconformable on Mesozoic	Diller, 1902; Maxson, 1933; Back, 1937

of the Bay resulted from post-glacial rise of sea level rather than from Recent subsidence (Louderback, 1951).

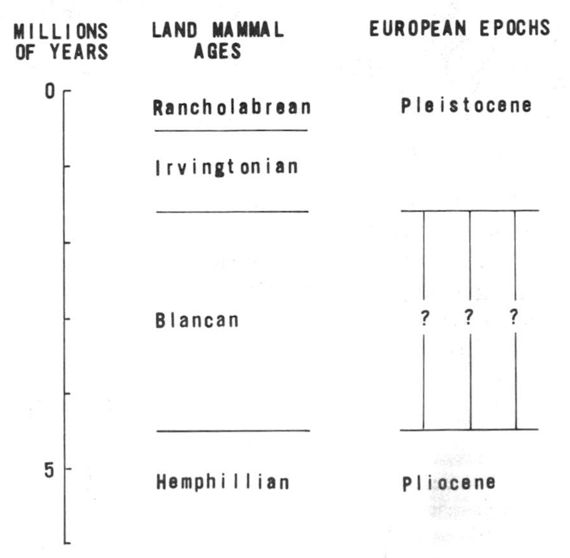

Figure 2. Duration of North American land mammal ages as indicated by radiometric age determinations. Adapted from Evernden and others, 1964, with additional data from Janda, 1965, and Carpenter, 1965.

STRUCTURE

The latest increments of Quaternary deformation have been graphically recorded by surface rupture on the Hayward fault in 1868, by right-lateral displacement of as much as 21 feet on the San Andreas fault in 1906 (Tocher, 1959), and now by continuing creep without accompanying seismic effects along the San Andreas fault south of Hollister (Tocher, 1960) and along the Hayward fault in Berkeley (Cluff 1965; Radbruch, 1965). The net lateral movement through Quaternary time is hard to assess. Russell (1926, p. 509) noted that stream valleys on the west side of the Berkeley Hills are apparently offset as much as 600 feet in a right-lateral sense where they cross the Hayward fault. Hinds (1952, p. 160) inferred as much as 3,000 feet of right-lateral displacement on the San Andreas fault from apparent offsets of streams. Hill (1952, p. 96) noted that Pleistocene gravels with contrasting composition are juxtaposed across the San Andreas fault on the west side of the Temblor Range; from this juxtaposition he inferred several miles of right-lateral displacement in Pleistocene time.

In the southern Coast Ranges, immediately adjacent to the active regional faults, Pleistocene strata are intensely deformed, and overthrust faults have been reported from several places (Crittenden, 1951; T. W. Dibblee, oral communication, 1964). Low-angle over-

Photo 2. Aerial view of The Geysers, northern Coast Ranges. ***Photo courtesy Pacific Gas and Electric Company.***

thrusts occur on the east side of the Temblor Range, but these seem to be large gravity slides (Arnold and Johnson, 1910; Taff, 1933; Hudson and White, 1941; Simonson and Krueger, 1942).

Away from the active regional faults deformation was concentrated around the flanks of the ranges. For example, at the boundary between the Diablo Range and the San Joaquin Valley, the Tulare Formation, including beds 600,000 years old, is sharply flexed (Carpenter, 1965); in the San Joaquin Valley to the east of this flexure, and in the Diablo Range to the west, strata of the same or greater age are flat lying or, at the most, broadly warped and cut by small faults (Bailey and Myers, 1942; Leith, 1949). Similarly, in many places along the east side of the Santa Lucia Range the angles of dip and amplitudes of structures in the Paso Robles Formation are much greater than they are in strata of the same age within the range. These ranges appear to have risen vertically, with movements concentrated on marginal flexures or faults, with only broad warping and minor faulting within the ranges.

While the ranges rose the valleys subsided. In Salinas Valley continental sediments occur to depths of 3,000 feet below sea level (Gribi, 1963a, p. 76). In Santa Clara Valley, south of San Francisco Bay, freshwater molluscs and peat have been found in alluvium 300 feet below sea level.

To a fair first approximation, then, generalized contours on the land surface of the Coast Ranges south of

San Francisco Bay correspond to vertical movements of these ranges during Quaternary time. No clear geometric relation of these vertical movements to the regional strikeslip faults is apparent. The regional faults do not bound the vertically moving crustal blocks; rather, they cut diagonally across some, parallel others. There is no necessary mechanical relation between the vertical and lateral movements.

In the north Coast Ranges the stratigraphic record of Quaternary deformation is less extensive. Here, too, however, the intensity of deformation clearly varied from place to place. The Merced and Ohlson Ranch Formations along the coast are broadly warped, but the Sonoma Volcanics, with which the Merced Formation interfingers, are more intensely folded and faulted. Along the east side of the north Coast Ranges the Tehama Formation in some places (for example, Rumsey Hills) is folded into anticlines and faulted; elsewhere it is essentially flat lying. Near Eureka the Carlotta Formation and underlying Pliocene strata have been folded into a syncline, the flanks of which are locally overturned and overthrust by Cretaceous strata. The various alluviated valleys are basinlike downwarps.

At the turn of the century A. C. Lawson (1894) and J. S. Diller (1902) postulated a series of peneplains in the north Coast Ranges that were supposed to have been cut during pauses in the bodily uplift of the ranges in Cenozoic time. Wahrhaftig and Birman (1965) have shown that the gipfelfluhr (topographic surface generalized from summit altitudes) does not have the regularity that one would expect of a peneplain. Deformation of Pliocene and Pleistocene strata shows that these ranges were complexly deformed rather than uplifted as a single unit.

MARINE TERRACES

Multiple levels of marine terraces occur in many places along the coastline. These terraces are discontinuous, and none can be traced for more than a few miles. Terraces are specially well developed at Santa Cruz; Bradley (1957) showed that each of these terraces was cut during a period of rising sea level and that the veneer of marine strata was deposited during a decline in sea level.

Wahrhaftig and Birman (1965) studied the elevations of terraces along the entire length of the Coast Ranges. Locally remnants of terraces with pholad borings and marine strata occur at elevations as high as 900 feet. The higher terraces are moderately deformed; the elevations of their shoreline angles vary by as much as a few tens of feet per mile parallel to the coast (see also, Alexander, 1953; Bradley, 1965). The lower terraces are less deformed but even those vary in elevation by as much as a few tens of feet in a few miles.

Even the highest marine terraces appear to be of late Pleistocene age. Near the Santa Ynez River marine terraces more than 700 feet above sea level are cut into folds involving lower and middle Pleistocene strata. The lowest terrace (100 feet) at Santa Cruz has been dated by Blanchard (1963), using experimental U, Th, Ra methods, as about 110,000 years, hence probably of Sangamon age.

The extreme elevations of the higher terraces and lateral variations in elevations of individual terraces record uplift and warping of the mountains as well as eustatic changes of sea level. The late Pleistocene age of all terraces combined with progressively greater deformation of the higher terraces indicates that deformation has been more or less continuous throughout the later Pleistocene.

There is a puzzling lack of evidence of pre-Wisconsin high sea levels in the interior valleys. The youngest Pleistocene terraces and marine deposits on San Francisco peninsula have no counterparts on the east side of San Francisco Bay. Well-developed terraces on the coastal side of the Santa Lucia Mountains have no counterparts on the Salinas Valley side; further, the deposits within Salinas Valley are almost entirely continental, with only minor marine incursions.

DRAINAGE PATTERNS

Drainage patterns throughout the Coast Ranges show clear evidence of crustal deformation. In the headwater areas in the ranges the patterns are markedly subsequent, with streams finely adjusted to the relative erodability of the bedrock. These patterns were probably established on islands in the mid-Cenozoic seas. As the seas withdrew, as ranges rose and depositional surfaces were tilted, younger increments of drainage were added downstream. In some areas consequent patterns developed, with rivers flowing down the dip of inclined strata, or along the troughs of synclinal structures, or across prograding deltas. In some places crustal movements defeated and reversed earlier drainages; elsewhere drainages maintained their courses across intervening structures and markedly antecedent patterns developed. Defeated patterns are most apparent in the southern ranges where the climate is now dry and volumes of rivers are small. Antecedent patterns are conspicuous in the moist northern ranges where the rivers are large.

Defeated drainages in the southern ranges can be inferred from comparison of physical features of Plio-Pleistocene strata with the pattern of the present drainage. The distribution of heavy minerals and the configurations of sedimentary structures in the extensive Paso Robles Formation at the southeastern end of Salinas Valley indicate that these strata were deposited by streams flowing southeastward, across the present Temblor Range, into the San Joaquin Valley (J. Galehouse, oral communication, 1964). The Nacimiento and San Antonio Rivers, two southeastward-flowing streams in the Santa Lucia Mountains, were apparently headwater tributaries of this drainage system. These

Photo 3. View southeast along San Andreas Fault (Tomales Bay). Bodega Head in foreground. Northern Coast Ranges.

strata of the Paso Robles Formation are now being eroded by the Salinas River, a consequent stream flowing northwestward along a structural trough. Apparently the Plio-Pleistocene drainage was defeated by a combination of the rise of the Temblor Range, westward tilting of the Gabilan Range, and subsidence of Salinas Valley. The upper Salinas River has captured the headwater tributaries of the early drainage. In the Diablo Range the San Benito Gravels (Griffin, Stanford Univ., Student Research Project), and probably also the Hans Grieve Formation, were deposited by eastward-flowing streams in Blancan(?) time; they are now being eroded by westward-flowing streams.

Antecedent patterns in the north Coast Ranges are shown by rivers with alluviated headwater basins, some with thousands of feet of fill, and deep, downstream bedrock gorges. The headwaters of Cache Creek, for example, are in the deeply alluviated basin of Clear Lake; downstream from the lake Cache Creek flows through a deep gorge across a ridge of Cretaceous rocks; below the gorge it becomes a consequent stream in Capay Valley, which is a syncline in the Tehama Formation. Putah Creek flows through two alluviated valleys and across two bedrock ridges before it enters the Sacramento Valley. The Russian River flows through a string of alluviated structural basins and intervening gorges, enters the north end of a plain that declines toward San Francisco Bay, then turns westward to follow a deep gorge through a bedrock plateau to the ocean. Higgins (1952) has shown that the river prograded its way to the west as the sea withdrew, maintaining its course across the uplift that developed subsequently. The Middle Fork of the Eel River makes almost a complete circuit around the alluviated structural depression of Round Valley but does not flow into the valley—even though the base of the alluvial deposits in the valley is several hundred feet below the bedrock channel of the river. Apparently the course of the river was established before Round Valley subsided; gravels of presumed Plio-Pleistocene age have been warped around the edge of Round Valley.

Estuaries and thick alluvial deposits along the lower courses of the larger rivers indicate that they excavated canyons that were graded to a sea level about 300 feet below the present level (Louderback, 1951; Higgins, 1952; Evenson, 1959). Upson (1949) showed that along the southern part of the coast these canyons are cut through the lowest marine terrace, hence they are of Wisconsin age. Studies of beach and offshore sands by Cherry (1964) and Minard (1964) have shown that much of the sand on the continental shelf was transported along a shoreline that was several miles west of the present shore.

DATING THE OROGENY

Deformed strata, marine terraces, and drainage anomalies all attest to the recency of tectonic activity in the Coast Ranges. The pattern of unconformities indicates that this activity began in Miocene time and occurred in a series of pulses, the intensity of which varied from place to place and time to time. Only in the areas of the major oil fields did the most intense pulse come after deposition of early Pleistocene strata. Progressively greater deformation of the older marine terraces indicates that deformation continued more or less steadily through later Pleistocene time. Modern seismic activity is a manifestation of continuing tectonism. The so-called "mid-Pleistocene" orogeny of the California Coast Ranges was but one phase of a process that has been operating rather continuously since late Miocene time at least.

REFERENCES

Alexander, C. S., 1953, The marine and stream terraces of the Capitola-Watsonville area: California Univ. Pubs. Geography, v. 10, no. 1, 44 p.

Allen, J. E., 1946, Geology of the San Juan Bautista quadrangle, California: California Div. Mines Bull. 133, p. 9–75.

Anderson, C. A., 1936, Volcanic history of the Clear Lake area, California: Geol. Soc. America Bull., v. 47, no. 5, p. 629–644.

Anderson, C. A., and Russell, R. D., 1939, Tertiary formations of northern Sacramento Valley, California: California Jour. Mines and Geology, v. 35, no. 3, p. 219–253.

Arnold, Ralph, and Johnson, H. R., 1910, Preliminary report on the McKittrick-Sunset oil region, Kern and San Luis Obispo Counties, California: U.S. Geol. Survey Bull. 406, 225 p.

Axelrod, D. I., 1944, The Sonoma Flora, *in* Chaney, R. W., ed., Pliocene floras of California and Oregon: Carnegie Inst. Washington Pub. 553, Contr. Paleontology, p. 167–206.

Back, William, 1957, Geology and ground-water features of the Smith River plain, Del Norte County, California: U.S. Geol. Survey Water-Supply Paper 1254, 76 p.

Bailey, E. H., and Myers, W. B., 1942, Quicksilver and antimony deposits of the Stayton district, California: U.S. Geol. Survey Bull. 931-Q, p. 405–434.

Blanchard, R. L., 1963, Uranium decay series disequilibrium in age determination of marine calcium carbonates: St. Louis, Mo., Washington Univ., Ph.D. thesis, 175 p.

Bradley, W. C., 1957, Origin of marine-terrace deposits in the Santa Cruz area, California: Geol. Soc. America Bull., v. 68, no. 4, p. 421–444.

—— 1965, Marine terraces on Ben Lomond Mountain, California, *in* Guidebook for Field Conference I, Northern Great Basin and California: INQUA (Internat. Assoc. Quaternary Research), 7th Cong. 1965, p. 148–150.

Branner, J. C., Newsom, F. S., and Arnold, Ralph, 1909, Description of the Santa Cruz quadrangle, California: U.S. Geol. Survey, Geol. Atlas, Folio 163, 11 p.

Brice, J. C., 1953, Geology of the Lower Lake quadrangle, California: California Div. Mines Bull. 166, 72 p.

California Department of Water Resources, Division of Resources Planning, 1958, Recommended water well construction and sealing standards, Mendocino County: California Dept. Water Resources, Div. Resources Plan. Bull. 62, p. 1–169.

Cardwell, G. T., 1958, Geology and ground water in the Santa Rosa and Petaluma Valley areas, Sonoma County, California: U.S. Geol. Survey Water-Supply Paper 1427, 273 p.

Carpenter, D. W., 1965, Pleistocene deformation in the vicinity of the Mile 18 pumping plant, *in* Guidebook for Field Conference I, Northern Great Basin and California: INQUA (Internat. Assoc. Quaternary Research), 7th Cong. 1965, p. 142–145.

Cherry, John, 1964, Sand movement along a portion of the northern California coast: California Univ. Hydraulic Eng. Lab., Tech. Rept., HEL—4–3, 150 p.

Cluff, Lloyd, 1965, Evidence of creep along the Hayward fault: Assoc. Eng. Geologists, First Ann. Joint Mtg. San Francisco-Sacramento secs.; paper delivered at Berkeley, Sept. 25, 1965.

Crittenden, M. D., Jr., 1951, Geology of the San Jose-Mount Hamilton area, California: California Div. Mines Bull. 157, 74 p.

Cummings, J. C., Touring, R. M., and Brabb, E. E., 1962, Geology of the northern Santa Cruz Mountains, California: California Div. Mines and Geology Bull. 181, p. 179–220.

Dibblee, T. W., Jr., 1950, Geology of southwestern Santa Barbara County, California; Point Arguello, Lompoc, Point Conception, Los Olivos, and Gaviota quadrangles: California Div. Mines Bull. 150, 95 p.

Diller, J. S., 1902, Topographic development of the Klamath Mountains: U.S. Geol. Survey Bull. 196, 69 p.

Durham, D. L., 1963, Geology of the Reliz Canyon, Thompson Canyon, and San Lucas quadrangles, Monterey County, California: U.S. Geol. Survey Bull. 1141-Q, 41 p.

Evenson, R. E., 1959, Geology and ground-water features of the Eureka area, Humboldt County, California: U.S. Geol. Survey Water-Supply Paper 1470, 80 p.

Evernden, J. F., and James, G. T., 1964, Potassium-argon dates and the Tertiary floras of North America: Am. Jour. Sci., v. 262, no. 8, p. 945–974.

Evernden, J. F., Savage, D. E., Curtis, G. H., and James, G. T., 1964, Potassium-argon dates and the Cenozoic mammalian chronology of North America: Am. Jour. Sci., v. 262, no. 2, p. 145–198.

Gealey, W. K., 1951, Geology of the Healdsburg quadrangle, California: California Div. Mines Bull. 161, p. 7–50.

Glen, William, 1959, Pliocene and lower Pleistocene of the western part of the San Francisco peninsula: California Univ. Pubs. Geol. Sci., v. 36, no. 2, p. 147–197.

Gribi, E. A., 1963a, Monroe Swell oil field, Monterey County, California *in* Guidebook to the geology of Salinas Valley and the San Andreas fault: Am. Assoc. Petroleum Geologists-Soc. Econ. Paleontologists and Mineralogists, Pacific Sec., Ann. Spring Field Trip 1963, p. 76–77.

—— 1963b, The Salinas basin oil province, *in* Guidebook to the geology of Salinas Valley and the San Andreas fault: Am. Assoc. Petroleum Geologists-Soc. Econ. Paleontologists and Mineralogists, Pacific Sec., Ann. Spring Field Trip 1963, p. 16–27.

Hall, C. A., Jr., 1959, Geology and paleontology of the Pleasanton area, Alameda and Contra Costa Counties, California: California Univ. Pubs. Geol. Sci., v. 34, no. 1, p. 1–89.

Hall, T. N., 1965, Late Cenozoic stratigraphy between Mussel Rock and Fleishhacker Zoo, San Francisco peninsula, *in* Guidebook for Field Conference I, Northern Great Basin and California: INQUA (Internat. Assoc. Quaternary Research), 7th Cong. 1965, p. 151–158.

Higgins, C. G., Jr., 1952, Lower course of the Russian River, California: California Univ. Pubs. Geol. Sci., v. 29, no. 5, p. 181–264.

—— 1960, Ohlson Ranch formation, Pliocene, northwestern Sonoma County, California: California Univ. Pubs. Geol. Sci., v. 36, no. 3, p. 199–231.

Hill, M. L., 1952, The San Andreas fault, *in* Field trip routes, geology, oil fields: Am. Assoc. Petroleum Geologists-Soc. Econ. Paleontologists and Mineralogists, Soc. Explor. Geophysicists Guidebook, Joint Ann. Mtg., Los Angeles, Calif., 1952, p. 96–98.

Hinds, N. E. A., 1952, Evolution of the California landscape: California Div. Mines Bull. 158, 240 p.

Hudson, F. S., and White, G. H., 1941, Thrust faulting and coarse clastics in the Temblor Range, California: Am. Assoc. Petroleum Geologists Bull., v. 25, no. 7, p. 1327–1342.

Huey, A. S., 1948, Geology of the Tesla quadrangle, California: California Div. Mines Bull. 140, 75 p.

Janda, R. J., 1965, Quaternary alluvium near Friant, California, *in* Guidebook for Field Conference I, Northern Great Basin and California: INQUA (Internat. Assoc. Quaternary Research), 7th Cong. 1965, p. 128–133.

Jennings, C. W., 1959, Geologic map of California, Olaf P. Jenkins edition, San Luis Obispo sheet: California Div. Mines, scale 1:250,000.

Jennings, C. W., and Strand, R. G., 1959, Geologic map of California, Olaf P. Jenkins edition, Santa Cruz sheet: California Div. Mines, scale 1:250,000.

Johnson, F. A., 1943, Petaluma region [California]: California Div. Mines Bull. 118, p. 622–627.

Koenig, J. B., 1963, Geologic map of California, Olaf P. Jenkins edition, Santa Rosa sheet: California Div. Mines and Geology, scale 1:250,000.

Kunkel, Fred, and Upson, J. E., 1960, Geology and ground water in Napa and Sonoma Valleys, Napa and Sonoma Counties, California: U.S. Geol. Survey Water-Supply Paper 1495, 252 p.

Lawson, A. C., 1894, The geomorphogeny of the coast of northern California: California Univ. Dept. Geology Bull., v. 1, p. 241–271.

—— 1914, Description of the San Francisco district, California: U.S. Geol. Survey Geol. Atlas, Folio 193 (Field ed., 1915, 180 p.).

Leith, C. J., 1949, Geology of the Quien Sabe quadrangle, California: California Div. Mines Bull. 147, p. 7–35.

Long, J. S., and Carpenter, D. W., 1963, Geology of the Mile 18 pumping plant area: Geol. Soc. of Sacramento, Guidebook for Field Trip, p. 53–57.

Louderback, G. D., 1951, Geologic history of San Francisco Bay: California Div. Mines Bull. 154, p. 75–94.

Maxson, J. H., 1933, Economic geology of portions of Del Norte and Siskiyou Counties, northwesternmost California: California Jour. Mines and Geology, v. 29, nos. 1–2, p. 123–160.

Minard, C. R., Jr., 1964, The erosional and depositional history of the coast of northern California: California Univ. Hydraulic Eng. Lab. Tech. Rept. HEL—2–10, 63 p.

Ogle, B. A., 1953, Geology of Eel River Valley area, Humboldt County, California: California Div. Mines Bull. 164, 128 p.

Peck, J. H., Jr., 1960, Paleontology and correlation of the Ohlson Ranch formation: California Univ. Pubs. Geol. Sci., v. 36, no. 4, p. 233–241.

Radbruch, D. H., 1957, Areal and engineering geology of the Oakland West quadrangle, California: U.S. Geol. Survey Misc. Geol. Inv. Map I-239, scale 1:24,000.

—— 1965, Approximate location of fault traces and historic surface ruptures within the Hayward fault zone between San Pablo and Warm Springs, California: U.S. Geol. Survey open-file map, scale 1:62,500.

Rose, R. L., and Colburn, I. P., 1963, Geology of the east-central part of the Priest Valley quadrangle, California, *in* Guidebook to the geology of Salinas Valley and the San Andreas fault: Am. Assoc. Petroleum Geologists-Soc. Econ. Paleontologists and Mineralogists, Pacific Sec., Ann. Spring Field Trip 1963, p. 38–45.

Russell, R. J., 1926, Recent horizontal offsets on the Haywards fault: Jour. Geology, v. 34, no. 6, p. 507–511.

Savage, D. E., 1951, Late Cenozoic vertebrates of the San Francisco Bay region: California Univ. Pubs. Dept. Geol. Sci. Bull., v. 28, no. 10, p. 215–314.

Schlocker, Julius, Bonilla, M. G., and Radbruch, D. H., 1958, Geology of the San Francisco North quadrangle, California: U.S. Geol. Survey Misc. Geol. Inv. Map I-272, scale 1:24,000.

Schombel, L. F., 1940, Preliminary report on the geology of Soledad quadrangle, Monterey County, California: California Univ., Berkeley, M.S. thesis.

Simonson, R. R., and Krueger, M. L., 1942, Crocker Flat landslide area, Temblor Range, California: Am. Assoc. Petroleum Geologists Bull., v. 26, no. 10, p. 1608–1631.

Stirton, R. A., 1936, Succession of North American continental Pliocene mammalian faunas: Am. Jour. Sci., 5th ser., v. 32, no. 189, p. 161–206.

—— 1952, Are Petaluma horse teeth reliable in correlation? [California]: Am. Assoc. Petroleum Geologists Bull., v. 36, no. 10, p. 2011–2025.

Taff, J. A., 1933, Geology of McKittrick oil field and vicinity, Kern County, California: Am. Assoc. Petroleum Geologists Bull., v. 17, no. 1, p. 1–15.

Taliaferro, N. L., 1943a, Geologic history and structure of the central Coast Ranges of California: California Div. Mines Bull. 118, p. 119–163.

—— 1943b, Bradley-San Miguel district [California]: California Div. Mines Bull. 118, p. 456–462.

—— 1951, Geology of the San Francisco Bay counties, *in* Jenkins, O. P., ed., Geologic guidebook of the San Francisco Bay counties: California Div. Mines Bull. 154, p. 117–150.

Tocher, Don, 1959, Seismic history of the San Francisco region, *in* San Francisco earthquake of March 1957: California Div. Mines Spec. Rept. 57, p. 39–48.

—— 1960, Creep on the San Andreas fault—Creep rate and related measurements at Vineyard, California: Seismol. Soc. America Bull., v. 50, no. 3, p. 398–404.

Trask, P. D., and Rolston, J. W., 1951, Engineering geology of San Francisco Bay, California: Geol. Soc. America Bull., v. 62, no. 9, p. 1079–1110.

Travis, R. B., 1952, Geology of the Sebastopol quadrangle, California: California Div. Mines Bull. 162, 32 p.

Upson, J. E., 1949, Late Pliocene and recent changes of sea level along the coast of Santa Barbara County, California: Am. Jour. Sci., v. 247, no. 2, p. 94–115.

Upson, J. E., and Kunkel, F. F., 1955, Ground water of the Lower Lake-Middletown area, Lake County, California: U.S. Geol. Survey Water-Supply Paper 1297, 83 p.

Upson, J. E., and Thomasson, H. G., Jr., 1951, Geology and water resources of the Santa Ynez River Basin, Santa Barbara County, California: U.S. Geol. Survey Water-Supply Paper 1107, 194 p.

VanderHoof, V. L., 1933, Additions to the fauna of the Tehama upper Pliocene of northern California: Am. Jour. Sci., 5th ser., v. 25, no. 149, p. 382–384.

Wahrhaftig, Clyde, and Birman, J. H., 1965, The Quaternary of the Pacific Mountain system in California, *in* Wright, H. E., Jr., and Frey, D. G., eds., The Quaternary of the United States—A review volume for the VII Congress of the International Association for Quaternary Research: Princeton, N. J., Princeton Univ. Press, p. 299–340.

Weaver, C. E., 1949, Geology of the Coast Ranges immediately north of the San Francisco Bay region, California: Geol. Soc. America Mem. 35, 242 p.

Wilson, I. F., 1943, Geology of the San Benito quadrangle, California: California Jour. Mines and Geology, v. 39, p. 183–270.

Woodford, A. O., 1951, Stream gradients and the Monterey sea valley: Geol. Soc. America Bull., v. 62, no. 7, p. 799–851.

Woodring, W. P., and Bramlette, M. N., 1950, Geology and paleontology of the Santa Maria district, California: U.S. Geol. Survey Prof. Paper 222, 185 p.

Woodring, W. P., Stewart, Ralph, and Richards, R. W., 1940, Geology of the Kettleman Hills oil field, California; stratigraphy, paleontology, and structure: U.S. Geol. Survey Prof. Paper 195, 170 p.

ECONOMIC MINERAL DEPOSITS IN THE COAST RANGES

By Fenelon F. Davis
California Division of Mines and Geology

Mercury mining in the Coast Ranges is the counterpart of gold mining in the Sierra Nevada. The histories of exploration for the two metals run parallel courses in the early mining development of the State, partly because the possession and use of mercury was essential for the recovery of gold by amalgamation. Actually the mining of mercury began in the Coast Ranges in 1845, prior to the discovery of gold in the Sierra Nevada, when "Indian Paint Rock" at New Almaden was identified as cinnabar, the chief ore of mercury. Subsequent successful developments encouraged prospecting both to the north and south and many more mercury deposits were discovered, as were also deposits of other metallic minerals, principally chromite, manganese oxide, and copper sulfides.

Later, as the population increased, demands for nonmetallic commodities, such as clay for brick, cement rock, lime, limestone, pumice, building stone, sand, and gravel, and other materials of construction developed, leading to the opening of pits and quarries in suitable formations close to the population centers. Also, as industry moved westward nonmetallic minerals to meet the needs for industrial products and chemical processes were found. This led to the exploitation of asbestos, barite, bromine, carbon dioxide, diatomite, dolomite, feldspar, gypsite, limestone, magnesite, perlite, pyrite, salt, and sulfur. Source areas of fuel and power were explored and developed, first resulting in the production of bituminous rock and coal in the late 1800's, and more recently in the production of petroleum, natural gas, and natural steam. The search for deposits of minerals of value is still in progress, and new discoveries are still being made.

The economic deposits of the Coast Ranges provided at least 43 separate mineral commodities to industry during the period 1850–1965, and the cumulative value of all these mineral commodities is estimated at $2,500,000,000. This figure includes not only the better known products but also many minor products, notably antimony ore, black sand, borax, gemstones, gold, graphite, silver, and uranium minerals. Additional commodities which occur in the province and have some potential for future production are nickel, olivine, and phosphate rock. The relative value of the individual mineral products is shown in Table 1.

Table 1. *Estimated value of minerals produced from California Coast Ranges, 1850–1965* [1]

Largest production (over $1,000,000,000)	Large production (over $100,000,000)	Moderate production ($1,000,000 to $100,000,000)	Small production ($100,000 to $1,000,000)	Little or no production (under $100,000)
Petroleum	Cement	Magnesia (sea water)	Perlite	Barite
	Sand and gravel	Limestone	Pumice	Antimony
	Mercury	Lime	Gypsite	Platinum
	Natural gas	Brick	Carbon dioxide gas	Graphite
	Rock products	Clay and shale	Natural steam	Black sand
	Salt	Coal	Gemstones	Uranium
		Chromite	Sulfur	Zinc
		Dolomite	Borax	Nickel
		Bromine		Tungsten
		Sand		Phosphate
		Feldspar		Sodium sulfate
		Mineral water		
		Magnesite		
		Manganese ore		
		Asbestos		
		Bituminous rock		
		Pyrites		
		Diatomite		
		Copper		
		Silver-gold		
		Sandstone (dimension)		

[1] Annual State production reports group commodity values where necessary to conceal confidential data of individual producers; hence, only approximate cumulative values are available.

Table 2. *Geologic environment of economic mineral deposits in the Coast Ranges.*

Age of host rock	Geologic Occurrence and host formation	Mineral deposit
Quaternary (Recent)	Sea water of San Francisco, San Pablo, and Monterey Bays.	*Salt* (sodium chloride) produced by solar evaporation of ponded sea water.
		Bromine recovered as a byproduct from salt-works bittern (only on San Francisco Bay).
		Magnesium compounds produced from sea water and bitterns by treatment with calcined dolomite. Principal plants at Newark and South San Francisco on San Francisco Bay and at Moss Landing on Monterey Bay.
	Mud and oyster shells in lenses on floor of San Francisco Bay.	*Cement* produced at tidewater near Redwood City from mud and shells recovered by floating suction dredges.
	Mud and waters of Borax playa lake southeast of Clear Lake.	*Borax and soda*, borax crystals recovered from water by pan evaporation; some soda potential.
	Surficial deposits from hot calcareous springs in Contra Costa and Solano Counties.	*Travertine* supplied cement plants for many years.
	Quartz veins in volcanic rocks.	*Silver and gold.* Production from two mines near Calistoga totaled over $1,000,000.
	Basalt, at Sulphur Bank hydrothermal area bordering Clear Lake.	*Sulfur and mercury.* In thermal area basalt above water table leached of all but silica and sulfur deposited; below water table clay alteration and formation of major mercury deposit.
	Surficial deposit in arid eastern foothills of province in Fresno County.	*Marl.* A "caliche" formed by evaporation of carbonate-bearing ground water.
Quaternary (Pleistocene to Recent)	Stream beds and terraces; river bars and banks; alluvial cones and fans.	*Sand and gravel* in the unconsolidated sediments close to metropolitan centers and major construction projects. Principal deposits in Livermore Valley, Niles Cone, Russian River, Salinas River, Sisquoc River, and Santa Maria River.
	Beaches and adjoining upland in Del Norte, Humboldt, and Santa Cruz Counties.	*Black sand* containing gold, platinum, and magnetite.
	Beaches and adjoining upland.	*Sand* in beaches and dunes north of Del Monte in Monterey County and at Oceano Beach in San Luis Obispo County.
	Dunes overlying and adjacent to granite basement at Pacific Grove, Monterey County.	*Feldspar and silica*, sand products separated by flotation or magnetic separation.
	Volcanic flows and pyroclastic rocks at the southern end of Clear Lake.	*Crushed stone* and decorative rock.
		Pumice and obsidian.
	Fractures in volcanic rocks in Lake and Napa Counties.	*Mineral water*, bottled and sold since 1856.
Quaternary-Tertiary (Plio-Pleistocene)	Irregular, discontinuous lenses of massive sulfide in intrusive-extrusive Leona rhyolite.	*Pyrites*, mined on west flank of Berkeley Hills and used in manufacture of sulfuric acid.
Tertiary (Pliocene)	Large bodies in flows of Sonoma volcanics.	*Perlite* in St. Helena area, Napa County, and Santa Rosa, Sonoma County.
	Layers of massive pyroclastic rocks in Sonoma volcanics.	*Pumice* and obsidian in Napa area of Napa County.
	Fresh water deposit interbedded with Sonoma volcanics near Napa.	*Diatomite*, used for pozzolanic properties.
(Lower Pliocene)	Calcareous "reefs" between diatomaceous shale and sandstone in Pancho Rico Formation in Monterey and San Luis Obispo Counties.	*Phosphate rock*, thin but extensive beds recently investigated.
(Miocene)	Fracture filling and replacement of quartz veins and breccia in volcanic rocks.	*Antimony and mercury.* Some mercury production; small antimony production.
(Late Miocene to late Eocene)	Sisquoc, Santa Margarita, upper Monterey and Kreyenhagen Formations.	*Diatomite* deposits are extensive in the southern Coast Ranges; occur in northern Coast Ranges as far north as Point Arena.
(Upper Miocene)	Light-colored friable marine sandstone of the Santa Margarita Formation.	*Sand*, large deposits and plants near Felton, Santa Cruz County.
	Multicolored, fine-grained, limy, siliceous sedimentary rocks of the Monterey Formation.	*Stone*, building stone and flagging.
	Overlying siliceous Monterey shale.	*Phosphate rock*, pellets in sand layers over wide area.
(Middle to Lower Miocene)	Steep dipping bed in Temblor Formation.	*Coal*, sub-bituminous mined in Stone Canyon, Monterey County.
(Lower Miocene)	Shell deposit in Vaqueros Formation.	*Limestone*, mined for sugar refining at Lime Mountain; San Luis Obispo County.
(Upper Eocene)	Zone in Kreyenhagen Formation crops out along flank of Vallecitos syncline, San Benito County.	*Bentonite*, swelling and non-swelling.
	Surficial edges of up-turned gypsiferous beds cropping out in the arid foothills along the eastern border of the province from Merced to Kern Counties.	*"Cap" gypsum* or gypsite with thin overburden on the hilltops.
(Middle Eocene)	Steep-dipping beds in Domengine and Tesla Formations.	*Coal*, sub-bituminous mined near Mount Diablo and Corral Hollow.
		Clay and sand, interbedded with coal.

Table 2. *Geologic environment of economic mineral deposits in the Coast Ranges—Continued*

Age of host rock	Geologic Occurrence and host formation	Mineral deposit
Tertiary (some Quaternary and Late Cretaceous)	Many formations of Tertiary age; greatest production, by far, from Miocene and Pliocene rocks. Minor amounts from other Tertiary formations, Pleistocene, and Cretaceous rocks. Traces from late Jurassic formations. Most of the reservoir rock is sandstone but some significant production from fractured shale. Type of structures involved are anticlines, faulted anticlines, and stratigraphic traps.	*Petroleum*, natural gas, greatest cumulative value of all Coast Ranges mineral commodities. Major fields are in the Tertiary marine basins, including Santa Maria, Cuyama, Salinas Valleys. Almost all petroleum of the Coast Ranges province has come from the southern ranges—Salinas Valley and south. Some of the great fields are San Ardo in Monterey County, Santa Maria Valley, and Cuyama and Russell Ranch fields in Santa Barbara County and the Coalinga anticline in Fresno County. A dry gas field near Eureka, Humboldt County.
Late Cretaceous (to Pliocene)	Marine shale and claystone. Numerous large deposits in the Coast Ranges.	Brick, clay products, expansible shale.
Late Cretaceous	Cretaceous sandstone.	*Stone*, dimension sandstone used extensively in construction of buildings at Stanford University, San Jose, and San Francisco during early 1900's.
	Fracture fillings and replacement in fractured Panoche shale and sandstone (and Franciscan sandstone) under New Idria thrust fault.	*Mercury*, the high degree of fracturing in the rocks has favored ore deposition. About 30 percent of California deposits occur in these rocks.
Late Cretaceous to Late Jurassic (Deposits associated with peridotite and serpentine, and serpentine hydrothermally altered to silica-carbonate rock).	Epithermal veins, fracture fillings, and replacement deposits in silica-carbonate rock (a hydrothermal alteration product of serpentine). About 50 percent of California deposits occur in fractured silica-carbonate rocks.	*Mercury*, Coast Ranges have supplied about 85 percent of United States production. Principal districts are New Almaden in Santa Clara County, New Idria in San Benito County, and Mayacmas in Sonoma, Lake, and Napa Counties.
	Recrystallization of fractured, massive serpentine by short-fiber chrysotile.	*Asbestos*, chrysotile, widely distributed throughout Coast Ranges, extensive new deposits being mined (1965) in southeastern San Benito County and adjacent Fresno County.
	Magmatic segregations of chromite in peridotite and peridotite altered to serpentine.	*Chromite*, widely distributed throughout the length of the Coast Ranges. No mining in 1965; greatest production has come from San Luis Obispo, Glenn, Del Norte Counties and Fresno County.
	Fracture fillings and replacement bodies in serpentine.	*Magnesite* formerly mined near common border of Santa Clara and Stanislaus Counties and elsewhere.
	Lateritic remnants of early Tertiary erosion surfaces developed on serpentine and peridotite in Mendocino County.	*Nickel* sulfide minerals of primary origin occur widely in the peridotites and serpentines. During laterization part of the nickel is dissolved and redeposited as garnierite in underlying silica boxwork. Some commercial potential.
	Fault zones in Franciscan rocks and serpentine; source of heat probably Quaternary volcanic rocks.	*Natural steam* produced for power at The Geysers, Sonoma County. *Carbon dioxide gas*, near Hopland. *Mineral Springs*, resorts popular in pre-motoring days.
(Deposits associated with sedimentary or metasedimentary rocks).	Massive lenticular sulfide body in rocks of the Franciscan Formation.	*Copper* from sulfide ores at Island Mountain, southern Trinity County.
	Veins of natrolite in fractured metamorphics included in serpentine.	Gemstone, benitoite, with neptunite and joaquinite.
	Lenses, pods, or veins within or near bodies of serpentine.	Nephrite, jadeite, orbicular jasper.
	Quartz veins in Francisan sandstone.	*Gold*, a number of small mines in Los Burros district of Monterey County.
	Calera Limestone member of Franciscan Formation. Highly fractured fault sliver in San Andreas Fault zone.	*Limestone and cement*. Permanente Cement Co. plant, Santa Clara County, is the largest producer of cement in California.
	Chert members of Franciscan Formation enclose lenses of sedimentary manganese materials later oxidized.	*Manganese* deposits throughout the Coast Ranges. Large percentage of Coast Range production from Ladd-Buckeye mines at junction Alameda, Santa Clara, San Joaquin, and Stanislaus Counties. Belt extends northwestward into Humboldt County.
Pre-Cretaceous rocks of Salinian block.	Roof pendants of highly deformed, metamorphosed marine sedimentary rocks in granite. "Gabilan crystalline Limestone" in Sur Series in Santa Cruz, Gabilan, and Santa Lucia Mountains.	*Limestone and cement*, major cement quarries and plants at Davenport in Santa Cruz County and San Juan Bautista in San Benito County. Limestone quarries near Santa Cruz.
	Replacement deposits of dolomite, cutting across limestone belts in Monterey and San Benito Counties.	*Dolomite* mined from major quarries at Natividad in Monterey County and south of Hollister in San Benito County.
	Replacement deposits in limestone.	*Barite* deposits near Fremont Peak supplied small production. Now in State park.

Table 2. *Geologic environment of economic mineral deposits in the Coast Ranges—Continued*

Age of host rock	Geologic Occurrence and host formation	Mineral deposit
Quaternary to Pre-Cretaceous	In various attitudes from flatlying to steepdipping. Quaternary to Miocene volcanic rocks; Miocene siliceous shale; Franciscan sandstone, limestone, chert, and greenstone; granitic rocks; Sur Series metamorphic rocks.	*Stone*, crushed and broken for use in metropolitan areas of San Francisco Bay and other centers of population.

ENVIRONMENT OF MINERAL DEPOSITS

The geologist exploring for mineral deposits in the Coast Ranges should understand the environment in which they have formed. Some deposits, called syngenetic, formed as part of the rock formation in which they occur, as for example, chromite deposits in ultramafic rock. Other deposits, called epigenetic, formed subsequent to their host rock, as did the quicksilver deposits. Mineral deposits are complex, however, and for the formation of many deposits more than one process is involved. Nevertheless, broad generalizations are warranted, and observations recorded at well-exposed deposits can often be extended successfully to nearby unexplored areas. Armed with a knowledge of origin and environment, the geologist concentrates his search in areas where suitable rock units exist, and thereby enhances his chance of discovery of the desired deposit. Some typical occurrences of mineral deposits in the Coast Ranges province are described below, and these and others are summarized in Table 2.

MAGMATIC SEGREGATIONS OF CHROMITE

Deposits of chromite occur in ultramafic rocks like peridotite, which consists of magnesium-iron silicates, chiefly of olivine and pyroxene. However, because these two minerals are easily altered to serpentine, while chromite remains unaltered, deposits of chromite are generally found in serpentine formed from peridotite or other ultramafic rock. The deposits may consist of compact, high-grade masses of chromite with little or no foreign material, or of low-grade deposits of chromite grains, nodules, stringers, or layers disseminated through the serpentine body.

Most of the deposits originated as erratically distributed magmatic segregations in peridotite, and no zones of altered chromite are available to guide the prospector. However, since chromite deposits often occur in clusters, bodies of serpentine known to contain chromite are likely places to prospect for additional deposits. Chromite released from its host rock is resistant to weathering and persists in stream canyons far below the outcrop, thus acting as a guide to the primary deposit. Occasionally, the detrital chromite may be sufficiently concentrated to form a workable secondary placer deposit.

As serpentine and peridotite host rocks are widely distributed throughout the Coast Ranges of California, chromite deposits are also widespread. Practically all counties have yielded some chromite, but the principal production in recent years has come from San Luis Obispo, Fresno, and Glenn Counties. California is the second largest producer of chromite of all the States. Most of the production, however, has been made during wartime emergency periods when premium prices were offered. Cumulative production from mines in the Coast Ranges is about 185,000 long tons valued at approximately $10,000,000.

EPITHERMAL DEPOSITS OF MERCURY

Mercury deposits in California, like those in most other parts of the world, are found in regions of Tertiary and Quaternary volcanic activity. The presence of cinnabar at Coso Hot Springs in Inyo County, at The Geysers in Sonoma County, at the Sulphur Bank mine in Lake County, and at Amedee Hot Springs in Lassen County demonstrates this association. In most districts, however, the cinnabar was deposited during an earlier period and only the roots of the spring systems remain.

The deposits were formed by the deposition of ore minerals from alkaline sulfide solutions at relatively low temperature and shallow depths. The mercury minerals fill fractures and pores or replace the host rock. Impervious rock overlying porous host rocks have proven to be especially effective traps. Some large and rich deposits have resulted from cinnabar replacing silica-carbonate rock—a hard, brittle rock formed by the hydrothermal alteration of serpentine to a mixture of quartz, opal, and a carbonate, usually magnesite. Over half of the larger mercury deposits occur in this rock with the cinnabar either replacing the rock or filling fractures. The New Almaden mine near San Jose provides an excellent example of ores in silica-carbonate rock. This mine produced over a million flasks of mercury sold for $50,000,000, but at 1965 prices worth ten times this amount. Although its workings reach a depth of 2,450 feet below the surface, the deepest of any mercury mine in the world, about half of its ore was mined above the 800 level.

Many mercury deposits occur in the extremely deformed sedimentary rocks of the Franciscan Formation with which the serpentine and silica-carbonate rocks are associated. Deposits also occur in the less-deformed rocks of the Knoxville, Paskenta, Chico, and Panoche sequences. The New Idria mine, in the heart of the Diablo Range, is an example of a major producer with ore bodies chiefly in overturned, altered, indurated, and fractured Panoche shale beneath a steep reverse fault. This mine has produced over 500,000

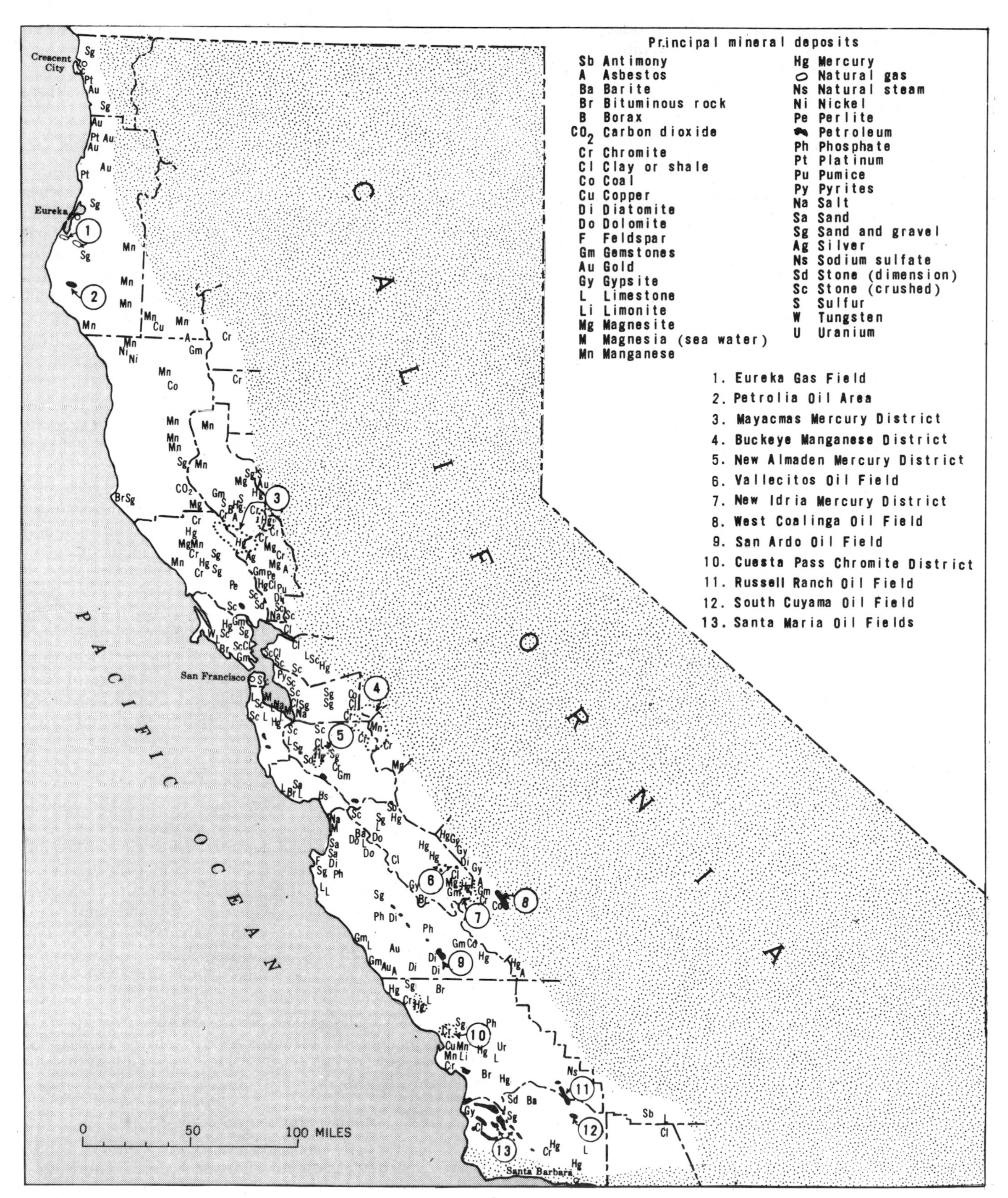

Figure 1. Map of northern California, showing the location of the principal mineral deposits, mining districts, and oil and gas fields in the Coast Ranges.

flasks and in 1965 was the largest producer in the United States. Elsewhere Tertiary sedimentary and volcanic rocks and Quaternary volcanic rocks contain major deposits. Recent small placer deposits also have been producers.

California quicksilver mines have produced about 85 percent of the mercury in the United States, and the great bulk of this production came from deposits in the Coast Ranges. The cumulative production of mercury in this province is about 2¾ million flasks valued at about $198,000,000.

HYDROTHERMAL DEPOSITS OF COPPER

Many occurrences of copper mineralization occur throughout the Coast Ranges, but only one deposit has yielded appreciable production. This is the massive sulfide body, consisting of pyrite, chalcopyrite, and pyrrhotite, located at the Island Mountain mine in southwestern Trinity County. The ore body occurs as a lenticular mass along a shear zone in slightly metamorphosed rocks of the Franciscan Formation. Replacement of the host rock was the dominant process in the formation of this deposit, although minor fracture filling is evident. The Island Mountain mine was active from 1915–30 when 9,000,000 pounds of copper, 144,000 ounces of silver, and 8,600 ounces of gold were produced. A geophysical survey suggests that some small unexposed ore bodies remain unmined.

METAMORPHIC DEPOSITS OF CHRYSOTILE ASBESTOS

Recently, a major asbestos industry has been developed in the Coast Ranges in western Fresno County. Here, a mass of serpentine, so intensely sheared that much of the rock has little coherence, yields smooth, flaky surfaces, similar to "mountain leather," bounded by polished chips of serpentine. On examination, the flexible leathery flakes were identified as matted, short-fiber chrysotile recrystallized from serpentine during the shearing process. Although the chrysotile fibre in this deposit is short, its ease of access to West Coast manufacturing makes it very valuable. Since 1960, four plants have located in the area to process the short-fiber asbestos for industrial usage.

CHEMICAL SEDIMENTARY DEPOSITS OF MANGANESE

Manganese deposits are associated with rocks of the Franciscan Formation, principally with the chert lenses which are widely distributed throughout the Coast Ranges. Franciscan chert ordinarily is thinly layered with shaly partings, but locally it forms large massive lenses which enclose concentrations of manganese minerals. The primary materials were manganese carbonates and silicates deposited in relatively flat lying positions in marine basins of restricted circulation. These materials and the enclosing rocks were folded, faulted, eroded, and oxidized to ores of the pyrolusite and psilomelane type. It is believed that the silica, manganese, and associated iron are of marine origin and were precipitated simultaneously.

Most of the manganese ore production has been made during wartime, and the Coast Ranges province has been the source of about half of the State's manganese ore. The principal production has come from the Ladd-Buckeye area south of Tracy.

SEDIMENTARY DEPOSITS OF LIMESTONE AND DOLOMITE

Large roof pendants of coarsely crystalline limestone and dolomite are found in the pre-Cretaceous rocks of the Santa Cruz Mountains, in the Gabilan Range and the Sierra de Salinas bounding the Salinas Valley, and in the Santa Lucia Range farther southeast in San Luis Obispo County. Included are bodies of high-grade limestone, dolomite, and mixed carbonate rocks in masses aggregating millions of tons. Practically all the dolomite consumed in northern California originates in quarries in the Gabilan Range.

The Calera limestone member of the Franciscan Formation provides a dense limestone used in the San Francisco area for making cement and for aggregate. The principal limestone quarries are on the San Francisco peninsula, and are located in the largest of many small discontinuous segments of the Calera member that are found extending along the San Andreas fault zone for a distance of about 30 miles. The limestone is thickest, about 400 feet, at the Permanente Cement Co. quarry about 40 miles south of San Francisco.

Large unmetamorphosed limestone deposits of Tertiary age are found in the southern Coast Ranges. The sugar refineries of the Salinas Valley currently use bedded shell limestone from the Vaqueros Formation, which is quarried at Lime Mountain northwest of Paso Robles. Lenses of oyster shells and mud are dredged from the floor of San Francisco Bay to manufacture cement at Redwood City.

SEDIMENTARY DEPOSITS OF CLAY AND SHALE

Conditions during Eocene time favored the deposition of high-grade sedimentary clays in lagoons bordering inland seas. Small deposits of fire-clay are found in the Tesla Formation in a narrow belt in southeastern Alameda County. The clay occurs in a synclinal structure with a sequence of white sand, subbituminous coal, shale, and anauxite clay. The structural conditions of the clay beds require expensive underground mining, and this factor has retarded their large-scale development.

Ceramic plants in the San Francisco area fill their requirements with shale quarried from the deposits of Jurassic and Cretaceous age which are widely distributed throughout the Coast Ranges province.

SEDIMENTARY DEPOSITS OF DIATOMITE

Extensive deposits of diatomaceous shale are found in the southern and central Coast Ranges where they are associated with volcanic ash and clastic sedimentary rocks. Deposits of commercial importance, which formed in a marine environment during Miocene and Pliocene time, crop out extensively from central

Monterey to southern Santa Barbara Counties and were formerly mined near Bradley. Additional marine beds occur in San Mateo and Santa Cruz Counties. Older marine diatomaceous beds of Eocene age crop out in western Fresno, Merced, and Stanislaus Counties. Fresh water deposits of Tertiary age occur in Napa County, where they are currently mined for use as a pozzolan. The chief uses of diatomite are for filters, insulation, and fillers.

SEDIMENTARY DEPOSITS OF SAND AND GRAVEL

Alluvial deposits of Quaternary age obtained from stream channels, terraces, flood plains, fans, and cones supply most of the sand and gravel required for concrete aggregate. Some of the principal source areas from north to south in the province are along the Eel, Mad, and Russian Rivers, Cache Creek, Alameda Creek, Arroyo Mocho, Corral Hollow, Coyote, and Los Gatos Creeks, and the Salinas, Santa Maria, and Sisquoc Rivers.

OTHER SEDIMENTARY DEPOSITS

Other economically important sedimentary deposits in the Coast Ranges contain bentonitic clay, bituminous rock, coal, and phosphate rock.

PETROLEUM

The natural habitat of petroleum is also in the sedimentary rocks. It is generally accepted that oil and gas are derived by natural distillation from organic remains buried in the sediments of marine basins. The principal basins of accumulation in the Coast Ranges are in, and adjoining, the Salinas, Santa Maria, and Cuyama Valleys.

At the San Ardo oil field in the Salinas Valley, beds of the Monterey Formation lie on a basement of eroded granite. Lower shale source beds of the Monterey Formation grade eastward into sandy reservoir beds, which are overlain by diatomaceous shale and by the Santa Margarita Formation of late Miocene age. Cumulative production from discovery in 1947 to 1963 inclusive was 135,000,000 barrels of 10-12 gravity oil from depths of 2,100 to 2,500 feet.

The Santa Maria Valley oil field occurs in a faulted stratigraphic trap, formed by an overlap of the Pliocene Sisquoc beds on the truncated reservoir sands of the Monterey Formation. Cumulative production from discovery in 1934 to 1963 inclusive was 136,000,000 barrels of 12-17 gravity oil from depths of 2,500-5,700 feet. Other fields in the Santa Maria basin are Arroyo Grande, Casmalia, Cat Canyon, Guadalupe, Lompoc, Orcutt, and Zaca, whose aggregate production to the end of 1963 was 353,000,000 barrels of oil.

In the Cuyama Valley the Russell Ranch field is in a homocline with closure against a normal fault. The principal production is from a thick body of sands in the Vaqueros Formation. Cumulative production from discovery in 1948 to 1963 inclusive was 58,000,000 barrels of 21–40 gravity oil from depths of 2,500–3,500 feet.

The South Cuyama field is an asymmetric faulted anticline with its principal production from the lower Miocene sand of the Vaqueros Formation. Cumulative production is 168,000,000 barrels of 26–35 gravity oil from depths of 3,600–4,300 feet.

Smaller oil fields are found in the Vallecitos syncline and in the Ciervo anticline, San Benito County; the Sargent anticline, and the Moody Gulch monoclinal fold in Santa Clara County; and the La Honda and Half Moon Bay fields in San Mateo County. Considerable quantities of natural gas have been produced from the various oil fields and also from the Eureka gas field in Humboldt County near the Pacific coast.

The total production of petroleum products in the Coast Ranges through 1965 is estimated at 920,000,000 barrels of oil and 700,000,000,000 cubic feet of gas.

REFERENCES

Bailey, E. H., and Everhard, D. L., 1964, Geology and quicksilver deposits of the New Almaden district, Santa Clara County, California: U. S. Geol. Survey Prof. Paper 360, 206 p.

California Division of Oil and Gas, 1961, California oil and gas fields, Pt. 2, Los Angeles-Ventura Basins and central coastal regions: San Francisco, California Div. Oil and Gas, p. 496–913.

Goldman, H. B., 1961, Sand and gravel in California, an inventory of deposits, Part A—Northern California: California Div. Mines and Geology Bull. 180-A, 38 p.

—— 1964, Sand and gravel in California, an inventory of deposits, Part B—Central California: California Div. Mines and Geology Bull. 180-B, 58 p.

Hart, E. W., in press, Mines and mineral resources of Monterey County: California Div. Mines and Geology.

Jenkins, O. P., 1943, Manganese in California: California Div. Mines Bull. 125, 387 p.

—— 1957, Mineral commodities of California: California Div. Mines and Geology Bull. 176, 736 p.

Rice, S. J., 1963, California asbestos industry: California Div. Mines and Geology, Mineral Inf. Service, v. 16, no. 9, p. 1–7.

Stinson, M. C., 1957, Geology of the Island Mountain copper mine, Trinity County, California: California Jour. Mines and Geology, v. 53, nos. 1–2, p. 9–33.

New Almaden quicksilver mine, California, 1852. By William Rich Hutton. Courtesy The Huntington Library, San Marino, California.

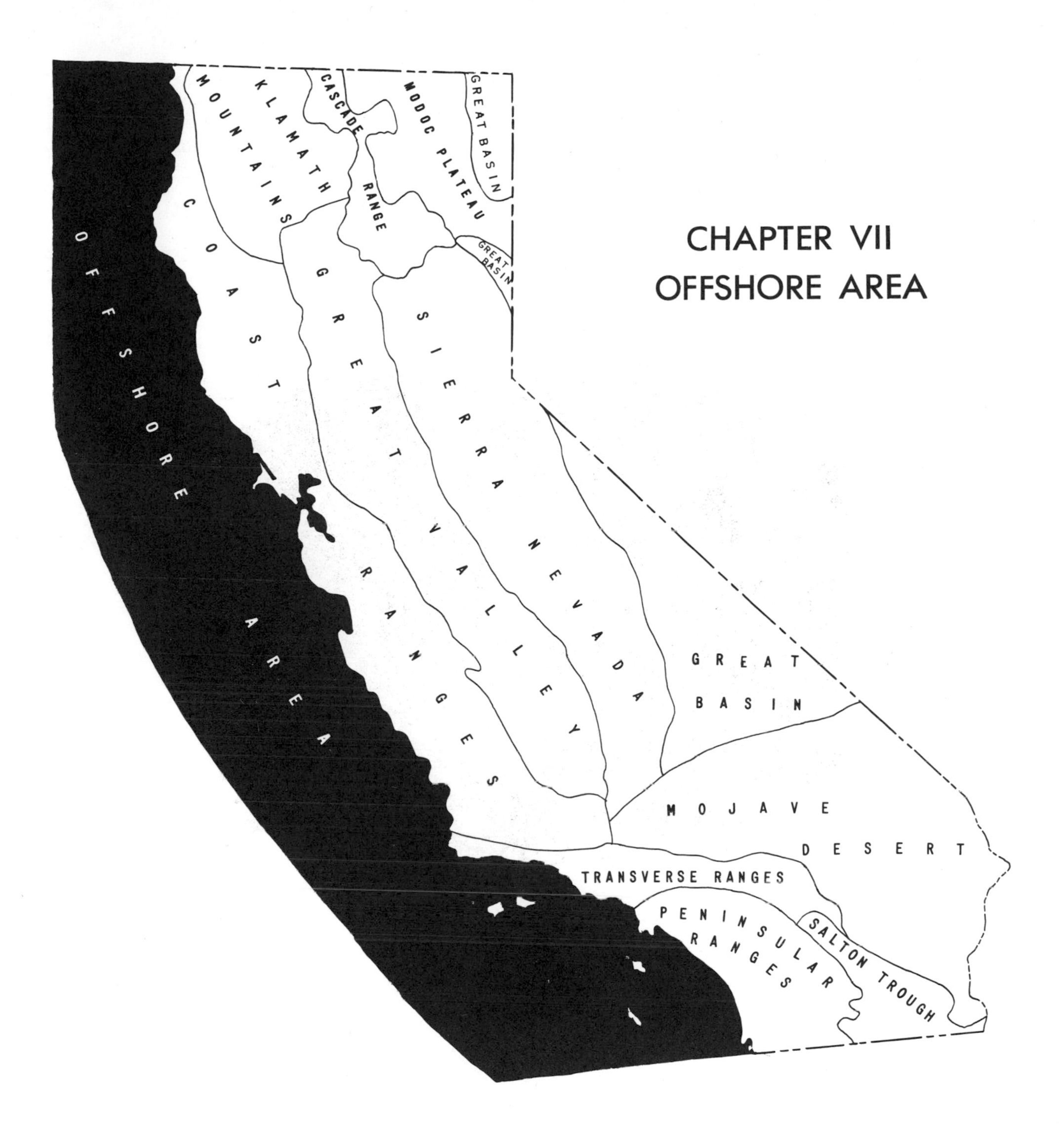

CHAPTER VII
OFFSHORE AREA

Page

THE CONTINENTAL MARGIN OF NORTHERN AND CENTRAL CALIFORNIA *

By Gene A. Rusnak
U.S. Geological Survey, Menlo Park, California

The geology of the continental margin offshore from northern and central California, though actively studied in recent years, is still very incompletely known. Much of the available data is in the remote sensing category, that is, it consists of measurements made at the ocean surface from which deductions have been made regarding the rocks and structures on the sea floor. The nature of the young sediments on the surface of the sea floor is moderately well known from dredge sampling, though not nearly so well known as in the broad shelf area off the coast of southern California. Bedrock that underlies these sediments has been sampled only by a few dredgings, but is, of course, exposed in a few islands and along the shore. The continental margin of northern and central California is unusually youthful, and thus this area is particularly suited for the study of basic problems of the development of continental shelves and slopes, and of the transition between continental and oceanic crustal rocks and structures.

The onshore limit of the continental margin is outlined by the western front of the California Coast Ranges, which is itself bounded to the south by the complex structure of the Transverse Ranges and to the north by the sharply defined lithologic boundary of the Klamath Mountains. Offshore the western edge of the continental margin is arbitrarily taken to be the 1,600 fm. (3,000-m) contour line, which lies at the foot of the steeper continental slope where it joins the lower declivity of the continental rise. To the north and south the extensive Mendocino and Murray fracture zones limit the morphological unit that constitutes the part of the continental margin to be described in this article. These major fractures trend from west to east towards the continents from the deep-sea oceanic crust and whether they abut directly against the continental crust or pass beneath is critical to understanding the geologic history of western California.

The narrow shelf and steep slope forms a distinctive morphological entity, which is clearly as different from the continental borderland south of the Transverse Ranges as it is different from the less steep and somewhat broader shelf and slope north of Cape Mendocino and opposite the western bulge of the Klamath Mountains (Irwin, 1960). A fundamental genetic association seems to exist between the submerged margin, the Coast Ranges, and the Great Valley by virtue of the very remarkable dimensional relationship of these structures to the major fracture zones of the sea floor (fig.1).

That relatively little data has been collected from the submerged margin in this area is partly because of the difficult working conditions to which ships are exposed offshore. The steep approach on the very narrow shelf offers little surface area upon which storm-generated seas can dissipate their energy. The severe winter storms generated regularly in the north Pacific during the northern hemisphere winter, and in the southern hemisphere during their winter, serve to create continuous heavy swells which peak sharply on this narrow continental shelf of California.

In contrast, a considerable amount of effort has been devoted to the study of the onshore geology because of the local occurrence of oil fields and the interest in the San Andreas fault system. That the geologic relations are still not entirely understood is partly because of the presence of the enigmatic suite of rocks which make up and are associated with the Franciscan assemblage (see for example, Taliaferro, 1943; Bailey, Irwin, and Jones, 1964). The Franciscan is well known for its thick sequence of graywacke, subordinate amounts of shale, chert, and limestone, some thick units of greenstone, and serpentine with and without glaucophane schist, and ultramafics. This great diversity of upper Jurassic through Cretaceous rocks, in addition to its variety, is unusual in that the base has not been observed and therefore the underlying units are unknown. It has been suggested that it represents an accumulation deposited directly on oceanic crust. Intense deformation of the Franciscan has resulted in the formation of major shear zones and much local crumpling, folding, and faulting, which developed a northwesterly trending grain that certainly must extend seaward. The major structural features of the region indicated in figure 2 have been compiled from the onshore studies summarized by Bailey, Irwin, and Jones (1964), and from the offshore studies of Uchupi and Emery (1963), and Curray (1965).

BATHYMETRY

Some conclusions regarding the late geologic history can be drawn from the submarine topography or bathymetry. The basic bathymetric charts of offshore

* Publication authorized by the Director, U.S. Geological Survey.

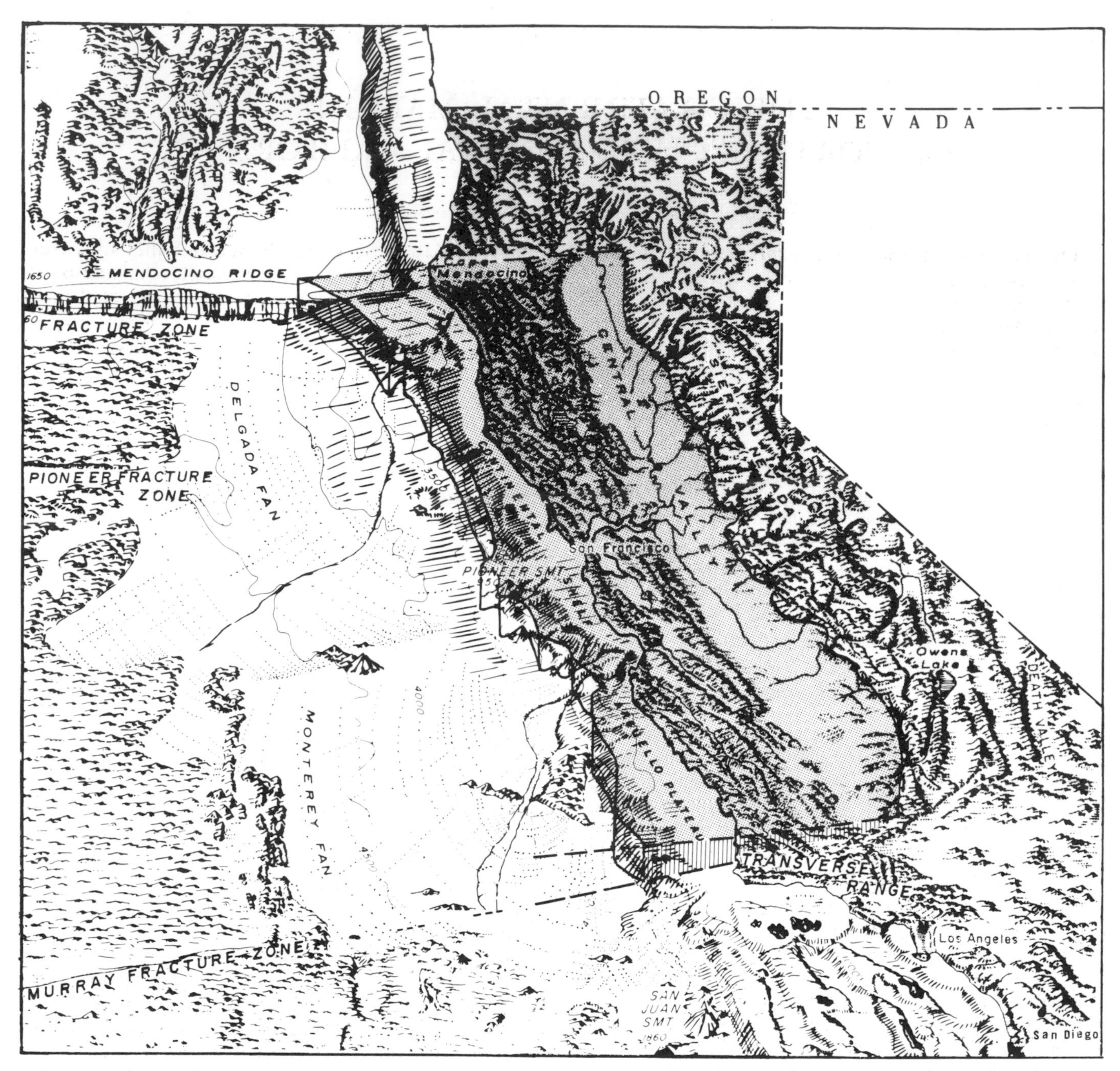

Figure 1. Physiographic setting of the northern and central California continental margin. Modified from Menard (1964); published by permission of McGraw-Hill Book Co.

California have been compiled by Shepard and Emery (1941). They have been incorporated in subsequent maps published by the California Division of Mines and Geology in their Geologic Map Series, and in a shaded relief map with offshore bathymetry shown in fathoms published by the U.S. Geological Survey in cooperation with the State of California. More recently, Uchupi and Emery (1963) have modified these basic charts to incorporate more recent soundings and to show the depths in meters.

The significant features of the northern and central California sea floor are its very narrow shelf with a slope averaging 3°, very steep canyon-cut slope, broad continental rise containing the Delgado and Monterey deep-sea fans, and the broad bank formed on the upper slope west of the Transverse Range. Typical profiles of the continental shelf and slope for various sections off the California coast, compared with the Sierra Nevada escarpment shown on the same scale are illustrated in figure 3.

The widest shelf area is found off the mouth of San Francisco Bay where the small group of Farallon Islands is developed. Width of the slope varies from 50 km off Point Pillar to 30 km west of Cordell bank.

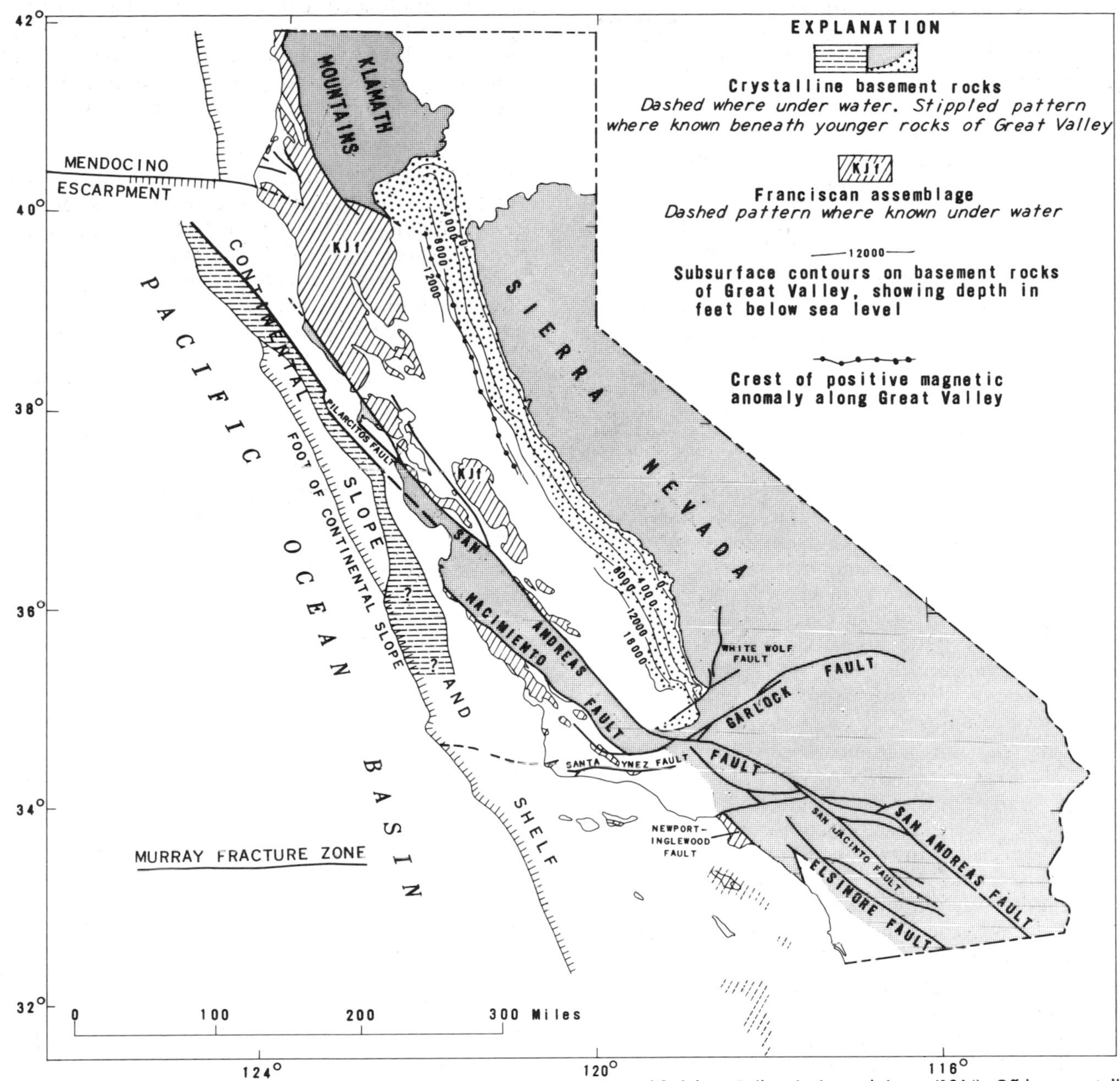

Figure 2: Principal structural features of the California continental margin modified from Bailey, Irwin, and Jones (1964). Offshore crystalline basement rock areas are after Uchupi and Emery (1963) and Curray (1965).

This shelf area is comparable to the still broader Arguello Plateau (fig. 4), which forms a broad bank that should be considered not as a part of the continental shelf but rather as a gentler part of the upper continental slope with an average gradient of 6.5° through its 50 km width (Uchupi and Emery, 1963). The shaded relief map of the State of California (1961) has this area designated as the Santa Lucia Bank and the very steep slope west of it is the Santa Lucia Escarpment.

Profiles of the continental margin at Point Arguello and off San Francisco (fig. 5) demonstrate the variety of surface irregularities on the sea floor. Small pinnacles at the foot of the slope, and locally higher, appear to be volcanic in origin, although most of the surface roughness is thought to be due to slump of sediments or rock.

SEDIMENTS

Sediments of the continental margin include shell sands and glauconitic sands on the shelves and banks, and a range from fine green sands through coarse silts to very fine olive-green silts on the slopes. The sand fraction of the slope deposits normally consist largely of detrital grains of quartz and feldspar with minor amounts of mica. The sand fraction of the Arguello Plateau, however, consists of glauconite, and phosphorate (see Wilson and Mero, this volume), together with benthonic foraminiferal tests and minor amounts

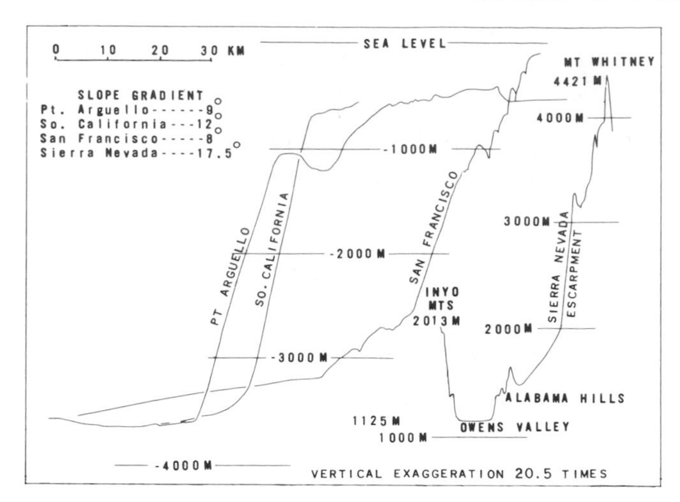

Figure 3. Comparison of three characteristic bottom profiles from the continental shelf, slope, and rise of the California continental margin with a profile of the Sierra Nevada escarpment. Modified after Uchupi and Emery (1963).

of diatoms, radiolarians, and fragments of shells. On the continental rise most of the sand consists of quartz and feldspar with minor amounts of mica, but the outermost lower portion of the rise consists mainly of radiolarians. The lithology of cores collected offshore from San Francisco and Point Arguello has been described by Uchupi and Emery (1963) in considerable detail, and one of their diagrams showing its variation is reproduced as figure 6.

Rates of sediment accumulation recorded for the slope areas are very low, being on the order of 2-6 cm/1,000 years. On the other hand, the shelves have been exposed to repeated periods of extensive wave planation, especially during the fall of eustatic sea level during the Pleistocene, with the result that the shelf areas are now largely nondepositional terraces mantled with only a thin veneer of winnowed materials (fig. 7, Moore and Shumway, 1959; Moore, 1960).

The Monterey, Delgado, and the Arguello deep-sea fans on the continental rise have gentle slopes that grade imperceptibly into the Deep Plain with a gradient of about 1°. These fans are associated with deep channels and with submarine canyons, which probably debouch turbidite deposits regularly to form these "deltas" or "deltalike" features (Menard, 1955, 1960). Recent studies of the Monterey Canyon and related fan deposits (Wilde, 1965; Martin, 1964; F. P. Shepard and R. F. Dill, oral communication, 1965) clearly demonstrate the depositional character of the deep-sea fans and their origin by turbidity currents. Shepard and Dill have recently recognized a well-developed meander at the base of Monterey Canyon which had been believed previously to represent two separate drainage channels for turbidity currents. Constructional levees about 25 m high border the channel, and, because of the Coriolis force induced by the earth's rotation, the right-hand levee is the higher of the two (Menard, 1955). The general absence of thick unconsolidated sediments on the shelf and slope, together with the presence of many outcrops of Miocene and older rocks, indicates that the bulk of sediment stripped from the continents in post-Miocene time has been deposited on these fans.

BEDROCK

Knowledge of the bedrock exposures on the continental margin is limited by the relatively small number of dredgings. Most of the dredge samples came from the area west of San Francisco, but a few samples have been recovered from Monterey Canyon (Shepard and Emery, 1941; Uchupi and Emery, 1963) and from the Rodriguez Seamount and Davis Seaknoll (Palmer, 1965) off the Arguello Plateau. Bedrock exposures are especially well known by subbottom acoustical-reflection techniques. One such profile for the Arguello Plateau and upper slope, as reported by Palmer (1965), is shown in figure 8. This section clearly indicates the general thickness of the unconsolidated sediments; it also reveals the attitude of the underlying semiconsolidated deposits of probable Miocene age (Uchupi and Emery, 1963). A similar cross section obtained from the San Francisco region by Curray (1965) shows considerable slumping of probable Miocene deposits (see dredge samples described by Uchupi and Emery, 1964) and several spurs of basement highs considered by Curray to be quartz diorite, because of proximity to known outcrops in the Farallon Islands. The relationship of sea-floor surface irregularities to underlying structure can be seen clearly here (see fig. 4 in Curray, this volume). The acoustical profile should be compared with the appearance of an adjacent bathymetric profile illustrated with a different vertical exaggeration in figure 5, profile 7.

Evidence from the Farallon Islands (Hanna, 1951, 1952; Chesterman, 1952) and adjacent banks demonstrates that Cretaceous granitic ridges paralleling the onshore structural grain form at least part of the basement offshore. Similarly, dredge samples from the lower slopes, especially the pinnacles, knolls, and seamounts (Uchupi and Emery, 1963), suggest that much of the area is underlain by a basement of volcanic origin that may represent offshore equivalents of greenstone units found in the Coast Range. Detailed sampling and chemical analyses will be required to describe adequately the general distribution of rock types and structures and to learn their relationships to onshore features. Curray (1965) suggests, for example, that a basement ridge of granite underlies the outer shelf and upper slope from a point south of Cape Mendocino for a distance of about 550 km, or to about 100 km south of Monterey. In keeping with the known structures onshore, W. P. Irwin suggests (oral communication, 1964) that the evidence available indicates a northwesterly continuation offshore toward the Farallon Islands, of the granite body lying between

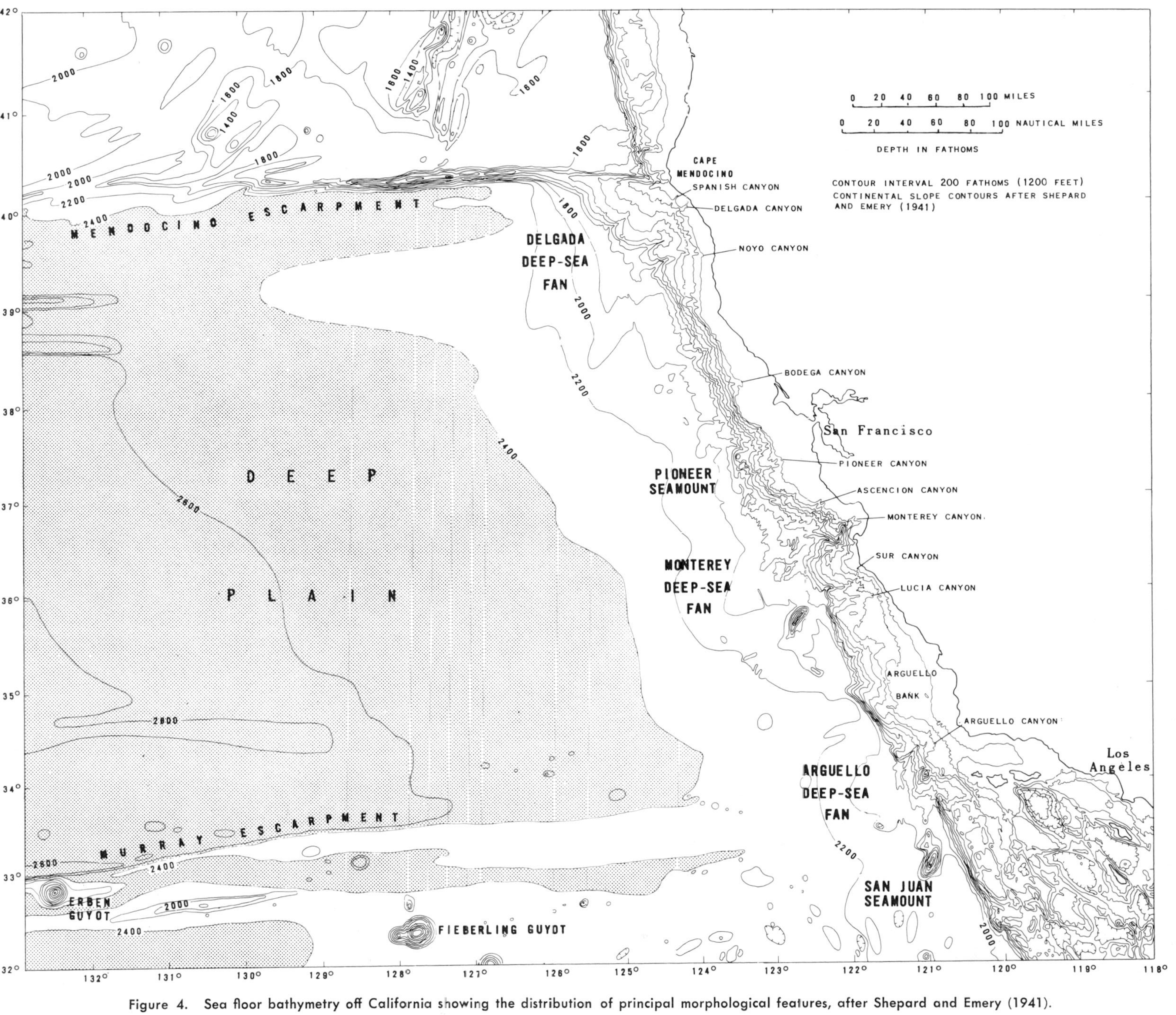

Figure 4. Sea floor bathymetry off California showing the distribution of principal morphological features, after Shepard and Emery (1941).

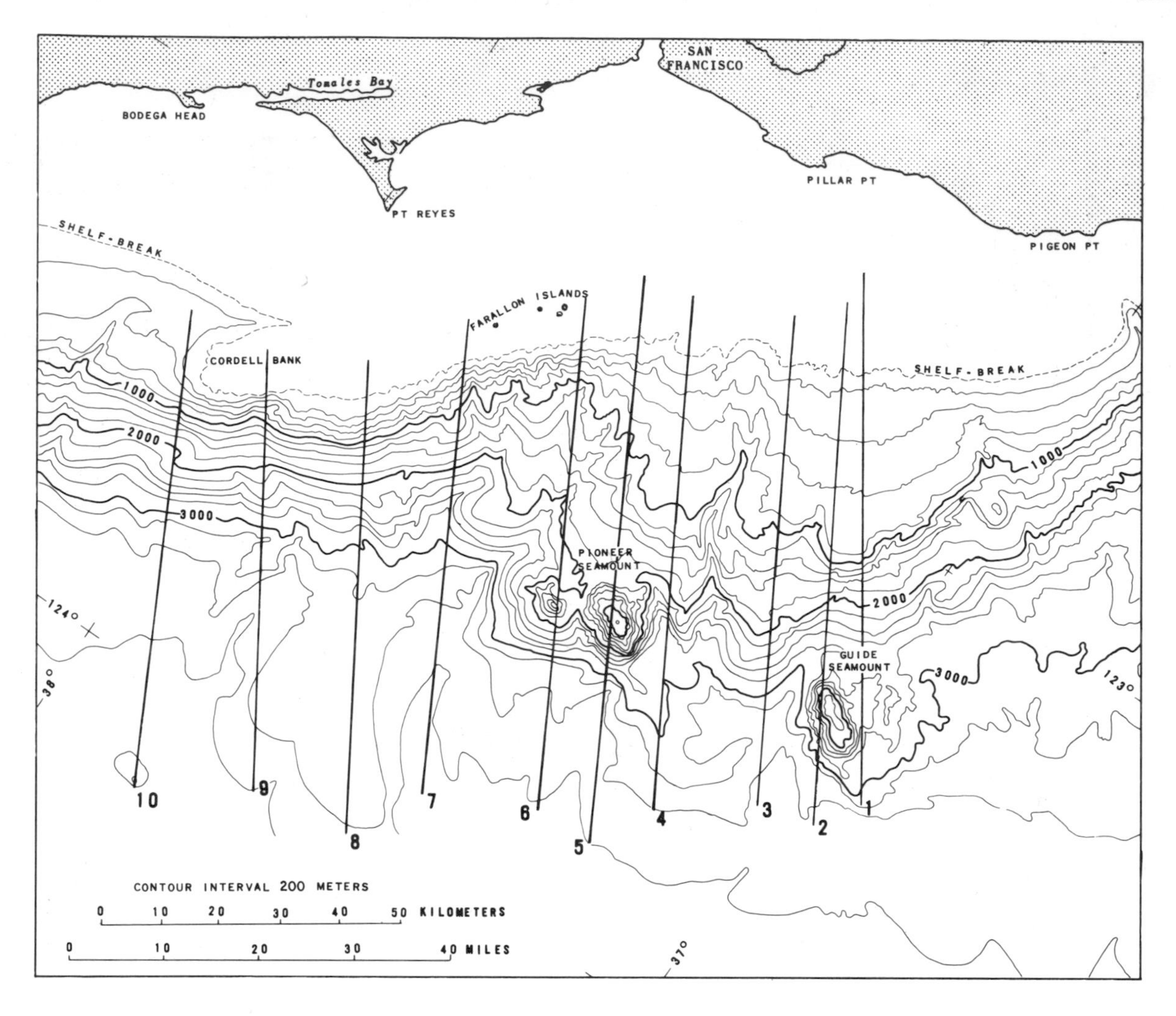

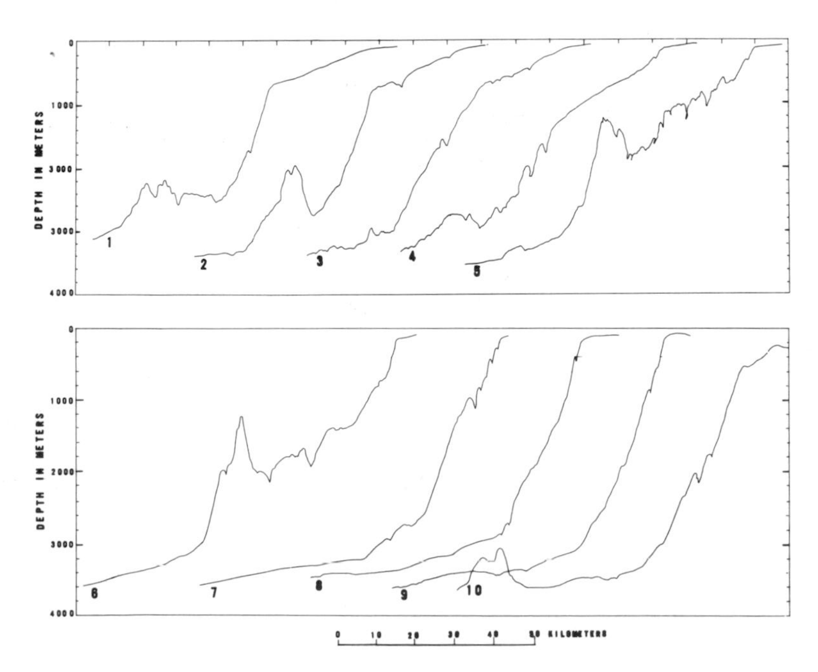

Figure 5. Bottom profiles of the sea floor off San Francisco, California, after Uchupi and Emery (1963).

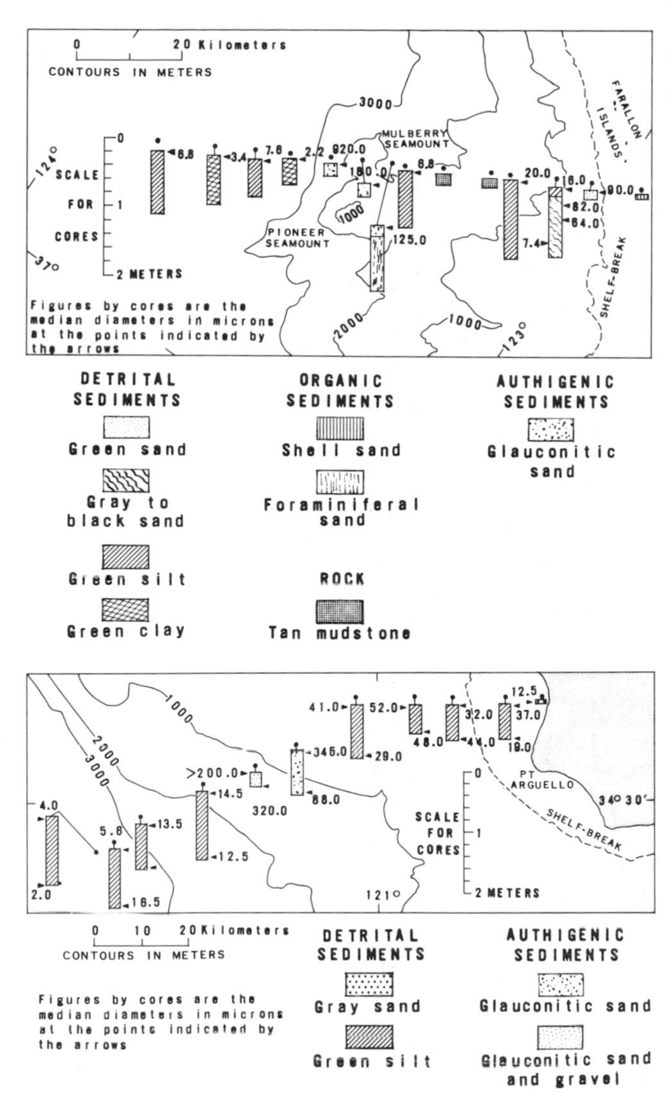

Figure 6. Lithology of surficial deposits off San Francisco (top) and Point Arguello (bottom) as described from cores by Uchupi and Emery (1963).

the Nacimiento and San Andreas faults on the San Francisco Peninsula, in which case no granite would lie near the continental slope south of San Francisco. On shore, granitic units are exposed in the Montara,

Figure 7 (below). Thickness of unconsolidated sediments off Pigeon Point, California, as compiled by Moore and Shumway (1959) from acoustic-reflection profiles.

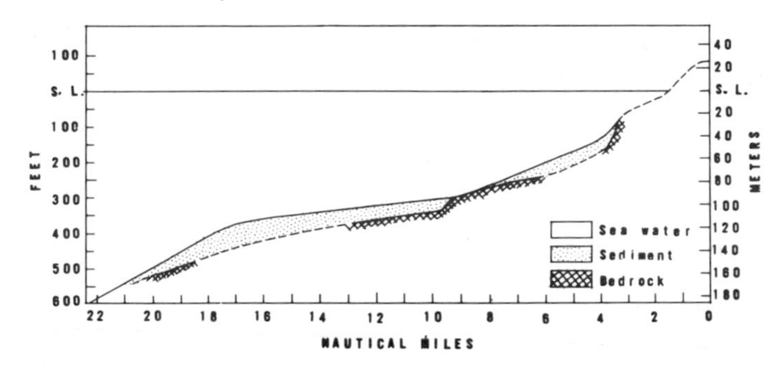

Ben Lomond, Gabilan, and Santa Lucia mountains, all of which lie between the San Andreas and the Nacimiento faults.

REGIONAL GEOPHYSICS

Geophysical data sufficiently detailed to allow a three-dimensional presentation and analysis for most of the area within the continental margin are not yet available. However, some data do provide considerable insight into the geologic structures hidden beneath the ocean in this area. The most complete body of data relating to the geophysics of the margin is based on local measurements of the magnetic field, and the mapping of anomalies in it. The intensive shipboard magnetometer surveys analyzed by Menard and Vacquier (1958), Vacquier, Raff, and Warren (1961), and Mason and Raff (1961) have been summarized by Menard (1964) who related the resulting interpretations to the geology of the eastern Pacific. Figure 9 illustrates the striking north-south pattern of magnetic anomalies associated with the deep-sea floor off the Pacific Coast from central California to Canada. Specific signature characteristics in the magnetic anomalies suggest very large horizontal displacements along the major faults of this area. Menard (1964) then included the sense and amount of lateral displacements in his discussion of the evolution of the crustal flexure of the East Pacific Rise and the subsequent lateral displacement of large east-west crustal units of the sea floor. The sense of motion along the Mendocino, Pioneer, and Murray fracture zone as shown in figure 10 is of particular interest here. It is inconceivable that east-west lateral movements measured in hundreds of kilometers could occur in the crust of the offshore area without disturbing the continents as well. However, it also seems that very little effect of the faults has been identified on the continent except for the seaward displacement of the continental crust south of the Mendocino scarp, where the continental slope has an inferred right-lateral offset of 100 km. Because the inferred movement along the Mendocino fault in its oceanic segment is left lateral, and because other relationships of continental crust tectonics have not been demonstrated, the exact nature of the associations between oceanic and continental segments is unclear.

Neither gravity studies nor seismic investigations in this area have shed much light on the relation between continental crustal movements and oceanic crustal movements. Possibly, an intensive magnetometer survey of the continental shelf and slope would be of help. Local magnetometer surveys around the San Francisco Bay area show only expected correlations with the known magnetic characteristics of the outcrops, according to Andrew Griscom (oral communication, 1965). Measured lateral displacements of continental rocks appear to be restricted to the northwest-southeast motions related to the structural grain of the San Andreas system. Bailey, Irwin, and Jones (1964) have suggested, however, an explanation of the struc-

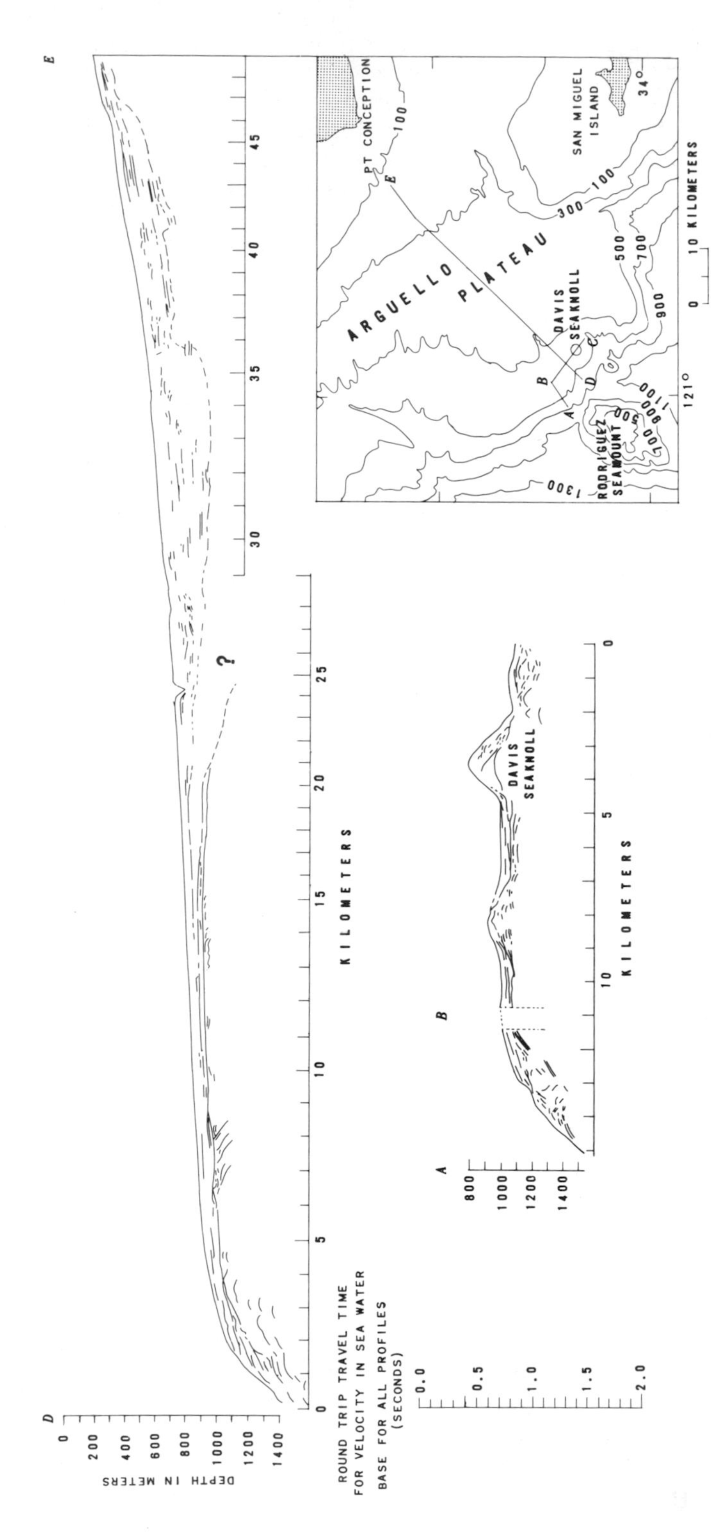

Figure 8. Acoustic-reflection profiles compiled by Palmer (1965) from "ARCER" records across the Arguello Plateau and Davis Seaknoll. Tracing from original records depicts better the stronger acoustical reflectors. Relatively thin, horizontally bedded sediments are in unconformable contact with underlying bedrock. The volcanic Davis Seaknoll is exposed through the thin cover of sediment on the Arguello Plateau. From Palmer (1965).

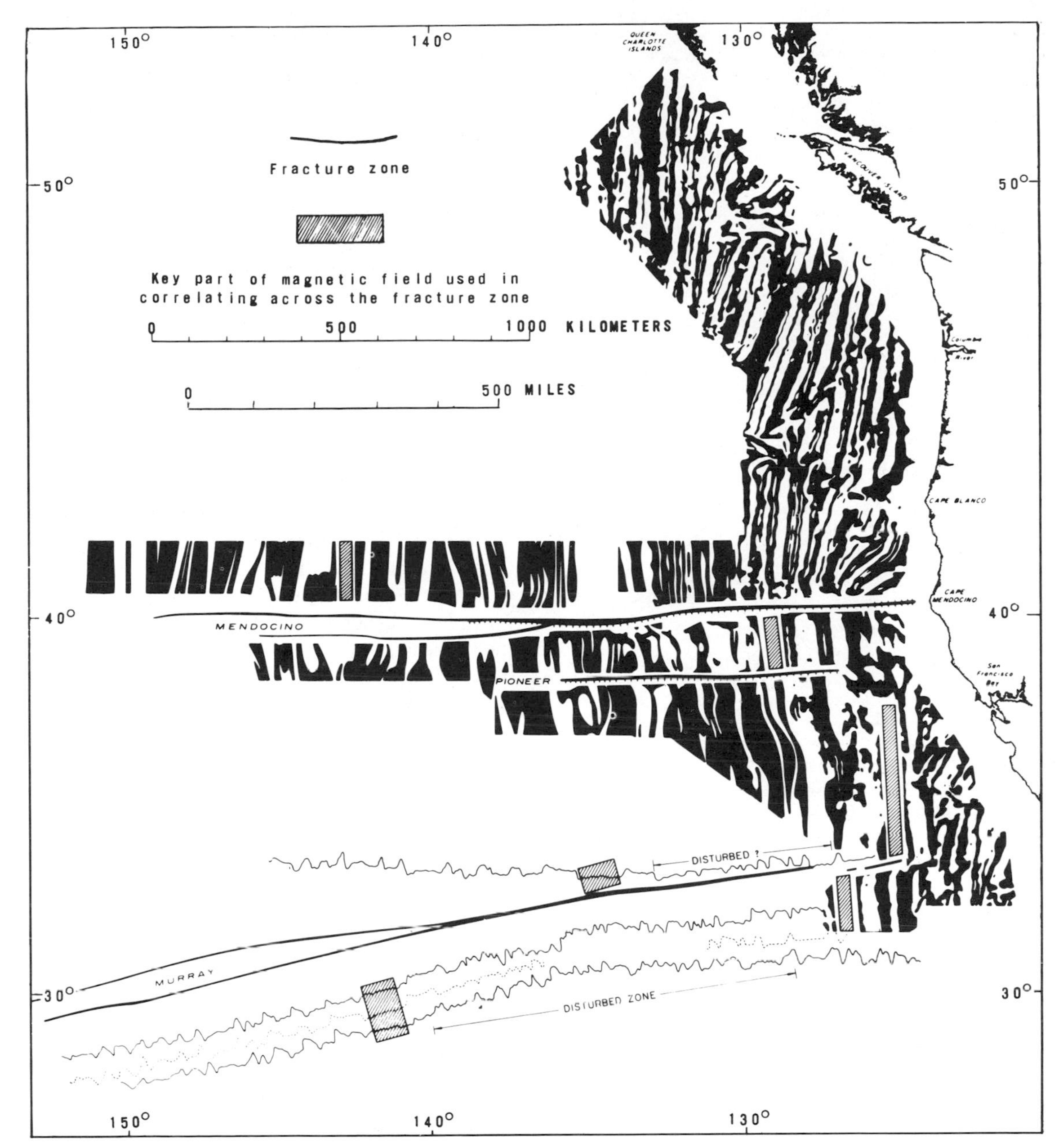

Figure 9. Pattern of magnetic anomalies showing major offsets in the Mendocino, Pioneer, and Murray fracture zones. From Menard (1964); published by permission of McGraw-Hill Book Co.

tural complexity in the northern California Coast Ranges and the Great Valley based on major westward migration of a block of continental-crustal material bounded on the east by an ancestral San Andreas fault. A similar explanation has been used by Rusnak and Fisher (1964) to explain the development of the Gulf of California and the origin of the continental borderland of southern California and Baja California, Mexico. An oblique-motion hypothesis was proposed by King (1959) for the Transverse Ranges which lie between these two areas.

Gravity measurements and seismic refraction studies compiled by Thompson and Talwani (1964a, 1964b) have provided information on the crustal structure of the continental margin (see fig. 4). It is especially noteworthy that the continental shelf east of the Farallon Islands has a mass deficiency similar in magnitude to the anomaly known to be correlated with the great thickness of sedimentary rocks in the Great Valley. This large negative anomaly on the shelf near San Francisco (Orlin, Fanning, Jones, and Garoutte, 1962) also seems to be related to a similar thick section of sediments of low mass, as suggested by the sub-bottom acoustical profile described by Curray (1965, and fig. 4).

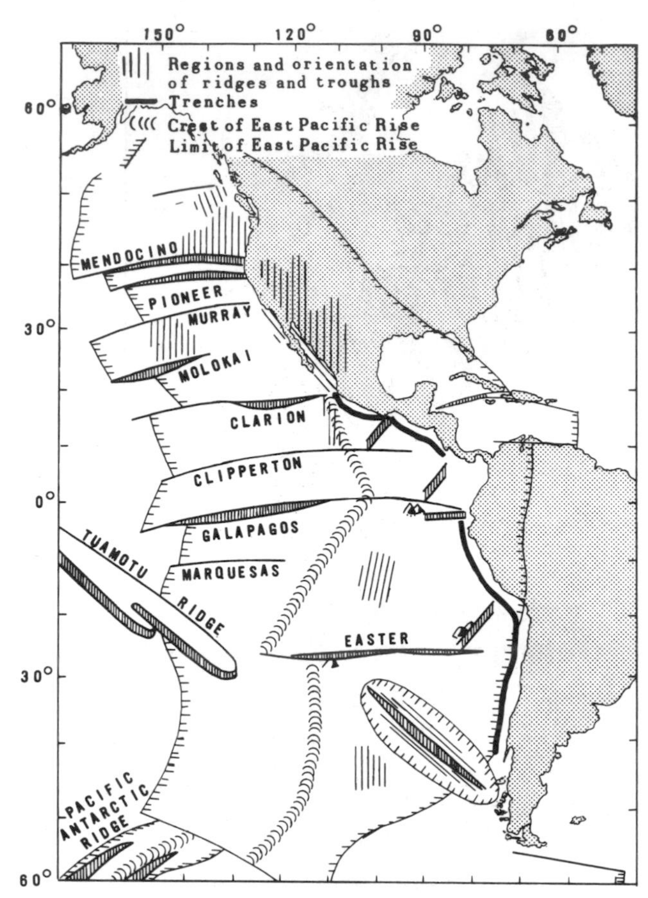

Figure 10. Interpretation of the history of development of the East Pacific Rise and its segmenting along major fracture zones. After Menard (1964); published by permission of McGraw-Hill Book Co.

The anomalies here may be compared with those reported for the Salton trough (Biehler, Kovach, and Allen, 1964) and the north end of the Gulf of California (Harrison and Mathur, 1964); these have been attributed to the crustal thinning that accompanied the westward lateral migration of Baja California following detachment from the mainland of Mexico (Rusnak and Fisher, 1964). The implication is that the similarity in style of the northern and central California continental margin to the Salton trough and the Gulf of California suggests a similar mechanical origin; thus, accounting for the absence of basement reported by Bailey, Irwin and Jones (1964) and strengthening their argument for lateral migration. The question of whether or not the Coast Range units are detached from the western edge of the Sierras must remain open until additional data become available.

The comparison of these two regions further suggests that the San Andreas fault follows the east face of the granitic core that makes up the Gabilan and Santa Lucia Ranges and is similar to the Sierra Juarez-San Pedro Martir-Sal si Puedas escarpment of the Gulf of California (Rusnak and Fisher, 1964). The conclusion of this argument would be to extend the San Andreas Fault seaward along the east face of the basement granite core from the Santa Lucia, Gabilan, Ben Lomond, and Montara mountains on shore past the Farallon Islands and northward to the Mendocino escarpment. One would then have to consider the fault traces drawn by Curray (1965, and this volume) as subsidiary faults of the San Andreas system, similar to those forming the fault pattern observed in the northern Coast Ranges. The question that arises is, if the argument is correct, what are the tectonics involved? The argument demands that two distinct tectonic motions be called upon: (1) westward lateral migration of Coast Range units away from the Sierra Nevada, followed by (2) strike-slip faulting towards the northwest along the San Andreas-Nacimiento-Hayward group, due to a northerly component of motion acting on the competent granitic core.

Two events have been postulated to explain the development of the Gulf of California by Rusnak and Fisher (1964). A double-event tectonic mechanism seems to satisfy equally well the suggestions made by Bailey, Irwin and Jones (1964), King (1959), and Benioff (1962) for the inferred tectonic motions derived from geologic and seismic analyses.

CONCLUSION

Although our knowledge of the northern and central California continental margin is still very fragmentary, the data give a broadly generalized picture of the geology and point to several working hypotheses that might explain the geological history of this complex area. Many questions have been raised by students of the continental margin; few have been answered. The data obtained from offshore studies, however, cannot be disregarded by those working on the mainland. The most intensive analyses of the puzzling geological associations of the central and northern California region, including much that is applicable to the continental margin, have been summarized recently by Bailey, Irwin, and Jones (1964).

REFERENCES

Bailey, E. H., Irwin, W. P., and Jones, D. L., 1964, Franciscan and related rocks, and their significance in the geology of western California: California Div. Mines and Geology Bull. 183, 177 p.

Benioff, Hugo, 1962, Movements on major transcurrent faults, *in* Runcorn, S. K., ed., Continental drift: New York, Academic Press, p. 103–134.

Biehler, Shawn, Kovach, R. L., and Allen, C. R., 1964, Geophysical framework of northern end of Gulf of California structural province, *in* Marine geology of the Gulf of California: Am. Assoc. Petroleum Geologists Mem. 3, p. 126–143.

Chesterman, C. W., 1952, Descriptive petrography of rocks dredged off the coast of central California: California Acad. Sci. Proc., 4th ser., v. 27, no. 10, p. 359–374.

Curray, J. R., 1965, Structure of the continental margin off central California: New York Acad. Sci. Trans., ser. 2, v. 27, p. 794–801.

Hanna, G. D., 1951, Geology of the Farallon Islands: California Div. Mines Bull., v. 154, p. 301–310.

—— 1952, Geology of the continental slope off central California: California Acad. Sci. Proc., 4th ser., v. 27, no. 9, p. 325–358.

Harrison, J. C., and Mathur, S. P., 1964, Gravity anomalies in Gulf of California, *in* Marine geology of the Gulf of California: Am. Assoc. Petroleum Geologists Mem. 3, p. 76–89.

Irwin, W. P., 1960, Geologic reconnaissance of the northern Coast Ranges and Klamath Mountains, California, with a summary of the mineral resources: California Div. Mines Bull., v. 179, 80 p.

King, P. B., 1959, The evolution of North America: Princeton, N. J., Princeton Univ. Press, 190 p.

Martin, B. D., 1964, Marine geology of Monterey Submarine Canyon: Southern California Univ., Los Angeles, Ph.D. thesis.

Mason, R. G., and Raff, A. D., 1961, Magnetic survey off the west coast of North America, 32° N. latitude to 42° N. latitude: Geol. Soc. America Bull., v. 72, no. 8, p. 1259–1265.

Menard, H. W., Jr., 1955, Deformation of the northeastern Pacific basin and the west coast of North America: Geol. Soc. America Bull., v. 66, no. 9, p. 1149–1198.

—— 1960, Possible pre-Pleistocene deep-sea fans off central California: Geol. Soc. America Bull., v. 71, no. 8, p. 1271–1278.

—— 1964, Marine geology of the Pacific: New York, McGraw-Hill Book Co., 271 p.

Menard, H. W., Jr., and Vacquier, Victor, 1958, Magnetic survey of part of the deep sea floor off the coast of California: [U.S.] Office Naval Research, Research Rev., June, p. 1–5.

Moore, D. G., 1960, Acoustic-reflection studies of the continental shelf and slope off southern California: Geol. Soc. America Bull., v. 71, no. 8, p. 1121–1136.

Moore, D. G., and Shumway, George, 1959, Sediment thickness and physical properties, Pigeon Point shelf, California: Jour. Geophys. Research, v. 64, no. 3, p. 367–374.

Orlin, H., Fanning, K. F., Jones, R. B., and Garoutte, S. K., 1962, Sea gravity phase oceanographic equipment evaluation range, San Francisco, California: U.S. Coast and Geodetic Survey-U.S. Navy Oceanog. Office, 24 p.

Palmer, H. D., 1965, Geologic significance of Davis Seaknoll, Arguello Plateau, California: Geol. Soc. America Bull., v. 76, no. 3, p. 379–384.

Rusnak, G. A., and Fisher, R. L., 1964, Structural history and evolution of Gulf of California, *in* Marine geology of the Gulf of California: Am. Assoc. Petroleum Geologists Mem. 3, p. 144–156.

Shepard, F. P., and Emery, K. O., 1941, Submarine topography off the California coast—canyons and tectonic interpretations: Geol. Soc. America Spec. Paper 31, 171 p.

Taliaferro, N. L., 1943, Franciscan-Knoxville problem: Am. Assoc. Petroleum Geologists Bull., v. 27, no. 2, p. 109–219.

Thompson, G. A., and Talwani, Manik, 1964a, Crustal structure from Pacific basin to central Nevada: Jour. Geophys. Research, v. 69, no. 22, p. 4813–4837.

—— 1964b, Geology of the crust and mantle, western United States: Science, v. 146, no. 3651, p. 1539–1549.

Uchupi, Elazar, and Emery, K. O., 1963, The continental slope between San Francisco, California, and Cedros Island, Mexico: Deep-Sea Research, v. 10, no. 4, p. 397–447.

Vacquier, Victor, Raff, A. D., and Warren, R. E., 1961, Horizontal displacements in the floor of the northeastern Pacific Ocean: Geol. Soc. America Bull., v. 72, no. 8, p. 1251–1258.

Wilde, Pat, 1965, Recent sediments of the Monterey Deep-Sea Fan: Harvard Univ., Cambridge, Mass., Ph.D. thesis, 156 p.; also in California Univ. Hydraulic Eng. Lab., Tech. Rept. HEL-2-13, 153 p.

The South Farallone Island. From J. M. Hutchings, *Scenes of wonder and curiosity in California*, 1865.

GEOLOGIC STRUCTURE ON THE CONTINENTAL MARGIN, FROM SUBBOTTOM PROFILES, NORTHERN AND CENTRAL CALIFORNIA

By Joseph R. Curray
Scripps Institution of Oceanography, La Jolla, California

The region offshore from northern and central California is a common type of continental margin, although it is atypical for the Pacific Ocean. Most of the margin of the Pacific Ocean basin is of the marginal depression or trench type, with narrow shelves and coastal plains, steep continental slopes, and a marginal depression or trench at the base of the slope. The Pacific margin off much of North America, on the other hand, is morphologically more similar to the margins of the Atlantic and Indian Oceans, with broad to intermediate width shelves, a typical continental slope, and a rise or series of deep-sea fans at the base of the slope. The area of investigation of this study is shown by submarine contours on figure 1, and by a physiographic diagram in figure 2. If a bordering oceanic depression or trench ever lay at the base of the slope in this area, it has been filled and buried beneath the Delgada and Monterey Fans, which together constitute the continental rise in this vicinity.

This article presents incomplete results of a study in progress on this region,[1] summarized from Curray (1965) and Curray and Nason (in press). It is based on continuous acoustic reflection profiling along the survey lines shown in figure 1, supplemented by bathymetry and other work of the Scripps Institution with modified Rayflex "Arcer" (or sparker-type) equipment, with input energy to the spark source of 20,000 joules, pulsing interval of 2 or 4 seconds, and bandpass filtering of the returning energy between 73 and 120 cycles per second.

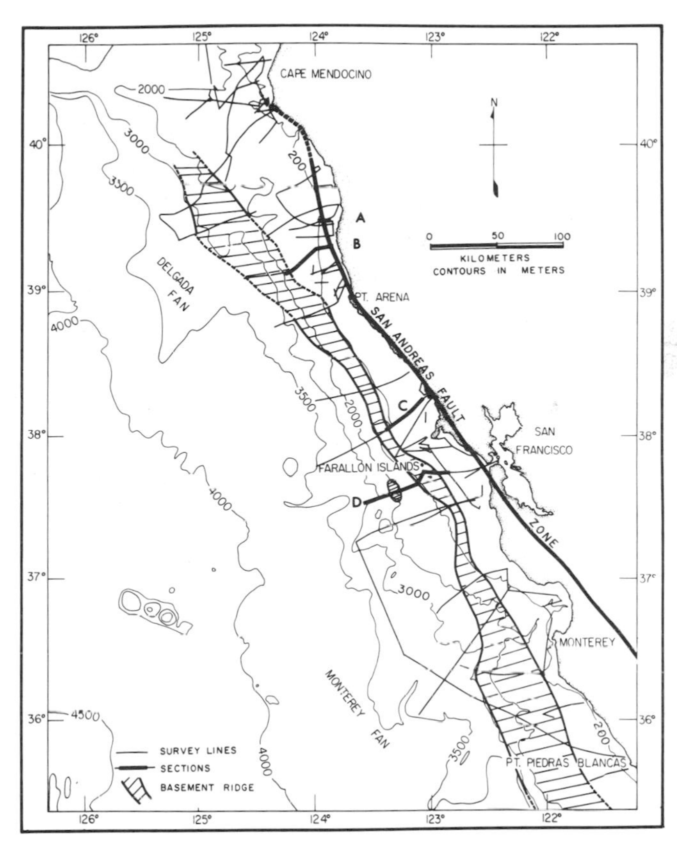

Figure 1. Chart of the area of investigation, showing reflection profile lines, locations of sections A through D, and some geological features. The continental shelf is approximately from the shoreline to 200 m, the continental slope is from 200 to 3,000 m, and the continental rise (Delgado and Monterey Fans) is below about 3,000 m.

SHALLOW STRUCTURE OF THE CONTINENTAL MARGIN

Gross structural features of the upper, predominantly sedimentary, portion of the continental margin have been delineated by the continuous acoustic reflection profiles shown in figure 1. Some examples of these profiles are included as figures 3, 4, 5, and 6, and others have been discussed by Curray (1965, figs. 2, 3, and 4). These figures include photographs and line tracings of major reflectors from the original records. No allowance has been made for variation in ship's speed, nor has any allowance been made for variation in the speed of sound with depth in the sediment and rock column. Thus, the horizontal scales are an average for each section, and the vertical scales show round trip travel time of the sound energy and depth at the velocity of sound in sea water (approximately 1500 m/sec). Actual sound velocities in the sediment and rock are unknown, but a usable approximation lending itself to easy calculation is 2 km/sec. Thus 1 second of penetration beneath the sea floor would represent about 1 km of section.

[1] Contribution from the Scripps Institution of Oceanography, University of California, La Jolla, California. Financial support was furnished by the National Science Foundation and the Office of Naval Research. The following have contributed greatly to this study by assisting in collecting and interpreting the reflection records: D. G. Moore, S. M. Smith, P. J. Crampton, R. D. Nason, C. C. Daetwyler, and many others.

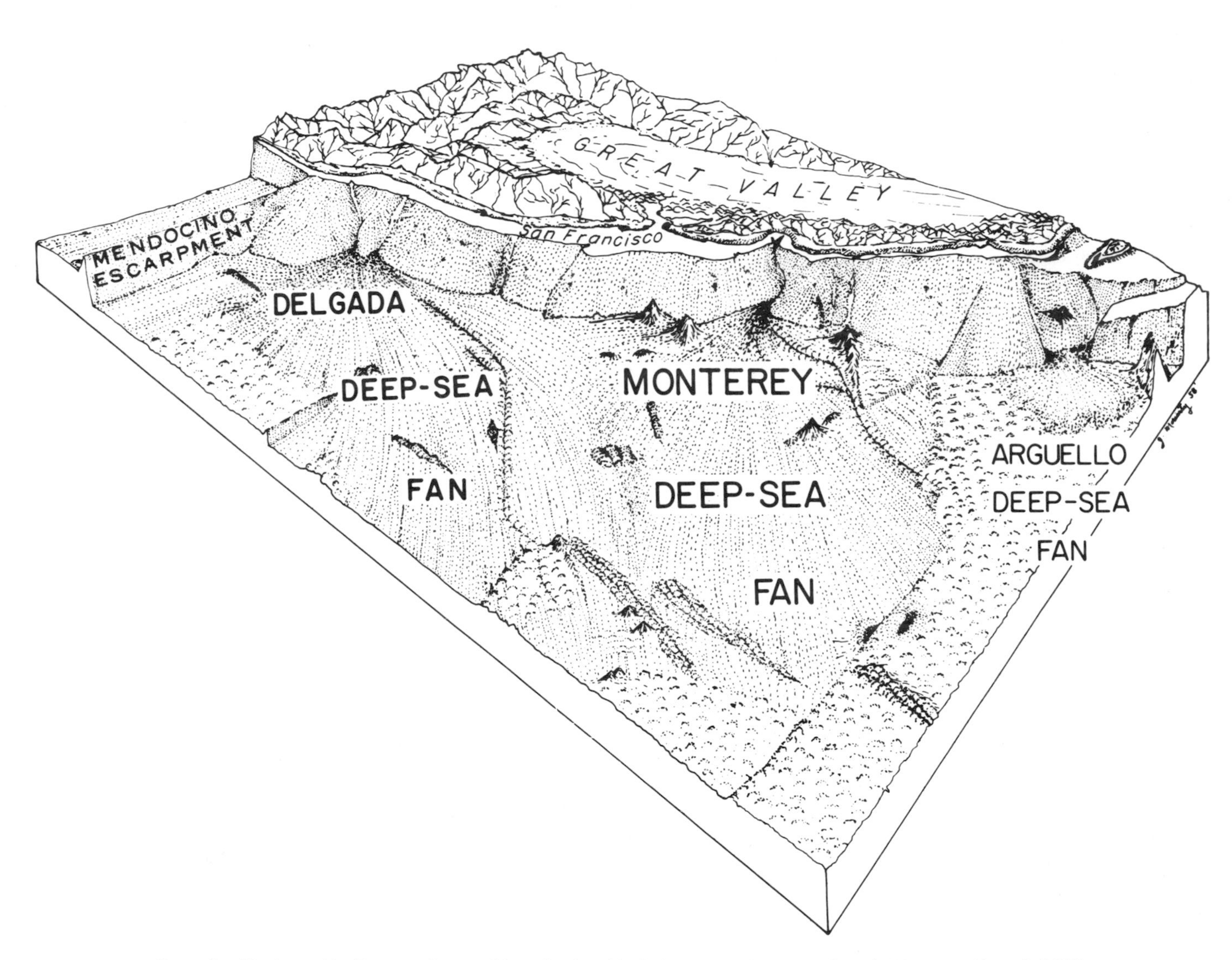

Figure 2. Physiographic diagram of area of investigation. Vertical exaggeration approximately 20x. From Menard (1960).

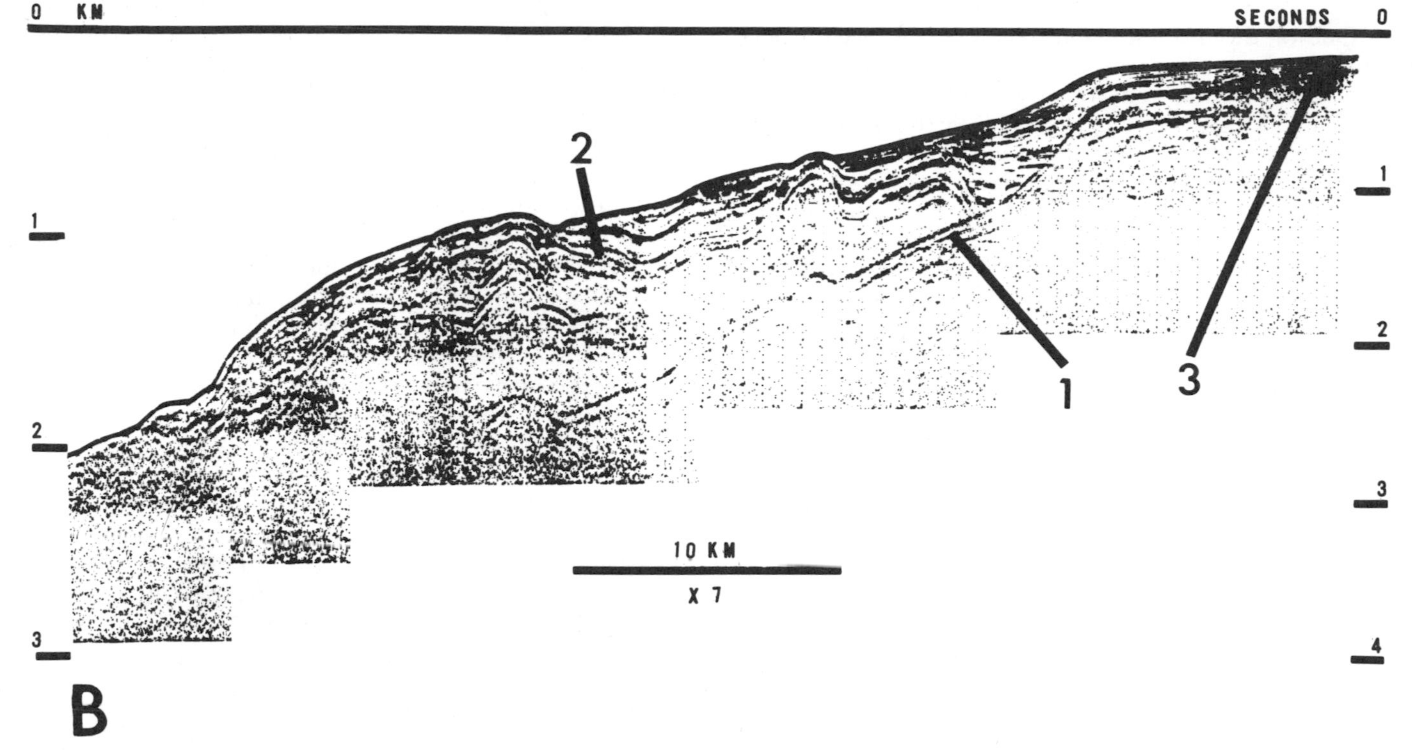

Figure 3. Acoustic reflection profile along line B of figure 1. Scale on right is round trip travel time, scale on left is approximate water depth at 1500 m/sec sound velocity. Note the following: (1) multiple of sea floor and sub-surface reflecting horizons, (2) reflecting horizons beneath the sea floor, with folds, unconformities, and truncation at the sea floor, but no evidence of major faults, (3) disturbed zone on the inner shelf probably representing the San Andreas fault zone.

Line B (fig. 3) extends across the shelf and down the slope seaward from the town of Mendocino, about 10 miles south of Fort Bragg. The slope here is underlain by a thick section of gently folded sedimentary rock, presumably Tertiary in age. Cretaceous (Franciscan) rock crops out along the coast, and some of the adjacent lines show the surface of this Cretaceous section dipping seaward beneath the shelf until it is lost in the disturbed zone of the seaward extension of the San Andreas fault. Other profiles in this area show a deeply submerged ridge of basement rock under the lower slope below a water depth of about 2,000 m.

Line D (fig. 4) is a tracing of a record off San Francisco that extends across the outer shelf, between the Farallon Islands, and down to the base of the slope. This record is replotted without vertical exaggeration in the lower part of this figure. Of special interest is the rather thick fill of sediment underlying the shelf and the thick fill underlying the continental rise at the base of the slope at a water depth of about 3,000 m. Most of the slope is underlain by a ridge of basement rock, known here to be the Cretaceous quartz diorite that crops out on the Farallon Islands and the Cordell Bank just to the north (Hanna, 1951, 1952; Chesterman, 1952; and Curtis, and others, 1958). This same ridge of basement rock can be observed under the outer shelf or slope in all but a few of the lines, and is presumed by correlation to be more or less continuous (fig. 1). The nature of its upper surface appears to be the same in all these records, but the possibility nevertheless exists that the age and lithology are not the same all the way along.

The depth below sea level to the top of this ridge varies from north to south. It lies about 2,000 m below sea level at the north, probably is even deeper seaward of the section shown in line B (fig. 3), is 250 m below sea level off Point Arena, and is at the sea floor or above sea level in the Farallon Islands. Farther south it is at about 500 m depth in Monterey Canyon, where granitic rock has been dredged (Shepard and Emery, 1941), and at about 1,000 m off Point Piedras Blancas. The best developments of the continental rise, Delgada and Monterey Fans, lie adjacent to the more deeply buried parts of the ridge. Each of these lobes is identified with a major canyon system, which is presumably the source of the bulk of the sediments of the fans (Menard, 1960). These have developed where the ridge is deepest and sediments may pass most easily over its top. Loading due to increased deposition may have caused subsidence and further deepened the ridge.

Another notable feature seen on figure 4 is the section of contorted sedimentary rocks underlying the slope. Miocene marine sediment has been dredged from this slope by Hanna (1952) and Uchupi and Emery (1963), so this slumped contorted mass is known to consist, at least in part, of Miocene rocks. It has presumably slumped part way down the slope because of oversteepening and instability.

FAULTS

One of the interesting problems in this region pertains to the position of the seaward extension of the San Andreas fault zone from where it leaves the coast at Point Arena. During the 1906 earthquake, surface rupture occurred along the fault zone from east of Monterey to Point Arena. Displacement also occurred along a fault at Shelter Cove, south of Cape Mendocino (about 40° N., fig. 1), and on this basis Lawson and others (1908) believed the fault zone curved to follow near the coastline from Point Arena to Shelter Cove. Shepard and Emery (1941) and Shepard (1957) also believed the fault zone followed the coast, although Tocher (1956) and Benioff (1962) thought on the basis of earthquake epicenters that the fault ran straight across the shelf, down the slope, and across the Gorda Escarpment off Cape Mendocino. Some of the evidence presented by Curray and Nason (in press) to prove that the fault zone curves as shown in figure 1 is reviewed here.

If the fault zone continued straight from Point Arena, it would cross the upper slope in line B, shown in figure 3, approximately between points 1 and 2. Two folds occur here, with possible secondary faults on their flanks, but the overlying younger sediments show no displacement or disturbance. Even though the dominant displacement on the San Andreas fault is horizontal, the fault should be visible in this and the other survey lines on the slope. This slope, and the others in this region, are remarkably devoid of faults of any kind in contrast to the shelf. In the same figure, a disturbed zone on the inner shelf is pointed out by point 3.

Figure 5 from a traverse along line A, shows a section on the shelf offshore from Fort Bragg. Note the zone of disturbed sediments and the seaward-facing escarpment at 3. This zone lines up with a similar disturbed zone in each successive survey line made of this shelf, and the escarpment is aligned with the escarpments of the other tracings. In some cases they face seaward as here, in others they face landward. This zone on the shelf is believed to be the San Andreas fault zone. It is headed toward the vicinity of Shelter Cove in the northernmost survey line that crosses it (about 39°50′ N.). North of Shelter Cove it apparently skims the coastline, cuts off the head of Delgada Canyon, and runs into Mattole Canyon at Punta Gorda, south of Cape Mendocino (40° 15′ N.). Immediately north of line A, in Noyo Canyon it causes a right-angle bend which appears to result from right-lateral displacement.

Faults appear to occur elsewhere on the shelf, but are especially well developed between Monterey and south of Point Arena. The slope, however, is here

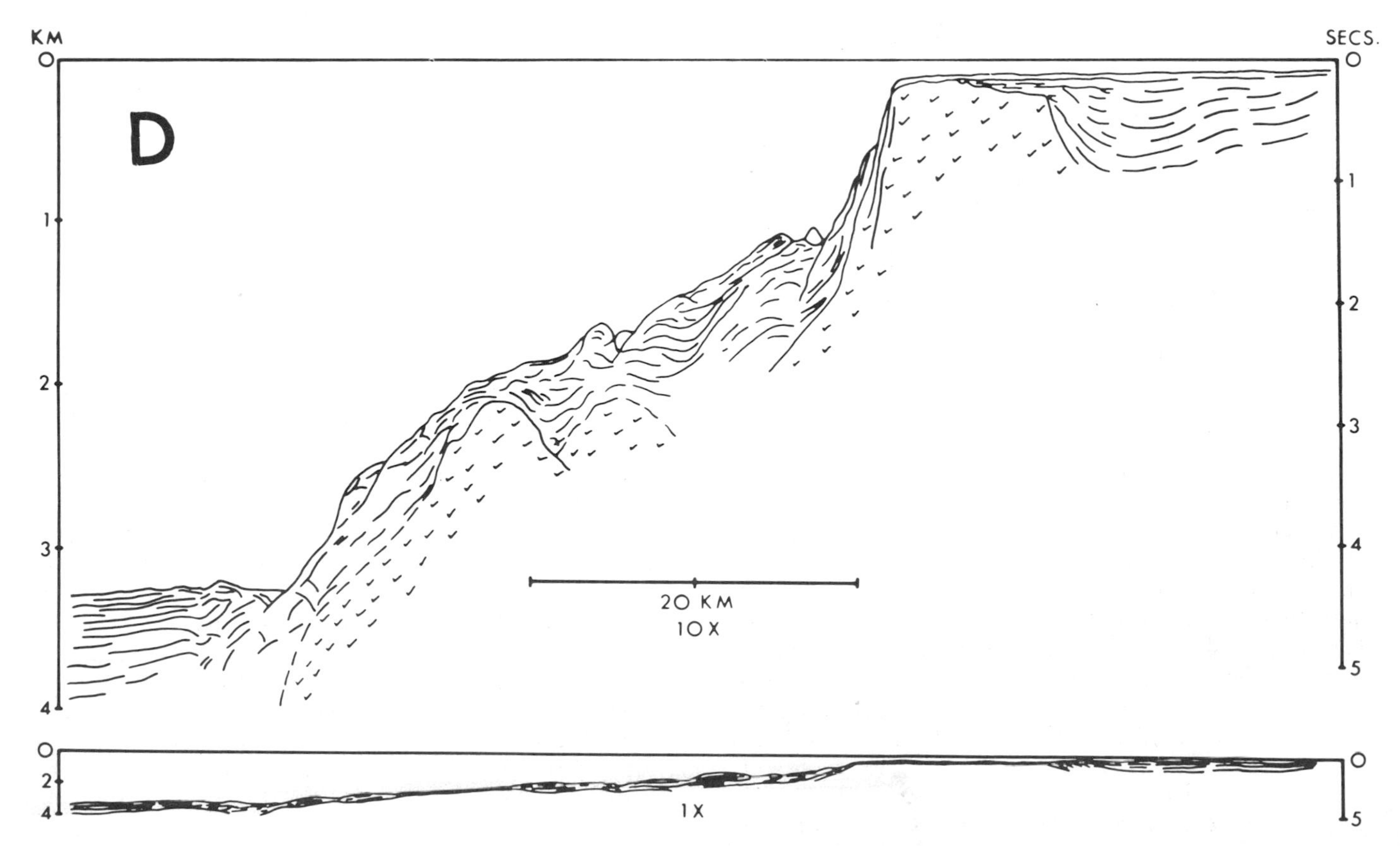

Figure 4. Line drawing of acoustic reflection record along line D of figure 1, passing between Farallon Islands on shelf edge. Upper section has vertical exaggeration 10:1; lower section is natural scale. Note locations of granitic rock (Cretaceous quartz diorite), sediment fill underlying continental shelf, sediment fill at base of slope underlying continental rise, and contorted nature of sedimentary rock (at least in part Miocene) overlying and slumping down on granitic rock on the slope.

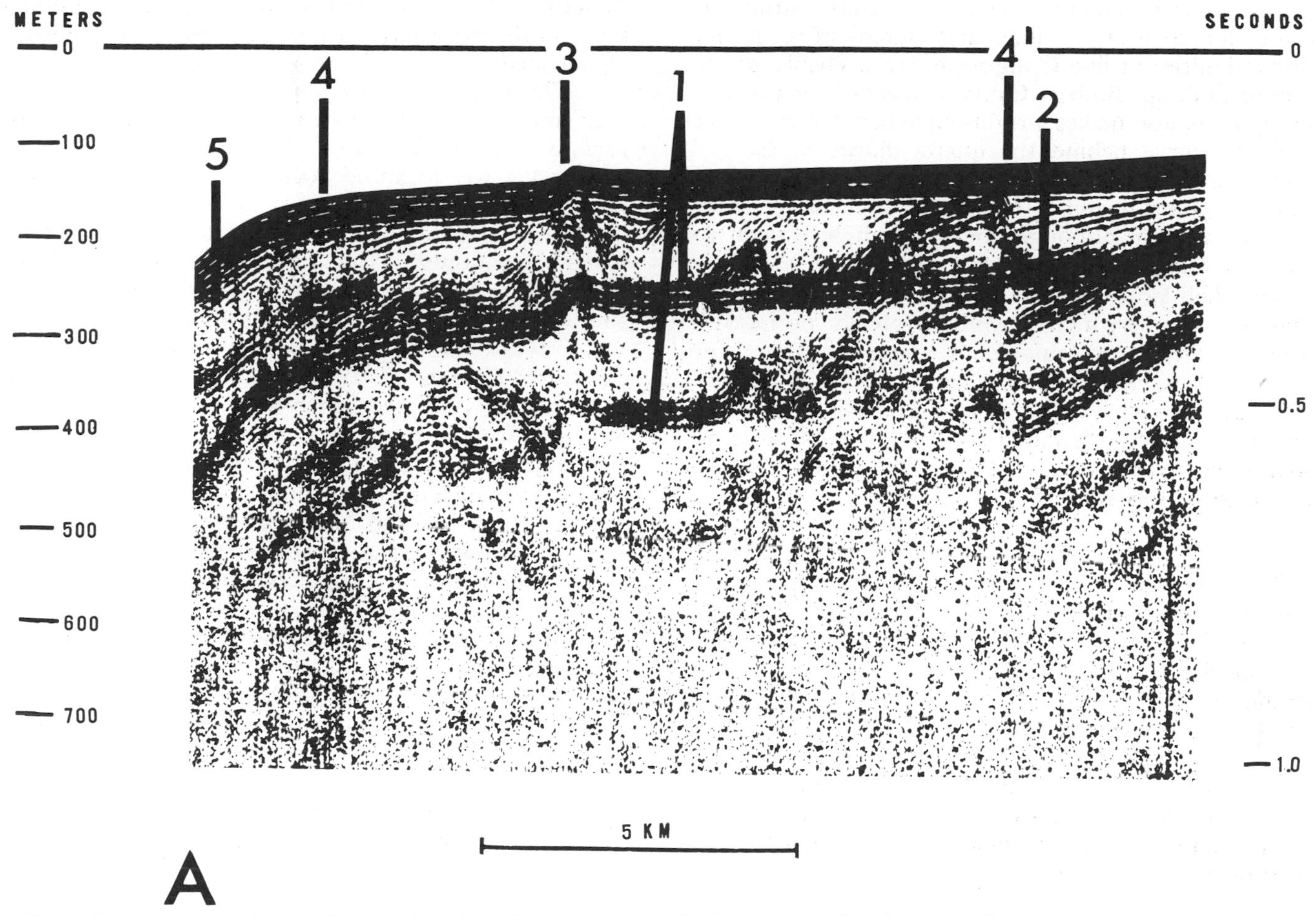

Figure 5. Acoustic reflection profile along line A on figure 1, showing disturbed region of San Andreas fault zone on the continental shelf. Note the following: (1) multiples of sea floor and sub-bottom reflectors, (2) probable top of Cretaceous, (3) 18 m. (60 feet) west-facing escarpment trending along fault zone, (4) to (4') disturbed contorted fault zone, and (5) undisturbed seaward dips, probably Tertiary, which continue on down the slope from here as in figure 3. Vertical exaggeration 15x.

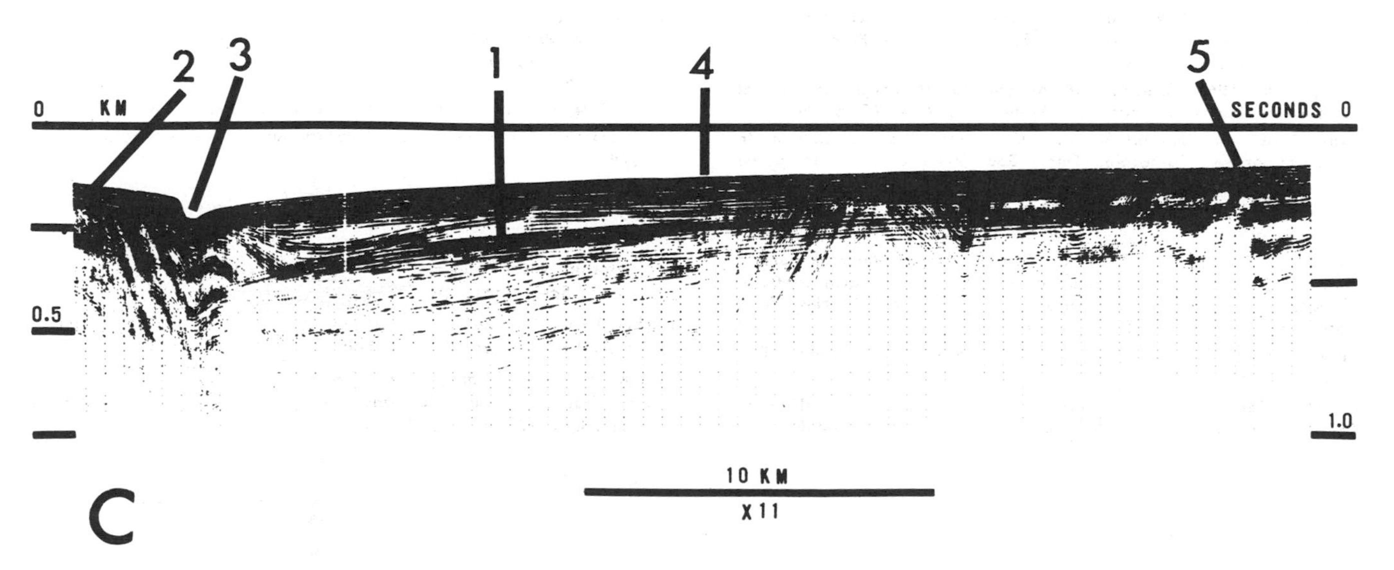

Figure 6. Acoustic reflection profile along line C on figure 1, showing the continental shelf off Bodega Bay. Note the following: (1) multiple of sea floor, (2) Cretaceous quartz diorite of Cordell Bank, (3) Bodega Canyon running along the contact between the quartz diorite and the sedimentary fill, presumed to be Pleistocene and Pliocene, (4) abrupt discontinuity, probably a fault of sedimentary fill against folded sediment section, probably partly Miocene as on Point Reyes, (5) probable fault contact against quartz diorite of Bodega Head.

again rather remarkably devoid of faults except for those due to gravity slides and slumps. The abrupt discontinuities in line C, figure 6, are probably partly due to faulting. Bodega Canyon, which is at point 3, on figure 6, also makes a right-angle bend on the outer shelf, to curve behind the quartz diorite of Cordell Bank shown at point 2. This discontinuity, as well as those at points 4 and 5, appears to be at least partly due to faulting, although they all can be shown to pass out into folds toward the south.

The shelf north of the point of Monterey is thoroughly cut up by faults, which probably tie in with some of the major fault zones mapped on land, for example, the Palo Colorado, Sur Thrust, Tularcitos, Nacimiento, etc. (Jennings and Strand, 1959). The pattern of faulting is much too complex, however, to suggest correlations on the basis of the reconnaissance coverage of this survey.

DISCUSSION AND CONCLUSIONS

This reconnaissance study has been based mainly on continuous acoustic reflection profiles, supplemented by consideration of the bathymetry and a few samples of rock dredged from the sea floor. No samples from drilling beneath the sea floor are available to confirm or deny the interpretations based on the reflection profiles; therefore, the conclusions are rather tenuous. The need for subsurface samples by drilling is obvious, and the possibilities of extrapolation of land geology by combined use of drilling samples and reflection records are tremendous.

Despite these limitations, however, some conclusions on the gross structure and details of the geology are justified:

1. The gross structure underlying the continental shelf and slope is dominated by a ridge of basement rock, which is at least partly Cretaceous granitic rock. This ridge has localized sediment deposition during the Tertiary, forming two thicker accumulations—one underlying the shelf and upper slope and the other under the continental rise at the base of the slope. The latter consists of two main lobes or fans, the Delgado and Monterey Fans, adjacent to the deeper and lower parts of the ridge. This is basically the same as the structure that lies off eastern United States north of Cape Hatteras (Drake and others, 1959), although it is not as well developed.

2. The Tertiary and Quaternary sediments underlying the steeper portions of the slope, generally on the seaward flank of the basement ridge, have locally slumped forming great slide masses as much as a kilometer thick and many kilometers in lateral dimension.

3. The San Andreas fault zone curves eastward from Point Arena to follow the shelf to the vicinity of Shelter Cove. From there it is presumed to continue close to the shoreline, which is therefore a fault line scarp, to Punta Gorda where it runs down Mattole Canyon.

4. Many other faults lie on the shelf with probable connections to faults mapped on land, but in the rocks on the continental slope relatively few faults have been observed.

REFERENCES

Benioff, Hugo, 1962, Movements on major transcurrent faults, *in* Runcorn, S. K., ed., Continental drift: New York, Academic Press, Internat. Geophys. Ser., v. 3, p. 103–134.

Chesterman, C. W., 1952, Descriptive petrography of rocks dredged off the coast of central California: California Acad. Sci. Proc., 4th ser., v. 27, no. 10, p. 359–374.

Curray, J. R., 1965, Structure of the continental margin off central California: New York Acad. Sci. Trans., ser. 2, v. 27, p. 794–801.

Curray, J. R., and Nason, R. D., 196__, San Andreas fault north of Point Arena, California: Geol. Soc. America Bull. (In press)

Curtis, G. H., Evernden, J. F., and Lipson, J. I., 1958, Age determination of some granitic rocks in California by the potassium-argon method: California Div. Mines Spec. Rept. 54, 16 p.

Drake, C. L., Ewing, M., and Sutton, G. H., 1959, Continental margins and geosynclines—the east coast of North America north of Cape Hatteras, *in* Physics and chemistry of the earth, Vol. 3: New York, Pergamon Press, p. 110–198.

Hanna, G. D., 1951, Geology of the Farallon Islands: California Div. Mines Bull. 154, p. 301–310.

—— 1952, Geology of the continental slope off central California: California Acad. Sci. Proc., 4th ser., v. 7, no. 9, p. 325–358.

Jennings, C. W., and Strand, R. G., 1959, Geologic map of California, Olaf P. Jenkins edition, Santa Cruz sheet: California Div. Mines, scale 1:250,000.

Lawson, A. C., and others, 1908, The California earthquake of April 13, 1906, Report of the State Earthquake Investigation Commission: Carnegie Inst., Washington, Pub. 87, v. 1, pt. 1, 254 p.; pt. 2, p. 255–451.

Menard, H. W., Jr., 1960, Possible pre-Pleistocene deep-sea fans off central California: Geol. Soc. America Bull., v. 71, no. 8, p. 1271–1278.

Shepard, F. P., 1957, Northward continuation of the San Andreas Fault: Seismol. Soc. America Bull., v. 47, no. 3, p. 263–266.

Shepard, F. P., and Emery, K. O., 1941, Submarine topography off the California coast—canyons and tectonic interpretation: Geol. Soc. America Spec. Paper 31, 171 p.

Tocher, Don, 1956, Earthquakes off the north Pacific Coast of the United States: Seismol. Soc. America Bull., v. 46, no. 3, p. 165–173.

Uchupi, Elazar, and Emery, K. O., 1963, The continental slope between San Francisco, California, and Cedros Island, Mexico: Deep-Sea Research, v. 10, no. 4, p. 397–447.

ECONOMIC DEPOSITS OF THE CALIFORNIA OFFSHORE AREA

By Thomas A. Wilson and John L. Mero
Ocean Resources, Inc., La Jolla, California

During recent years marine sediments have attracted ever increasing attention, because certain types that contain appreciable amounts of valuable metals and minerals could become commercial sources of industrial raw materials in the near future. To best discuss the economic aspects of the mineral deposits that lie on the sea floor off California, it is preferable to divide the ocean bordering the State into three general geographic regions: the beach and nearshore area, the continental shelf and slope, and the deep-sea floor. Mineral resources in all of these regions are considerable and are virtually untapped.

The beach and nearshore areas of the California coast are favorable zones for the occurrence of black sand and precious metal placers. The continental shelf and slope are known to contain authigenic materials of commercial interest such as glauconite and phosphorite, as well as sizeable reserves of petroleum and natural gas. The deep-sea floor contains extensive deposits of manganese and other metals in the form of nodules. Of all of these potential mineral resources available from the oceanic area off California only one, petroleum, is being recovered on a large-scale basis today.

BEACH AND NEARSHORE PLACER DEPOSITS

The world contains many commercial beach placers that have been mined for their heavy mineral content for generations. While the average concentration of heavy minerals in marine placer deposits is usually low, the combination of modern dredging techniques and low-cost benefication has greatly expanded the amount and variety of occurrences that can be considered economic resources. Heavy mineral deposits found on present beaches are part of the marine environment because they lie within the influence of the ocean and are continually reworked and enriched by surf action. In addition, many modern beach deposits represent only the small land-exposed border of a large mineral-bearing zone that extends seaward several miles.

The principal deposits along the ocean beach, and in submerged beaches, are a result of the natural concentration of minerals in sands that have been carried to the ocean by streams or that have resulted from the cutting back of sedimentary bluffs by waves. The winnowing action of the surf forms erratic and changing deposits, which take the shape of lenticular beds, or, more commonly, thin layers of concentrated black sand interstratified with layers of gray sand. The greatest accumulation of valuable minerals is usually found on the landward side of these deposits where the wave action was strongest. All placer deposits vary somewhat in appearance and configuration, however, marine placers tend to be individually larger, and may be even higher in grade, than many dry-land placers.

The present beaches of the State of California are known to contain many zones favorable for heavy mineral accumulations, and in fact, several beach areas have been mined intermittently for many years. Early-day miners were limited to low-tide operations; however, present technology places large portions of the State's submerged lands in the category of available prospecting ground. Concentrations of placer minerals may be found as far seaward as 300 to 400 feet below the present sea level on the continental shelf of California. The repeated changes in sea level during Pleistocene time, and the low stands that were attained, resulted in exposure and subsequent erosion of much of the inner shelf of California. Rivers discharging into the ocean at that time would have cut canyons and formed placers in areas seaward of the present shoreline and developed beaches along the then existing strandline.

Marine placers usually contain concentrations of heavy, tough, chemically resistant minerals; the most abundant of these minerals found in California waters are probably magnetite and ilmenite. The largest quantities of both of these have been derived from the erosion of the ferromagnesian rocks of the Coast Ranges and their related sediments. Less abundant, but nonetheless commonly associated with these black sands, are gold and the platinum group metals, and many of the inert oxides and silicates such as chromite, rutile, zircon, monazite, uranoan thorite, garnet, and gemstones. Relatively insoluble sulfides such as cinnabar have also been recovered in small amounts from the beach placers of California.

Black sands of the Pacific coast have been exploited periodically since the 1870's, originally for gold and platinum but more recently for iron and titanium. During early periods of mining activity, the richest and most successful deposits were worked at a good profit. From that time onward, however, other ventures that have attempted to recover minerals from beach sands have not proven as successful.

Most of the titaniferous magnetite mined in California has been produced from Los Angeles County, and beach sands recovered from Redondo and Her-

Photo 1. Beaches are interesting areas in which to prospect for mineral deposits. Not only is much of the processing done by the crushing, grinding, and concentrating action of the ocean surf, but the beaches are frequently of overwhelming beauty.

mosa Beaches supplied a large part of this production. The placer deposits occur between Redondo Beach and Palos Verdes Point, covering about 2½ miles of beach. In this placer are found some concentrations of almost pure ilmenite and magnetite, in a 3:2 ratio. The valuable placer minerals occur in lenticular bodies of heavy sand that are about 5 feet thick, 100 feet wide, and 150 feet long. Near Clifton a sand worked in 1927, was reported to contain 20 percent "titaniferous iron" and magnetite, with a residue of quartz, olivine, epidote, garnet, and zircon (Tucker, 1927, p. 287).

A beach deposit farther north near Aptos, in Santa Cruz County, has been worked periodically for its titanium and iron content by several companies. Of these, the principal consumer was Triumph Steel Co., which utilized the sands for producing sponge iron, alloy steel, and briquetted magnetite by a unique smelting process. The early mining at Aptos Beach, however, was for gold, but it was reportedly unsuccessful. These black sand placer deposits occur in both the present beach and in older marine terraces away from the shoreline. The sands contain magnetite, ilmenite, chromite, garnet, zircon and quartz. Irregular crescents of black sand, 100 to 200 feet long and as much as 50 feet wide, that occur along the foot of sandy bluffs are said to be mostly magnetite, with some martite, and enough ilmenite to assay 16 percent TiO_2.

Black sand concentrations occur in beaches at quite a few other locations along the California coast, and many have been sampled or mined periodically in search for gold. Some amounts of gold have been recovered from beach sands in Humboldt County, particularly at Gold Bluff where occasional high values of gold and small amounts of platinum have been found with magnetite and chromite sands. Beach sands near the Oregon border in Del Norte County contain high concentrations of iron and chromium minerals. One sample of sand from this area assayed 480 pounds of magnetite, 210 pounds of chromite, and 56 pounds of monazite per ton, and also contained a small amount of gold. Most placers containing unusually large amount of chromite are found along the northern coast of California, however, an extremely high-value sample of chromite, running over 1,000 pounds per ton of natural sand, was reported to have been taken from the beach in San Mateo County.

High concentrations of garnet occur in the beach deposits near Fort Bragg, in Mendocino County, and at Point Sal, in Santa Barbara County. The garnet found in beach deposits is generally too fine to have commercial value as an abrasive; however, small quantities have been sold for other purposes.

No known concentrations of monazite sand of present commercial importance exist in California, although sands near Cresent City in Del Norte County have been found to contain economically significant, but sporadic, accumulations of monazite.

Uranium minerals occur in small quantities in some beach alluvial deposits, but no commercial amounts have been discovered. A few years ago, uranoan thorite was discovered along the beach between Half Moon Bay and Monterey. A ton of sand taken along these beaches will yield one pound of uranoan thorite which contains 7 percent uranium oxide; a concentration too low to be commercial (Hutton, 1959, p. 80–90). More recent studies have shown the range of thorite occurrences in beaches and offshore areas to extend north beyond San Francisco.

Diamonds are occasionally found as a mineralogical curiosity in the beach sands of San Mateo County, and also reportedly in Humboldt County. Typically, the diamonds are in the form of highly irregular fragments and nowhere are they concentrated enough to have commercial value.

Jade is the only gem material known to occur in recoverable quantities in California beach deposits. Nephrite jade was discovered in the late 1930's along a 2-mile stretch of coast in southern Monterey County, midway between Morro Bay and the City of Monterey. Some excellent quality nephrite has been collected on the narrow pebble beach in what has become known as the Jade Cove area. Gem material ranging in size from small pebbles to large beachworn boulders have been found, but while many of the pebbles forming the beach are composed of nephrite, only a few of these were found to be of desirable color and translucency. Later, pods of nephrite jade were found to crop out in place along the sea cliffs that border the beach. In the cliffs gray schists and mylonite predominate, and many intrusions of peridotite, now serpentine, have altered the schists forming the bedrock nephrite, which is always near such bodies of serpentine. Chances of finding alluvial concentrations of nephrite in offshore gravels are very favorable. Jade is also believed to occur off the coast of southern California at Laguna Beach, as a sizeable block of this material was reported to have been recovered by skin divers.

A small but important part of the total sand and gravel output of California comes from beach and nearshore sand deposits. Although beach deposits consist mostly of well-sorted sand of fairly uniform composition, gravels of a type used for construction purposes are normally absent in shoreline areas. Deposits from which specialty sands are mined are even less common than those containing aggregate-grade material. Beach sands derived from granitic rocks and notably rich in quartz occur at several places south of San Francisco along the present coast and are mined both for specialty products and aggregate.

Most aggregate sand material recovered from beach deposits is obtained from the sands that rim Monterey Bay from Sunset Bay in Santa Cruz County to the City of Monterey for a distance of more than 30 miles.

In these modern beaches that border Monterey Bay the sand sizes and compositions vary considerably with location, consequently, not all of the sand is of commercial interest and only those containing coarse sand have been mined. Because wave activity varies continually, the average grain size at any given beach changes from time to time, especially with the seasons.

In late 1965 four companies operated five modern beach deposits and one older beach deposit (Hart, 1965). The coarse beach sand that is mined is used mainly for aggregate in plaster, concrete, asphalt paving material, and as sandblasting sand. Small amounts are used for filter sand, roofing granules, foundry, and engine sand. Modern beach sand reserves are difficult to determine because of erosion and depositional action, but in recent years several operators report that their beaches are retreating. Shore erosion in the vicinity is considered by the Beach Erosion Board to be severe, and this problem is under study. Development of offshore sand reserves may provide a solution and lead to restoration of the storm-destroyed beaches for recreational and residential, as well as industrial, purposes.

On the western margin of Monterey Bay, near Pacific Grove, fine white beach sands are being utilized for glass manufacture, and for ceramic, abrasive, and refractory uses. As early as 1867, some of these deposits were worked for the production of glass. The deposits near Pacific Grove, which are derived from the abrasion of granitic rocks, are unlike any other beach sands in California because of their uncommonly white color, and general lack of clay, iron-bearing materials, and rock fragments. They consist of about 53 percent quartz grains, 46.5 percent feldspar, and 0.5 percent other minerals including biotite, ilmenite, garnet, zircon and monazite. Nearly all of the sand grains of this deposit will pass through a 20-mesh sieve.

No commercial operations to recover calcareous sands from the shelf areas of California have been attempted. However, Recent deposits of shells and mud, dredged from San Francisco Bay, provide the principal raw materials for a portland cement plant at the Port of Redwood City.

PETROLEUM

Petroleum is the mineral resource that occurs in the waters adjacent to the California coast having the greatest present value and the most promising potential for future large-scale increase in production. Oil fields along the California coast are localized in deep sedimentary basins containing sharply folded rocks. Great quantities of oil have been found in the relatively small basins of Los Angeles, Ventura, and Santa Maria, but elsewhere in the coastal region only small pools have been developed. Productive basins are normally at an angle to the general trend of the coast, and they extend westward some distance beyond the shoreline out under the Pacific Ocean. These submerged areas are excellent prospecting grounds for potentially large petroleum and natural gas resources.

While much oil has been produced from offshore wells in California, there is still a paucity of general geological knowledge of the subsea floor in most areas of the State; an exception is the part of offshore southern California situated south of Point Conception. Rocks of this province consist of schist and granitic basement, of Jurassic age or older, overlain by Cretaceous and Tertiary sediments. Cretaceous and Eocene rocks are exposed over a small percentage of the province, generally on or near islands along the shelf. Oligocene rocks are not known to be exposed on the sea floor; however, oil wells have penetrated such rocks in several places beneath the shelf off Santa Barbara and Ventura Counties. Miocene rocks, widespread petroleum producers on land, are believed to be common offshore, but rocks younger than Miocene are scarce. Pliocene formations have been encountered in several offshore wells in both the Los Angeles and

Table 1. Mineral deposits of the sea

Source area	Minerals of interest
Sea water	Common salt, magnesium for metal and magnesium compounds, bromine, potash, soda, and gypsum—potentially, sulfur, strontium, and borax. Many other elements can be found in sea water; however, processes fundamentally different from those now used would have to be developed in order to extract these elements.
Marine beaches	Placer gold, platinum, diamonds, magnetite, ilmenite, zircon, rutile, columbite, chromite, cassiterite, scheelite, wolframite, monazite. Quartz, calcium carbonate, and sand and gravel.
Continental shelves	Calcareous shells, phosphorite, glauconite, barium sulphate nodules, sand and gravels; placer deposits of tin, platinum, gold, and other minerals in drowned river valleys.
Deep-sea floor	Clays suitable for structural uses, possibly also as a source of alumina, copper, cobalt, nickel, and other metals. Calcareous oozes for cement rock and other calcium carbonate applications. Siliceous oozes for silica and in diatomaceous earth applications. Animal remains as a source of phosphates, and possibly certain metals such as tin, silver, lead, and nickel. Zeolites as a source of potash. Manganese nodules as a source of manganese, iron, cobalt, nickel, copper, molybdenum, vanadium, and perhaps other elements.
Rocks beneath subsea floor	Oil, gas, sulfur, salt, coal, iron ore, and possibly other mineral deposits in veins and other forms as in the rocks on land.

Ventura basins, and are probably more common on the shelf than indicated by surface samples on the sea floor (Calif. Div. Mines, 1959).

The sub-sea area of central and northern California is, of course, far less known geologically and topographically than is the rest of the State. From an economic viewpoint, two-thirds of the California coast is bordered by Tertiary and Cretaceous rocks having oil-producing potential. Two of these sedimentary regions, the Los Angeles and Ventura basins, have already yielded a great amount of oil and gas from their offshore portions, and undoubtedly a substantial proportion of their reserves still remains to be discovered. Probably, the most favorable sedimentary basins that extend into adjacent shelf areas from land are the Santa Maria basin of Santa Barbara and San Luis Obispo Counties, and the Eel River basin of Humboldt County. However, other favorable ground that is not an extension of onshore basins surely exists. Potentially petroliferous zones lie offshore from the sedimentary sequences of Marin, Sonoma, and southern Mendocino Counties.

The California coast is the scene of rapidly increasing offshore activity because of the State's growing demand for fuel, the development of technological skills to drill and operate in extremely deep water, recent successes in the Ventura basin, and Federal offshore lease sales in northern California in the past two years. The Federal decision to open for oil exploration more than 1,000 square miles of offshore acreage beyond California's 3-mile limit makes this region the best remaining block of wildcat territory in the Nation. Much of the area represents the seaward extension of the Los Angeles basin, which has produced 40 percent of California's oil and is the world's most prolific basin in terms of established reserves per cubic mile of sediment.

Los Angeles basin activity has become enhanced by significant extensions of the Huntington Beach field and by the solution of legal problems involving development of the East Wilmington field. East Wilmington field is the largest undeveloped known oil reserve in the United States, containing an estimated 1.2 billion barrels of recoverable oil. Five companies have won 80 percent of the field by offering 95.56 percent of net profits as royalty. Building of four 10-acre drilling islands is underway and production is expected to reach 200,000 bpd within a decade.

The Ventura basin has seen considerable offshore development in recent years. This activity continues with the report of a new field recently discovered offshore from Carpinteria. In addition, new gas reserves have been developed off the Santa Barbara coast and directional drilling is underway from beach locations at Gaviota.

The first wildcat ever drilled in Federal waters off the State was completed in 1964 just north of San Francisco in the Point Reyes area. The hole was drilled in 360 feet of water and was taken to 4,400 feet with inconclusive results. A second hole is now being attempted in the same general location.

In 1965 a wildcat was being drilled north of Santa Barbara, off Morro Bay, in 630 feet of water on Federal lands beyond the 3-mile limit. While drilling in this depth of water may seem amazing, oil companies now feel that it is feasible to drill throughout the year in California in places where the water is as deep as 1,000 feet.

TAR DEPOSITS

Unusual occurrences of submarine tar deposits have been observed in shallow water on the sea floor off southern California in at least three localities; the Point Conception area, Coal Oil Point near Goleta, and off Carpinteria (Vernon, 1963). Scuba-diving geologists mapping underwater for oil companies first discovered these tar deposits in the mid-1950's. Although the potential economic importance and true extent of the deposits is unknown, it is believed that tar recovery could be accomplished by known mining processes if the deposits prove to be sizeable.

Tar is most abundant in the Point Conception area where a sheet of the material covers at least one-fourth square mile and forms a 10- to 12-foot scarp at its seaward edge. East of the Point, individual deposits that range up to 100 feet in diameter and 8 feet in height have been reported.

The deposits are irregularly distributed along the east-west trend of faulted anticlines exposed in shale outcroppings on the ocean floor. Most of the tar occurs in mounds that have roughly circular outlines and resemble miniature volcanos with sides sloping gradually upward toward a vent at a central high point. The mounds are essentially discrete masses of tar in the form of flows. Fresh material is being extruded continuously from the vents of most mounds, and a whiplike strand of fresh tar is commonly found floating above the central vents. Rotary cores taken near one group of tar mounds show that the tar fills fractures in the shale to a depth of 10 feet, but below this depth the fractures in the bedrock are essentially free of tar.

Studies of the tar deposits indicate that Late Quaternary fluctuations in sea level uncovered the site of the tar deposits and wave action removed previous accumulations, and probably also removed several tens of feet of shale forming the surface on which the mounds are now accumulating. It is suggested that the present deposits must have developed since the last major rise in sea level, about 9,000 years ago.

BARITE DEPOSITS

Limited deposits of barite concretions have been found embedded in marine mud at depths between 2,000 and 2,400 feet along the northeast side of San Clemente Island off the coast of southern California. About 250 loosely mixed concretions, along with about 100 kilograms of green mud, have been dredged from this area. They are irregularly shaped nodules, and range from 1 to 25 cm in length. Chemically and min-

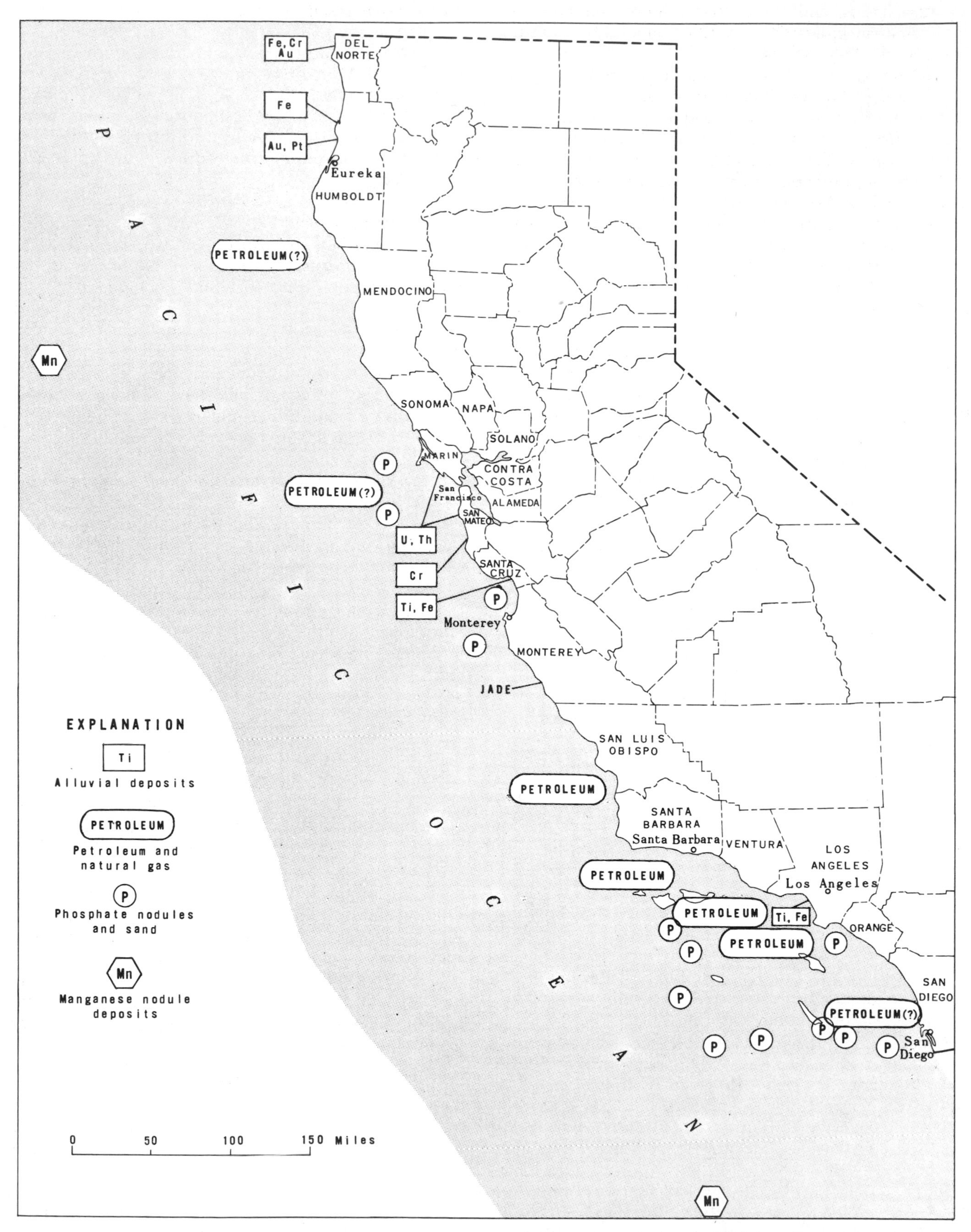

Figure 1. Sketch map showing the California offshore area and the location of various types of mineral deposits found therein.

eralogically they are similar to other barite concretions found on land or recovered from the sea floor. Barium sulphate is present in the nodules in amounts from 62 to 77 percent.

It is believed the barite concretions originated by a reaction between hot solutions ascending along a fault and the interstitial seawater of the sediments (Revelle and Emery, 1951, p. 707). This suggestion is supported by the fact that all known nodule localities are situated on or near large faults, which could have provided an avenue of escape for the hot barium-bearing solutions. It appears likely that the deposits of barite concretions are quite localized, and they should not be considered a potential offshore resource.

GLAUCONITE

Glauconite is an authigenic sea-floor mineral of potential economic interest that is found in widespread occurrence off the Coast of California. This mineral contains from 2 to 9 percent K_2O and could serve as a future source of potash and soil conditioner for agricultural use, or as a source of potassium or potassium salts. Compared to continental deposits of potash salts, marine glauconite sediments could not be considered a rich source of supply, however, mining costs would be relatively cheap and mechanical concentration might possibly produce a product with a significant amount of contained potash.

Glauconite is widely distributed in the terrigenous sediments off the coast of the State, occurring in water depths ranging from 100 to 200 fathoms. The highest concentrations of glauconite occur in environments in which detrital sedimentation is slow or virtually absent, such as banks, ridges, and upper slopes of basins of the continental shelf. Distribution of the mineral is normally patchy both laterally and vertically.

Deposits of glauconite are either *in situ*, having been formed where they now are found, or else reworked, having been transported into the environment in which they are found. Transported glauconite can be recognized because it is usually characterized by fine grains, some of which show evidence of fragmentation. Individual grains of glauconite found in marine muds are in some places as large as 3 mm, although normally they are much smaller. Glauconites off California range from dark green illitic types to pale and yellowish-green montmorillonitic types.

Glauconite deposits of offshore California range in age from Miocene to Late Pleistocene. They have been found in abundance in Recent sediments that form the shelf south of Santa Barbara, where they appear to be reworked from glauconitic sediments of Late Pliocene age. Similar, but less extensive deposits of reworked glauconite are present in other areas off the California coast. Both Santa Monica Bay and the Palos Verdes shelf contain vast areas of glauconitic sands of low concentration. The sea area off Monterey Bay contains local sediments at the shelf break that run as high as 40 percent glauconite, and individual layers in some offshore areas are known to grade as high as 80 percent glauconite (Pratt, 1962, p. 233).

PHOSPHORITE

Authigenic phosphorite is one of the truly important kinds of rock on the sea floor off California from an economic standpoint. It has been shown by recent scientific and engineering studies to offer great potential as a present-day source of chemical raw materials. Extensive deposits of phosphorite are common in many places off the coast, and are quite near to potential areas of consumption and centers of processing and marketing.

Phosphatic concretions were first discovered on the ocean floor by scientists of the famous Challenger Expedition in the 1870's; however, they were not recognized off the California coast until 1937. Since that time many additional locations have been discovered in the State's coastal waters, and in several of these phosphorite has been found to be the most abundant surface rock. Deposits of phosphorite nodules are now known to extend from the coastal waters off Point Reyes, north of San Francisco, southward to the mouth of the Gulf of California, a distance of 1,300 miles. The nodules occur in some places within a few miles of the coast and they extend as far from shore as the inner edge of the continental slope. The greatest depth from which nodules have been dredged is 8,400 feet, while the shallowest is about 100 feet off southern California. The total area that is known or believed to be covered by phosphorite is about 6,000 square miles (Emery, 1946, p. 69). If it is assumed that the nodule layer has an average thickness of one inch, the

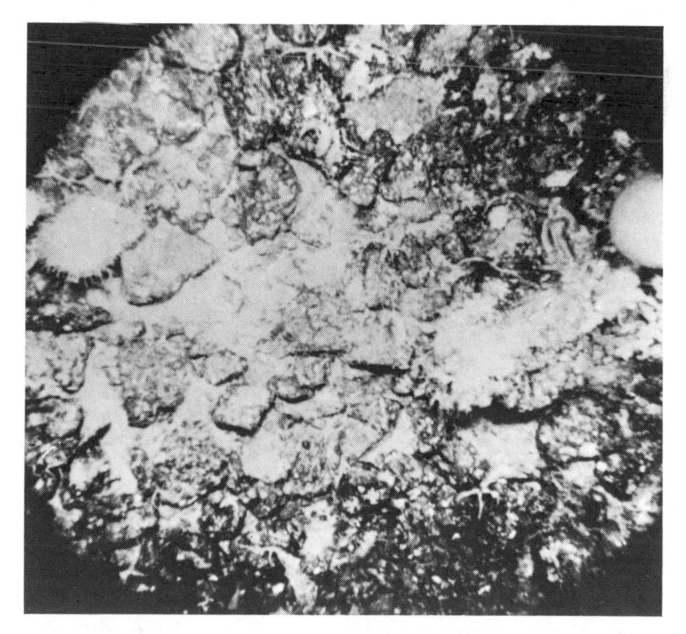

Photo 2. Phosphorite on the Forty Mile Bank area at a depth of 108 fathoms. This photo shows an area of about 16 square feet. The quantity of phosphorite, assuming a monolayer of rock on the surface of the sea floor, is about 500,000 tons per square mile of sea floor. Individual nodules range in size from oolites to blocks with a major dimension of about 2 feet.

region could contain approximately one billion tons of phosphorite rock.

Dredging has indicated that an especially great abundance of phosphorite exists in the continental borderland area of southern California, particularly in the vicinity of Thirty Mile and Forty Mile Banks off San Diego. Deposits have also been identified near Santa Catalina Island, and farther north off Santa Rosa and Santa Cruz Islands. Off central California, phosphorite nodules have been dredged from deposits in Monterey Bay and from the outer shelf in this region as well. West of San Francisco, several hundred pounds of nodules were recovered from dredge hauls in water depths between 400 to 600 fathoms (Chesterman, 1952, p. 366). To the northwest of San Francisco in the vicinity of Cordell Bank, at water depths ranging from 200 to 400 fathoms, over 800 pounds of nodules were taken during sampling. They ranged from 2 to 8 inches in diameter and appeared to be nearly pure phosphatic material. The percentage of sand recovered with the nodules in this region was very low.

Sea-floor phosphorite is known to occur in a wide variety of topographic environments. It has been dredged from the tops and sides of banks and ridges, from deep hills, on steep escarpments, on the walls of submarine canyons, and on the break of the continental slope. Small grains or oölites are common in many inshore areas as well as in the coarse sediment seaward of the main shelf. Most samples of phosphorite, however, have been taken from areas characterized by a slow rate of deposition. In these environments ocean bottom currents are concentrated so that any sediment that reaches the nodules is soon removed and no permanent deposit of fine sediment remains. Sea-floor phosphorite occurs as a veneer or mono-layer covering the ocean bottom for many square miles; no evidence has been found that indicates phosphorites occur to any depth beneath the surface of the ocean floor.

California phosphorites typically occur as nodules and sands, ranging from flat slabs and irregular masses to oolites. They vary in size from small grains of less than 1 mm to nodules well over 3 feet in diameter. Pieces of phosphorite weighing 100 pounds have been recovered in dredge hauls and larger pieces are likely to exist. The nodules generally have flat bottoms and nodelike tops, and their surfaces appear glazed as they are normally coated with a thin film of manganese oxides. From place to place nodular phosphorites vary in color from light brown to black; those from a particular area typically have a group resemblance.

Internally, the nodules display a wide range of structures and purity. Most small nodules have a very fine grained texture and a homogeneous composition, while most of the larger nodules contain some nonphosphatic material, usually composed of sand and glauconite and fragments of nearby bedrock. Frequently, phosphorite forms a thin coating on fragments of local rocks that are lying on the sea floor. In places old-appearing nodules are cemented together to form a conglomeratic mass. The majority of sea-floor phosphorite shows signs of internal layering either visually or microscopically. These layers are irregular and nonconcentric, and vary in thickness from less than a millimeter to a few centimeters.

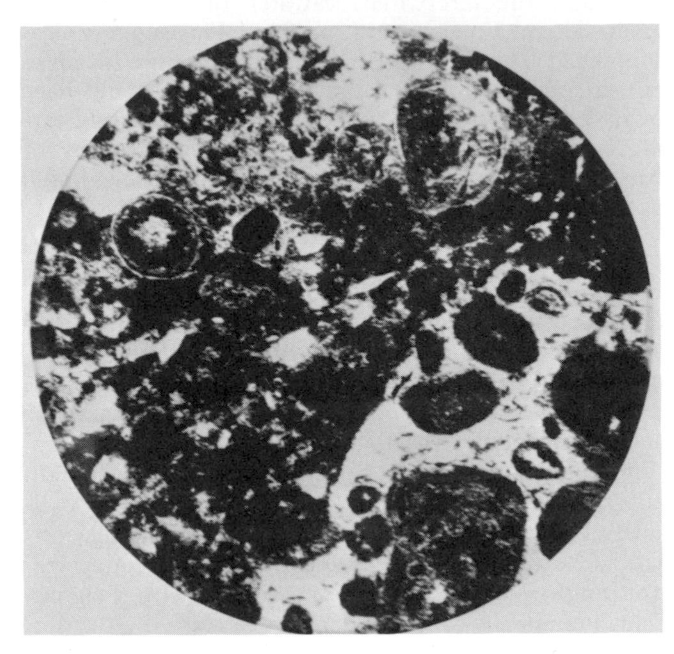

Photo 3. Photomicrograph of a thin section of phosphorite from Forty Mile Bank, showing the oolitic structure of these nodules (x 50).

Sea-floor phosphorites are firm and dense, with a specific gravity of 2.62 and a hardness of 5 on the Mohs' scale. Chemical and mineralogical analysis has proved the nodules to be composed almost entirely of collophane, a nearly isotropic fluorapatite. Associated with collophane in minor amounts is francolite, also a carbonate fluorapatite mineral. Chemical analyses indicate that sea-floor phosphorite is nearly the same composition as reported for deposits of land phosphorites in the United States and elsewhere. It generally contains 20 to 31 percent P_2O_5 and can be upgraded by physical processing to contain 32 to 34 percent P_2O_5 (Mero, 1965).

The process of formation of these unique blanket deposits of nodular phosphorite is still unknown. The evidence available strongly suggests that most of the phosphorite originated as a primary or syngenetic mineral formed *in situ.* Deposits of nodules are most abundant along coasts where there are great and rapid changes of temperature resulting from the meeting of cold and warm ocean currents. In these areas, large numbers of pelagic or deep-water organisms are killed by temperature changes and may accumulate to form sizeable layers of decomposing phosphatic matter on the ocean bottom. In areas where there are large amounts of decaying phosphatic matter, an environment that allows the phosphate to dissolve in sea water is created. The dissolved phosphate migrates away from this area into the prevailing oxidizing environment of the ocean, and is precipitated in colloidal form. Under certain conditions these phosphate colloids can agglomerate to form nodules.

Another suggested origin is that the phosphorite is precipitated from sea water in areas of strong upwelling ocean currents. In these areas where cooler deep water containing a high concentration of phosphate ions and other nutrients rises to the surface the sea water undergoes an increase in pH and temperature and a decrease of pressure. Carbon dioxide, which serves to hold phosphate in solution, is released. This combination of events serves to explain the modern occurrence of phosphorite in the oxidizing environments of waters along California and other coasts, at least some of which are also areas of upwelling.

Many fossils are found incorporated in the phosphorite nodules. They range from bones and teeth of fishes to sponge spicules and tests of Forminifera. Of these the Foraminifera are by far the most abundant in the phosphorite, and they are quite useful in determining the age of formation of the deposit. Foraminifera in the California nodules fall into two general groups: middle and late Miocene types in dark brown, older-appearing nodules, and late Pliocene to Recent types in the matrix of light brown forms. Evidence indicates most nodules formed during Miocene time; however, subsequent exposure of nodules on the sea floor may have provided nuclei for renewed Quaternary deposition of phosphorite.

Although phosphatic pebbles are found in the sedimentary strata in some land areas of California (see Dickert, this bulletin), no deposit of rock phosphate within the State has yet proved economic to mine. It appears likely that if offshore deposits of phosphorite prove to be sufficiently extensive, they can offer a substantial source of low-grade ore. Not all of the phosphorite found off California will be economic to recover, as some deposits are too marginal or too scattered to be profitable and others are too mixed with nonphosphatic rocks or too unfavorably located for commercial recovery. However, if it is economic to mine only 10 percent of the phosphorite speculated to be off the coast of California, there is a reserve for about 200 years of mining at a rate of 500,000 tons per year.

MANGANESE NODULES

The most promising of ocean-floor mineral occurrences found off California are the deep-sea deposits of manganese nodules. Nodular manganese as a pelagic sediment is probably one of the most common forms of hard rock found at the surface of the lithosphere, but although its existence has been known since the 1870's, its potential economic significance was not apparent until widespread dredging in the Pacific Ocean during the International Geophysical Year revealed its vast extent. The amount of nodules on the Pacific Ocean floor alone has been estimated to be in excess of 1.5 trillion tons. Furthermore, recent engineering studies on the mining of nodules from the sea floor suggest that such operations may be both technically and economically practical.

Concretionary deposits of ferromanganese minerals are found ubiquitously spread over the ocean bottom where oxidizing conditions prevail at the sediment-water interface. It has been estimated that between 20 and 50 percent of the deep-sea floor in the southwestern Pacific is covered with these concretions, and although their relative abundance in the northeastern Pacific is not yet as well known, sporadic dredging has indicated several potentially large and highly concentrated deposits.

Ocean-floor manganese minerals are most commonly found as loose-lying concretions or nodules at the surface of soft sea-floor sediments. The manganese nodules range in color from light brown to earthy black, are friable with a hardness that does not exceed 3 or 4 on the Mohs' scale, and have a density of from 2.1 to 3.1. On an ocean-wide basis, they have an average diameter of 3 cm; however, they locally vary in size from 1 cm to 25 cm with a few that are even larger. One extremely large nodule recovered from the Pacific weighed 1,700 pounds.

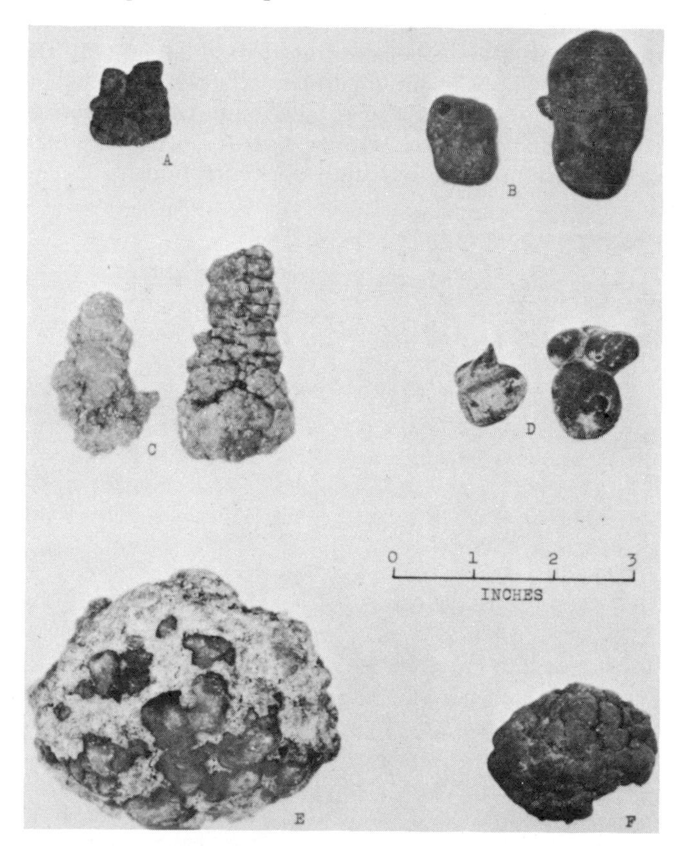

Photo 4. Manganese nodules from the north Pacific, illustrating a few of the many shapes they assume in their growth process. The location data for the individual nodules are: A.) N. 29° 58', W. 125° 55', depth 4,325 m.; B.) N. 23° 17', W. 138° 15', depth 4,890 m.; C.) N. 22° 30', W. 113° 08', depth 3,600 m.; D.) N. 14° 11', W. 161° 08', depth 5,652 m.; E.) N. 9° 57', W. 137° 47', depth 4,930 m.; F.) N. 21° 27', W. 126° 43', depth 4,300 m.

In physical appearance, the nodules exhibit a variety of shapes, such as marbles, tablets, potato shapes, cylinders, slabs, and irregular masses. Nodules from different parts of the ocean generally have unique physical characteristics, but those within a given deposit show a group resemblance. Their external form commonly depends on the shape of the nucleus. Some, however, show several nuclei because growing nodules have coalesced to form slab-like concretions with multiple knobs. (See photo 4.)

The mineralogy of the nodules is complex. As a number of distinct minerals are generally present the nodules may be classified most appropriately as rocks. In addition to the common detrital silica and alumina minerals, such minerals as opal, rutile, anatase, barite, nontronite, goethite, and at least three manganese oxide minerals of major importance have been recognized in the nodules. Generally these minerals occur as intimately intergrown crystallites. Grutter and Buser (1957, p. 132) found that the structure consists of layers of MnO_2 in an irregular pile of quasi two-dimensional crystals. Their X-ray diffraction pattern is of a type similar to that of the mineral lithiophorite. They suggest a structure of two MnO_2 layers, 10 Å apart, separated by a layer consisting of $Mn(OH)_2$ and $Fe(OH)_3$, and possibly sodium ions. Many of the nodules contain more iron than can be accommodated in the in-between hydroxyl layer and the excess iron appears in the form of goethite. The in-between layer seems also to accommodate a group of cations, such as nickel, copper, cobalt, and zinc, which may be found in rather high concentrations.

Several hypotheses have been suggested concerning the formation of the nodules. The most plausible inorganic theory of formation, as based on presently available data, begins with sea-water saturated with manganese and iron, which has been derived largely from streams, continental erosion, and volcanic eruptions. With the evaporation of the sea water at the ocean surface, manganese and iron are forced to precipitate as colloidal particles, which filter down through the sea water scavenging nickel, copper, cobalt, vanadium, molybdenum and other metals from solution. The manganese and iron sols are swept along by bottom currents and accrete on the sea floor around physical nuclei such as clay particles, organic material, coral, or pumice.

Deposits of manganese nodules appear to occur essentially as a mono-layer on the surface of the deep-sea floor. Some nodules do occur at discrete levels within superficial sea-floor sediments, but they are in less abundance than on the surface itself, at least in the more explored upper meter or so of the sediments. Detailed information on the distribution and concentration of macroscopic nodules on the sea floor has been obtained through bottom photography and by sampling. Crusts and large nodules appear to develop on topographic highs or in areas where there is a low rate of total deposition, probably because in these areas growing nuclei are not so quickly buried by other sedimentary components. In general, the concentration of nodules in individual deposits tends to increase toward the center of the Pacific Ocean. Measurements in the eastern Pacific gave an average nodule

Photo 5. Manganese nodules on the ocean floor at N. 26°, W. 135°, in 4,330 m of water between California and Hawaii. The largest slablike nodule is about 23 cm in diameter. Many of the blocklike nodules in this photo may be only manganese dioxide encrusted blocks of pumice. *Photo by Carl Shipek, U.S. Naval Electronics Laboratory, San Diego, California.*

concentration of 0.9 gms/cm^2; measurements in the central Pacific average 1.8 gms/cm^2 (Photo 5).

Definite regional variation in the composition of manganese nodules has been observed in the Pacific Ocean. The chemical basis for determining whether a nodule is "high" in regard to the amount of a particular element is rather arbitrary; however, using a detritus-free weight percentage base of about 1 percent for cobalt, nickel, and copper, a geochemical pattern becomes apparent. In the case of manganese, a weight percentage of 40 percent is considered "high", and if the manganese/iron ratio is less than unity, a nodule is assumed to be "high" in iron. In the central part of the eastern Pacific, nodules are found to be "high" in nickel and copper. In the central Pacific, nodules are "high" in cobalt, but contain very little copper. Nodules near the west coast of the United States are characterized by a manganese/iron ratio of less than one and an iron/cobalt ratio that is greater than that of other regions. Nodules from the region that borders the North American Pacific coast have an average chemical composition, on a detrital-free mineral basis, in percent of: iron—28.3, manganese—21.7, cobalt—0.35, nickel—0.46, and copper—0.32.

Although no nodule deposits have been reported as occurring on the continental shelf and slope of California, much manganese dioxide has been found there in the form of coatings around rock fragments. For example, in a seahill area about 30 miles off the coast near San Diego large quantities of manganese dioxide have been reported cementing andesite fragments. Elsewhere off California in deeper water, a considerable number of rocks with manganese crusts have been dredged. These are generally angular slabs and tabular masses with a core of altered pumice fragments, and between the slabs in many places nodules have been found to cover much of the bottom.

Manganese nodules may occur over an extensive region of the deep-sea floor due west of Cape Mendocino. Samples recovered from as close to the continent as 250 miles contain approximately 19 percent manganese, 8 percent iron, 0.6 percent nickel, and 0.4 percent copper. From about 680 miles to 2,100 miles west of Cape Mendocino, recovered nodules contain an average of 14 percent Mn, 8 percent Fe, 0.5 percent Ni, 0.4 percent Cu, and 0.28 percent Co. Approximately 2,000 miles west of San Francisco, nodules were found to contain about 20 percent Mn, 14 percent Fe, 0.4 percent Ni, 0.25 percent Cu, and 0.13 percent Co. To the south in a zone 1,000 miles west of Cape San Martin, nodules recovered contained 10 percent Mn, 13 percent Fe, 0.3 percent Co, 0.3 percent Ni, and 0.3 percent Cu. West of Los Angeles, approximately 1,600 miles at sea, a dredge haul retrieved nodules that contained 15 percent Mn, 12 percent Fe, 0.6 percent Ni, 0.3 percent Cu, and 0.3 percent Co. Most of the nodules taken in waters off California occur in a depth range from 4,500 to 5,500 meters.

The feasibility of mining deposits of manganese nodules has been studied in some detail by Mero (1965), and he concludes that a proven engineering system such as drag dredging or suction dredging could economically recover nodules from specific deposits off California. Before seriously considering mining these deposits, however, it will be necessary to learn far more about their environment and occurrence so that the best sites for operations can be selected. Should these deep-sea deposits prove to be ores of various metals, the reserves in the Pacific Ocean are staggering, as the indicated reserves for many of the metals range into quantities sufficient to support mining for hundreds of thousands of years. From a mining standpoint, the nodules rich in cobalt, copper, and nickel are of greatest interest. Maximum concentrations of these metals found in nodules thus far are 3 percent copper, 2 percent cobalt, and 2 percent nickel. Economic incentive may soon provide sufficient information to bring deep-sea nodules into the realm of true ore deposits.

REFERENCES

California Division of Mines, 1959, Offshore geology and oil resources: California Div. Mines Mineral Inf. Serv., v. 12, no. 5, p. 1–7.

Chesterman, C. W., 1952, Descriptive petrography of rocks dredged off the coast of central California: California Acad. Sci. Proc., 4th ser., v. 27, p. 359–374.

Emery, K. O., 1960, The sea off southern California, a modern habitat of petroleum: New York, John Wiley and Sons, Inc., 366 p.

Grutter, A., and Buser, W., 1957, Untersuchungen an Mangansedimenten: Chimia (Aarau) 11, p. 132–133.

Hart, E. W., 1965, Mines and mineral resources of Monterey County: California Div. Mines and Geology, County Rept. 5. (In press)

Hutton, C. O., 1959, Mineralogy of beach sands between Halfmoon and Monterey Bays, California: California Div. Mines Spec. Rept. 59, 32 p.

Mero, J. L., 1964, Mineral resources of the sea: New York, Am. Elsevier Publishing Co., 312 p.

Pratt, W. L., 1962, The origin and distribution of glauconite from the sea floor off California and Baja California: Southern California Univ., Los Angeles, Ph.D. thesis, 296 p.

Revelle, R. D., and Emery, K. O., 1951, Barite concretions from the ocean floor: Geol. Soc. America Bull., v. 62, no. 7, p. 707–723.

Tucker, W. B., 1927, Los Angeles County: California Mining Bur., 23d Rept. State Mineralogist, no. 3, p. 287–313.

Vernon, J. W., and Slater, R. A., 1963, Submarine tar mounds, Santa Barbara County, California: Am. Assoc. Petroleum Geologists Bull., v. 47, no. 8, p. 1624–1627.

From J. W. Hutchings, *Scenes of wonder and curiosity in California*, 1865.

CHAPTER VIII
SAN ANDREAS FAULT

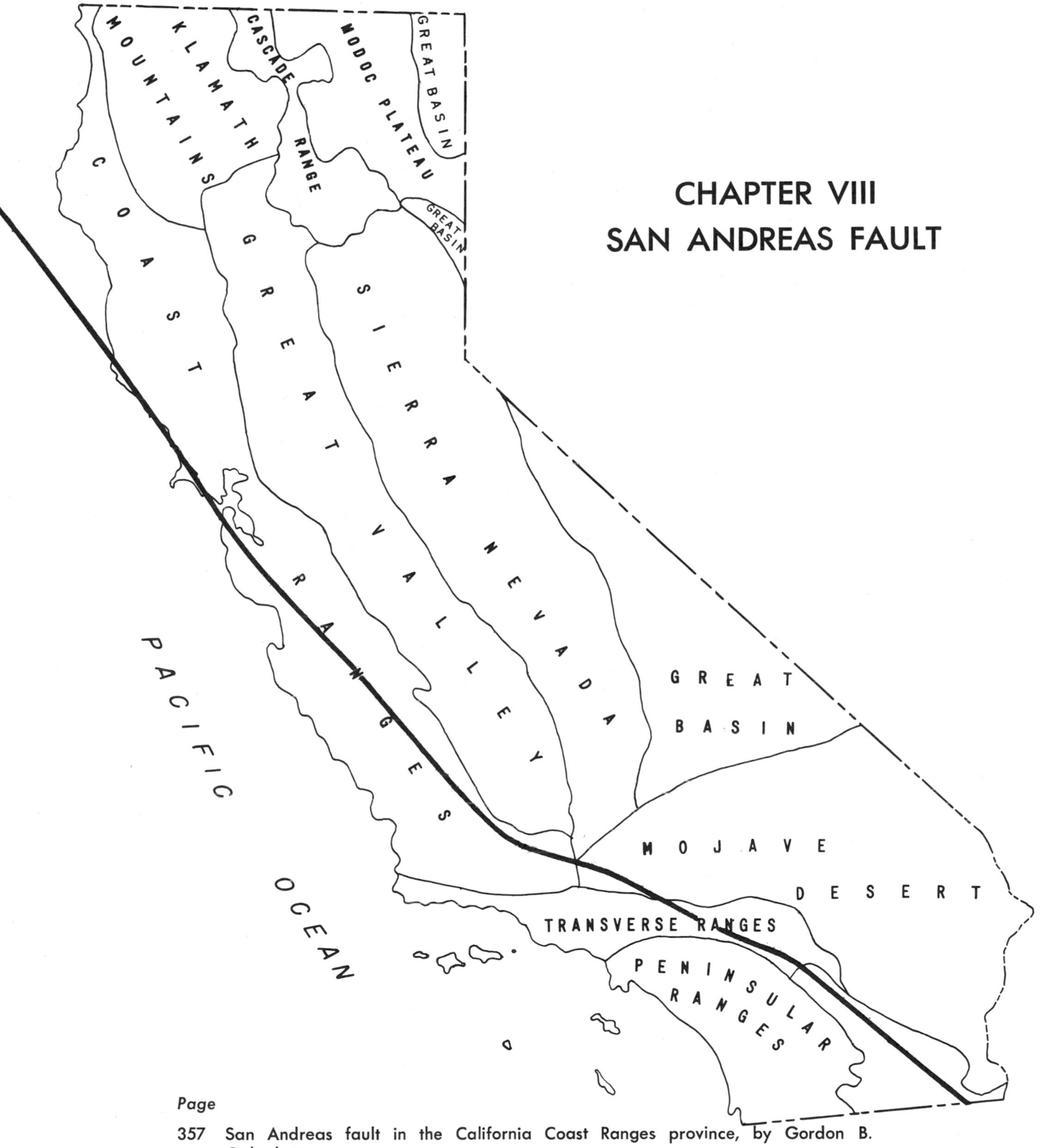

Page

SAN ANDREAS FAULT IN THE CALIFORNIA COAST RANGES PROVINCE

By Gordon B. Oakeshott
California Division of Mines and Geology

The San Andreas fault (p. 355) is California's most spectacular and widely known structural feature. Few specific geologic features on earth have received more public attention. Sound reasons for this are found in the series of historic earthquakes which have originated in movements in the San Andreas fault zone, and in continuing surface displacements, both accompanied and unaccompanied by earthquakes. This active fault is of tremendous engineering significance, for no engineering structure can cross it without jeopardy, and all major structures within its potential area of seismicity must incorporate aseismic design features. Recently a proposal for a great nuclear power plant installation on Bodega Head, north of San Francisco, was abandoned because of public controversy over the dangers of renewed movements and earthquakes on the nearby fault (Koenig, 1963; and fig. 1, photo 1). Expensive design features are being incorporated into the State's plan to transport some of northern California's excess of water to water-deficient southern California in order to ensure uninterrupted service across the fault in the event of fault movements and earthquakes in the Tehachapi area (James, 1964).

Worldwide attention of geologists and seismologists to the San Andreas fault has resulted from: (1) the great ($M = 8.25$) San Francisco earthquake of 1906 (Lawson and others, 1908) and many lesser shocks which have originated in the fault zone, (2) development of the "elastic rebound" theory by H. F. Reid in the Lawson report, (3) striking geologic effects of former and continuing surface movements in the fault zone, and (4) postulated gigantic right-slip displacement (Hill and Dibblee, 1953). The San Andreas has been frequently and widely cited in the scientific and popular literature as a classic example of a strike-slip fault with cumulative horizontal displacement of several hundred miles; this in spite of the highly controversial nature of the geologic evidence that can be documented!

LOCATION AND EXTENT

The San Andreas fault strikes approximately N. 35° W. in a nearly straight line in the Coast Ranges province and extends southward for a total length of about 650 miles from Shelter Cove in Humboldt County to the Salton Sea. This carries it at a low angle completely across structures and lineation of the Coast Ranges, south across the Transverse Ranges, and into the Salton Trough. Latest movement in the fault zone, as noted by Lawson and others (1908) who named and traced it, has thus been clearly later than all major structural features of those provinces. This recent movement may, however, be an expression of renewed activity along an older fault zone that antedated differentiation of the geologic provinces now in existence. If so, we need to distinguish between the ancestral "San Andreas" fault zone and the Quaternary San Andreas fault proper (pl. 1, Geologic map of California).

The long northwesterly trend of the fault zone is interrupted in three places (pl. 1): (1) At Cape Mendocino, where it turns abruptly westward to enter the Mendocino fault zone, as reflected in the Mendocino Escarpment, or is offset left laterally and continues northwestward from that escarpment; (2) at the south end where the Coast Ranges adjoin the Transverse Ranges and the fault turns to strike east into the complex knot of major faults in the Frazier Mountain area and on emerging splits into the 50-mile-wide system of related faults, including the San Andreas fault proper, in southern California; and (3) in the San Gorgonio Pass area where the San Andreas fault proper appears to change direction again and butt into the Mission Creek-Banning fault zone which continues into the Salton Trough. That these three changes in trend are of profound structural significance, most geologists would agree, but there is wide disagreement on possible explanations.

HISTORY OF GEOLOGICAL INVESTIGATIONS

A. C. Lawson (1893) first recognized faulting in the San Andreas fault zone when he said "The line of demarcation between the Pliocene and the Mesozoic rocks, which extends from Mussel Rock southeastward is, in part, also, the trace of a post-Pliocene fault." In 1899, F. M. Anderson recognized evidence of major faulting on the Marin peninsula "both in the topography and in the general stratigraphic and petrographic relations". However, he projected this fault southeastward into Lawson's fault along the western margin of San Bruno Mountain, rather than connecting it with the major "post-Pliocene" fault mentioned by Lawson. Neither of these two geologists gave a name, at that time, to the San Andreas fault.

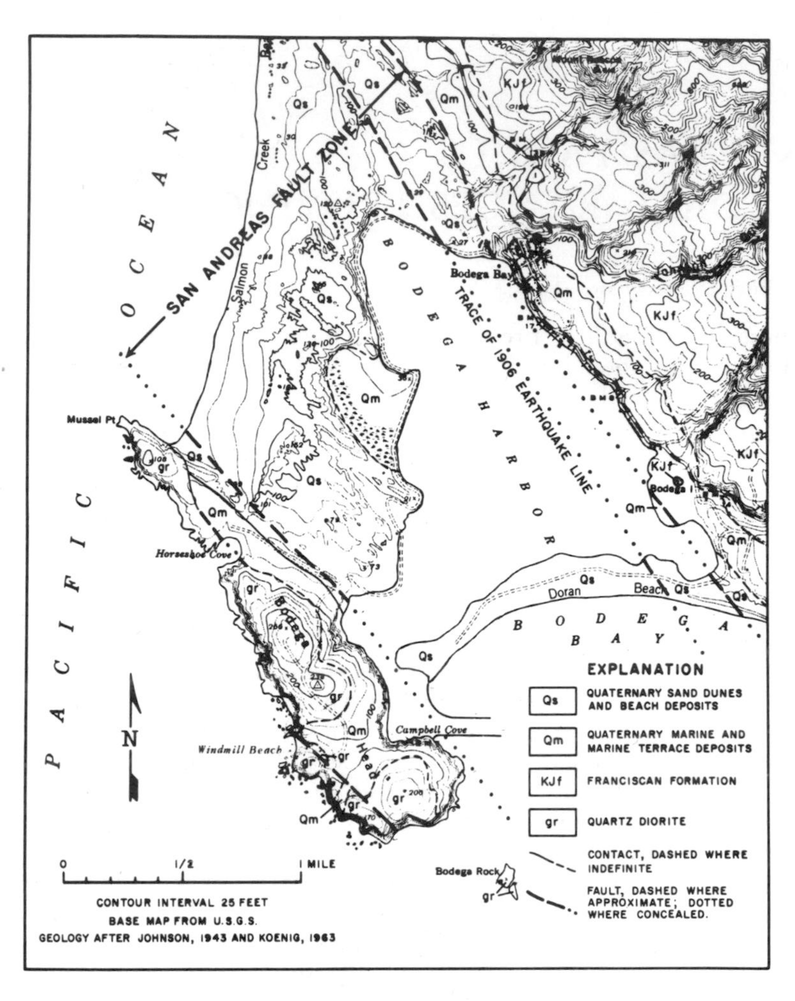

Figure 1. Geologic map of San Andreas fault zone at Bodega Head. *From California Div. Mines and Geology Mineral Inf. Service, v. 16, no. 7, 1963.*

The great San Francisco earthquake of 1906 and the obvious surface rupture focused attention of leading California geologists of the day on the fault, and resulted in publication of the monumental report of the State Earthquake Investigation Commission (Lawson, 1908). Lawson was assisted by many American geologists, prominent then or later, including Robert Anderson, J. C. Branner, A. S. Eakle, H. W. Fairbanks, G. K. Gilbert, F. E. Matthes, G. D. Louderback, and G. A. Waring. They described surface fault ruptures from Shelter Cove in Humboldt County to San Juan Bautista in San Benito County, a distance of approximately 250 miles, but they also followed the Recent fault into San Bernardino County. In this report Lawson first named the San Andreas fault after its rift-valley expression in the San Andreas Lake area of the San Francisco peninsula.

In volume II of the Earthquake Commission Report, not published until 1910, H. F. Reid developed his "elastic rebound theory" to account for the origin of earthquakes. This report contains a number of seismograms and isoseismal maps. This volume, like volume I, is abundantly illustrated and is a fascinating geologic document.

Other significant outgrowths of the 1906 earthquake were the founding of the Seismological Society of America, the publication of the first Bulletin of the Society in 1911, and the installation of new seismographs by the University of California at Berkeley and at Lick Observatory in 1910.

In 1914 the U.S. Geological Survey published the San Francisco Folio by Lawson, still a standard reference for geology of the Bay area, although long since out of print.

During the past 25 years many geologic maps have been published of parts of the Coast Ranges which include segments of the San Andreas fault zone, and more mapping is in progress. A complete list of these through 1960 has been published in Special Reports 52 and 52A by the California Division of Mines and Geology (Strand, Koenig and Jennings, 1958; Koenig, 1962). Their 1:250,000-scale sheets of the State Geologic Map that include both published and unpublished geologic mapping across the San Andreas fault zone in the Coast Ranges province are: Redding (1962), Ukiah (1960), Santa Rosa (1963), San Francisco (1961), San Jose (in press 1966), Santa Cruz (1959), San Luis Obispo (1959), and Bakersfield (1965).

Oakeshott (1959) in a report on the *San Francisco earthquake of March 1957* included summary papers by various authors on the geology, seismic history, and structural damage of a Bay area segment of the

Photo 1. Aerial view of Bodega Head, looking northward, with village of Bodega Bay at center of the photograph. The steep cliffs at the bottom of the picture reach a height of about 170 feet. Sandy beach in the middle ground, connecting Bodega Head to the mainland, corresponds to the seismically active San Andreas fault zone. *From California Div. Mines and Geology Mineral Inf. Service, v. 16, no. 7, 1963. Photo by Aero Photographers, Sausalito, California.*

San Andreas fault zone. Special Report 74 (Jennings and Strand, 1963) of the Division of Mines and Geology lists graduate theses on California geology. The latest listing of current research projects by colleges and universities on subjects pertaining to California geology, including some which have direct bearing on San Andreas fault problems is in the July 1964 issue of the Division's *Mineral Information Service* (Campbell and Jennings, 1964).

In December 1964, The Resources Agency, State of California, held a public scientific conference on earthquake hazards (California Resources Agency, 1964), and this agency, through its Division of Mines and Geology and Department of Water Resources, has embarked on a long-range program of fault and earthquake investigations, particularly emphasizing the San Andreas fault. In May 1965, The Resources Agency held a second geologic hazards conference in which the emphasis was placed on landslides and subsidence (California Resources Agency, in press, November 1965). At the time this report was being prepared (November 1, 1965), announcements were being made of several long-range, far-reaching programs designed to learn more of the San Andreas fault, in particular, and of faulting and earthquakes in general. A recent summary of earthquake investigations in progress, and planned, in California may be found in the California Resources Agency publication (1964) just cited.

The University of California Seismograph Station has received approval of the Regents to start construction of a multipurpose geophysical observatory to be located in granitic rock just west of an active segment of the San Andreas fault a few miles south of Hollister. This installation will provide instrumentation for long-term recording of elastic and acoustic waves, tilt, strain, and conductivity fluctuations as well as varia-

Photo 2. San Andreas(?) fault scarp at Shelter Cove in Humboldt County, photographed in 1963. East side (left) is up about 6 feet. Cut at base of scarp was made for a road. *Photo by K. V. Steinbrugge.*

tions in the magnetic, gravity, and heat fields near the fault.

The U.S. Coast and Geodetic Survey is continuing and increasing its long-time program of strong motion studies and resurveys across the fault zone (Meade and Small, this bulletin).

The U.S. Geological Survey, in July 1965, began accelerating its geologic and geophysical analysis of the western earthquake belt, particularly along the San Andreas fault zone. Geologic investigations included geomorphic studies of Quaternary displacements, analyzing the development and offset of Tertiary basins, and offsets of granitic, metamorphic, and volcanic blocks and gravels derived therefrom. Geologic maps and sections representing transects of the fault and a synthesis of the regional tectonics were being prepared at scales of 1:62,500 and 1:125,000. A variety of geophysical studies including emphasis on seismic-refraction profiling and study of near earthquakes, and studies of tilt-measuring, strain seismometry, and electronic distance measurement among other techniques were begun in and near the fault zone. In October 1965, the U.S. Department of the Interior announced establishment of a National Center for Earthquake Research within the Geological Survey to stimulate and coordinate research on the causes and prediction of earthquakes.

By an understanding in effect for many years, earthquakes north of the Kern County line have been studied particularly by the University of California Seismograph Station, while those originating in Kern County and south have been the prime responsibility of the Seismological Laboratory of the California Institute of Technology.

EARTHQUAKE HISTORY

Earthquake history of California is extremely short. The earliest earthquake in written records was felt by explorer Gaspar de Portolá and his party in 1769 while camped on the Santa Ana River about 30 miles southeast of Los Angeles. The earliest seismographs in use in California, and also the earliest in the United States (Louderback, 1942), were installed by the University of California at Lick Observatory on Mount Hamilton, and at the University at Berkeley in 1887. Earliest seismograms of a major California earthquake are those of the San Francisco earthquake of 1906, which was recorded at seven California stations as well as elsewhere throughout the world. Townley and Allen (1939) is the standard reference on earthquakes prior to 1929. Byerly (1951), VanderHoof (1955), Richter (1958), and Tocher (1959) have published accounts of earthquakes in the Coast Ranges.

One of the Bay area's largest earthquakes centered on the Hayward fault (within the San Andreas fault zone) in the East Bay on June 10, 1836. Surface faulting took place at the base of the Berkeley Hills from Mission San José to San Pablo. On October 21, 1868, another large earthquake centered on the Hayward fault with surface faulting for about 20 miles from Warm Springs to San Leandro (Radbruch, 1965). Maximum right-lateral offset was about 3 feet.

In June of 1838 a strong earthquake originating on the San Andreas fault was accompanied by surface rupturing from Santa Clara almost to San Francisco.

This damaged the Presidio at San Francisco and the missions at San Jose, Santa Clara, and San Francisco. Another strong earthquake centered on the San Andreas fault in the Santa Cruz Mountains on October 8, 1865. This was accompanied by ground cracks, landslides and dust clouds; buildings were damaged in San Francisco and at the New Almaden mercury mine, which was only a few miles east of the active part of the fault.

On April 24, 1890, a strong earthquake damaged Watsonville, Hollister, and Gilroy. Mr. Joe Anzar, who was a young boy living in the San Andreas rift valley in the nearby Chittenden Pass area at the time of that earthquake, was interviewed in 1963 by Olaf P. Jenkins and Oakeshott. Anzar clearly remembered ground breakage, which caused Anzar Lake to drain, and landslides, which closed the railroad and highway where the fault trace crosses Chittenden Pass. He judged the motion to be stronger (at his home) than during the San Francisco earthquake of 1906.

The famous San Francisco earthquake, 5:12 a.m. local time, April 18, 1906, was probably California's greatest. Visible surface faulting occurred from San Juan Bautista to Point Arena, where the San Andreas fault enters the ocean. At the same time surface faulting also occurred 75 miles north of Point Arena at Shelter Cove in Humboldt County, but it is not certain whether this was along the San Andreas fault proper or whether the breakage took place on an *en echelon* fault in the same zone. The 1906 scarp viewed at Shelter Cove in 1963 (photo 3, 4) clearly shows upthrow of 6 to 8 feet on the east side; there was no evidence of a horizontal component of displacement. However, offset of a line of old trees and an old fence viewed east of Point Arena in 1963 gave clear evidence of right-lateral displacement on the order of about 14 feet. The epicenter of the earthquake was near Olema, at the south end of Tomales Bay, near where a road was offset 20 feet in a right-lateral sense. Richter magnitude is generally computed at about 8.25. Damage has been estimated at from $350 million to $1 billion. An estimated 700 people were killed. A large part of the loss was due to the tremendous fires in San Francisco, which resulted from broken gas mains and lack of water owing to numerous ruptures in the lines.

Another of California's great earthquakes, comparable in magnitude to the San Francisco 1906 earthquake, was caused by displacement on a segment of the San Andreas fault extending through the southern part of the Coast Ranges province and on beyond across the Transverse Ranges. This Fort Tejon earthquake of January 9, 1857, probably centered in the region between Fort Tejon in the Tehachapi Mountains and the Carrizo Plain in the southern Coast Ranges. Surface faulting extended for 200 to 275 miles from Cholame Valley along the northeast side of the Carrizo Plain through Tejon Pass, Elizabeth Lake, Cajon Pass and along the south side of the San Bernardino Mountains. Accounts of this earthquake are unsatisfactory and inconclusive, but surface displacement almost certainly amounted to several feet in a right-lateral sense (Lawson and others, 1908; Townley and Allen, 1939; Wood, 1955).

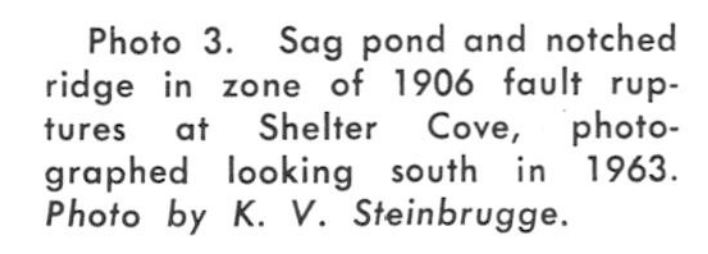

Photo 3. Sag pond and notched ridge in zone of 1906 fault ruptures at Shelter Cove, photographed looking south in 1963. *Photo by K. V. Steinbrugge.*

Photo 4. Aerial view of San Andreas fault in the northern Temblor Range, looking toward the north. Long narrow valley toward upper right is Antelope Valley. The fault trace here lies within gravels and sands of the Plio-Pleistocene Paso Robles Formation. *John S. Shelton photo.*

Thus, there have been in historic times two great earthquakes originating on the San Andreas fault, each accompanied by over 200 miles of surface ruptures: one at the southern end of the Coast Ranges and one in the north. Between is left a segment, roughly 90 miles long, in the southern Coast Ranges, which has not been disrupted by surface faulting in historic time. It is interesting to note that the two ends of this segment—the Hollister area and the Parkfield area—are now the most seismically active in the southern Coast Ranges. The extreme southern segment—south of the Tehachapi Mountains—is quiet on the San Andreas fault proper, but very active on the closely related San Jacinto, Elsinore, Inglewood, and Imperial faults (Allen and others, 1965). In the segment of surface rupture in 1906 many earthquakes have originated in the central and southern part of the San Andreas fault and its auxiliary faults in the East Bay—the Hayward and Calaveras faults. However, since 1906 there have been no earthquakes on the most northerly segment from Marin to Humboldt Counties (Tocher, 1959). The strongest earthquake in the Bay area since 1906 was the San Francisco earthquake of March 22, 1957, of magnitude 5.3. It originated at shallow depth near Mussel Rock, off the coast a few miles south of San Francisco; there was no surface faulting.

GEOMORPHIC FEATURES

Extensive activity along the San Andreas fault zone in Quaternary time has developed a linear depression, marked by all the features of a classic rift valley, extending the entire length of the fault and encompassing a width from a few hundred feet to over a mile and a half. Rift-valley features are particularly well expressed in the San Francisco Bay area (Oakeshott, 1959). Within the rift zone always occurs fault gouge and breccia and a disorganized jumble of fault-brecciated rocks of both the eastern and western blocks, the result of hundreds of repeated ruptures on different fault planes in late Pleistocene and Recent time. Features of the rift valleys have resulted from: (1) Repeated, discontinuous fault ruptures on the surface, often with the development of minor graben, horsts, and pressure ridges; (2) landsliding, triggered by earthquake waves and surface faulting; and (3) erosion of brecciated, readily weathered rock. Within the rift-valley troughs, it is common to find late Pliocene to Recent sediments.

Many of the observations made after the earthquake of 1906 are of great significance in understanding the origin and development of rift valleys and the nature of movement on the San Andreas fault: (1) Open ruptures were mapped along the fault trace from San Juan Bautista to Point Arena, and at Telegraph Hill north of Shelter Cove in Humboldt County; (2) individual fault ruptures were not continuous, but extended for a few feet to a mile or a little more, with the continuations of the displacements being picked up along *en echelon* breaks; (3) the ruptures were often complex, with small grabens and horsts developed between breaks; (4) apparent movements were dominantly right lateral, with lesser vertical displacements; and (5) the amount of displacement varied irregularly along the fault trace, but in a gross way decreased in both directions from the maximum at the south end of Tomales Bay.

North of San Francisco, across Marin County, the fault follows a remarkably straight course approximately N. 35° W. The most prominent features are Bolinas Bay and the long, linear Tomales Bay which lie in portions of the rift valley drowned by rising sea waters following the Pleistocene glacial epoch. Between these bays, the rift zone is a steep-sided trough, in places as deep as 1,500 feet, with its lower levels characterized by a remarkable succession of minor, alternating ridges and gullies parallel to the general trend of the fault zone. Surfaces of the ridges and gullies are spotted by irregular hummocks and hollows; many of the hollows are undrained and have developed sag ponds, so common along the San Andreas rift. Geologically Recent adjustment of the drainage in the rift zone leaves little positive evidence of the amount and direction of Recent displacement, except for that which took place in 1906. Offset lines of trees in this area still show the 13- to 14-foot right slip of 1906, and just south of Point Arena they also serve to show the 1906 offset. A large-scale plane-table map of the Fort Ross region by Matthes, published in the Earthquake Commission report (Lawson and others, 1908), is the best record of that portion of the rift zone in 1906. In the long stretch northward from Fort Ross to a point a few miles south of Point Arena, the broad expression of the rift zone is clear, but minor features within the zone have been obscured by erosion of the Gualala and Garcia Rivers and by the dense forest cover of the area.

South of San Francisco across San Mateo County the San Andreas fault zone follows the same trend as to the north but is less straight and is complicated by several subparallel faults. Near Mussel Rock, where the fault enters the land south of San Francisco, are great landslides which obscure the trace, and for a few miles to the southeast is a succession of sag ponds, notched ridges, and rift-valley lakes within a deeply trenched valley. The long, narrow San Andreas Lake and Crystal Springs Lakes are natural lakes which were enlarged many years ago by the artificial dams built to impound San Francisco's water supply. Similar rift-valley features mark the fault southward to the Tehachapi Mountains; because of the local aridity, they are particularly clear and striking in the Temblor Range area, in the Cholame Valley, and in the Carrizo Plain (photo 5, fig. 2). As the fault enters its eastward bend in the San Emigdio Mountains area, the rift-valley features become less striking, perhaps because the contrast between the basement rocks in the east and west blocks disappears where the fault lies wholly within granitic rocks and older schists (Crowell and others, 1964).

STRATIGRAPHY ALONG THE FAULT ZONE NORTH OF THE TEHACHAPI MOUNTAINS

The Coast Ranges province is a series of north-northwest-trending mountain ranges and intermontane valleys bounded on the east by the Great Valley and on the west by the Pacific Ocean. Since the San Andreas fault trends slightly more to the west than the general trend of the province, the fault zone completely crosses the Coast Ranges from its suboceanic junction with the Mendocino Escarpment on the north to the foothills on the western margin of the San Joaquin Valley in the south. The fault zone therefore crosses all essential elements of the extremely complex geology of the Coast Ranges. This geology has been treated earlier in this bulletin by Ben M. Page; I wish only to emphasize here those features which seem to have the greatest bearing on geologic history of the great San Andreas fault.

Perhaps the most geologically significant feature of the San Andreas fault in the Coast Ranges is that it separates two regions containing entirely different "basement" rocks—the Sur Series and quartz diorite to the west, and the Late Jurassic to Late Cretaceous Franciscan Formation to the east. There are apparent exceptions to this. It is unknown whether the fault under the ocean north of Point Arena continues to mark such a separation; the short segment on which surface displacement took place near Shelter Cove, in south coastal Humboldt County, in 1906 appears to lie wholly within Franciscan-type rocks. It may well be, however, that the Humboldt County fault is an *en echelon* fault within the San Andreas zone, and is not on the fault trace proper. On the San Francisco peninsula, the active San Andreas fault also lies wholly within the Franciscan Formation for a few miles where

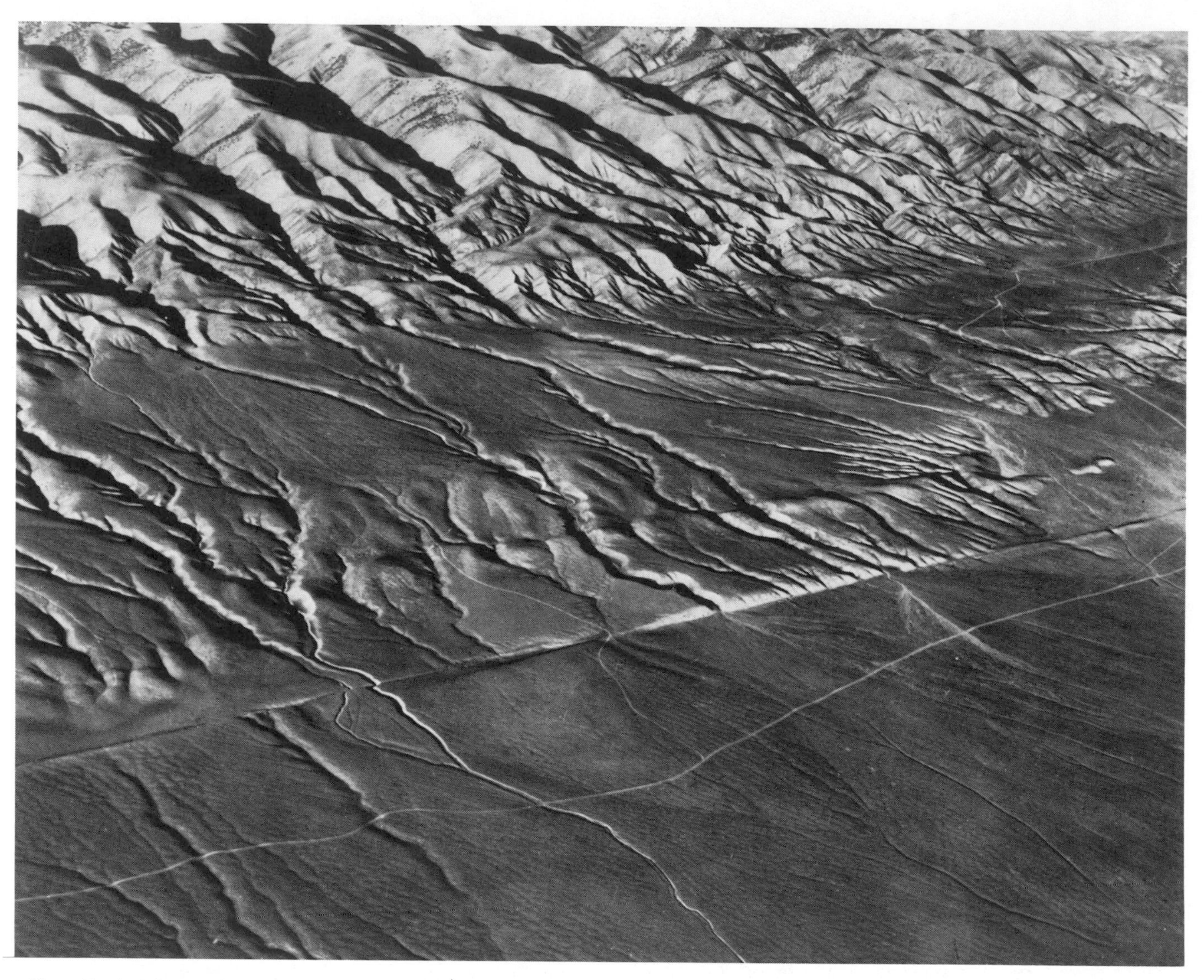

Photo 5. Aerial view of San Andreas fault on the east side of Carrizo Plain, looking east. This area is about 35 miles south of that shown in figure 5. Note that at least three *en echelon* fault traces are visible here. The youngest trace is that out on the valley floor, and as it is the only one which has offset modern drainage, it may be part of the surface fault associated with the 1857 Fort Tejon earthquake. Here the youngest fault trace appears to be the contact between valley alluvium and the Paso Robles Formation.

the older, inactive Pilarcitos fault forms the major rock-province contact. At the southern end of the Coast Ranges, where the San Andreas fault begins its sharp bend to enter the Transverse Ranges province, the fault is wholly within Late Mesozoic granitic rocks that appear to be continuous from the Sierra Nevada around the southern end of the San Joaquin Valley into the Coast Ranges. Farther south, the San Andreas fault is entirely within the "granitic" province. Any hope of unraveling pre-Tertiary history of the fault lies in understanding the origin, age, and geologic history of the two great lithologic units it separates. Herein lie serious difficulties.

Franciscan Formation

The Franciscan Formation is a heterogeneous unit of eugeosynclinal marine sedimentary and volcanic rocks which consists predominantly of massively bedded graywacke with interbedded dark shale, minor amounts of chert and limestone, altered volcanic rock (greenstone), and various metamorphic rocks of the zeolite, blueschist, greenschist, and eclogite facies. These rocks have been intruded by sill-like masses of peridotite, mostly serpentinized, which are prevalent in some parts of the San Andreas and related fault zones. The serpentine is highly mobile and much of it appears as "cold intrusions." A comprehensive paper by Bailey, Irwin, and Jones (1964) summarizes knowledge of the Franciscan and adds much new material based on modern geologic mapping and laboratory research. Rocks of the Franciscan Formation crop out very widely in all parts of the Coast Ranges, except between the San Andreas and Nacimiento fault zones. The formation is perhaps as much as 50,000 feet thick, but no top or base has been observed; the sediments and volcanics were probably deposited on ultramafic

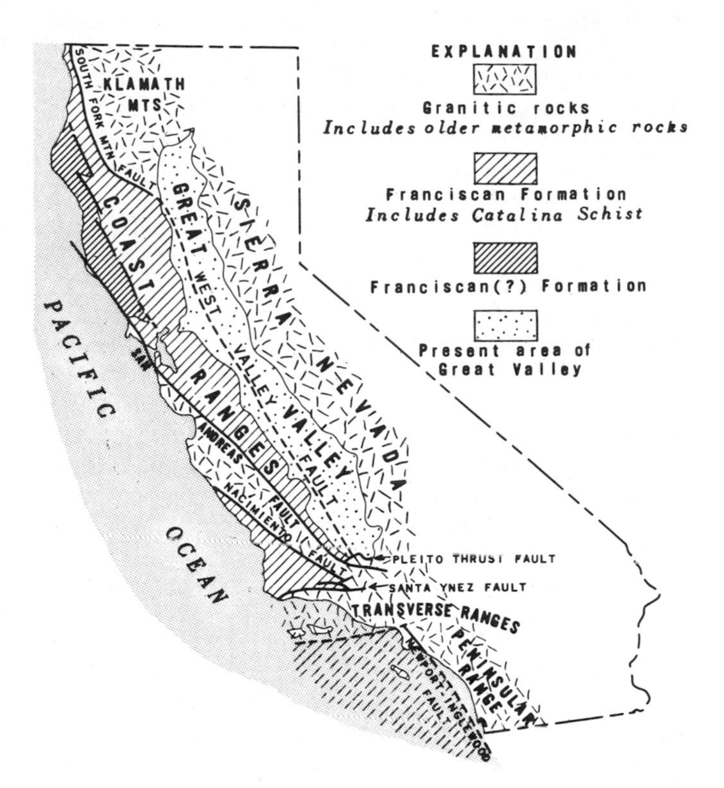

Figure 2. Franciscan-granite contacts, with shelf-facies rocks of Late Jurassic and younger age removed. Three great fault zones—Nacimiento, San Andreas, South Fork Mountain-West Valley—separate Franciscan "basement" rocks from granitic rocks (including older schists and gneisses and some unmetamorphosed rocks).

materials of the upper mantle (peridotite and serpentine), or on the "oceanic" layer, in deep, narrow, geosynclinal troughs by slides and turbidity currents, at the foot of the continental slope.

The large area shown on the Santa Rosa sheet of the State Geologic Map as "undivided Cretaceous marine" rocks in the coastal belt extending from Fort Ross to Point Arena, entirely east of the San Andreas fault, will be regarded here, as it was by Bailey and others, as a volcanic-poor unit of the Franciscan Formation of Cretaceous age. Fossils are very scarce throughout the entire Franciscan Formation, but the age range seems to be from Late Jurassic to Late Cretaceous. In any one area it is usually either Late Jurassic *or* Late Cretaceous. The older unit appears to be east of the Hayward fault and its northward projection.

Based on considerations of the pressure-temperature conditions of formation of the blueschists, Bailey and others postulate the metamorphic rocks indicate temperatures of less than 300°C, but pressures of 5 or more kilobars. They believe that these rocks must therefore have reached a depth of something like 70,000 feet, through accumulation and downwarping, so rapidly that a normal thermal gradient was not established. Uplift must have been equally rapid. If this sort of reasoning is valid, then "absolute" uplift of the Franciscan Formation on the San Andreas fault may have been on the order of 13 miles, perhaps beginning at the close of the Jurassic. Geochemical research is rapidly developing new information which may greatly affect any such conclusions (Coleman and Lee, 1963; Essene and others, 1965).

Granitic Rocks and Sur Series

The Sur Series gneisses, schists, and marble, discussed by R. R. Compton in this bulletin appear to consist of thick sedimentary and perhaps volcanic formations, of possible Late Paleozoic(?) age, which have been affected by high-grade metamorphism. They crop out most extensively in the Santa Cruz and Santa Lucia Mountains where they are intruded by, and occur as inclusions in, granitic rocks. These rocks form the basement in the strip between the San Andreas and Nacimiento-Sur fault zones. No fossils have been found in the Sur Series and their structures are so complex that reasonable estimates of thickness have not been made.

Most of the granitic rocks, such as at Point Reyes, Montara Mountain, and in the La Panza high appear to be quartz diorite but granodiorite and adamellite are present. Several radiometric dates are in the Late Cretaceous range, although a number have been obtained which appear anomalous. Hornblende from a "granitic-appearing" amphibolite at Gold Hill, in the San Andreas fault zone east of Paso Robles, yielded a date of 143 m.y., or Late Jurassic (Hay, 1963). Unpublished hornblende dates I obtained from the hornblende diorite gneiss in the fault zone at Logan, San Benito County, and on hornblende from a similar rock in the fault zone about a mile south of Logan yielded dates which appear to confirm the Jurassic age of these rocks. Closer dating is not yet justified.

Most probably some of the granitic rocks are of Late Jurassic and Late Cretaceous ages and are therefore essentially contemporaneous with the Franciscan Formation. To reach their present exposed situation the granitic rocks and Sur Series must have been elevated, both by faulting and folding, by many thousands of feet—perhaps 5 miles, or more. But what is their precise relationship to the Franciscan? Since these two major rock groups are never found in anything but *fault* contact, we can only speculate on their fundamental relationship.

Upper Jurassic To Upper Cretaceous Shelf-Facies Rocks

Further to complicate relationships in the Coast Ranges and therefore also understanding of the history of the San Andreas fault, a major group of sedimentary rocks representing all epochs from Late Jurassic to Late Cretaceous age crops out in the Coast Ranges on both sides of the fault zone. They comprise an aggregate thickness on the order of 30,000 feet of unmetamorphosed shelf-facies sandstone, shale, siltstone, and minor conglomerate and limestone. They are found, in a few places, lying on the granitic rocks, Sur Series, and Franciscan, but the thickest, most continuous section lies east of the Hayward fault zone (projected) and dips under the Great Valley from the east flanks of the Diablo and Mendocino Ranges. The Late Jurassic part of this section is predominantly dark shale; the Lower and Upper Cretaceous rocks are mainly graywacke and arkose with minor shale and conglomerate. They contain larger proportions of K-feldspar grains than does the Franciscan (Bailey and others, 1964). These rocks are, at least in considerable part, contemporaneous with the Franciscan and with the granitic rocks. The older shelf-facies rocks are in fault contact with both the Franciscan and granitic rocks, but the latest Cretaceous rocks lie depositionally on each "basement" rock.

Tertiary and Quaternary Formations

Cenozoic formations comprise a great variety of sedimentary and volcanic rocks, but all are of shallow marine (shelf and slope) and continental origin. Intermittent folding, faulting, and volcanism, often of limited areal extent in this era, are reflected in rapid changes in facies and thicknesses. Most local basins of deposition were oriented in a northwesterly direction, *approximately parallel to the trend of the San Andreas fault*, and deposits were derived from a westerly or easterly direction. Facies and thickness changes are most marked at the margins of the basins and take place commonly in an east-west direction *across the trend of the San Andreas fault*. These conditions have made it particularly difficult to convincingly match rock units or facies across the fault in order to document its displacement.

Paleocene marine sedimentary rocks are quite similar to those in Upper Cretaceous formations, but are not as thick or as widespread. Progressively more restricted seaways from Paleocene to late Eocene time limited the deposition of marine sands, muds, and clays to relatively narrow basins in the area of the Coast Ranges. Paleocene and Eocene formations are found in fault blocks on both sides of the San Andreas fault in the Bay area. The presence of formations of this age only west of the fault in the coastal "Gualala" strip from Fort Ross to Point Arena suggests late Eocene or post-Eocene displacement, but whether this has been produced by strike slip, dip slip, or oblique slip is not known; the formations have not been successfully matched with those in the block east of the fault. There are, however, faulted remnants of marine Paleocene and Eocene rocks in the east block along the Middle Fork of the Eel River about 70 miles north of the Gualala strip.

From late Eocene to middle Miocene time, seaways in the Coast Range region were severely restricted and climates became markedly seasonal and locally semiarid. Conglomerate, sandstone, shale and mudstone of these epochs include shallow marine materials and widespread, locally thick, continental red beds. Oligocene formations crop out only in the southern Coast Ranges; probably the northern Coast Range area was above sea level during Oligocene time. In the Santa Cruz, Santa Lucia, and Diablo Ranges, shallow-water marine sandstone, shale, some conglomerate, and local tuff beds represent deposits in rather restricted embayments and channels. Distribution of these sedimentary units is both east and west of the San Andreas fault in the ranges named, without any considerable lateral displacement required to explain their present position.

Early and middle Miocene formations consist of marine, shelf-facies sandstone, conglomerate, shale, and mudstone, which were deposited in rather narrow basins extensively in the southern Coast Ranges and in a narrow trough as far north as the central Mendocino Range in the northern Coast Ranges. Middle Miocene seas were more widespread than those of the early Miocene. Great volumes of volcanic materials were extruded during middle Miocene time—tuff, breccia, agglomerate, rhyolitic to andesitic flows, and plugs. Matching of such volcanic units across the San Andreas fault offers possibilities for documenting evidence of its nature and amounts of displacement, but is frustrating because of particularly rapid changes in facies and thicknesses.

In early late Miocene time shallow seas reached a maximum extent. The most widespread Tertiary formation is the Monterey Formation, of middle to late Miocene age, which is found throughout the Coast Ranges as far north as Point Arena. All common sedimentary rocks are represented, but must characteristic are siliceous shale, chert, and diatomaceous shale. The Miocene Epoch closed with deposition of coarser, sandy, marine sedimentary facies, such as the Santa Margarita, Sisquoc, and San Pablo Formations in more restricted basins between the rising Coast Ranges. The upper parts of these formations are of early Pliocene age.

In Pliocene time, sands, muds, and some tuff were deposited in narrow, shallow marine embayments throughout the Coast Ranges as far north as the Eel River basin. Most of the formations appear to thin or pinch out in the anticlinal-crest areas, reflecting uplift and folding of many of the individual ranges. Late Pliocene and early Pleistocene time was marked by restricted and thin local marine beds in narrow basins, and by a remarkably widespread and locally thick series of coarse, nonmarine sediments. Floods of gravel and coarse sand, which were deposited in the channels, deltas, and flood plains of streams, almost covered the site of the southern Coast Ranges and extended locally along the margins of the northern Coast Ranges. Volcanism was important in limited areas, but the activity did not compare with that of the great middle Miocene volcanic epoch.

In the San Francisco Bay area in late Pliocene and early Pleistocene time, a shallow, narrow seaway developed from the vicinity of Lake Merced southeastward through Merced Valley lying between the elevated blocks of the San Bruno and Montara Mountains. Over 5,000 feet of sand, silt, gravel, sandy mudstone, and layers of volcanic ash accumulated to form the Merced Formation. On the southwestern margin of this trough, and along the rift valley of the San Andreas fault, stream and alluvial-fan gravels, sand, and mud accumulated to form the Santa Clara Formation. Fossiliferous, slightly consolidated, rocks of the Merced Formation crop out in the San Andreas fault zone from Bolinas Bay for about 5 miles to the north, spreading broadly across more than 50 square miles of northern Marin County, east of the fault. Distribution and local thicknesses of the Merced and Santa Clara suggest that their deposition was strongly controlled by the San Andreas fault trough; these formations, however, spread thinly and widely both east and west of the fault.

Late Quaternary deposition is represented by coastal marine terrace deposits, bay mud, dune sands, and thin sediments along the San Andreas rift. Loosely consolidated arkosic sands crop out in the ridges and troughs within the San Andreas fault zone between Olema and Tomales Bay. Bolinas Lagoon and Tomales Bay are nearly landlocked bays in the rift valley.

STRUCTURAL HISTORY

In spite of the interests of geologists, and the very considerable amount of time and attention given by geologists and seismologists to study of the San Andreas fault, it remains very incompletely known and understood. There is no agreement on answers to such fundamental questions as: When did the fault originate? Should the Late Quaternary and "ancestral" San Andreas be regarded as different faults, developed by different stresses, and with entirely different characteristics and displacements? Have the sense and direction of displacement (right slip—east block moving south) always been the same, or has great vertical movement taken place? If the latter, which is the upthrown block? (Or has this changed from one side to the other in some segments during geologic time?) If dominantly right-lateral strike slip, has the present rate of displacement or strain, as discussed by Meade and Small in this bulletin (p. 385), been about the same since Cretaceous time? Is the cumulative displacement on the fault a few thousand feet or several hundred miles? To what depth does the faulting extend—5 or 6 miles, as suggested by the depth of earthquake foci, or several times this? Is the San Andreas fault becoming more, or less, active? Are earthquakes, which center in the San Andreas fault zone, relieving stresses and thus lessening the chances of future earthquakes, or do the continuing earthquakes merely indicate a high level of seismic activity portending many future earthquakes?

Three Great Faults

The San Andreas fault is but one of three great north-northwest-trending fault zones which appear to dominate the structural pattern of the Coast Ranges (fig. 3). The most westerly of these is the Nacimiento-Sur fault zone which separates the western coastal block of Franciscan basement rocks from the granitic block east of that fault zone. This fault is probably essentially normal, with perhaps some local right-lateral strike slip, but in its northerly projection extends into the Sur thrust zone which dips 30°–60° E. This fault zone has had a long and complex history. It comprises a large number of *en echelon* faults which are, in many places, apparently offset by cross faults. At the southern end of the Coast Ranges, the Nacimiento fault butts into the northeast-trending, left-lateral Big Pine fault yet faults farther west (for example, Suey fault) in the Nacimiento zone appear to bend continuously along the strike into the Big Pine fault. At the north end of the zone, the Sur thrust enters the ocean a few miles south of Monterey. In this area, in Pfeiffer Big Sur State Park, the fault involves upper Miocene rocks but does not cut Pleistocene terrace gravels (Oakeshot, 1951). The Nacimiento-Sur fault zone does not show the rift-valley features that are so characteristic of the San Andreas, and no earthquake epicenters along its trace have been reported.

The second great fault is the San Andreas, separating the granitic block on the west from the eastern block with Franciscan "basement." As its characteristics are discussed throughout this report, they require no special treatment here.

A third great fault zone, probably related to the Nacimiento and San Andreas in origin, is the South Fork Mountain-West Valley fault, which separates a Franciscan block on the west from granitic-metamorphic rocks on the east. This fault zone constitutes the

Figure 3. San Andreas fault zone, essentially as traced by Lawson and others in 1906. Dotted segment shows surface faulting in 1906; the dashed-line segment indicates surface faulting in 1857.

geologic, structural boundary between the Coast Ranges province and the Klamath-Sierra Nevada province. The South Fork Mountain fault, marked by a zone of pre-Cretaceous(?) schists several miles wide, forms the western and southwestern margin of the Klamath Mountains block (Irwin, 1960). Granitic rocks in the Klamath Mountains block, and in the western foothills of the Sierra Nevada, have yielded Late Jurassic radiometric dates. Along its southern continuation, the South Fork Mountain fault has been intruded by serpentine and appears to be overlapped by the Early Cretaceous miogeosynclinal rocks of the west side of the Great Valley. The southward projection of this great fault (Bailey and others, 1964; Oakeshott, 1964, 1965) may well form the contact between Sierra Nevada granitic rocks on the east and Franciscan rocks on the west. Gravity and magnetic anomalies mark this contact zone (Chapman, this bulletin; Griscom, this bulletin). It may have been active at the close of the Jurassic Period.

The Nacimiento-Sur, San Andreas, and South Fork Mountain-West Valley faults merge southward into the knot of major faults at the junction of the Coast Ranges, Sierra Nevada, and Transverse Ranges provinces. All three northwest-trending fault zones are completely interrupted by the east-west structures of the Transverse Ranges.

Age of the San Andreas Fault

Since there can be no disagreement that the San Andreas fault is presently active, the principal question is when movements began. Taliaferro (1943) emphasized the importance of distinguishing between the Quaternary San Andreas fault, on which displacements are still occurring, and the "ancestral" San Andreas which he regarded as "a profound normal fault developed in the early Eocene along the eastern side of the Gabilan Mesa * * *", and which always marks the boundary between the "crystalline basement complex and Mesozoic sedimentary rocks." Hill and Dibblee (1953), expressing fundamentally different views from Taliaferro, suggested very large cumulative right-lateral displacements of "perhaps 350 miles since Jurassic time," and "10 miles since the Pleistocene." Bailey, Irwin, and Jones (1964) suggest yet another mechanism in which the block west of the West Side fault separates from the eastern block in Late Jurassic time and drifts westward. The opening between blocks is filled with rocks of the Franciscan Formation and the eastern margin of the drifting block becomes the ancestral San Andreas fault. Since reaching its present position in Late Cretaceous time, Bailey suggests the fault has had no more than 50 miles of strike-slip movement.

In the segment of the San Andreas fault from the Tehachapi south, Crowell (1962) and Crowell and Walker (1962) have shown that Oligocene and all older rocks in the San Gabriel and Orocopia Mountains seem to have been displaced by the same amount. From this, and other evidence, the San Andreas fault in southern California need be no older than early Miocene. This is one of a number of profound differences between the geologic features of the fault in northern and southern California.

Evidences of mountain building in the Coast Ranges at the close of the Jurassic (Taliaferro, 1943; Page, this bulletin), accompanied by intrusion of granitic rocks and the development of narrow troughs into which great thicknesses of Franciscan sediments and volcanics were dumped, make it appear likely that development of an ancestral San Andreas fault began as early as closing Jurassic time. Repeated movements have doubtless taken place in this fault zone, accompanying other movements in orogenic epochs culminating in the greatest orogeny of the Coast Ranges in late Pliocene to mid-Pleistocene time and continuing to the present day.

Nature and Amount of Displacement

In 1953, Hill and Dibblee advanced the possibility of cumulative right-lateral displacement of hundreds of miles since Jurassic time on the San Andreas fault. This hypothesis has received very wide acceptance among earth scientists, has intrigued geologists, and has been an important factor in stimulating work on the fault. The concept of large strike slip on the San Andreas was not original with Hill and Dibblee, for Noble (1926) suggested a horizontal shift of apparently 24 miles since deposition of the "Martinez" (Paleocene) beds in the Transverse Ranges of southern California. Hill and Dibblee used lithologic, faunal, and facies similarities in attempting correlations across the fault to suggest right-lateral separation of 10 miles since the Pleistocene, 65 miles since upper Miocene, 175 miles since early Miocene, 225 miles since late Eocene, 320 miles since Cretaceous, and 350 miles since the Jurassic Period (see Dibblee this bulletin, p). This analysis is especially impressive because Dibblee had personally mapped about 300 miles along the San Andreas fault zone on the mile-to-the-inch scale. It is interesting to note that Taliaferro (1943), who had previously mapped more of the fault zone than any other geologist save Dibblee, felt less confident about such correlations and stated unequivocally that horizontal movement on the San Andreas fault north of Parkfield has been less than 1 mile!

Geologic evidence is so varied that geologists have drawn conflicting interpretations of the geologic history and characteristics of the fault; at one extreme are those who believe that there has been several hundred miles of right slip since Late Jurassic time, and at the other are those who consider that there has been large vertical displacement on an ancestral San Andreas fault and relatively small lateral displacement in Late Tertiary and Quaternary time. I have adaptd the following discussion of some of the evidence for displacement from two recent papers (Oakeshott, 1964, 1965).

Seismologic evidence, geodetic measurements, and geomorphic observations point strongly, but not entirely, to right-lateral displacement in historic and Late Quaternary time. This type of evidence and the remarkable rift-valley features are too well known to justify more than a sketchy review here. Observers who contributed to the monumental report of the State Earthquake Investigation Commission after 1906 (Lawson and others, 1908) cited the obvious preponderance of right separation along the fault trace, up to a maximum of 20 feet; but they also noted that the western block moved relatively upward a probable maximum of 3 feet. Re-surveys of first-order triangulation nets by the Coast and Geodetic Survey suggest that strain or displacement on the San Andreas fault north of the 36th parallel has averaged about 1 to 3 cm a year since 1885, the east block moving south (Whitten, 1955; Meade and Small, this bulletin, p. 385). South of that parallel Meade and Small found no significant horizontal displacement but do cite evidence of uplift (this bulletin). In a talk presented to the Stanford Journal Club in October 1963, Robert D. Burford reported on an analysis of C. A. Whitten's vectors across the San Andreas fault system near Hollister. His analysis showed right displacement on the northwest-trending faults, left displacement on two northeast-trending faults, and extension at right angles to the trace of the San Andreas fault. He concluded that displacement near the San Andreas fault in that locality has been at the rate of 3 cm per year, and a few miles to the west and east, at the rate of 2 cm per year. Wallace (1949) computed a displacement of 0.2 inch per year since 1857 by adding known displacements associated with historic earthquakes.

Tocher (1960) has measured slow creep at the winery south of Hollister at about half an inch per year. This occurs in "spasms" of a few days, separated by intervals of weeks or months. Hill and Dibblee (1953) computed average displacement of 0.2 to 0.3 inches per year, based on their postulated movements for various ages as far back as Late Jurassic time. Cluff (1965) and Radbruch (1965) have reported several cases of well-substantiated right-lateral creep on the order of an eighth to a quarter of an inch per year, averaged for about 40 years, along the 1868 trace of the Hayward fault from Irvington to the University of California Stadium.[1]

Recently, the State Department of Water Resources, in its crustal strain investigation program (Gibson, 1961, and State Department of Water Resources, 1963), has made geodimeter measurements of 2,600 miles of surveying across the San Andreas and related faults. That Department's statement is "* * * a preliminary evaluation of measurements across the San Andreas fault suggests right-lateral movement between Hollister and Simmler. The few repeat measurements available between Simmler and the intersection of the San Andreas and Garlock faults [farther south] suggest left-lateral movement. South of the Garlock fault, it has not been possible to establish a consistent pattern of movement."

An interesting departure from the pattern of right-slip movements has been recorded by Tocher (1959) for the San Francisco earthquake of March 1957. In applying Byerly's method for deducing the nature of faulting from seismograms, Tocher concluded that the movement causing that earthquake was not a repetition of the observed right-lateral movement of 1906, but instead was largely vertical displacement on a steeply dipping reverse fault with the east block moving relatively upward. Thus, it would appear that increments of movement on the San Andreas fault may be of different sense at different times and places.

Most of the geomorphic evidence for Quaternary displacement on the San Andreas fault has been based on offset drainage features. Nature of the evidence may be seen from the following examples: Noble (1926) reported four deep ravines which were offset 150 feet at a point 3 miles southeast of Cajon Pass; Allen (1946) noted offsets of drainage amounting to 3,800 feet in the Gabilan Range; Wallace recorded drainage features offset up to 1½ miles on the north side of the San Gabriel Mountains; and Hill and Dibblee saw 3,000 feet of stream offset in the Temblor Range. Higgins (1961) did detailed mapping in the fault zone north of San Francisco Bay and concluded that there the fault was active before middle Pliocene time, but that the evidence was insufficient to allow determination of either the type or amount of pre-middle Pliocene displacement. None of the anomalous stream courses in that area gave clear evidence of lateral displacement; all can best be attributed to deflection by slides or earthflows, to headward erosion along softened rocks in the fault zone, to vertical movement of fault slivers, and to other minor structural controls within the fault zone. Galloway (1962) has been working on these problems in the San Andreas fault zone in the Bolinas-Point Reyes area for several years. His detailed mapping in the zone has disclosed no evidence of either the sense or amount of displacement.

Seismologic evidence, geodetic measurements, and geomorphic observations generally strongly suggest right slip in very late Quaternary time, but also indicate that the sense of movement in increments of slip has not always been the same. *Extrapolation of this very short experience back over geologic periods of many millions of years appears wholly unjustifiable.*

Unraveling of the pre-Quaternary history of the San Andreas fault is much more difficult than deciphering its later history, and uncertainties multiply as we attempt to trace the fault displacements back into Early Tertiary time and to document a possible pre-

[1] See six related papers on Slippage on the Hayward fault: (Cluff and Steinbrugge, 1966; Bonilla, 1966; Blanchard and Laverty, 1966; Radbruch and Lennert, 1966; Bolt and Marion, 1966; Pope, Stearn, and Whitten, 1966).

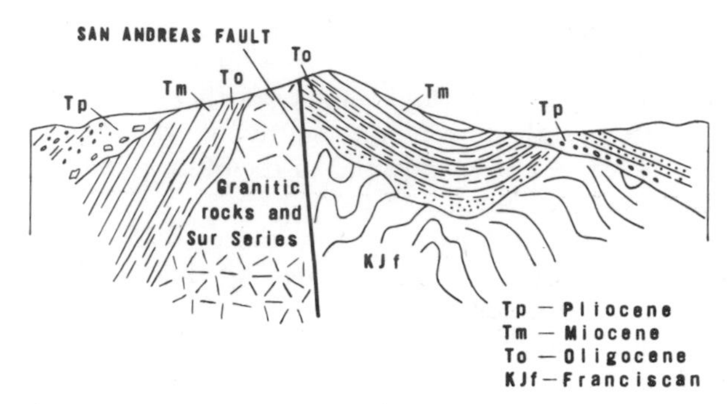

Figure 4. Diagrammatic section near Pajaro Gap, Santa Cruz-San Benito Counties, showing similarity of geologic units on both sides of San Andreas fault.

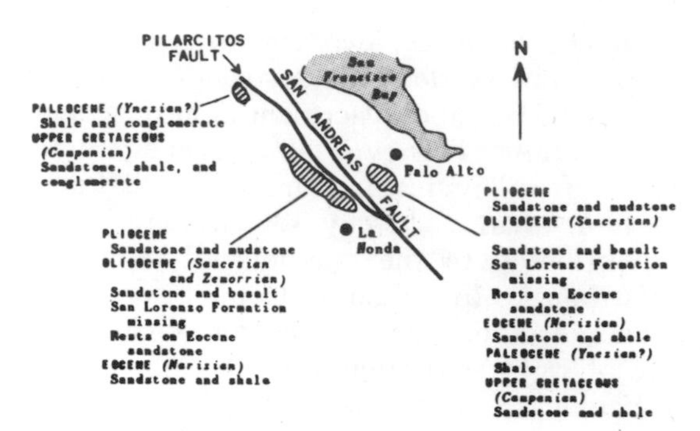

Figure 6. Big Basin area, Santa Cruz Mountains, showing how Cretaceous and Tertiary rocks correlate across the San Andreas fault zone. *After Cummings, Touring, and Brabb, 1962.*

Tertiary history. We shall now examine a small part of that evidence in selected areas in the segment north of the Tehachapi (more completely reviewed in Oakeshott, 1965).

Figure 3 shows the San Andreas fault much as it was mapped by Lawson and others, in 1906, and it also includes other faults that will be discussed. The dotted segment of the fault, from San Juan Bautista to the ocean north of Point Arena, denotes the surface fracture associated with the 1906 San Francisco earthquake. Surface faulting (east block raised) that took place at the same time along an *en echelon* fault at Shelter Cove in southern Humboldt County is indicated by the northernmost fault line. On the San Francisco peninsula the Late Quaternary San Andreas fault

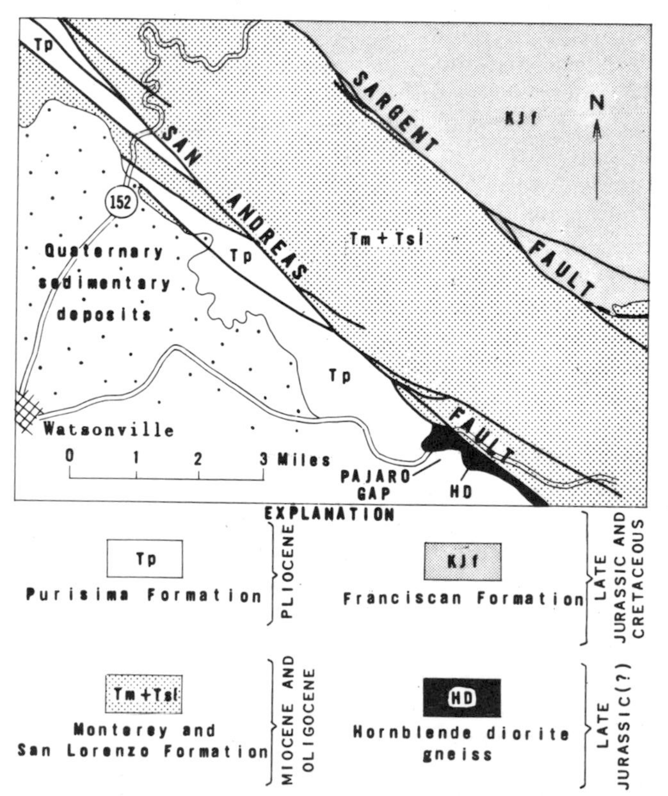

Figure 5. Pattern of faults in the Pajaro River area, according to Allen (1946).

departs from the old major fault zone as the important fault which separates distinctive geologic units here is the Pilarcitos, not the San Andreas as named by Lawson (1908). Surface faulting which took place at the time of the 1857 Fort Tejon earthquake, from Priest Valley to San Bernardino, is shown by the dashed-line segment in that area.

Figure 4 is a diagrammatic section (my field interpretation from Allen, 1946) representing the rock formations that are exposed in the Pajaro River Gap and vicinity across the southern end of the Santa Cruz Mountains. Figure 5 shows the pattern of faulting in this area, according to Allen (1946). Here the San Andreas fault is unusually well exposed. Basement rocks in the west block consist of the Sur Series gneisses and schists of pre-Cretaceous age which have been intruded by Late Jurassic and Cretaceous granitic rocks. On the east are the complex rocks of the Late Jurassic to Late Cretaceous Franciscan Formation. Three Tertiary formations, which are exposed above the basement rocks on both sides of the fault, appear lithologically, structurally, and stratigraphically identical. Oligocene marine shale crops out on both sides of the fault and grades upward into the distinctive, thin-bedded sandstone and siliceous shale of the Miocene Monterey Formation. Unconformably lying on the Monterey Formation on both sides of the fault are the much coarser sandstones and conglomerates of the Pliocene Purisima Formation. The Purisima overlaps the older Tertiary units to lie unconformably on Franciscan in the east block and on granitic rocks and Sur Series on the west. At one nearby locality the basal beds of the Purisima that lie on granitic rock contain an abundance of extremely coarse clasts of Franciscan rocks which must have come across the fault zone. There is thus no evidence for, and no necessity for, large Tertiary or post-Tertiary displacement on the San Andreas fault in this region.

In figure 4 the west side of the section is the southern end of the Santa Cruz basin, the east side is the north end of the Hollister Trough. If there has been large-lateral displacement on the San Andreas fault, these two Tertiary basins would not be continuous but would be matched by sedimentary-rock sections many miles apart across the fault. After years of work in this region, Gribi (1963) recently had this to say:

> "'Slippers' would match the Hollister Trough sediments with rocks in some basin far to the northwest on the west side of the San Andreas fault. However, the rocks from Eocene into middle Miocene of the southeast end of the Santa Cruz Basin are similar to their counterparts immediately across the fault in the northwest end of the Hollister Trough in lithology, thickness, and faunal content. Upper Miocene and Pliocene rocks show some differing characteristics, but these differences are no greater than have been demonstrated by simple facies and thickness changes in similar rocks in areas not affected by lateral faulting. Therefore, as a working hypothesis here it is assumed that the Hollister Trough is the depositional and structural continuation of the Half Moon Bay-Santa Cruz Basin. With its definite connection to the San Benito Trough, Vallecitos Syncline, Priest Valley-Warthan Canyon Syncline, the San Joaquin Valley, and probably the Bitterwater Basin and the Salinas Basin, the Hollister Trough becomes an integral part of California Tertiary sedimentary history and particularly of a great linear zone of weakness, a portion of which coincides with the present-day San Andreas fault."

At San Juan Bautista, about 6 miles southeast of Pajaro Gap, the west block of the fault, in which Sur Series gneisses and granitic rocks are exposed, is at least 10,000 feet structurally higher than the Hollister Trough immediately across the fault to the east.

Farther north in the Santa Cruz Mountains, Brabb (1960) and associates (Cummings, Touring, and Brabb, 1962) did large-scale, detailed geologic mapping west of the San Andreas fault and compared the Late Cretaceous-to-Pliocene geologic columns and histories across the San Andreas-Pilarcitos fault zone, as shown on figure 6. Lithology, stratigraphy, fossil zones, and geologic history correlate so strikingly across the faults here from Late Cretaceous (Campanian) to Pliocene time as to apparently preclude any cumulative offset measurable in miles since the Late Cretaceous. Evidence from the given examples of matching geology across the fault suggests that there are no compelling geological reasons for lateral displacements measurable in miles since Late Cretaceous (Santonian?) time.

It is evident that, in the present state of knowledge, the origin, nature, and history of movement on the San Andreas and related faults are not clear. Late Quaternary evidence strongly, but not exclusively, favors predominant right-slip displacement. Late Cretaceous and Tertiary stratigraphy, structure, and geologic history which can be matched across the fault in central and northern California leave little room for strike-slip displacement of more than a mile or two. Abrupt thickness and facies changes in rock units of these ages and very complex structures throw great difficulties in the way of matching geological elements across the fault. Distribution of Late Mesozoic Franciscan rocks and granitic rocks of near-equivalent age cannot be satisfactorily explained by large strike-slip movement, but does appear to require vertical displacements on the order of more than 10 miles. *For the present, geologists, seismologists, and geophysicists should retain multiple working hypotheses concerning displacement on the San Andreas and related major faults.*

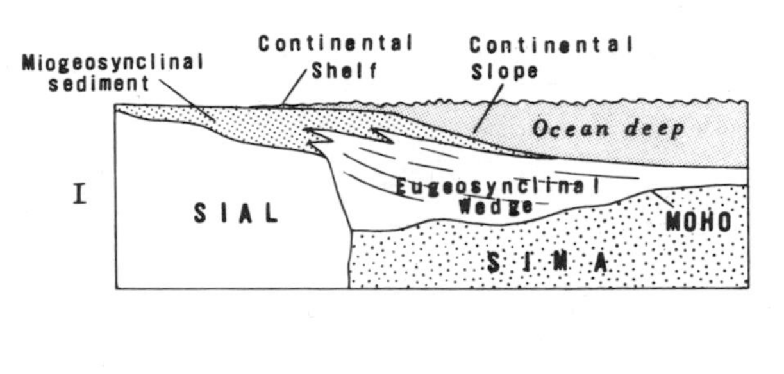

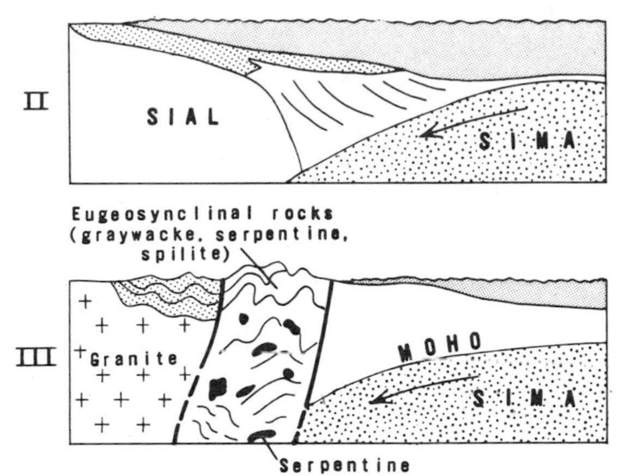

Figure 7. Stages in Alpine orogeny, after Dietz, 1963, with hypothetical faults added.

ORIGIN OF THE FAULT SYSTEM

How and why did the San Andreas fault system, including its associated northwest-trending fault—the Nacimiento-Sur and the South Fork Mountain-West Valley faults—originate?

Here we move into the realm of speculation, but we are not wholly without some basis for discussion. We have noted earlier that geologic relationships between the Franciscan Formation and the granitic blocks seem to require absolute vertical elevation of the Franciscan on the order of 10 miles, and elevation relative to the granitic segments of the crust of an unestimated amount. Bailey (1963) and Bailey and others (1964) proposed westward continental drifting and rifting to form "sphenochasms" between blocks of continental crust, thus providing sites for deposition of the Franciscan Formation directly on sima. In any case, initiation of this great faulting at the juncture of the ocean basin and continental platform was probably in closing Jurassic time; additional first-order faulting took place in Late Cretaceous time. Slivers and pods of ultramafic rocks were caught up and intruded into the lower part of the Franciscan from the upper mantle at the time the eugeosynclinal trough reached its maximum depression. Figure 7, after Dietz (1963A, 1963B), suggests how this sort of thing might happen. This diagram shows three stages in alpine orogeny after Dietz' concept of geosynclines and mountain building, a concept which appears compatible with the great fault features of western California which have been so briefly outlined. I have modified his diagrams somewhat and have added hypothetical faults in stage III.

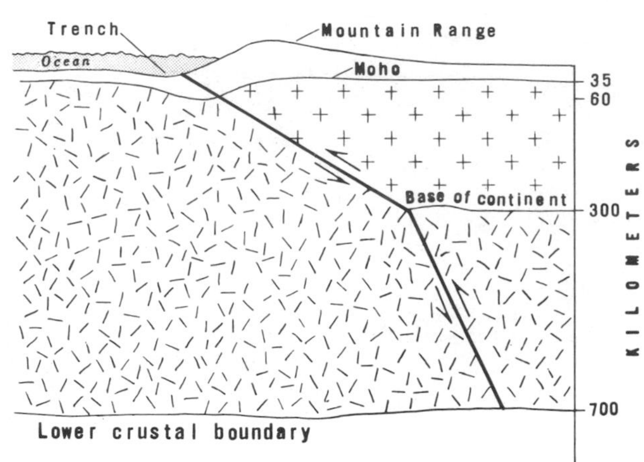

Figure 8. Continental crustal section with orogenic fault type. *After Benioff, 1954.*

The three stages as applied to the Coast Ranges might be:

I. Franciscan sediments and volcanics are rapidly deposited in a eugeosynclinal wedge at the base of the continental slope, generally seaward from nearly contemporaneous deposition of shelf, or miogeosynclinal, deposits.

II. Sea-floor spreading (under a force perhaps supplied by thermal convection cells in the mantle) provides the initial thrust which causes the sima to slip under the sial of the continent. The bottom of the prism of deep-sea turbidites is forced even deeper and is intruded by, and picks up, fragments of the simatic basement.

III. The mantle tends to shear beneath the continental platform, granitic intrusion begins early in the thrusting, and the prism is intensely folded, faulted, and elevated to form coastal mountains. The generalized, diagrammatic faults emphasize the prominent role that steep, dip-slip, reverse faults probably play in this history.

Benioff (1954) studied the elastic strain-rebound characteristics and related spatial distribution of foci of hundreds of seismic sequences to demonstrate the characteristics of oceanic and marginal orogenic faults. Figure 8 is his diagram showing a continental crustal section with orogenic fault type. The fault-dip angles of 32° to a depth of 300 km and 60° to 700 km should not be taken quantitatively, but it is significant that seismology, quite independently, develops a diagram showing deep major faulting extending under the continental margin and dipping toward the continent. Although the San Andreas fault appears to be nearly vertical, it is quite possible that it flattens near the Moho and that Benioff's section is more applicable than it appears to be at first glance.

REFERENCES

Allen, C. R., St. Amand, P., Richter, C. F., and Nordquist, J. M., 1965, Relationship between seismicity and geologic structure in the southern California region: Seismol. Soc. America Bull., v. 55, no. 4, p. 753–797.

Allen, J. E., 1946, Geology of the San Juan Bautista quadrangle, California: California Div. Mines Bull. 133, p. 9–75.

Anderson, F. M., 1899, The geology of Point Reyes Peninsula: California Univ. Dept. Geology Bull., v. 2, no. 5, p. 119–153.

Bailey, E. H., 1964, Mesozoic sphenochasmic rifting along the San Andreas fault north of the Transverse Ranges [abs.]: Geol. Soc. America Spec. Paper 76, p. 186–187.

Bailey, E. H., Irwin, W. P., and Jones, D. L., 1964, Franciscan and related rocks, and their significance in the geology of western California: California Div. Mines and Geology Bull. 183, 177 p.

Benioff, H., 1954, Orogenesis and deep crustal structure—additional evidence from seismology: Geol. Soc. America Bull., v. 65, no. 5, p. 385–400.

Blanchard, F. B., and Laverty, C. L., 1966, Displacements in the Claremont water tunnel at the intersection with the Hayward fault: Seismol. Soc. America Bull., v. 56, no. 2.

Bolt, Bruce A., and Marion, Walter C., 1966, Instrumental measurement of slippage on the Hayward fault: Seismol. Soc. America Bull. v. 56, no. 2.

Bonilla, M. G., 1966, Deformation of railroad tracks by slippage on the Hayward fault in the Niles district of Fremont, California: Seismol. Soc. America Bull., v. 56, no. 2.

Brabb, E. E., 1960, Geology of the Big Basin area, Santa Cruz Mountains, California: Stanford Univ., Stanford, Ph.D. thesis, 192 p.

Burford, R. D., 1963, Strain analysis across the San Andreas fault system near Hollister, California: Stanford Journal Club talk, Oct. 1963.

Byerly, Perry, 1951, History of earthquakes in the San Francisco Bay area: California Div. Mines Bull. 154, p. 151–160.

California Department of Water Resources, 1963, Crustal strain and fault measurement investigation—progress report: California Dept. Water Resources, Bull. 116-1, 37 p. and map.

California Division of Mines and Geology, 1958–1965, Geologic map of California, Olaf. P. Jenkins edition, published sheets: California Div. Mines and Geology, scale 1:250,000.

California Resources Agency, 1964, Earthquake and geologic hazards conference, December 7 and 8, 1964, San Francisco, Calif., 154 p.

California Resources Agency, 1965, Landslide and subsidence conference, San Francisco, Calif. (In press)

Campbell, Ian, and Jennings, C. W., 1964, University research projects on California geology: California Div. Mines and Geology, Mineral Inf. Serv., v. 17, no. 7, p. 111–118.

Cluff, Lloyd, 1965, Evidence of creep along the Hayward fault: Assoc. Eng. Geologists, First Ann. Joint Mtg. San Francisco-Sacramento Sec., paper delivered at Berkeley, Sept. 25, 1965.

Cluff, Lloyd S., and Steinbrugge, Karl V., 1966, Hayward fault slippage in the Irvington-Niles districts of Fremont, California: Seismol. Soc. America Bull., v. 56, no. 2.

Coleman, R. G., and Lee, D. E., 1963, Glaucophane-bearing metamorphic rock types of the Cazadero area, California: Jour. Petrology [Oxford], v. 4, no. 2, p. 260–301.

Crowell, J. C., 1962, Displacement along the San Andreas fault, California: Geol. Soc. America Spec. Paper 71, 61 p.

Crowell, J. C., and Walker, W. R., 1962, Anorthosite and related rocks along the San Andreas fault, southern California: California Univ. Pubs. Geol. Sci., v. 40, no. 4, p. 219–287.

Crowell, J. C., and others, 1964, The San Andreas fault zone from the Temblor Mountains to Antelope Valley, southern California: Am. Assoc. Petroleum Geologists-Soc. Econ. Paleontologists and Mineralogists, Pacific Sec., and San Joaquin Geol. Soc. Guidebook, 51 p.

Cummings, J. C., Touring, R. M., and Brabb, E. E., 1962, Geology of the northern Santa Cruz Mountains, California: California Div. Mines and Geology Bull. 181, p. 179–220.

Dietz, R. S., 1963a, Alpine serpentines as oceanic rind fragments: Geol. Soc. America Bull., v. 74, no. 7, p. 947–952.

——1963b, Collapsing continental rises—an actualistic concept of geosynclines and mountain building: Jour. Geology, v. 71, no. 3, p. 314–333.

Essene, E. J., Fyfe, W. S., and Turner, F. J., 1965, Genesis of Franciscan metamorphic types in California [abs.]: Geol. Soc. America, Ann. Mtg., Kansas City, Mo., 1965, program, p. 52.

Gibson, W. M., 1961, Geodimeter measurements across the San Andreas fault, California [abs.]: Geol. Soc. America, Cordilleran Sec.–Seismol. Soc. America–Paleontol. Soc., Pacific Coast Sec., Ann. Mtg., San Diego, Calif., 1961, program, p. 37.

Gribi, E. A., Jr., 1963, Hollister Trough oil province: Geol. Soc. Sacramento, Guidebook Ann. Field Trip, San Juan Bautista to Yosemite Valley, Calif., 1963, p. 77–80.

Hay, E. A., 1963, Age and relationships of the Gold Hill pluton, Cholame Valley, California, Guidebook to the geology of Salinas Valley and the San Andreas fault: Am. Assoc Petroleum Geologists-Soc. Econ. Paleontologists and Mineralogists, Ann. Spring field trip, 1963, p. 113–115.

Higgins, C. G., 1961, San Andreas fault north of San Francisco, California: Geol. Soc. America Bull., v. 72, no. 1, p. 51–68.

Hill, M. L., and Dibblee, T. W., Jr., 1953, San Andreas, Garlock, and Big Pine faults, California—a study of the character, history, and tectonic significance of their displacements: Geol. Soc. America Bull., v. 64, no. 4, p. 443–458.

Irwin, W. P., 1960, Geologic reconnaissance of the northern Coast Ranges and Klamath Mountains, California, with a summary of the mineral resources: California Div. Mines Bull. 179, 80 p.

James, L. B., 1964, The role of engineering geology in planning the route for the California Aqueduct across the Tehachapi Mountains: Am. Assoc. Petroleum Geologists-Soc. Econ. Paleontologists and Mineralogists, Pacific Sec., and San Joaquin Geol. Soc. Guidebook, p. 47–48.

Jennings, C. W., and Strand, R. G., 1963, Index to graduate theses on California geology to December 31, 1961: California Div. Mines and Geology Spec. Rept. 74, 39 p.

Koenig, J. B., 1962, Index to geologic maps of California, 1957–1960: California Div. Mines and Geology Spec. Rept. 52A, 60 p.

——1963, The geologic setting of Bodega Head: California Div. Mines and Geology, Mineral Inf. Serv., v. 16, no. 7, p. 1–10.

Lawson, A. C., 1893, The post-Pliocene diastrophism of the coast of southern California: California Univ. Dept. Geology Bull., v. 1, no. 4, p. 115–160.

——1914, San Francisco, California: U.S. Geol. Survey Geol. Atlas, Folio 193, 24 p. (field ed., 1915, 180 p.)

Lawson, A. C., and others, 1908, The California earthquake of April 18, 1906, Report of the State Earthquake Investigation Committee: Carnegie Inst. Washington Pub. 87, v. 1, pts. 1–2, 451 p.

Noble, L. F., 1926, The San Andreas rift and some other active faults in the desert region of southeastern California: Carnegie Inst. Washington Yearbook 25, 1925–1926, p. 415–428; reprinted in 1927, Seismol. Soc. America Bull., v. 17, no. 1, p. 25–40.

Oakeshott, G. B., 1951, Guide to the geology of Pfeiffer Big Sur State Park, Monterey County, California: California Div. Mines Spec. Rept. 11, 16 p.

——ed., 1959, San Francisco earthquakes of March 1957: California Div. Mines Spec. Rept. 57, 127 p.

——1959, San Andreas fault in Marin and San Mateo Counties, *in* San Francisco earthquake of March 1957: California Div. Mines Spec. Rept. 57, p. 7–24.

——1964a, The San Andreas Fault—predominant lateral or vertical displacement?: Pacific Petroleum Geologists, v. 18, no. 12, p. 3; also, 1965, San Joaquin Geol. Soc., Selected Papers, v. 3, p. 5–18.

——1964b, San Andreas fault revisited—evidence for displacement [abs.]: Seismol. Soc. America, Cordilleran Sec., 60th Ann. Mtg., Seattle, Wash., 1964, program, p. 48.

Pope, A. J., Stearn, J. L., and Whitten, C. A., 1966, Surveys for crustal movement along the Hayward fault: Seismol. Soc. America Bull., v. 56, no. 2.

Radbruch, D. H., 1965, Approximate location of fault traces and historic surface ruptures within the Hayward fault zone between San Pablo and Warm Springs, California: U.S. Geol. Survey open-file map, scale 1:62,500.

Radbruch, D. H., and Lennert, Ben J., 1966, Damage to culvert under Memorial Stadium, University of California, Berkeley, caused by slippage in the Hayward fault zone: Seismol. Soc. America Bull., v. 56, no. 2.

Richter, C. F., 1958, Elementary seismology: San Francisco, Calif., W. H. Freeman and Co., 768 p.

Strand, R. G., Koenig, J. B., and Jennings, C. W., 1958, Index to geologic maps of California to December 31, 1956: California Div. Mines Spec. Rept. 52, 128 p.

Taliaferro, N. L., 1943, Geologic history and structure of the central Coast Ranges of California: California Div. Mines Bull. 118, p. 119–163.

Tocher, Don, 1959, Seismographic results from the 1957 San Francisco earthquakes: California Div. Mines Spec. Rept. 57, p. 59–71.

——1960, Creep on the San Andreas fault—Creep rate and related measurements at Vineyard, California: Seismol. Soc. America Bull., v. 50, no. 3, p. 398–404.

Townley, S. D., and Allen, M. W., 1939, Descriptive catalog of earthquakes of the Pacific Coast of the United States, 1769 to 1928: Seismol. Soc. America Bull., v. 29, no. 1, p. 1–297.

VanderHoof, V. L., 1955, The major earthquakes of California—a historical summary: California Div. Mines Bull. 171, p. 137–142.

Wallace, R. E., 1949, Structure of a portion of the San Andreas rift in southern California: Geol. Soc. America Bull., v. 60, no. 4, p. 781–806.

Whitten, C. A., 1955, Measurements of earth movements in California: California Div. Mines Bull. 171, p. 75–80.

Wood, H. O., 1955, The 1857 earthquake in California: Seismol. Soc. America Bull., v. 45, no. 1, p. 47–67.

San Francisco earthquake of 1865. From *Roughing It,* by Mark Twain, 1872.

EVIDENCE FOR CUMULATIVE OFFSET ON THE SAN ANDREAS FAULT IN CENTRAL AND NORTHERN CALIFORNIA *

By T. W. Dibblee, Jr.
U.S. Geological Survey, Menlo Park, California

INTRODUCTION

It is agreed among all geologists who have investigated the San Andreas fault that the latest movements are horizontal in the right-lateral (dextral) sense. However, as indicated in the preceding summary article, geologists do not agree on the type, direction, and magnitude of earlier movements. Their interpretations vary according to the parts of the fault they have investigated, and with the way in which they have mapped and interpreted the related geology.

The geology on both sides of all but a few segments of the San Andreas fault has been mapped or partly mapped by the writer, and his initial interpretations of the time, direction, and magnitude of movements on this master fault have already been presented (Hill and Dibblee, 1953, p. 445–450). Additional field observations by the writer since that time cast more light on those inferences, calling for some modifications in magnitude, but do not alter the basic concept of large cumulative right-lateral movement since the inception of this generally vertical fault.

This progress report presents the evidences of lateral offsets, as now interpreted, on the central and northwestern parts of the San Andreas fault—the parts within the Coast Ranges province. The latest offsets are most clearly discernible and are described first, followed by descriptions of earlier offsets which become progressively less discernible with age. For evidence of right-lateral offsets on the southern continuation of the San Andreas fault southeast from Gorman, the reader is referred to descriptions by Noble (1954) and Crowell (1960, 1962).

* Publication authorized by the Director, U.S. Geological Survey.

Photo 1. Aerial view southwest across low scarp of San Andreas fault exposed in the Carrizo Plain, Painted Rock quadrangle. Arroyo in Quaternary alluvial sediments shows 400 feet of right-lateral offset along fault.

OFFSETS DURING QUATERNARY TIME

Physiographic features formed by the latest Quaternary lateral movements on the San Andreas fault are described in detail in many publications that describe the fault. Most stream channels that drain southwestward across the fault are consistently offset to the northwest, and those that drain northeastward across it are offset to the southeast. These relations can be seen along the entire 600-mile known length of the fault and are the most positive evidence of right-lateral movement. Offset stream channels are especially evident in the Carrizo Plain where some channels that drain southwestward from the Temblor Range apparently are offset as much as 3,000 feet (Hill and Dibblee, 1953, p. 446). In the Santa Cruz Mountains a number of channels, including the Pajaro River, are offset about 3,800 feet (Allen, 1946, p. 50). North of San Francisco similar offsets near Point Arena have been described by Higgins (1961, p. 53, 59). These displacements occurred in very late Pleistocene and Recent times, perhaps during the last 30,000 or 40,000 years. This would amount to about 1 inch of right-lateral movement per year during that interval.

Photo 2. View southwest across San Andreas fault in Carrizo Plain, McKittrick Summit quadrangle, showing at least two, and probably three, offsets. Recent(?) right-lateral movement of nearly 100 feet is shown by abrupt bend in pair of channels in crossing the fault. Larger, and older, offset is indicated by the headless pair of channels on right, and an intermediate offset probably is indicated by less well-developed swales to left of road beyond fault.

Displacements since earlier Quaternary time can be inferred by comparing the detrital fragments of Pleistocene alluvial gravel adjacent to or near the fault, particularly the early or middle Pleistocene gravel, and by relating these gravels to their probable source rocks. This is especially significant because throughout Quaternary time segments on both sides of the fault were elevated and shed detritus, the gravel accumulating in valleys or lowlands on the opposite side. Thus it is possible to determine the source area of much of the Pleistocene gravel adjacent to the fault, especially if some unique or particularly distinctive rocks are involved; and if the source area has been shifted from its original position by lateral movement on the fault one may estimate the amount of shift since the gravel accumulated. Similar inferences can be applied to Pleistocene landslide masses that may have slumped across the fault.

In the north-central Santa Cruz Mountains (fig. 1), about 2,000 feet of Pliocene and Pleistocene alluvial gravels, the Santa Clara Formation, occurs on both sides of the San Andreas fault. East of the fault the gravel is composed of detritus of the Franciscan Formation derived from the adjacent mountains lying on the same side of the fault. Remnants of the gravel on the west side contain Franciscan detritus. But in addition the gravel contains abundant boulders of a distinctive cobble conglomerate and fragments of sandstone and shale lithologically identical to Upper Cretaceous(?) conglomerate, shale, and sandstone now exposed only on the east side of the fault some 20 miles southeast on Loma Prieta Mountain (fig. 1). If that area was the source of the fragments, the gravels provide evidence of the amount of movement along the fault since their deposition.

Farther southeast, on the west side of the San Andreas fault near Peachtree Valley northeast of Salinas Valley (fig. 2), about 1,000 feet of Pliocene and Pleistocene(?) alluvial gravel, the Paso Robles Formation, unconformably overlies lower Pliocene siliceous mudstone which rests on granitic basement. The gravel, however, is composed mostly of Franciscan detritus and dips under a strip of shattered Franciscan rocks and serpentine adjacent to the fault. Either these shat-

Photo 3. View northwest along San Andreas rift zone in Santa Cruz Mountains in northern part of area shown on figure 4. Long straight canyon draining to lower right is that of Stevens Creek, which follows the San Andreas fault. Mountains left of fault underlain by marine sedimentary rocks of lower Miocene age; mountains to right of fault, including grass-covered Black Mountain, are underlain by Franciscan eugeosynclinal rocks which here are Cretaceous in age.

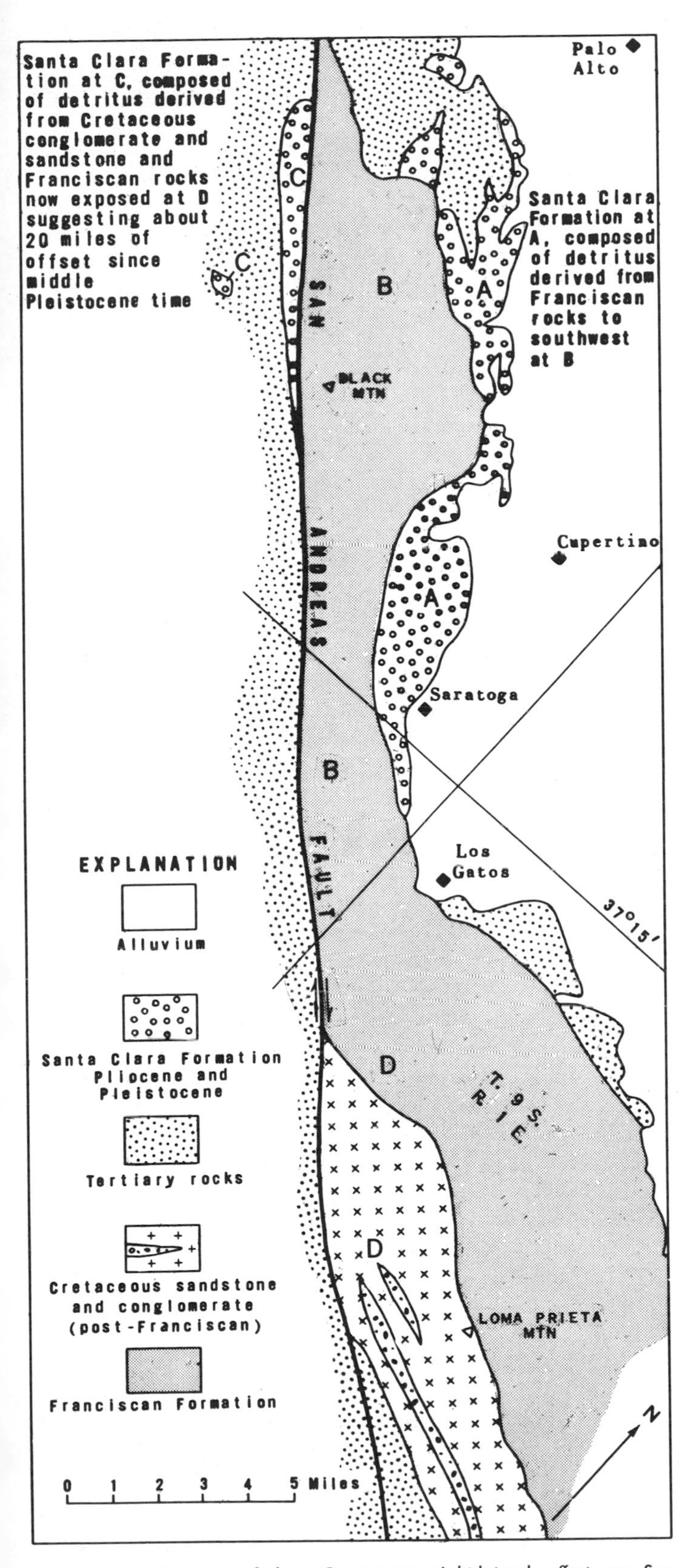

Figure 1. Evidence of late Quaternary right-lateral offset on San Andreas fault in the Santa Cruz Mountains.

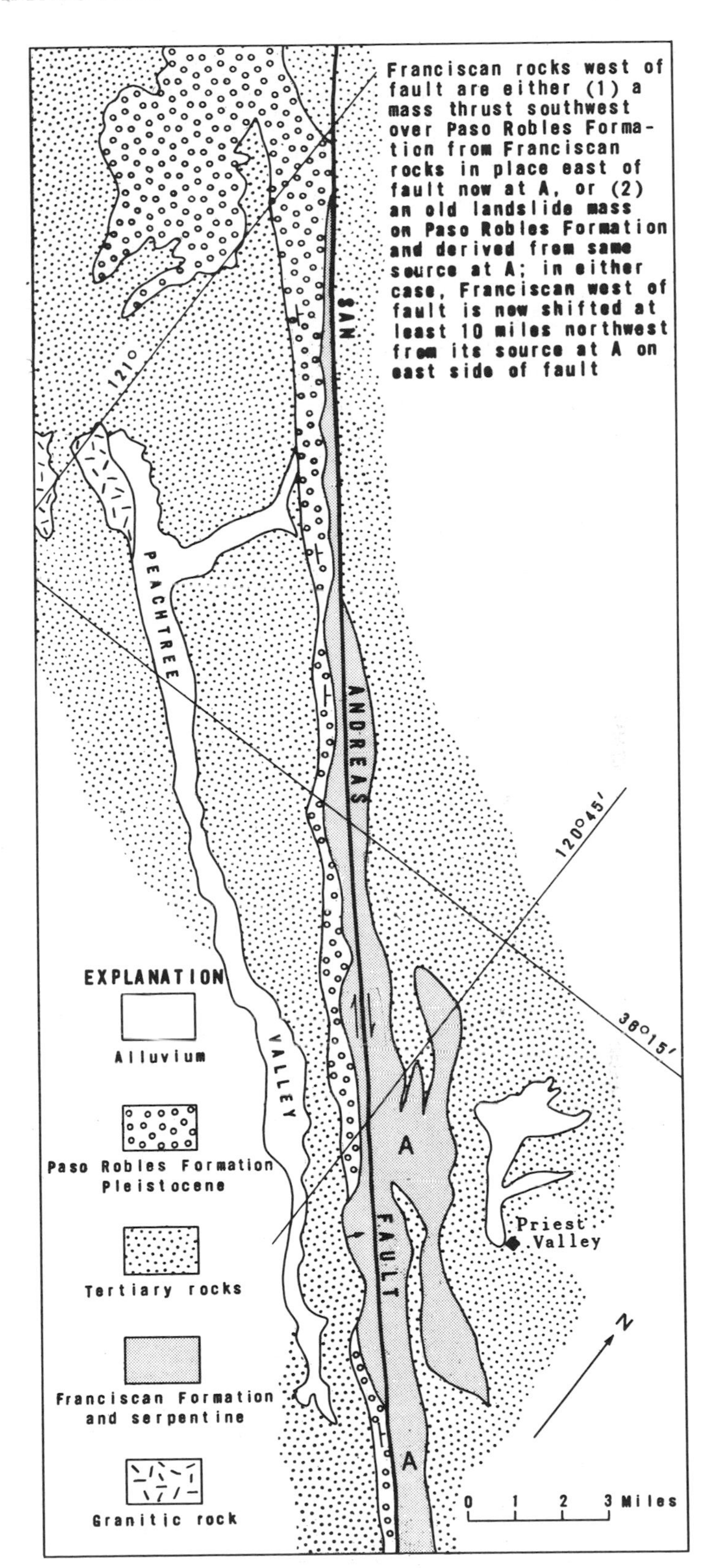

Figure 2. Evidence of late Quaternary right-lateral offset on San Andreas fault in Peachtree Valley area.

tered rocks were thrust over the gravel or they slumped over it from the northeast. In either case the source rocks must have been in the large mass of Franciscan rocks and serpentine northeast across the fault, but which now are some 10 miles to the southeast (fig. 2).

A few miles northwest of Peachtree Valley, in Bear Valley east of the Gabilan Mountains, additional suggestion of offset may be obtained from somewhat complex relations. Here lower Pleistocene gravel, the San Benito Gravels of Lawson (1893), lies on marine Pliocene sediments on the east side of the San Andreas fault; but on the west side of the fault this same gravel is underlain by brecciated Franciscan rocks. These rocks west of the San Andreas fault were mapped as being in *fault contact* on their west with Miocene sediments lying on granitic basement of the Gabilan Mountains (Wilson, 1943, pl. III). Interpretations on these relations vary greatly (Wilson, 1943, p. 227, 251–253; Hill and Dibblee, 1953, p. 449), and it is not certain whether this contact between the Franciscan and the Miocene rocks is a major fault, a minor fault, or an unconformity. It appears most likely that there is an unconformity at the base of the gravel, and that the Franciscan rocks beneath are landslide, or possibly overthrust, masses. If so, these Franciscan masses can have had no local source and probably were derived from the area of Franciscan rocks exposed at A in figure 2 before the gravel was deposited. If this is a correct interpretation, it suggests a right-lateral offset of at least 20 miles since the basal part of the San Benito Gravels was deposited.

Still farther southeast, the valley of Carrizo Plain is partly filled with lower Pleistocene alluvial gravel, in this area assigned to the Paso Robles Formation, to a depth of about 2,000 feet. In the southeast end of this plain and southeastward (fig. 3), much of the gravel on the east side of the San Andreas fault is composed of siliceous shale pebbles derived from Miocene siliceous shale of the adjacent Temblor Range. But on the west side of the fault, gravel of the same age is composed of detritus and small landslide masses derived from distinctive crystalline rocks and Tertiary sedimentary rocks now exposed a dozen miles to the southeast in the San Emigdio Mountains east of the fault (fig. 3). These relations strongly suggest that right-lateral shift on the fault since deposition of the early Pleistocene gravel has been about 12 miles.

Similar offsets of Pleistocene gravel on the fault have been found still farther southeast in the Mojave Desert region near Palmdale.

DISPLACEMENTS OF PLIOCENE FORMATIONS

In the Santa Cruz Mountains, as shown on figure 4, the northern limit of fossiliferous marine sandstone and siltstone of the Purisima Formation of early and middle Pliocene age east of the San Andreas fault appears to be offset some 20 miles, or possibly 40 miles, from its northern limit west of the fault. This offset suggests a lateral displacement of this magnitude since deposition of the Pliocene marine sediments.

Similarly, in the Salinas Valley-Carrizo Plain region far to the southeast, shown on figure 5, the southern limit of lower to middle Pliocene marine formations exposed east of the fault near Carrizo Plain appears to be offset about 50 miles from the southern limit of its counterpart west of the fault in Salinas Valley. Well data in the Salinas Valley indicate that these marine sediments extend southward under the alluvium not more than 12 miles, south of which the Pliocene is entirely nonmarine.

DISPLACEMENTS OF MIOCENE FORMATIONS

West of Bakersfield on the east flank of the Temblor Range, east of the San Andreas fault, the uppermost Miocene section is a marine diatomaceous shale, commonly called the Reef Ridge Shale. But to the southwest within this range the shale intertongues into a coarse breccia facies of granitic rock, schist, and marble detritus which consists in part of several landslide masses of these rocks. Obviously this coarse detritus was derived from an adjacent mountain range of crystalline rocks that must have been prominent in the area directly west across the fault in late Miocene time. This source has since been shifted many miles away, presumably to the northwest, because upper Miocene sedimentary rocks underlie much of Carrizo Plain to the west, as indicated by drill holes. The nearest possible source of such crystalline rocks without a cover of upper Miocene sediments west of the fault is now in the Gabilan Range some 80 miles to the northwest, suggesting a right-lateral displacement of that amount since late Miocene time (Dibblee, 1962, p. 8).

In the Carrizo Plain, Caliente Range, and southeastward, west of the San Andreas fault, as shown on figure 6, much of the upper and middle Miocene section is marine and locally contains abundant large tropical shallow-water molluscan fossils. Eastward in these areas the section grades laterally into nonmarine red beds. Toward the fault these red beds coarsen into conglomerate composed of detritus derived from an area of granitic and metamorphic rocks that presumably existed east of the fault. However, in the Temblor Range and western San Emigdio Mountains, on the east side of the fault, the equivalent Miocene section is *all marine*, composed of shale with deep-water microfaunas, and standstone with sparse, dwarfed molluscan faunas. In going eastward this marine section grades laterally through littoral sands into nonmarine sediments at the eastern margin of southern San Joaquin Valley, giving relations like those in the area west of the fault. The transition zone from marine to nonmarine beds, or strand line, if once continuous across the fault, has been displaced since Miocene time by cumulative right-lateral movement on the fault, as shown on figure 6 (Hill and Dibblee, 1953, p. 446–448;

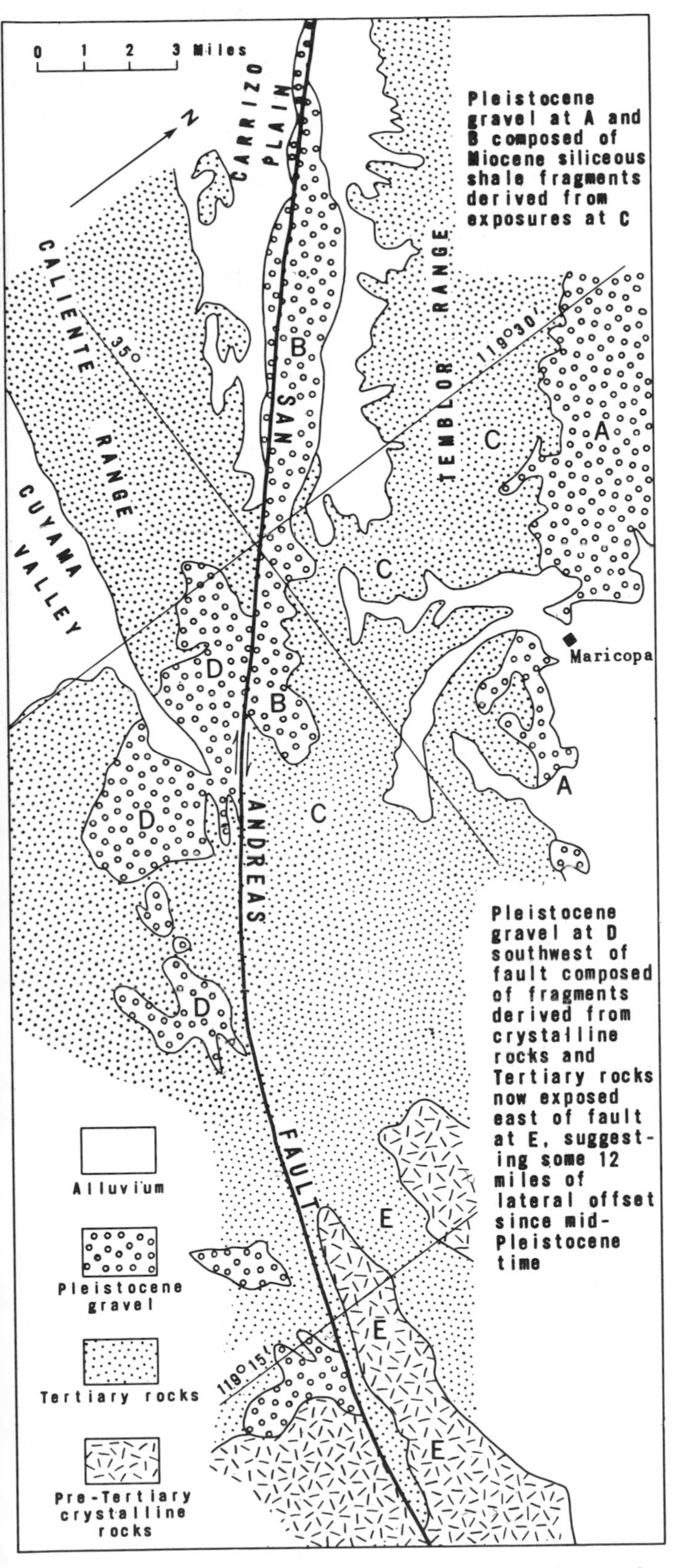

Figure 3. Evidence of late Quaternary right-lateral offset on San Andreas fault southeast of Carrizo Plain.

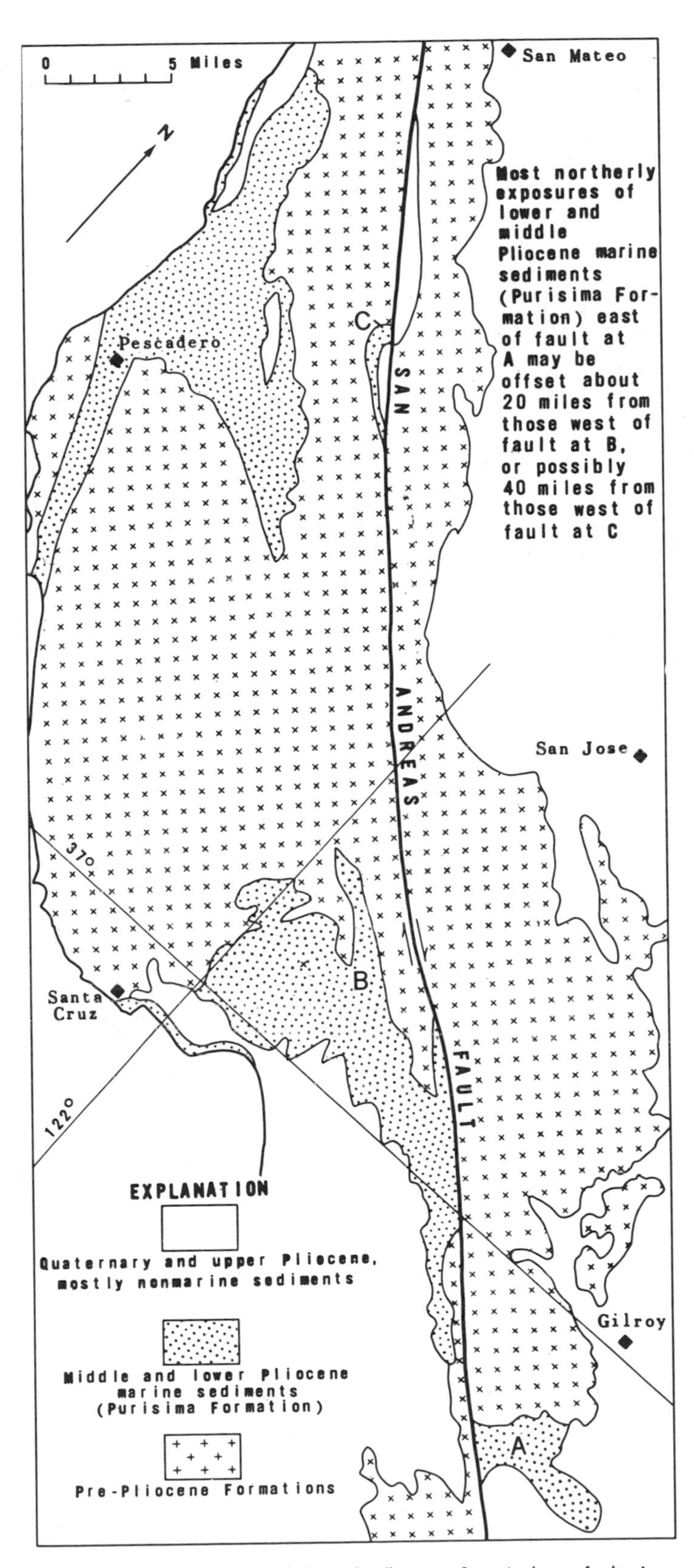

Figure 4. Evidence of right-lateral offset on San Andreas fault since middle Pliocene time in the Santa Cruz Mountains.

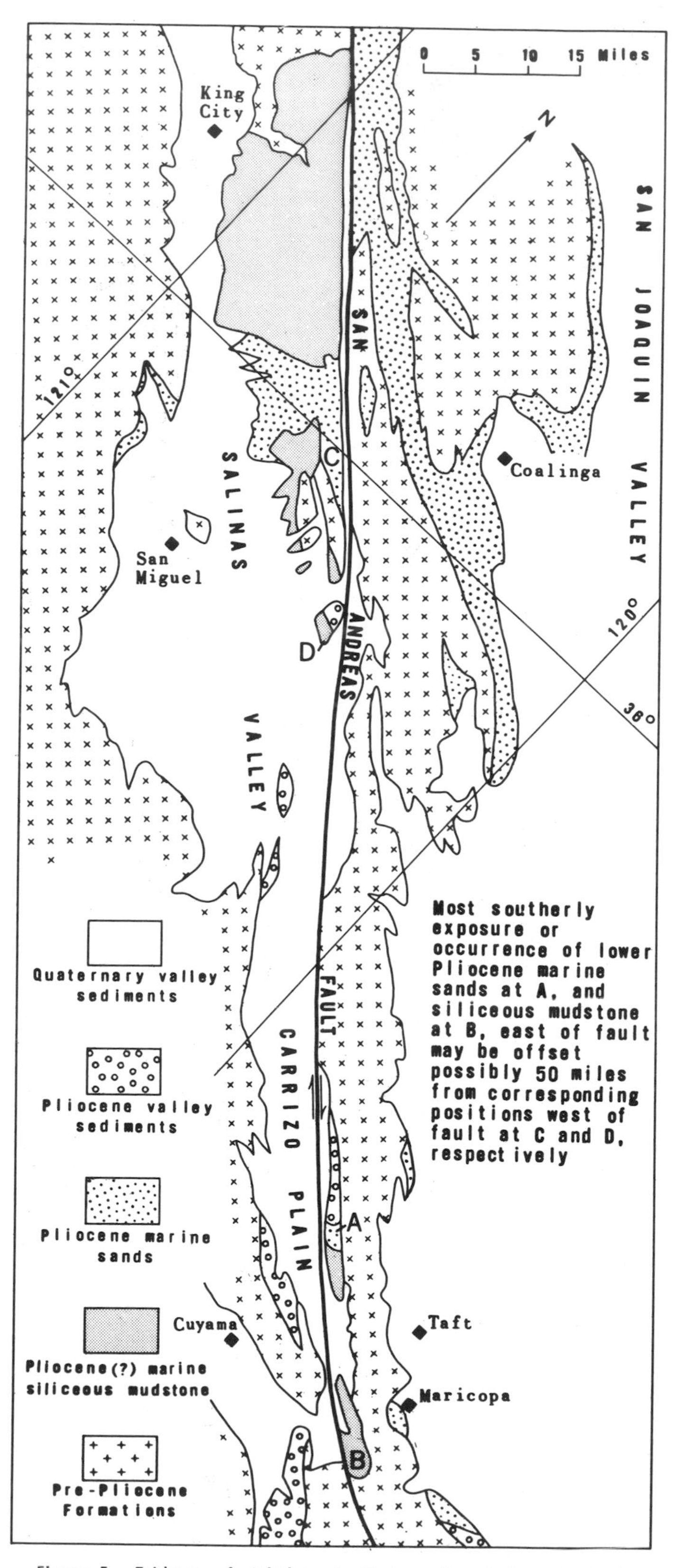

Figure 5. Evidence of right-lateral offset on San Andreas fault since early Pliocene time in the area from King City to Cuyama.

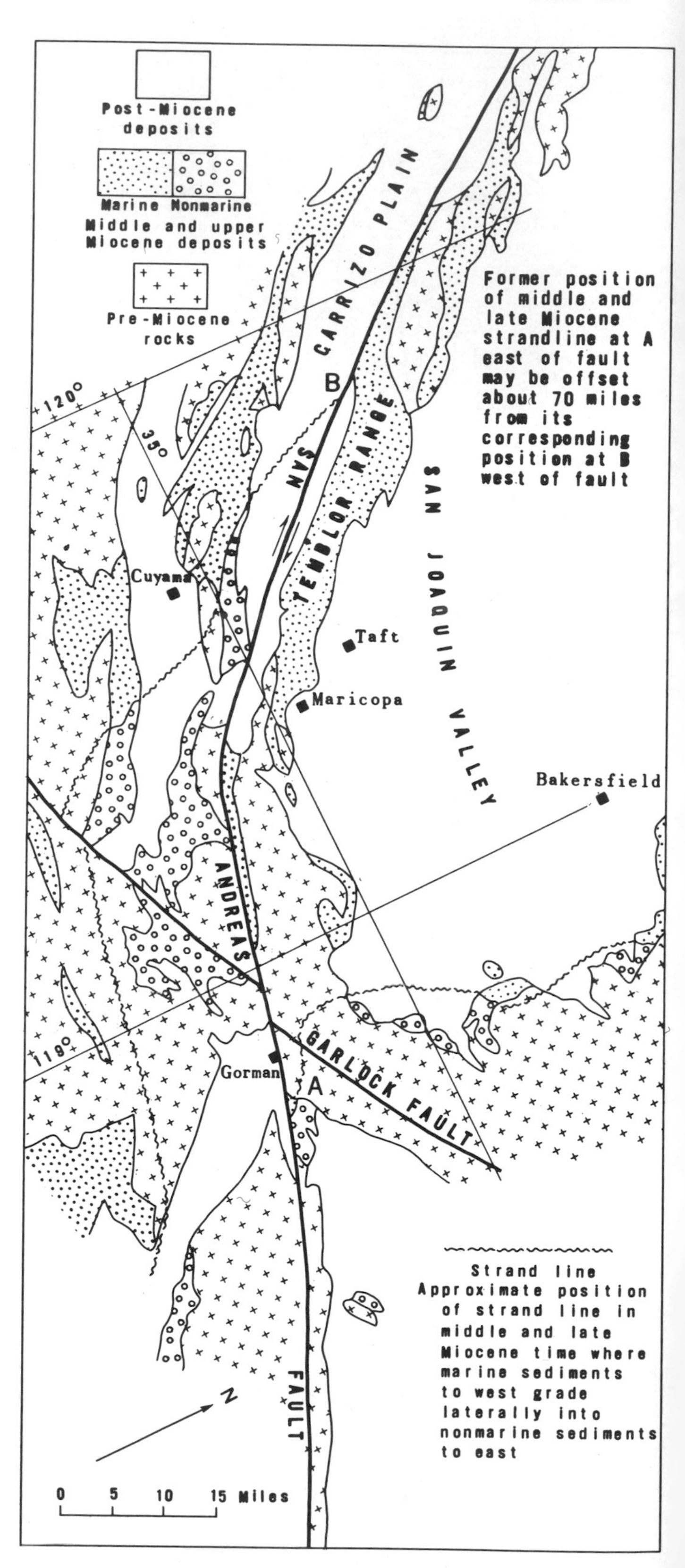

Figure 6. Evidence of right-lateral offset on San Andreas fault since late Miocene time in the vicinity of southern San Joaquin Valley.

Dibblee, 1962, p. 5). Because of possible irregularities in the strand line the post-Miocene offset cannot be precisely determined, but it is apparently about 70 miles.

DISPLACEMENTS OF OLIGOCENE AND LOWER MIOCENE FORMATIONS

West of the San Andreas fault, sedimentary rocks of Oligocene and lower Miocene (Refugian and Zemorrian) age are present in many areas. In the Santa Cruz Mountains they are all marine and are assigned to the San Lorenzo Formation and Vaqueros Sandstone. To the southeast, at the north end of the Gabilan Range (about 15 miles east of Monterey Bay), the sandstone becomes nonmarine and includes volcanic flows. Southeastward from the Gabilan and Santa Lucia Mountains the lower part of the section is all nonmarine throughout the State except in the Point Conception area.

East of the San Andreas fault, Oligocene and lower Miocene formations are recognized in southern San Joaquin Valley and the bordering hills and mountains. The formations here are all marine northwestward from the San Emigdio Mountains. In these mountains, the lower part of the section is represented by the marine San Emigdio Formation, which is lithologically and faunally similar to the San Lorenzo Formation west of the San Andreas fault, and the overlying marine sandstone grades eastward into nonmarine beds which contain volcanic flows, similar to the nonmarine beds at the north end of the Gabilan Range west of the fault. Farther east, around the southeast end of San Joaquin Valley, the entire section becomes nonmarine. If the strand line between marine and nonmarine beds was once continuous across the fault, it has been displaced about 175 miles since early Miocene time (Hill and Dibblee, 1953, p. 448–449).

DISPLACEMENTS OF EOCENE FORMATIONS

Formations of Eocene, Paleocene, and Late Cretaceous age throughout the Coast Range and Great Valley provinces are nearly all marine and clastic sedimentary rocks, with no strand-line offset by the San Andreas fault. Lateral displacements of the marine sections could be great but would be very difficult to recognize. The lithologic and faunal similarities of the Eocene section of the San Emigdio-Temblor Range to that of the Santa Cruz Mountains suggests some 225 miles of separation since late Eocene time, as noted by Hill and Dibblee (1953, p. 449).

DISPLACEMENTS OF MESOZOIC FORMATIONS

The San Andreas fault forms the boundary between an area of granitic-metamorphic basement on the west and an area of Franciscan and serpentine basement to the east. Nowhere are these two vastly different basement types found in depositional or intrusive contact, although laboratory and fossil studies seem to suggest that they are both within the same age range in the Mesozoic (Bailey, Irwin, and Jones, 1964, p. 154, pl. 1). If this is so, then their juxtaposition must be the result of large lateral movement on the fault. The 350-mile right-lateral displacement of the contact between these basements from near the southern end of the San Joaquin Valley to some point undersea northwest of Point Arena, as postulated by Hill and Dibblee (1953, p. 449), is therefore still a possibility.

OTHER DISPLACEMENTS ON NORTHERN PART OF SAN ANDREAS FAULT

On the segment of the San Andreas fault zone northwest of San Francisco the pre-Pleistocene rock units on opposite sides are entirely dissimilar. Near the fault zone none of the rock units present on one side are present on the other. This segment separates a western area of granitic basement overlain by marine sandstone and shale of latest Cretaceous, Eocene, and early Miocene age, marine siliceous shale (Monterey) of Miocene age, and marine diatomaceous mudstone (Purisima) of early Pliocene age, from an eastern area of Franciscan rocks overlain by nonmarine and volcanic rocks of Pliocene age and marine sands of middle(?) and late Pliocene age. This juxtaposition of dissimilar sequences along the fault zone must be the result of very large cumulative lateral displacement. The fault is also strongly expressed physiographically by a rift zone that offsets streams in a right-lateral sense. There is no indication of any decreasing displacement as it enters the ocean near Point Arena.

Higgins (1961, p. 67) infers that there was probably not more than 1 or 1½ miles of right-lateral displacement on the fault since deposition of the marine Pliocene sands first began east of the fault. However, owing to the absence of the Pliocene sands west of the fault there seems to be no positive way to determine the displacement on this part of the fault since that time.

The Pilarcitos fault in the northern Santa Cruz Mountains is an important branch of the San Andreas fault. While it shows little topographic expression, and no physiographic evidence of Recent or late Pleistocene activity, it, rather than the San Andreas fault, forms the boundary between the area of Franciscan basement and the area of granitic basement to the west, as shown on figure 7. It presumably rejoins the San Andreas undersea west of the Golden Gate. The Pilarcitos fault in most places dips steeply northeastward toward the San Andreas fault. Throughout the narrow strip between these two faults, the sequence and structural relations of rock units from Franciscan to and including the Miocene Monterey Shale is much the same as that of the block northeast of the San Andreas. The sequence is, however, shifted northwesterly from its counterpart northeast of the fault about 20 miles, as shown on figure 7.

Photo 5. View southeast along San Andreas fault from over south end of Tomales Bay. Dark peak in upper left is Mount Tamalpais. In this area the San Andreas rift zone is marked by two parallel branches, half a mile or less apart, bounding the alluviated valley. Timbered mountains on the right have a granitic basement overlain by Miocene sandstone and siliceous shale; hills and mountains left of fault are composed chiefly of Franciscan rocks.

Photo 4. Aerial view northwest along San Andreas fault in the Elkhorn Hills in Carrizo Plain, Elkhorn Hills quadrangle. Uplifted and dissected area traversed by the fault is composed of the Pleistocene alluvial sediments of the Paso Robles Formation. The black streak at the left edge of the hills is not the result of faulting, but is formed by tumbleweed collecting along a fence line. Temblor Range at upper right is underlain by Miocene sedimentary rocks.

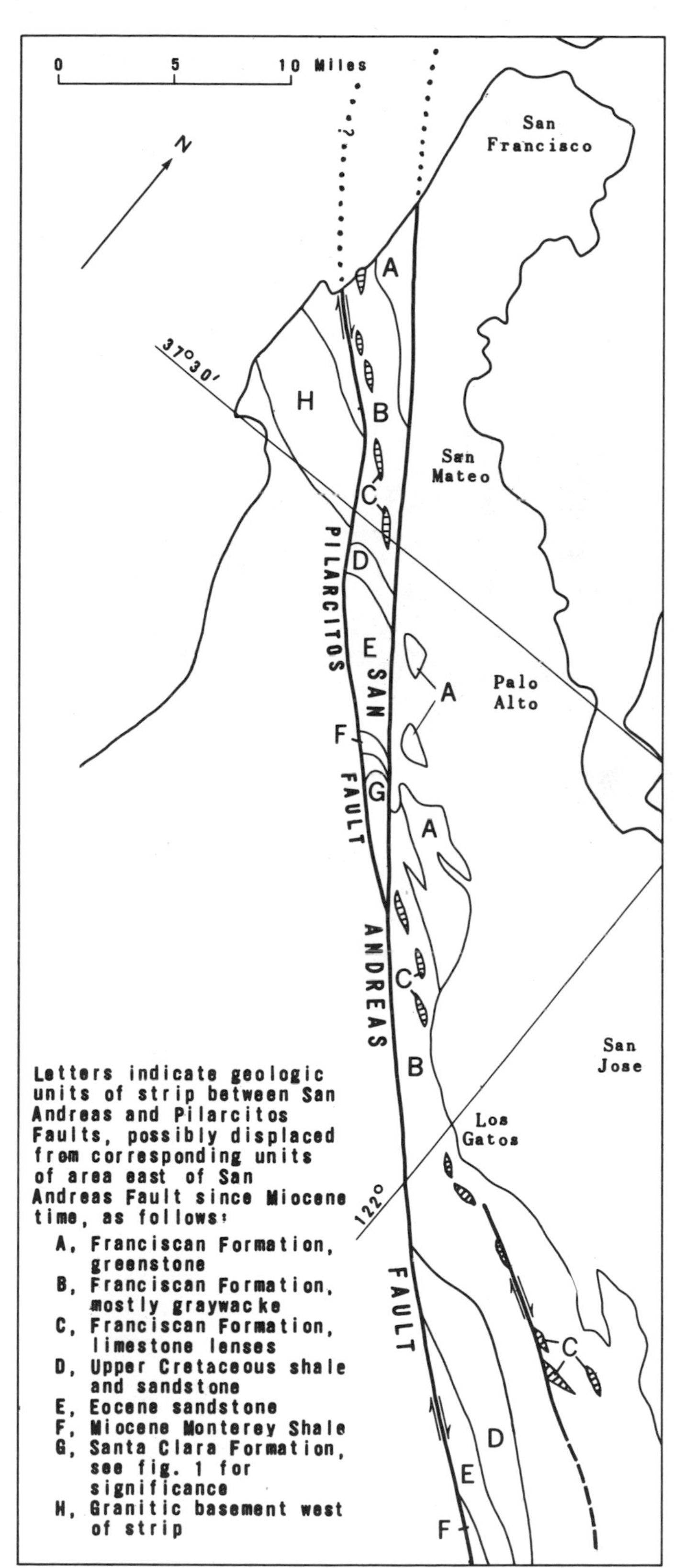

Figure 7. Evidence of right-lateral offset of strip between Pilarcitos and San Andreas faults in northern Santa Cruz Mountains.

The above relation strongly suggests that the Pilarcitos fault was the main active line of movement of the San Andreas zone until after deposition of the Miocene Monterey Shale. The marine Pliocene sandstone that unconformably overlies the Monterey Shale in the area between the faults is similar to that west of the Pilarcitos fault and probably accumulated across it, as did the Santa Clara Gravel. This suggests that since Pliocene time the Pilarcitos fault has been inactive and the present San Andreas fault has been the active line of movement.

In the New Almaden mining district southeast of Los Gatos, the Franciscan rocks, which here dip mostly to the northeast, are transected by a pre-Tertiary shear zone (Ben Trovato shear zone) and associated minor north-branching faults, about 5 miles east of and parallel to the San Andreas fault. The stratigraphic portion of the Franciscan rocks that contains discontinuous lenses of limestone is apparently offset several (less than 10) miles in a right-lateral sense on this shear zone (see fig. 7), as postulated by Bailey and Everhart (1964, p. 79, 80, 91, pl. 1).

CONCLUSION

From both the physiographic expression and the geologic relations it seems evident that the San Andreas fault is a generally vertical plane of right-lateral shear movement active during most, if not all, of the Cenozoic Era, with very large cumulative offset or displacement. This is indicated or suggested not only by the displacements of geologic units that have been described, but also by the structural pattern associated with the fault. This pattern is expressed in the severely folded condition of the bordering Cretaceous and Cenozoic sedimentary formations in which the axes of folds on both sides trend slightly more east-west than does the fault. As the folds approach the San Andreas fault they become more severely compressed and their axes veer more nearly parallel to it. This persistent pattern all along the fault is no doubt the effect of right-lateral drag on the fault combined with the pressure of one block against the other.

REFERENCES

Allen, J. E., 1946, Geology of the San Juan Bautista quadrangle, California: California Div. Mines Bull. 133, p. 9–75, map.

Bailey, E. H., and Everhart, D. L., 1964, Geology and quicksilver deposits of the New Almaden district, Santa Clara County, California: U.S. Geol. Survey Prof. Paper 360, 202 p.

Bailey, E. H., Irwin, W. P., and Jones, D. L., 1964, Franciscan and related rocks, and their significance in the geology of western California: California Div. Mines and Geology Bull. 183, 177 p.

Crowell, J. C., 1960, The San Andreas fault in southern California: Internat. Geol. Cong., 21st, Copenhagen, 1960, Proc., pt. 18, p. 45–52.

——1962, Displacement along the San Andreas fault, California: Geol. Soc. America Spec. Paper 71, 61 p.

Dibblee, T. W., Jr., 1962, Displacements on the San Andreas Rift zone and related structure in Carrizo Plain and vicinity, *in* Geology of

Carrizo Plains and San Andreas fault: San Joaquin Valley Geol. Soc. [Guidebook] Field trip 1962, p. 5–12, map.

Higgins, C. G., 1961, San Andreas fault north of San Francisco, California: Geol. Soc. America Bull., v. 72, no. 1, p. 51–68.

Hill, M. L., and Dibblee, T. W., Jr., 1953, San Andreas, Garlock, and Big Pine faults, California—a study of the character, history, and tectonic significance of their displacements: Geol. Soc. America Bull., v. 64, no. 4, p. 443–458.

Lawson, A. C., 1893, The post-Pliocene diastrophism of the coast of southern California: California Univ., Dept. Geology Bull., v. 1, p. 115–160.

Noble, L. F., 1954, The San Andreas fault zone from Soledad Pass to Cajon Pass, California, [Pt.] 5 *in* Chap. 4 of Jahns, R. H. ed., Geology of southern California: California Div. Mines Bull. 170, p. 37–48.

Wilson, I. F., 1943, Geology of the San Benito quadrangle, California: California Jour. Mines and Geology, v. 39, no. 2, p. 183–270.

Train of the North Shore Railway at Point Reyes Station, Marin County. Engine and cars were overturned by the April 1906 earthquake. From the collection of Roy D. Graves.

CURRENT AND RECENT MOVEMENT ON THE SAN ANDREAS FAULT

By Buford K. Meade and James B. Small
U.S. Coast and Geodetic Survey, Rockville, Maryland

PART 1. HORIZONTAL MOVEMENT

By B. K. Meade
Chief, Triangulation Branch, U.S. Coast and Geodetic Survey

A general program for the study of horizontal crustal movement in California was started by the U.S. Coast and Geodetic Survey about 1930. The areas selected for these studies were based on the recommendations of geologists, seismologists, engineers, and geodesists.

After the San Francisco earthquake of 1906, the primary network of triangulation in the area, originally observed in 1880–1885, was reobserved to determine the extent of horizontal movement. The network was reobserved again in 1922. Results obtained from these repeat surveys disclosed conclusively that relative movement between points could be detected in areas of seismic activity.

The survey networks observed for the study of horizontal movement were established at various places along the major faults. These networks have been reobserved at periodic intervals, and horizontal movement is disclosed by changes in the final coordinates at each station in the net. The results which indicate movements are always given in relative terms. On opposite sides of a fault, the relative movement between points may be either right or left lateral. Right-lateral movement is indicated when the azimuth between two points is increased, or the line joining the points rotates in a clockwise direction. When the azimuth is decreased, relative movement between the points is left lateral or counterclockwise.

In each area along the San Andreas fault where the surveys have indicated movement, the direction of movement has been right lateral. That is, the west side of the fault has moved northwest relative to the east side, or the east side has moved southeast relative to the west side. Table 1 shows the dates of survey and indicated annual rate of movement at various localities from Point Reyes to El Centro. A summary of the results at each numbered locality is given in the correspondingly numbered paragraphs that follow.

Table 1. Annual rate of movement along San Andreas fault at localities discussed in text.

Locality	Position		Dates of survey	Annual rate of movement (cm)
	Lat.	Long.		
1	38.1°	122.8°	1930–38–60	1.3
2	37.6	122.0	1951–57–63	2.5
3	36.8	121.5	1930–51–62	1.6
4	36.7	121.4	1957–59–60–61–62–63–65	1.5
5	36.4	120.9	1944–63	3.0
6	35.7	120.3	1932–51–62	0.3
7a	35.0	119.4	1938–49–59	0
7b	34.8	118.8	1938–49	0
7c	34.5	118.1	1938–47–58	0
7d	34.3	117.5	1949–63	0
8	32.8	115.5	1935–41–54	3.0*

* Annual rate from 1941 to 1954.

(1). Point Reyes to Petaluma

This network starting at Point Reyes on the coast extends northeastward across the San Andreas fault to Petaluma. The net was established in 1930 and was reobserved in 1938 and again in 1960. Results of these surveys indicate that relative movement between points near and on opposite sides of the fault was on the order of 2 cm per year for the period from 1930 to 1938. During the interval from 1938 to 1960 the annual rate of movement was about 1 cm.

(2). Vicinity of Hayward

Surveys for the study of horizontal movement were established in this area in 1951. This network of triangles, with sides 9 to 12 km in length, straddles the Calaveras and Hayward faults, and the San Andreas fault extends along the western side of the area. Horizontal movement between surveys of 1951 and 1963 is indicated by vectors in figure 1. These results are based on least-square adjustments using the same control for each set of observations. The geographic position of station 18 was held fixed in the adjustment and also the azimuth and length of the line to station 17. Adjusted results of the 1957 survey are in very close agreement with results obtained from the 1963 observations. There is no indication of any significant movement during this 6-year period.

The quadrilateral involving stations 17, 18, 19, and 20 was first observed in 1882, and observations were repeated in 1906, 1922, and 1947. Results from these observations showed that station 19 moved northwesterly about 5 cm per year during the period 1882–1947. During this same 65-year period, station 20 moved southeasterly about 2 cm per year (Whitten, 1949).

Results of the 1951 and 1963 surveys show that stations 19 and 20 moved northwesterly about the same amount, 6 cm per year, during this 12-year pe-

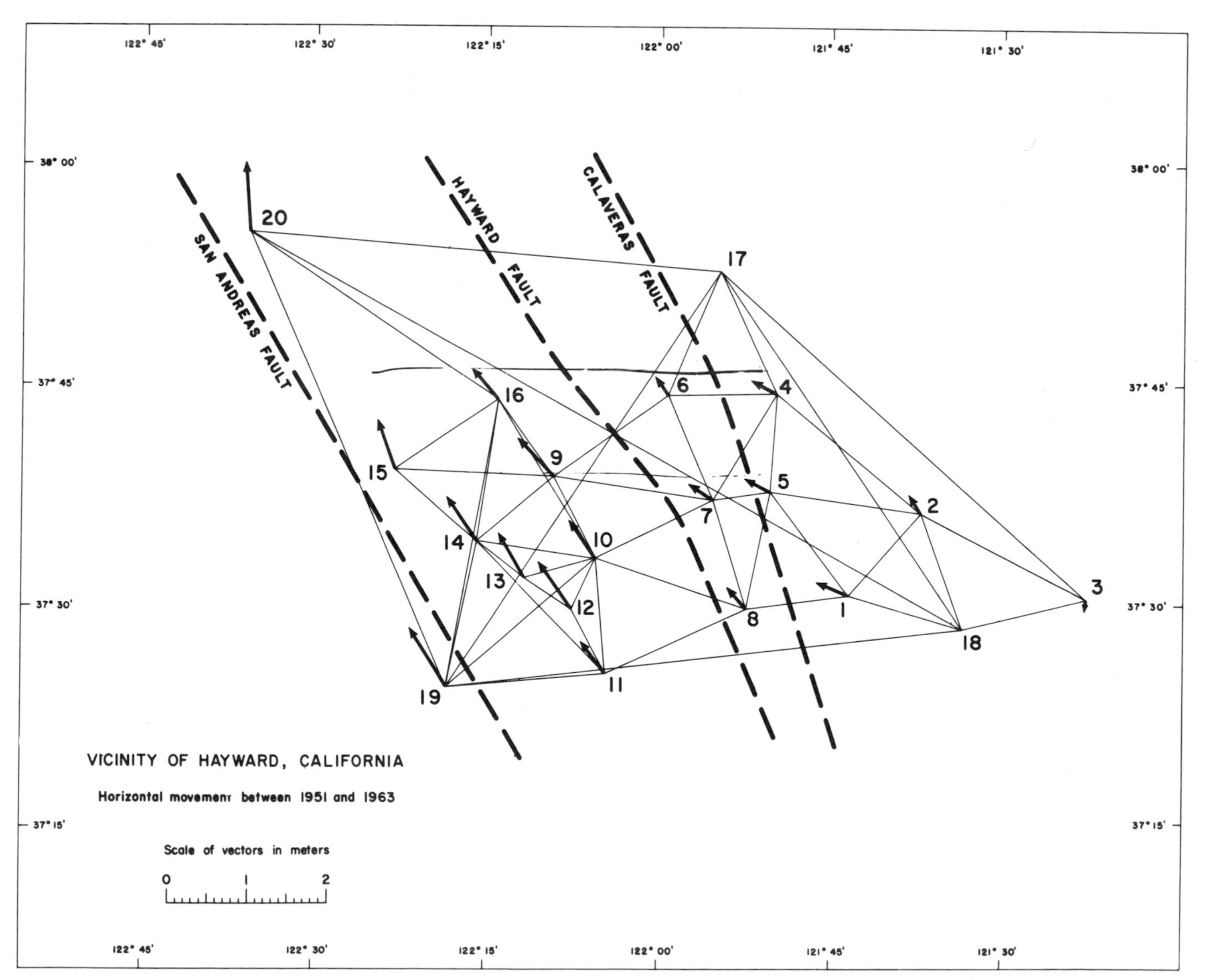

Figure 1. Triangulation network extending from Mount Tamalpais to Mount Oso, showing amount of horizontal movement between 1951 and 1963.

riod. The movement indicated at stations 19 and 20 is relative to the control stations 17–18, and part of this movement could be due to a change in the orientation of the figure. Final data for each survey are based on the assumption that the azimuth of the control line did not change.

The magnitude of the vectors at points near and on opposite sides of the Hayward fault indicates relative movement of about 0.3 m for the 12-year period or an annual rate of 2.5 cm. The change in the direction of the vectors indicates a possibility of compression in this area.

For future studies of horizontal movement, the Coast and Geodetic Survey has made tentative plans to establish two small nets straddling the Hayward fault in this area. The sides of these figures will be 200 to 400 m in length. Three nets of this type, two straddling the Hayward fault and one the Calaveras fault, were established in this area in 1965. Surveys involving these nets are described under a cooperative project with the California Department of Water Resources.

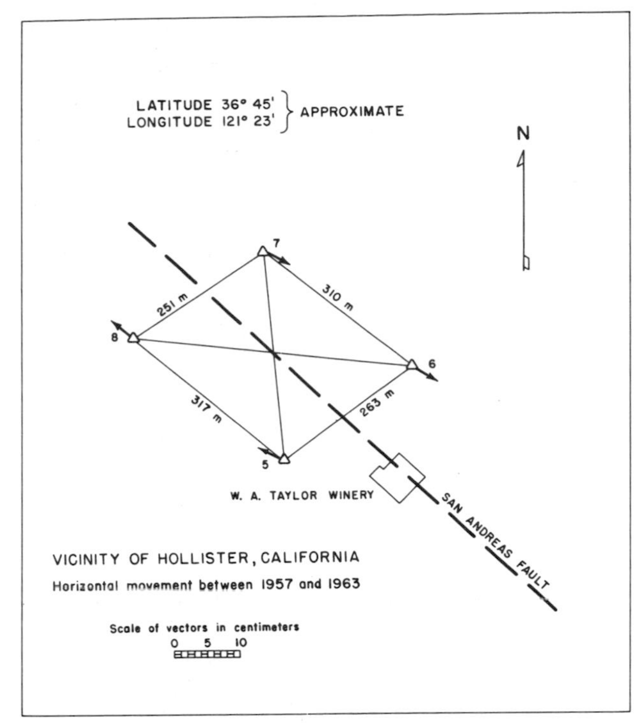

Figure 2. Quadrilateral near winery south of Hollister, showing cumulative horizontal movement between 1957 and 1963.

(3). Vicinity of Monterey Bay

This net extends from the coast at Monterey Bay northeastward through Salinas and crosses the San Andreas fault near Hollister. Observations were first made in 1930 and repeat observations were made in 1951 and 1962. Results of the surveys show the same rate of movement during the two intervals, 1930–1951 and 1951–1962. During each of these periods, the annual rate of movement was 1.6 cm between points on opposite sides of the fault.

(4). Vicinity of Hollister

A quadrilateral straddling the San Andreas fault, with sides approximately 300 m in length, was established near a winery south of Hollister in 1957. The quadrilateral was reobserved in 1959, 1960, 1961, 1962, and 1963. Relative movement, divided equally between points on opposite sides of the fault, is shown by vectors in figure 2. This relative movement, averaging 1.5 cm per year, is based on the difference between surveys of 1957 and 1963. However, the difference between consecutive surveys indicates the movement is fairly uniform and on the order of 1.5 cm per year. The two sides parallel to the fault have not shown any significant change in direction or length. Sides 5–6 and 7–8, perpendicular to the fault, have increased in azimuth an average of 11 seconds per year. The diagonal 6–8 increased 7.7 cm in length, and the other diagonal decreased 5.9 cm during the 6-year period 1957–1963.

A resurvey of this figure was completed in June 1965. During the 20-month interval from October 1963 to June 1965, results showed relative movement of 1.7 cm between points on opposite sides of the fault.

The annual rate of movement determined from these surveys is in close agreement with the rate obtained from creep recorders installed near the winery in 1957 and 1958 (Tocher, 1960).

(5). Salinas River Valley

This triangulation network extending along the San Andreas fault from the 36th parallel northwesterly for a distance of approximately 100 km was observed in 1944 as an extension of the national horizontal control net. An extension of this net in 1962 indicated that movement had taken place between points on opposite sides of the fault. In order to determine the extent of movement in the area, the 1944 network was reobserved in 1963.

Differences between the adjusted results of the 1944 and 1963 observations are indicated by vectors in figure 3. The movement indicated is relative to the fixed control station, number 11. For all stations on the western side of the fault, observations made in 1963 were in very close agreement with those of 1944. Differences between the adjusted lengths and azimuths of 9 lines crossing the fault are given below. Numbers identifying the lines are shown in figure 3.

The maximum changes in length are on lines crossing and in the general direction of the fault, as indicated under (a). Maximum changes in azimuth are on

Table 2.

Line	Length meters	1963 minus 1944	
		Length meters	Azimuth
(a) 3– 9	17,059	−0.50	− 1.9″
9–15	13,114	+0.69	+ 0.9
14–23	36,415	+0.71	+ 1.0
(b) 12–15	15,651	+0.27	+ 8.2
17–15	14,179	−0.09	+ 8.5
21–23	13,109	+0.04	+ 8.5
25–24	14,957	+0.20	+ 9.6
25–22	5,882	+0.21	+21.2
28–29	14,739	+0.23	+ 7.8

lines approximately perpendicular to and crossing the fault. When the lengths are used to convert azimuth changes to displacement, the following values are obtained for lines under (b).

Table 3.

Line	Displacement meters
12–15	+0.62
17–15	+0.58
21–23	+0.54
25–24	+0.70
25–22	+0.60
28–29	+0.56
average	+0.60

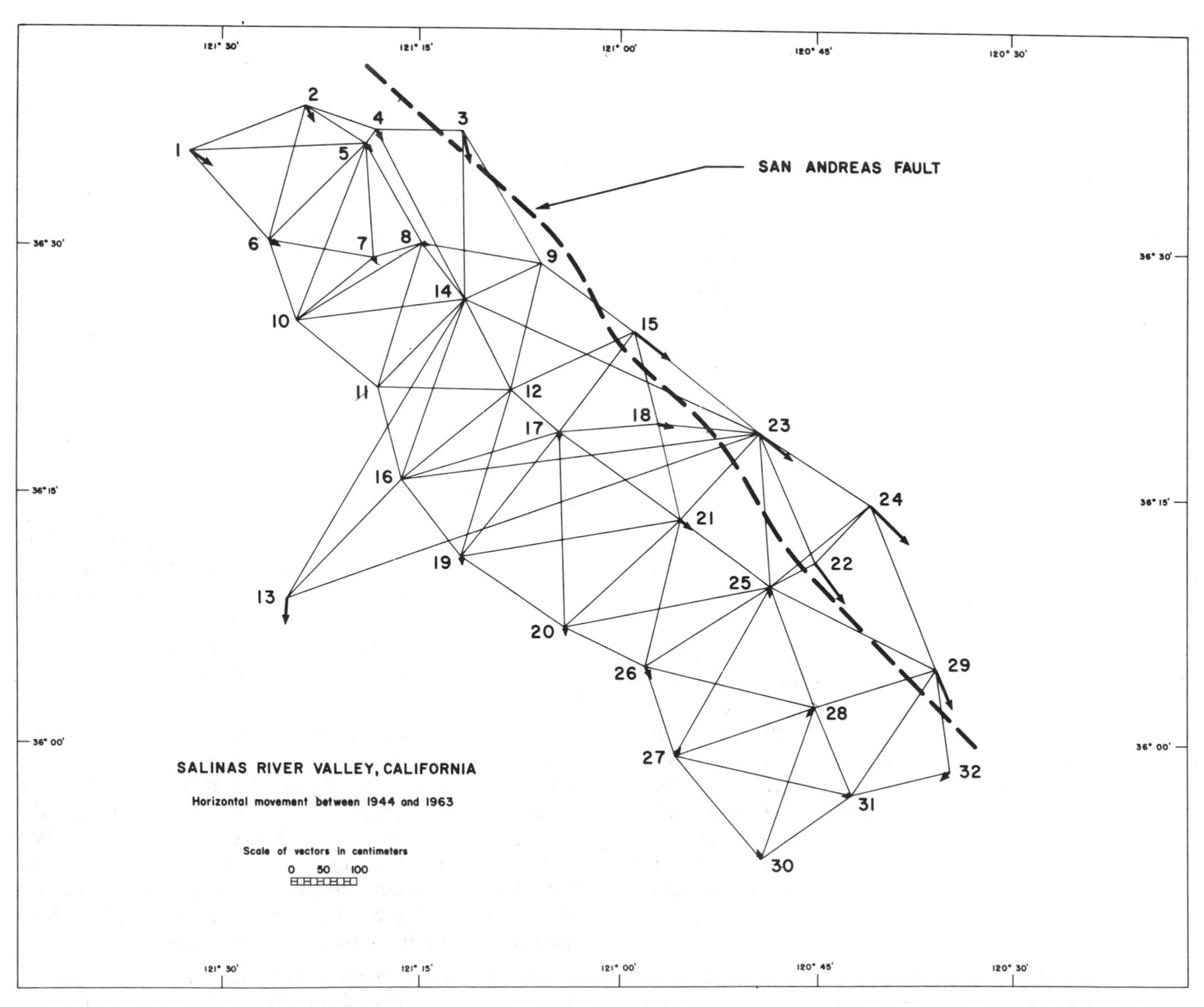

Figure 3. Triangulation network extending from a few miles southeast of Salinas to a point several miles northwest of Parkfield, showing horizontal movement between 1944 and 1963.

The average value for this displacement is in close agreement with the length changes under (a), lines in the direction of and on opposite sides of the fault.

The relative movement determined from results of the 1944 and 1963 surveys is fairly uniform along the San Andreas fault in this area. Between points on opposite sides of the fault the average relative movement was 3 cm per year (Meade, 1965).

(6). San Luis Obispo to Avenal

This triangulation net, about 100 km in length, crosses the San Andreas fault in the vicinity of Cholame. The original survey was accomplished in 1932 and reobservations were made in 1951 and 1962. For stations near the fault, the relative movement was 5 cm for the 20-year interval 1932–1951. During the period from 1951 to 1962, the relative movement was about the same as that for 1932–1951.

(7). The 35th Parallel to Cajon Pass

Along the San Andreas fault from the 35th parallel to Cajon Pass, repeat surveys for the study of crustal movements have been made in the vicinities of (a) Maricopa, (b) Gorman, (c) Palmdale, and (d) Cajon Pass. The various surveys in these areas have not disclosed any significant movement.

(8). Imperial Valley, Vicinity of El Centro

The San Andreas fault crosses the middle of this area which is adjacent to the Mexican border. The original survey was made in 1935 and resurveys were made in 1941 and 1954. Large relative movements between points on opposite sides of the fault were disclosed from results of the 1935 and 1941 surveys. These changes occurred at the time of the severe earthquake in the area in 1940. The annual rate of movement between points on opposite sides of the fault was 3 cm during the period 1941–1954 (Meade, 1963).

Taft-Mojave Area

An extensive triangulation net was established in 1959–60 over the area where the San Andreas, Garlock, White Wolf, and other faults converge. Previous surveys along the San Andreas fault in this area have not disclosed significant movements. Along the 35th parallel from Wheeler Ridge to the east, surveys of 1932, 1952, and 1963 indicate a possibility of left-lateral movement along the Garlock fault.

A resurvey of this extensive network will furnish valuable information on crustal movements along the various faults in this area.

Cooperative Project With Department of Water Resources

In cooperation with the California Department of Water Resources, surveys for the study of crustal movements were started in 1964 in areas where a proposed aqueduct and its branches parallel or cross known fault lines. The figures established at these crossings range in size from 150 by 260 m to 500 by 900 m. A typical net of this type is shown in figure 4.

Seventeen aqueduct-fault crossings of the type shown in figure 4 were established and observed in 1964. A precise base line was measured and an astronomic azimuth was observed in each net. These nets are located at various intervals along the major faults of southern California extending from approximate position 34.1° N., 117.3° W. to 35.7° N., 120.2° W. A complete resurvey of each of the 17 nets was completed during the spring of 1965. Results of the surveys did not show conclusively that horizontal movement had taken place.

Four additional nets of the type mentioned above were established in the San Francisco Bay area in 1965. Also another net at the site of the proposed Cedar Springs Reservoir about 15 miles north of San Bernardino was added to the project early in 1965. It was surveyed in February 1965 and again at the end of the season's work in May 1965. No movement between surveys was apparent. Tentative plans have been made to resurvey each of the 22 nets straddling the faults at intervals of 1 or 2 years.

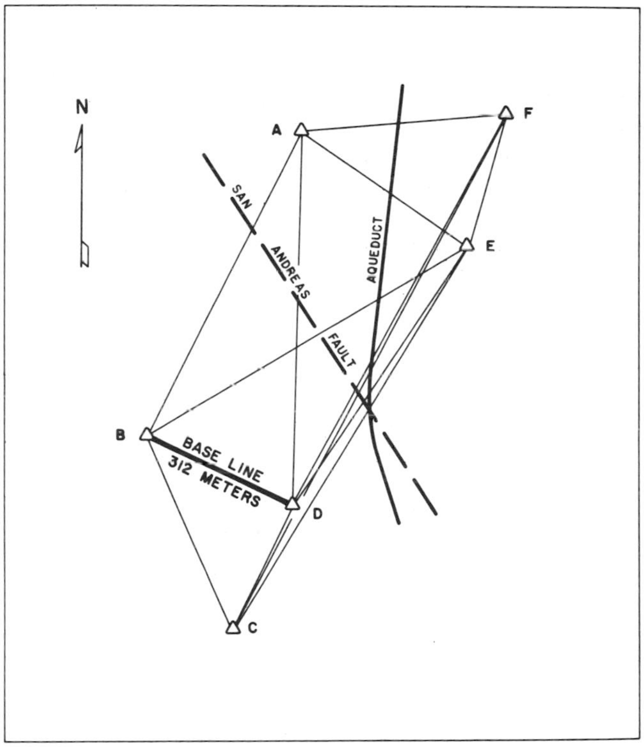

Figure 4. A typical triangulation net about proposed aqueduct-fault crossing.

Along the San Andreas fault from the vicinity of Point Reyes to the 36th parallel, repeat surveys for the study of crustal movement continue to show right-lateral movement. From the vicinity of the 36th parallel to Cajon Pass these surveys have not disclosed any significant movement along the fault. In the Imperial Valley the relative movement is in the same direction and about the same magnitude as that along the fault from Hayward to the 36th parallel.

PART 2. VERTICAL MOVEMENT

By J. B. Small

Chief, Leveling Branch, U.S. Coast and Geodetic Survey

The Coast and Geodetic Survey is responsible for the basic vertical control net of the United States. The first leveling undertaken in California in the development of this net was in 1906. About 30,000 miles of first-order leveling and 20,000 miles of second-order leveling have been undertaken in California, including the original leveling and releveling to determine vertical changes. California is considered one of the most difficult areas in which to undertake leveling because of the many factors contributing to change, some of which are: removal of underground water, oil, and gas; changing moisture content of the soil; fault lines; earthquakes; tectonic and secular changes. To determine the magnitude of change in an absolute sense, the releveling needs to be extended to what are considered stable areas or to coastal locations where mean sea level has been determined through tide gauge records. Often it is difficult to determine what areas to consider stable, since even the survey markers established in bedrock to serve as anchors are subject to some small slow changes.

The most concentrated releveling has been in cooperation with the California Department of Water Resources in the San Joaquin Valley. Areas of most rapid subsidence have been where there is a removal of underground water, oil, or gas. In the San Joaquin Valley, the maximum subsidence was 22.890 feet from 1943 to 1964 at a location about 10 miles southwest of Mendota. Another cone of subsidence in the San Joaquin Valley is located in the Delano area. The maximum subsidence was 11.437 feet from 1930 to 1964 at a location 2 miles north of Earlimart. In the vicinity of San Jose, at the southern end of San Francisco Bay, the maximum subsidence from 1912 to 1963 has been 11.2 feet. There has been an accelerated rate of subsidence from 1960 to 1963 with a maximum during this period of 1.94 feet. Usually the vertical changes are considered to be subsidence; however, there are some areas where relevelings indicate some small upheaval. One aspect of particular interest in this study is the movement of marks in bedrock. About 5 miles southeast of San Jose and west of the Hayward fault line, there is a group of bench marks in bedrock which is classed as ultrabasic. These marks are relatively stable and have been used as tie marks between the various levelings because they agree best when checking with tidal bench marks at San Francisco. There is another group of bedrock marks in Alum Rock Park which is about 7 miles northeast of San Jose on the east side of the Hayward fault trace. Between 1948 and 1963, the bedrock marks in Alum Rock Park raised about 0.213 foot in relation to those southeast of San Jose. The various relevelings have shown this to be a gradual rise. The length of the leveling connecting these two groups of marks is about 12 miles. In the vicinity of Lebec, near the San Andreas fault, releveling in 1964 carried from San Pedro indicates an upheaval of 0.55 foot, and releveling of 1965 indicates an upheaval of 0.82 foot.

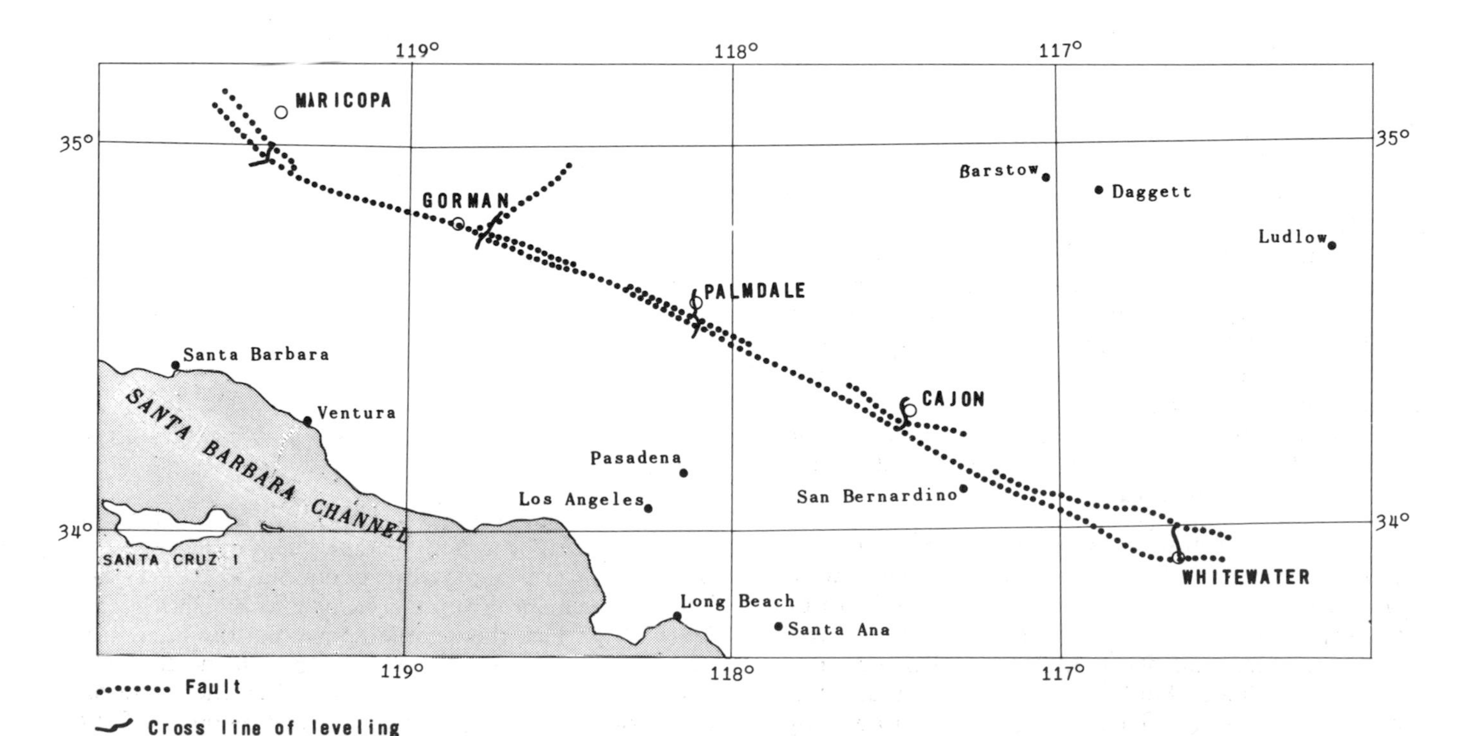

Figure 5. Locations of special levelings established in 1935 across San Andreas fault between Maricopa and Whitewater.

In 1935, five lines of leveling were established at right angles to the San Andreas fault (see fig. 5). The level lines were about 10 miles in length with about 200 bench marks on each line. The marks were established approximately 100 feet apart for the first mile each way from the fault line, 200 feet apart for the second mile, 300 feet for the third mile, 400 feet for the fourth mile, and 500 feet for the fifth mile.

The locations at which these lines were established and the dates of the leveling are as follows:

Table 4.

Line no.	Location	Dates of leveling
1.	Vicinity of Whitewater	1935, 1949. (2 levelings).
2.	Vicinity of Cajon Pass	1935, 1943–4 (Part), 1956, 1961. (4 levelings).
3.	Vicinity of Palmdale	1935, 1938, 1947, 1955, 1960 (Part), 1961, 1964, 1965. (8 levelings).
4.	Vicinity of Gorman	1935, 1938, 1953, 1961, 1964. (5 levelings).
5.	Vicinity of Maricopa	1935, 1938, 1948 (Part), 1953, 1956, 1959, 1964. (7 levelings).

The maximum and average divergence between levelings for the above lines are as follows:

Table 5.

Line no.	Maximum divergence between levelings	Average divergence
1.	0.174 meter or 0.571 foot	0.01 meter or 0.03 foot
2.	0.071 meter or 0.233 foot	0.04 meter or 0.13 foot
3.	0.363 meter or 1.191 feet	0.07 meter or 0.23 foot
4.	0.066 meter or 0.217 foot	0.04 meter or 0.13 foot
5.	0.439 meter or 1.440 feet	0.03 meter or 0.10 foot

In 1964, small groups of marks were set at 22 locations stradling the San Andreas and other major faults. In 1965, releveling was undertaken at 15 of these locations.

The maximum vertical relative changes are as follows:

Table 6.

Site no.	Location	Latitude	Longitude	Vertical change 1964 to 1965 (mm)
1	Colt	34.1°	117.3°	2.6
2	Rialto	34.1	117.3	5.7
3	Devil	34.2	117.3	8.2
4	Cedar	34.3	117.3	5.0
5	Wright	34.4	117.7	7.2
6	Pear	34.5	117.9	4.8
7	Barrel	34.5	118.1	10.1
8	Palm	34.6	118.2	12.7
9	Hughes	34.7	118.5	7.8
10	Warm	34.6	118.5	26.4
11	Cast	34.5	118.6	11.4
12	Quail	34.8	118.8	4.4
13	Ranch	34.9	118.8	22.4
14	Tejon	34.9	118.8	11.8
15	Mettler	35.0	119.0	8.1

REFERENCES

Meade, B. K., 1963, Horizontal crustal movements in the United States—Report to the Commission on Recent Crustal Movements: U.S. Coast and Geodetic Survey, Internat. Union Geodesy and Geophysics, Gen. Assembly, Berkeley, Calif., 1963, 25 p.

—— 1965, Report to the Commission on Recent Crustal Movements: Internat. Assoc. Geodesy, Symposium on Recent Crustal Movements, Aulanko, Finland, August 1965, 25 p.

Tocher, Don, 1960, Creep on the San Andreas fault—Creep rate and related measurements at Vineyard, California: Seismol. Soc. America Bull., v. 50, no. 3, p. 396–403.

Whitten, C. A., 1949, Horizontal earth movement in California: U.S. Coast and Geodetic Survey Jour., no. 2, April 1949, p. 84–88.

Chapel at Mission San Juan Capistrano, ruined by the earthquake of 1812. Courtesy of San Francisco Chronicle.

Relief camp set up after earthquake of 1906, San Francisco.

CHAPTER IX
SUBCRUSTAL STRUCTURE

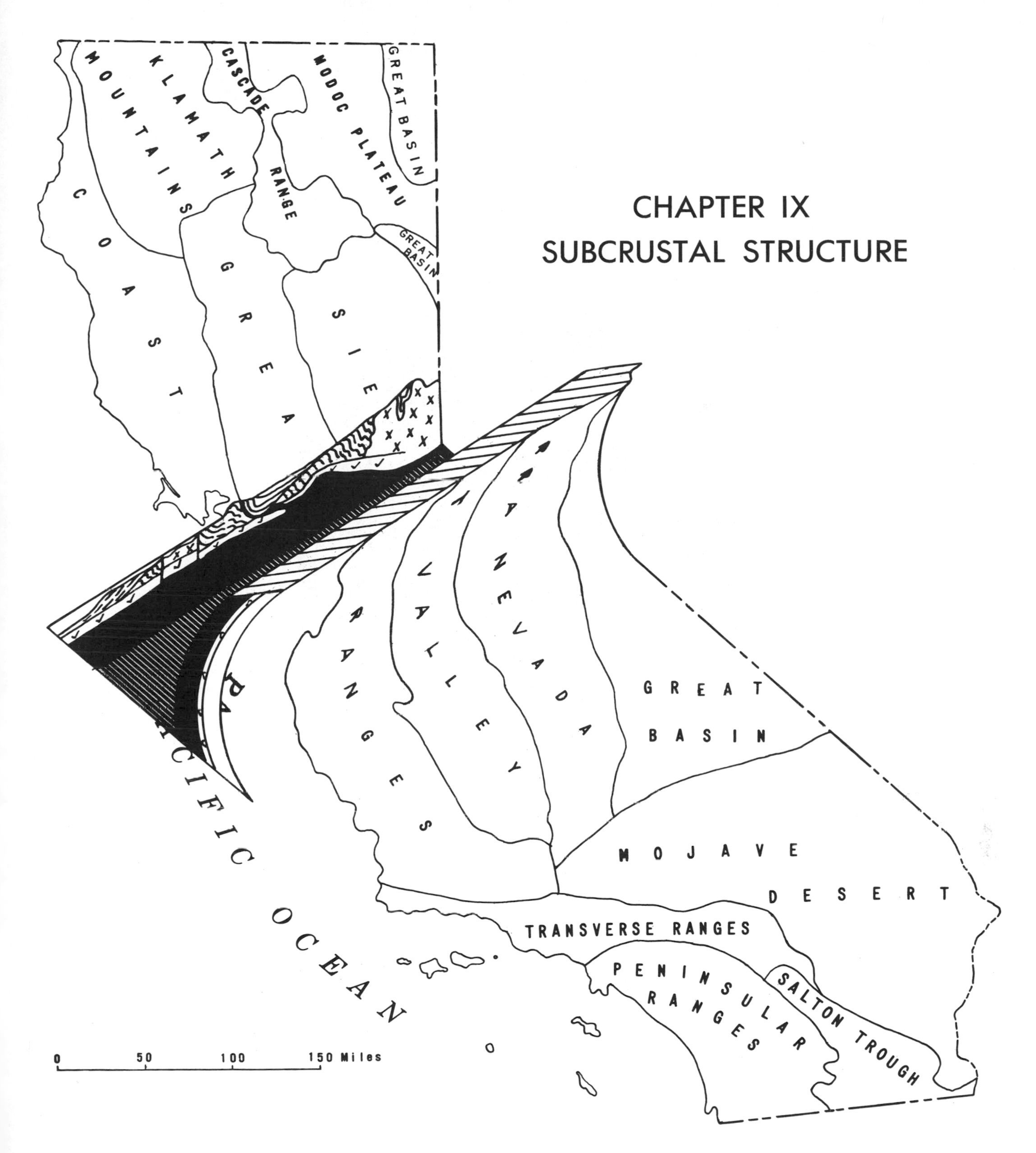

THE GRAVITY FIELD IN NORTHERN CALIFORNIA

By Rodger H. Chapman
California Division of Mines and Geology

Gravity surveys have proved useful in the study of the geology of northern California, particularly in interpreting some of the varied and complex structures found in this part of the State. Such surveys have been conducted by Federal and State government agencies, universities, and private industry. The U.S. Geological Survey is responsible for most of the published gravity data in the State, as a result of both Survey projects and student theses supported by the Survey. Oil companies have conducted extensive gravity surveys in the northern part of California, largely in potential gas or petroleum producing areas. Some local surveys and regional data have been released by the companies but most of this kind of data has remained confidential. A large number of projects are currently underway in California, including work by the U.S. Geological Survey and the California Division of Mines and Geology (Oliver, 1965; Chapman, 1965).

The present gravity coverage in northern California is far from uniform: good regional coverage is now available in parts of the Great Valley, the Sierra Nevada, some central parts of the Coast Ranges, and the southern Cascade Mountains, for example, but little has been done in many other areas in the State, such as the northern Coast Ranges.

A gravity measurement is the summation of many mass effects. Ideally, if we can assume that the effects of elevation, topography, latitude, and tides have been correctly removed, the anomalies in a map of the gravity field are caused by lateral density changes in the materials composing the earth. Geologic structures often bring into contact rocks of different densities, hence, gravity surveys may help locate these structures where they are hidden or buried. Local gravity surveys are frequently used directly in the search for mineral deposits, oil and gas, and in solving geologic problems. Regional surveys yield data on larger geologic features, such as the thickness and density of the earth's crust and the nature of isostatic compensation.

GENERAL FEATURES OF THE GRAVITY FIELD

Figure 1, a generalized Bouguer gravity map of the northern part of California with a contour interval of 20 mgal, has been adapted from a recently published 10 mgal map of the United States (Woollard and Joesting, 1964). This map was compiled from many sources and includes airport gravity base stations (Woollard, 1958) and regional traverses by the University of Wisconsin, as well as data from oil companies, universities, the U.S. Geological Survey, and the U.S. Coast and Geodetic Survey. The data were reduced using a density of 2.67 g/cm^3, yielding Bouguer gravity values, but terrain corrections are included only for the Sierra Nevada region between latitudes of 35°45′ and 37°00′.

The Bouguer gravity values along the coastal areas usually are positive or slightly negative, being often about 0 mgal. These decrease eastward to strongly negative values, —200 mgal or less, in the vicinity of the Sierra Nevada and Great Basin provinces. Superimposed on this general trend are numerous smaller anomalies ranging in size from some that are as large as a geologic province to others too small to be shown at the contour interval and scale of figure 1.

Thompson and Talwani (1964, p. 4820) have analyzed in detail a gravity profile that extends from the Pacific Basin in a northeasterly direction, approximately normal to the regional geologic structure, through the Coast Ranges near San Francisco, the Great Valley, the Sierra Nevada, and the western Great Basin provinces to a point near Fallon, Nevada (profile A-A′, figs. 1 and 2). The starting point for their crustal section, which is derived from the gravity anomaly profile, is based on seismic evidence that the depth to the base of the crust in the San Francisco Bay area is 21 km (Thompson and Talwani, 1964, p. 4823, who cite Healy, 1963, and Eaton, 1963). According to this interpretation, the regional anomaly from the Pacific Basin to the Great Basin, as shown on figure 2, is caused primarily by the effect of the crust, which thickens eastward from the margin of the continent, and secondarily by a decrease in the density of both the crust and upper mantle in the same direction. A gradation in the density of the crust from 2.9 g/cm^3 in the oceanic area to 2.8 g/cm^3 in the continental area was assumed to take place under the continental slope. Also assumed is an anomalous upper mantle with a density of 3.3 g/cm^3 under the continental area separated from the normal mantle with a density of 3.4 g/cm^3 at a depth of about 50 km (Thompson and Talwani, 1964, p. 4822).

The local anomalies, shown on both the contour map (fig. 1) and profile (fig. 2) are caused principally by density differences in the rocks of the upper crust, although in some cases deeper effects, including isostatic compensation, are also believed to be present. The locations of some of these anomalies are identified

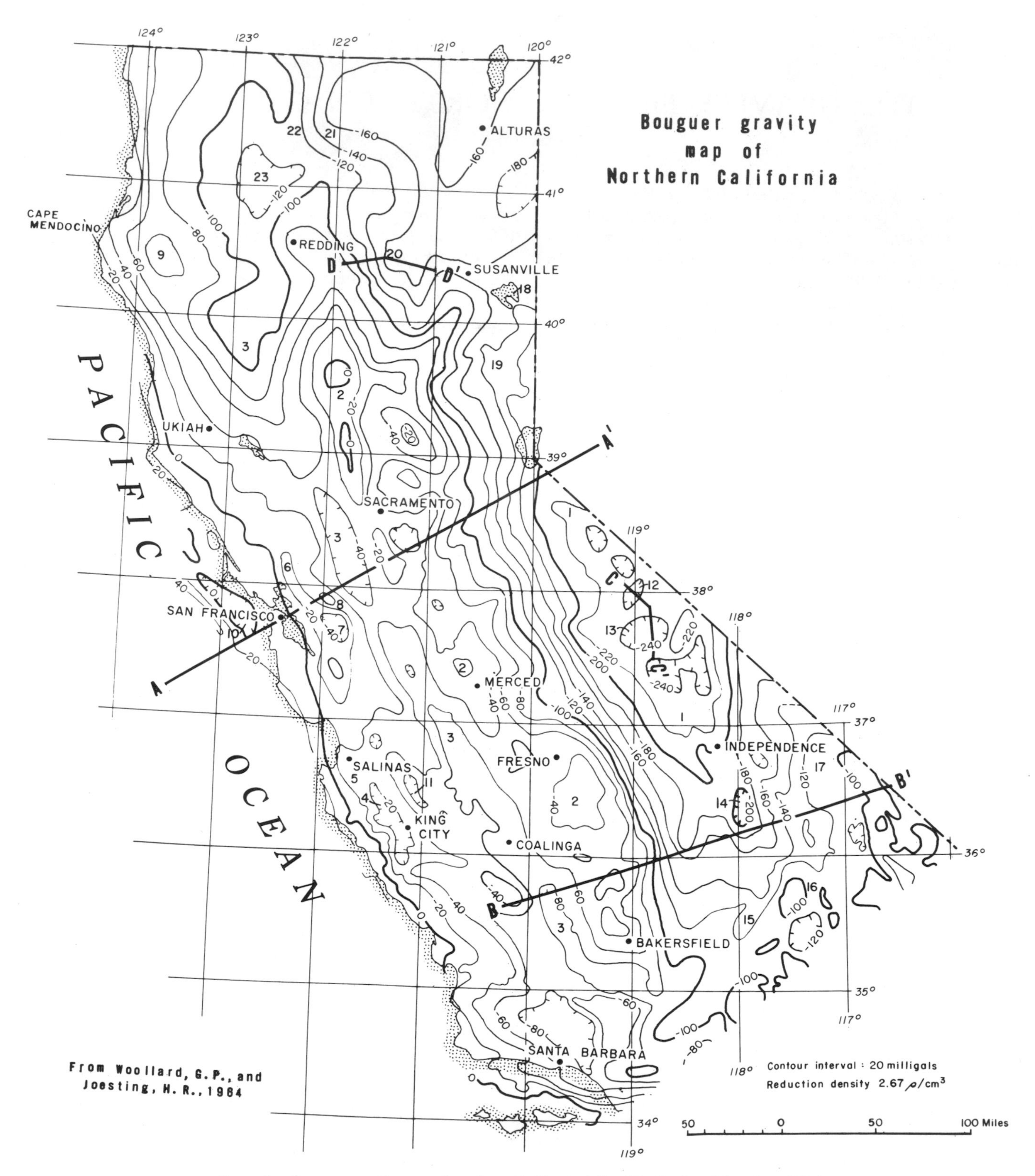

Figure 1. Bouguer gravity map of northern California (after Woollard and Joesting, 1964).

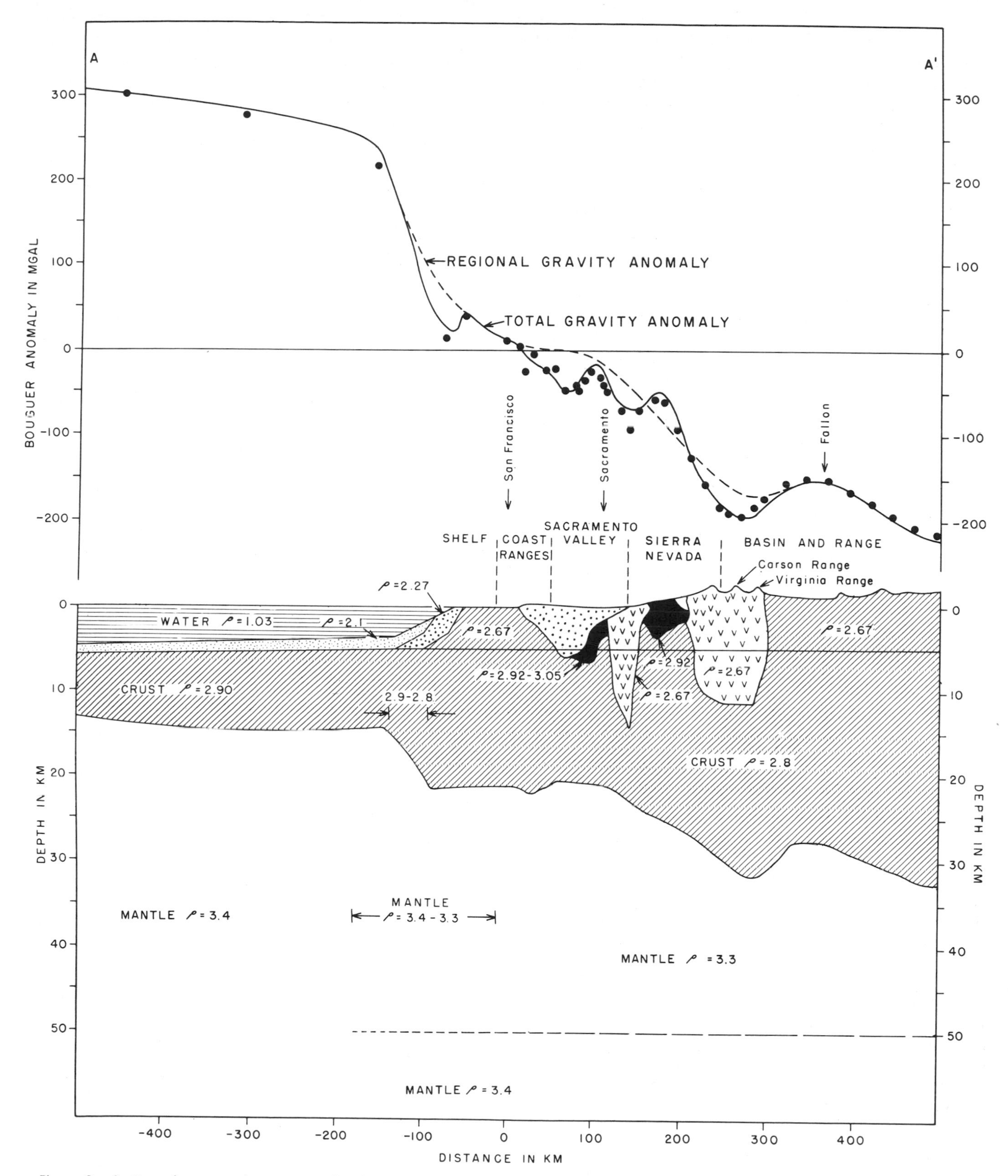

Figure 2. Section of crust and upper mantle along A-A', figure 1, showing gravity anomaly computed from section compared with observed points. Dotted patterns represent sedimentary rocks; checks, granitic rocks; shading, greenstone (after Thompson and Talwani, 1964, fig. 4).

on figures 1 and 2 by numbers. Three of the more prominent northwest-trending anomalies that can be seen on the map include a gravity minimum (No. 1) associated with the Sierra Nevada, a gravity high (No. 2) extending along the length of the Great Valley on its east side from near Redding to Bakersfield, and a gravity minimum (No. 3) located on the east side of the Coast Ranges and west side of the Great Valley. The local anomalies will be discussed in more detail in the following sections on the individual geologic provinces.

COAST RANGES PROVINCE AND OFFSHORE AREAS

In many parts of the Coast Ranges of California there is only a small amount of gravity data available. The Coast Ranges in the area north and south of San Francisco have received the most attention. Figure 1 shows that in general the gravity field decreases from between +20 and 0 mgal at the coast to as low as −80 mgal in the eastern part of the Coast Ranges and western part of the Great Valley.

Local studies have usually found gravity lows associated with large thicknesses of Cretaceous and Cenozoic rocks and almost normal or high gravity values over the more dense Franciscan Formation and granitic basement rocks of the Coast Ranges. Thicknesses of the sedimentary rocks have been estimated in some areas from the gravity data. These estimations depend critically on the density contrasts selected unless independent seismic data are available, and for many areas the densities are not well established.

In the Salinas Valley-San Antonio Hills area northwest of King City, P. E. Byerly (1966, fig. 2) found a negative anomaly of about −30 mgal (fig. 1, No. 4) which he attributes largely to a 6,000-foot-thick section of Miocene shale. Farther north in the Salinas Valley, J. W. Fairborn (1963, student project, Stanford Univ., p. 17) analyzed a −38 mgal anomaly (fig. 1, No. 5) south of the city of Salinas. He concluded that this is caused by a thickness of approximately 9,000 feet of Tertiary sediments bounded on the east by granitic basement rocks of the Gabilan Range and on the west by the King City fault and basement rocks in the Sierra de Salinas.

Parts of the south San Francisco Bay and northern Santa Clara Valley area have been studied by S. G. Taylor (1956) and G. M. Greve (1962). Additional work has also been done recently in this area by the California Division of Mines and Geology and the California Department of Water Resources (California Dept. Water Resources, 1965) and near San Jose by Stephens Robbins (oral communication, 1964). These studies have revealed steep gravity gradients and large gravity lows of up to −30 mgal in parts of the valley, and these indicate the presence of faults separating several major structural blocks. The gravity evidence suggests that younger sediments with thicknesses up to 5,000 feet may overlie the basement of Franciscan rocks in parts of the valley.

In the vicinity of San Pablo Bay, northeast of San Francisco, Clement (1965, p. 4) has outlined another major gravity low (fig. 1, No. 6) which he believes is caused primarily by a downfaulted and folded block of Tertiary rocks bounded by Jurassic and Cretaceous rocks on the west and east. In addition, C. F. Petersen (1962, student project, Stanford Univ., p. 3) found a negative anomaly with a westerly trend and an amplitude of about 30 mgal over a thick accumulation of sediments in the Livermore Valley, east of the San Francisco Bay area (fig. 1, No. 7).

Gravity highs in the Coast Ranges are often related to exposed basement rocks, particularly greenstone masses in the Franciscan Formation and intrusive granitic, mafic, and ultramafic bodies. Examples are highs over the granitic rocks of Montara Mountain and Point Reyes in the San Francisco Bay area (Greve, 1962, p. 21; Clement, 1965, p. 5) and a high east of the San Andreas fault in Marin County caused by a belt of greenstone and ultramafic rocks (Clement, 1965, p. 5). A surprisingly large positive anomaly of approximately 50 mgal (fig. 1, No. 8) found in a survey of the Mount Diablo area by Wood (1964, p. 33) indicates by its size that the diabase exposures northwest of the central peak of Mount Diablo represent a very large deepseated mass. Another prominent broad gravity high (fig. 1, No. 9) in the Coast Ranges, east of Cape Mendocino, is based on very few measurements but corresponds in general to a wide belt of Franciscan Formation rocks.

Masses of ultramafic rock in the Coast Ranges are believed to be largely serpentinized. The range of densities for dunite, peridotite and pyroxenite is about 3.1 to 3.3 g/cm^3 (Birch, 1942, p. 14), but for serpentine it is about 2.2 to 2.8 g/cm^3. Thus, an ultramafic body in contact with Franciscan graywacke which has an average density between 2.60 and 2.65 (Bailey and others, 1964, p. 141) might cause either a gravity high or low depending on the proportion of serpentine present.

Gravity surveys of several ultramafic masses in the Coast Ranges have been made to determine the nature of these bodies at depth. For example, P. E. Byerly (1966), using a reduction density of 2.67 g/cm^3, found a negative anomaly over a serpentinized laccolith or thick sill north of Coalinga in the Diablo Range. He concluded that there could be no large amount of unaltered ultramafic rock in the core of the mass. Studies of exposed dunite bodies at Cazadero, in Sonoma County, and Burro Mountain, in Monterey County, reveal relatively small gravity anomalies that indicate "shallow depths of dunite and a probable abundance of concealed serpentine" (Thompson, 1963, p. 228). A possible exception to these findings is the ultramafic mass in the eastern Klamath Mountains discussed in a later part of this article.

Published offshore gravity data in northern California are meager. Profile A-A′, shown in figure 2, makes use of sea pendulum stations by Harrison and others (1957) and Vening Meinesz (1948) and a station on Farallon Island. This profile shows a 40 mgal negative residual anomaly in the vicinity of the continental slope, which Thompson and Talwani (1964, p. 4829) suggest is caused by a thickness of about 3 km of sedimentary rocks. A survey offshore in the San Francisco area by the U.S. Coast and Geodetic Survey (Jones, 1963, p. 32) revealed a gravity low bounded by steep gravity gradients (fig. 1, No. 8) between the Farallon Islands and the mainland. This suggests a fault-controlled basin, or graben, filled with sediments.

In the vicinity of the Mendocino fracture zone off northern California some gravity stations have been occupied by Worzel and others (1955) and Harrison and others (1957). A more detailed investigation of this area was recently completed by geophysicists of Oregon State University, using a shipborne gravity meter (Peter Dehlinger, written communication, 1965).

An interpretation of the structure across the Mendocino fracture zone based on the gravity data available at that time has been presented by Talwani and others (1959, p. 55). According to this interpretation, which assumed that the crust consists of a single homogeneous layer overlain by sediments and water, the crust was found to be about 3 km thicker north of the fracture zone than south of it in the area studied. There is also an indication of a mass deficiency under the escarpment which may represent a local thickening of the crust. Limited data obtained by Bowers (1958) in the Cape Mendocino area east of the Mendocino and Gordo escarpments does not provide evidence for the shoreward continuation of these structural features.

San Andreas fault. Many of the gravity anomalies in the Coast Ranges are related to faulting, which has brought rocks of contrasting densities into contact. Where rock types on each side of the faults are similar, or have similar densities, there may be no associated anomaly. It is conceivable, however, that a major fault zone, such as the San Andreas, could displace the base of the earth's crust or layers deep within the crust and have a characteristic anomaly related to this relatively deepseated displacement even though the surface rocks have similar densities.

If we examine gravity maps of the area along the San Andreas fault zone we find in some areas anomalies associated with the fault, but in others essentially no anomalies. P. E. Byerly (1966), for example, found northeast of King City, a negative anomaly (fig. 1, No. 11) of about 40 mgal just southwest of and parallel to the San Andreas fault zone. This anomaly is probably caused by a thick section of Miocene and Pliocene sedimentary rocks, which lies between the fault and the exposed crystalline rocks of the Gabilan Range to the southwest. A Bouguer anomaly profile across the Coast Ranges and San Joaquin Valley (P. E. Byerly, 1966, pl. 1) which has been corrected for near-surface geologic effects shows no evidence of an anomaly related to the San Andreas fault.

In the San Francisco Bay area there are both negative and positive anomalies found close to the San Andreas fault, but these are also clearly related to near-surface geologic features. In the vicinity of Tomales Bay, for example, there are no local anomalies to distort the smooth regional surface, and Clement (1965, p. 5) has concluded that there is no characteristic anomaly associated with the fault. A study of the regional magnetic data leads to a similar conclusion with respect to the San Andreas fault according to Griscom (this bulletin, p. 408).

GREAT VALLEY PROVINCE

The Great Valley of California, which includes the Sacramento Valley on the north and the San Joaquin Valley on the south, is a broad alluviated depression near sea level in elevation. Structurally, it is an asymmetrical synclinorium containing on its western side 30,000 feet or more of Cretaceous and Cenozoic sediments (Kilkenny, 1951, p. 215). As would be expected, the western side of the valley and the eastern side of the Coast Ranges are characterized by a prominent gravity low (fig. 1, No. 3) owing to this great thickness of sedimentary rock. A surprising gravity feature in the Great Valley, however, is a nearly continuous gravity high (fig. 1, No. 2) that trends down the length of the valley and is nearly in the middle from east to west, except for a southernmost segment which is nearer the eastern side. On profile A-A′ (fig. 2), for example, the gravity values increase from less than −50 mgal along the western edge to about −20 mgal near the center of the valley. Both of these major gravity anomalies extend throughout the length of the valley.

The gravity high in the Great Valley has been the subject of great interest and speculation, partly because it tends to obscure smaller effects of possible oil-bearing structures (Ivanhoe, 1957, p. 64). Associated with the gravity anomaly is a prominent magnetic high (Grantz and Zeitz, 1960, p. B346), and both anomalies probably result from the same geologic feature. Several explanations for this high have been suggested. Woollard (1943, p. 778) observed this gravity anomaly and the related magnetic high in the Bakersfield area, and he pointed out that it is one of three major positive anomalies encountered on a transcontinental traverse. He suggested a gabbro intrusive as a possible cause. Bowers (1958, p. 20–23) attributed the gravity high near Marysville in the Sacramento Valley to a combination of a buried basement ridge and an upwarp of the earth's crust. The results of drilling in the Great Valley, however, show that basement topography is probably not an important factor in the cause of the anomaly. The Cenozoic intrusive and volcanic rocks at Sutter Buttes, near Marysville, suggest another possible cause for the anomaly in this area, but similar volcanic rocks are not found in other parts of the valley.

Ivanhoe (1957, p. 62) interpreted the positive anomaly belt as only a relative maximum located between the negative anomaly associated with the valley sediments and a negative anomaly caused by isostatic compensation of the Sierra Nevada. This explanation, however, does not account for the associated magnetic anomaly.

Bayoumi (1961, p. 32) concluded that the positive anomalies in an area generally between Merced and Fresno in the San Joaquin Valley are caused mainly by lithologic variations in the basement rocks. He supports this idea with a large number of density and magnetic susceptibility measurements from drill cores and outcrops. Similarly, Thompson and Talwani (1959, p. 1688) concluded that the positive anomaly belt is "directly associated with the greenstone belt, partly exposed and partly concealed beneath the Great Valley sediments." However, according to Griscom (this bulletin, p. 410), the results of recent aeromagnetic surveys by the U.S. Geological Survey do not support this explanation because no positive magnetic anomaly is associated with the exposed greenstone in the central Sierra foothills belt.

Grantz and Zietz (1960, p. B346) suggest igneous rock masses, at a depth of from 5 to 10 miles, as a cause of the aeromagnetic anomaly in the Great Valley. As a result of a study of gravity and magnetic data in the San Joaquin Valley, Oliver and Mabey (1963, p. 1293) conclude that the mass responsible for the anomaly is in the lower part of the earth's crust at a depth of 5 to 10 miles, and is conceivably related to the more mafic rocks of the earth's upper mantle. Seismic data suggest that the crust may thin to less than 20 km or 12 miles in this area, possibly as a result of an isostatic adjustment to balance the thick section of low-density sediments. Bailey (1964) has suggested that the anomalous zone represents a Mesozoic sphenochasmic rift in the continental crust caused by westward drifting of a crustal block. This rift might represent the boundary between Sierran granitic and Coast Range Franciscan basement rocks, and could also explain a rise of dense, magnetic upper mantle rocks below the Great Valley.

Oil companies have conducted extensive gravity surveys of the Great Valley in the search for possible oil- and gas-bearing structures. Although few results

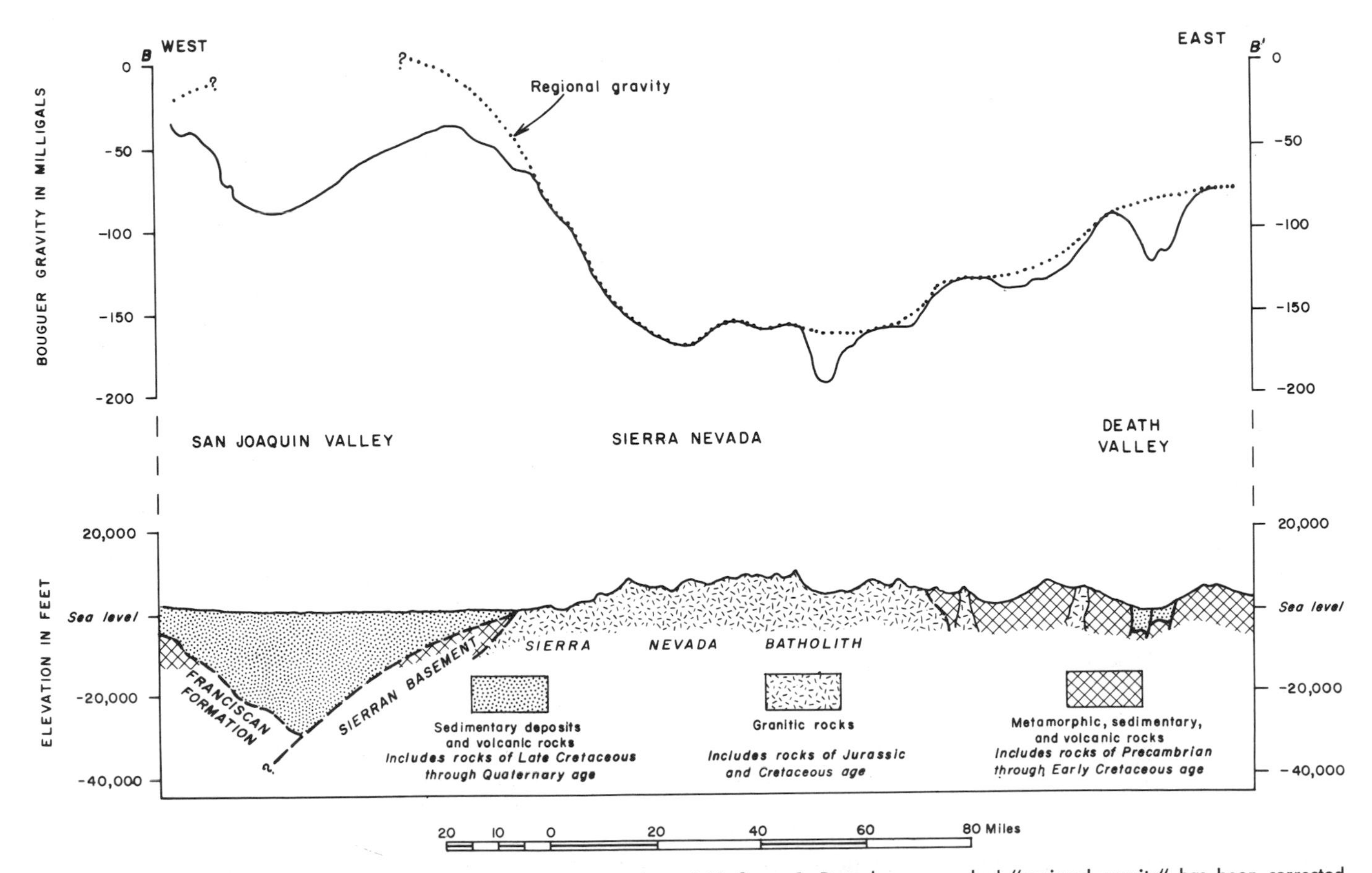

Figure 3. Bouguer gravity profile and geologic cross section along B-B', figure 1. Dotted curve marked "regional gravity" has been corrected for the effect of sedimentary deposits and volcanic rocks of late Cretaceous through Quaternary age (after Oliver and Mabey, 1963, fig. 1).

of these studies are available, some examples of the more unusual features and difficulties encountered in interpreting local anomalies have been published. Born (1956, p. 302) described a positive gravity anomaly near Dinuba in Tulare County that is caused by a buried topographic feature, which was also detected by other geophysical methods. Boyd (1949, p. 523–528) shows how a gravity high at the Kettleman Hills domes, southeast of Coalinga, becomes a gravity minimum along the same structural trend at the Lost Hills anticline. This effect is apparently caused by a transition in the sedimentary rocks from clays and shales at Kettleman Hills to light, diatomaceous shales at Lost Hills.

SIERRA NEVADA AND GREAT BASIN PROVINCES

Gravity values decrease rapidly eastward in the western foothills of the Sierra Nevada. The total decrease from the foothills to the vicinity of the High Sierra is as much as 200 mgal and gravity gradients are as high as 7 mgals/mile (Oliver and Mabey, 1963, p. 1295). In the Central Sierra Nevada this decrease culminates just west of the crest of the mountain range (profile B-B′, fig. 3). Farther north, according to Thompson and Sandberg (1958, p. 1278), the gravity minimum is reached just east of the Carson Range in western Nevada (profile A-A′, fig. 2). East of the Sierra Nevada low, gravity values tend to increase in an eastward direction in the mountain blocks of the Great Basin province, but the intermontane basin areas are characterized by local lows.

A large part of the negative gravity anomaly associated with the Sierra Nevada is believed to be caused by isostatic compensation, indicating a root composed of relatively light rocks extends downward into the earth's mantle (Oliver, 1960, p. B314; Oliver and others, 1961, fig. 3). A portion of this anomaly is probably caused by the difference in density between the granitic rocks of the Sierra Nevada batholith and the bordering basement rocks (Thompson and Sandberg, 1958, p. 1280; Oliver and Mabey, 1963, p. 1296). Whether the thickness of the granitic rocks actually is greater under the Sierra Nevada than elsewhere, however, cannot be determined from gravity data alone.

Oliver and others (1961, p. 4268) estimated from gravity data that in the central Sierras a root of crustal material may extend to a depth of 50 km. On the basis of seismic data obtained subsequently by the U.S. Geological Survey, Eaton (1963, p. 5805) estimated that the earth's crust is more than 40 km thick beneath the crest of the northern Sierra Nevada near Lake Tahoe. This does not agree well with Section A-A′ (fig. 2) where the base of the crust is shown to be at a depth slightly greater than 30 km. Thompson and Talwani (1964, p. 4832) suggest, however, that the calculated thickness would be increased and the gravity interpretation brought into accord with the seismic results if the lower part of the crust under the Sierra Nevada batholith is unusually dense. This condition is not unreasonable; the batholiths are lighter than normal, and if they were formed by differentiation within the crust the rocks remaining below them should be heavier than normal.

The Great Basin province east of the Sierra Nevada has been the subject of several gravity investigations. Gravity augmented by some seismic control has been found very useful in this province in the study of some structures, particularly in learning the depth of Cenozoic deposits and in locating hidden high-angle faults. As might be expected, the gravity field tends to be low in the valleys and basins containing relatively low-density sediments and volcanic rocks of

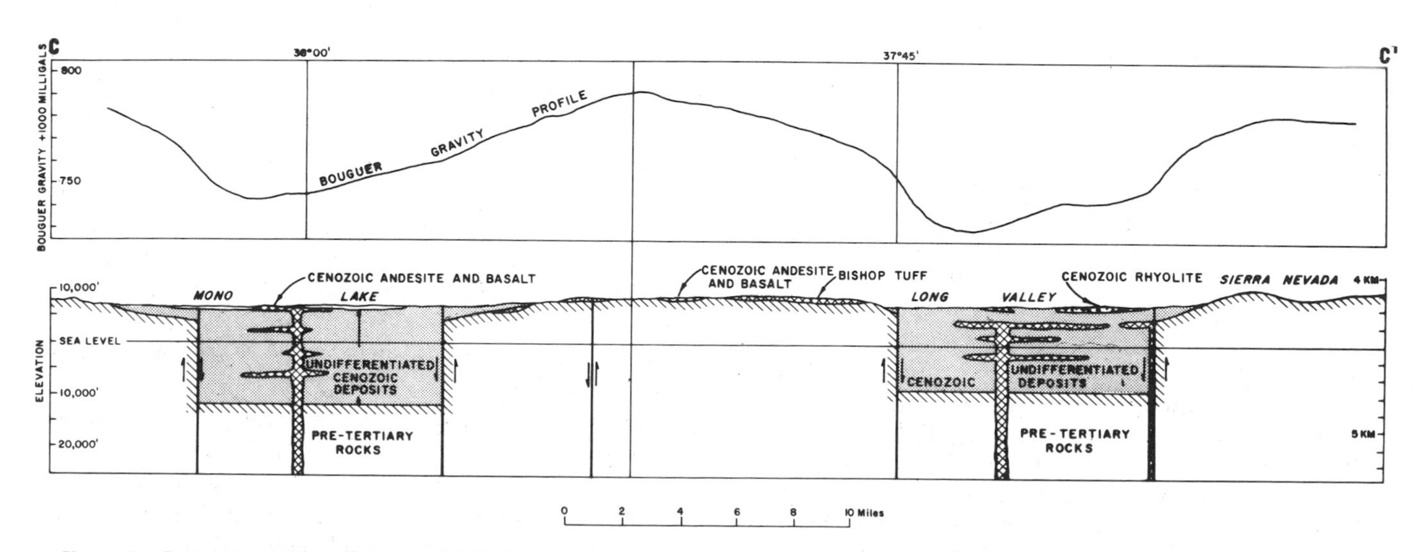

Figure 4. Bouguer gravity profile along C-C′, figure 1, across Mono Basin and Long Valley, showing assumed subsurface structure (after Pakiser and others, 1964, fig. 9).

Cenozoic age and high in the ranges where pre-Tertiary rocks predominate. A study of Mono Lake basin (fig. 1, No. 12) by Pakiser and others (1960) revealed a remarkable volcano-tectonic basin structure bounded by steep faults and containing a maximum thickness of 18,000 feet of Cenozoic deposits. Similar studies of Long Valley (fig. 1, No. 13) (Pakiser, 1961, p. B252) and southern Owens Valley (fig. 1, No. 14) (Kane and Pakiser, 1961, fig. 7) yielded estimates for the maximum thicknesses of Cenozoic deposits of 12,000 and 8,000 feet, respectively. Figure 4 (after Pakiser, 1964, fig. 9) shows the gravity anomalies and the assumed subsurface structure on a profile (profile C-C′, fig. 1) crossing Long Valley and Mono Lake. The gravity low over Long Valley, superimposed on the low regional value in this area, results in a value of less than −270 mgal, and is the largest negative Bouguer gravity value in California.

Gravity and seismic data at Indian Wells Valley (fig. 1, No. 15) and Searles Lake (fig. 1, No. 16) indicate maximum thicknesses of Cenozoic deposits of over 7,000 and 3,400 feet, respectively, according to Healy and Press (1964, fig. 10), von Huene (1960, pl. 3), and Mabey (1956, fig. 6). In the Death Valley region, according to a gravity survey by Mabey (1963), the Cenozoic fill reaches a thickness of about 10,000 feet in Mesquite Flat (fig. 1, No. 17).

Farther north in Honey Lake Valley (fig. 1, No. 18) in southeastern Lassen County, a gravity study suggests a thickness of about 5,000 feet of Cenozoic deposits in the basin bounded by granitic basement rocks (California Department of Water Resources, Bull. 98, 1963, p. 210). A study of Sierra Valley (fig. 1, No. 19), in parts of Sierra and Plumas Counties near the north end of the Sierra Nevada, indicates a minimum from 2,500 to 3,000 feet of Cenozoic fill (Jackson and others, 1961, p. B254). On the basis of the gravity data and outcropping volcanic rocks, Pakiser (1960, p. B413) has suggested that Sierra Valley may be a volcano-tectonic depression similar to Mono Basin and Long Valley.

CASCADE MOUNTAINS AND MODOC PLATEAU PROVINCES

Regional gravity surveys now extend over the entire southern Cascade Mountains and the western part of the Modoc Plateau, which consist almost entirely of sequences of Cenozoic lava and include the well-known eruptive centers of Mount Shasta and Lassen Peak.

A large gravity low in the Lassen Peak area was discovered by Bowers (1958, p. 24) while making a regional gravity survey in northern California. This survey was later extended by the U.S. Geological Survey to obtain more detail and more regional data (Pakiser, 1964). These studies have revealed that the gravity low in this area (fig. 1, No. 20) has a maximum amplitude of 70 mgal and an area of about 2,000 square miles. Although analysis of the anomaly is made difficult by the fact that the entire area is covered by Cenozoic volcanic rocks, Pakiser (1964, p. 617) suggests as possible causes for the anomaly the following geologic structures: (1) a batholith of silicic rock beneath the volcanic rock, (2) a thick buried accumulation of low-density sedimentary rocks of Cretaceous(?) age, (3) a low-density mass caused by thermal expansion of crustal rocks by heat from igneous activity, as originally suggested by Bowers (1958, p. 26), and (4) a volcano-tectonic depression filled with volcanic rock of low-average density.

Because subsidence in major volcanic source areas is very common and may be a characteristic condition, Pakiser (1964, p. 619) concludes that "* * * volcano-tectonic subsidence was a major element contributing to formation of the large mass of low density material buried in the Lassen Peak area." However, some of the other suggested causes may also contribute to the anomaly. Figure 5 shows a gravity profile (profile D-D′, fig. 1) across the Lassen Peak area with an assumed cross section and calculated anomaly based on the volcano-tectonic subsidence theory.

Farther north in the Cascade Mountains, in the Mount Shasta area (fig. 1, No. 21) LaFehr (1965a, 1965b) found a negative anomaly of from -35 to -50 mgal, which is very similar in amplitude, gradients, and general size to the Lassen Peak anomaly. Both anomalies are found within a broad gravity low with a width of about 50 km and a length of 75 km following the axis of the southern Cascades (LaFehr, 1965a, p. 11). Thus, it is reasonable to suppose that both the Mount Shasta and Mount Lassen anomalies have a similar cause: a large volume of low-density material at a shallow depth. LaFehr (1965b, p. 5581) calculated that this anomalous mass cannot be wholly below a depth ranging between 4 and 10 km in the Mount Shasta area, and he suggests that part of this low may be caused by the presence of shallow magma chambers containing silicic intrusive rocks. It is also possible that a part of the anomalies could be caused by a thickening of the crust below the volcanic province, but the largest part must have a relatively shallow source.

Both Pakiser (1964, p. 616) and LaFehr (1965b) applied Gauss' theorem to determine the mass deficiencies represented by the residual gravity lows, and compared this figure with the mass excesses represented by the mountains. The results at both Mount Shasta and Lassen Peak are that the mass deficiencies and mass excesses have the same order of magnitude. This significant result indicates that compensation of these large mountain masses must be largely a local rather than a regional phenomenon. LaFehr (1965a, p. 13) notes that the average free air gravity anomaly in the western portion of the Modoc Plateau is nearly zero, suggesting that the Modoc Plateau region is in nearly complete isostatic equilibrium.

KLAMATH MOUNTAINS PROVINCE

The gravity contours shown in figure 1 for the Klamath Mountains area in northwestern California are based on only a few stations. A part of the eastern side of this area, however, has now been covered by LaFehr (1965a) in his regional survey of the Mount Shasta and southern Cascade Mountains, but these data have not been incorporated into the map.

The rocks of the eastern portion of the Klamath Mountains range from pre-Silurian to Jurassic in age and consist predominantly of metasedimentary and metavolcanic rocks intruded by Mesozoic ultramafic, mafic, and granitic rocks (Irwin, 1960, p. 14–15).

The recent survey by LaFehr (1965a, p. 10) revealed a major north-trending positive gravity anomaly with a width of about 25 km and an amplitude of about 50 mgal centered near the high peaks of the Scott Mountains, the easternmost uplift of the Klamath Mountains. This anomaly is not properly shown by the contours on figure 1 but its position is indicated by number 22. LaFehr (in press) points out that this is evidently one of the few large positive gravity anomalies associated with a structural uplift on the North American continent.

The anomaly appears to be associated with an ultramafic intrusive mass, perhaps a thick sill occupying the crest of an anticlinal structure, although the surface geology and density samples do not provide conclusive evidence for this. The anomaly could also be caused by mafic intrusive rocks which have been mapped in the same general area. Calculations indicate that the maximum possible depth to the anomalous mass is 4 km (LaFehr, in press); thus, the source is shallow and may actually crop out. If the ultramafic mass is largely serpentine, as suggested by surface samples, rather than unaltered ultramafic or mafic rock, it is doubtful that there would be sufficient density contrast with the normal basement rocks to account for the anomaly. Therefore, if an ultramafic sill is actually the cause of the anomaly, serpentinization must decrease with depth in the sill.

The broad gravity low (fig. 1, No. 23) northwest of Redding and centered in the vicinity of the Trinity Alps, is based on few gravity stations. It corresponds in general to an area of Mesozoic ultramafic and mafic rocks intruded by large Mesozoic granitic batholiths, but additional gravity data are needed to better define the anomaly.

SUMMARY AND CONCLUSIONS

Our knowledge of the regional geology of northern California has been enhanced substantially by the information obtained from gravity surveys, as exemplified by some of the structures described in the preceding sections of this article. Additional gravity data in parts of the State not now covered adequately will further increase our knowledge of many of its major structures. A few examples of the many diverse projects in progress might include: (1) a study in the Burro Mountain area in Monterey County, by the U.S. Geological Survey, expected to yield new information on the nature of ultramafic intrusions, (2) a survey in the vicinity of Mount Konocti and Mayac-

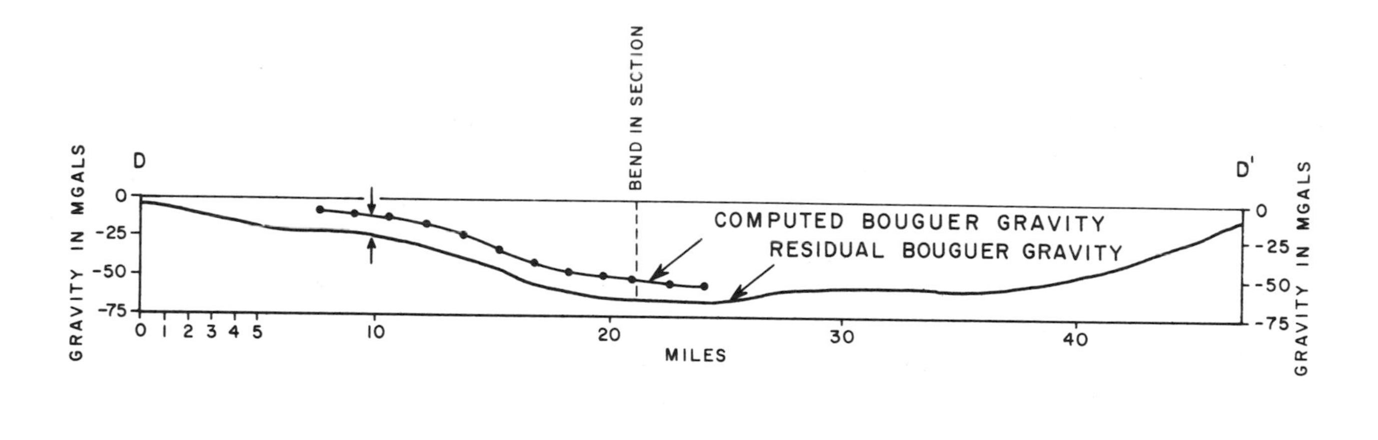

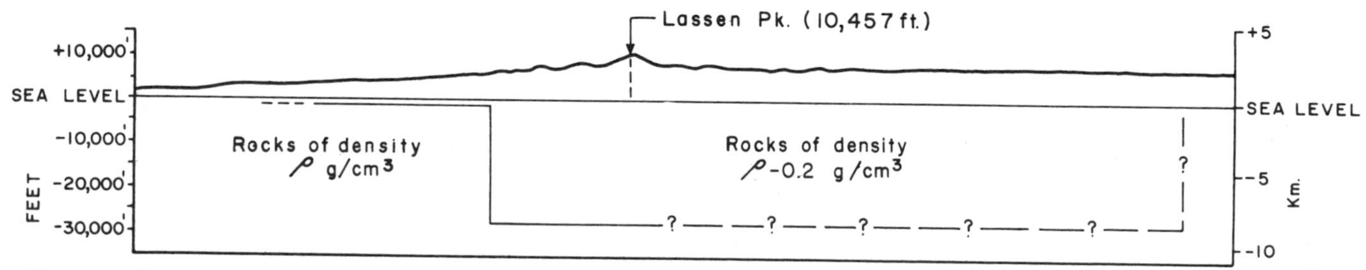

Figure 5. Bouguer gravity profile along D-D′, figure 1, across Lassen Peak and the southern Cascade Range area showing assumed subsurface structure (after Pakiser, 1964, fig. 3).

mas uplift in Lake and Sonoma Counties, by the California Division of Mines and Geology, will add to our knowledge of Quaternary structure and volcanism in the Coast Ranges, and (3) sea gravity investigations off northern California, by Oregon State University, leading to better knowledge of the offshore geologic structure.

Detailed gravity surveys in areas now covered only by regional data will be justified in many cases because of the evidence they will bring to bear on local problems. One of the goals of the Division of Mines and Geology is to publish gravity maps of California on the state map scale (1:250,000), as sufficient data become available, in the belief that maps on this scale will prove to be useful for many relatively local problems.

Additional gravity studies both on land and offshore are needed for an understanding of such broad problems as the nature of the transition from oceanic to continental crust, the differences in the crust and upper mantle in different areas, and the nature of isostatic compensation. Specific major problems identified but not solved include: (1) the Great Valley anomaly, (2) the degree of isostatic compensation of the Coast Ranges and Great Valley, (3) the possible shoreward continuation of the structures represented by the Mendocino and Gordo escarpments.

Because of the nature of the gravity field, structure cannot be determined from gravity data alone. Thus, there is a need for not only seismic and other geophysical data, but for geologic mapping, drilling information, and measurements of physical properties of rocks underlying northern California in order that the full benefit of both present and future gravity surveys may be realized.

REFERENCES

Bailey, E. H., 1964, Mesozoic sphenochasmic rifting along the San Andreas fault north of the Transverse Ranges [abs.]: Geol. Soc. America Spec. Paper 76, p. 186–187.

Bailey, E. H., Irwin, W. P., and Jones, D. L., 1964, Franciscan and related rocks, and their significance in the geology of western California: California Div. Mines and Geology Bull. 183, 177 p.

Bayoumi, I. A., 1961, Gravity and magnetic study in the San Joaquin Valley: Stanford Univ., Stanford, Calif., Ph.D. thesis.

Birch, Francis, Schairer, J. F., and Spicer, H. C., eds., 1942, Handbook of physical constants: Geol. Soc. America Spec. Paper 36, 325 p.

Born, M. C., 1956, Geophysical comparisons at Dinuba, Tulare County, California: Geophys. Case Histories, v. 2, p. 299–309.

Bowers, R. A., 1958, Gravity in northern California: California Univ., Berkeley, Ph.D. thesis.

Boyd, L. H., 1949, Gravity meter survey of the Kettleman Hills-Lost Hills trend, California: Geophys. Case Histories, v. 1, p. 523–528.

Byerly, P. E., 1966, Interpretations of gravity data from the central Coast Ranges and San Joaquin Valley, California: Geol. Soc. America Bull., v. 77, p. 83–94.

California Department of Water Resources, 1963, Northeastern counties ground water investigation: California Dept. Water Resources Bull. 98, 223 p.

—— 196__, Evaluation of ground water resources, south San Francisco Bay area: California Dept. Water Resources Bull. 118-1 (In press).

Chapman, R. H., 1965, The California Division of Mines and Geology gravity program: Am. Geophys. Union Trans., v. 46, no. 1, p. 223–224.

Clement, W. G., 1965, Complete Bouguer gravity map of the northern part of the San Francisco Bay area and its geological interpretation: U. S. Geol. Survey Map GP-468, 6 p., scale 1:125,000.

Eaton, J. P., 1963, Crustal structure from San Francisco, California, to Eureka, Nevada, from seismic-refraction measurements: Jour. Geophys. Research, v. 68, no. 20, p. 5789–5806.

Grantz, Arthur, and Zietz, Isidore, 1960, Possible significance of broad magnetic highs over belts of moderately deformed sedimentary rocks in Alaska and California: U.S. Geol. Survey Prof. Paper 400-B, art. 158, p. B342–B347.

Greve, G. M., 1962, An investigation of the earth's gravitational and magnetic fields on the San Francisco peninsula, California: Stanford Univ., Stanford, Calif., Ph.D. thesis, 209 p.

Harrison, J. C., Brown, G. L., and Spiess, F. N., 1957, Gravity measurements in the northeastern Pacific Ocean: Am. Geophys. Union Trans., v. 38, no. 6, p. 835–840.

Healy, J. H., 1963, Crustal structure along the coast of California from seismic-refraction measurements: Jour. Geophys. Research, v. 68, no. 20, p. 5777–5787.

Healy, J. H., and Press, Frank, 1964, Geophysical studies of basin structures along the eastern front of the Sierra Nevada, California: Geophysics, v. 29, no. 3, p. 337–359.

Irwin, W. P., 1960, Geologic reconnaissance of the northern Coast Ranges and Klamath Mountains, California: California Div. Mines Bull. 179, 80 p.

Ivanhoe, L. F., Jr., 1957, A gravity maximum in the Great Valley of California due to isostatic effect of the Sierra Nevada: Geophysics, v. 22, no. 1, p. 62–66.

Jackson, W. H., Shawe, F. R., and Pakiser, L. C., 1961, Gravity study of the structural geology of Sierra Valley, California: U.S. Geol. Survey Prof. Paper 424-B, art. 107, p. B254–B256.

Jones, R. B., 1963, A geophysical interpretation of an offshore gravity survey near San Francisco [abs.]: Am. Geophys. Union Trans., v. 44, no. 1, p. 32.

Kane, M. F., and Pakiser, L. C., 1961, Geophysical study of subsurface structure in southern Owens Valley, California: Geophysics, v. 26, no. 1, p. 12–26.

Kilkenny, J. E., 1951, San Joaquin Valley [California], *in* Ball, M. W., ed., Possible future petroleum provinces of North America: Am. Assoc. Petroleum Geologists Bull., v. 35, no. 2, p. 215–218.

LaFehr, T. R., 1965a, Gravity survey in the southern Cascade Range, California: U.S. Geol. Survey open-file report, September 20, 1965, 21 p., plus 48 p. app.

LaFehr, T. R., 1965b, Gravity, isostasy, and crustal structure in the southern Cascade Ranges: Jour. Geophys. Research, v. 70, p. 5581–5597.

LaFehr, T. R., 196__, Gravity in the Eastern Klamath Mountains, California: Geol. Soc. America Bull. (In press)

Mabey, D. R., 1956, Geophysical studies in the intermontane basins in southern California: Geophysics, v. 21, no. 3, p. 839–853.

—— 1963, Complete Bouguer anomaly map of the Death Valley region, California: U.S. Geol. Survey Geophys. Inv. Map GP-305, scale 1:250,000.

Oliver, H. W., 1960, Gravity anomalies at Mount Whitney, California: U.S. Geol. Survey Prof. Paper 400-B, art. 146, p. B313–B315.

—— 1965, The U.S. Geological Survey's gravity program in California, Hawaii, Nevada, and Oregon: Am. Geophys. Union Trans., v. 46, no. 1, p. 218–222.

Oliver, H. W., and Mabey, D. R., 1963, Anomalous gravity field in east-central California: Geol. Soc. America Bull., v. 74, no. 10, p. 1293–1298.

Oliver, H. W., Pakiser, L. C., and Kane, M. F., 1961, Gravity anomalies in the central Sierra Nevada, California: Jour. Geophys. Research, v. 66, no. 12, p. 4265–4271.

Pakiser, L. C., 1960, Volcanism in eastern California—a proposed eruption mechanism: U.S. Geol. Survey Prof. Paper 400-B, art. 189, p. B411–B414.

—— 1961, Gravity, volcanism, and crustal deformation in Long Valley, California: U.S. Geol. Survey Prof. Paper 424-B, art. 106, p. B250–B253.

—— 1964, Gravity, volcanism, and crustal structure in the southern Cascade Range, California: Geol. Soc. America Bull., v. 75, no. 7, p. 611–620.

Pakiser, L. C., Kane, M. F., and Jackson, W. H., 1964, Structural geology and volcanism of Owens Valley region, California—a geophysical study: U.S. Geol. Survey Prof. Paper 438, 68 p.

Pakiser, L. C., Press, Frank, and Kane, M. F., 1960, Geophysical investigation of Mono Basin, California: Geol. Soc. America Bull., v. 71, no. 4, p. 415–447.

Talwani, Manik, Worzel, J. L., and Landisman, M. G., 1959, Rapid gravity computations for two-dimensional bodies with application to the Mendocino submarine fracture zone [Pacific Ocean]: Jour. Geophys. Research, v. 64, no. 1, p. 49–59.

Taylor, S. G., Jr., 1956, Gravity investigation of the southern San Francisco Bay area, California: Stanford Univ., Stanford, Calif., Ph.D. thesis.

Thompson, G. A., 1963, Geophysical investigation of the dunite at Twin Sisters, Washington [abs.]: Geol. Soc. America Spec. Paper 76, p. 227–228.

Thompson, G. A., and Talwani, Manik, 1959, Crustal section across California and Sierra Nevada [abs.]: Geol. Soc. America Bull., v. 70, no. 12, pt. 2, p. 1688.

—— 1964, Crustal structure from Pacific basin to central Nevada: Jour. Geophys. Research, v. 69, no. 22, p. 4813–4837.

Thompson, G. A., and Sandberg, C. H., 1958, Structural significance of gravity surveys in the Virginia City-Mount Rose area, Nevada and California: Geol. Soc. America Bull., v. 69, no. 10, p. 1269–1281.

Vening Meinesz, F. A., 1948, Gravity expeditions at sea, 1923–1938; v. IV, Complete results with isostatic reduction; interpretation of the results: Netherlands Geod. Commission, Delft, 233 p.

von Huene, R. E., 1960, Structural geology and gravimetry of Indian Wells Valley, southeastern California: California Univ., Los Angeles, Ph.D. thesis.

Wood, L. C., 1964, A gravity survey of the Mount Diablo area, California, *in* Guidebook to the Mount Diablo field trip: Geol. Soc. Sacramento, p. 33–36.

Woollard, G. P., 1943, Transcontinental gravitational and magnetic profile of North America and its relation to geologic structure: Geol. Soc. America Bull., v. 54, no. 6, p. 747–789.

—— 1958, Results for a gravity control network at airports in the United States: Geophysics, v. 23, no. 3, p. 520–535.

Woollard, G. P., chm., and Joesting, H. R., coordinator, 1964, Bouguer gravity anomaly map of the United States (exclusive of Alaska and Hawaii): Am. Geophys. Union, Spec. Comm. Geophys. and Geology Study of Continents, and U.S. Geol. Survey, scale 1:250,000.

Worzel, J. L., Shurbet, G. L., and Ewing, Maurice, 1955, Gravity measurements at sea, 1952 and 1953: Am. Geophys. Union Trans., v. 36, no. 2, p. 326–334.

Empire mine, Grass Valley.

MAGNETIC DATA AND REGIONAL STRUCTURE IN NORTHERN CALIFORNIA[1]

By Andrew Griscom
U.S. Geological Survey, Menlo Park, California

In the 20 years that have passed since the advent of the airborne magnetometer, much aeromagnetic data have been collected in California. Measurements have been made both by Federal agencies, including the U.S. Geological Survey, the U.S. Coast and Geodetic Survey, and the U.S. Naval Oceanographic Office, and by private companies, primarily for the use of State agencies and the petroleum and mining industries. Most of the company data, which covers virtually all potentially petroliferous areas in the State, is not available to the public and will not be further discussed here. Measurements made for State agencies generally were related to specific problems, such as planning for dams and other structures, and have not generally been published. The published or released aeromagnetic data, however, contain a wealth of information concerning details of California geology, and in addition indicate several broad regional magnetic features associated with the major tectonic or crustal units of the State. It is these major features which are the prime concern of this paper, and for convenience, the discussion will treat the State from west to east. However, because the aeromagnetic coverage of northern California is so extremely incomplete, especially north of lat 40°N., this paper can only be a preliminary report.

COAST RANGES AND CONTINENTAL MARGIN

Pacific Ocean

A north-south trending pattern of linear magnetic anomalies in the deep ocean area west of the continental slope has been described by Mason and Raff (1961) and by Raff and Mason (1961). Near the continental margin the north-south grain swings to a trend of N. 30° E—particularly in the region southwest of San Francisco—and continues to where it intersects the continental margin. In addition, near the continental margin the anomaly amplitudes diminish and the lengths of the horizontal projections of the marginal gradients increase, strongly suggesting that the magnetic material causing the anomalies becomes much more deeply buried as the continent is approached. These facts bear on the space problem caused by the left-lateral displacement of 735 miles along the Mendocino fault as deduced from the magnetic pattern offset by Vacquier, Raff, and Warren (1961). This east-west fault intersects the California coast at Cape Mendocino, and Vacquier and colleagues have suggested as one possibility that the oceanic crust may be sliding smoothly under the continent without disrupting the magnetic pattern. According to Affleck (1962), near-surface magnetic anomaly trends over the postulated eastward extension of the fault into California support the hypothesis that the fault is also present in the continental crust. Using a crustal thickness of 12 miles at San Francisco (Eaton, 1963) and an average geothermal gradient, the Curie point isotherm is likely to be near the base of the crust so that no magnetic anomalies can be expected from greater depths even though former oceanic crust material may now be present there. Moderately high heat flow has been measured from the continental slope off San Francisco (Von Herzen, 1964). Thus the Curie point isotherm under the continental shelf in this area may be located a substantial distance above the base of the crust.

A contoured transcontinental strip of aeromagnetic data 100 miles wide flown by the U.S. Naval Oceanographic Office (Zietz and others, 1965) extends west through San Francisco, a distance of 120 miles into the deep ocean. The magnetic pattern over the oceanic crust is well displayed and clearly terminates at the foot of the continental slope near the 1,500-fathom contour. A portion of a profile from this aeromagnetic survey is illustrated in figure 1.

Continental Shelf

The continental shelf from Santa Cruz to Point Arena is a block of crystalline basement rocks overlain by Cretaceous and younger sedimentary rocks. This block is bounded on the east by the San Andreas fault and on the west probably by an extension of the Nacimiento fault (Bailey, Irwin, and Jones, 1964), which here may define the western limit of continental crystalline basement rocks. Gravity minima and seismic data offshore from San Francisco suggest the presence of large basins of low-density Tertiary sedimentary deposits both west of the Farallon Islands on the continental slope (Thompson and Talwani, 1964, p. 4829; Curray, 1965) and also east of the granitic Farallon Islands, where Jones (1963) inferred a graben of sedimentary rocks with border faults parallel to the San Andreas fault. The Bouguer gravity low associated with the graben has an amplitude of about 50 mgal,[2]

[1] Publication authorized by the Director, U.S. Geological Survey.

[2] Orlin, Hyman, Fanning, K. F., Jones, R. B., and Garoutte, S. K., 1962, Sea gravity phase, oceanographic equipment evaluation range, San Francisco, California: U.S. Coast and Geod. Survey and U. S. Naval Oceanographic Office, July 1962, 24 p.

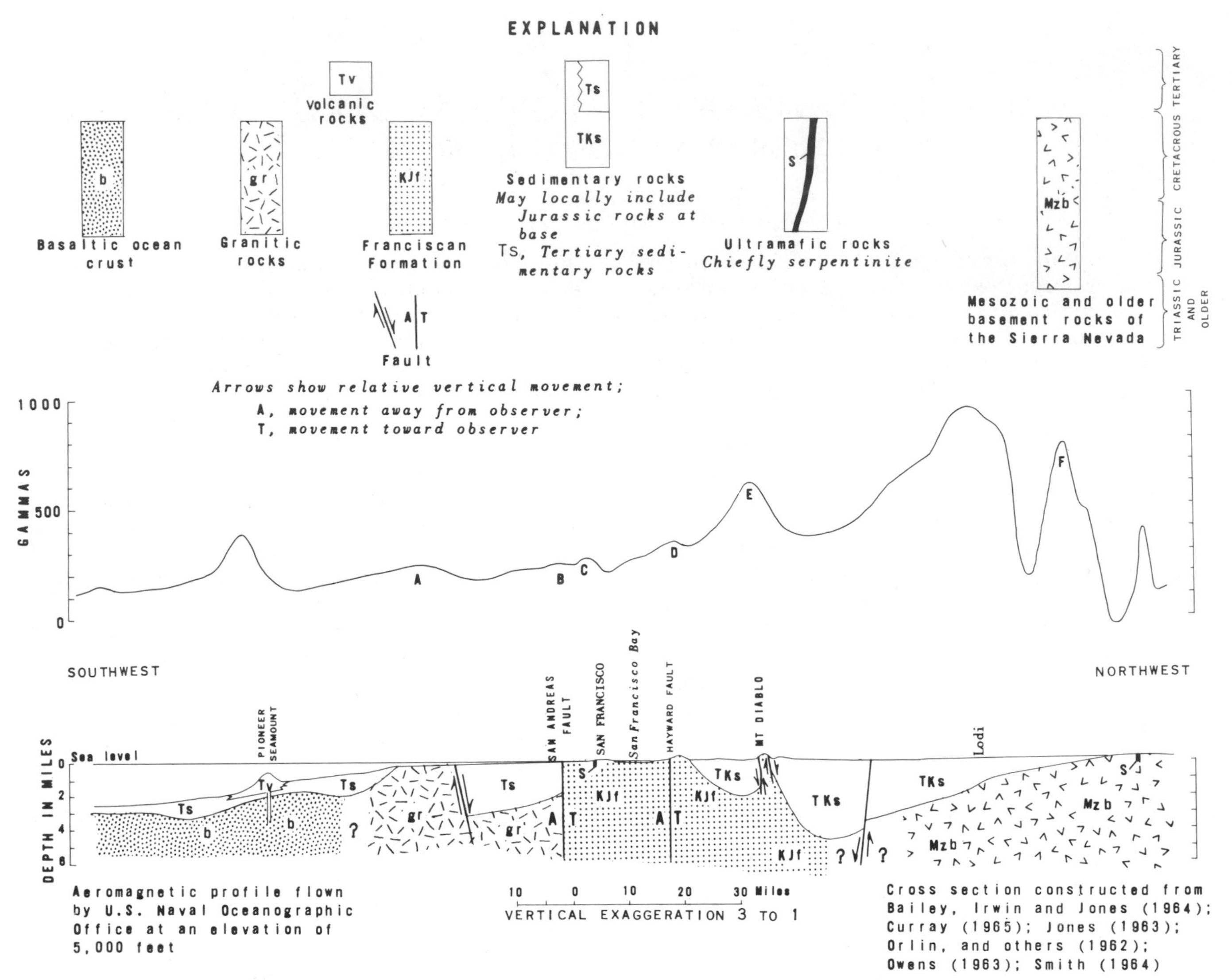

Figure 1. Total intensity aeromagnetic profile and generalized geologic cross-section from the Pacific Ocean through San Francisco to the Sierra Nevada.

indicating a rock thickness of about 2.5 miles, assuming a density contrast of 0.3 g/cm^3. Because this contrast is probably a maximum, the calculated thickness is a minimum. The granitic ridge (quartz diorite) associated with the Farallon Islands produces a broad magnetic high, shown as Point A on figure 1, and the inflection point on the east side of the magnetic anomaly corresponds in position with the fault inferred from the gravity data.

San Andreas Fault

Affleck (1962) traced the San Andreas fault northwest into the Pacific from Point Arena (39°N. lat) for a distance of 40 miles by means of aeromagnetic data, and his aeromagnetic map is reproduced here (fig. 2). An elongate magnetic high with an amplitude of about 200 gammas is clearly cut off on its northeast side by the fault. The anomaly is at least 10 miles wide and 40 miles long, and because of its distinctive character, suggests the possibility of searching on the opposite side of the fault for the missing portion of the magnetic mass in order to measure the displacement along the San Andreas. Available aeromagnetic data indicate that the missing magnetic mass is probably not north of Hollister, and in 1966 the U.S. Geological Survey will make reconnaissance aeromagnetic measurements over the more southerly extension of the fault zone. Assuming possible strike-slip movement of 350 miles since Jurassic time (Hill and Dibblee, 1953) and magnetic source rocks of nearly similar age, one might expect the missing portion of the magnetic anomaly to be located near the south end of the San Joaquin Valley. Another possibility is considered in a later section discussing the magnetic anomaly on the east side of the Great Valley.

At the projected intersection of the San Andreas fault with the Mendocino fault, Menard (1960) has pointed out that the Mendocino fault offsets the con-

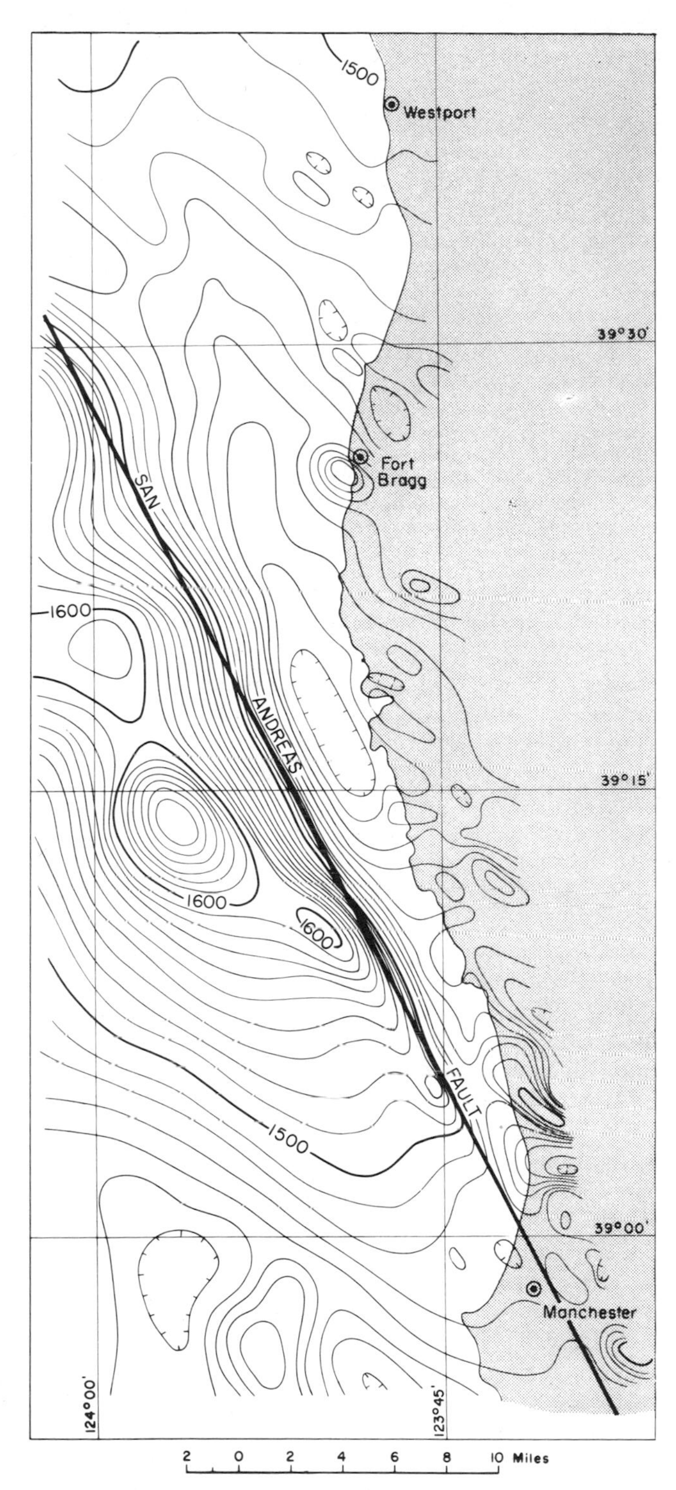

Figure 2. Total intensity aeromagnetic map showing the extension of the San Andreas fault on the continental shelf north of 39° N latitude (after Affleck, 1962). Contour interval 10 gammas.

tinental slope in northern California, a distance of about 65 miles in a right-lateral sense, the reverse of the sense of movement determined from magnetic data. The San Andreas fault, being also right lateral, may curve to the west at its north end and merge with the Mendocino fracture zone. The north-south linear magnetic grain north of the Mendocino fracture zone (Raff and Mason, 1961) shows no sign of offset in the area on strike with the San Andreas fault, so that if the fault continues north beyond the Mendocino fault, it cannot extend on strike toward the deep ocean but must bend northward at Cape Mendocino, following the continental slope. At lat 42°N. the magnetic data suggest that the fault, if present, must still be at the top of the continental slope, but a northwest-trending discontinuity in the magnetic pattern permits the speculation that the fault may extend into the Pacific Ocean north of this latitude (Wilson, 1965).

Aeromagnetic profiles across the San Andreas fault (fig. 1) indicate that in general the rocks on both sides of the fault are relatively nonmagnetic and that there are no regional magnetic anomalies which might indicate significant crustal differences on the two sides. Thompson and Talwani (1964a, p. 4823) make a similar statement about gravity data which indicates "no systematic density difference in crustal rocks on the two sides." In contrast with the above is the seismic refraction data of Eaton (1963), which show that the crustal velocity of P is 6.0 km/sec west of the San Andreas fault but only 5.6 km/sec east of the fault. Local magnetic highs over the fault, such as B on figure 1, are known from magnetic data elsewhere to be caused by serpentinite masses within the fault, and this explanation is adopted for anomaly B. The frequent occurrence of magnetic highs over the San Andreas fault suggests that serpentinite may be more common in the fault at shallow depth than is indicated by geologic mapping.

Franciscan Formation

The belt of Franciscan rocks lying between the San Andreas fault and the Great Valley sequence of sedimentary rocks (Bailey and others, 1964) is characterized by abundant serpentinite masses which account for most of the small magnetic anomalies associated with this unit on figure 1. In general, the Tertiary volcanic rocks are not sufficiently thick to generate magnetic anomalies at a flight elevation of 5,000 feet. The serpentinites of San Francisco form a 50-gamma magnetic high (C on fig. 1) and the serpentinite belt along the Hayward fault also generates a magnetic anomaly (D on fig. 1).

The large magnetic high over Mount Diablo (E on fig. 1) is a unique feature deserving separate comment. The northern half of the Mount Diablo piercement structure is shown as Franciscan rocks by Bailey, Irwin, and Jones (1964) and is mapped as intrusive diabase by Pampeyan (1963), who states that although it seems very similar to Franciscan greenstones in the southern half of the structure, it is younger than the Franciscan Formation. No other area of Franciscan greenstone is known to generate such a large magnetic anomaly. The great width of magnetic anomaly E indicates a magnetic mass approximately 7 miles wide along the profile, whereas the exposed diabase has a maximum mapped width of only about 3 miles in this same direction. A large positive gravity anomaly associated with this diabase mass has an amplitude of about 50 mgal and has been studied in detail by Wood (1964). He calculates a laccolithic or mushroom-shaped mass of diabase about 1.5 miles thick and 8 miles in diameter, having a stem about 2 miles wide and extending downward about 8 miles. The association of the two geophysical anomalies and the similar anomalous mass widths determined from the data indicate that both anomalies are caused by the same mass, that is, the diabase. In addition, the unique magnetic and gravity expression of this mass indicates that it should not be regarded as a part of the Franciscan Formation.

The eastern contact of the Franciscan Formation with the sedimentary rocks of the Great Valley sequence is generally a zone of faulting, and a sheet of serpentinite or other ultramafic rock commonly intervenes beneath the Great Valley sequence but above the Franciscan Formation. Irwin (1964) and Bailey, Irwin, and Jones (1964) hypothesize that the Great Valley sequence may have been thrust toward the west over the Franciscan rocks and that a sheet of ultramafic rocks, including serpentinite, simultaneously has been emplaced along the thrust plane. Ultramafic rocks such as pyroxenite and peridotite are usually not very magnetic but their altered equivalent, serpentinite, is highly magnetic because of the magnetite formed during the alteration of the anhydrous silicates to serpentine minerals. Aeromagnetic data of the U.S. Naval Oceanographic Office indicate a continuous magnetic high which can be traced along the eastern border of the Franciscan Formation at least as far south as Pacheco Pass (lat 37°N.). The magnetic data support the concept of a nearly continuous belt of ultramafic rock, predominantly serpentinite, along the eastern margin of the area of the Franciscan, and thus support the hypothesis of Irwin (1964). At Pacheco Pass, ground magnetic and gravity data (Woollard, 1943; Schroll, 1963) show that at the exposed east contact of the Franciscan a small gravity high may be associated with the magnetic high. Here, in addition to serpentinite, relatively unaltered ultramafic rock may be present to account for the gravity anomaly.

An important magnetic feature is found associated with this same serpentinite belt farther north, between lat 39°15'N. and 30°45'N. Here, aeromagnetic data released by the California Department of Water Resources (unpublished data, July 1966) and also aeromagnetic data collected by the U.S. Geological Survey (Irwin and Bath, 1962) show a broad regional magnetic anomaly associated with a sharp, local magnetic anomaly generated by the exposed ultramafic rock. The regional anomaly is apparently caused by a buried magnetic mass lying 1 to 2 miles below the surface along the belt of ultramafic rocks. The upper surface of the mass dips both east and west from its highest point at average angles of less than 15°, and its total width must exceed 12 miles. The association of this regional magnetic anomaly with exposed serpentinite suggests that it is caused by a large concealed mass of serpentinite, possibly a gently folded thick sheet. The western half of the sheet would underlie Franciscan rocks, and from its crest a zone of serpentine-filled, eastward-dipping thrust faults would extend up to the earth's surface.

GREAT VALLEY

Great Valley Magnetic Anomaly

A large broad magnetic high extends the entire length of the Great Valley of California from Red Bluff to Bakersfield. This feature has been known at least since 1932 (Jenny, 1932), and a contoured aeromagnetic map with flight intervals of 3 to 12 miles has been published by Grantz and Zietz (1960) for the interval between lat 37°30'N. and 40°N. The close association of the magnetic high with a corresponding gravity high was noted by Woollard (1943), and subsequent publications (Bayoumi, 1961; Oliver and Mabey, 1963; Thompson and Talwani, 1964a) have emphasized the good correlation of the two highs along the entire valley, although contoured magnetic data are not generally available between approximately lat 35°40'N. and 36°40'N.

The explanations for this major geophysical feature fall into two general categories. Some writers have suggested a large mass of mafic intrusive igneous rock; such writers include: Woollard (1943), who interpreted the anomaly as caused by a mass of gabbro with its top 3.6 miles below the surface; Grantz and Zietz (1960); Irwin and Bath (1962), who believe the anomaly may be caused primarily by ultramafic rock; and Oliver and Mabey (1963). The second proposed explanation (Thompson and Talwani, 1959; Bayoumi, 1961; Thompson and Talwani, 1964a) is that the Great Valley anomaly is caused by old deformed extrusive mafic volcanic rocks like those exposed in the western Sierra Nevada foothills. The evidence upon which these dissimilar conclusions are based includes: basement rock samples from drill holes in the Great Valley, a supposed continuation of the anomaly north of the Great Valley, and analogies with the geophysical expression of rock units of the western Sierra Nevada foothills.

Available data from drill holes over the anomaly north of lat 37°30'N. are scanty and have been discussed by Irwin and Bath (1962, p. B67). They mention 10 holes which penetrate "chiefly intrusive rocks of intermediate composition," and they note one core of gabbro and one of ultramafic rock. Basement lithology in the Fresno-Madera area near lat 37°N. is illustrated by Thompson and Talwani (1964a, fig. 5) with data modified from Bayoumi (1961). Here, along the higher portion of the gravity anomaly are shown 7 mafic metaigneous cores, 1 serpentine core, and 14 granitic cores. The gravity high in this area is broad and relatively low in amplitude, but depth calculations by Bayoumi (1961) based on contoured ground magnetic data suggest that the anomaly-producing rocks crop out at the basement surface. Abundant basement core data are available for the Bakersfield area (May and Hewitt, 1948; Thompson and Talwani, 1964a, fig. 6) where gravity and magnetic highs are associated with 4 gabbro cores, 2 diabase cores, 2 serpentine cores, and at least 13 mafic metaigneous cores in addition to other cores of granitic and metasedimentary rocks. It should be noted that the abundant quartz diorite samples recorded from the Great Valley basement are classified as granitic rocks because of their low density and generally low magnetization.

Evidence for continuation of the gravity and magnetic anomalies north of the valley is uncertain. The gravity high between lat 40°15′N. and 40°45′N. near Redding shown in figure 1 of Chapman (this bulletin, page 396) is probably only a relative high caused by the large flanking gravity lows to the east and west. The northern extension of the Great Valley magnetic anomaly to the magnetic gabbroic and ultramafic rocks of the Klamath Mountains is suggested by Irwin and Bath (1962) on the basis of a few widely spaced aeromagnetic profiles and the fact that the major magnetic anomalies, where definitely explained, are caused by ultramafic rocks, chiefly serpentinite. A small map published by Affleck (1962, p. 170) shows in the area north and northwest of Red Bluff magnetic anomaly axes trending east-west directly across the projected trend of the Great Valley anomaly; farther north, however, a return to the Great Valley trend is suggested. The magnetic data of Affleck (1962), and the probable absence of an associated gravity high at the north end of the Great Valley, raise considerable doubt as to the validity of this postulated northern extension of the anomaly.

The explanation that the Great Valley magnetic and gravity feature is caused primarily by mafic volcanic rocks is based largely on the presumption that the greenstone belt of the Sierra Nevada foothills is both magnetic and of relatively high density (Thompson and Talwani, 1964a). The abundant gravity and magnetic data now available from the foothills indicate that the volcanic rocks probably do not cause substantial magnetic or gravity highs. Most of the major gravity and magnetic highs known in the western Sierra Nevada foothills (see, for example, fig. 1; Balsley, 1953; Henderson, 1953) are caused by belts of serpentinite and mafic intrusions associated with the serpentinites. One gravity high of uncertain origin is crossed by the gravity profile of Thompson and Talwani (1964a) about 30 miles northwest of Sacramento, but it is precisely at this location that a belt of serpentinite and associated small mafic intrusions intersects the gravity profile. Furthermore, a large mafic pluton about 10 miles long and 5 miles wide is located less than 10 miles south of, and on strike with, the gravity anomaly. Gravity measurements over this pluton by the U.S. Geological Survey indicate a local Bouguer gravity high of about 25-mgal amplitude. Thompson and Talwani (1964b) believe that the gravity anomalies of this area merge to the southwest with the Great Valley anomaly, thus proving the greenstone association. However, more recent gravity data suggest that the two gravity features may not be connected (H. W. Oliver, oral communication, 1965). Even if they should prove to be connected, the indicated lithologic association is mafic intrusive rocks rather than extrusive greenstone. It appears that geophysical evidence from the rock units of the Sierra Nevada foothills does not favor the interpretation that mafic volcanic rocks similar to those of the greenstone belt cause the Great Valley feature.

A detailed aeromagnetic map of the Great Valley in the area between lat 37°15′N. and 39°10′N. is illustrated in figure 3. Small isolated local anomalies on individual flight lines are caused by well casings or industrial areas. The broad regional anomaly is well shown, as also are the smaller, sharper anomalies which are probably caused by magnetic rock masses extending up to the basement surface. A few anomalies, such as those along the northwest border of the map near Colusa, are caused by igneous rocks, presumably volcanic rocks, located relatively high in the sedimentary section above the basement. The Great Valley magnetic anomaly is situated approximately in the center of figure 3, trending parallel to the long direction of the map. The northeastern limit of the high is a relatively steep magnetic gradient extending downward into a rather linear associated magnetic low. The low is commonly below the regional magnetic level and is probably in part a polarization low associated with a relatively steep northeast-dipping contact on the northeast side of a magnetic mass of rock, the declination being N.17°E. and the inclination of the earth's field being 63°. A belt of relatively nonmagnetic basement rocks is presumably associated with the magnetic low, and it is not necessary to invoke reverse remanent magnetization to explain this low. The southwestern side of the Great Valley magnetic anomaly has a relatively even slope of great width which suggests that the west contact of the magnetic rock mass dips to the southwest but is below the basement surface.

As far south as Stockton, well-defined inflection points are observed on each transverse profile high on the southwest side of the magnetic anomaly. This line of inflection points probably defines the approximate location of the southwest contact of the magnetic rock mass where exposed at the basement surface. A width of 6 to 10 miles at the basement surface is indicated for this basement unit north of Stockton and the unit must become much wider at depth. The excellent correlation of this feature with the gravity high can be noted by comparing figure 3 with the gravity map (fig. 1 of Chapman, 1966, this bulletin).

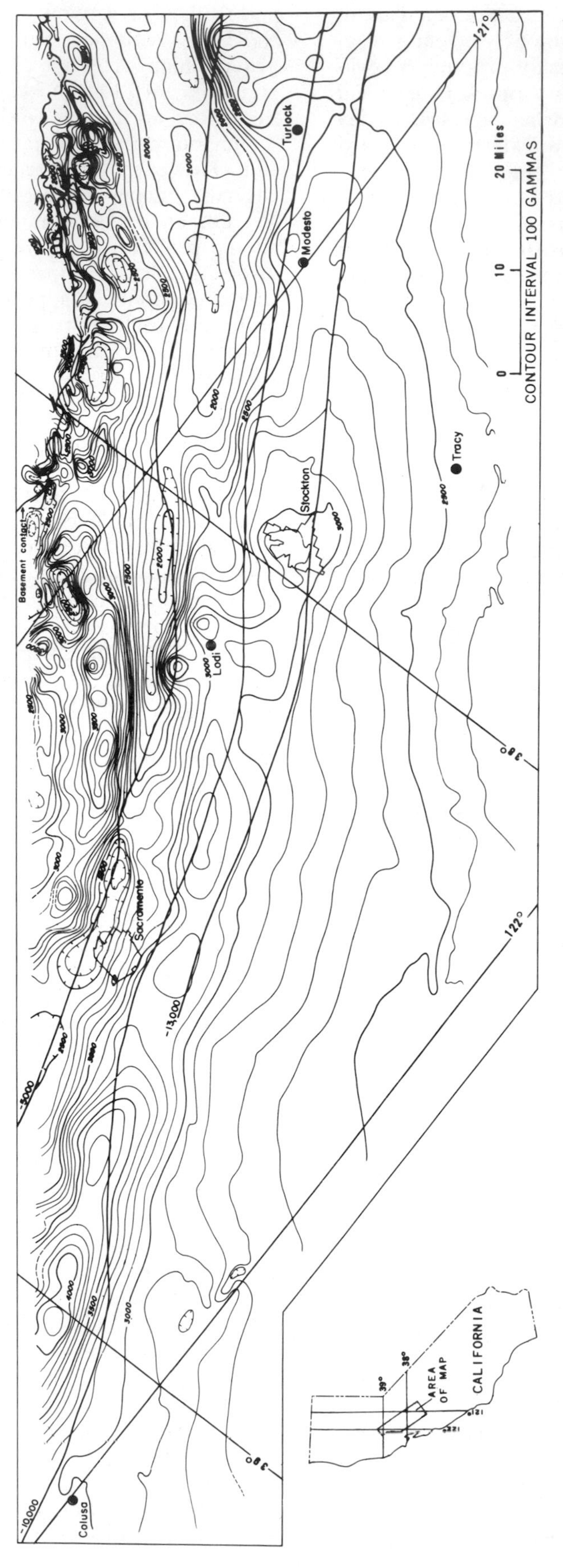

Figure 3. Total intensity aeromagnetic map of portions of the Sacramento and San Joaquin River valleys, California, after Meuschke and others, 1966. Flown 500 feet above ground at a traverse spacing of 1 mile. Basement depth contours in feet below sea level from Smith (1964).

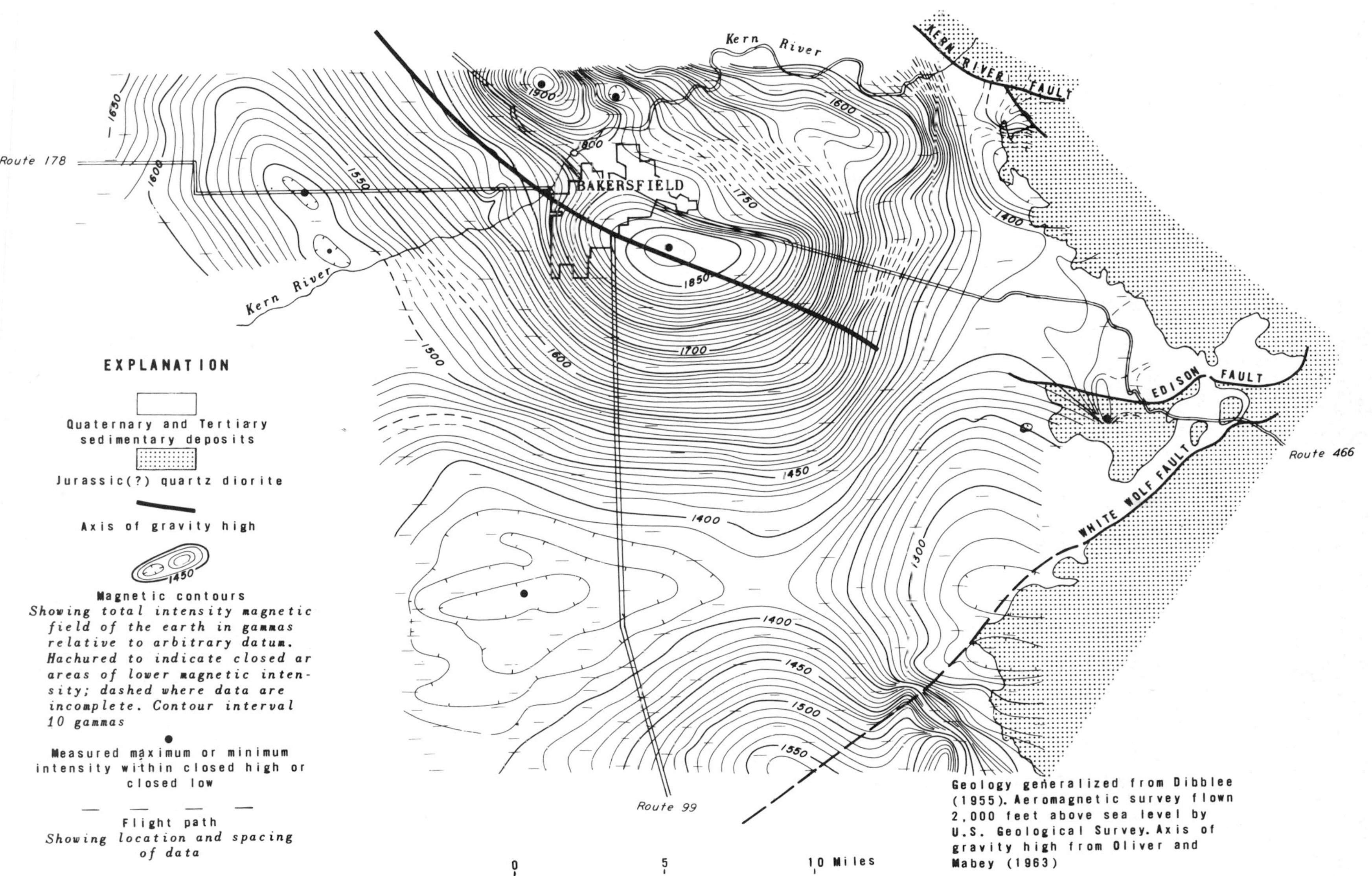

Figure 4. Total intensity aeromagnetic and generalized geologic map of the Bakersfield area, California, showing correlation of magnetic high with axis of the Great Valley gravity high.

The gravity data cannot be used to provide much information about the southwest contact of this magnetic, high-density rock responsible for the anomaly because of the large but poorly known thickness of low-density sediments on the west side of the Great Valley (Repenning, 1960). Southeast of Stockton as far as Turlock, the southwest contact of the magnetic rock mass is poorly defined and there are no inflection points high on the southwest side of the feature. Throughout this distance the gravity map indicates a low saddle on the associated Great Valley gravity ridge, so it is possible that the magnetic rock unit here may not be exposed at the basement surface, except perhaps locally at the magnetic high 2 miles east of Modesto. Southwest of Turlock the magnetic anomaly resumes an appearance more similar to the portion northwest of Stockton, and at the same location the associated gravity anomaly resumes its former amplitude.

At the extreme southern end of the Great Valley, in the Bakersfield area, both the magnetic high and the gravity high (fig. 4) do not extend to the place where the basement rocks crop out on the southeast side of the White Wolf fault. In the area of figure 4, the exposed basement rocks are predominantly quartz diorite which appears to be relatively nonmagnetic. The association of the positive gravity anomaly with mafic basement rocks in this area has been well documented by Thompson and Talwani (1964a), and by using their figure 6, it is possible to draw a geologic contact about 10 miles long between mafic and granitic rocks. This line approximates the position of the 1,450-gamma contour line southeast of Bakersfield on figure 4, the mafic rocks being northwest of the contact and associated with the magnetic high. It is difficult to decide from the drill-hole samples whether mafic plutonic or volcanic rocks (or both) are the main source of the magnetic and gravity anomalies. The northern magnetic high clearly is not associated with the gravity high.

The magnetic contours southeast of the White Wolf fault indicate by steep, narrow gradients the shallow depth to basement relative to the northwest side of the fault. In addition the magnetic contours suggest that left-lateral movement of the fault must be less than a mile. The 1.5-mile-downward displacement of the northwest side shown by Smith (1964) at the location where the 1,450-gamma contour crosses the fault is probably sufficient to cause the left-lateral offset in the magnetic contour line, owing to increase in distance of the magnetic rocks from the aircraft. This conclusion contradicts various writers who consider the fault movement to be predominantly strike slip and confirms the statement of Dibblee (1955, p. 23) that the "White Wolf fault is essentially a reverse fault, locally a thrust, elevated in the southeast block, with a small left-lateral component of movement."

In summary, the close association of the magnetic and gravity highs trending the length of the Great Valley demonstrates that the gravity anomaly is at least in part caused by a mass of high-density magnetic rock, and that it is not merely a relative maximum between the gravity lows caused by the valley sediments to the west and the Sierra Nevada to the east, as suggested by Ivanhoe (1957). The Great Valley magnetic anomaly can be considered the expression of one of the principal structural features in California (Bailey and others, 1964, p. 150), and an explanation of its origin should take into consideration the regional structural setting. The anomaly is located in the central portion of the Great Valley, an asymmetrical elongate synclinal sedimentary basin which is parallel to the uplifted Sierra Nevada to the east and of about the same length. The anomaly appears to be situated at the contact between two very different geologic and tectonic terranes, the Franciscan rocks to the west and the Sierra Nevada basement rocks to the east. Two major east-west oceanic fault zones, the Mendocino fault to the north and the Murray fault to the south, intersect the continental margin at the approximate latitude of the north and south ends of both the anomaly and the Sierra Nevada. The sense of movement of continental strike-slip faults on strike with these oceanic faults suggests that the continental block west of the magnetic anomaly and between the faults may be moving west relative to the adjacent portions of the continent. Yet the sense of movement on the oceanic faults as determined from magnetic data (Vacquier and others, 1961) is the reverse.

The oblique-rifting hypothesis of Bailey (1964) and Bailey, Irwin, and Jones (1964, p. 160) offers a possible way to synthesize the regional structural setting with the geologic and geophysical information concerning the Great Valley feature. This hypothesis proposes that beginning in Late Jurassic time the block of granitic rocks "between the San Andreas and Nacimiento faults has drifted laterally from a position adjacent to the present central part of the Great Valley" (Bailey, Irwin, and Jones, 1964, p. 162), the north end of the block moving along the Mendocino fault. It seems logical that the Late Jurassic zone of tension and fracture along the present location of the Great Valley might have been intruded at that time by substantial masses of mafic and ultramafic rocks, coming possibly from the upper mantle (Oliver and Mabey, 1963). This large elongate mass of magnetic high-density rocks would be the source of the Great Valley anomaly and could possibly contain associated volcanic rocks, and locally, some serpentinite. The association of the structural depression of the Great Valley with this high-density mass implies that the valley may in part be caused by the subsidence of this block of mafic rock, perhaps in order to regain isostatic equilibrium after it was intruded; however, other factors must also have been operating because isostatic equilibrium can be regained relatively rapidly and the Great Valley has been subsiding at least since Cretaceous time. The parallel association of the high-density descending mass of valley basement with the complementary low-density rising mass of the Sierra Nevada suggests that these two areas behaved in the main as a single crustal block rotating in response to isostatic forces about a horizontal axis trending slightly west of north. This idea has been advanced by Kane (*in* Kane and Carlson, 1961) for ranges in Nevada. Presumably the Sierran root has been growing during the uplift, and perhaps the crust under the Great Valley has thinned during its descent.

Magnetic Anomaly on the East Side of the Great Valley

Another major regional belt of magnetic highs follows along the northeast border of figure 3 to the latitude of Sacramento, where it appears to terminate against the circular, mostly covered mass of granite that causes the large gravity low northeast of Sacramento (Thompson and Talwani, 1964a). This magnetic high does not seem to be present north of Sacramento, according to the limited data that was available to Irwin and Bath (1962). Along the very linear high-amplitude portion of this magnetic anomaly between a point 8 miles east of Sacramento and another point 10 miles northeast of Lodi, there is a large associated gravity high, interpreted as caused by a mafic intrusion, but farther to the southeast the amplitude of the magnetic anomaly is lower and the gravity expression is subdued. The more complex pattern of local magnetic highs and lows along this regional magnetic high can be attributed for the most part to the relatively shallow depth of the magnetic rocks below the aircraft (about 1,500 feet), and the profile of figure 1 gives an indication of the appearance of this anomaly northeast of Lodi at F under circumstances where the magnetic rocks are approximately 6,000 feet below the aircraft. The shape of this magnetic anomaly, its generally lower amplitude than that of the Great Valley magnetic anomaly, and the absence of a major associated gravity high except for the local linear feature a few miles southeast of Sacramento, suggest that this anomaly is not caused by rocks similar to those causing the Great Valley anomaly. The irregular pattern of smaller magnetic highs and lows is similar to magnetic patterns observed over volcanic rocks in many areas of the United States, but the volcanic rocks of this belt would have to contrast sharply in their magnetic properties with the volcanic rocks of the Sierra foothills. Another possible explanation (Henderson, Stromquist, and Jespersen, in press) is a second major belt of ultramafic rocks, similar to, and parallel with, the belt of associated ultramafic and gabbroic rocks in the Sierra foothills. This hypothesis is not confirmed by any geologic mapping or drill-hole data.

South of 38°15′N. the northeast border of the magnetic map (fig. 3) locally overlaps exposed basement rocks for distances of up to 3 miles, and the source of the magnetic anomalies must crop out. In this area a detailed aeromagnetic map that extends from long 120°W. to 121°W. (Henderson and Bass, 1953; Henderson, Stromquist, and Jespersen, in press) indicates that although the volcanic rocks of the foothills give rise to a few low-amplitude magnetic anomalies, these rocks are at best weakly magnetic and major magnetic anomalies are caused by serpentinite masses in fault zones. At the western border of this detailed aeromagnetic map, the belt of magnetic rocks associated with the northeast side of the Great Valley is mostly covered by younger sediments, but H. W. Oliver (written communication, 1964) has noted that one magnetic anomaly of this belt correlates well with volcanic rocks of the Logtown Ridge Formation of Taliaferro and Solari (1948). No serpentinite has been mapped along this edge of the Great Valley, so the best evidence points to a volcanic rock source for this belt of magnetic anomalies.

The apparent termination of this anomaly belt in the vicinity of Sacramento gives rise to a speculation based on the oblique-rifting hypothesis of Bailey (1964). If, as previously mentioned, the granitic block between the San Andreas and Nacimiento faults achieved its present position by drifting westward from a former location in the Great Valley, it might be possible to locate the northwest extension of this seemingly terminated magnetic anomaly belt by examining magnetic patterns on the west side of the San Andreas fault. Bailey, Irwin, and Jones (1964, fig. 33, p. 161) indicate that the original location and subsequent direction of oblique rifting may have been in such a manner that basement rocks once in the Sacramento area would now lie a few miles northwest of Manchester (fig. 2). Perhaps by coincidence, this is the precise location of the unusual linear magnetic high shown on figure 2, and it would thus be of considerable interest to compare the rocks causing this anomaly west of the San Andreas fault with those rocks causing the magnetic anomaly belt on the east side of the Great Valley southeast of Sacramento.

SIERRA NEVADA

Aeromagnetic profiles flown across the Sierra Nevada by the U.S. Geological Survey and the U.S. Naval Oceanographic Office (Zietz and others, 1965) indicate a regional magnetic high with a peak amplitude at the crest of the range of about 400 gammas. This regional magnetic high trends parallel with the mountain range, and its margins extend from the edge of the Great Valley on the west to the Owens River Valley on the east. North of 38°N. (the latitude of Mono Lake) the anomaly becomes less distinct, and it is not visible on two profiles crossing the Sierra Nevada between lat 39°15′N. and 39°30′N. (Balsley, 1953; Agocs, Rollins, and Bangs, 1954). The anomaly may be present on the ground magnetic profile of Woollard (1943), which crosses the southern end of the Sierra Nevada at 35°40′N., but his data can also be interpreted as indicating two separate local highs superimposed on a broad regional high of only 150 gammas. The amplitude of the Sierra Nevada magnetic anomaly is such that the topography, assuming a reasonable susceptibility, cannot cause the feature (H. W. Oliver, oral communication, 1965). Correlation of the magnetic anomaly with the regional topography of the Sierra Nevada south of Mono Lake is good, but the geologic correlation is uncertain. There may be a correlation with the southern portion of the Sierra Nevada batholith, but it is then unclear why the magnetic anomaly does not persist over the northern portion of the batholith. The anomaly may be related in some way to the deeper root under the central and southern portions of the Sierra Nevada. Seismic evidence for this deeper root is discussed by Romney (1957) and by Eaton (this bulletin). A regional depression of the Curie point isotherm could account for the anomaly and might be related to the deeper root, but data on heat flow and on the thickness of the more radioactive granitic rocks of the batholith are still needed in order to evaluate this hypothesis.

An unexplained feature on the two northerly profiles across the Sierra (Balsley, 1953; Agocs, Rollins, and Bangs, 1954) is the large abrupt eastward increase (800–1,300 gammas) in the magnetic field encountered while crossing the crest of the range. Agocs, Rollins, and Bangs (1954) explain this increase as probably caused by surficial volcanic rocks, but it seems unlikely that this is a sufficient explanation because the increase shown on the profile of Balsley (1953) occurs shortly after crossing into the Sierra Nevada batholith and before reaching any substantial or continuous outcrops of volcanic rocks. It is possible that the sudden increase is caused by exposed or shallow-depth rocks of the Sierra Nevada batholith, but data on the magnetic properties of these rocks are not available.

GREAT BASIN

East of the Sierra Nevada, the Mono Lake volcano-tectonic depression has been studied by combined geophysical techniques, including aeromagnetic profiles (Pakiser, Press, and Kane, 1960). A magnetic high over the center of Mono Lake coincides with a small, poorly defined gravity high and "may be caused by a pile of intrusive and flow rocks that were emplaced during the deposition of the basin fill" (Pakiser, Press, and Kane, 1960, p. 435). A larger and wider magnetic high is also associated with the center of Long Valley, a calderalike volcano-tectonic depression located about 20 miles south of Mono Lake (Pakiser, 1961; Henderson, White, and others, 1963; Pakiser, Kane, and Jackson, 1964). The depth to this magnetic anomaly has been determined by Isidore Zietz (Pakiser, Kane, and Jackson, 1964, p. 41) to be about 3,000 feet below the ground surface. The preferred interpretation (in Pakiser, Kane, and Jackson, 1964) of this central magnetic feature is that it is caused by volcanic necks surrounded by a sequence of associated flows located high up in the valley fill of Cenozoic clastic deposits. It is also possible that the anomaly may represent a relatively shallow intrusion within the caldera.

Farther south, at lat 35°45′N., an aeromagnetic survey by the U.S. Geological Survey has been described by Zbur (1963). His magnetic map covers Indian Wells Valley on the east side of the Sierra Nevada fault at China Lake. Two magnetic highs are attributed to basaltic volcanic rocks interbedded in the Cenozoic sedimentary rocks, while two other magnetic highs are thought to be caused by mafic plutonic rocks within the basement because they are associated with gravity highs.

In the Darwin area, at lat 36°20′N. between Owens Lake and Panamint Valley (pl. 1), an aeromagnetic survey located a large magnetic high about 5 miles in diameter, interpreted by Mabey (1961) as being caused by a large intrusive body. On the east side of Death Valley, aeromagnetic data over the Black Mountains (Andreasen and Petrafeso, 1963) show a series of broad aeromagnetic highs which appear to be caused for the most part by the Mesozoic grantic plutons along the crest of the range. Aeromagnetic surveys in the Great Basin have proved extremely useful in the delineation of concealed stocks and other plutons, and they thus provide a valuable method for locating areas of potential economic interest.

REFERENCES

Affleck, James, 1962, Exploration for petroleum by the magnetic method, *in* Nagata, Takesi, ed., Benedum earth magnetism symposium: Pittsburgh, Pa., Univ. Pittsburgh Press, p. 159–175.

Agocs, W. B., Rollins, J. C., and Bangs, E., 1954, Airborne magnetometer profile from Portland, Oregon, to Albuquerque, New Mexico: Geophysics, v. 19, no. 2, p. 270–280.

Andreasen, G. E., and Petrafeso, F. A., 1963, Aeromagnetic map of the east-central part of the Death Valley National Monument, Inyo County, California: U.S. Geol. Survey Geophys. Inv. Map GP-428, scale 1:62,500.

Bailey, E. H., 1964, Mesozoic sphenochasmic rifting along the San Andreas fault north of the Transverse Ranges [abs.]: Geol. Soc. America Spec. Paper 76, p. 186–187.

Bailey, E. H., Irwin, W. P., and Jones, D. L., 1964, Franciscan and related rocks, and their significance in the geology of western California: California Div. Mines and Geology Bull. 183, 177 p.

Balsley, J. R., Jr., 1953, Total-intensity aeromagnetic profile from Denver, Colorado, to Point Reyes, California: U. S. Geol. Survey open-file report, Mar. 30, 1953.

Bayoumi, A. R. I., 1961, Gravity and magnetic study in the San Joaquin Valley: Stanford University, Stanford, Calif., Ph.D. thesis, 48 p.

Curray, J. R., 1965, Structure of the continental margin off central California: New York Acad. Sci. Trans., v. 27, no. 7, p. 794–801.

Dibblee, T. W., Jr., 1955, Geology of the southeastern margin of the San Joaquin Valley, California, pt. 1 of Oakeshott, G. B., ed., Earthquakes in Kern County, California, during 1952: California Div. Mines Bull. 171, p. 23–34.

Eaton, J. P., 1963, Crustal structure from San Francisco, California, to Eureka, Nevada, from seismic-refraction measurements: Jour. Geophys. Research, v. 68, no. 20, p. 5789–5806.

Grantz, Arthur, and Zietz, Isidore, 1960, Possible significance of broad magnetic highs over belts of moderately deformed sedimentary rocks in Alaska and California: U.S. Geol. Survey Prof. Paper 400-B, art. 158, p. B342–B347.

Henderson, J. R., 1953, Preliminary total intensity aeromagnetic maps of the Mother Lode district, California: U.S. Geol. Survey open-file maps, July 23, 1953.

Henderson, J. R., Stromquist, A. A., and Jespersen, Anna, 196.., Geologic interpretation of an aeromagnetic survey across the Mother Lode gold-mining district, California: U.S. Geol. Survey Geophysical Inv. Map. (In press)

Henderson, J. R., White, B. L., and others, 1963, Aeromagnetic map of Long Valley and northern Owens Valley, California: U.S. Geol. Survey Geophys. Inv. Map GP-329, scale 1:62,500.

Hill, M. L., and Dibblee, T. W., Jr., 1953, San Andreas, Garlock, and Big Pine faults, California—a study of the character, history, and tectonic significance of their displacements: Geol. Soc. America Bull., v. 64, no. 4, p. 443–448.

Irwin, W. P., 1964, Late Mesozoic orogenies in the ultramafic belts of northwestern California and southwestern Oregon: U.S. Geol. Survey Prof. Paper 501-C, p. C1–C9.

Irwin, W. P., and Bath, G. D., 1962, Magnetic anomalies and ultramafic rock in northern California: U.S. Geol. Survey Prof. Paper 450-B, art. 25, p. B65–B67.

Ivanhoe, L. F., Jr., 1957, A gravity maximum in the Great Valley of California due to the isostatic effect of the Sierra Nevada: Geophysics, v. 22, no. 1, p. 62–66.

Jenny, W. P., 1932, Magnetic vector study of regional and local geologic structure in principal oil states: Am. Assoc. Petroleum Geologists Bull., v. 16, no. 12, p. 1177–1203.

Jones, R. B., 1963, A geophysical interpretation of an offshore gravity survey near San Francisco [abs.]: Am. Geophys. Union Trans., v. 44, no. 1, p. 32.

Kane, M. F., and Carlson, J. E., 1961, Gravity anomalies, isostasy, and geologic structure in Clark County, Nevada: U.S. Geol. Survey Prof. Paper 424-D, art. 390, p. D274–D277.

Mabey, D. R., 1961, Regional magnetic and gravity anomalies in the Darwin area, California: U.S. Geol. Survey Prof. Paper 424-C, art. 249, p. C276–C279.

Mason, R. G., and Raff, A. D., 1961, Magnetic survey off the west coast of North America, 32° N. latitude to 42° N. latitude: Geol. Soc. America Bull., v. 72, no. 8, p. 1259–1266.

May, J. C., and Hewitt, R. L., 1948, The basement complex in well samples from the Sacramento and San Joaquin Valleys: California Jour. Mines and Geol., v. 44, no. 2, p. 129–158.

Menard, H. W., Jr., 1960, The East Pacific Rise: Science, v. 132, no. 3441, p. 1737–1746.

Meuschke, J. L., Pitkin, J. A., and Smith, C. W., 1966, Aeromagnetic map of Sacramento and vicinity, California: U.S. Geol. Survey Geophys. Inv. Map GP-574, scale 1:250,000.

Oliver, H. W., and Mabey, D. R., 1963, Anomalous gravity field in east-central California: Geol. Soc. America Bull., v. 74, no. 10, p. 1293–1298.

Owens, L. D., 1963, Regional geology of the central portion of the Great Valley of California, *in* Richter, R. C., ed., Guidebook to the Annual Field Trip: Geol. Soc. Sacramento, p. 88–97.

Pakiser, L. C., 1961, Gravity, volcanism, and crustal deformation in Long Valley, California: U.S. Geol. Survey Prof. Paper 424-B, art. 106, p. B250–B253.

Pakiser, L. C., Kane, M. F., and Jackson, W. H., 1964, Structural geology and volcanism of Owens Valley region, California—a geophysical study: U.S. Geol. Survey Prof. Paper 438, 68 p.

Pakiser, L. C., Press, Frank, and Kane, M. F., 1960, Geophysical investigation of Mono Basin, California: Geol. Soc. America Bull., v. 71, no. 4, p. 415–447.

Pampeyan, E. H., 1963, Geology and mineral deposits of Mount Diablo, Contra Costa County, California: California Div. Mines and Geology Spec. Rept. 80, 31 p.

Raff, A. D., and Mason, R. G., 1961, Magnetic survey off the west coast of North America, 40° N. latitude to 52° N. latitude: Geol. Soc. America Bull., v. 72, no. 8, p. 1267–1270.

Repenning, C. A., 1960, Geologic summary of the central valley of California with reference to the disposal of liquid radioactive waste: U.S. Geol. Survey TEI Rept. 769, 69 p.

Romney, C. F., 1957, Seismic waves from the Dixie Valley-Fairview Peak earthquake [Nevada]: Seismol. Soc. America Bull., v. 47, no. 4, p. 301–319.

Schroll, C. L., 1963, Gravity and magnetic profile—San Juan Bautista to Yosemite, *in* Richter, R. C., ed., Guidebook to the Annual Field Trip: Geol. Soc. Sacramento, p. 108–111.

Smith, M. B., 1964, Map showing distribution and configuration of basement rocks in California: U.S. Geol. Survey Oil and Gas Inv. Map OM-215, scale 1:500,000.

Taliaferro, N. L., and Solari, A. J., 1948, Geologic map of the Copperopolis quadrangle, California: California Div. Mines Bull. 145, 1 sheet, scale 1:62,500.

Thompson, G. A., and Talwani, Manik, 1959, Crustal section across California and Sierra Nevada [abs.]: Geol. Soc. America Bull., v. 70, no. 12, pt. 2, p. 1688.

—— 1964a, Crustal structure from Pacific basin to central Nevada: Jour. Geophys. Research, v. 69, no. 22, p. 4813–4837.

—— 1964b, Geology of the crust and mantle, western United States: Science, v. 146, no. 3651, p. 1539–1549.

Vacquier, Victor, Raff, A. D., and Warren, R. E., 1961, Horizontal displacements in the floor of the northeastern Pacific Ocean: Geol. Soc. America Bull., v. 72, no. 8, p. 1251–1258.

Von Herzen, R. P., 1964, Ocean-floor heat-flow measurements west of the United States and Baja California: Marine Geology, v. 1, no. 3, p. 225–239.

Wilson, J. T., 1965, Transform faults, oceanic ridges, and magnetic anomalies southwest of Vancouver Island: Science, v. 150, no. 3695, p. 482–485.

Wood, L. C., 1964, A gravity survey of the Mount Diablo area, California, *in* Guidebook to the Mount Diablo field trip: Geol. Soc. Sacramento, June 6, 1964, p. 33–36.

Woollard, G. P., 1943, Transcontinental gravitational and magnetic profile of North America and its relation to geologic structure: Geol. Soc. America Bull., v. 54, no. 6, p. 747–789.

Zbur, R. T., 1963, A geophysical investigation of Indian Wells Valley, California: U.S. Naval Ordnance Test Station Tech. Pub. 2795, 98 p.

Zietz, Isidore, Lorentzen, G. R., Griscom, Andrew, and King, E. R., 1965, Crustal study of a transcontinental strip west of the Rocky Mountains [abs.]: Soc. Explor. Geophysicists, 35th Ann. Internat. Mtg., Dallas, Texas, 1965, program.

Empire mine, Grass Valley.

CRUSTAL STRUCTURE IN NORTHERN AND CENTRAL CALIFORNIA FROM SEISMIC EVIDENCE *

By Jerry P. Eaton
U.S. Geological Survey, Menlo Park, California

The location of California along the continental margin, and the differentiation of the State into a number of strikingly dissimilar geologic provinces, have led to the expectation that within the State the gross composition and structure of the crust should vary considerably from place to place. Documentation, by seismic means, of major differences in crustal structure from region to region began more than 25 years ago, when Perry Byerly adduced evidence that the Sierra Nevada has a root that extends much deeper into the mantle than the base of the crust beneath the Coast Ranges. Recent seismic refraction studies by the U.S. Geological Survey in California and adjacent portions of the western United States have explored regional variations in crustal structure in greater detail.

This article will outline the nature and limitations of the principal seismic methods used in detailed investigations of the crust, and it will also review the seismic coverage available in northern and central California, summarize the observations and results so far obtained, and convey some impression of the reliability of those results. In the interest of brevity, no discussion of important supplementary techniques, such as analysis of P-wave delays and surface-wave dispersion, will be included. Not all of the earthquake and refraction studies carried out in the region will be considered, but only those which relate most directly to the present theme.

METHODS

Until quite recently, the opportunity to conduct detailed seismic studies of the deep crust and upper mantle of the earth has been limited to regions that have both frequent, shallow earthquakes and specialized networks of seismographs. The principal task of such networks, like that of the University of California in the central Coast Ranges, has been to study the earthquakes themselves; and stations have been concentrated in zones of high seismicity at sites that facilitate locating the epicenters of small to moderate earthquakes. Information on crustal structure in these regions has been obtained as a byproduct of earthquake-wave traveltime studies that have been carried out to improve the accuracy of epicenter and focal depth determinations.

Because the number of recording stations normally is small, data from many earthquakes with epicenters scattered at random through the network are usually combined to establish the empirical traveltime curves from which a mathematical crustal model is calculated. To determine the traveltime curve of waves refracted along the top of the mantle, observations at distant stations located outside the primary region of study, even in different geologic provinces, are frequently used. To interpret traveltime curves established by such heterogeneous data, it is customary to assume a uniform structure for the entire region studied. Traveltime perturbations caused by regional variations in structure are normally too poorly defined to bring such structural variations to light. The crustal model resulting from such an investigation is a poorly defined average of conditions over the entire region containing the earthquakes and the recording stations employed. Moreover, serious uncertainties in focal depth of most of the earthquakes studied further decrease the reliability of values obtained for the total thickness of the crust and for the depths of boundaries within it.

Many of the obstacles that impair determinations of crustal structure by near-earthquake traveltime studies are removed when accurately timed and located large explosive charges are substituted for natural earthquakes, and when well-laid-out profiles of portable high-performance seismic systems are used in place of regional near-earthquake seismic networks. Investigations can be carried out in aseismic as well as seismic areas, profiles can be laid out with regard to major geologic provinces, problems arising from uncertainties in the time and location of the seismic source are eliminated, and observations that are sufficiently dense and continuous along the profile to permit "tracking" of individual seismic phases through their entire range of occurrence can be obtained. On the other hand, the high cost of explosives requires the use of the smallest practicable charges for distant observations, and waves refracted from the mantle usually cannot be traced to the large distance that would be desirable. This difficulty is largely offset by the use of "later arrivals," including waves reflected from the top of the mantle and intermediate boundaries within the crust. Such waves can be identified and traced far more reliably on seismograms from profiles with close-spaced instruments along a single line than on the seismograms of scattered earthquakes recorded on instruments spaced irregularly throughout a large area.

* Publication authorized by the Director, U.S. Geological Survey.

Since near-earthquake and explosion-seismic data are interpreted on the same theoretical basis (the analysis of traveltimes of refracted and, to a lesser extent, reflected waves), the two techniques are limited by some of the same factors. A region with a crust that is relatively homogeneous, or that varies only in a simple manner over a distance of 8 to 10 times the thickness of the crust, is essential if arbitrary assumptions about crustal parameters are to be avoided. Near-surface conditions, especially the thickness of very low velocity rocks, should be nearly uniform in the region studied. With unfavorable velocity-depth relationships, such as appear to exist in many regions, "masked" layers that are very difficult to detect may exist in the lower crust. Particularly complete (or better, moderately redundant) systems of observations are needed to detect such layers, which are not represented by "first arrivals" over some part of the profile.

Traveltime curves of compressional waves in most regions consist of two principal branches that are readily distinguishable because they represent the first waves recorded on the seismograms over considerable distances. Waves refracted through the upper, sialic or "granitic," part of the continental crust below the irregular superficial blanket of lower velocity near-surface rocks (P_g waves) fall close to a traveltime line with a reciprocal slope (velocity) of 6 km/sec and an intercept of about 1 sec. They are first arrivals from the vicinity of the shotpoint, or epicenter of a shallow earthquake, to a distance of 100 to 250 km, depending on the thickness of the crust. These waves through the upper part of the crust are succeeded as first arrivals at larger distances by waves that are refracted through the upper part of the mantle (P_n waves) below the Mohorovicic discontinuity. P_n arrivals fall close to a traveltime line with a velocity near 8 km/sec and an intercept between 5 and 10 sec, depending on the thickness of the crust. Other phases, with velocities in the range of 6.5 to 7.0 km/sec, that have been refracted horizontally through an "intermediate layer" in the lower crust can sometimes be detected as first arrivals at intermediate distances between the domains of P_g and P_n. More commonly, at least in continental regions, such intermediate phases (P*) do not appear as first arrivals, and the existence of an intermediate layer is inferred from later arrivals that appear to be reflected from, or refracted along, its upper surface.

Although intermediate layers are difficult to detect and do not strongly influence first-arrival traveltimes, they tend to be very prominent in crustal models computed from seismic data. Healy (1963) has illustrated how a complex crust 37 km thick can produce the same first-arrival traveltimes as a single layer crust only 28 km thick, though such an extreme case seems unlikely. When rock compositions or densities are inferred from seismic-wave velocities, extremely serious errors in estimates of average values of these parameters in the crust will result if intermediate layers go undetected.

EVIDENCE ON CRUSTAL STRUCTURE FROM NEAR EARTHQUAKES

The only area in northern and central California that has had a sufficient concentration of earthquakes and seismograph stations to permit the calculation of a reasonably well-documented near-earthquake crustal model is the part of the Coast Ranges southeast of San Francisco.

The principal analysis of crustal structure in this region, which has been studied by Perry Byerly and his students at the University of California for several decades, was reported by Byerly (1939). He concluded that the crust is about 32 km thick and is divided into two principal layers. The upper crust appeared to vary in thickness from about 10 to about 20 km, and the velocity of P waves in it (established along paths that lay east of the San Andreas fault in a region with Franciscan basement rocks) was found to be 5.6 km/sec. P waves through the lower part of the crust, which appeared to have a velocity of about 6.7 km/sec, were nowhere observed as first arrivals; so their traveltime curve was not firmly established.

To determine the traveltime curve of waves through the upper mantle (P_n), Byerly was obliged to use observations at stations in southern California in addition to those in the central Coast Ranges. The P_n velocity so obtained (8.02 km/sec) and the total thickness of the crust reported were, therefore, influenced by conditions outside the region in which the velocity in the upper crust was obtained.

The most important seismic contribution to our understanding of central California crustal structure outside of the Coast Ranges was also made by Byerly (1938), who demonstrated that P_n waves from earthquakes along the San Andreas fault in the central Coast Ranges arrived late at stations in Owens Valley. He attributed this delay to a thick root of low-velocity crustal rock extending into the mantle beneath the high southern Sierra Nevada.

EVIDENCE FROM EXPLOSION SEISMIC REFRACTION PROFILES

In the fall of 1961 the U.S. Geological Survey began an extensive investigation of crustal structure in the western United States as part of the VELA Uniform project of ARPA. In northern and central California, major seismic refraction profiles were run longitudinally in the Coast Ranges between San Francisco and Santa Monica, with an intermediate shotpoint at Camp Roberts, and in the Sierra Nevada from Shasta Lake to China Lake, with an intermediate shotpoint at Mono Lake (fig. 1). Two other profiles were run transverse to these (and to major structures of the region): one between San Francisco and Fallon, and one between San Luis Obispo and the Nevada Test Site, through Owens Valley (fig. 1). Additional profiles were run south and east of these to study the bordering geologic

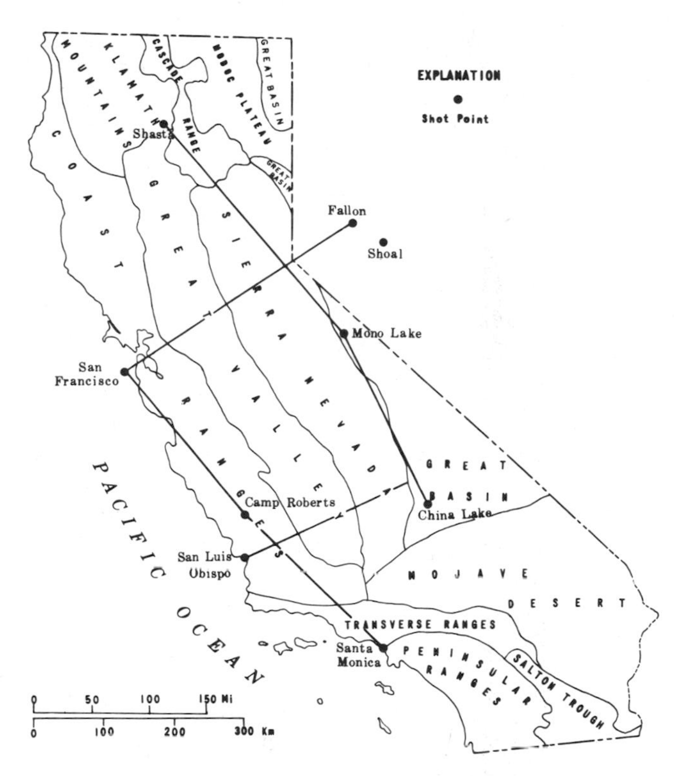

Figure 1. Map showing shot points and seismic refraction profiles made by the U.S. Geological Survey in the northern and central part of California.

provinces: the Transverse Ranges, Mojave Desert, and Great Basin.

Analyses of the Coast Range profile and the northern transverse profile have been reported previously (Healy, 1963; Eaton, 1963) and will be only summarized here. Results from these profiles will be compared with those from the Sierra Nevada profile, which will be more fully documented because it has not been reported previously. Both longitudinal profiles were sufficiently long and well recorded that we may accept their results with reasonable confidence. A few problems of wave identification and interpretation remain, but it is unlikely that the recording of additional explosions and reinterpretation of the augmented data would lead to significantly different results. The interpretation of the transverse profiles, however, is far less certain. They serve chiefly to set limits on where and how major units of the crust vary between the longitudinal profiles. Additional profiles along the strike of the major geologic structures will be required to resolve problems that have been identified from the transverse profiles.

Descriptions of instrumentation (Warrick and others, 1961) and field procedures (Jackson and others, 1963) used in the Survey's crustal refraction work, and discussions of techniques used in detailed analysis of the field data (Eaton, 1963), have been reported previously. The principal results of such work in the western United States, including California, were summarized by Pakiser (1963), who discussed the gross geologic implications of the pattern of crustal thickness and P_n velocities obtained.

Sierra Nevada Profile

Series of nitrocarbonitrate charges ranging in size from 2,000 to 6,000 lbs were detonated in Shasta Lake, Mono Lake, and in drill holes near China Lake, and were recorded along a pair of end-to-end profiles running the length of the Sierra Nevada. The northern profile crosses a portion of the Cascade Mountains west of Mount Lassen and then runs down the crest of the Sierra Nevada just west of Lake Tahoe and on to Mono Lake. The southern profile runs along the east face of the Sierra Nevada southeast of Mono Lake, along the western edge of Owens Valley, to China Lake. Because the eastern face of the Sierra Nevada is convex eastward in this region, refraction paths from the Mono Lake and China Lake shotpoints to recording points at distances greater than 150 km pass beneath the highest peaks of the range.

In the interpretation of the recorded seismograms, record sections were constructed to facilitate correlation of wave arrivals and identification of phases. Traveltimes of the principal phases were measured on the monitor records (or on playbacks, with filter corrections subtracted) and were plotted on a reduced scale (that is, $T-\Delta/6$ vs Δ, where T is traveltime and Δ is distance) to establish traveltime curves. Phases used in the calculation of the seismic cross section were either first arrivals over a reasonable distance or were second arrivals that were strongly supported by reflected phases. Parameters of the traveltime lines of these phases, and a statement of the nature of the wave arrivals and the approximate range over which they were recorded, are given in table 1.

The seismic cross section calculated from these curves (fig. 2) shows a three-layered crust with a maximum thickness of about 54 km beneath the high southern part of the range. Beneath a thin weathered(?) zone, the speed of longitudinal waves (in the granite) is very close to 6.0 km/sec. At a depth of about 14 km the velocity appears to increase to 6.4 km/sec; and at about 27 km it increases to 6.9 km/sec. The 6.4 km/sec layer produced first arrivals from 135 to 205 km on the Mono Lake to China Lake profile, and the 6.9 km/sec layer produced first arrivals from 160 to 250 km on the China Lake to Mono Lake profile.

Beneath the crest of the Sierra Nevada west of Lake Tahoe the crust thins to about 47 km and the top of the 6.4 km/sec layer rises to about 10 km. The best determination of the velocity of P_n was between Shasta Lake and Mono Lake, where it appears to be slightly more than 7.9 km/sec.

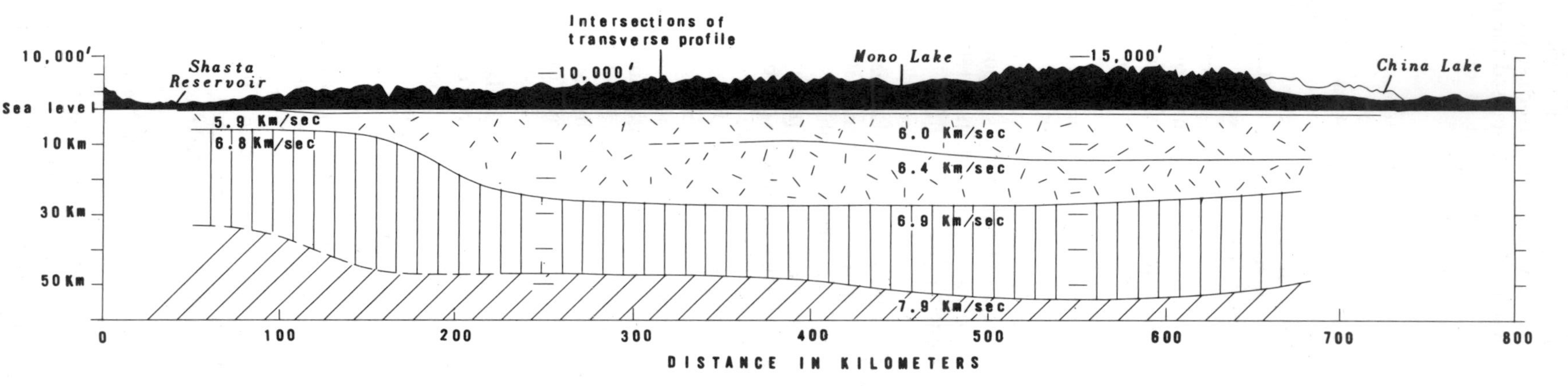

Figure 2. Longitudinal seismic cross section through the Sierra Nevada from near Shasta Reservoir to China Lake.

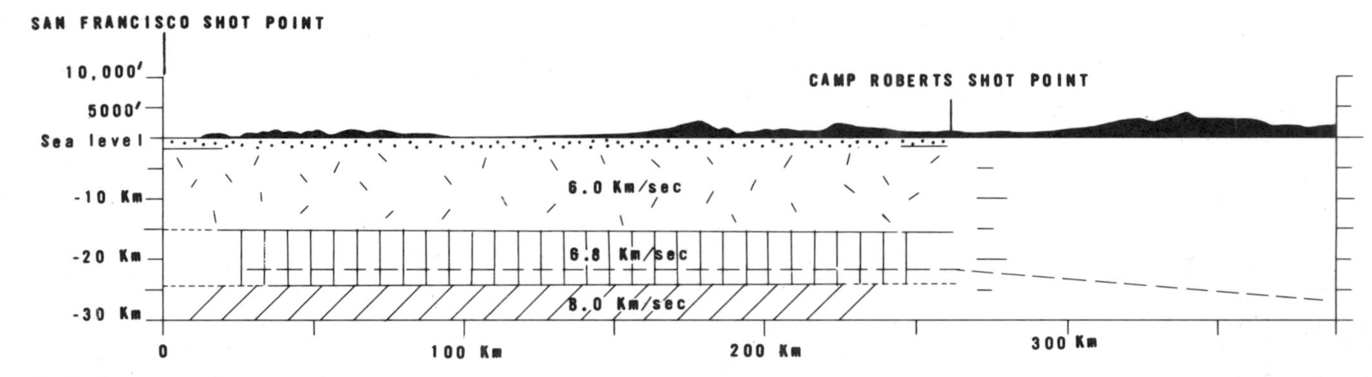

Figure 3. Longitudinal seismic cross section through the Central Coast Ranges from San Francisco to Camp Roberts. The dashed line shows the single-layer interpretation of the first-arrival traveltimes. Solid lines show the two-layer interpretation with the thickest intermediate layer of velocity 6.8 km/sec that would not produce first arrivals on some part of the profile.

Table 1. Traveltime curves of the Sierra Nevada refraction profile.

Phase	*Traveltime line*	*Nature and range of arrival*
(Shasta Lake to Mono Lake)		
P_g	$0.4 + \Delta/5.9$	First arrival, 10 to 40 km
P^*_a	$1.4 + \Delta/6.8$	First arrival, 40 to 80 km
P^*_b	$1.7 + \Delta/6.8$	First arrival, 90 to 140 km
P^*_c	$3.0 + \Delta/6.8$	First arrival, 215 to 250 km
P_n	$8.0 + \Delta/7.9$	First arrival, 250 to 405 km
(Mono Lake to Shasta Lake)		
P_g	$1.2 + \Delta/6.0$	First arrival, 10 to 85 km
P^*_1	$1.9 + \Delta/6.3$	First arrival, 85 to 175 km
P^*_2	$4.5 + \Delta/6.8$	Reflections, 100 to 250 km
P_n	$9.2 + \Delta/8.0$	First arrival, 210 to 400 km and Shasta Lake to Mono Lake reciprocal point
(Mono Lake to China Lake)		
P_g	$1.0 + \Delta/6.0$	First arrival, 10 to 135 km
P^*_1	$2.6 + \Delta/6.4$	First arrival, 135 to 205 km
P^*_2	$4.7 + \Delta/6.9$	Reflections primarily, 100 to 230 km
P_n	$10.6 + \Delta/8.1$	First arrival, 280 to 310 km, and reflections, 150 to 250 km
(China Lake to Mono Lake)		
P_g	$1.1 + \Delta/6.1$	First arrival, 5 to 160 km
P^*_1	$2.3 + \Delta/6.3$	Reflections, 55 to 170 km
P^*_2	$4.2 + \Delta/6.9$	First arrival beyond 160 km
P_n	$8.7 + \Delta/7.7$	Reflections, 100 to 250 km, and Mono Lake to China Lake reciprocal point

Just southeast of Shasta Lake a velocity of 6.8 km/sec was encountered at a depth of only 6 km. Details of deeper structure in this region are obscure. Rapid thickening of the upper crustal layers appears to begin near the canyon of the North Fork of the Feather River about 60 km south-southeast of Mount Lassen. Very similar conditions in the upper crust have been encountered in the Snake River plain south of Boise, Idaho (Hill and Pakiser, 1963).

Coast Range Profile

To insure compatibility with the Sierra Nevada profile, the data reported by Healy for the reversed profile between San Francisco and Camp Roberts were replotted to obtain reduced traveltime curves in the manner just indicated. P_n was well recorded between 195 and 305 km southeast of San Francisco and established the line $5.9 + \Delta/8.03$ sec. From Camp Roberts, P_n was less well recorded: a line drawn through the data points (175 to 245 km) and constrained to pass through the well-established San Francisco to Camp Roberts P_n reciprocal point is given by $5.8 + \Delta/8.01$ sec. The line $1.3 + \Delta/6.0$ sec fits 10 well-recorded P_g arrivals northwest of Camp Roberts; and a line $1.4 + \Delta/6.0$ sec is compatible with (but is not established by) four P_g(?) arrivals southeast of San Francisco. The 6.1 km/sec P_g velocity obtained by Healy fits the data equally well.

Inconclusive evidence for an intermediate layer is provided by later arrivals from both shotpoints and by two somewhat early P_g(?) arrivals about 100 km north of Camp Roberts. These heterogeneous arrivals are approximately represented by the line $3.5 + \Delta/6.8$ sec, which passes through the crossover point of P_g and P_n waves from the San Francisco shotpoint. High noise levels in the Salinas Valley seriously impaired the quality of recordings that were needed to test the existence of an intermediate layer.

If evidence for an intermediate layer is ignored, the crust appears to be about 22 km thick between San Francisco and Camp Roberts (dashed line, fig. 3). It thickens southeastward from Camp Roberts to Santa Monica (Healy, 1963), where it is 35 km thick. Inclusion of the possible intermediate layer discussed above yields the structure represented by solid lines in figure 3: low-velocity near-surface zone to 1.5 to 2 km, 6.0 km/sec to 15.4 km, 6.8 km/sec to 24.3 km, and 8.0 km/sec in the upper mantle.

When comparing the P_g velocity obtained along the San Francisco to Camp Roberts profile (6.0 to 6.1 km/sec) with that reported by Byerly for the central Coast Ranges (5.6 km/sec), it is important to note that the explosion-refraction profiles sampled only the granite corridor southwest of the San Andreas fault whereas Byerly's material on $\overline{P}$ (P_g in the present notation) sampled only the region of Franciscan basement rocks northeast of the fault. Additional evidence for an abnormally low P velocity northeast of the San Andreas fault in the San Francisco Bay region was provided by the San Francisco to Fallon profile (Eaton, 1963).

The velocity of P_n beneath the Coast Ranges deduced from the refraction profiles agrees closely with that found by Byerly.

Transverse Profiles

An attempt to construct a cross-section transverse to the Sierra Nevada on the basis of limited data from refraction profiles between San Francisco and Fallon has been reported by Eaton (1963). Inadequate recordings at large distances seriously restricted interpretation of those profiles, and the maximum thickness of the Sierra root was estimated by extrapolating results obtained on the flanks of the range toward its center. Recordings from the San Francisco shotpoint were especially difficult to interpret: the thick sediments of the Great Valley, with their high noise level and very low seismic velocity, nearly blotted out the profile in the critical range of 80 to 160 km. Only between 160 and 275 km, from the western foothills to the crest of the Sierra Nevada, were adequate seismograms recorded.

Better results were obtained from the Fallon shotpoint, which provided evidence on the location of the

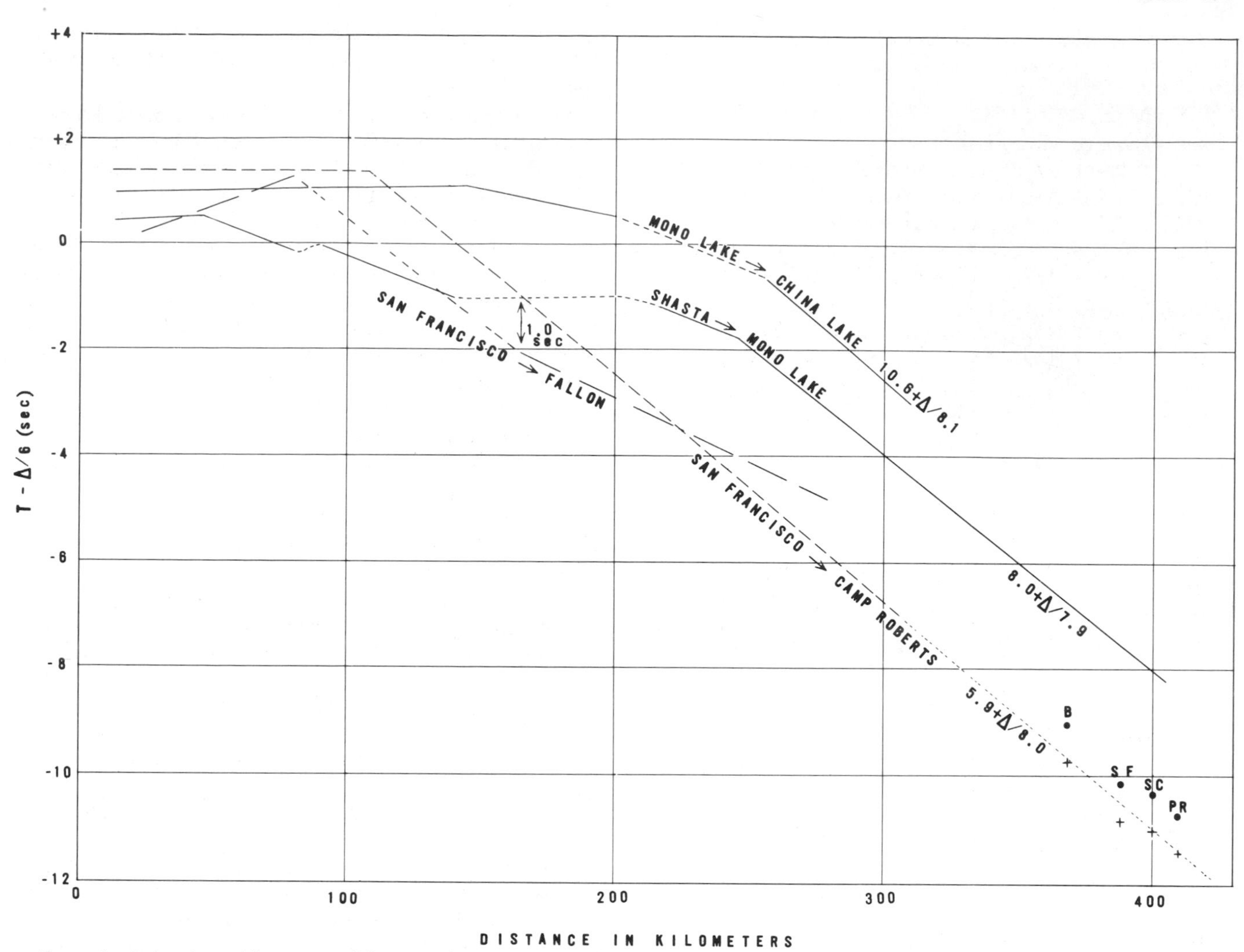

Figure 4. Reduced traveltime curves of first arrivals on selected profiles shown on figure 1. T-Δ/6, where T is traveltime in seconds and Δ is shot to receiver distance in kilometers, is plotted against Δ. Uncorrected reduced traveltimes versus distance from SHOAL to seismograph stations near the San Francisco Shotpoint are shown as solid circles (B, Berkeley; SF, San Francisco; SC, Santa Cruz; and PR, Point Reyes). After correction for diffraction around the Sierra Nevada root (fig. 5), they are shown as crosses.

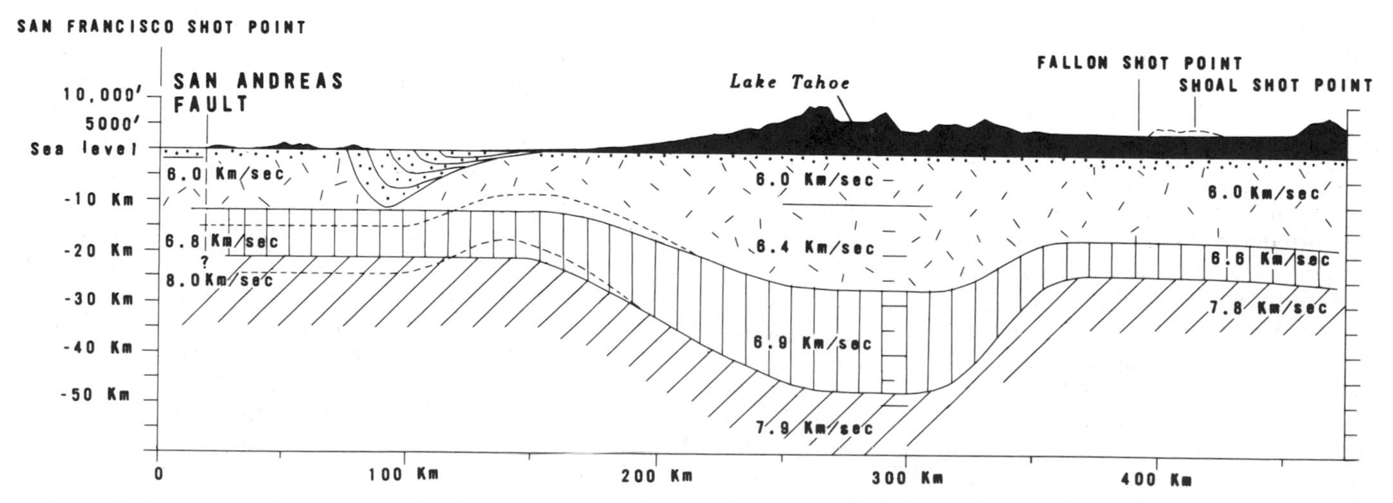

Figure 5. Transverse cross section from San Francisco to Fallon based on seismic-refraction data. Alternate structures beneath the Great Valley are shown in solid and dashed lines.

steep eastern boundary of the Sierra Nevada root. Profiles from Fallon to Owens Valley and between Fallon and Eureka further defined the eastern portion of the root and established the crustal structure of the Basin and Range province farther east (Eaton, 1963).

A more reliable picture of the structure of the crust between San Francisco and Fallon can now be drawn. Beneath the Coast Ranges and Sierra Nevada the structure is quite well determined by the longitudinal profiles; and results from the Fallon shotpoint serve to establish the structure of the eastern end of the section. Recordings between 160 and 275 km from San Francisco set additional constraints on the behavior of crustal boundaries beneath the Great Valley and Sierra Nevada foothills.

To evaluate the profile from San Francisco toward Fallon, it is useful to compare first arrivals recorded along it with those recorded along other critical profiles in the region. For this purpose, reduced first-arrival traveltime curves for the profiles San Francisco to Camp Roberts, Mono Lake to China Lake, and Shasta Lake to Mono Lake are plotted with that for San Francisco to Fallon in figure 4.

Plotting reduced time ($T-\Delta/6$) vs distance (Δ) permits the use of an expanded time scale and greatly increases the difference in slope of two lines representing slightly different velocities. At any particular distance, however, differences in arrival time on the various curves can be read directly from the graph. The near-horizontal portions of the curves at small distances represent the P_g phase, longitudinal waves propagating through the upper crust beneath superficial low-velocity materials. The nearly parallel portions of the curves at large distances represent the P_n phase, longitudinal waves with the deepest parts of their paths through the upper mantle just beneath the crust. Portions of the curves with intermediate slopes (for example, Shasta Lake to Mono Lake, Mono Lake to China Lake) usually represent waves refracted through rocks of intermediate-velocity in the lower part of the crust.

With certain reservations, the average thickness of the crust beneath the shotpoint and receiving stations is proportional to the intercept of the P_n line. Thus, for the profile San Francisco to Camp Roberts, which traverses a relatively regular crust less than 25 km thick, the P_n intercept is only 5.9 sec while for the profile from Mono Lake to China Lake, which runs longitudinally through the thick Sierra Nevada crust, the P_n intercept is 10.6 sec (fig. 4). With similar reservations, the average thickness of the upper part of the crust beneath the shotpoint and the receiving stations is proportional to the intercept of the traveltime line of any intermediate layer that might be detected. Steplike increases in the intercepts of the 6.8 km/sec intermediate layer traveltime line segments recorded southeast of Shasta Lake (fig. 4) suggest steplike increases in the thickness of the upper crust as that profile crosses from the southern Cascades into the Sierra Nevada.

The significance of the most crucial (and also the most reliable) recordings on the profile from San Francisco to Fallon is best brought out by comparison with arrivals at the same distance along the San Francisco to Camp Roberts profile. At 160 km, waves from the San Francisco shotpoint emerge at the western edge of the Sierra Nevada foothills on the transverse profile a full second earlier than they emerge at the same distance on the longitudinal profile. By 220 km first arrivals on the transverse profile have fallen back to the same time as those on the longitudinal profile, and by 275 km they have fallen nearly a full second behind.

Because these arrivals on the San Francisco to Fallon profile have an apparent velocity of about 7 km/sec, it is tempting to attribute them to a very shallow intermediate layer with such a velocity. This possibility appears to be ruled out by the persistence of the phase to the crest of the Sierra Nevada, which was shown by the longitudinal Sierra profile to have a thick section of rocks with velocities of 6.0 to 6.4 km/sec. Failure of the phase to appear as a first arrival west of the Great Valley also argues against this solution.

A more likely explanation is that this phase is P_n emerging from beneath a progressively thickening crust as the profile crosses into the Sierra Nevada. If thickening of the crust were due to an increase in thickness of a 6.0 km/sec layer in the upper crust, the Mohorovicic discontinuity would have to dip northeastward along the profile at about 11°; and if crustal thickening were due to the overall thickening of a composite crust with an average velocity of 6.4 km/sec, the dip of the Moho would be nearly 16°. Explanation of the early arrival of P_n at the western edge of the Sierra foothills requires a thinner crust beneath the Great Valley or higher crustal velocities beneath the valley and foothills, or both, than beneath the central Coast Ranges. As much as 0.3 sec of the 1 sec lead might be explained by a thinner zone of superficial low-velocity material in the Sierra Nevada foothills than in the Coast Ranges. To account for the remaining 0.7 sec by variations in the crust requires rather large changes in boundaries between layers.

Two modifications of the two-layer-crust solution for the Coast Range profile that would satisfy observations along the San Francisco to Fallon profile are indicated in figure 5, which summarizes current seismic refraction information on the structure of the crust between San Francisco and Fallon. The structure shown by solid lines (thin crust extending southwestward approximately to the San Andreas fault) also accounts for the early arrival of P_n in the Great Valley suggested by observations that were corrected for delays in the sediments (fig. 4 and Eaton, 1963). Other models with somewhat greater depths to the mantle and a very shallow intermediate layer beneath the eastern part of the valley and the Sierra Nevada foothills satisfy the observations equally well.

Preliminary analysis of the San Luis Obispo to Owens Valley transverse profile shows that it has striking similarities to the northern transverse profile. Waves from the San Luis Obispo shotpoint are late, as expected, where they emerge through the thick sediments of the valley; but beyond 180 km they fall very close to the line established by arrivals beyond 160 km on the northern profile. P_g arrivals and apparent reflections from the mantle and an intermediate layer in the southern Coast Ranges northeast of San Luis Obispo suggest a two-layer crust that is about 3 km thicker than that between San Francisco and Camp Roberts. As on the northern profile, thinning of the crust beneath the valley or increase in the velocity of crustal rocks beneath the valley and foothills is required to explain the early P_n arrivals in the Sierra Nevada foothills.

Failure to record P_n east of the Sierra Nevada from shots at San Francisco left that profile incomplete. This defect was remedied by recordings at the University of California seismograph stations Berkeley, Santa Cruz, San Francisco, and Point Reyes near the San Francisco shotpoint (Mikumo, 1965), of waves from the SHOAL nuclear explosion, about 50 km southeast of Fallon, fig. 1. SHOAL P_n arrivals at these stations are plotted as solid circles on figure 4. The increase in path length required for propagation around the Sierra Nevada root shown in figure 5 would delay these arrivals about 0.7 sec. The corrected arrivals, which are plotted as crosses, fall on the extension of the San Francisco to Camp Roberts P_n line. Thus, unless the average velocity of P in the upper mantle between San Francisco and Fallon is significantly higher than 8.0 km/sec, which seems unlikely, the crust at SHOAL cannot be significantly thicker than that near Camp Roberts. This result tends to corroborate the thin crust (24 km) near the Shoal site deduced from the Fallon to Eureka profile (Eaton, 1963).

SUMMARY

A longitudinal seismic refraction profile in the Sierra Nevada shows that the high southern part of the range is underlain by a crust about 54 km thick. The crust thins beneath the northern end of the range and changes drastically in character at the Sierra Nevada-Cascade Range boundary. A similar profile through the central Coast Ranges indicates that the crust is only 22 to 25 km thick in that region. Early wave arrivals at the western foothills of the Sierra Nevada from explosions along the Pacific shore suggest that the crust is thinner, or is composed of rocks with higher seismic velocities, beneath the Great Valley than beneath the central Coast Ranges.

The velocity of P waves in the upper mantle appears to be somewhat less beneath the Sierra Nevada (7.9 km/sec) than beneath the central Coast Ranges (8.0 km/sec). The velocity of P waves in the upper part of the crystalline crust is the same beneath the Sierra Nevada and the central Coast Ranges west of the San Andreas fault (6.0 km/sec). Earthquake studies and meager refraction data suggest that the velocity of P waves in the upper crust beneath the central Coast Ranges east of the San Andreas fault is only 5.6 km/sec. This lower velocity may characterize a very thick accumulation of Franciscan rocks, which form the basement in this region.

Rocks with intermediate P wave velocities (6.4 to 6.9 km/sec) form a major part of the Sierra Nevada root, but they thin to 10 km or less toward both the northeast and southwest. They are probably a major constituent of the crust beneath the eastern Great Valley and the Sierra Nevada foothills.

Evidence from seismology on the detailed structure of the crust and upper mantle in northern California outside the regions described above is almost entirely lacking. Except for the tantalizing but limited evidence from the two transverse refraction profiles, the crust beneath the Great Valley remains essentially unexplored; and the Coast Ranges north of San Francisco, as well as the Klamath Mountains, have received even less attention. Extrapolations of results from one region into a neighboring one is of dubious value in light of the drastic changes encountered at the boundary between the Sierra Nevada and the provinces that surround it.

REFERENCES

Byerly, Perry, 1938, Comment on "The Sierra Nevada in the light of isostasy," by A. C. Lawson: Geol. Soc. America Bull., v. 48, no. 12, p. 2025–2031.

—— 1939, Near earthquakes in central California: Seismol. Soc. America Bull., v. 29, p. 427–462.

Eaton, J. P., 1963, Crustal structure between Eureka, Nevada, and San Francisco, California, from seismic-refraction measurements: Jour. Geophys. Research, v. 68, no. 20, p. 5789–5806.

Healy, J. H., 1963, Crustal structure along the coast of California from seismic-refraction measurements: Jour. Geophys. Research, v. 68, no. 20, p. 5777–5787.

Hill, D. P., and Pakiser, L. C., 1963, Crustal structure from seismic-refraction measurements between Eureka, Nevada, and Boise, Idaho [abs.]: Am. Geophys. Union Trans., v. 44, p. 890.

Jackson, W. H., Stewart, S. W., and Pakiser, L. C., 1963, Crustal structure in eastern Colorado from seismic-refraction measurements: Jour. Geophys. Research, v. 68, no. 20, p. 5767–5776.

Mikumo, Takeshi, 1965, Crustal structure in central California in relation to the Sierra Nevada: Seismol. Soc. America Bull., v. 55, no. 1, p. 65–84.

Pakiser, L. C., 1963, Structure of the crust and upper mantle in the western United States: Jour. Geophys. Research, v. 68, no. 20, p. 5747–5756.

Warrick, R. E., Hoover, D. B., Jackson, W. H., Pakiser, L. C., and Roller, J. C., 1961, The specification and testing of a seismic-refraction system for crustal studies: Geophysics, v. 26, no. 6, p. 820–824.

CHAPTER X
FIELD TRIP GUIDES

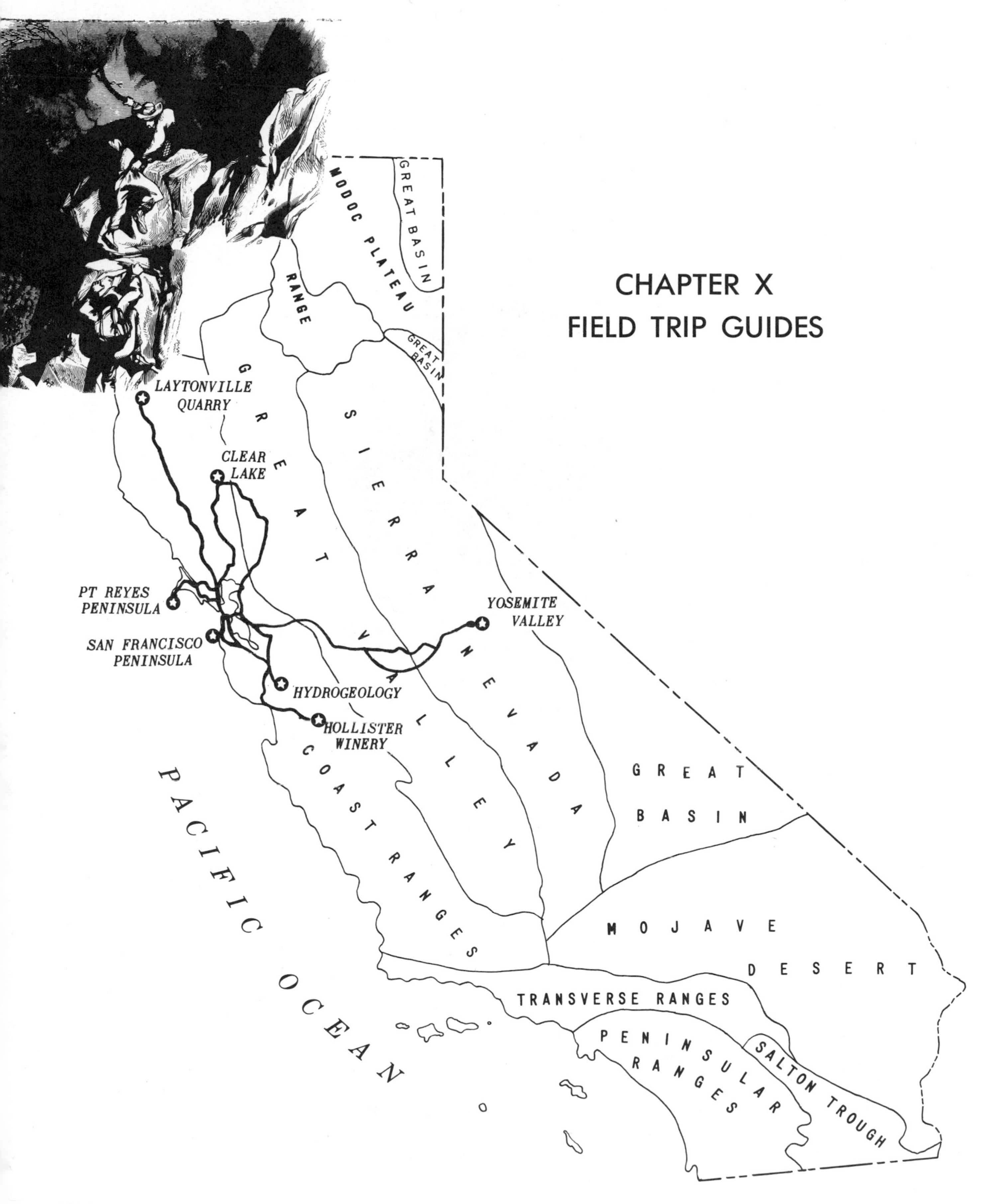

FIELD TRIP GUIDES

FIELD TRIP
POINT REYES PENINSULA AND SAN ANDREAS FAULT ZONE

By Alan J. Galloway
California Academy of Sciences, San Francisco, California

SAN FRANCISCO—GOLDEN GATE BRIDGE—STINSON BEACH—OLEMA—BEAR VALLEY—INVERNESS—DRAKES BEACH—POINT REYES LIGHTHOUSE—SAMUEL P. TAYLOR STATE PARK—GREENBRAE—SAN FRANCISCO

Sketch of Geology

The itinerary for this field trip will start from the toll gate at the south end of the Golden Gate Bridge and proceed north across the bridge. The country immediately north of San Francisco consists of Franciscan rocks of Jurassic to Cretaceous age, including sandstone, shale, radiolarian chert, pillow lava, and pyroclastic rocks along with serpentine intrusives—a typical eugeosynclinal assemblage. These rocks are well exposed along U.S. Highway 101 just north of the Golden Gate Bridge (photo 1), and the route stays in them all the way to where it reaches the San Andreas fault near Bolinas. They are seen again on the return route along the Sir Francis Drake Highway between Olema and San Francisco. The structure of these rocks is complex, and in places they have been altered hydrothermally.

In the northern part of the Franciscan terrain shown on the map (fig. 1), immediately adjoining the San Andreas fault zone, the Franciscan beds are principally dirty sandstones or graywackes dipping homoclinally northeastward. These are overlain to the northeast by a thick series of spilitic volcanic rocks including well-developed pillow lavas.

In the southern part of the area the structure is generally much more complex, and indeed the coastline south of Stinson Beach appears to mark a highly disturbed zone containing large blocks of many different kinds of rocks.

From the head of Bolinas Lagoon to Inverness, the trip follows the course of the San Andreas fault along the Olema Valley (photo 5). Most of the way the road lies 1,000 to 2,000 feet east of the rupture produced at the time of the 1906 earthquake, but all the way the road is within the overall zone of faulting. Along the fault zone can be seen striking examples of fault topography, and reminders of the large lateral displacement that took place at the time of the San Francisco earthquake of April 18, 1906.

To the west of the fault the rocks consist of relatively undisturbed Tertiary beds lying on the quartz diorite basement. They form a sharp contrast with the Franciscan rocks to the east.

On reaching Inverness, the route turns west and then south across the quartz diorite and Tertiary rocks of the peninsula. A side road to Drakes Beach provides access to an excellent place for a picnic lunch. Thence, after retracing a few miles, the route continues westward to Point Reyes lighthouse where an interesting Paleocene conglomerate is exposed.

On the return trip the same route is followed back as far as Olema, at which point it diverges eastward through the Franciscan terrain back to San Francisco.

This trip involves no extensive walking side trips and ordinary sports or business clothing are adequate.

The general course of the route can be followed on the accompanying geological map (fig. 1).

History

Historically the Point Reyes peninsula is of considerable interest, since many historians believe it was here that Sir Francis Drake, the Elizabethan freebooter, spent 6 weeks in the summer of 1579 in the course of his circumnavigation of the globe, and claimed the land for Queen Elizabeth I of England. (The Pilgrims did not land in Massachusetts until 1620, and the first successful settlement in Virginia was in 1607.) But Drake did not stay to settle the land (he didn't like the cold foggy summer weather!); the Spanish did not settle the area until the early part of the 19th century.

Following California's joining the Union in 1850 and the rise of San Francisco, the Point Reyes area was divided into large dairy and cattle ranches, and it has stayed almost in that condition until now, although it is close to the expanding 3 million population of the Bay region. This lack of real estate development is due to its inaccessibility over hilly, winding roads, and its generally foggy and cool summer climate. In an effort to preserve the area in its relatively untouched condition, the land is gradually being purchased by the National Park Service and included in a "National Seashore," part of the National Park System.

Inverness Ridge
Mt Tamalpais
San Andreas fault zone

Photo 1 (opposite). The Marin Peninsula. Aerial view northwest toward the San Andreas fault and Point Reyes from a point southwest of Angel Island. The dissected hills of the peninsula, which culminate in Mount Tamalpais, are composed of graywacke, shale, radiolarian chert, greenstone, and limestone of the Franciscan Formation of Late Jurassic and Cretaceous age, and intrusive serpentine. The trench of the San Andreas fault zone separates the Franciscan Formation from the Mesozoic granitic rocks and Tertiary sedimentary rocks of the Point Reyes Peninsula, including Inverness Ridge. The field trip follows Highway 101, seen in left foreground passing through Waldo tunnel, and cut into the hills above Sausalito in central foreground. Just beyond where the highway descends to water level is the turnoff for Highway 1, the route up Tamalpais Valley and over the ridge to the coast. *Photo courtesy Aero Photographers, Sausalito.*

Oil

Bolinas, at the south end of the Point Reyes peninsula, had an oil boom as long ago as 1865, and it was enthusiastic enough to result in the building of a Petroleum Hotel, although no commercial oil has ever been found. Early stories tell of a live gas seep at Duxbury Point, a mile west of Bolinas, and there are oil-filled joints and asphaltic clastic dikes in the Miocene shale in this vicinity. Farther north up the coast are massive tar sands and oil sands, in middle Miocene beds. A number of test wells have been drilled in the last 100 years, the first being drilled as long ago as 1865, but no commercial oil or gas has yet been found.

Acknowledgments

The writer wishes to acknowledge the assistance of many persons in the preparation of this manuscript and map. Much information on the Franciscan has been taken from Harold J. Gluskoter's unpublished report on the "Geology of a portion of western Marin County, California," which was kindly made available by the California Division of Mines and Geology. In addition the writer is indebted to many persons in the U.S. Geological Survey, the California Division of Mines and Geology, and the California Academy of Sciences. The work is adapted from a road log originally prepared by the writer for the California Division of Mines and Geology Bulletin 181 (1962).

REFERENCES

Anderson, F. M., 1899, The geology of Point Reyes peninsula: California Univ. Dept. Geology Bull., v. 2, p. 119–153.

Bailey, E. H., Irwin, W. P., and Jones, D. L., 1964, Franciscan and related rocks and their significance in the geology of western California: California Div. Mines and Geology Bull. 183, 171 p.

Bradley, W. W., 1916, Marin County: California Mining Bur., 14th Rept. State Mineralogist, pt. 2, p. 241–261.

Douglas, J. M., 1943, Duxbury Point region [California]: California Div. Mines Bull. 118, p. 621.

Galloway, A. J., 1961, The geology of the Point Reyes peninsula: U.S. Nat. Park Service, Land Use Survey, proposed Point Reyes Nat. Seashore, Region Four Office, San Francisco, Calif., p. 30–34.

—— 1962, Field Trip 3: Point Reyes peninsula and San Andreas fault zone: California Div. Mines and Geology Bull. 181, p. 391–398, pl. 26.

Gluskoter, H. J., 1964, Orthoclase distribution and authigenesis in the Franciscan Formation of a portion of western Marin County, California: Jour. Sed. Petrology, v. 34, no. 2, p. 335–343.

—— 1966, Geology of a portion of western Marin County, California: California Div. Mines and Geology, Map Sheet 11, (in press).

Hinds, N. E. A., 1952, Evolution of the California landscape: California Div. Mines Bull. 158, 240 p.

Jenkins, O. P., ed., 1951, Geologic guidebook of the San Francisco Bay counties—history, landscape, geology, fossils, minerals, industry, and routes to travel: California Div. Mines Bull. 154, 392 p.

Lawson, A. C., 1914, Description of the San Francisco district; Tamalpais, San Francisco, Concord, San Mateo, and Hayward quadrangles: U.S. Geol. Survey Geol. Atlas, Folio 193, 24 p.

Lawson, A. C., and others, 1908, The California earthquake of April 18, 1906—Report of the State Earthquake Investigation Commission: Carnegie Inst. Washington Pub. 87, v. 1, 451 p.

Weaver, C. E., 1949, Geology of the Coast Ranges immediately north of the San Francisco Bay region, California: Geol. Soc. America Mem. 35, 242 p.

ROAD LOG

00.0 *Golden Gate Bridge toll gate.* Across the bridge to the north can be seen Fort Baker Military Reservation, and to the west the Golden Gate and Point Bonita. To the east is Alcatraz Island. The south pier of the bridge rests on serpentine of relatively low strength; the north pier on stronger basalt, chert, and sandstone of the Franciscan Formation. The length of the main span is 4,200 feet. The Golden Gate itself is a drowned river valley eroded by the ancestral Sacramento-San Joaquin River. The present channel at the bridge is more than 300 feet deep.

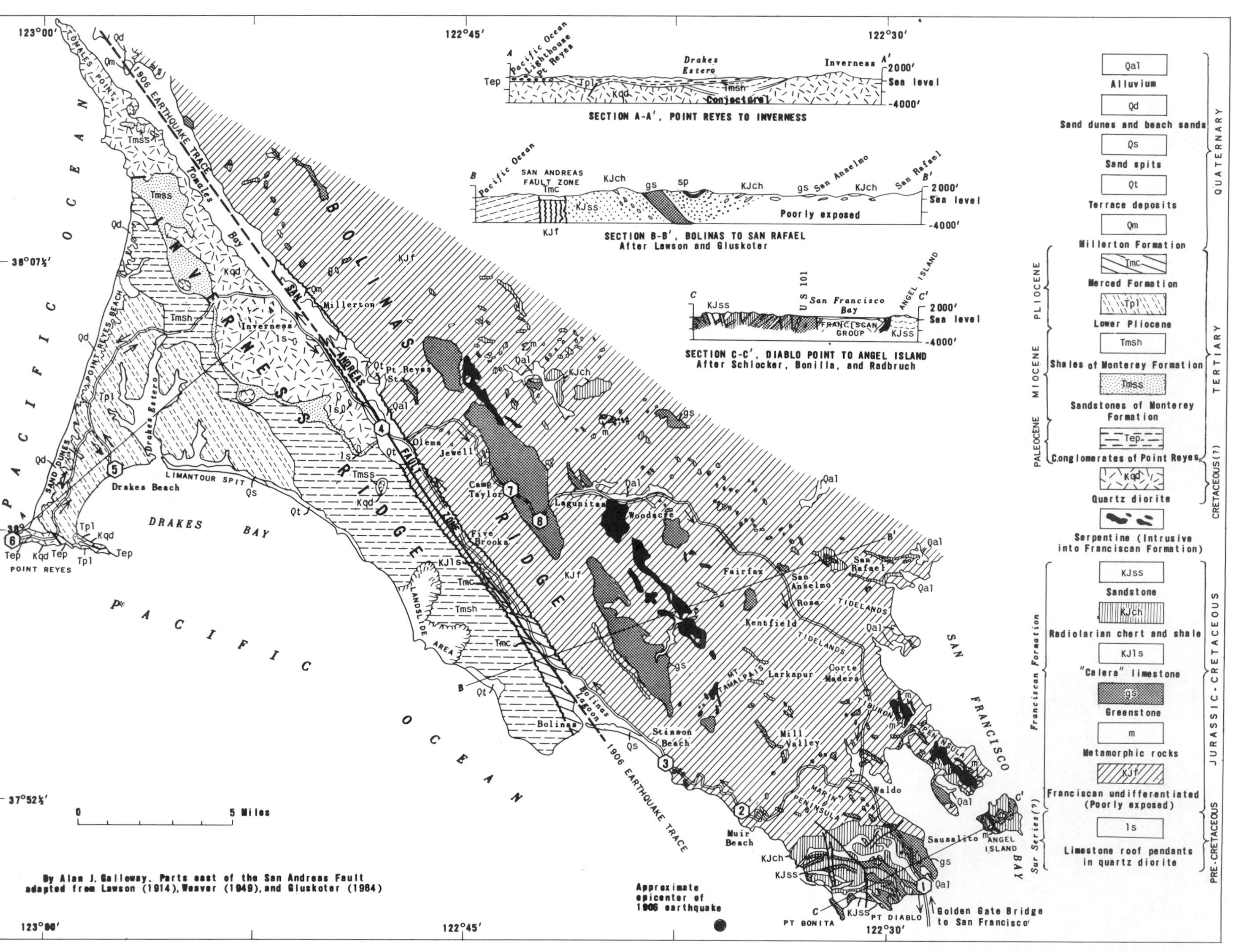

Figure 1. Index map of area extending northwest of San Francisco to Point Reyes and Tomales Point, showing geology and route of field trip. Stops in road log are indicated by numbers in hexagons.

Photo 2. The Golden Gate Bridge. View northeast toward Marin County. *Photo by Sarah Ann Davis.*

02.0 Turn off at Vista Point; view of San Francisco to south.

02.1 *Stop 1.* Vista Point. Looking north we see Franciscan beds dipping southwest. To the right (east) of the highway tunnel the rocks are mainly volcanic: the prominent hills to the left (west) of the tunnel are mainly radiolarian chert and graywacke sandstone. These beds form the west limb of an anticline whose axis is in Richardson's Bay to the east (see cross section C-C′, fig. 1). The route will remain in Franciscan rocks to where it meets the San Andreas fault at Bolinas Lagoon, 21 miles from here.

02.5 Franciscan sandstone in roadcut.

03.0 Radiolarian chert at entrance to tunnel.

03.5 Well-developed blackish-green pillow basalt full of calcite veinlets. Pillow basalt is common in the Franciscan and is often associated with chert, which can be seen just ahead on both sides of the road.

06.0 Fork right onto State Highway 1, the Coast Highway. To the north can be seen Mount Tamalpais, elevation 2,604 feet. The route proceeds westward across the southern slope of Mount Tamalpais in the outbound portion, and eastward on the northern side on the return, so that the mountain will be seen from all angles.

07.0 Turn left on Highway 1.

09.7 Junction with Panoramic Highway which leads to Muir Woods and Mount Tamalpais.

11.5 Green Gulch Ranch on left (south).

11.9 On right (east) prominent outcrop of grayish-green chert; Muir Beach on left.

12.4 Intersection with road to Muir Woods via Frank Valley. Turn left up ridge.

13.8 *Stop 2.* Tamalpais and Frank Valley on right (northeast). Green chert outcrop in Franciscan to right.

To the left (west) on a clear day may be seen the Farallon Islands, composed of quartz diorite similar to that of Point Reyes.

14.6 To the left, the Slide Ranch—situated on a large landslide. There are many such slides along this strip of coast.

15.5 To the left, good views of Slide Ranch landslide.

17.0 To the right, outcrop of serpentine in Franciscan beds.

17.5 To the left, Steep Ravine resort and landslide.

17.9 Quarry in red manganiferous chert to right.

18.4 *Stop 3.* View of Stinson Beach sandspit, Bolinas Lagoon, and on a good clear day, Point Reyes. Sedimentation by streams will eventually fill Bolinas Lagoon to form first a marsh, and finally a coastal plain. Topographically, the lagoon is an expression of the San Andreas fault zone which here emerges from the sea on its way north. Leaving Bolinas Lagoon, the fault zone occupies a long straight valley, the Olema Valley, for 12 miles, and then the narrow Tomales Bay which is 15 miles long, before submerging below the Pacific Ocean again (photo 5).

Up to now the whole trip has been in Franciscan (Jurassic-Cretaceous) terrain. But from this point one can look westward across the fault zone and see the yellow cliffs of Bolinas which are soft siltstone and fine sandstone of the marine Pliocene (Merced). Farther west, one can see Duxbury Reef which is made up of southwest dipping hard Miocene siliceous shale. At Duxbury Reef there are oil-filled joints in the cliffs, and a reported gas-seep.

Photo 3. Contorted chert beds in the Franciscan Formation atop Wolfback Ridge, Marin County. ***Photo by Mary Hill.***

Photo 4. The San Andreas fault just north of Bear Valley Ranch headquarters, Highway 1, Marin County. Erosion since 1906 has exposed this portion of the fault, along which large surface displacements took place in 1906. ***Photo by Mary Hill.***

Photo 5. Aerial view of western Marin County and Point Reyes; view northwest from near Stinson Beach. The San Andreas fault zone extends across the width of the trough lying between Bolinas Lagoon in the foreground and Tomales Bay in the upper right. *Photo by Clyde Sunderland, Aerial Photographs, Oakland.*

Photo 6. Duxbury Reef, near Bolinas, Marin County, at low tide. Exploration for petroleum in this region began as early as 1865, attracted by asphalt seeps, heavy oil, and gas. *Photo by Sarah Ann Davis.*

18.6 Junction with Panoramic Highway from Mount Tamalpais. Village of Stinson Beach.

23.3 Coarse talus breccia—probably Quaternary, tilted east.

23.5 Intersection with road to Bolinas.

24.1 Intersection with Horseshoe Hill Road. Trace of 1906 earthquake crack immediately to left. Beds are the Merced Formation of Pliocene age.

24.5 On the right is Coppermine Canyon where a copper mine was opened in 1863 in Franciscan rocks. It was never commercial, but a little ore was shipped from it during the first World War. On the left is a grove of eucalyptus trees; in this grove can be found a line of trees which was offset 13½ feet by right-lateral movement of the 1906 earthquake.

25.1 Texeira Ranch—the fault trace of 1906 traverses the meadow to our left (west).

27.1 On the left, the old Biesler Ranch: Mr. Biesler was milking a cow when the earthquake hit, and the crack developed within 6 feet of where he was. Would that he had been a geologist and could have told us just how the movement on the fault proceeded.

At this point the topography is so affected by the San Andreas fault zone that there are two streams, about 1,000 feet apart and parallel to one another, the eastern one flowing north and emptying into Tomales Bay and the western one flowing south and emptying into Bolinas Lagoon. Each of these streams is actively eroding along an old fault trace. The whole faulted zone is about half a mile wide.

28.6 On the left at the bottom of the creek are some old lime kilns, built to burn limestone from an outcrop of Calera (Franciscan) limestone in the side of the canyon. For many years it was thought that these lime kilns were built by the Russians, who were established 50 miles north of here in 1812. But it is now known that they were built by American settlers in 1850 (see photo 7).

29.4 The lumber mill to the left (west) stands directly on the 1906 earthquake fault trace.

31.0 On the right (east) of the road is a prominent sag pond, typical of many along the fault zone. This one is not on the 1906 fault trace, but on a well-marked older trace lying 1,400 feet east of it, near the east edge of the faulted zone.

33.1 Village of Olema—junction with Sir Francis Drake Highway from San Rafael.

33.2 Turn left on Bear Valley Ranch road.

33.7 *Stop 4.* Bear Valley, headquarters of Point Reyes National Seashore. Here the road is right on top of the 1906 fault trace. Survey markers were established here in 1907 to assist in measuring the next movement on the trace; two are visible from the road. Here the path leading up to an old house (no longer standing) was offset 15 feet laterally. At the next ranch south, the Shafter place, a cow fell headfirst into a fault crevice. "The closure which immediately followed left only the tail visible" (G. K. Gilbert).

Photo 7. Ruins of Olema lime kiln, built around 1850 for burning white, calera-type limestone from the Franciscan Formation. *Photo by Mary Hill.*

Photo 8. Detail of fissured earth north of Bear Valley Ranch, 3 miles northwest of Olema, Marin County. Marshlands of Tomales Bay may be seen in the background. *Photo from J. C. Branner collection, courtesy Stanford University.*

34.9 Turn left. The crack caused by the 1906 earthquake is on the hillside immediately to the east of us.

35.5 Junction with Highway 1. On the road to the right (east), occurred the greatest measured lateral displacement of the 1906 movement, amounting to 20 feet. The road has been straightened, but the eye of the faithful can still, with a little imagination, see the bend caused by the earthquake.

On the west the rocks are mostly quartz diorite, but up the canyon to the left lies one of several roof pendants of crystalline limestone enclosed in the quartz diorite. The limestone contains scheelite (calcium tungstate).

35.7 White House Pool. Fifty to a hundred years ago this was a loading point for schooners which took the lumber and dairy products of the area to San Francisco. They also took lime, obtained from another roof pendant of crystalline limestone well exposed up the road to the left.

36.9 Adams real estate office. Behind this building is an exposure of mica schist included in the quartz diorite.

38.0 Willow Point. Up the canyon to the left (west) is another pendant of metamorphosed crystalline limestone containing scheelite.

38.8 Village of Inverness.

40.1 Road turns west over Inverness Ridge. Exposure of schist in quartz diorite on left.

41.4 Take left fork to Point Reyes: right fork goes to Tomales Point.

41.8 In roadcut to right—basal Miocene sands (inlier).

42.2 Quarry on right in quartz diorite.

42.8 Quarry on right in typical rhythmically bedded white-weathering Monterey shale.

44.5 Left (south): head of Drake's Estero, a drowned valley occupying the Point Reyes syncline. Its outlet is at Drakes Bay to the south.

45.3 R.C.A. trans-Pacific receiving station and A.T. & T. receiving station.

49.3 Fork left to Drakes Beach.

51.0 *Stop 5.* Drakes Beach. Picnic tables available here. The white cliffs, which Drake likened to the chalk cliffs of England, are composed of fine sandstone, siltstone, and a subordinate amount of siliceous shale of lower Pliocene age. These beds fill the gentle syncline of Point Reyes peninsula, lying unconformably on the Paleocene and quartz diorite of Point Reyes to the west, and on the middle Miocene chert to the east.

At the base of these lower Pliocene beds are glauconite-bearing "greensands" locally rich in bones of whales and other marine fossils. The unconformity between the Pliocene and the underlying middle Miocene is exposed at low tide on the beach to the east. The middle Miocene cherty beds are steeply folded. Drake is supposed to have careened his ship, the *Golden Hinde*, close to this spot.

52.7 Return to Sir Francis Drake Highway, turn left (south) toward Point Reyes.

53.3 Road to Point Reyes Beach on west.

53.8 Sand dune across highway.

57.0 Nunes Ranch.

57.6 Radio relay station is located on quartz diorite.

58.5 *Stop 6*. Parking lot, Point Reyes Lighthouse. Here one may walk down to the top of the lighthouse steps. On the way are fine exposures of the coarse Paleocene conglomerate which here overlies the quartz diorite. This conglomerate dips at a high angle to the northwest, and is found in three separate faulted blocks on the point. Interesting sedimentary structures, including channeling, are to be seen. The glauconite-bearing basal sand of the lower Pliocene lies unconformably on both quartz diorite and conglomerate at the east end of the point; the contact is obscured by blown sand at this end of the point.

To the north lies the 12-mile-long Point Reyes Beach, a spectacular sight on a clear day, (photo 10).

73.9 Retrace the road to Olema—junction of Coast Highway 1 and Sir Francis Drake Highway. Turn left (east) on Sir Francis Drake Highway. The remainder of the trip will be in Franciscan rocks. In the road-cut ahead Franciscan sandstone is well exposed.

88.8 *Stop* 7. Samuel P. Taylor State Park, a fine grove of second-growth redwoods. The stumps of the original trees, cut in the 1850's are still here and measure up to 16 feet in diameter.

91.1 *Stop 8*. Confluence of Lagunitas and San Geronimo Creeks. Pillow lava exposed in roadcut to south contains numerous glassy feldspar crystals. Pillow structure is well demonstrated; it is believed to indicate rapid cooling of the molten rock in a very wet medium.

Photo 9. Pillow structures in volcanic rocks at Nicasio Dam, Marin County. *Photo by Mary Hill.*

93.4 Lagunitas District School: on the north side of the road can be seen yellowish-brown silica-carbonate rock, an alteration product of serpentine, along with green serpentine and Franciscan sandstone and chert.

96.8 White's Hill. A fine section of interbedded Franciscan sandstone and shale is exposed in roadcuts at the summit.

104.8 Greenbrae. Turn right (south) on Highway 101. These marshlands, typical of drowned valleys, now are nearly filled by Recent sediments (and subdivisions). The San Francisco-Marin fault block on which one has been traveling since leaving the San Andreas fault is tilted eastward, producing these drowned valleys extending into San Francisco Bay.

In the hills north of Greenbrae was found in 1956 the "plate of brasse" which Sir Francis Drake affixed in 1579 to a point believed to be at Drakes Bay, claiming the land of "New Albion" for Queen Elizabeth. The plate has passed all tests for genuineness.

113.5 Golden Gate Bridge.

Photo 10. Aerial view north toward Point Reyes. On the left, perched near the water, can be seen the lighthouse. The bedded sedimentary rocks at the left (west) end of the Point are Paleocene conglomerates, which lie on Mesozoic granitic rock. In the middle distance, the Pliocene beds of Drake's Bay fill a syncline which is marked by the drowned valley of Drake's Estero. The San Andreas fault is just behind the first dark-colored distant ridge. *Photo courtesy Aero Photographers, Sausalito.*

FIELD TRIP
SAN FRANCISCO PENINSULA

BY M. G. BONILLA AND JULIUS SCHLOCKER
U.S. GEOLOGICAL SURVEY, MENLO PARK, CALIFORNIA

SAN FRANCISCO—TELEGRAPH HILL—FORT POINT—OCEAN BEACH—THORNTON BEACH—PACIFICA—DEVILS SLIDE—MONTARA MOUNTAIN—HALF MOON BAY—CRYSTAL SPRINGS RESERVOIR—SAN ANDREAS FAULT ZONE—CITY COLLEGE FAULT ZONE—SAN BRUNO MOUNTAIN—TWIN PEAKS—MISSION SWAMP SUBSIDING AREA

The trip starts at the Hilton Hotel in San Francisco and initially follows the edge of San Francisco Peninsula from Telegraph Hill on the northeast to Fort Point on the north, and the Cliff House on the west (fig. 1). The route is then south along the Pacific Ocean, across the San Andreas fault zone near its junction with the coastline, to Half Moon Bay. The Santa Cruz Range is crossed along Pilarcitos Creek and the San Andreas fault zone is followed northwestward for more than 10 miles. San Francisco is seen in a panorama view from Twin Peaks before the trip returns to the Hilton Hotel.

San Francisco is the type area for the Franciscan Formation. Most of the varieties of rocks in that extensive and controversial formation will be seen, as well as the ultramafics which intrude it and the younger rocks which cover it.

The Franciscan Formation is found throughout the Coast Ranges of California. It consists mostly of sandstone (graywacke type), shale, and volcanic rock with minor amounts of ferruginous chert, conglomerate, limestone, and metamorphic rocks. Accumulation of the rocks was probably in a deep-sea eugeosynclinal environment. The metamorphic rocks resulted mostly from deep burial and local high shear stress. Some of the metamorphic rocks have been moved by faulting and diapir intrusion and are now found as isolated bodies surrounded by unmetamorphosed rock or rock of lower or higher metamorphic grade; others formed in the spatial relationship now seen. All of the Franciscan rocks were intruded by serpentine either during or following Franciscan time.

For many years the Franciscan Formation was considered to be limited in age to the latest Jurassic (Taliaferro, 1943, p. 195). Recent discoveries of Early and Late Cretaceous fossils in the Franciscan Formation in the type area and elsewhere have forced geologists to assign a younger age to parts of it (Irwin, 1957, p. 2289; Bailey, Irwin, and Jones, 1964). Lack of marker beds, scarcity of fossils, and pervasive structural complexities prevent geologists from devising a standard stratigraphic section or accurately determining the thickness of the formation.

Petrologic methods of characterizing the Franciscan Formation and other upper Mesozoic sedimentary

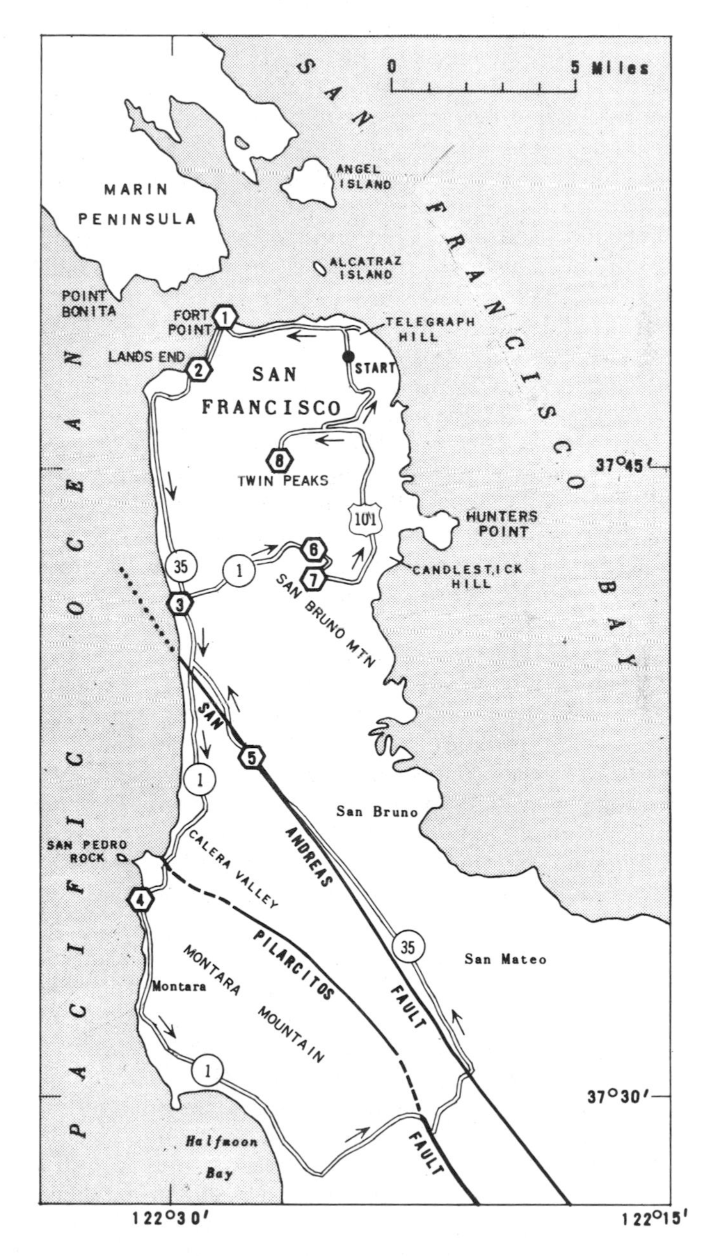

Figure 1. Index map of San Francisco peninsula showing route of field trip; stops in road log indicated by numbers in hexagons.

rocks have been tried with moderate success in solving local as well as regional stratigraphic and structural problems. For example, Bailey and Irwin (1959, p. 2806) used a simple stain technique in studying a thick, conformable sequence of fossiliferous shelf and slope facies sandstones of Late Jurassic to Late Cretaceous age along the west side of the Sacramento Valley. They found that the amount of detrital potassium feldspar increases progressively in rocks of decreasing age. This stain technique showed that most sandstones of the Franciscan Formation contain no potassium feldspar, though locally significant amounts are present, especially in the western part of the Coast Ranges. Bailey, Irwin, and Jones (1964, p. 141) suggest that sandstones of the Franciscan Formation that contain more than a few percent potassium feldspar are probably Cretaceous in age, but that sandstones of the Franciscan Formation that contain little or no potassium feldspar may be either Cretaceous or Jurassic in age.

In the type area of the Franciscan Formation, eugeosynclinal-type sandstones contain little or no detrital potassium feldspar. The sandstones of San Bruno Mountain, south of San Francisco, however, which were included in Lawson's (1914) Franciscan group, were found to consistently contain potassium feldspar in large amounts in some places. This mineralogical difference, as well as other features thought to be atypical of sandstone of the eugeosynclinal environment, such as persistent bedding, general lack of pervasive fracturing and shearing, and general absence of volcanic rocks and radiolarian chert, casts doubt on the correlation of the sedimentary rocks of San Bruno Mountain with the eugeosynclinal assemblage of rocks of the Franciscan Formation in the City of San Francisco.

Sedimentary rocks of an entirely different facies are represented by Upper Cretaceous(?) and Paleocene shale, sandstone, and conglomerate to be seen lying on granitic rock of Montara Mountain in the area south of the Pilarcitos fault. Other still younger sedimentary rocks seen on the trip are the Monterey shale and unnamed formations of Miocene age, the Purisima Formation of Pliocene age, the Merced Formation of Pliocene and Pleistocene age, and the Colma Formation of Pleistocene age.

The geologic structure of San Francisco Peninsula is not thoroughly understood despite considerable study. Franciscan rocks north of the Fort Point-Hunters Point shear zone and sandstone and shale of San Bruno Mountain south of the City College-Lands End shear zone are folded along northwest-trending axes. The block bounded by these shear zones consists of rocks of the Franciscan Formation, mostly radiolarian chert and volcanic rocks, folded on east-west and north-south axes. The marine Merced Formation of Pliocene and Pleistocene age lies on the Franciscan Formation west and south of San Bruno Mountain; it appears to be folded into a large northwest-trending syncline. Franciscan rocks, mostly pyroclastics, make up the block between the San Andreas and Pilarcitos faults. South of the Pilarcitos fault no Franciscan rocks are found and granitic rocks are mantled by younger Mesozoic and Tertiary sedimentary deposits. The crustal segment between the San Andreas and Hayward faults is probably a complex structural block consisting mostly of small blocks bounded by northwest-trending faults and folds. San Francisco Bay, which occupies much of it, is the drowned lower end of Santa Clara Valley, a down-faulted and folded segment. The granitic rocks of Montara Mountain may be a part of an adjoining structural block tilted down on the northeast.

The great variation in topography, rock type, and geologic structure, and the presence of a large city, afford an excellent opportunity to observe relations between geology and engineering. In San Francisco the low areas are generally underlain by young, unconsolidated sediments whereas the hills are of indurated Franciscan rocks. Engineering practice is directed towards reducing subsidence of structures built on weak, unconsolidated sediments and preventing slope failures of indurated rocks in the hills. Earthquake damage prevention is also a factor in engineering design. Shear zones, an inch to a mile wide, in the Franciscan Formation consist mostly of firm to soft, finely sheared, material that encloses hard rock pieces from an inch to hundreds of feet in diameter. The shear zones present troublesome problems to the engineer because of their overall weakness and the random presence in them of hard rock pieces of unpredictable size. On the trip, such shear zones will be seen, as well as subsiding structures built on filled-in parts of San Francisco Bay, and large residential areas underlain by dune sand.

REFERENCES

Bailey, E. H., and Irwin, W. P., 1959, K-feldspar content of Jurassic and Cretaceous graywackes of the northern Coast Ranges and Sacramento Valley, California: Am. Assoc. Petroleum Geologists Bull, v. 43, no. 12, p. 2797–2809.

Bailey, E. H., Irwin, W. P., and Jones, D. L., 1964, Franciscan and related rocks, and their significance in the geology of western California: California Div. Mines and Geology Bull. 183, 177 p.

Bonilla, M. G., 1965, Geologic map of the San Francisco South quadrangle, California: U.S. Geol. Survey open-file map, scale 1:20,000.

Curtis, G. H., Evernden, J. F., and Lipson, J. I., 1958, Age determination of some granitic rocks in California by the potassium-argon method: California Div. Mines Spec. Rept. 54, 16 p.

Irwin, W. P., 1957, Franciscan group in Coast Ranges and its equivalents in Sacramento Valley, California: Am. Assoc. Petroleum Geologists Bull., v. 41, no. 10, p. 2284–2297.

Lawson, A. C., 1914, Description of the San Francisco district; Tamalpais, San Francisco, Concord, San Mateo, and Hayward quadrangles: U.S. Geol. Survey Geol. Atlas, Folio 193, 24 p.

Lawson, A. C., and others, 1908, The California earthquake of April 18, 1906. Report of the State Earthquake Investigation Commission: Carnegie Inst. Washington Pub. 87, v. 1, pt. 1, 254 p.; pt. 2, p. 255–451.

Schlocker, Julius, Bonilla, M. G., and Radbruch, D. H., 1958, Geology of the San Francisco North quadrangle, California: U.S. Geol. Survey Misc. Geol. Inv. Map I-272, scale 1:24,000.

Schussler, Herman, 1906, The water supply of San Francisco, California, before, during, and after the earthquake of April 18, 1906, and the subsequent conflagration: New York, M. B. Brown Press, 103 p.

Taliaferro, N. L., 1943, Franciscan-Knoxville problem: Am. Assoc. Petroleum Geologists Bull., v. 27, no. 2, p. 109–219.

ROAD LOG

Mileage

0.0 *Hilton Hotel, Mason and Eddy Streets.* Go one block west on Eddy Street.

0.1 Turn right (north) on Taylor Street.

1.0 Taylor Street crosses Broadway twin-bore, vehicular tunnel. Massive sandstone and sheared, thin-bedded sandstone and shale of the Franciscan Formation were encountered in excavating the tunnels. No potassium feldspar occurs in the sandstones.

1.1 Vallejo Street, Coolbrith Park. Potassium feldspar-free sandstone and shale of the Franciscan Formation on both sides of street. Rocks are sheared, fractured, thrust-faulted and overturned. View of Alcatraz and Angel Islands.

1.2 Telegraph Hill on right.

1.4 Cross Columbus Avenue.

1.5 Turn right (east) onto Bay Street.

2.0 Turn right onto Kearney Street and go 1 block south.

2.1 Massive sandstone of the Franciscan Formation in quarry face, northeast side of Telegraph Hill. No potassium feldspar is present in this rock. Southwest dip is shown by thin shale beds. Thin-bedded sandstone and shale form the west side of Telegraph Hill. Rocks of Telegraph Hill and Russian Hill are part of northwest-plunging syncline (Schlocker, Bonilla, and Radbruch, 1958).

2.2 Retrace route and turn left (west) onto Bay Street.

3.6 Turn right (north) onto Laguna Street. This is the east edge of a large area of beach sand and land reclaimed from the bay.

3.7 Turn left (west) onto Marina Boulevard.

4.4 Yacht Harbor and view of Golden Gate Bridge.

4.7 Site of Pan-Pacific Exposition, 1914–1915. Enter Golden Gate Bridge approach.

4.8 Presidio military reservation. This area was set aside in 1776 by the Spanish Government for military purposes, and it is still held for military use as headquarters of U.S. Sixth Army.

5.9 Route crosses Hunters Point-Fort Point shear zone. Sheared rocks of Franciscan Formation and serpentine are exposed in cuts.

6.3 Turn to right where sign says "View Area" just before reaching Golden Gate Bridge toll gates.

6.4 Turn left on Lincoln Boulevard.

6.6 Turn left on Long Avenue, then left on Marine Drive. Road cuts are in serpentine. Landslide blocks of altered serpentine exposed in cliffs on south side of Marine Drive. This serpentine is derived from dunite and saxonite, and relict enstatite is common.

7.2 *Stop 1.* Fort Winfield Scott, built in 1853. Serpentine here is altered to:

Hydro-magnesite	$Mg_4CO_3(OH)_2 \cdot 3H_2O$
Pyroaurite	$Mg_6Fe_2CO_3(OH)_{16} \cdot 4H_2O$
Coalingite	$Mg_{10}Fe_2CO_3(OH)_{24} \cdot 2H_2O$
Nesquehonite	$MgCO_3 \cdot 3H_2O$

Sjögrenite, the hexagonal polymorph of pyroaurite (rhombohedral), and brugnatellite ($Mg_6FeCO_3(OH)_{12} \cdot 4H_2O$) are also reported from the Fort Point area. In other nearby localities, serpentine is altered to montmorillonite rich in magnesium, nickeloan nontronite, opal, chalcedony, artinite ($Mg_2CO_3(OH)_2 \cdot 3H_2O$), and magnesite ($MgCO_3$).

Walk around east side of the fort for view of Golden Gate Bridge. South tower of bridge is founded on serpentine 100 feet below surface of the water. During construction a strong controversy arose between two prominent geologists, Andrew C. Lawson and Bailey Willis, regarding the safety of this tower.

Retrace route and turn right on Lincoln Blvd., following the latter onto El Camino del Mar.

11.3 *Stop 2.*—East edge of Lincoln Park Golf Course. Walk north on path along former street car line. About 75 feet from El Camino del Mar path is on landslide. From north to south are seen: Golden Gate Bridge; landslides in serpentine along the shore on the west edge of the Presidio; Bakers Beach; Phelan Beach State Park. The narrow spur north of the stop is a fossil locality where a Cretaceous ammonite, *Douvilleiceras*, was found in sandstone of the Franciscan Formation. This sandstone contains 2 percent potassium feldspar. The Franciscan Formation here consists mostly of eastward-dipping sandstone and shale with small amounts of radiolarian chert and greenstone; the structure is locally disturbed by faults and landslides. Serpentine is found in a shear zone cutting the formation at Phelan Beach, 1,000 feet east of the stop. The large rock, about 10 feet high, lying on the west edge of Phelan Beach, is altered volcanic rock (greenstone) of the Franciscan Formation. It is probably a tectonic inclusion in the shear zone.

The cliffs on the north side of the Golden Gate show a section of radiolarian chert, greenstone, and sandstone, dipping mostly southwest. Pillow lavas dip eastward at Point Bonita, the site of the lighthouse at the north portal of the Golden Gate.

Mile Rock Lighthouse, west of stop 1 and about one-half mile offshore, is on greenstone that is

Photo 1. Earthquake damage to road on shore of Lake Merced, 1957. The landslides probably were caused by liquefaction during shaking of water-saturated sand.

probably a tectonic inclusion in the shear zone that can be seen on shore at Lands End. Continue west on El Camino del Mar.

11.8 Turn left in front of Legion of Honor Art Gallery. Landslides have closed El Camino del Mar to the west despite efforts to control them.

12.3 Turn right onto Geary Street and go 8 blocks to Point Lobos Avenue. Continue on Point Lobos Avenue which becomes the Esplanade south of the Cliff House.

13.4 Cliff House. Massive, fractured sandstone exposed in cliffs east of road. The simulated rock face is a concrete coating placed to stabilize cliff. Sandstones here contain more than 5 percent potassium feldspar.

13.5 North end of Ocean Beach. Seal Rocks to north and sea cliffs below Cliff House are mostly sandstone. Sandstone is hydrothermally altered at the contact with the Colma Formation but is fresh about 100 feet north of the contact. East of the Esplanade, at the north end of the amusement park, the Colma Formation, probably of Late Pleistocene age, lies on sandstone and is overlain by dune sand. The base of the Colma Formation here consists of steeply dipping rubble beds derived from the underlying massive sandstone. The upper part of the formation is orange, clayey sand, which dips about 8° to the south. At this locality, the clayey sand of the Colma Formation is probably marine, though the rubble beds may be nonmarine.

The beach extends southward for about 7 miles. Sand on the San Francisco part of the beach is probably derived from the south. The arcuate sandy shoals that extend as far as 5 miles offshore, opposite the Golden Gate, may be a result of the north-drifting sand being deflected from shore by the ebb tide from San Francisco Bay.

13.8 Amundsen's ship "Gjoa" on the left was the first to make the Northwest Passage.

14.3 Cross Lincoln Avenue. Enter north end of Great Highway.

Dune sand blown eastward from Ocean Beach covers much of northern San Francisco. The sand was also blown over the 700-foot-high ridge 2 miles to the left (east) and accumulated to a depth of more than 30 feet on the lee side. Most of the fill material used to reclaim land from the Bay east of Montgomery Street in downtown San Francisco was obtained from sand dunes in that area. Movement of sand is now mostly confined to the area west of Great Highway, though sand persistently enters tunnels under Great Highway.

16.3 Fleishhacker Zoo. Cross Sloat Boulevard and continue south on Park Road and Skyline Boulevard.

17.1 Lake Merced. The earthquake of March 1957 caused large sections of road along the shores to slide into the lake (photo 1). Lake Merced is a drowned stream valley separated from the ocean by beach- and dune-sand.

18.8 Landslide on right.

19.2 *Stop 3*. Alemany Boulevard at Thornton Beach. Walk about 1 block west. Flat-lying sand of the Colma Formation, exposed along east side of abandoned highway, overlies the Pleistocene part of the Merced Formation with slight discordance. Half a mile to the south, the Pliocene part of the Merced dips as much as 70°. Large landslides are found here and for 1 mile to the north (Bonilla, 1965). Highway to the south has been abandoned because of landslides.

19.7 Continue south on routes 1 and 35, Skyline Boulevard. Houses on right (west) were moderately damaged by earthquake of March 1957 (photo 2).

20.4 Cross Westmoor Avenue. Merced Formation underlies this general area.

21.5 Turn right on State Highway 1 where sign points to Santa Cruz.

22.2 Cross San Andreas fault zone. This is the northernmost point on the San Francisco Peninsula where the fault trace could be accurately located in 1906; from here it was followed for many miles to the southeast.

Photo 2. House damaged by earthquake of March 22, 1957, Westlake Palisades area, Daly City.

Photo 3. Devils Slide area. Field trip stop 4 is on highway just left of center. Note the bedding in sedimentary rocks above and below highway. ***Photo by E. E. Brabb.***

24.9 Sharp Park Golf Course. The lagoon to the right (west) is on the drowned south edge of a tilted marine terrace which 2 miles north of here is almost 200 feet above sea level.

25.2 Hills to the south are sandstone and altered pyroclastic rock (greenstone) of the Franciscan Formation.

25.7 Entering Calera Valley, type locality of the Calera Limestone Member of the Franciscan Formation.

25.9 The Calera Limestone is exposed in Rockaway Quarry on the right. This is the northernmost exposure of the Calera Limestone Member of the type locality. The limestone is interbedded with sandstone that Lawson (1914) designated the oldest formation of his Franciscan Group. The limestone, however, contains abundant Cenomanian (Late Cretaceous) Foraminifera, which suggests it is one of the youngest parts of the Franciscan Formation.

26.7 Dark-gray Calera Limestone Member in roadcut on left.

26.8 Road cut in shear zone exposes a confused mixture of several rock types of the Franciscan Formation. Shear zone may be part of Pilarcitos fault discussed below.

27.3 Portola expedition marker. From a camp near this point scouts of the expedition discovered San Francisco Bay in 1769.

27.6 Intersection with road to Pedro Valley section of the City of Pacifica.

The southeast-trending Pilarcitos fault lies in Pedro Valley. The fault is a major boundary between a block with basement of Franciscan Formation to the northeast and another block with basement of granitic rocks to the southwest. Some geologists believe that the Pilarcitos fault was the active branch of the San Andreas fault in late Pleistocene time. The western projection of the coastline, on the south side of Pedro Valley, has been cited as evidence for Quaternary right-lateral movement. In contrast the coastline is only slightly irregular where it is cut by the San Andreas fault, 5 miles north of Pedro Valley.

27.9 Thin-bedded, fine-grained sandstones and shales, possibly of Late Cretaceous age, dip southward in the roadcuts.

28.7 In roadcut on right granitic boulder conglomerate of probable Paleocene age lies unconformably on Upper Cretaceous(?) beds.

29.1 Paleocene beds dip northward on south limb of syncline.

29.3 *Stop 4.* Devils Slide area. Roadcut, several hundred feet high, exposes tightly folded, thin-bedded sandstone and shale of Paleocene age. Slivers of rock, mostly of gray shale of Late Cretaceous(?) age, are visible in the large landslides also exposed in the roadcut. San Pedro Rock, the small island to the north with conspicuous bedding, consists of Upper Cretaceous (?) rocks. Granitic rocks are exposed along the highway for more than a mile south of Devils Slide (photo 3).

29.8 Road crosses large landslide in sheared and shattered granitic and sedimentary rocks. Crown of landslide is more than 600 feet above the road. The highway has been completely blocked many times by movement of this slide, especially following long periods of heavy rainfall. Control of the slide movement and relocation of the highway both present difficult problems.

31.6 Town of Montara. The highway is on Half Moon Bay marine terrace, developed during a Pleistocene interglacial period and subsequently warped and faulted.

32.8 Roadcut in continental terrace sediments which overlie marine sediments that in turn lie on the wave-cut terrace surface.

33.3 Moss Beach on southwestern flank of Montara Mountain.

The granitic rocks of Montara Mountain are exposed over an area of more than 30 square miles. They have not been mapped in detail, but are known to vary from granite to quartz diorite. A sample collected five miles eastward gave a potassium-argon date on biotite of 91.6 million years (Curtis and others, 1958, p. 9). Cretaceous and Paleocene strata evidently were stripped from this area before the deposition of the marine Pliocene sediments, which lie on granitic rocks and are exposed in small folds along the beach and on the wave-cut bench at low tide.

34.7 Road is on the Half Moon Bay marine terrace. Hill to right is of marine Pliocene beds slightly older than those of the type Merced Formation. Northeast face of hill is probably a recent fault scarp formed by movement along the Seal Cove fault.

36.9 El Granada Beach. Structurally low portion of the warped Half Moon Bay marine terrace.

37.8 Rocks exposed about three-fourths of a mile left (east) of highway are sandstone and shale of Miocene age.

40.0 Turn left (east) onto Half Moon Bay road. Sign points to San Mateo. Town of Half Moon Bay is at northern limits of an area of seepages of gas and high-gravity oil from Miocene and Pliocene sedimentary rocks. Commercial production of oil has been small, and it is mostly from wells on a northwest-trending anticline that intersects the coast about 4 miles south of the town.

The route crosses part of the Santa Cruz Mountains and drops into the valley eroded along the San Andreas fault zone. The road, for about 3 miles, is in a deep canyon cut by Pilarcitos Creek. Evidence of Quaternary and possibly Tertiary uplift can be inferred from several marine terraces that are higher than the Half Moon Bay terrace, and from stream terraces that appear as flat benches on the spurs jutting into the canyon of Pilarcitos Creek. The Montara Mountain granitic rock mass plunges southeastward beneath a cover of Tertiary and Quaternary rocks.

40.6 Purisima Formation exposed in roadcut on left is a marine sandstone of Pliocene age.

40.9 Monterey Shale exposed in roadcut on left. At this locality the shale contains middle Miocene (Luisian) fossils. It grades downward into sandstone which can be seen at mileages 42.5 and 42.7.

42.5 On left and ahead, view of hogback of basal arkosic sandstone of Monterey Shale dipping westward.

42.7 Same basal sandstone exposed in quarry on left.

43.2 Granitic rock in roadcut on left.

43.8 In roadcut on left conglomerate of Pliocene(?) age is thrust over sheared granitic rocks.

44.1 In roadcut on left sandstone, shale, and basalt of early Miocene (Zemorrian) age are faulted against conglomerate of Pliocene(?) age.

44.5 Good locality for collecting lower Miocene (Zemorrian) Foraminifera in shale in roadcut on left.

44.7 Pilarcitos fault crosses the road. It is the eastern border of the granitic rocks in this area. Beyond the fault the exposure of sandstone and conglomerate, mapped as Franciscan Formation, has yielded Cretaceous Rudistids.

45.8 Intersection with Skyline Boulevard (State Highway No. 35). Continue eastward on Skyline Boulevard.

46.4 Good view eastward of: The valley of the San Andreas fault zone; hills east of the fault truncated by a flat to rolling Pleistocene erosion surface 600 to 800 feet above sea level cut on serpentine and Franciscan Formation; San Francisco Bay; and the Berkeley Hills and Diablo Range. The active Hayward fault lies on or near the west edge of the hills beyond (east of) San Francisco Bay.

Crystal Springs Lake in the valley of the San Andreas fault zone supplies water to San Francisco Peninsula towns. Most of the water comes from Hetch Hetchy Valley in the Sierra Nevada.

47.2 Causeway on Crystal Springs Lake. Right-lateral offset of the causeway along the surface trace of the San Andreas fault in 1906 at this point was 8 feet.

47.4 Turn left (north) toward San Francisco.

48.2 Serpentine derived from peridotite, in roadcut on right, here consists of hard blocks, rounded by shearing.

48.3 Serpentine in cuts on both sides of road.

48.4 Intersection with Bunkerhill Drive.

48.9 Skyline Boulevard crosses Crystal Springs Dam which, when completed in 1888, was one of the largest concrete dams in the world. The trace of the 1906 surface rupture along the San Andreas fault lies only 1,000 feet west of the dam, but the dam was not damaged by the 1906 earthquake.

49.1 Intersection with Crystal Springs Road.

49.5 Tectonic inclusion of rocks of the Franciscan Formation within serpentine in roadcut on right.

50.2 The Pleistocene erosion surface on which Skyline Boulevard was built is well exposed here.

50.6 Intersection with Black Mountain Road.

50.7 Volcanic rock (greenstone) of the Franciscan Formation altered to a red-brown, friable rock.

50.9 Crystal Springs Golf Course. View westward across the San Andreas fault valley shows two erosion surfaces, developed at about 1,200 and 1,800 feet above sea level.

52.6 Knob on right about 200 feet east of Skyline Boulevard consists of several schistose metamorphic rocks containing the blue amphibole glaucophane. Similar isolated knobs of metamorphic rocks are common in many areas underlain by the Franciscan Formation.

54.2 Skyline Boulevard intersection with Hillcrest Boulevard in City of Millbrae.

56.8 San Bruno Avenue. Skyline Boulevard here crosses 1906 trace of San Andreas fault at an acute angle and remains close to the trace for the next 1.2 miles.

58.0 Berkshire Drive. Rupture in 1906 was through a small sag pond that lay just east of Skyline Boulevard.

58.5 *Stop 5.* Observation point on the east side of Skyline Boulevard, on greenstone of the Franciscan Formation. Artificial fill, beneath the houses in the valley in the immediate foreground, conceals a formerly well-defined valley that marked the trace of the San Andreas fault. Before the houses were built, evidence of the 1906 movement of the San Andreas fault could be seen, such as a break in the former San Francisco water supply pipeline and a broken fence. The fence was offset about 6 feet at the break but it was also bent so that the total horizontal displacement was 13 feet. A diagram of the fence is shown in Lawson and others (1908, v. 1, p. 94). Photo 4 shows the fence as it appeared in 1956 and photo 5 shows this scene in 1962.

The Merced Formation lies east of the fault. A well drilled about one-half mile north of here on the east side of the fault was still in the Merced Formation at a depth of more than 3,000 feet. Near the base of San Bruno Mountain, which is visible to the northeast, is the San Bruno fault. Lawson (1914, p. 16) estimated the vertical "differential displacement" on this fault as not less than 7,000 feet. Gravity surveys and recent geologic mapping indicate, however, that the vertical separation on the fault is much less, and logs of borings near the south end of San Bruno Mountain show that the separation there can be no more than a few hundred feet.

The Colma Formation overlies the Merced Formation in the flat valley southwest of San Bruno Mountain.

59.6 Road crosses trace of the 1906 movement of the San Andreas fault. On the right (south) sag ponds were visible in the valley before grading was done for the subdivision. On the left (north), a small notch in the side of the hill marks the line of movement in 1906.

60.1 To the right is a view of a Chinese cemetery. South of the cemetery, in the little valley to the right, a well-formed terrace is visible along a branch of Colma Creek. Radiocarbon dating of wood collected at the base of this stream terrace gave an age of about 10,500 years.

60.4 A sag pond could be seen in the San Andreas fault zone about 1,000 feet left (southwest) of the road prior to construction of the houses. The

Photo 4. Fence that was ruptured, bent, and shifted bodily more than 5 feet by movement of the San Andreas fault in 1906. Solid line shows trace of fault. Arrow points to building that is also shown in photo 5. Photograph taken in 1956.

Photo 5. Same view as photo 4, but taken in 1962 during construction of housing tract. Arrow points to building Indicated on photo 4. Some of the trees have been removed, the hills graded, and the valleys filled.

trace of the 1906 movement was along the west edge of the pond.

61.4 Intersection with State Highway 1. Continue northward.

61.8 Green building straight ahead is a water reservoir. During the March 1957 earthquake water poured out of a large crack that formed in the side of the reservoir. Because of fear that the reservoir would fail completely, people were evacuated from homes immediately below it.

62.4 Westmore Avenue. A volcanic ash bed, uncovered in the Merced Formation during grading for the houses northeast of this intersection, was traced intermittently to the northwest for about 2 miles down to the beach. This is the lower of two ash beds that have been found in the Merced Formation.

63.5 Turn right onto Alemany Boulevard. Follow sign pointing to road to San Francisco.

65.0 Left turn onto Junipero Serra Boulevard.

65.3 Right turn onto Alemany Boulevard. Sign reads "Civic Center-Bay Bridge-Cow Palace."

66.0 The road crosses a former railroad line into San Francisco. Road is on Colma Formation; the hills on either side are of Franciscan Formation.

67.2 Turn right onto Geneva Avenue, cross Mission Street, and continue on Geneva Avenue another 8 blocks.

67.6 Turn left onto Athens Street and go 5 blocks.

68.1 Turn right onto Persia Street and go about 5 blocks.

68.5 *Stop 6*. City College fault zone. Sheared sandstone, shale, greenstone, chert, and metamorphic rocks can be seen in the roadcut. North of this locality the Franciscan Formation includes much chert and greenstone; the sandstones generally contain no potassium feldspar. South of here San Bruno Mountain consists largely of sandstone and shale with relatively little chert or greenstone; the sandstones have as much as 20 percent potassium feldspar. The former quarry visible just south of here is our next stop.

70.0 Turn right onto Santos Street. Large mass of sandstone and shale on left (east) near Geneva Avenue is a tectonic inclusion in the fault zone. This sandstone contains only a trace of potassium feldspar.

70.3 Turn right onto Geneva Avenue.

70.7 *Stop* 7. Turn left into parking lot of Castle Lanes Sport Center, where restrooms are available.

This former quarry provides a good exposure of the sedimentary rocks that make up San Bruno Mountain. They are well bedded, and are less faulted and sheared than are most outcrops of the Franciscan Formation. Graded bedding and bedding plane markings can be seen in the interbedded graywacke and shale. The quarry is on the northeastern limit of the potassium feldspar-rich sandstone and is at the north end of the San Bruno Mountain mass. Attitudes of bedding in San Bruno Mountain suggest that the mountain is an asymmetric anticline with a steep limb on the southwest side and a relatively gentle limb on the northeast side. The hill north of the quarry is in the City College fault zone.

70.7 Turn right onto Geneva Avenue from parking lot.

71.9 Turn left onto Bayshore Highway.

72.8 On the right, view of shear zone in cut on Candlestick Hill east of Bayshore Freeway, where highly sheared shale and sandstone have tectonic inclusions of greenstone and chert. Chert and greenstone crop out at the crest of the hill. The hillslope has many small earthflows, some of which have damaged a former public housing project. The excavations on the side of the hill are borrow areas where rock was obtained for the garbage disposal operation to the south. The San Francisco Giants' baseball park is on the east side of this hill.

Turn left onto James Lick Freeway.

74.3 Intersection with Alemany Boulevard (Southern Freeway). A tidal channel, Islais Creek, formerly extended 0.4 mile westward from this intersection. Channels cut in bedrock, probably during a time of Pleistocene glaciation, extend more than 60 feet below sea level here and more than 200 feet below sea level near the mouth of the creek.

75.0 A small landslide here delayed construction of the freeway. Note horizontal drains on left (west).

75.6 Concrete struts, crushed rock, and horizontal drains on right (east) were installed to control a landslide that developed in sheared rock at the contact between sandstone and serpentine.

75.9 Cuts are in serpentine.

76.7 Take Vermont Street exit and go 1 block north on Vermont; turn left (west) on 17th Street.

76.9 Serpentine is exposed on right near Hampshire Street.

77.2 Cross railroad tracks where 17th Street turns slightly left. This is the east edge of an area of artificial fill which the route crosses for the next quarter of a mile. In the 1868 and 1906 earthquakes, damage was generally greater on filled ground such as this than on natural ground.

77.3 East slope of Twin Peaks visible forward (west).

77.6 Cross Mission Street. Mission Street is one of the oldest streets in San Francisco; in early days it

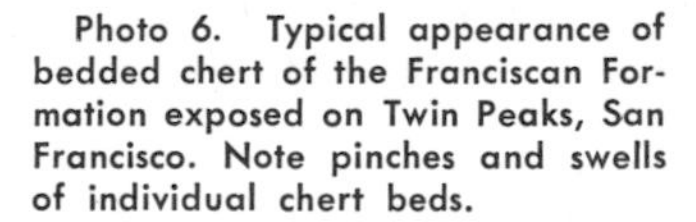
Photo 6. Typical appearance of bedded chert of the Franciscan Formation exposed on Twin Peaks, San Francisco. Note pinches and swells of individual chert beds.

connected the harbor settlement, which was near Chinatown, with the settlement developed about the Spanish Mission.

77.7 Cross Valencia Street. During the 1906 earthquake, artificial fill of poor quality on Valencia Street between 18th and 19th Streets settled 1 to 5 feet and shifted horizontally as much as 7 feet. These movements ruptured iron water mains, the brick sewer, gas pipes, and electric conduits (Schussler, 1906, p. 35, 93, 95).

78.4 Cross Market Street, continue west on 17th Street. To left can be seen the east portal of the 2-mile Twin Peaks Tunnel, which is for street cars only.

79.0 Cross Roosevelt Avenue. Mostly thick-bedded radiolarian chert of the Franciscan Formation on right.

79.1 Turn left onto Clayton Street and go south 1 block.

79.2 Turn right onto Twin Peaks Boulevard. Greenstone, here largely altered to clay minerals, is the brown friable material that apparently intrudes radiolarian chert in cut on right.

79.4 Intersection with Clarendon Avenue. Turn left and stay on Twin Peaks Boulevard.

79.6 Extensive exposures of red-brown radiolarian chert. Beds dip north on nose of north-plunging anticline.

79.9 Radiolarian chert hydrothermally altered to grayish-orange color in small fault on left.

80.0 Take road on west (right) side of Twin Peaks.

80.1 *Stop 8.* Roadcut on west side of north Twin Peaks shows radiolarian chert lying on greenstone. Greenstone at and near contact is altered to a soft clayey material. Chert beds 3 to 5 inches thick, separated by thin shale parting, pinch and swell and generally wedge out in 20 to 30 feet (photo 6). Radiolaria, which appear under the hand lens as pin-head size, round, dark bodies are abundant in both chert and shale. These sedimentary rocks are believed to have been a colloidal gel formed by precipitation of silica and small amounts of iron and aluminum oxides from sea water. The shale-like partings probably represent impurities in the gel (Bailey and others, 1964, p. 65–68). Near the north end of the roadcut, west of north Twin Peaks, the chert and shale beds are tightly folded, and axial fold planes are nearly horizontal. Folding evidently took place before the gel hardened.

A small body of chert lying on greenstone makes up the south Twin Peaks. Roadcuts also reveal former valleys that are now filled with Quaternary sediments. Their size, shape, and location suggest that the former topography of the Twin Peaks summit area was not as steep or as youthful as it is today.

80.3 Continue south on road west of crest. Note pillow structure in altered greenstone southwest of southern peak.

80.6 Turn north on the circular road around the south end of Twin Peaks. Pause for view of

Photo 7. Building on Clara Street in San Francisco showing subsidence of filled ground over former swamp. Street and sidewalk have been raised to their original level by additional fill, and as a result the top of the garage door on left side of the house is only about 2 feet above the sidewalk.

eastern half of San Francisco. The wide street is Market Street. The U.S. Mint, the gray building north of Market Street with the long vertical windows is built on serpentine within the Fort Point-Hunters Point shear zone. The same shear zone includes both Potrero Hill, mostly serpentine, due east and near the Bay, and Hunters Point, the hills to the southeast that jut into the Bay. The south tower of the Golden Gate Bridge rests on serpentine near the northwest end of the shear zone. The hills immediately east of Twin Peaks are predominantly northeast-dipping sandstone and greenstone and lenses of radiolarian chert, all of the Franciscan Formation. San Bruno Mountain is the high hill far to the southeast. Yerba Buena Island, along the Bay Bridge route, is mostly northeast-dipping sandstone beds of the Franciscan Formation covered with thick deposits of clayey sand. Lower Market Street area is land reclaimed from the Bay.

Retrace route down Twin Peaks.

81.5 Left turn onto Clayton Street. Go one block north to 17th Street.

81.6 Right turn onto 17th Street.

82.2 Cross Market Street, continue on 17th Street for 3 blocks to Church Street.

82.6 Turn left onto Church Street and go 1 block.

82.7 Turn right onto 16th Street.

82.8 Mission Dolores, one of the chain of Franciscan Missions that extended in California from San Diego to Sonoma. The mission site was selected because here a small stream furnished fresh water and the land was suitable for farming. Grazing lands on the east side of the Bay were also developed by the mission authorities.

83.7 Turn left onto Bryant Street.

84.5 Land reclaimed from Mission swamp. Buildings in this former swamp area are tilted and otherwise disturbed by subsidence. Note irregularity of alignment of adjacent buildings.

84.8 Turn left onto Fifth Street.

85.0 Turn left onto Shipley Street. Subsidence is especially noticeable here because a few years ago the street and sidewalks were brought up to the level they had before subsidence. Now the level of the sidewalk and street is several feet above the bottoms of the doorways (photo 7). Subsidence here is probably due to dewatering of bay mud under load of artificial fill and buildings.

85.2 Turn right onto Sixth Street. More views of subsiding buildings, especially on the right along Clementina and Tehama Streets.

85.4 Mission Street, north edge of the filled-in area.

85.6 Cross Market Street and turn half right onto Taylor Street.

86.3 Turn right onto California Street. Dune sand is more than 25 feet thick here. It rests on sheared sandstone and shale of the Franciscan Formation.

86.4 Back to starting point.

FIELD TRIP
SAN ANDREAS FAULT FROM SAN FRANCISCO TO HOLLISTER *

By Earl E. Brabb, Marshall E. Maddock, and Robert E. Wallace
U.S. Geological Survey, Washington, D.C.; San Jose State College, San Jose, California; U.S. Geological Survey, Menlo Park, California

SAN FRANCISCO—CRYSTAL SPRINGS LAKES—LOS GATOS—SANTA CRUZ—SEA CLIFF STATE PARK—WATSONVILLE—HECKER PASS —PAJARO GAP—MISSION SAN JUAN BAUTISTA— HARRIS RANCH—ALMADEN WINERY

The San Francisco earthquake of April 18, 1906, focused attention on a then little known geologic structure of California—the San Andreas fault. Fences, roads, pipelines, stream channels, and other structures and features were drastically offset along the fault, demonstrating vividly the right-lateral strike-slip nature of its displacement. Maximum displacement attributable to the 1906 rupture was 21 feet near the head of Tomales Bay, about 30 miles north of San Francisco.

Publication by the Carnegie Institute of Washington of the monumental report by the State Earthquake Investigation Commission, including the elastic-rebound theory proposed by Reid, made the San Andreas fault one of the most widely known geologic structures in the world. Even now, however, more than 60 years since the great earthquake, a great deal remains to be learned about the fault; for example, few geologic maps at a scale of 1:62,500 or larger of areas along the fault have been published. Thus, interpretation of incomplete data has led to considerable controversy about the origin of the fault, when it first originated, and the amount and characteristics of displacement along it. For example, there still is debate as to whether the total displacement on the fault is hundreds of miles or only a few miles.

The San Andreas fault can be traced almost continuously from Point Arena, in northern California, to San Gorgonio Pass in southern California, a distance of about 500 miles, but it is only one strand of a complex fault system which may exceed 1,000 miles in length. In gross pattern the fault cuts obliquely across the trends of major geomorphic elements, such as the San Joaquin Valley, Coast Ranges, Transverse Ranges, and the Pacific margin. In its course the fault crosses, and in many places clearly offsets, minor geomorphic elements such as stream and river valleys, terraces, and ridges. In many places its trace is marked by a distinct topographic trough underlain by extensively fractured and brecciated rocks. In central and northern California, the San Andreas and subsidiary faults are thought to mark the boundary between eugeosynclinal rocks deposited on a basaltic or "oceanic" crust, and miogeosynclinal rocks deposited on a granitic or "continental" crust.

The route of the field trip in part follows, and in part crisscrosses, a 100-mile segment of the San Andreas fault extending from San Francisco southward to the Almaden winery 8 miles south of Hollister. Geomorphic features associated with the fault, such as sag ponds and scarps, offset tree rows, and springs, can be seen at several localities. Some of the destruction caused by movement along the fault in 1906, 1957, and 1963 can be observed. The hight point of the trip is a visit to the Almaden winery, one of the few places in the world where nearly continuous fault slippage is literally tearing a building apart.

* Publication authorized by the Director, U.S. Geological Survey.

REFERENCES

Allen, J. E., 1946, Geology of the San Juan Bautista quadrangle, California: California Div. Mines Bull. 133, p. 9–75.

Crowell, J. C., 1962, Displacement along the San Andreas fault, California: Geol. Soc. America Spec. Paper 71, 61 p.

Hill, M. L., and Dibblee, T. W., Jr., 1953, San Andreas, Garlock, and Big Pine faults, California: Geol. Soc. America Bull., v. 64, p. 443–458.

Jennings, C. W., and Strand, R. G., 1959, Geologic map of California, Olaf P. Jenkins edition, Santa Cruz sheet: California Div. Mines, scale 1:250,000.

Jennings, C. W., and Burnett, J. L., 1961, Geologic map of California, Olaf P. Jenkins edition, San Francisco sheet: California Div. Mines, scale 1:250,000.

Lawson, A. C., 1914, Description of the San Francisco district; Tamalpais, San Francisco, Concord, San Mateo, and Hayward quadrangles: U.S. Geol. Survey Geol. Atlas, Folio 193, 24 p.

Lawson, A. C., and others, 1908, The California earthquake of April 18, 1906—Report of the State Earthquake Investigation Commission: Carnegie Inst. Washington, Pub. 87, v. 1, 451 p.

Rogers, T. H., 196__, Geologic map of California, Olaf P. Jenkins edition, San Jose sheet: California Div. Mines and Geology, scale 1:250,000 (In press).

Oakeshott, G. B., ed., 1959, San Francisco earthquakes of March 1957: California Div. Mines Spec. Rept. 57, 127 p.

Schlocker, Julius, Bonilla, M. G., and Radbruch, D. H., 1958, Geology of the San Francisco North quadrangle, California: U.S. Geol. Survey Misc. Geol. Inv. Map I-272, scale 1:24,000.

Taliaferro, N. L., 1948, Geology of the Hollister quadrangle, California: California Div. Mines Bull. 143, scale 1:62,500.

Tocher, Don, 1960, Creep on the San Andreas fault—Creep rate and related measurements at Vineyard, California: Seismol. Soc. America Bull., v. 50, no. 3, p. 396–403.

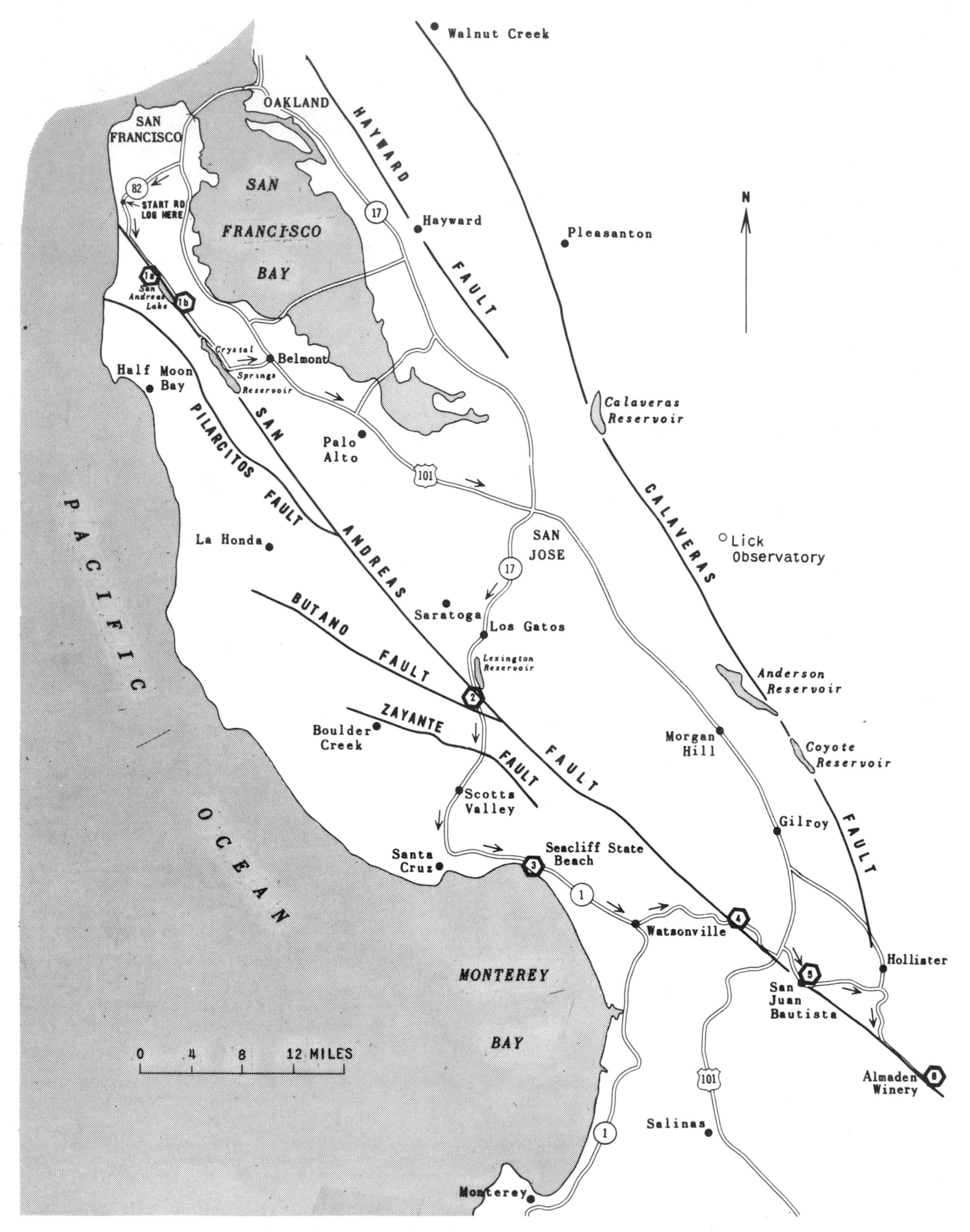

Figure 1. Index map showing field trip route; stops in road log indicated by numbers in hexagons.

Photo 1. San Francisco after the 1906 earthquake and fire. View of Fairmont Hotel (left) and City Hall (right). Taken from Lawrence captive airship at elevation 1,500 feet. Looking south. *Photograph courtesy of California Historical Society.*

ROAD LOG

The road log begins at the intersection of Alemany and Skyline Boulevards, 12 miles from downtown San Francisco via James Lick Freeway (U.S. 101), Southern Freeway (Calif. 82), and Alemany Boulevard (Calif. 1).

Mileage

00.0 Proceed south on Skyline Boulevard.

1.2 Cross Westmoor Avenue. The epicenter of the March 1957 earthquake was near here. Large green building on hill west (right) of highway is a water reservoir which cracked and released water during the quake (photo 2). Many homes had to be evacuated until the reservoir could be drained. Other homes, buildings, and structures in the area suffered at least $1,000,000 damage. For further details the interested reader is referred to California Division of Mines Special Report 57, San Francisco Earthquakes of March 1957.

2.3 Highway 1 diverges from Skyline Boulevard (California 5); keep left and continue south on Skyline Boulevard.

Mileage

The 1906 trace of the San Andreas fault is approximately parallel to, and 1,000 feet southwest (right) of, Skyline Boulevard.

4.2 Serramonte subdivision sign. 1906 trace of San Andreas fault crosses Skyline Boulevard and trends about S. 40° E. through gap in eucalyptus trees in distance. Note sag pond on west (right) side of highway. Sag ponds on east (left) side of highway have been filled. Two large pipes are exposed near the fault, possibly for easy access if they should rupture during an earthquake.

4.8 View of San Bruno Mountain to northeast (left). This mountain has been mentioned as a source for filling about 30 square miles of San Francisco Bay.

Photo 2. Leak in east wall of Westlake Palisades Reservoir developed during 1957 earthquake. *Photograph courtesy of San Francisco Examiner.*

5.2 Westborough Boulevard–Sharp Park Road. From this point before the houses were built a fence offset along the 1906 trace of the San Andreas fault could be seen east (left) of the highway. The fence was offset right laterally about 6 feet at the break, but as it was also bent near the break the total offset was 13 feet. A large water main in this area was ruptured during the 1906 earthquake, thereby contributing to the water shortage during the great San Francisco fire.

6.1 Intersection of Berkshire Drive and College Drive with Skyline Boulevard. Fault is just to left of highway.

Highway crosses 1906 trace of San Andreas fault at or just south of intersection with San Bruno Avenue.

6.8 *Stop 1.* View of San Andreas Lake and the valley along the San Andreas fault zone. At intersection of Skyline Boulevard and Sneath Lane, turn right on Sneath Lane 1 block to Monterey Drive, left on Monterey Drive 6 blocks to Lake Drive, and left on Lake Drive to cul-de-sac at the end of the street. Park and walk about 200 yards along narrow road leading to water tanks for best view of fault zone. Return to intersection of Skyline Boulevard and Sneath Lane and proceed south (right) on Skyline. (Approximate 1.4-mile side trip is not included in road log mileage.)

7.7 View of San Andreas Lake (photo 3), one of the principal reservoirs for San Francisco, west (right) of the highway.

10.4 *Alternate Stop 1A.* View of valley along San Andreas fault zone from dam at south end of San Andreas Lake (photo 4). Crystal Springs Reservoir can be seen to the southeast along the fault zone. At intersection of Skyline Boulevard and Millbrae Avenue-Sawyer Camp Road turn right on Sawyer Camp Road about 1 mile to west end of San Andreas Lake dam. Park and walk to middle of dam for views northwest and southeast along the valley of the fault zone. Return to Skyline Boulevard and proceed south (right) on Skyline. (Approximate 2-mile side trip is not included in road-log mileage.)

11.3 Volcanic rocks (greenstone) of the Franciscan Formation of Jurassic and Cretaceous age exposed along highway.

14.1 Intersection with Black Mountain Road. Skyline Boulevard extends along Buri Buri Ridge; note Pleistocene erosion surface forming crest of ridge.

15.3 View of Crystal Springs Reservoir (photo 5) and the valley along the San Andreas fault zone. The 1906 trace was approximately along the center of the lake. Most of the water in the lake comes from the Hetch Hetchy Reservoir north of Yosemite Valley in the Sierra Nevada.

Sheared serpentine and tectonic inclusions of the Franciscan Formation on east (left) side of highway.

15.8 Vista Point. Another view of Crystal Springs Reservoir.

15.9 Skyline Boulevard crosses Crystal Springs Dam which, when completed in 1888, was one of the largest concrete dams in the world. Although the 1906 trace of the San Andreas fault is about 1,000 feet west of the dam, the dam itself was not damaged by the 1906 earthquake.

16.5 Serpentine in roadcuts.

16.8 View of abandoned limestone quarry in the Calera Limestone Member of the Franciscan Formation on southwest side of Crystal Springs Reservoir. The nearest outcrops of the Calera Limestone Member on the northeast side of the fault are at Black Mountain, about 16 miles to the southeast.

17.5 Intersection with Ralston Avenue. The causeway across Crystal Springs Reservoir to the southwest (right) was offset about 8 feet during the 1906 earthquake (photo 6). A good view

Photo 3. Aerial view showing San Andreas Lake and Crystal Springs Reservoir which lie in the San Andreas fault trough. Line is approximate trace of 1906 break. Arrow indicates view point. Looking southeast.

Photo 4. Aerial view of San Andreas Lake. Line is approximate trace of 1906 break. Looking northwest.

Photo 5. Aerial view of Crystal Springs Reservoir. Line is approximate trace of 1906 break. Pulgas Temple is at outlet of pipelines bringing water from Sierra Nevada. Looking northwest.

Photo 6. Causeway over Crystal Springs Reservoir offset during 1906 earthquake. ***Photograph courtesy of Branner Library, Stanford University.***

of the valley along the San Andreas fault can be obtained from center of causeway, but parking and access problems are formidable. Turn east (left) on Ralston Road toward Belmont.

17.8 Serpentine in roadcuts.

18.5 Intersection with Cañada Road. Continue on Ralston Road.

19.3 Sheared rocks of the Franciscan Formation along road.

20.5 Intersection with El Camino Real. Continue on Ralston.

22.9 Enter Bayshore Freeway (U.S. 101) and proceed south toward San Jose.

24.9 View of piles of salt east (left) of highway. Salt is produced by solar evaporation of bay water in shallow ponds along the margins of southern San Francisco Bay. From the air the evaporating ponds are easily recognized by their red and green colorations caused by algae.

Farther to the east, beyond the salt piles, the Ideal Cement Company produces cement from oyster shells and mud dredged from San Francisco Bay.

31.5 Willow Road Overpass.

39.2 Moffett Field (U.S. Naval Air Station) on left. Large buildings here were formerly used as dirigible hangers.

Ground in this area has subsided more than 6 feet since 1912. The subsidence is apparently caused by withdrawal of ground water.

48.1 View of Diablo Range to east (left ahead). Mountains are composed mostly of folded sedimentary rocks of Jurassic, Cretaceous, and Tertiary age.

The active Hayward fault, which was associated with severe earthquakes and extensive damage in 1836 and 1868, is along the base of the mountains.

49.2 Intersection with Interstate 280 (Highway 17). Turn right toward Santa Cruz and Los Gatos.

57.8 Percolation ponds west (right) of highway. Since July 1965 water from the delta region of the Sacramento River has been brought to the Santa Clara Valley via the State's South Bay Aqueduct. Much of this water is percolated directly into the valley alluvium for storage. Santa Cruz Mountains straight ahead.

60.4 Vasona Dam. Another larger percolation facility now also used for recreational purposes.

62.6 Sheared rocks of the Franciscan Formation on west (right) side of highway.

63.6 Lexington Dam and reservoir on east (left) side of highway. This dam and others like it in the mountains nearby were built by the Santa Clara Valley Water Conservation District to impound water which would otherwise be lost by runoff

Photo 7. View of San Andreas fault at Pajaro Gap near Chittenden. Tertiary shale (right), Cretaceous quartz diorite (left). The fault exposure was recently covered by a landslide. Looking north. *Photograph by J. B. Macelwane, 1923, reprinted by permission Prentice-Hall, Inc.*

after heavy rains. The water is released slowly and spread in percolation ponds in the valley to recharge a formerly rapidly sinking water table.

65.6 *Stop 2.* Entrance to Alma College, on the San Andreas fault zone. The fault is not obvious at this locality and is not marked by a distinct valley like the one at Crystal Springs Reservoir. Highly contorted Tertiary rocks in the fault zone can be seen between the entrance to Alma College and the highway bridge across Aldercroft Creek. About 3½ miles southeast of this locality, near Wrights Station, right-lateral movement along the 1906 trace of the San Andreas fault offset a railway tunnel about 5 feet.

67.1 Site of Moody Gulch Oil Field, one of the oldest oil fields in California. About 125,000 barrels of oil were produced from the San Lorenzo Formation of late Eocene and Oligocene age before the field was abandoned in the late 1930's. The highway now goes across the field.

69.3 Intersection with Summit Road. The site of the Morrell Ranch is about 2.7 miles southeast along Summit Road, approximately 1,500 feet west-northwest of Loma Prieta School. The Morrell ranch house was torn in half in 1906 by left-lateral movement, possibly along the Butano fault, a subsidiary of the San Andreas fault. The Butano fault extends approximately to the intersection of Highway 17 and Summit Road and brings Butano Sandstone of late Eocene age to the southwest against Vaqueros Sandstone of Zemorrian age to the northeast. The Zemorrian Stage is considered Oligocene by some geologists and early Miocene by others.

70.5 Possible stop for view of Ben Lomond Mountain from parking lot of restaurant west (left) of highway.

71.2 Inspiration Point. Outcrops of San Lorenzo Formation of late Eocene and Oligocene age along highway.

71.9 Vaqueros Sandstone along highway. An abandoned railroad tunnel, extending 1.1 miles from Glenwood to Laurel, underlies the highway.

72.7 Purisima Formation of Pliocene age exposed along highway.

74.0 Crossing the Zayante fault, which at this locality has brought an unnamed shale of Miocene age against the Butano Sandstone of late Eocene age.

77.2 Scotts Valley area. The prominent white sandstone exposed in quarries and on hills near the highway is the Santa Margarita Sandstone, which at this locality is of Clarendonian (late Miocene

Photo 8. Walls of Mission San Juan Bautista damaged during 1906 earthquake. *Photograph from Harry Downie collection.*

Photo 9. Aerial view northwest along fault. Mission San Juan Bautista in foreground (arrow). Line is approximate trace of fault.

and/or early Pliocene) age. The sandstone is probably a deltaic deposit and contains a curious mixture of marine and terrestrial fossils including remains of camels, horses, sharks, sea cows, marine birds, whales, porpoises, desmostylids, sea lions, sand dollars, snails, and clams.

80.6 Santa Margarita Sandstone resting on quartz diorite can be seen on east (left) side of highway near base of roadcut.

83.2 Take exit ramp toward Watsonville. Proceed south on State Highway 1.

90.2 Turn right toward Sea Cliff State Park. View of Pacific Ocean. Fossiliferous Purisima Formation (Pliocene) was used to make walls around lunch pavilion.

90.9 *Stop 3.* Seacliff State Beach provides a convenient place to stop for lunch.

91.3 Return to State Highway 1 and turn south (right) toward Watsonville.

93.6 Pleistocene terrace deposits along highway.

96.3 Aromas Red Sands of Allen (1946). The sands are thought to be of Pleistocene age.

103.0 Watsonville. Turn east (left) on Bridge Road. Proceed eastward along valley of Pajaro River, an area noted for apple orchards and truck gardens.

106.5 Johnson Corner. San Andreas fault cuts across hills about 2 miles northeast of Riverside Road. The trace is marked by a line of sag ponds and offset streams.

109.0 Entrance to Chittenden Pass. Along north (left) side of road, fossiliferous sandstone of Pliocene age rests unconformably on shale that is possibly of Oligocene age.

111.5 Quartz diorite in cuts to north (left) and in Logan Quarry to east (right).

111.9 *Stop 4.* Pajaro Gap. One of the few localities in northern California where the surface of the San Andreas fault, now covered by slides, was formerly clearly exposed (photo 7). Marine shale of Oligocene age, presumably resting on a "basement" of Franciscan Formation of Jurassic and Cretaceous age, is seen on the northeastern side of the San Andreas fault; quartz diorite, presumably of mid-Cretaceous age, overlapped by sedimentary rocks of Pliocene age, is exposed on the southwestern side. Landslides recently covered the contact.

Pajaro Gap is in the center of one of the most seismically active regions in the conterminous United States.

Movement along the San Andreas fault in 1906 displaced the railroad bridge across the Pajaro River. The westernmost pier and abutment were moved laterally about 3½ feet and the east abutment moved about 1½ inches with respect to the bridge span. The fault evidently passes directly beneath the bridge.

112.8 Village of Chittenden. The following account by G. A. Waring on the effects of the 1906 earthquake in Chittenden is from the report of the California Earthquake Commission:

> "At Chittenden Station evidence of a most violent disturbance was found. The cottage of the foreman was moved 5 inches westward; an upright piano was thrown northwestward upon its back, and electric drop-lights swung so as to break against the ceiling. A large frame dairy building on underpinning was moved 3 feet northward, as was a smaller building. The oil in a large tank was thrown southeastward, badly bending the tank and smashing the protecting shed. The railroad office was not moved from its foundations, but the porch roof was jerked nearly off and a 1,000-pound safe was thrown southeastward upon its back. Three freight cars on the side-track, loaded with beans, were tipt over to the northeastward. At the time of the shock a northbound freight train was running at about 30 miles an hour, a short distance south of the bridge over the Pajaro. About 10 cars in the middle of the train were thrown off on both sides of the track. The track at the southern end of the Pajaro bridge sank from 2 to 4 feet for a distance of 150 yards, and between Chittenden and the bridge the track was bent in an S-shaped curve in several places. The concrete piers of the bridge were cracked, and the granite cappings shifted as before noticed. There is much sulfur, oil, gas, and water in the hills here. A marked increase was noted in the flow of oil and water, and more gas and sulfur became associated with them."

113.5 Soda lake north (left) of highway is along an abandoned meander and terrace of the Pajaro River.

114.1 Highway bridge across Pajaro River was extensively damaged during earthquake of 1906 and was slightly damaged during earthquake of September 14, 1963.

114.5 Turn south (right) on School Road.

115.2 View of valley of Pajaro River looking north toward Pajaro Gap.

115.5 Turn west (right) on Forest Road. Cross main trace of San Andreas fault. No distinctive topographic features reveal the presence of the fault at this locality.

116.0 Turn southeast (left) on Anzar Road.

116.1 Anzar Lake, a sag pond along a subsidiary fault of the San Andreas. Mr. Anzar reportedly stated that during the 1906 earthquake water drained from this lake into a fissure.

117.0 Quartz diorite in quarry on south (right) side of road.

117.5 Intersection with Cannon Road. Cross trace of San Andreas fault. The fault is nearly parallel to Anzar Road. A fence somewhere in this area was offset 3½ feet during the 1906 earthquake.

118.5 Cross U.S. 101 and continue on Anzar Road.

119.6 Turn south (right) on San Juan Highway.

Photo 10. Aerial view of fault trace where it passes under Almaden winery south of Hollister. Line is approximate trace of fault. Looking northwest.

121.1 Intersection with Prescott Road. Cross 1906 trace of San Andreas fault. Surface rupture along the fault in 1906 had its southern end in the field a short distance southeast of this locality. From there the surface rupture extended northwestward to Point Arena and beyond under the ocean—a distance of at least 190 miles.

122.0 Turn southeast (left) on Monterey Street.

122.4 *Stop 5.* Mission San Juan Bautista, named for John the Baptist. The first church on this site, completed in 1798, was extensively damaged by earthquakes. The present structure was completed in 1812. It was intended to be the first California mission with three aisles, but the builders, fearful of earthquake damage, filled in the vaulted passages leading to the outer aisles before the church was finished. During the 1906 earthquake, parts of the outer walls of the mission collapsed (photo 8). Concrete buttresses and other supports were added to the remaining structure, but the broken walls were not restored and can still be seen.

The grandstand east of the mission is built on a scarp (photo 9) that apparently was formed by movement along the San Andreas fault prior to 1798.

Return to Third Street (San Juan Highway) and continue south toward Hollister.

122.8 Turn east (left) on California Highway 156.

123.1 Ideal Cement Plant on south (right) side of highway utilizes as raw materials Sur Series marble, weathered granite and schist, and clay shale hauled in from Chittenden.

127.4 Turn south (right) on Union Road. Continental deposits of Pliocene age are exposed along road.

130.5 Keep right on Union Road.

131.5 Turn southeast (right) on Cienega Road.

133.1 Turn southwest (right). Keep on Cienega Road. Continental silt and sand of Pliocene age along road.

135.6 Marine sandstone and shale of Pliocene age.

136.4 View of brush-covered slopes of the Gabilan Range to the southeast. The San Andreas fault extends along the valley at the base of the slopes.

137.4 Harris Ranch. Site of University of California seismic research station. Cienega Road is along San Andreas fault zone.

139.4 Sag pond to northeast (left). Offset trees, small scarp and springs can be seen along southwest (right) side of road.

139.7 *Stop 6.* Almaden winery (photo 10).

HYDROGEOLOGY FIELD TRIP
EAST BAY AREA AND NORTHERN SANTA CLARA VALLEY

By S. N. Davis
Stanford University, Stanford, California

SAN FRANCISCO—UNIVERSITY OF CALIFORNIA ENGINEERING FIELD STATION—ALAMEDA CREEK ALLUVIAL FAN—NILES CANYON—SUNOL VALLEY—MISSION SAN JOSÉ—U.S.G.S. SUBSIDENCE RECORDER IN SAN JOSE—GUADALUPE-LOS ALAMITOS RECHARGE BASINS

Introduction

Most of the water used in the San Francisco Bay area comes from surface streams, and to satisfy the requirements of the metropolitan area much of this surface water must be imported from streams in the Sierra Nevada. Local ground water, nevertheless, still forms an important supplementary supply, particularly in Colma, Fremont, San Jose, Santa Clara, and surrounding suburban and rural areas. The lower cost of ground water has been its main advantage. Declining water levels in wells and the superior chemical quality of the imported water, however, have caused a relative decrease in the importance of ground water during the past 40 years.

The purpose of the hydrogeology trip is to obtain in a brief period an understanding of the ground-water geology of the area adjacent to the southern part of the San Francisco Bay (fig. 1). Although the area is fairly restricted in geographic extent, it presents a wide variety of special problems. Some of these are declining ground-water levels, land subsidence, sea-water intrusion, correlation of aquifers and aquicludes, location and design of recharge basins, and the barrier effects of active faults. All field-trip stops described in the road log are on private land, and permission for access for all except the Sunol stop should be obtained before going on the properties.

Aquifer materials in the region surrounding the San Francisco Bay include limestone, sandstone, fractured shale, basalt, serpentine, and alluvium. From the standpoint of both areal extent and total production, the alluvium is much more important than any of the other aquifer types. The alluvial aquifers are mostly irregular beds or lenses of gravel which are, in certain localities, permeable enough to yield more than 3,000 gallons per minute to wells. In contrast, the indurated aquifers rarely yield to wells more than 5 gallons per minute. These low-yield wells, nevertheless, have an importance far out of proportion with their production because they allow the development of otherwise useless land for livestock grazing and, in recent years, for country estates.

The distribution of major geologic units is controlled primarily by numerous faults and folds, most of which trend in a north-northwesterly direction (fig. 1). Although only lateral movement has been observed along the well-known San Andreas and Hayward faults during the past 70 years, offset beds and steep mountain fronts suggest that vertical movement along these and other major faults has been very important in forming San Francisco Bay and associated alluvial valleys.

The history of deposition within the alluvial valleys has been complicated by almost constant tectonic

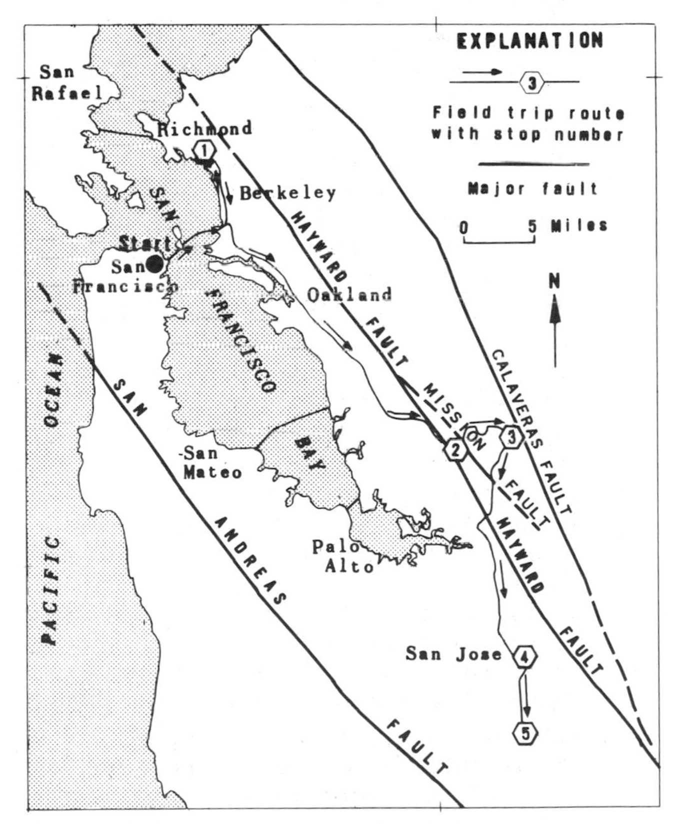

Figure 1. Map of southern San Francisco Bay area showing route of trip and location of major faults. Stops in road log indicated by numbers in hexagons.

activity superimposed on the effects of a fluctuating sea level. Evidence from stable coastal regions in other parts of the world indicates that the sea level has been as much as 100 feet higher and 300 feet lower than present levels, all within the past 150,000 years. Widespread gray clay, commonly called "blue clay" by well drillers, may indicate former marine deposits within alluvium adjacent to the present San Francisco Bay. Some of these clays may also be deltaic or lacustrine. Most wells near the present shoreline, however, appear to encounter alluvial silts, sands, and gravels, with less than half of the deposits having a possible marine or lagoonal origin. Inland from the shore the deposits appear to be mostly alluvial, with less than 10 percent gray clay in the deposits penetrated by wells along the basal slopes of the mountains.

REFERENCES

California Department of Public Works, Division of Water Resources, 1955, Geology, App. H of Water Project Authority of the State of California, report on feasibility of construction by the state of barriers in the San Francisco Bay system: Sacramento, Calif., 62 p.

California Department of Water Resources, Division of Resources Planning, 1960, Intrusion of salt water into ground water basins of southern Alameda County: California Dept. Water Resources Div. Resources Plan. Bull. 81, [64] p.

California State Water Resources Board, 1955, Santa Clara Valley investigation: California State Water Resources Board Bull., no. 7, 154 p.

Clark, W. O., 1924, Ground water in the Santa Clara Valley, California: U.S. Geol. Survey Water-Supply Paper 519, 209 p.

Hall, C. A., Jr., 1958, Geology and paleontology of the Pleasanton area, Alameda and Contra Costa Counties, California: California Univ., Dept. Geol. Sci. Bull., v. 34, no. 1, p. 1–90.

Matthai, H. F., Back, William, Orth, R. P., and Brennan, Robert, 1957, Water resources of the San Francisco Bay area, California: U.S. Geol. Survey Circ. 378, 55 p.

Poland, J. F., and Green, J. H., 1962, Subsidence in the Santa Clara Valley, California—a progress report: U.S. Geol. Survey Water-Supply Paper 1619-C, p. C1–C16.

Sanitary Engineering Research Laboratory, California Univ., Berkeley, 1954, Report on the investigation of travel of pollution: California State Water Pollution Control Board Pub. 11, 218 p.

Spring Valley Water Company, 1912, The future water supply of San Francisco: San Francisco, Calif., Rincon Pub. Co., for private distribution by the Spring Valley Water Co., 506 p.

Tolman, C. F., and Poland, J. F., 1940, Ground-water, salt-water infiltration, and ground-surface recession in Santa Clara Valley, Santa Clara County, California: Am. Geophys. Union Trans., pt. 1, p. 23–35.

Zohdy, A. A. R., 1965, Geoelectrical and seismic refraction investigations near San Jose, California: Ground Water, v. 3, no. 3, p. 41–48.

ROAD LOG

Mileage

00.0 *Onramp to west end of San Francisco-Oakland Bay Bridge.* (Interstate 80)

The western span of this bridge has its pier foundations on the highly indurated rocks of the Franciscan Formation, which are here chiefly graywacke. Recent and Pleistocene sands, silts, and clays overlying the Franciscan reach a maximum thickness of about 120 feet near the San Francisco side of the span. Water depth is generally between 80 and 110 feet beneath the western span.

02.2 Yerba Buena Island. This small island is composed entirely of Franciscan shale and sandstone (graywacke). Treasure Island, just to the north, is an artificial island constructed originally for the Golden Gate International Exposition in 1939.

02.5 The eastern segment of the bridge passes over Recent and Pleistocene sediments that have a combined thickness of more than 300 feet. Water depth, however, is only 10 to 20 feet through most of the distance to the eastern terminus of the bridge. Pier foundations for the bridge east of the island are within the compact Pleistocene sediments below the soft bay mud.

05.4 Toll plaza. Compaction and displacement of soft bay muds has caused continuing problems with settlement, particularly around the plaza buildings. Early subsidence was most rapid, being about 9 feet between 1935 and 1950.

06.3 Turn north-northeast (left) on Eastshore Freeway (Interstate Highway 80 to Sacramento).

10.7 Turn north (left) on Hoffman Boulevard (State Highway 17 to Richmond-San Rafael Bridge). El Cerrito, the hill east of the highway, is underlain by Franciscan sandstone. For many years a quarry was operated on the west side of the hill.

13.2 Turn southwest (left) on South 47th Street.

13.3 Turn north (right) into the University of California Engineering Field Station.

Stop 1. The Engineering Field Station was established after World War II as a locality where researchers in various branches of engineering could conduct projects that required more space than was available on the Berkeley campus. An extensive well field, constructed in 1951 and 1952, has served for numerous experiments in the study of subsurface travel of biological, chemical, and radiochemical contaminants.

The well field consists of about 26 observation wells distributed around a central pumped well. Most of the observation wells are 6 inches in diameter and are within 100 feet of the pumped well, although the most distant is 500 feet to the south. The pumped well is a 12-inch, gravel-packed well which has been grouted from the surface to a depth of 88 feet. This central well and the observation wells penetrate an aquifer of fine gravel and sand at an average depth of 95 feet. The aquifer ranges in thickness from 3 to 7 feet. Test results indicate a transmissivity of about 2,000 gals/day foot and a storage coefficient of roughly 2.5×10^{-4} (fig. 2).

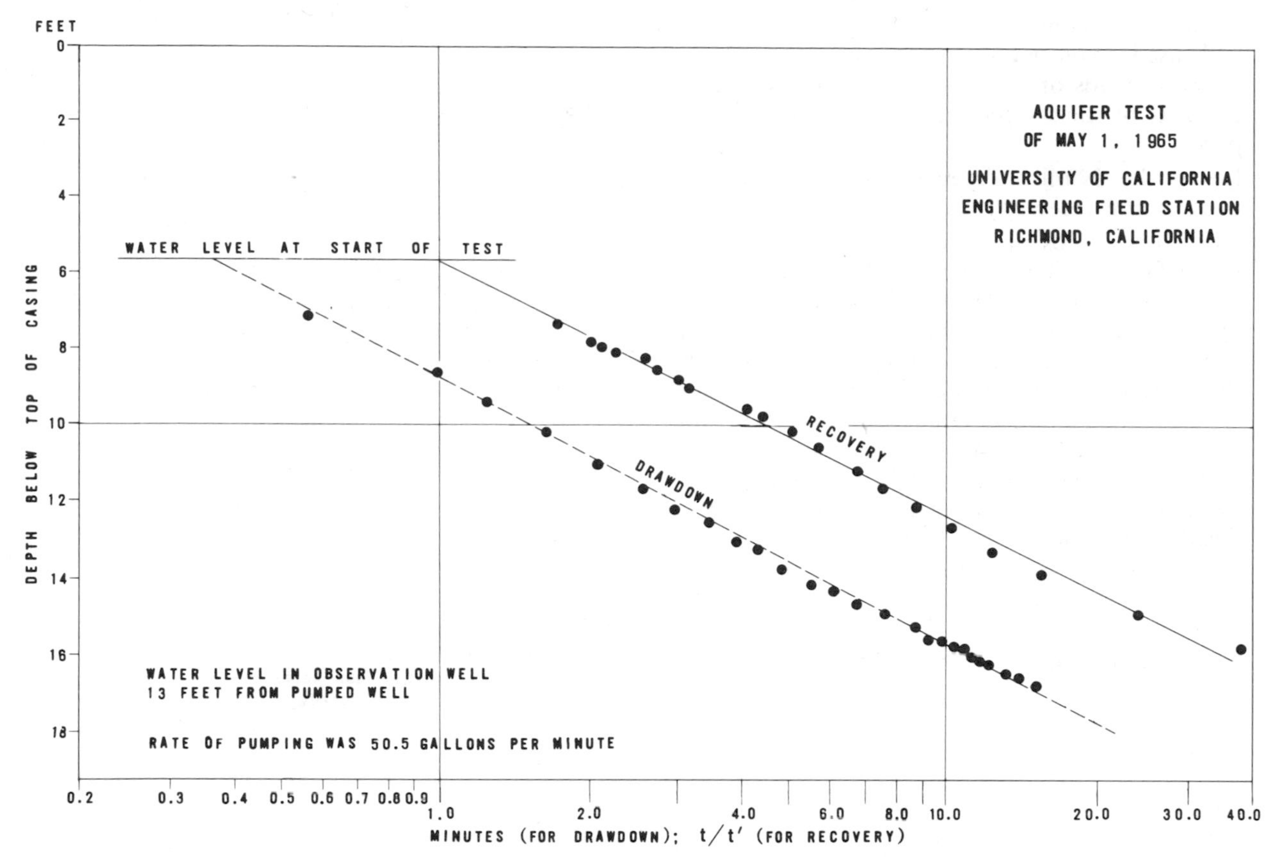

Figure. 2. Drawdown and recovery of pumped well at Richmond Field Station.

The aquifer is overlain by a continuous clay layer that ranges in thickness from 20 to 45 feet. A second aquifer, about 4 feet thick, is found at a depth of about 30 feet, but it is not connected with the test wells.

Both discharge and recharge tests have been made through the central well. In one series of tests sewage was injected at a rate of 37 gallons per minute. Even though the sewage had been allowed to settle and was screened, the well had to be redeveloped once a week to maintain the recharge rate. The water from the sewage traveled a total distance of more than 225 feet. Micro-organisms, however, were not found in wells beyond 100 feet down the hydraulic gradient or beyond 63 feet in other directions. Initial coliform concentrations in the sewage were roughly 2.4 x 10^6 per 100 ml, which was reduced to only 23 per 100 ml after the water traveled 100 feet downgradient.

13.5 Return to Hoffman Boulevard and retrace route southward via Eastshore Freeway.

19.9 Intersection with Bay Bridge approach. Continue south on C. W. Nimitz Freeway (State Highway 17).

The Merritt Formation of Pleistocene age is at the surface in this part of Oakland. Most of the formation is well-sorted sand and silt with the coarser material having eolianlike crossbedding.

23.2 Downtown Oakland to the east (left) and Oakland Inner Harbor to the west (right). Continue south on the Nimitz Freeway.

Recent and upper Pleistocene tidal flat deposits and artificial fill are at the surface for the next 6 miles. The fine-grained materials extend to the west under the water of the San Francisco Bay and serve to retard, and in some places prevent, the intrusion of saline bay water into the shallow aquifers.

27.6 Area office of the East Bay Municipal Utilities District west (right) of the freeway. The East Bay Municipal Utilities District is one of the organizations in the San Francisco Bay area which imports water for local distribution. This publicly owned system purchased local water companies in 1928 and soon thereafter had water delivered to the area from the Mokelumne River in the Sierra Nevada. Although the East Bay Municipal Utilities District services Richmond, Berkeley, Oakland, San Leandro, and many smaller communities, ground-water supplies are still used extensively for large industries. In general, yields of wells are greater in the southern part of the service area than in the northern part.

41.0 Leave the Nimitz Freeway and proceed east (left of the freeway) on Whipple Avenue.

The road climbs up the gentle slope of the alluvial fan of Alameda Creek. This fan is sometimes called the "Niles alluvial cone" after the old town of Niles that once stood at its apex. Low hills visible south (right) of the road in the near distance are the Coyote Hills, which are part of an elongate fault block that protrudes from the alluvium. The hills are composed of a variety of rocks of the Franciscan Formation, some of which are highly fractured and partly weathered. These make ideal land-fill material for construction on the soft bay muds, and quarrying has removed a large part of the southern section of the hills. Inasmuch as the hills form a local barrier to the movement of ground water within the Cenozoic aquifers, they are also important hydrogeologic features.

44.0 Turn south (right) on State Highway 238.

The steep mountain front to the east is caused by uplift along two prominent faults—the Mission fault and the Hayward fault. Rocks in the higher mountains are mostly Cretaceous conglomerates, sandstones, and shale, and in the nearby hills, they include intrusive Cretaceous rocks as well as extrusive rhyolite of possible Pliocene age.

The Hayward fault is about 400 feet east of the highway and parallel with the base of the mountains. Movement at the surface occurred along this part of the fault during the strong earthquakes of 1836 and 1868, and there is evidence that slow creep is taking place along it now. The Mission fault, about 1,500 feet east of the highway, has not been observed to be active within historical time.

46.5 Turn southwest (right) onto Nursery Road.

47.0 Turn into gravel-pit area. Access roads within this area are not fixed, so one should inquire about the best route when obtaining permission to enter.

Stop 2. Recharge operations have been conducted here for a number of years using Alameda Creek water which is discharged into the abandoned gravel pits. Walls of the pits expose typical coarse-grained sediments found in the apex area of the Alameda Creek alluvial fan. In the more distal parts of the fan the gravel is interstratified with finer grained sediments, which act as confining and partially confining beds. Initially, water levels in the wells within this region sloped toward the bay. By 1913

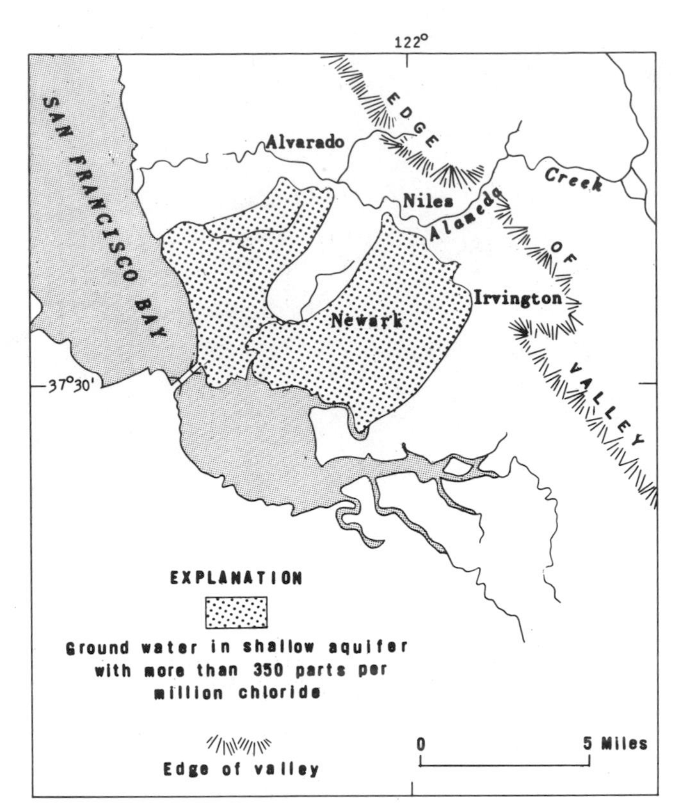

Figure 3. Map of a part of southern Alameda County showing extent of saline-water intrusion in 1958. *California Dept. Water Resources Div. Resources Plan, Bull. 81, 1960.*

water levels in many of the wells were below sea level, and by 1924 the intrusion of water from the bay became evident in the uppermost aquifer. By 1958 intrusion of saline water had advanced more than 4½ miles inland (fig. 3). Degradation of water quality in the upper aquifer forced water users to drill to a lower aquifer, locally called the "200-foot" aquifer. Subsequent pumping has reduced the head in the lower aquifer, and this in turn has induced a downward migration of saline water through abandoned wells and stratigraphic breaks in the confining layers (fig. 4).

The influence of the Hayward fault on ground-water migration in this area is of particular interest. As early as 1915 it was realized that the fault created a subsurface barrier which at that time produced a discontinuity in the water levels of the upper aquifer of as much as 25 feet. This barrier has been exposed from time to time in various excavations in the Niles area, where it appears as a crushed band which is more indurated than the surrounding sediments.

48.4 Turn southwest (right) on State Highway 238 after returning from the gravel pits.

50.2 Turn northeast (left) on State Highway 84.

Bridge about 400 feet southwest of the intersection crosses over Alameda Creek. At this

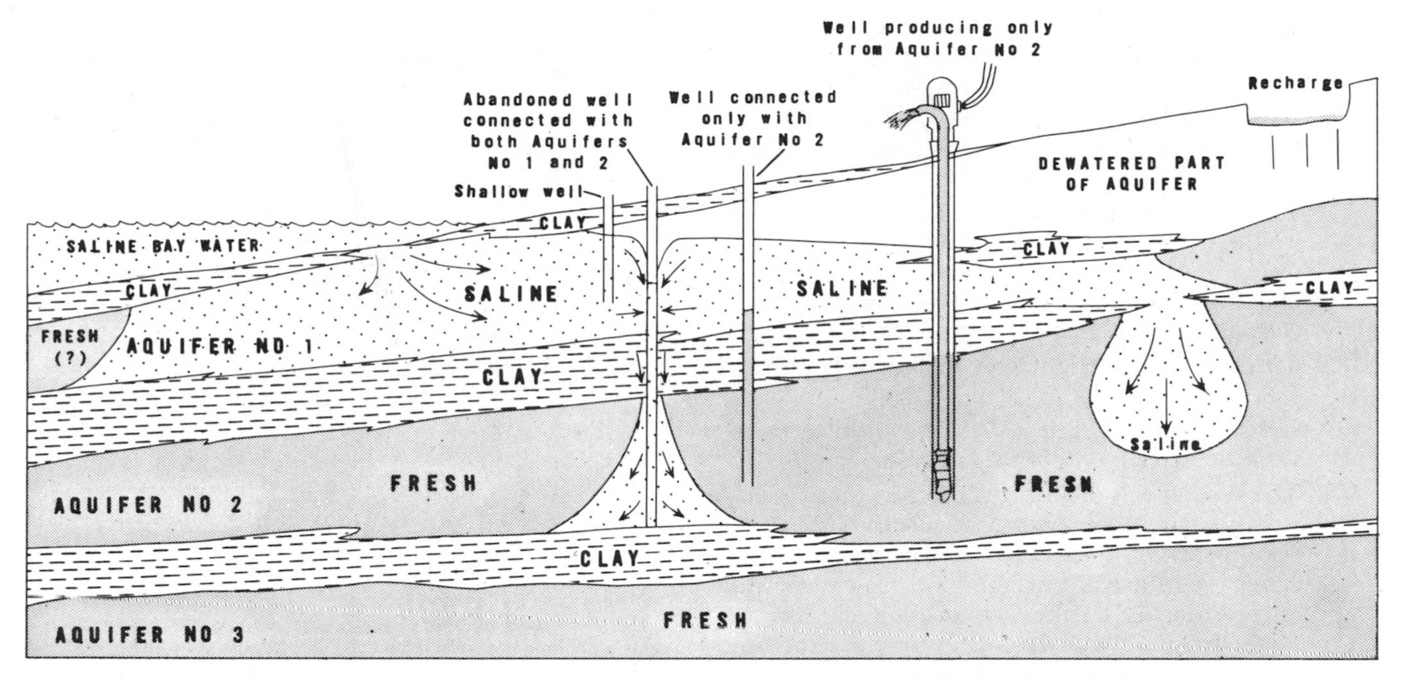

Figure 4. Schematic cross section showing probable migration of saline water in southern Alameda County, California.

point the channel is quite wide and serves as part of the recharge system for the underlying aquifers.

50.9 Note well-developed terraces east of the creek. The highest terraces are about 80 feet above flood level. The canyon ahead is known as Niles Canyon, and the road will follow this canyon for about 5 miles. All the outcrops exposed along the road are Lower Cretaceous sandstone and shale of the Niles Canyon Formation.

51.6 Railroad underpass.

A small landslide mass is exposed in the roadcut just beyond the underpass. In this area almost continuous highway maintenance is necessary to remove small rockfalls originating from the unstable hillside.

Although Alameda Creek is normally a very small stream, its extensive drainage basin to the west can contribute large amounts of runoff during winter storms. During the severe storms of the winter of 1955 the highway in this section was flooded.

53.6 Old concrete water conduit along the highway carries water from the Sunol area to reservoirs of the San Francisco Water Department on the San Francisco Peninsula.

The canyon is about 1,200 feet deep at this point. The steepness of the canyon walls, the recency of orogenic movements, and the presence of lower passes to the sea all strongly suggest that Alameda Creek has maintained its ancient course across the slowly rising Mount Hamilton Range.

54.9 Shale deposit is being developed north (left) of the highway. The shale will be expanded by heating and will be used for lightweight concrete aggregate.

57.0 Turn south (right) through large gateway to the "water temple."

57.6 *Stop 3.* Picnic grounds. The "water temple" is in Sunol Valley, one of many broad but isolated valleys that are typical of the Coast Ranges in California. Most of these valleys owe their origin to Pleistocene folding and faulting. The major fault that passes through Sunol Valley is the Calaveras fault. Because some earthquake centers seem to plot along it, the fault may be active, but it has not shown any surface offset within historic time.

The Sunol infiltration galleries discharge their water into the "water temple," which in turn feeds the water into the cross-bay conduit. The infiltration works were originally designed to filter surface water through the natural gravels. They were completed in 1900, and consist of rectangular concrete tunnels with thousands of 1½-inch pipes driven into the gravel on either side of the tunnels. Most of the water is recovered in the tunnels after winter rains have brought runoff into the adjacent creek. Groundwater levels during the dry part of the year are normally below most of the intake pipes.

The Sunol operation originally included the importation of water from a well field near Pleasanton, 4 miles to the north of Sunol. Since the City of San Francisco purchased the system from the Spring Valley Water Company in 1932, the well field has been gradually abandoned, and in 1965 only a very small amount of water was being pumped for local users.

58.2 Return to the highway and continue southeast (right) on State Highway 21.

The Calaveras fault borders the northeast side of the valley and is about 200 feet northeast (left) of the road. Hills beyond the fault are underlain by upper Pliocene to lower Pleistocene Livermore gravels.

58.9 Turn southwest (right) on Interstate Highway 680.

59.7 Cross Alameda Creek. Well-developed terraces flank the stream on both sides.

60.2 The road at this point starts to cross the Mission Pass syncline. The lower Cretaceous Niles Canyon Formation forms the outer part of the syncline, and Miocene sandstone and shale that rests unconformably on the Cretaceous rock fills the axial part. Poor exposures prevent the structure from being seen from the highway.

62.2 The road crosses the Vargas anticline at this point. The poorly exposed rocks along the road are Miocene sandstone and shale.

63.5 Cross the Mission fault.

63.6 Turn southeast (left) on State Highway 238.

64.2 Mission San José founded in 1797 by Padre Lasuen. This was one of the largest and most successful of the California missions founded by the Spanish padres.

The Irvington gravel pits, about 2 miles east of the mission, have yielded a rich vertebrate fauna of early to middle Pleistocene age.

65.1 Pleistocene silt, sand, and gravel exposed in roadcuts.

67.2 Cross Hayward fault.

68.6 Turn south (left) on Interstate Highway 680.

76.2 Turn southeast (to downtown San Jose) onto First Street, and continue southeast through the center of the city.

78.8 Turn northeast (left) on East Reed Street.

79.6 Turn southeast (right) on 12th Street.

80.0 *Stop 4.* Subsidence recorder of the U.S. Geological Survey at the San Jose Water Works pumping station near the intersection of Martha and 12th Streets.

The compaction-recorder installation is in the central part of the subsidence area in the Santa Clara Valley (fig. 5), and has been operating since May 1960. It was installed by the U.S. Geological Survey in an unused municipal well 907 feet deep. A stainless steel cable ⅛-inch in diameter leads from an anchor bench mark at well bottom over sheaves at the land surface and is counterweighted to produce tension. Another

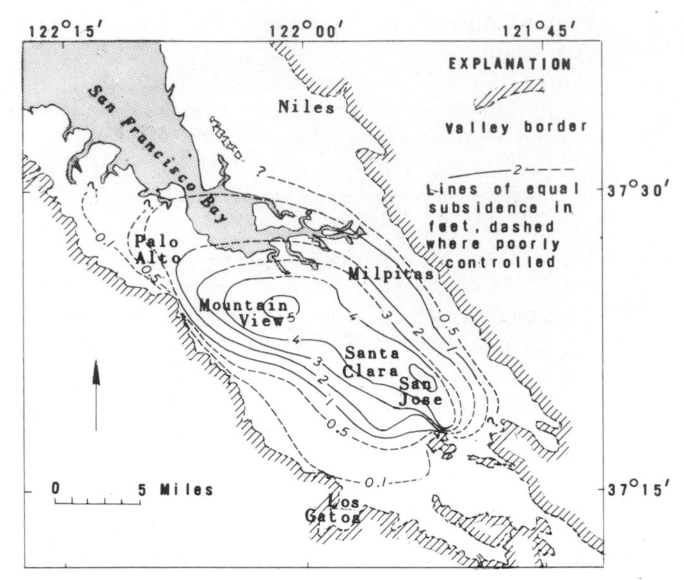

Figure 5. Map of Santa Clara Valley showing lines of equal land subsidence from 1934 to 1960. *Simplified from an unpublished map by J. F. Poland.*

cable firmly fastened to the anchor cable at land surface actuates a recorder to supply a 1:1 continuous record of any change in the distance between the anchor bench mark and the land surface due to compaction of the deposits. A second recorder driven by the first supplies a 24:1 record of compaction. A third recorder furnishes a continuous record of water-level fluctuation in the same well. Figure 6 shows as an example the record of the compaction and water level obtained in September and October 1963.

This well taps several sand and gravel beds (aquifers) separated by beds of silty clay of low permeability. The water in the aquifers is confined and under artesian pressure and wells flowed here initially. About 11 feet of land subsidence and about 250 feet of water-level decline have occurred at this site since 1915.

The compaction recorder shows 2.86 feet of compaction (to 900 feet) from August 1960 to September 1965. The rate of compaction varies in accord with the water-level trend, increasing during the summer drawdown and decreasing during the winter recovery of water levels.

80.0 Continue southeast for two blocks on 12th Street.

80.2 Turn southwest (right) on Keyes Street, continue on Keyes Street to its end, angle right on Graham Street, and angle left on Willow Street. Continue on Willow for only 1½ blocks.

81.1 Turn southeast (left) on Vine Street. Continue on Vine Street until it merges with Almaden Road. Continue south on Almaden Road and Almaden Expressway to 15420 Almaden Road.

87.3 *Stop 5.* Headquarters of the Santa Clara Valley Water Conservation District and the Guadalupe-Los Alamitos recharge basins. The Santa Clara Valley Water Conservation District started operation in 1934 and is the earliest large-scale, ground-water recharge operation in northern California. The Conservation District obtains its recharge water from the South Bay Aqueduct of the State of California and from the storage of local stream water. The total reservoir capacity is 174,400 acre-feet, spread among ten separate reservoirs. Future importation of water through a tunnel near Pacheco Pass is planned for the southern part of the Santa Clara Valley. This water will come from the large Central Valley Project reservoir near Los Banos.

Ground-water recharge here is accomplished through the release of stored water into natural stream beds and into about 12 percolation pond systems. A recent expansion of the percolation pond systems required extensive exploration for areas underlain by permeable gravel. This exploration work has been accomplished by surface resistivity geophysical measurements combined with test drilling.

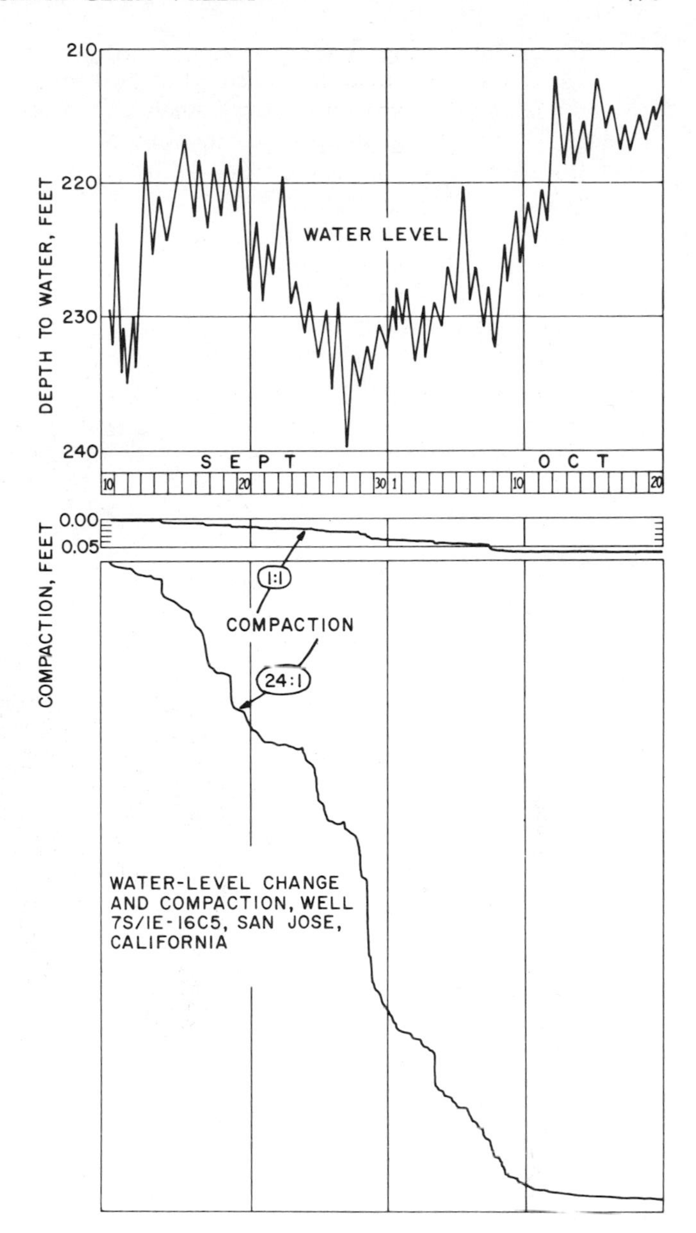

Figure 6 (opposite). Sample of graph from the 12th and Martha Street compaction recorder. *J. F. Poland, unpublished data.*

FIELD TRIP
SACRAMENTO VALLEY AND NORTHERN COAST RANGES

By D. O. Emerson and E. I. Rich
University of California, Davis; U.S. Geological Survey
and Stanford University, Stanford, California

SAN FRANCISCO—OAKLAND—VALLEJO—PUTAH CANYON—LAKE BERRYESSA—CAPAY VALLEY—CACHE CREEK—CLEAR LAKE —SULPHUR BANK MERCURY MINE—MIDDLETOWN— MOUNT ST. HELENA—CALISTOGA—NAPA VALLEY

This trip, which extends through 2 days with an overnight stop in the resort area bordering Clear Lake, provides an opportunity to see typical sedimentary and volcanic rocks of the western Sacramento Valley and northern Coast Ranges, as well as "sedimentary" and intrusive masses of serpentine and an unusually interesting major mercury mine.

On the first day, the trip will cross the Coast Ranges to the Sacramento Valley by way of the depression through which the Sacramento-San Joaquin River flows into San Francisco Bay. It will then go north weaving its way through the hills on the west side of the Sacramento Valley. Then, turning due west, the Coast Ranges are penetrated to Clear Lake, which lies in the midst of a Late Tertiary and Quaternary volcanic field.

The second day will begin with a look at some of the volcanic rocks followed by an examination of the famous Sulphur Bank mercury mine. From the mine the trip heads back through the Coast Ranges to San Francisco, with stops being made to examine serpentine contacts, to see the rocks of the Sonoma Volcanic Series, and to view the Palisades of the Mayacmas Mountains.

Sketch of Geology

The Coast Ranges and western Sacramento Valley in the area extending north from San Francisco to Clear Lake consist chiefly of two very thick sequences of Late Jurassic to Late Cretaceous age, one of which was deposited in a deep eugeosynclinal environment and the other on the continental shelf and slope. The eugeosynclinal assemblage is the Franciscan Formation consisting of graywacke, shale, altered mafic volcanic rock, chert, limestone, and locally metamorphic rocks of the blueschist facies. It is not emphasized in this trip, as other trips, particularly the San Francisco Peninsula trip, provide better opportunities to see these rocks. The shelf and slope facies, which has been called the Great Valley sequence, consists largely of clastic sediments, sandstone, shale, and conglomerate. So far as is known, these two great sequences, though coeval, do not interdigitate, and in many places they are separated by a sheet of serpentine. It has been suggested that the Great Valley sequence has been thrust over the Franciscan and the serpentine was intruded along the fault plane, perhaps aiding the movement by serving as a lubricant. In the area of the trip, these rocks and some accompanying Eocene sediments are broadly folded into a southeastward-plunging antiform, whose axis runs northwestward through Clear Lake. Along the axial areas are Pliocene to Recent volcanic rocks, ranging in composition from basalt to rhyolite. Northwesterly trending faults transect the western part of the area cutting all but the very youngest volcanic rocks. Hydrothermal solutions rising along faults and serpentine contacts have deposited cinnabar in several areas making this one of the main mercury mining regions in the United States.

The first day of the trip is devoted chiefly to viewing the Cretaceous strata of the Great Valley sequence in the exposed steep western limb of the Great Valley syncline. The section here is at least 30,000 feet thick and in outcrop is seemingly conformable from the Upper Jurassic (Tithonian) into the lower Eocene. It is overlapped by the continental Pliocene Tehama Formation that contains a rhyolitic tuff, the Nomlaki Tuff Member, near its base. The Cretaceous part of the Great Valley sequence is notable for its sedimentary structures—groove casts, flute casts, other kinds of sole markings, shale pull-aparts, and large submarine slumps. Fossils are present but are not common.

Of unusual interest are beds of "sedimentary serpentine" that will be seen in the Lower Cretaceous part of the section. Some of these are over 1,000 feet thick, and as they consist almost entirely of shreds and blocks of serpentine, they closely resemble the normal sheared serpentine sills found through much of the Coast Ranges. Others, however, are very thin, some being less than an inch thick, and in places they form dozens of layers alternating with equally thin layers of black Paskenta shale. Locally the "sedimentary serpentine" beds contain lenses of very fossiliferous limestone. This unusual sediment is thought to have formed as a result of serpentine slides descending

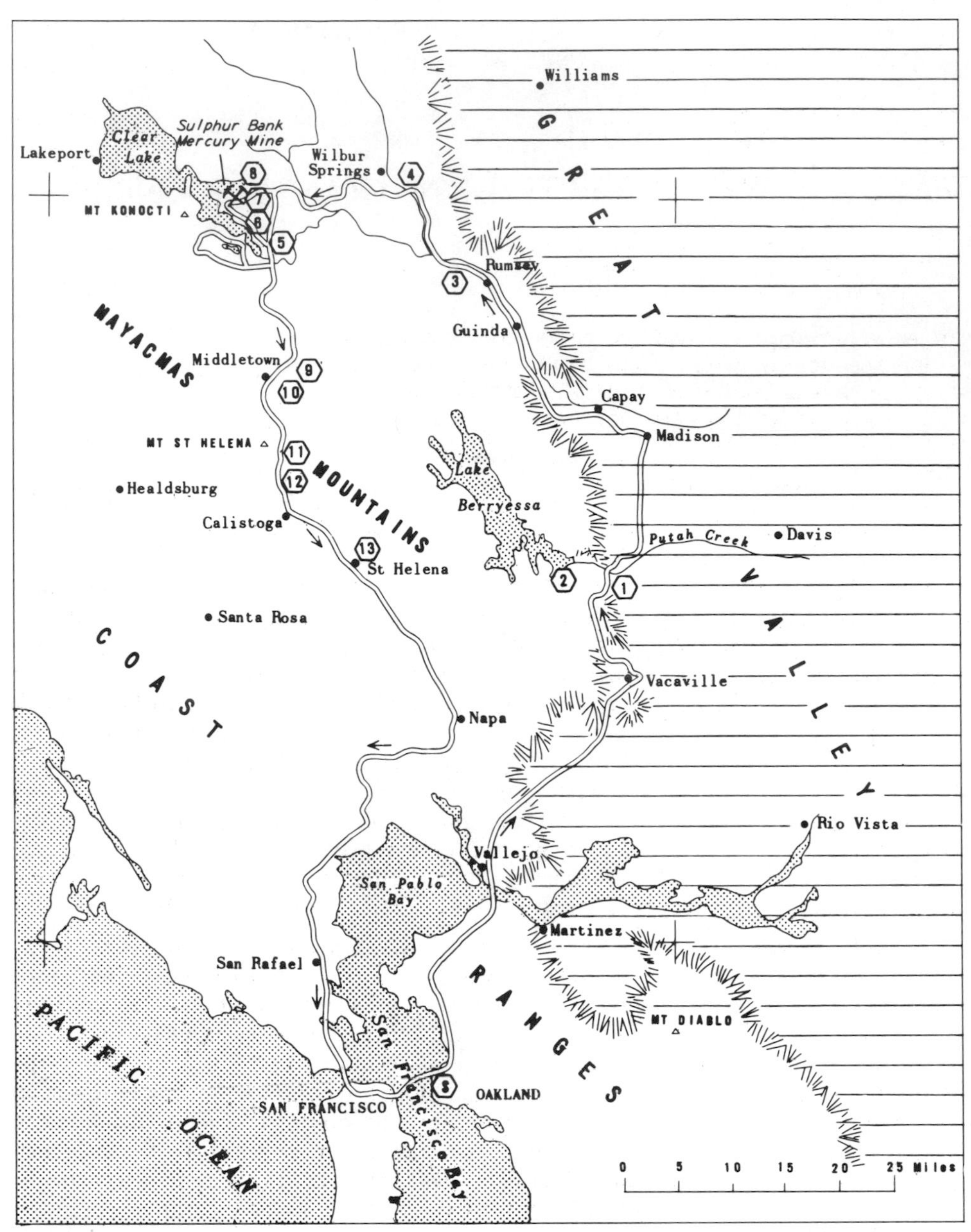

Figure 1. Index map of area between San Francisco and Clear Lake, showing boundary between Coast Ranges and Great Valley and route of field trip. Stops in road log are indicated by numbers in hexagons.

into the seas during the deposition of the Paskenta mudstones.

Volcanic rocks of Pleistocene to Recent age, the Clear Lake Volcanic Series of Brice (1953), are found about the southern half of Clear Lake, and the lake itself results from the outlet being dammed by one of these volcanic flows. The volcanic rocks show great diversity both in composition, which ranges from olivine basalt to rhyolitic obsidian, and in kind of accumulation, which ranges from formless volcanic fields to tableland flows, obsidian domes, and volcanoes so young they still retain their conical shape and central crater depressions. They have been extensively studied by C. A. Anderson (1936) and Brice (1953).

The Sonoma Volcanics, which will be seen extending from a point 15 miles south of Clear Lake essentially to San Francisco Bay, are Pliocene and therefore older than the Clear Lake Volcanic Series. Although they are widespread, they have not yet been adequately studied. Included in the Sonoma Volcanics are basalt flows and breccias, extensive andesitic breccias and tuffs, and rhyolitic tuffs and welded tuffs. In many areas they are prevasively altered either by deep weathering or by hydrothermal solutions perhaps related to those that formed the mercury deposits in the span from Calistoga to Clear Lake.

The trip passes through several mercury districts which are in order: the Wilbur Springs district, where the sedimentary serpentines are seen; the Clear Lake district, where an examination of the Sulphur Bank mine is included in the itinerary; and the Mayacmas district, in the main Mayacmas range crossed between Clear Lake and Calistoga. These districts together have yielded about a fifth of the mercury recovered in the

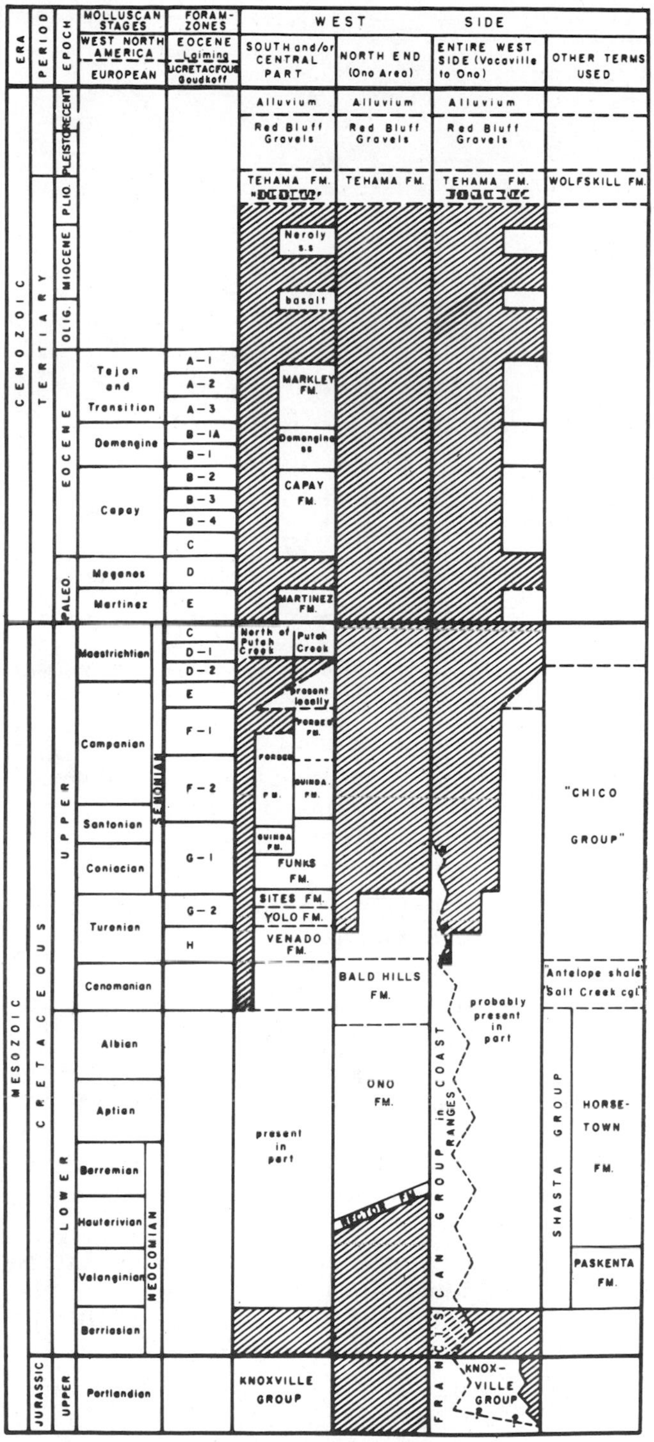

Figure 2. Stratigraphic chart showing units exposed along the west side of the Sacramento Valley. *From Lachenbruch (1962).*

United States. Most of the mercury deposits are in Franciscan rocks or in silica-carbonate rock formed from serpentine. The mineralization, however, is very young, being Pleistocene or Recent in age. At the Sulphur Bank mine, hot waters are now depositing mercury, and at The Geysers in the western part of the Mayacmas district, natural steam is being used for the commercial generation of electricity.

REFERENCES

Anderson, C. A., 1936, Volcanic history of Clear Lake, California: Geol. Soc. America Bull., v. 47, no. 5, p. 629–664.

Anderson, F. M., 1938, Lower Cretaceous deposits in California and Oregon: Geol. Soc. America Spec. Paper 16, 339 p.

—— 1945, Knoxville series in California Mesozoic: Geol. Soc. America Bull., v. 56, no. 10, p. 909–1014.

Bailey, E. H., 1946, Quicksilver deposits of the western Mayacmas district, Sonoma County, California: California Jour. Mines and Geology, v. 42, no. 3, p. 199–240.

Bailey, E. H., Irwin, W. P., and Jones, D. L., 1964, Franciscan and related rocks, and their significance in the geology of western California: California Div. Mines and Geology Bull. 183, 177 p.

Bowen, Oliver, E., ed., 1962, Geologic guide to the gas and oil fields of northern California: California Div. Mines and Geology Bull. 181, 412 p.

Brice, J. C., 1953, Geology of Lower Lake quadrangle, California: California Div. Mines Bull. 166, 72 p.

Erd, R. C., White, D. E., Fahey, J. J., and Lee, D. E., 1964, Buddingtonite, and ammonium feldspar with zeolitic water: Am. Mineralogist, v. 49, nos. 7–8, p. 831–850.

Everhart, D. L., 1946, Quicksilver deposits at the Sulphur Bank mine, Lake County, California: California Jour. Mines and Geology, v. 42, no. 2, p. 125–153.

Irwin, W. P., 1964, Late Mesozoic orogenies in the ultramafic belts of northwestern California and southwestern Oregon: U.S. Geol. Survey Prof. Paper 501-C, p. C1–C9.

Jennings, C. W., and Strand, R. G., 1960, Geologic map of California, Olaf P. Jenkins edition, Ukiah sheet: California Div. Mines and Geology, scale 1:250,000.

Kirby, J. M., 1943, Upper Cretaceous stratigraphy of the west side of Sacramento Valley south of Willows, Glenn County, California: Am: Assoc. Petroleum Geologists Bull. v. 27, no. 3, p. 207–305.

Koenig, J. B., 1963, Geologic map of California, Olaf P. Jenkins edition, Santa Rosa sheet: California Div. Mines and Geology, scale 1:250,000.

Lachenbruch, M. C., 1962, Geology of the west side of the Sacramento Valley, California: California Div. Mines and Geology Bull. 181, p. 53–66.

Lawton, J. E., 1956, Geology of the north half of the Morgan Valley quadrangle and the south half of the Wilbur Springs quadrangle [California]: Stanford Univ., Stanford, Calif., Ph.D. thesis.

Safonov, Anatole, 1962, The challenge of the Sacramento Valley, California: California Div. Mines and Geology Bull. 181, p. 77–100.

Weaver, C. E., 1949, Geology and mineral deposits of an area north of San Francisco Bay, California—Vacaville, Antioch, Mount Vaca, Carquinez, Mare Island, Sonoma, Santa Rosa, Petluma, and Point Reyes quadrangles: California Div. Mines Bull. 149, 135 p.

White, D. E., and Roberson, C. E., 1962, Sulphur Bank, California, a major hot-spring quicksilver deposit, *in* Engel, A. E. J., James, H. L., and Leonard, B. F., eds., Petrologic studies: Geol. Soc. America, Buddington Volume, p. 397–428.

Yates, R. G., and Hilpert, L. S., 1946, Quicksilver deposits of eastern Mayacmas district, Lake and Napa Counties, California: California Jour. Mines and Geology, v. 42, no. 3, p. 231–286.

ROAD LOG

The route on the trip leaves San Francisco via the Bay Bridge, and the zero mileage point is at the toll gate at the east end of the crossing. From the main span forming the western part of the bridge one can see on the left the small Alcatraz Island, which formerly was the site of a Federal prison, and farther north is Angel Island. Franciscan sedimentary and volcanic rocks of Late Jurassic and Cretaceous age underlie these islands and form the bedrock beneath the muds of most of San Francisco Bay. The bay itself

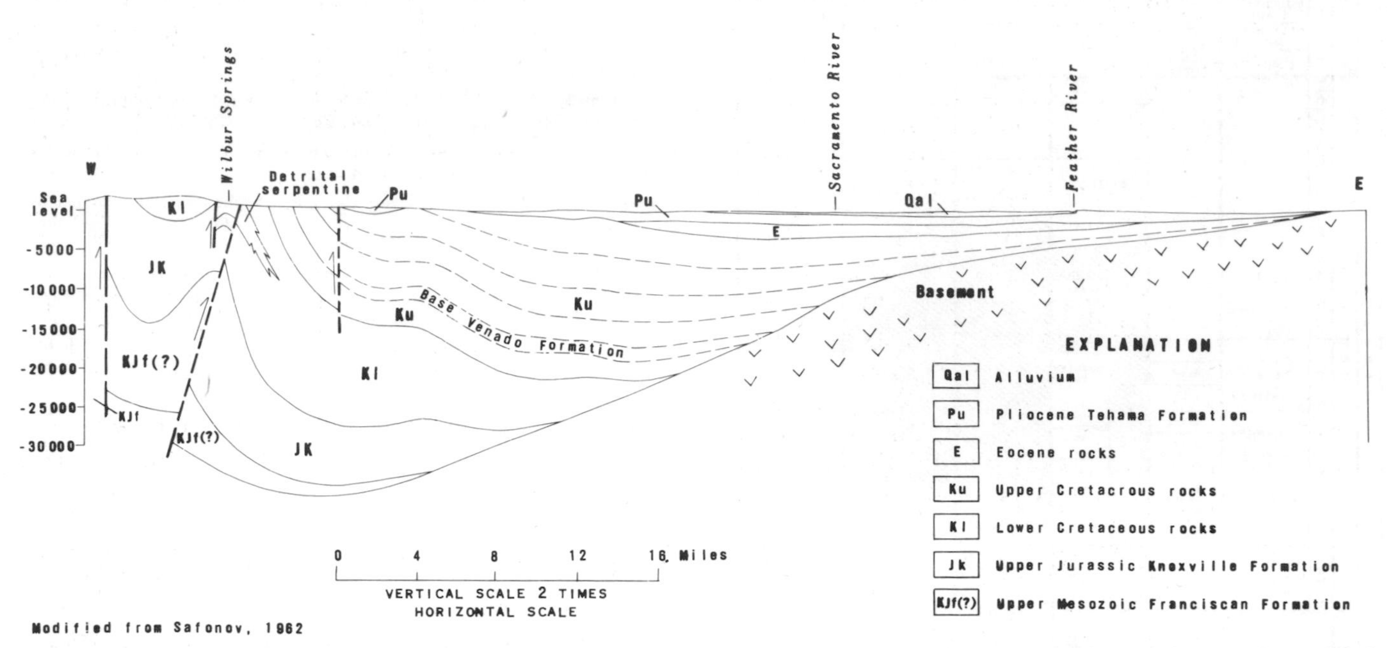

Figure 3. Generalized E-W section across the Sacramento Valley from near Wilbur Springs to a point a few miles east of Marysville. *Modified from Safonov (1962).*

is a result of local subsidence of river valleys during the Pleistocene. Yerba Buena Island near the midpoint of the bridge crossing consists of Franciscan graywacke and shale, which are well exposed on its southwestern side. Man-made Treasure Island, the site of the Golden Gate International Exposition in 1936, adjoins the north end of Yerba Buena Island.

Mileage

00.0 *Toll Plaza.* East side of San Francisco Bay Bridge.

0.5 Keep left on Interstate 80 (U.S. Highway 40).

3.9 University Avenue exit. University of California, Berkeley campus to the right.

5.3 Keep right to avoid Richmond exit. Franciscan graywacke is well exposed in the large quarry on El Cerrito Hill ahead and to the right.

10.5 San Pablo Dam Road exit. Within the next half a mile, the highway curves westward and crosses the Hayward fault. This fault or fault zone, buried under alluvium at this location, generally separates the Franciscan of the San Francisco-Marin block from the younger sedimentary rocks of the Berkeley Hills block to the east. For about 9 miles beyond this fault, the highway crosses a folded and faulted series of Tertiary sedimentary rocks that is notable for rapid lateral facies changes. The formations included are the nonmarine Pliocene Orinda Formation, the Pinole Tuff, the marine middle Miocene Monterey Formation, the marine upper Miocene San Pablo Group, and at the far eastern side the marine Paleocene Martinez Formation.

16.5 California Highway 4 exit.

17.3 Rodeo (Willow Avenue) exit.

17.8 Gently dipping San Pablo Group sandstone and shale can be seen here on both sides of highway.

18.3 Union Oil Company Oleum refinery on the left side of highway.

18.7 Near-vertical Cierbo Sandstone Formation of the San Pablo Group.

19.3 Cummings Skyway exit.

19.6 Roadcut through dark gray Monterey shale.

20.2 The Franklin fault, a fault dipping steeply to the northeast is crossed nearly at right angles by this large roadcut, and is best seen on the left side of the highway near the eastern end of the cut. Along the Franklin fault undifferentiated Upper Cretaceous rocks are thrust from the east over the Tertiary section.

20.4 Carquinez Bridge across Carquinez Straits, through which drain the waters of the Sacramento-San Joaquin Rivers from Suisun Bay on the right to San Pablo Bay on the left.

21.3 Undifferentiated Upper Cretaceous sandstone and shale are exposed on both sides of the highway.

21.7 Toll Plaza for Carquinez Bridge. From here, through the town of Vallejo, the highway traverses Upper Cretaceous rocks that are poorly exposed.

26.6 Napa (California Highway 37) exit. Sulphur Springs Mountain on the left.

27.0 Bold outcrops of red, radiolaria-bearing chert of the Franciscan Formation are exposed on the left. The chert, together with associated sandstone, serpentine, and the Jurassic Knoxville Formation have been raised along numerous faults up into the Cretaceous section.

27.6 Fault contact of Upper Cretaceous shale with Franciscan chert and sandstone to the east. The rust-brown rock exposed in the roadcut ahead is silica-carbonate rock, a hydrothermal alteration product of serpentine, which in many places is the host rock for mercury deposits.

27.8 Parking area. Serpentine is well exposed along the eastern end of the parking strip.

28.7 Greatly contorted fault contact of serpentine against Lower Cretaceous sedimentary rocks.

28.9 The gray-colored "Solano" diabase or hornblendite is exposed along the left side of the highway. These intrusives into the Knoxville Formation are thought to be of pre-Eocene age.

29.7 Ahead and to the left, Eocene sandstone resting unconformably on Lower Cretaceous shale. The lowest Tertiary formation in this American Canyon section is the Domengine Sandstone. Above this 200-foot-thick sandstone is the thick upper Eocene Markley Sandstone Member of the Kreyenhagen Formation.

32.9 Red-weathering Pliocene Sonoma Volcanics seen ahead and to the left are lying unconformably on Markley Sandstone.

33.4 Junction with California Highway 12. The hills ahead, across Green Valley and on both sides of the highway, are underlain by the Sonoma Volcanics.

36.2 Crossing alluvial plain of Gordon Valley.

38.3 On a clear day, Mount Diablo is visible 28 miles to the right of the highway. This prominent

Photo 1. Aerial view of strata of the Great Valley sequence forming the Vaca Mountains, Lake Berryessa, and Vaca quadrangles. View south from a point about 4 miles north of Monticello dam. Great Valley in background, Mt. Diablo beyond. Most of the rocks are Upper Cretaceous, some lower Tertiary strata at upper left, beyond narrow Vaca Valley.

Photo 2. Pebbly mudstone with displaced blocks of interbedded sandstone and shale, at base of Venado Formation (Late Cretaceous, Turonian) near Monticello Dam on State Highway 128, Capay quadrangle.

peak is a diapiric intrusion of Franciscan rocks piercing Jurassic and younger sediments of the Great Valley sequence. It is notable as the zero point for the Land Office grid in central California.

38.8 Fairfield exit. Hills on either side of the highway for the next 6.5 miles comprise the southern end of the Vaca Mountains and are underlain by Upper Cretaceous rocks.

40.0 Cement Hill, ahead and to the right. Travertine deposits on the southern side of this hill were quarried for cement from 1903–1927. Mineral springs along faults are still depositing travertine.

42.9 Pleasants Valley exit in Lagoon Valley. This basin, which lacks external drainage, is the result of faulting.

44.8 The rocks in roadcut on left are Upper Cretaceous Forbes Formation sandstone and shale dipping eastward. The contact with Tertiary sediments is just east of these outcrops and nearly conformable, but it is buried under alluvium.

46.0 Railroad underpass. Just ahead and on the right are exposures of the upper Eocene Markley Sandstone.

47.0 Seen in the roadcut on the left is the unconformable contact between the whitish, tuffaceous sediments of the marine Miocene San Pablo Sandstone and the nonmarine Pliocene Tehama Formation.

48.7 Turn off of the freeway at the Monte Vista Avenue exit, and circle back over the freeway.

49.2 Turn left onto Monte Vista Avenue.

49.3 Here the route again crosses the contact between the gently dipping Tehama Formation and the tuffaceous San Pablo Formation.

49.8 Railroad crossing.

49.9 Continue straight ahead. Do not turn.

50.0 Turn right on Vine Street at top of hill.

51.1 Ahead and to the left are outcrops of a Tertiary basalt resting unconformably on upper Miocene Markley Sandstone. This basalt, considered to be of local origin and Miocene age by some, is correlated by others with the Oligocene Lovejoy Basalt of the Feather River area.

51.6 Ahead is Pleasants Valley with the Vaca Mountains on the horizon. To the right, Markley Sandstone dips to the east.

51.7 Turn right onto Gibson Canyon Road.

51.9 Turn left onto Farrell Road.

52.2 Intersection; continue straight ahead on Vaca Valley Road.

52.4 On the left, resistant middle Eocene Domengine Sandstone overlying Capay Shale and overlain by Markley Sandstone. The Capay Shale underlies much of Pleasants Valley, but it is very poorly exposed.

53.6 Turn right onto Pleasants Valley Road. About 600 feet east of this road, and trending parallel to it, is the contact between the Paleocene Martinez Formation and the Upper Cretaceous Forbes Formation to the west.

56.2 Here is the approximate contact of the Martinez Formation and the Capay Shale to the east.

58.0 Mix Canyon Road is to the left, and on the right the highest point of the English Hills, Putnam Peak, is capped by Tertiary basalt.

61.7 Markley Sandstone in roadcut at left. To the right, conglomerate of the Tehama Formation rests unconformably on Markley Sandstone.

62.0 Turn right onto Putah Creek Road.

62.6 On the right is a large roadcut through the "Nomlaki" Tuff Member of the Tehama Formation. Continue on 0.2 miles, turn around and return to this roadcut.

Stop 1. Here, at the edge of the Sacramento Valley, the "Nomlaki" Tuff Member of the Pliocene Tehama Formation is exposed in a section that dips gently to the northeast. Euhedral sodic plagioclase crystals, released from the pumice fragments by weathering, are concentrated in a buff-colored zone. The gravels of the Tehama Formation are cemented with a carbonate. They thicken rapidly towards the mouth of Putah Creek, and represent alluvial material deposited by this creek about at the time the Sonoma Volcanics were deposited to the west and the thick gravels of the Cache Formation were laid down farther north near the present head of Putah Creek. The tuff is roughly equivalent in age to the type Nomlaki tuff on the west side of the Sacramento Valley, west of Corning about 85 miles to the north, but it has a different source area.

63.6 Turn right on Pleasants Valley Road.

63.7 Contact of basal conglomerate of the Tehama Formation with Markley Sandstone.

64.1 Small quarries in the "Nomlaki" tuff along right side of road.

64.5 Bridge over Putah Creek.

64.6 Turn left onto California Highway 128 and proceed up Putah Creek.

64.8 "Nomlaki" tuff is exposed in roadcuts on the right.

65.2 Basal Tehama gravel and conglomerate visible in roadcut on the right.

66.0 Small hill ahead and to the right is a slumped block of the Tehama Formation.

67.0 Black Rocks of Putah Creek. Large slump blocks of columnar jointed basalt have slid from the top of the ridge ahead and to the right into Putah Creek. This is the approximate contact of Tertiary rocks with the underlying Forbes Sandstone (Upper Cretaceous, Campanian).

68.1 Approximate basal contact of Forbes Sandstone on Dobbins Shale (Upper Cretaceous, Santonian).

68.3 Cannonball Park. Painted concretion across creek is in the Guinda Sandstone (Upper Cretaceous, Coniacian?).

68.4 Basal contact of Guinda Sandstone on Funks Shale (Upper Cretaceous, Coniacian?).

68.6 Basal contact of Funks Shale on Sites Sandstone (Upper Cretaceous, Turonian).

69.2 Recreation beach.

69.4 Bridge across Putah Creek. The basal contact of Sites sandstone on Yolo shale is below the bridge. Excellent view of Monticello Dam on the right.

69.9 Approximate basal contact of Yolo Shale on Venado Sandstone.

70.2 *Stop 2.* Monticello Dam. Many sedimentary features and some tectonic structures can be seen in this classical exposure of the Venado Formation (Upper Cretaceous, Turonian). They range from drag folds at the far eastern end of the parking area, through internal structures in thin-bedded graywacke sandstone and shale near the dam, to large displaced blocks of interbedded sandstone and shale in pebbly mudstone 150 yards west of the dam. Just beyond the zone of displaced blocks is the basal contact of the Venado upon the "Antelope Shale". The last conglomerate to the west and the sandstone above it are included in the "Antelope Shale" and have yielded fossils of Upper Cretaceous, Cenomanian age.

Photo 3. Aerial view of Mt. Konocti, a Recent dacitic volcano on the southern shore of Clear Lake in the Kelseyville quadrangle. Both the Clear Lake volcanic field and another field of similar size lying largely in the Quien Sabe quadrangle are along the axial part of the Diablo antiform.

72.1 Turn around and proceed back down Putah Creek to Cannonball Park, a pleasant place for a picnic lunch.

Continue on down Putah Creek on California Highway 128 toward Winters.

75.8 Intersection with Pleasants Valley Road; go straight ahead.

77.2 Road turns right onto the alluvial plain of the Sacramento Valley. On both sides of the highway leading into Winters are numerous apricot orchards.

80.0 Turn left toward Madison on the Winters-Madison Road.

81.7 On the left, about 2 miles away, in the gently rolling hills underlain by the Tehama Formation is the Pleasant Creek gas field. On the right, about 3 miles away, is the Winters field, which contains the only producing oil well in the Sacramento Valley. Production here is from Upper Cretaceous sands which lie above those exposed in Putah Creek.

91.1 Junction with California Highway 16. Turn left toward Esparto.

93.8 Follow highway right toward Esparto.

94.3 Follow highway left toward Capay.

96.5 Capay. From here to Brooks the highway passes through the Tehama Formation. Cache Creek flows through Capay Valley. The valley is bounded on the east by the Rumsey Hills, which have an Upper Cretaceous core directly overlain by the Pliocene Tehama Formation, and on the west by the Blue Ridge of the Vaca Mountains.

103.9 Brooks. The type locality of the lower Eocene Capay Formation is in Smith Canyon about 2 miles northwest of Brooks. From north of Brooks the Capay Formation rapidly changes from a section of channel conglomerates to fine-grained estuarine deposits to the south. The crest of Blue Ridge on the left is underlain by the Upper Cretaceous Venado Sandstone.

110.4 Guinda. Rumsey Hills on the right is a faulted anticlinal structure about 22 miles long and striking northwest. The prominent escarpment on the western front of the Rumsey Hills is the trace of the high-angle reverse Sweitzer fault. The displacement along this fault rarely exceeds the actual height of the escarpment, and although it varies from place to place only locally does it exceed 450 feet. North of Guinda, the crestal zone of the anticline is further complicated by the low-angle Eisner thrust fault, which thrusts Cretaceous beds over Tehama gravels.

114.1 Blue Slides in the Tehama Formation on the right. The blue color has been attributed to iron that has been reduced by natural gas seeping out along faults through the Rumsey Hills.

115.1 Rumsey.

117.9 *Stop 3.* Excellent examples of flute casts and current lineations are exposed on the lower surfaces of the sandstone beds of the Sites Sandstone. Across Cache Creek, deformation along the northern end of the Sweitzer fault cuts the beds and tilts them to nearly vertical.

118.8 Basal contact of Sites Sandstone on the type section of the Yolo Shale. The Yolo is about 800 feet thick.

119.8 Basal contact of Venado Sandstone on the "Antelope shale." Throughout the next 3 miles this shale shows deformation due to local faulting.

123.4 Highway 16 leaves Cache Creek and follows a tributary named Bear Creek.

125.9 First bridge over Bear Creek. Beyond the bridge, and exposed on the left, is one of several highway crossings of the Salt Creek conglomerate. Pebbles in this thin, persistent bed, are reworked from the underlying Lower Cretaceous Paskenta beds and are chiefly clay-ironstone concretions or well-rounded, very durable rocks. The Salt Creek conglomerate is a stratigraphic marker that can be traced 30 miles to the north; it separates Upper from Lower Cretaceous rocks and is thought by some to indicate an unconformity. Excellent flute casts are exposed at this location.

126.1 Excellent summer-time swimming hole on the right.

126.5 Second bridge over Bear Creek.

126.6 Salt Creek conglomerate again.

127.0 Last crossing of Salt Creek conglomerate exposed in the roadcut on the right. The highway cuts across the Paskenta sandstone and into an area of shale and "detrital serpentine."

128.4 Bare-hill exposures of "detrital serpentine" to the left (west).

129.5 Turn left toward Clear Lake on California Highway 20.

129.6 *Stop 4.* Roadcut in "detrital serpentine." For the next 7 miles to the west, Highway 20 passes through 5,000 to 7,500 feet of Lower Cretaceous breccia. This breccia is made up almost entirely of serpentine detritus with rare pebbles of shale, limestone, and chert. Work in this area has indicated that Upper Jurassic serpentine was elevated above sea level to form headlands during Lower Cretaceous time from which huge serpentine slides moved eastward into an adjacent sea. As these slides continued intermittently during a large part of the Lower Cretaceous, the slide breccia is interbedded with Lower Cretaceous sandstone and shale. Ocean currents and wave action reworked and spread the serpentine breccia to the north and south, drawing out breccia beds so that they interfinger with the other sediments.

131.0 Quarry site on the left. Lower Cretaceous sandstone, shale, and silica-carbonate rock is overlain by "detrital serpentine."

131.4 Coarse breccia of "detrital serpentine" on the left.

131.7 Lower Cretaceous sandstone is exposed in roadcut. Highway continues through areas of sandstone and detrital serpentine for the next 5 miles.

135.4 On the right is the headframe and mill of the Abbott mine. The cinnibar mined here occurs chiefly in silica-carbonate rock formed from sedimentary serpentine near its contacts with Lower Cretaceous sandstones.

136.9 Oasis. One mile west, the highway will wind through a 2-mile complex of Jurassic Knoxville shale, intrusive serpentine, and graywacke, shale, and greenstone of the Franciscan assemblage.

139.9 Grizzly Spring. Here we leave the serpentine and enter a basin filled with gravels of the nonmarine Plio-Pleistocene Cache Formation. Whitish travertine from Grizzly Spring can be seen on the slope on the right.

141.5 Carbonate-cemented concretions are conspicuous in the Cache beds on the left. The Cache deposits of gravel and silt are interbedded with some tuffaceous sand, marl, pebbly limestone, and diatomite near the top of the section. The maximum thickness is reported to be 6,500 feet. These sediments must have collected in large tectonic basins that subsided by faulting and minor downwarping.

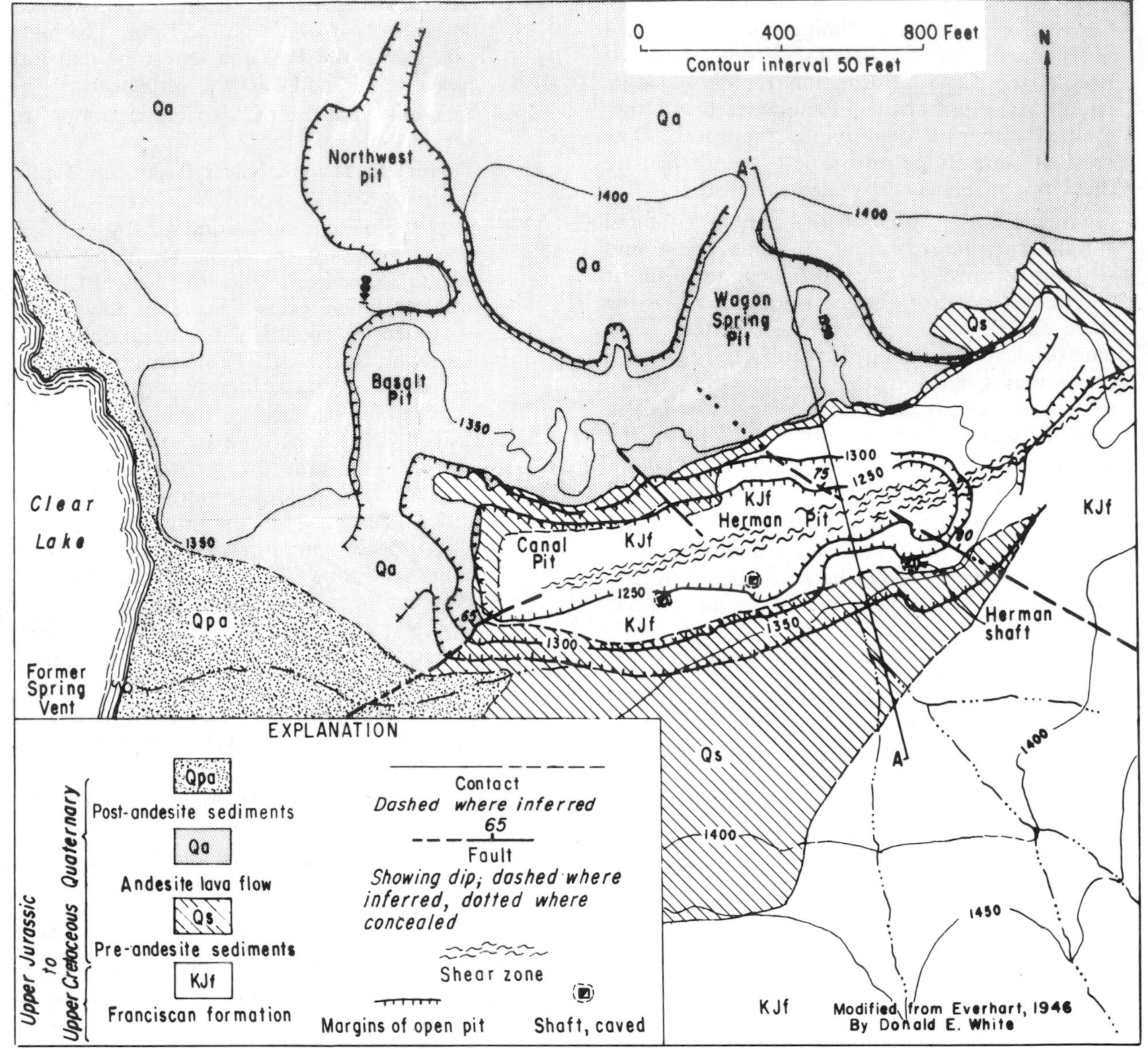

Figure 4. Geologic map of the Sulphur Bank mercury mine area.

142.7 Bridge over the North Fork of Cache Creek.

144.6 West-dipping Cache beds to the right across the gravel pit and creek.

146.6 The cliffs ahead and to the left are quartz-bearing olivine basalt flows that are interbedded with the uppermost sediments of the Cache Formation.

147.5 Fault contact with Franciscan metavolcanics to the west.

147.9 Divide above Clear Lake basin. Ahead are Recent cinder cones composed of reddish basaltic lapilli, and beyond is Clear Lake.

148.4 Turn left toward Lower Lake on California Highway 53.

149.1 Re-cross fault contact from the Franciscan into the olivine basalt of the Cache Formation.

152.1 To the right, across Clear Lake (elev. 1326′) is Mount Konocti (elev. 4200′). This composite volcanic cone of rhyodacite consists of several summit craters and parasitic cones developed during the middle or upper Pleistocene. Quackenbush Mountain on the left, is underlain by olivine basalt. (See air photo with the Santa Rosa Sheet, Geologic Map of California.)

152.3 *Stop 5.* Quartz-bearing, olivine basalt is interbedded with the gravels of the Cache Formation. The medium-gray, inconspicuously porphyritic basalt contains small (2 mm) crystals of olivine, pyroxene, and locally some plagioclase. An unusual feature is the presence of inclusions of clear, shattered quartz which in this area average about 2 mm in length but in other areas attain lengths of 15 cm. These are locally known as "Lake County Diamonds."

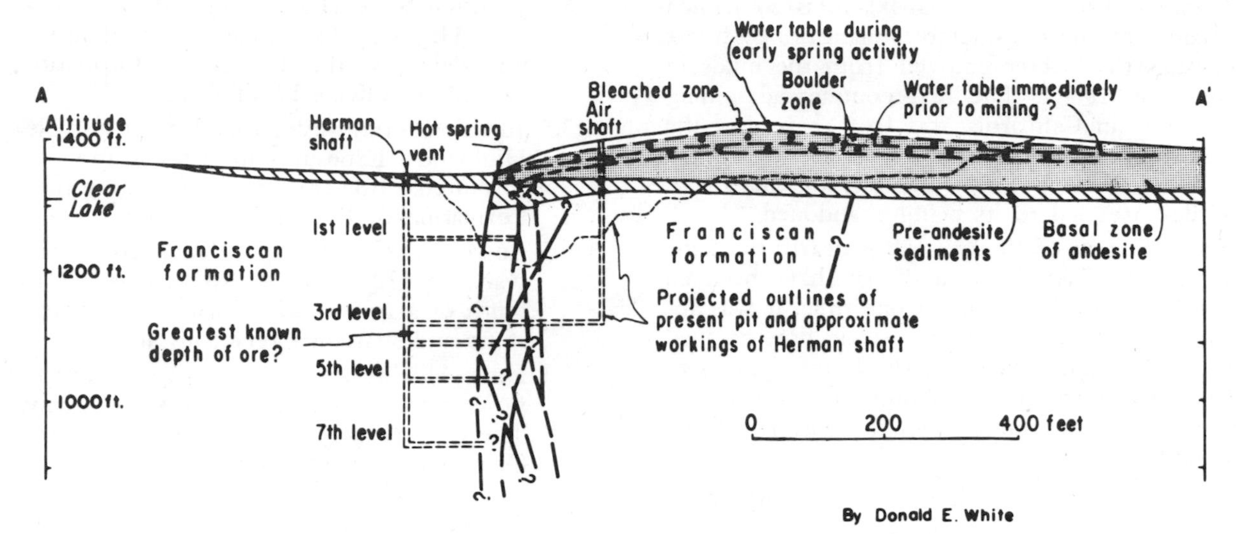

Figure 5. Geologic section through the Sulphur Bank mine area along line A-A', of figure 4.

153.0 Clearlake Highlands turn off.

155.0 Bridge over Cache Creek. The discharge from this creek, which is the outlet to Clear Lake, is controlled by a dam about 3 miles down stream.

156.1 Lower Lake. The end of California Highway 53. Turn right toward Kelseyville on California Highway 29.

157.2 Undifferentiated Cretaceous sandstone. Within the next half mile, these sands are overlain by the poorly exposed Cache Formation which, in turn, is overlain by the rhyodacite of Mount Konocti.

158.0 Turn right onto Jago Bay Road. Here one traverses a small, late basaltic lava flow from the Recent cinder cone of Roundtop Mountain ahead and to the right.

158.8 Small quarry in the basaltic cinders of Roundtop Mountain. This cone post-dates all nearby volcanic activity and appears to be the same age as the cinder cones seen earlier near the junction of Highway 59 and 20.

160.8 Lake Thurston on the left. This flat-bottomed basin has no outlet and is filled by a shallow lake. The basin, which is floored by Cache sediments, formed when viscous rhyodacite flows failed to coalesce.

162.2 Keep left toward Soda Bay on the Point Lake View Road.

162.7 On the right jutting into Clear Lake is Baylis Point of Franciscan rocks that escaped being covered by the Konocti volcanics.

165.5 Turn left, away from the lake, on Soda Bay Road. To the right at several places along this road are good views of Mount Konocti.

167.0 Recent obsidian flow is exposed in roadcut on the left.

167.5 Turn left toward Lower Lake on California Highway 29, which for the next 2 miles crosses flows of obsidian.

173.4 Jago Bay turnoff. Continue straight ahead on Highway 29.

175.3 Lower Lake. Turn left toward Clearlake Highlands on Highway 53.

178.4 Turn left on road to Clearlake Highlands.

178.8 Continue straight ahead on Lake Shore Drive.

179.2 Rosebud Park, Clearlake Highlands.

179.8 Resorts in Clearlake Highlands provide excellent overnight accommodations, and the first day of the field trip terminates here.

0.0 The second day of the trip starts from the U.S. Post Office in Clearlake Highlands.

1.0 *Stop 6.* Intersection Pomo Road and Arrowhead Road in Clearlake Highlands. Continue northward on Pomo Road about 500 feet from this intersection to quarry to examine one of several exposures of vesiculated obsidian in the Clearlake Highlands area. The steep dip of banded structures along the margins of the quarry, the brecciated eastern margin, and the vesiculation of the glass are all rare in other obsidian flows, and these features have led to the interpretation that at least some of the obsidian here is intrusive. The gray bands in the obsidian are formed by swarms of microlites in parallel arrangement. Inclusions and phenocrysts are common. A chemical analysis of the glass and its refractive index of about 1.489 indicate the obsidian is rhyolitic.

Return to intersection of Pomo Road and Arrowhead Road; turn right on Arrowhead Road. Follow Arrowhead Road to Borax Lake Road, and bear right onto Borax Lake Road.

3.0 View of Borax Lake. This lake is so named because of the considerable quantities of borax crystals that were removed from the muds in the early 1860's. The first commercial mining of borax in California was from here, but the discovery of the much larger ulexite (1873) and colemanite (1882) deposits of the Death Valley area led to its being abandoned.

The elevation of Borax Lake is nearly the same as that of Clear Lake, and may have been an extension of Clear Lake at one time. It was apparently formed when an obsidian flow damned the valley. The source of the borax appears to have been a group of hot solfataric springs, now almost extinct, issuing from the obsidian at the southeastern end of the lake.

4.5 *Stop* 7. View of Sulphur Bank mercury mine, Clear Lake, and east toward breached cinder cone and quarrying operations. Interbedded sedimentary rocks of the Franciscan Formation are exposed in roadcuts.

5.4 *Stop 8*. Sulphur Bank mercury mine. The mine was originally opened in 1865 as a sulphur mine and produced over 2 million pounds of sulphur during the ensuing 3 years. The falling price of sulphur and increasing contamination by cinnabar forced the closure of the mine in 1868. It was reopened in 1873 to exploit the mercury ores, and from the period 1873–1965 more than 129,000 flasks of mercury were produced. At today's prices (1965, $500 a flask) the output would be worth about $65,000,000, though when mined it was worth much less than this. The known rich ores have been mined but the deposit still contains low grade ore. Today the ore that has been roasted to remove the mercury is used for the manufacture of concrete blocks.

The sulphur is found above the water table as a product of near-surface oxidation of H_2S. The cinnabar was deposited from solution below the water table as incrustations on boulders and blocks of altered andesite. At depth along the faults, which act as channels for the escape of thermal fluids, cinnabar has been deposited in Quaternary volcanic rocks and lake beds, and in metagraywacke of the Franciscan Formation. Hot waters and vapors charged with carbon dioxide, hydrogen sulfide, methane gas, nitrogen, and minor mercury still issue from vents at Sulphur Bank.

6.8 Junction of Sulphur Bank mine entrance road and State Highway 20. Turn right onto Highway 20.

7.2 Cinder quarry in breached cinder cone. Cinders from this quarry are used as road metal, as aggregate, and perhaps more commonly as decorative material in landscape gardening.

8.9 Junction State Highway 20 and 53; turn right onto Highway 53. Ridge to left of highway is underlain by the Franciscan Formation and capped by olivine basalt flows.

13.5 Junction Highway 53 and road to Clearlake Highlands. Exposures in roadcut just south of this intersection are tuffaceous beds in the Cache Formation of Plio-Pleistocene age.

16.5 Lower Lake. Highway 53 ends, continue southward on Highway 29. Rocks exposed about a tenth of a mile south of Lower Lake are sandstone and shale of Cretaceous age.

19.1 Perin Hill at 2 o'clock is capped by andesite flows with abundant xenoliths and xenocrysts. The xenocrysts form the so-called "Lake County Diamonds," which are in fact irregular grains and masses of unusually clear quartz. Hills at 10 o'clock are held up by minor sandstone beds in the dominantly shaly Cretaceous formations. Tree-covered slope near road is landslide material.

21.0 Cretaceous rocks, undifferentiated but probably of Late Cretaceous age, strike about N.60W. and dip 65° to 70° northeast. They are on the southwestern flank of a broad syncline, in the center of which, about three-fourths of a mile east of the highway, fossiliferous Eocene Martinez Formation is exposed.

21.7 Massive Cretaceous sandstone seen in roadcut at 9 o'clock strikes nearly parallel with highway and dips 75° into the hill. Sole markings are well exposed on base of many of the sandstone beds. Directional markings suggest the depositional currents flowed from north to south.

24.6 Hills along road are underlain by Cretaceous rocks and capped by andesitic flows. At about this point the Cretaceous rocks are separated from the underlying Jurassic Knoxville Formation by the Childers Peak Fault. Gravels in roadcut represent a small remnant patch of Cache Formation of Plio-Pleistocene age which was deposited across the structure.

26.2 Bridge across Putah Creek. Hills on right are underlain by serpentinized ultrabasic rocks.

26.9 *Stop 9*. Serpentine in roadcuts and adjacent hills. Massive serpentine here is fractured into large blocks, which are themselves nearly devoid of shears. Note in these blocks the relict texture of the original coarse-grained ultrabasic rock, especially the shiny yellow-green crystals of bastite that pseudomorph a pyroxene, probably enstatite.

Walk south along highway about 0.4 mile to the next roadcut where a contact of serpentine against the Jurassic Knoxville Formation is exposed. Closely spaced shear planes in serpentine dip steeply to the north as do the intruded sediments. Bands of light serpentine mark the strongest shear planes. Texture here is sugary or locally fine-grained, possibly indicating alteration from dunite rather than from coarser grained peridotite. Disseminated flecks of chromite are locally concentrated along shear planes. This contact is typical of many in the Coast Ranges and illustrates well the difficulty of establishing whether the emplacement was by the intrusion of magma, or of serpentine, or whether the serpentine is merely faulted to the position where we see it.

28.7 *Stop 10.* Contact of serpentine and Jurassic Knoxville Formation. Pectolite (a complex hydrous sodium-calcium silicate) occurring in veins, and anorthite in intricate networks of veinlets and small irregular pods, have been collected from the serpentine closely associated with the sedimentary rocks. The origin of the pectolite is problematical, but it is thought to be either metasomatic metamorphism along intrusive contacts or hydrothermal mineralization similar to that forming the silica-carbonate rocks common in this area. About 1 mile west of this point a vein of pectolite about 30 feet wide and several hundred feet long is associated with a diabasic breccia.

29.7 Bridge across St. Helena Creek at northern city limits of Middletown.

34.7 Mirabel Mines left side road across St. Helena Creek. This mercury mine lies at the border of a large serpentine mass and is in a zone of faulted and sheared Franciscan rocks. Most of the rocks are altered: Graywacke is softened by kaolinization or hardened by silicification, greenstones are converted to clay or altered to sheared chloritic rock, and serpentine is altered to silica-carbonate rock. Cinnabar occurs in the silica-carbonate rock as shoots of both tabular and pipelike forms. With the cinnabar is also found metacinnabar and native mercury. Associated with these are pyrite, hydrocarbons, and veinlets of dolomite and quartz.

This mine first opened in the early 1870's and continued operation until 1898. It was reopened in 1930 through a well planned program of exploration and was in production until 1946. Its output is more than 41,000 flasks of mercury, and it is but one of the many mercury mines of the Mayacmas district, which has an aggregate production of nearly half a million flasks.

36.8 Contact of serpentine and Sonoma Volcanics visible on right side of road. Nearly all exposures of the Sonoma Volcanics along the highway have been involved in landslides, so that the relations of volcanics to serpentine and individual flows to each other are obscure.

39.4 *Stop 11.* Entrance to Robert Louis Stevenson State Park at the top of the grade. Relatively poor and highly altered exposures of some of the Sonoma Volcanics can be examined here. The Sonoma Volcanics are predominantly andesitic with some rhyolite flows, pyroclastics, and intrusive equivalents. In general the series is basaltic at the base and is composed of rhyolitic tuffs, tuff-breccia, and probably welded tuffs at the top. The eruptive sources are unknown; although Mount St. Helena to the west superficially resembles an eroded volcano, its internal structures suggest that it probably is not an old vent.

The famous author, Robert Louis Stevenson, lived in a miner's small cabin about one mile west of this point while writing his novel Silverado Squatters, based on the Silverado mines lying on the slope of Mount St. Helena.

43.1 *Stop 12.* View of Palisades, Mount St. Helena, and Napa Valley. The Palisades are made up principally of flows, debris flows, and welded tuffs. The horizontal banding defines individual flows. Vertical jointing in the uppermost layers is clearly visible. The Palisades mine, the only really productive silver mine in the Coast Range, lies in the canyon southeast of here, but it cannot be seen from the highway. To the north Mount St. Helena rises to a height of 4,343 feet.

48.0 Junction Highways 29 and 128 in town of Calistoga. Turn left at Junction. From this point southward the highway is in the Napa Valley that is famed for its wines. The alluviated valley is bordered by hills of Cretaceous and Jurassic sedimentary rocks. The hills on the east (left) are capped by the Sonoma Volcanics. The valley occupies the Napa Valley syncline which is thought to be downdropped along a fault trending nearly parallel with the valley along its eastern side.

52.9 Old Bale Mill on left side of highway. This old grist mill was erected by Dr. E. T. Bale, grantee of the Carne Humann Ranch, in 1846. Water wheel measures about 30 feet in diameter.

55.2 Entrance of Charles Krug winery at St. Helena. This winery, like many others in western California, provides visitors with an opportunity to sample their products and to view the wine making process.

103.1 Toll plaza at south end of Golden Gate bridge.

Coffee break. *Harper's Weekly*, 1866

FIELD TRIP
YOSEMITE VALLEY AND SIERRA NEVADA BATHOLITH *

By Dallas L. Peck, Clyde Wahrhaftig, and Lorin D. Clark
U.S. Geological Survey, Menlo Park; University of California; U.S. Geological Survey, Washington, D.C.

SAN FRANCISCO—OAKLAND—DIABLO RANGE—GREAT VALLEY—TRACY —TURLOCK—MERCED RIVER VALLEY—HORNITOS—MARIPOSA— EL PORTAL—YOSEMITE VALLEY—MIRROR LAKE—YOSEMITE NATIONAL PARK HEADQUARTERS AND MUSEUM

The focal point of this field trip is the world famous Yosemite Valley where one may see not only magnificent views of towering waterfalls, precipitous cliffs, majestic domes, and verdant meadows, but also notable exposures of the granitic rocks of the Sierra Nevada batholith. En route from San Francisco one passes through the Coast Ranges, with its folded and faulted Upper Mesozoic and Cenozoic strata, and the Central Valley underlain by similar rocks but largely mantled by alluvium. Owing to the length of the trip no stops to see the geology of these areas are scheduled, but the road log calls attention to particularly interesting geologic features that may be seen en route. The western foothills of the Sierra Nevada contain many geologic features, but these also must be slighted in order to conserve time for observations in the main Yosemite Valley—only one stop to view the prebatholithic metamorphic rocks is included. However, descriptions of many features of the metamorphic rocks, the postbatholithic rocks, the glacial geology, the geomorphology, and of the colorful history of the portion of the gold belt that is crossed on the trip are included in the road log.

Sketch of Geology

East of San Francisco, the field trip route (fig. 1) follows U.S. Highway 50 across the Bay Bridge. Sandstone referred to the Franciscan Formation of Jurassic and Cretaceous age is exposed on Alcatraz Island, 3 miles to the north, and at the enrance to the tunnel on Yerba Buena Island. From the east abutment of the bridge, the route traverses the bay-margin flats along the Nimitz Freeway to Hayward, where it turns east again and rejoins U.S. Highway 50 across the Diablo Range.

Along the route the Diablo Range is broken into two high-standing areas separated by the Livermore Valley—the Berkeley Hills block on the west and the Altamont anticline on the east. The northwest-trending Berkeley Hills block is bounded by major fault zones of the San Andreas system—the Hayward and the Chabot faults on the southwest side and the Sunol-Calaveras fault on the northeast side. Two and two-tenths miles after leaving the Nimitz Freeway, we see in roadcuts on the left serpentinized ultramafic rocks which lie in fault slivers between the Hayward and Chabot faults.

The Berkeley Hills block where crossed by U.S. Highway 50 is composed of sandstone, shale, and conglomerate of Cretaceous, Miocene, and Pliocene age. A major unconformity separates the Cretaceous and Miocene rocks. During late Miocene and Pliocene time, the area of San Francisco Bay was a highland, which shed sediment eastward into a marine embayment on the site of the Diablo Range. Continental sediments derived from the Franciscan Formation on the Bay block interfinger eastward with marine Miocene sediments and overlap them. In late Pliocene time the entire sequence was tightly folded, and the region was reduced to relatively low relief, either during the folding or soon thereafter.

The present distribution of mountains and structural valleys was blocked out after the late Pliocene orogeny. The San Francisco Bay block and the Livermore Valley subsided, while the Berkeley Hills and the Mount Diablo-Altamont areas were upwarped. This deformation began in mid-Pleistocene time, and is probably still continuing. Approximately 4,000 feet of Pliocene(?) and Pleistocene deposits, the Livermore Gravels of Clark (1930), accumulated in the Livermore Valley area and were subsequently tilted down to the northeast. Gently dipping beds of the Livermore Gravels, exposed in low hills on both sides of the highway 1.0 mile east of the Livermore turnoff, have yielded a middle Pleistocene Irvingtonian fauna, and the undeformed creek gravels that rest across the truncated edges of these beds in the same area have yielded a late Pleistocene Rancholabrean fauna.

At the east edge of Livermore Valley, the highway crosses the concealed Greenville fault and passes onto Miocene rocks on the flank of the Altamont anticline. For the next 7 miles the route traverses well-exposed Cretaceous sandstone and shale forming the core of the broad northwest-trending Altamont anticline. On

* Publication authorized by the Director, U.S. Geological Survey.

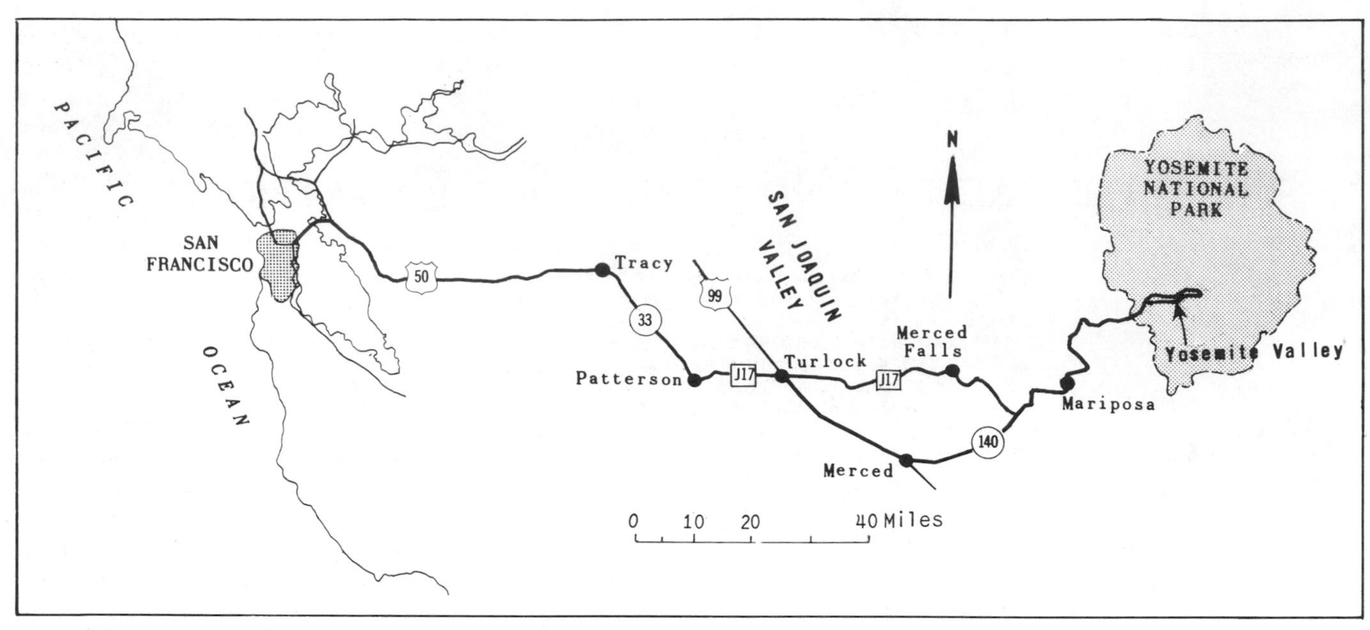

Figure 1. Index map showing route of field trip from San Francisco to Yosemite Valley.

the flanks of the anticline, Cretaceous beds are overlapped unconformably by upper Miocene conglomerate, sandstone, and shale. The unconformity is well exposed in a cut on the north side of the highway at the Byron Turnoff, where andesitic conglomerates of the Neroly Formation (upper Miocene) overlies truncated beds of the Panoche Formation (Upper Cretaceous). At a point 1.5 miles farther east, lacustrine clay, sand, and gravel of the Tulare Formation (Pliocene and Pleistocene) dipping 2°–3° eastward are exposed on the left.

The route continues eastward across the fertile San Joaquin Valley via Tracy, Patterson, and Turlock. The San Joaquin Valley is a flat alluvial plain underlain by sedimentary deposits of Cretaceous, Tertiary, and Quaternary age. These deposits, which are about 20,000 feet thick where we cross the valley, were derived mostly from the Sierra Nevada and Coast Ranges. On the east side of the valley they lap onto granite and metamorphic rocks of the west-tilted Sierra Nevada block. The deposits are in wedge-shaped beds that taper eastward; their lithology and bedding provide clues to the later history of the range.

The Cenozoic rocks first seen along the Merced River east of Turlock have been described by Arkley (1962). Most are poorly consolidated sedimentary rocks; all are non-marine except the oldest, the Ione Formation of Eocene age. Pleistocene formations that are exposed in roadcuts along our route to the east are alluvial sand and silt of arkosic composition; in ascending order the units are designated by Davis and Hall (1959) the Turlock Lake Formation of early Pleistocene age, the Riverbank Formation of middle Pleistocene age, and the Modesto Formation of late Pleistocene age.

Merced Falls lies at the boundary between the Cenozoic deposits of the Great Valley and strongly deformed and regionally metamorphosed strata of Paleozoic and Jurassic age in the western foothills of the Sierra Nevada. The metamorphic rocks consist chiefly of slate, phyllite, and metamorphosed graywacke, chert, conglomerate, and volcanics, including tuff, breccia, and pillow lava. The volcanic rocks are chiefly of intermediate to basaltic composition. Graded beds in graywackes and tuffs make it possible to decipher the principal structural features despite pervasive cleavage, lineation, and minor folds of diverse orientation.

These metamorphosed strata are in the west limb of a complex faulted synclinorium that spans the Sierra Nevada and provides the structural setting of the Sierra Nevada batholith. This major structure, however, is obscure because older rocks now lie east of younger rocks owing to displacement along the Melones and Bear Mountain faults (Clark, 1963). Nevertheless, the structure within each block is homoclinal with younger beds to the east. The two more westerly blocks both contain strata of Late Jurassic age, but the youngest strata are in the most westerly block. The strata in the most easterly block belong to the Calaveras Formation, which is very thick and for the most part unfossiliferous but has yielded Permian fossils from its upper part.

The Sierra Nevada batholith is a composite batholith made up of sharply bounded discrete plutons, locally separated by thin septa of metamorphic or mafic igneous rocks. The plutons are composed chiefly of quartz-bearing granitic rocks ranging from quartz diorite to alaskite, but include less abundant darker plutonic rocks. Mineralogical composition of the intrusive rocks

TABLE 1.—Granitic rocks of the Yosemite Valley region.

Series	Name	Lithology
Tuolumne Intrusive Series	Johnson Granite Porphyry	Light-gray, fine-grained quartz monzonite prophyry containing a little biotite but no hornblende.
	Cathedral Peak Granite	Light-gray quartz monzonite containing abundant large phenocrysts of K-feldspar in a medium-grained groundmass containing both biotite and hornblende.
	Half Dome Quartz Monzonite	Light- to medium-gray granodiorite and quartz monzonite containing well-formed crystals of biotite and hornblende. Includes both a nonporphyritic and a porphyritic facies, the latter resembling the Cathedral Peak Granite but containing better formed biotite and hornblende.
	Sentinel Granodiorite	Medium-dark-gray granodiorite and quartz diorite, variable in color and texture; typically well foliated.
Minor intrusive bodies	Diorite of the "Map of North America"	Very-dark-gray diorite similar to the diorite of the Rockslides but finer grained.
	Quartz-mica diorite	Medium-dark-gray, medium-fine-grained quartz mica diorite.
	Bridalveil Granite	Medium-gray, fine-grained granodiorite; moderately abundant biotite gives the rock a "salt and pepper" appearance.
	Leaning Tower Quartz Monzonite	Medium-gray, medium-grained granodiorite; clusters of biotite and hornblende give the rock a speckled appearance.
Western intrusive series	Taft Granite	Very-light-gray, fine-grained quartz monzonite, finer grained and more uniform than the El Capitan Granite.
	El Capitan Granite	Light-gray, medium-coarse-grained biotite quartz monzonite and granodiorite. Vaguely porphyritic in part.
	Granodiorite of The Gateway	Dark-gray, medium-grained quartz diorite and granodiorite.
	Granite of Arch Rock	Medium-light-gray, medium-grained, biotite quartz monzonite and granodiorite; contain characteristic poikilitic K-feldspar grains.
	Diorite of the Rockslides	Very-dark-gray, coarse- to medium-grained diorite, quartz diorite, and gabbro. Very variable.

of Yosemite Valley has been determined by Dodge (1963). Potassium-argon ratios of biotite from the granitic rocks of the Yosemite region have yielded Cretaceous isotopic ages ranging from 95 to 84 million years (Curtis and others, 1958), but recent work by Kistler and others (1965) farther east in the batholith suggest that some of the older plutons may be older, their mineral ages having been reduced during emplacement of the younger plutons. The geology across the central part of the batholith has been summarized by Bateman and others (1963).

The major granitic plutons of the Yosemite region were emplaced from west to east. Most of the granitic rocks are grouped into two series, the older western intrusive series, and the younger Tuolumne Intrusive Series (Calkins, 1930; Calkins and Peck, 1962). The Tuolumne probably represents a single very large zoned pluton in which repeated movements of the magma took place in the core during crystallization. The distribution of the intrusive rocks is shown in figure 4, and their lithology is summarized in table 1.

The Merced River canyon is cut in a broad upland surface of moderate local relief that was formed by erosion mostly during the Late Cretaceous and early Tertiary. A narrow, steep-walled stream canyon was cut in late Pliocene and early Pleistocene, which was later widened and deepened by glacial erosion. The geomorphology of the Yosemite Valley region has been described by Matthes (1930) and summarized by Wahrhaftig (1962) and Wahrhaftig and Birman (1965). During the Pleistocene, glaciers descended about 25 miles down the Merced Canyon, to El Portal and beyond. Glaciers advanced down the Merced Canyon at least 3 and perhaps 4 times. The Merced Glacier completely filled Yosemite Valley at its maximum and spilled over the rim onto the upland on either side (fig. 6). During a later glaciation, the Tenaya Glaciation of Birman (1964), the glacier only partially filled Yosemite Valley, and left a set of six moraines between Bridalveil Meadow and El Capitan Bridge. During the last major glaciation, the Tioga Glaciation, the glacier stopped short of the valley, and left a set of moraines at the lower end of Little Yosemite Valley.

REFERENCES

Allen, V. T., 1929, The Ione formation of California: California Univ., Dept. Geol. Sci. Bull., v. 18, no. 14, p. 347–448.

Arkley, R. J., 1962, The geology, geomorphology, and soils of the San Joaquin Valley in the vicinity of the Merced River, California: California Div. Mines and Geology Bull. 182, p. 25–32.

Bateman, P. C., Clark, L. D., Huber, N. K., Moore, J. G., and Rinehart, C. D., 1963, The Sierra Nevada batholith—a synthesis of recent work across the central part: U.S. Geol. Survey Prof. Paper 414-D, p. D1–D46.

Best, Myron G., 1963a, Petrology and structural analysis of metamorphic rocks in the southwestern Sierra Nevada foothills, California: California Univ., Dept. Geol. Sci. Bull., v. 42, p. 111–158.

—— 1963b, Petrology of the Guadelupe igneous complex, southwestern Sierra Nevada foothills, California: Journal of Petrology, v. 4, p. 223–259.

Birman, J. H., 1964, Glacial geology across the crest of the Sierra Nevada, California: Geol. Soc. America Spec. Paper 75, 80 p.

Bowen, O. E., Jr., and Gray, C. H., Jr., 1957, Mines and mineral deposits of Mariposa County, California: California Jour. Mines and Geology, v. 53, p. 34–243.

Calkins, F. C., 1930, The granitic rocks of the Yosemite region, *in* Matthes, F. E., Geologic history of the Yosemite Valley: U.S. Geol. Survey Prof. Paper 160, p. 120–129.

Calkins, F. C., and Peck, D. L., 1962, Granitic rocks of the Yosemite Valley area, California, *in* Geologic guide to the Merced Canyon and Yosemite Valley: California Div. Mines and Geology Bull. 182, p. 17–24.

Clark, L. D., 1962, Summary of the pre-Tertiary geology of the western Sierra Nevada metamorphic belt, California: California Div. Mines and Geology Bull. 182, p. 15–16.

Photo 1. Granite domes of the Sierra Nevada batholith, exposed in the high country above Yosemite Valley. *Photo by Mary Hill.*

—— 1964, Stratigraphy and structure of part of the western Sierra Nevada metamorphic belt, California: U.S. Geol. Survey Prof. Paper 410, 70 p.

Curtis, G. H., Evernden, J. F., and Lipson, J. I., 1958, Age determination of some granitic rocks in California by the potassium-argon method: California Div. Mines Spec. Report 54, 16 p.

Davis, S. N., and Hall, F. R., 1959, Water quality of eastern Stanislaus and northern Merced Counties, California: Stanford Univ. Pubs. Geol. Sci., v. 6, no. 1, 112 p.

Dodge, F. C. W., 1963, A mineralogical study of the instrusive rocks of the Yosemite Valley area, California: Stanford Univ., Stanford, Calif., Ph.D. thesis, 158 p.

Gutenberg, Beno, Buwalda, J. P., and Sharp, R. P., 1956, Seismic explorations of the floor of Yosemite Valley, California: Geol. Soc. America Bull., v. 67, no. 8, p. 1051–1078.

Hudson, F. S., 1960, Post-Pliocene uplift of the Sierra Nevada, California: Geol. Soc. America Bull., v. 71, no. 11, p. 1547–1573.

Kistler, R. W., Bateman, P. C., and Brannock, W. W., 1965, Isotopic ages of minerals from granitic rocks of the central Sierra Nevada and Inyo Mountains, California: Geol. Soc. America Bull., v. 76, no. 2, p. 155–164.

Matthes, F. E., 1930, Geologic history of Yosemite Valley: U.S. Geol. Survey Prof. Paper 160, 137 p.

Piper, A. M., Gale, N. S., Thomas, H. E., and Robinson, T. W., 1939, Geology and ground-water hydrology of the Mokelumne area, California: U.S. Geol. Survey Water-Supply Paper 780, 230 p.

Turner, H. W., and Ransome, F. L., 1897, Geology of the Sonora quadrangle, California: U.S. Geol. Survey Geol. Atlas, Folio 41, [7] p., 4 maps.

Wahrhaftig, Clyde, 1962, Geomorphology of the Yosemite Valley region, California: California Div. Mines and Geology Bull. 182, p. 33–46.

Wahrhaftig, Clyde, and Birman, J. H., 1965, The Quaternary of the Pacific Mountain system in California, *in* Wright, H. E., Jr., and Frey, D. G., eds., The Quaternary of the United States—A review volume for the VII Congress of the International Association for Quaternary Research: Princeton, N. J., Princeton Univ. Press, p. 299–340.

ROAD LOG

Mileage

00.0 *Center of Turlock* (intersection Main and U.S. 99)—proceed south on U.S. 99.

0.1 First street past stoplight. Turn left (east) on East Ave.; follow road to Snelling.
The road crosses the depositional surface on top of the Pleistocene Modesto Formation of Davis and Hall (1959), equivalent to the upper part of the late Pleistocene Victor Formation (Piper and others, 1939).

5.8 The road leaves the smooth depositional surface and enters slightly rolling topography carved in the Pleistocene Riverbank Formation of Davis and Hall (1959), equivalent to the lower part of the Victor Formation. Outcrops of reddish sandy alluvium along the road at 7.6 are probably of this formation.
To the north can be seen a line of low, flat-topped hills carved in the Turlock Lake Formation of Davis and Hall (1959).

12.3 The road enters the area of Turlock Lake Formation characterized by rolling country carved in reddish sandy alluvium.

14.7 North bank of Dry Creek. The roadcuts along the grade down to the creek expose two layers of thinly bedded fine sand and silt interbedded with coarse sand. These may represent glacial lake deposits (glacial rock flour) laid down by the Merced River. The terrace traversed by the road beyond Dry Creek is underlain by the Riverbank Formation.

15.2 The China Hat pediment can be seen across the Merced River, above the trees at 2:00 o'clock. Just beyond this point the road descends 20 feet to the terrace surface of the Modesto Formation.

17.0 On the skyline to the east across the river can be seen the westward-sloping China Hat pediment.

17.7 The road descends the terrace to the modern floodplain of the Merced River. The small outcrop at the base of the bluff is of thinly bedded fine sand and silt. This is overlain by 20 to 30 feet of well-sorted medium-grained sand of granitic detritus.

21.4 The abandoned grade visible at intervals on the right is that of the Yosemite Valley Railroad, which extended from Merced to El Portal and operated from 1907 to 1945. Its chief business was freight, but during the summer the railroad carried many travelers to Yosemite.

25.3 Snelling. Small white courthouse at Snelling, erected in 1857, was the first in Merced County. Between Snelling and Merced Falls the road passes piles of dredge tailings. The gold mining dredges are large barges with chains of scoop buckets that gnaw away on one side of the artificial pond on which the dredge floats. The buckets feed into a large trommel on the dredge that separates the coarse gravel from the fine gold-bearing sand. This sand passes from the trommel over a complicated series of riffles which trap the gold. The barren gravel is carried up a long stacking arm by an endless belt and dumped on the side of the pond opposite from where it was dug. By excavating at one end and back-filling at the opposite end, the dredge carries along the pond on which it floats as it mines the gold. The dredge is anchored to the shore by cables and swings from side to side by pulling alternately on the cables, digging and stacking as it goes. This back and forth swinging from a fixed point gives the curious cross ridges of the dredge tailings, which look from the air like stacks of coins that have fallen over.
The gravel that has been dredged here is apparently post-glacial alluvium deposited in the shallow steep-walled valley that the Merced River carved in the Pleistocene Modesto and Riverbank Formations. The large boulders in the gravel are a concentrate from the alluvial formations. From the dredgings, in addition to gold, a small amount of platinum was recovered.
With luck, one can see to the south the profile of the China Hat pediment.

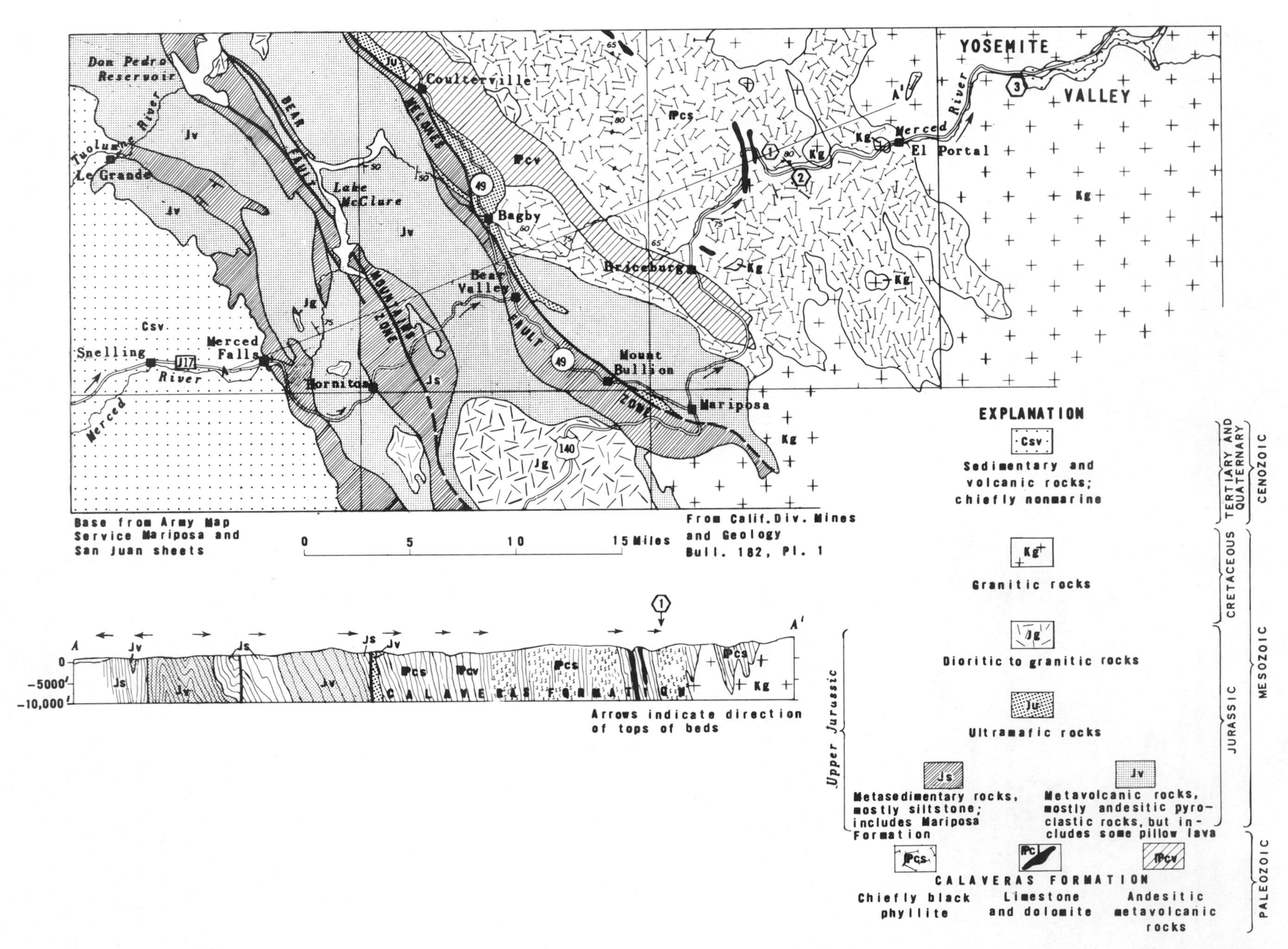

Figure 2. Geologic map and section of the southern part of the western Sierra Nevada metamorphic belt and Yosemite Valley, showing route of field trip. Numbers in hexagons indicate stops referred to in text.

31.8 Merced Falls.

31.9 Merced Falls Dam and powerplant on right. The dam rests on the westernmost outcrop of bedrock, which consists of black slate with interbedded graywacke.

32.1 Sawmill ruins on right.

32.3 Cross abandoned grade of the Yosemite Valley Railroad. Exposures of steeply dipping Upper Jurassic slate. The metasedimentary rocks extending from here eastward for 2 miles are on the western limb of a large anticline (fig. 2). Although the beds are in places complexly folded, tops are westward in intervening areas where bedding is not crumpled.

The pre-Tertiary geology of the western Sierra Nevada metamorphic belt has been described by Clark (1962, 1964). Metamorphic rocks near the Merced River are of Paleozoic and Jurassic age, and form the western limb of a complex synclinorium, the axial parts of which were intruded by the Sierra Nevada batholith. They occur in three structural blocks, separated by the Melones and Bear Mountain fault zones. Within each block the structure is generally homoclinal, with younger beds to the east; but the overall sequence has been reversed by movement along the faults, so that the youngest metamorphic rocks are exposed in the western block and the oldest in the eastern block. The Paleozoic rocks, which are all included in the Calaveras Formation, are exposed only in the block east of the Melones fault zone. They consist of phyllite, metavolcanic rock, and less abundant metachert, limestone, and dolomite. Mesozoic rocks that make up the central and western fault blocks consist of intertonguing metavolcanic and metasedimentary rocks of Late Jurassic age. The metavolcanic rocks are derived chiefly from tuff and breccia of intermediate composition, but include basalt and felsite. The metasedimentary rocks were derived chiefly from siltstone, but graywacke, metaconglomerate, and metachert are locally abundant. Graded beds are common in both tuff and graywacke. The metamorphic rocks are intruded by ultramafic and mafic bodies of Late Jurassic or Early Cretaceous age and by the granitic rocks of the Sierra Nevada batholith.

Nearby McSwain Dam is constructed of rockfill with an impervious earthfill core. The dam is 1,500 feet long with a crest elevation of 425 feet, and it impounds a reservoir with a gross capacity of 9,400 acre-feet of water. This dam and the New Exchequer Dam, about 6 miles farther upstream, were built as part of the Merced River Development Project to store water for agricultural purposes, to generate electricity, to provide downstream flood control, and to make available recreational facilities.

32.5 Cross Merced River.

33.5 The flat-topped hill just west of the road is capped by about 100 feet of coarse crossbedded sandstone and conglomerate of the Ione Formation (Eocene), which rests on deeply weathered Jurassic slate. At the base of the hill the slate is black and unweathered, but near the top of the hill, the slate below the sandstone is bleached white. The sandstone contains pebbles of the bleached slate, volcanic rocks, and quartz. It is largely a quartz-kaolin sandstone with a very low percentage of resistant heavy minerals, and was apparently derived from the erosion of a terrain that had been deeply weathered in a tropical climate. Casts of *Venericardia planicosta* have been reported from the sandstone in this hill (Allen, 1929, p. 361).

The flat-topped hills to the southeast, which slope gently southwestward, are also capped by about 100 feet of similar sandstone of the Ione, resting unconformably on the upturned edges of the Jurassic slate. The eastward projection of the surface made by these hillcrests coincides roughly in height with the even-topped ridges in the distance to the east, the foothill ridges of the Sierra. These ridges are underlain by metavolcanic rocks.

33.7 The road for the next 3 miles passes through rolling country surmounted by the flat-topped mesas of the sandstone of the Ione Formation. On the low, rolling hills can be seen the curious "hogwallow" microrelief of evenly spaced mounds 2 to 3 feet high, and about 20 to 40 feet across.

36.7 Whitish-weathered schistose felsite, probably Upper Jurassic.

39.3 Road crosses into Jurassic metavolcanic rocks.

39.5 Roadcuts in schistose metavolcanic rocks.

40.1 Hornitos (take left fork).

40.2 Adobe and stone buildings, some in ruins but others still occupied. Hornitos was settled in 1850 by Mexicans who were invited to leave the town of Quartzburg, about 4 miles to the northeast. Joaquin Murrieta, a bandit idolized by some in Mother Lode history, is alleged to have once escaped through a tunnel leading from a building here. One of the ruined buildings once housed the store of D. Ghirardelli, who later went into the chocolate business. From the Wells Fargo office, established in 1852, gold shipments of $40,000 per day are reported, and the population of Hornitos reached a high point of about 15,000. The name "Hornitos" means "little ovens" and was derived from the dome-like bake ovens constructed here by a group of

Germans. Return to junction at south edge of Hornitos.

40.3 Turn left on road to Cathay Valley.
For the next 5 miles the road passes through mica-quartz-feldspar schist, thin-bedded black argillite, and intercalated layers of metavolcanic rock presumed to be of Jurassic age. In the bed of Eldorado Creek on the north side of the road are tailing piles from placer mining. Prospect pits, adits, and shafts can be seen here and there on the surrounding hills.

42.3 Road to right goes to Indian Gulch. Take left fork, which goes to Bear Valley and Cathay Valley.

44.8 Ruins of the Ruth Pierce gold mine, which yielded $600,000 worth of gold from a quartz vein, on the hill to the south (right). The vein is exposed at the road just east of the mine (Bowen and Gray, 1957, p. 165). Beyond the Ruth Pierce mine, the road crosses a belt of metavolcanic rocks (Best, 1963a, fig. 4).

45.8 Entering the Guadelupe intrusive complex (Best, 1963b). This layered and differentiated intrusion is exposed in an elliptical area approximately 12 miles long in a northwest direction and 6 miles wide. Its contacts are generally parallel to the foliation of the surrounding rocks; the west contact dips steeply eastward beneath the intrusion or is vertical, and the east contact appears to dip more gently to the east. The rock types included in the complex are the following: layered gabbro, consisting largely of plagioclase and clinopyroxene, with minor amounts of olivine, orthopyroxene, or hornblende, exposed in the western part of the intrusion; meladiorite, consisting about 50 percent of plagioclase and 40 to 50 percent of hornblende, and quartz-monzonite, exposed in the central part; and granite and granophyre in the eastern part. An unusual feature of the complex is the presence of a broad belt of agmatite (a fragmental plutonic rock with a more or less granitic matrix or cement) extending due north across the body between the meladiorite and the granite. The inclusions in the agmatite are compositionally similar to the meladiorite, and the matrix passes upward without lithologic change into massive granite.
According to Best (1963, p. 245–257), the Guadelupe intrusive complex formed by in place differentiation of a fairly water-rich magma with a composition of diabase containing about 50 percent SiO_2. During the early stages of crystallization the mineral components of the gabbro (plagioclase, pyroxene, and olivine) accumulated toward the floor of the chamber, in part by crystal settling and in part by convection currents. Removal of these minerals, plus crystallization of meladiorite and quartz-monzonite along the walls and roof of the chamber, left a central core filled with granitic magma. The shell of meladiorite along the roof collapsed and its fragments have sunk through the granitic magma to accumulate as the fragmental phase of the agmatite.
For the first three miles in the intrusive complex the route is over gabbroic rocks of the western (basal) part, close to the north margin. In this area the layering is not distinct. Schultz Mountain, the high mountain to the south, consists of layered gabbro. It will be possible to see the layered character of the rock in this mountain from the Yosemite-Merced Highway on the route followed on the return trip.

47.6 Road branches to left toward Bear Valley. Keep to right on road to Cathay Valley.

49.0 Bridge across Bear Creek. Here the route enters the belt of meladiorite and quartz-monzonite. The route is over these rocks to the junction with Highway 140 and for about 1 mile beyond.

52.5 Junction with Highway 140 at settlement of Cathay (or Cathey's) Valley. Turn left on Highway 140 for Mariposa and Yosemite.

53.5 Entering belt of agmatite. Guadelupe Mountain ahead.

54.0 Begin grade up west side of Guadelupe Mountain. Excellent exposures of the agmatite are to be seen in roadcuts for the next two miles. Unfortunately, there is no place to park along this road.

56.0 Exposure of agmatite in roadcuts on right. Just beyond, the highway swings eastward around the north end of Guadelupe Mountain.

57.0 Road branches to left toward Bear Valley. Stay on Highway 140. The route ahead is over the granite and granophyre of the upper part of the intrusive complex.

58.5 Route enters the slate and graywacke of the Mariposa Formation, of Jurassic (late Oxfordian to early Kimmeridgian) age (Clark, 1964, p. 25).

59.5 Road and creek pass through ridge held up by resistant unit in the Mariposa Formation. Slate beds, striking northwest and dipping steeply northeast, can be seen in roadcuts and on hillside.

59.6 Flagstone quarry in interbedded slate and graywacke on south bank of creek to right.

65.8 Enter Mariposa, county seat of Mariposa County. In this town the route crosses the southern end of the Mother Lode (Melones Fault Zone). "Mariposa" is Spanish for "butterfly". The Mariposa mine (gold-quartz) is on the hill to the right as we enter the town. The mine is reported to have been discovered by Kit Carson in the spring of 1849. It was worked, with periods of interruption, until 1956, yielding a total known production valued at $2,400,-000 at the old price of gold. The ore occurred in a branching vein of milky quartz 2 to 8 feet thick, which contained native gold, pyrite, and arsenopyrite. Individual local pockets yielded as much as $30,000 worth of gold, but at the time of closing the average tenor of the ore was $8 to $15 per ton. The vein was worked to a depth of 1,500 feet (Bowen and Gray, 1957, p. 128–130).

67.1 Junction California 140 and 49. Continue ahead on 140. For the next 4 miles steeply dipping metavolcanic rocks with some interbedded slate are exposed in most of the roadcuts.

68.6 Small body of talc-antigorite schist enclosed in metavolcanic rocks.

70.7 Mariposa summit. For the next 4 miles, the highway passes down the valley of Bear Creek, a broad gentle valley probably graded approximately to the Merced River of the Broad Valley stage (Hudson, 1960, fig. 2, p. 1551).

71.4 Highway enters an area underlain by a granitic rock.

72.0 Highway passes from the granitic area back onto metavolcanic rocks.

75.2 The grade of Bear Creek steepens somewhat, the canyon narrows, and the stream has carved incised meanders. The segment of the stream from 75.2 to 77.3 was probably graded to the Merced River of the Mountain Valley stage.

77.0 Bridge over Bear Creek.

77.3 Bear Creek here plunges over a fall held up by the resistant metavolcanic rock and descends the abrupt canyon ahead to the Merced River. This is probably the nickpoint between the upstream segment of Bear Creek graded to the Mountain Valley stage and to the present stage in its canyon downstream (fig. 3).

77.9 Contact between steeply dipping metavolcanic and metasedimentary rocks, both parts of the Calaveras Formation of Paleozoic age.

77.9 to 79.6 Steeply dipping planar structure in Paleozoic slate exposed on the left is cleavage. Bedding is in general nearly parallel to the cleavage, but in many places crosses it.

79.6 Briceburg.

79.7 Slate and thin-bedded chert of the Calaveras Formation are here greatly sheared, and the only structures remaining are the steeply plunging lineations and minor folds related to the last stage of deformation. For the next 5 miles, the Calaveras Formation consists of phyllite derived from siltstone that locally contained interbedded chert. Bedding is preserved in part of this interval, but in other parts has been destroyed by shearing, as it is here.

Granitic boulders are abundant in glacial outwash resting on water-polished bedrock in cuts on the south side of the road. Since the gravel consists largely of well-rounded boulders of granite and granodiorite, it must have been transported by the river, for the bedrock for many miles upstream from this point consists of metasedimentary rocks. Over the outwash gravel is colluvium derived from the slope above.

80.8 On the right in large cut boudinage in steeply dipping mafic dike.

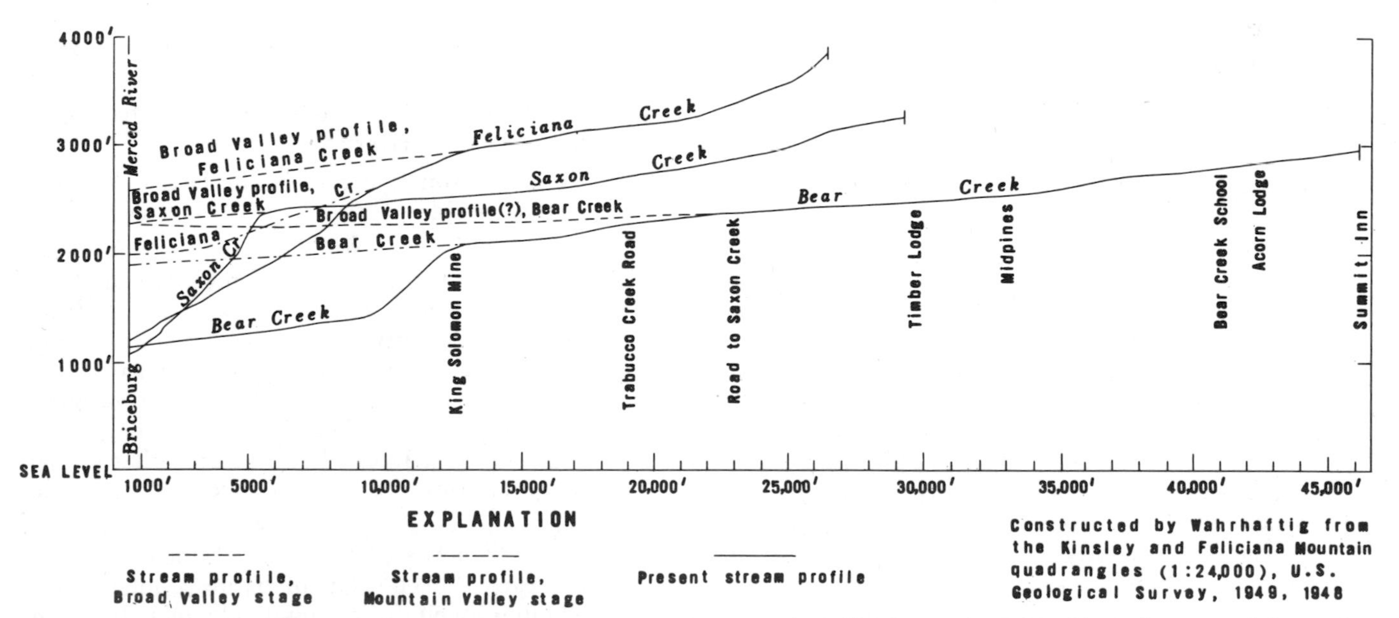

Figure 3. Profiles of three tributaries of the Merced River in El Portal quadrangle, California, showing knickpoints to the stages of downcutting of the Merced River. *From California Div. Mines and Geology Bull. 182, figure 2.*

81.6 Outwash gravel exposed in the roadcut may indicate two layers of outwash, separated by a period of dissection when ice retreated in the headwaters of the river. In the lower 10 feet of the gravel many of the boulders of granodiorite and granite are rotted to granite sand; maximum size of the boulders is about 4 feet, but this is no larger than boulders now being moved by the Merced River on the other side of the road. The upper 20 feet of the exposure, separated from the lower part by a row of boulders slumped from the hillside above, consists of finer gravel (about 1 foot average size) composed of largely unweathered boulders of granite and granodiorite. The upper gravel may be of Tioga or Tenaya (Birman, 1964) age, probably the latter, and the lower gravel Tahoe or Sherwin in age.

83.8 Crossing Feliciana Creek, one of Matthes' (1930) classic areas of the Broad Valley stage.

83.9 Quartz ladder veins in dikes to the right.

84.7 Thin-bedded metachert of the Calaveras Formation, locally contorted. The light-gray-weathering more massive rock is limestone, traceable for about 2½ miles north.

85.8 Small granitic stock to the north across the river.

86.0 Inactive limestone quarry which formerly supplied limestone used in Merced for the manufacture of portland cement. The geologic structure on hillsides to the north (left) is brought out by the resistant metachert and limestone beds.

87.8 *Stop 1.* Geologic marker. Tightly and complexly folded metachert and black phyllite of the Calaveras Formation. The folds all plunge steeply, but the bearing of the fold axes and attitudes of axial planes are not consistent.

88.6 Landslide debris in roadcut on the right. The scarp at the top of the slide, not visible from this point, is near the crest of the ridge. Looking downstream from this point the V-shaped canyon of the Merced River is well displayed.

88.9 *Stop 2.* Glacial outwash gravel, consisting largely of rounded cobbles and boulders of granodiorite and quartz-monzonite, is exposed in benched quarry on the right. The cobbles in the lower bench are so thoroughly weathered that they wear back flat to the face of the cut. The cobbles of the upper bench, although considerably weathered, are firm enough to stand out from the bluff in relief. Presumably these are two separate deposits of outwash gravel, separated by a time interval during which the lower unit was eroded and weathered. As will be seen at Stop 2 tomorrow, the cobbles in the younger gravel here are much more deeply weathered than boulders in the outwash and till of moraines at the lower end of Yosemite Valley, which are correlated with the Tenaya Glaciation of Birman (1964) of presumed middle or late Wisconsin age. These gravels indicate that here the Merced River cut its gorge to its present depth by at least early Wisconsin time; and if two different ages of weathered outwash are indeed present, the Merced Gorge reached its present depth by Illinoian time.

89.4 Bridge across the South Fork of the Merced River.

90.9 Waste dumps of the Clearing House mine can be seen to the east across the river. The ore was discovered in 1860, and before mining ceased in 1937, the mine had yielded more than $3,350,000 in gold, some silver, and small amounts of copper and lead. Granodiorite exposed on hill north of the mine.

91.1 Southwestern contact of an isolated granitic pluton.

91.3 Gold star mine on right. The mine produced small amounts of gold from 1936 to 1952.

91.5 On the spur on the canyon wall to the north (left) can be seen the trace of the incline where log-laden flatcars were lowered from spurlines on the gently rolling upland surface above to the main line of the Yosemite Valley Railroad near the river level.

91.6 Dumps at the Rutherford gold mine are visible north of the river. The production is not recorded but there are several reports of high-grade ore.

92.0 Outwash gravel in roadcut.

92.4 Northeastern contact of granitic pluton.

92.5 Spheroidally weathered boulders of granitic rock.

93.9 Southwestern contact of a granitic body crossed in the next half mile.

94.6 The flat area to the left marks an abandoned meander of the river.

94.8 The sheet-iron structure at the base of the hill on the far side of the river is a mill that processed tungsten ore from mines in this vicinity.

95.3 At this point, the canyon of the Merced River widens out and is U-shaped. Downstream from this point the canyon is V-shaped and winding, and there is some question as to how far below this point ice actually extended. There is, however, no question that ice reached this far downstream on the Merced River in the oldest glacial stages recognized on the west side of the Sierra.

95.4 Tunnels in the sharp ridge north of the river are workings of the El Portal barite mine. Most of the nearly 400,000 tons of barite produced was used in oil-well drilling mud. The mine has been idle since 1948.

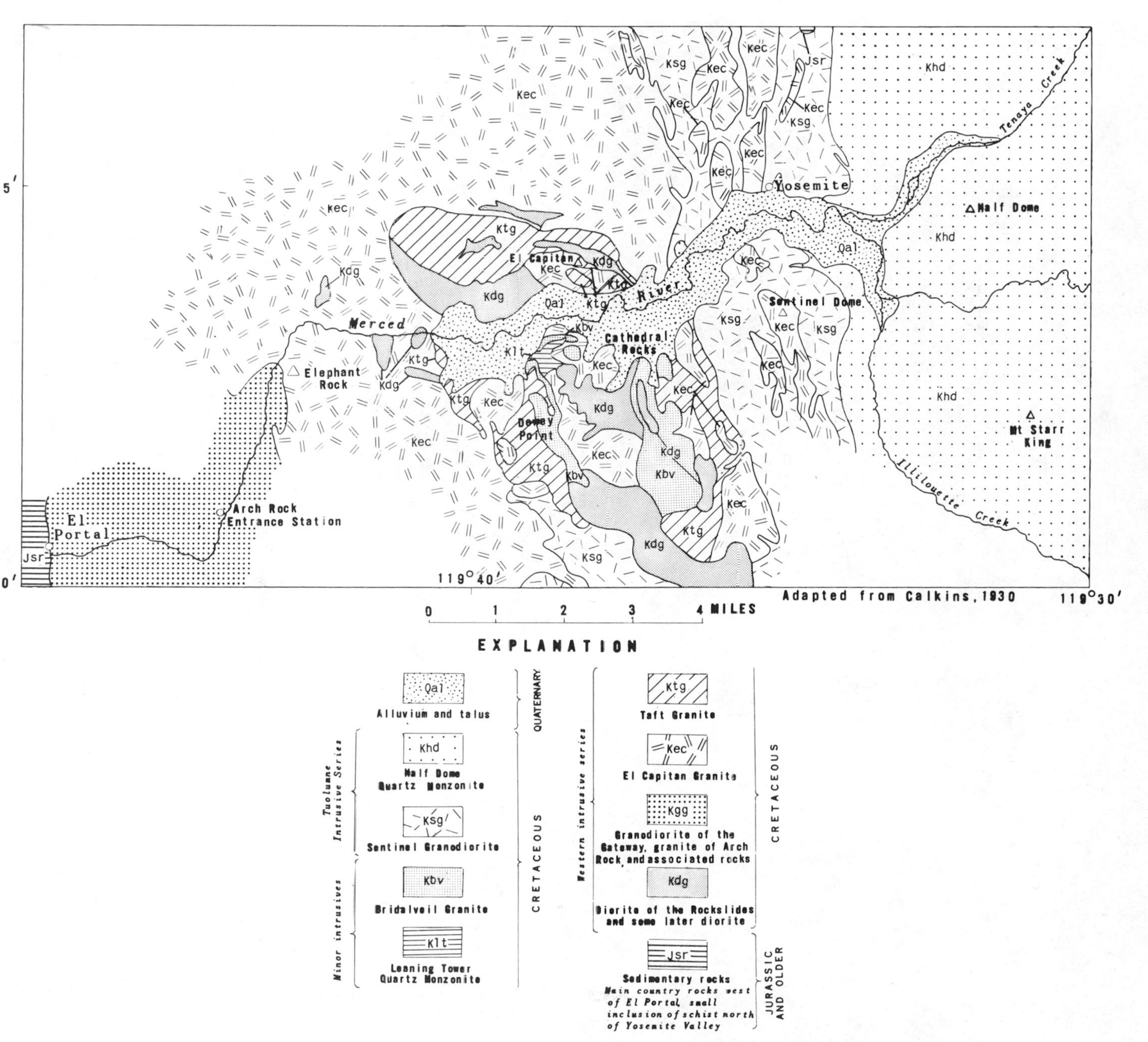

Figure 4. Generalized geologic map of the Yosemite Valley area. *From California Div. Mines and Geology Bull. 182, figure 1.*

Photo 2. "Tombstone rocks" (metamorphosed volcanic rocks) near Cattown, Mariposa County. *Photo by Mary Hill.*

96.2 Bridge across Merced River.

96.5 Metamorphic rocks across river to the right.

96.8 El Portal. This was formerly the terminus of the Yosemite Valley Road. The contact between Calaveras Formation (late Paleozoic) and the granitic rocks of the Yosemite area trends due north a few hundred feet east of here (fig. 4). The marginal intrusive rocks include coarse diorite and some norite. The gorge of the Merced River ahead of us was glaciated during two pre-Wisconsin stages, when the glaciers extended about 1 mile below here, but was not glaciated during the Wisconsin.

100.3 Arch Rock Entrance Station, National Park Service.

100.4 Arch Rock. Two large fallen blocks are in contact at the top but are separated at the bottom by enough space for passage of the old road. Talus of granite (table 1), is exposed in a quarry on the north side of the road. The granite contains sparse inclusions of an unidentified darker gray rock similar in appearance to the granodorite at The Gateway.

101.5 Elephant Rock is straight ahead.

102.8 Junction with the Coulterville Road, the first road into Yosemite Valley (completed as a toll road on June 17, 1874.)

103.0 Wildcat Creek. El Capitan Granite is exposed at the falls just west of here.

103.3 Cascade Creek. El Capitan Granite is exposed in a nearby cliff, and some large fallen blocks of it can be seen from the road.

105.2 Junction with the Big Oak Flat Road. The original road, which lies farther up the slope, was completed a month after the Coulterville Road. At the road junction are exposures and talus of older diorite. Here the diorite contains light-colored aggregates consisting mainly of plagioclase that probably formed as the result of metamorphism by the nearby El Capitan Granite.

106.2 Turn right across Pohono Bridge.

107.2 Turn right on Wawona Road.

109.0 *Stop 3.* Parking lot at the east portal of Wawona Tunnel. View to the east of El Capitan, Sentinel Rock, Cathedral Rocks, the hanging valley of Bridalveil Creek, and Bridalveil Fall. Nearby exposures of various granitic rocks and of diorite.

The abundance of joints in the diorite in the opposite valley wall (directly north of here) contrasts strongly with their scarcity in the massive cliffs of El Capitan and the Cathedral Rocks (composed mostly of El Capitan, Bridalveil, and Taft Granites, all probably of Cretaceous age). The constriction in the valley between El Capitan and the Cathedral Rocks may be due to the massive nature of the granitic rocks at this point. The great abundance of talus in the cliffs directly north of here, in contrast to the paucity of talus farther up the valley, is due to the close jointing of the diorite of the cliffs.

The U-shape of Yosemite Valley, in contrast to the V-shape of the gorge of the Merced below El Portal, is well displayed here. The bottom of the U, however, is much flatter than in typical glaciated valleys. According to Gutenberg, Buwalda, and Sharp (1956, pl. 5), the bedrock surface lies almost 1,000 feet beneath the floor of the valley between El Capitan and Cathedral Rocks, and what we see is essentially a plain floored by lake sediments.

The top of the highest glacier in Yosemite Valley, according to Matthes (1930), reached about to the brow of El Capitan, and was about 300 feet above the top of the Cathedral Rocks. The glacier swept around the flank of Sentinel Dome, but did not cover the dome. The upper 700 feet of Half Dome, likewise, was unglaciated. These domes owe their form to concentric spalling of massive unjointed rock, not to glacial erosion.

The steep lower course of Bridalveil Creek above Bridalveil Fall is graded to the level established by the Merced River during the most recent of three distinct stages of preglacial erosion (from oldest to youngest, the Broad Valley, Mountain Valley, and Canyon stages of Matthes, 1930, p. 45–50); hence it helps to define the amount of glacial erosion in Yosemite Valley. The V-shaped form of the gorge of the creek, although typical of stream erosion, is preserved because the sloping walls of the gorge coincide with throughgoing joints in the otherwise nearly unjointed rock. The upper part of Fireplace Creek, a little downstream from us on the opposite wall, is graded to the Mountain Valley stage of the Merced Canyon according to Matthes. Ribbon Creek, above the head of Ribbon Fall (which cannot be seen from here, but can be seen on the north wall of the canyon from places a mile or two down the road), is graded to the Broad Valley stage of the Merced (fig. 3) according to Matthes.

The blasted rock face at the west end of the parking lot exposes a complicated mixture of diorite and El Capitan Granite. The porphyritic phase of the Taft Granite is well exposed on the slope just to the west. El Capitan Granite along the south side of the road contains blocks of partially assimilated diorite, and has a steeply dipping foliation.

This ends the first day of the field trip. Tomorrow's log begins with mileage zero at the Yosemite Lodge parking lot.

Circuit of Yosemite Valley

Mileage

00.0 *West entrance to Yosemite Lodge parking lot,* the starting point for the trip following the route shown on figure 5. View of Sentinel Rock across valley. Along the cascade of Sentinel Creek to the right (west) of the rock, can be seen recesses caused by spalling of the granitic rocks around the cascade. Enlargement of the recesses appears to be developing vertical waterfalls from this sloping cascade.

0.3 View of El Capitan straight ahead.

1.2 Junction at north end of El Capitan Bridge: continue straight ahead.

1.4 *Stop 1.* El Capitan Meadow. Walk north up trail to rock face at base of El Capitan. Talus en route includes El Capitan Granite, finer-grained Taft Granite, diorite, and quartz-mica diorite. On the rock face can be seen dikes of quartz-mica diorite cutting El Capitan Granite, which contains inclusions of older diorite. Across the valley on the faces of the Cathedral Rocks can be seen nearly horizontal light-colored dikes of Bridalveil Granite cutting a maze of other granitic and dioritic rocks.

Return to the road and continue west.

2.9 (At V-26 sign.) The low ridge to the left is the easternmost of a series of Wisconsin terminal moraines, which held in the former Lake Yosemite. The lake was filled with as much as 300 feet of silt and sand deposited in advancing deltas by the Merced River and Tenaya Creek; this debris was possibly supplied by glaciers of Tioga age, which reached only as far downstream as the lip of Nevada Fall and the upper part of Tenaya Canyon (fig. 6).

3.2 Turnout. Pause for view of Bridalveil Fall, Leaning Tower, and Cathedral Rocks across valley.

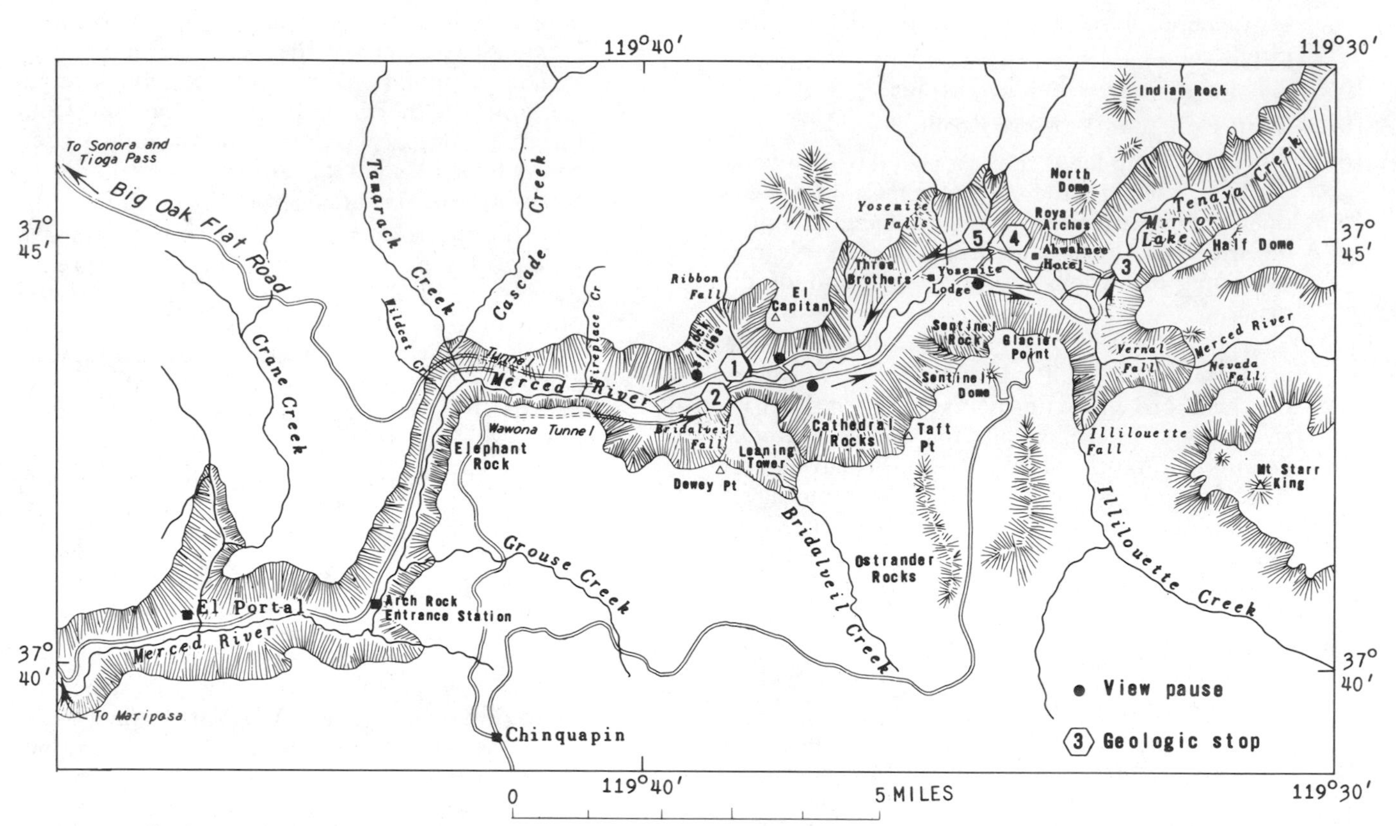

Figure 5. Sketch map showing the route to be followed in the circuit of Yosemite Valley. Numbers in hexagons are the stops described in the road log.

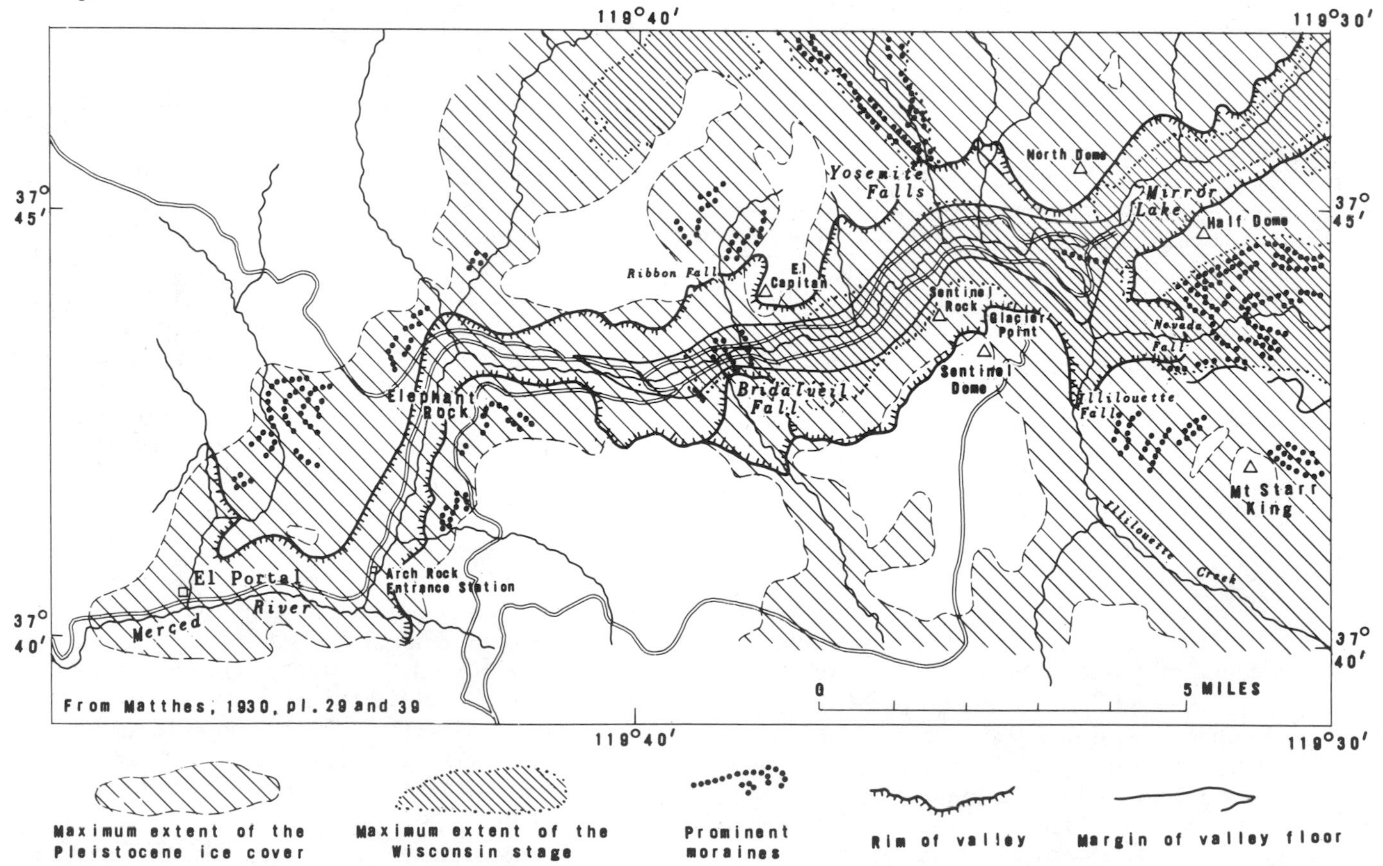

Figure 6. Sketch map showing former extent of glacial ice in and around Yosemite Valley.

4.1 Valley View turnout. Pause for view of El Capitan, Clouds Rest, and Sentinel Rock to the east and Cathedral Rocks and Bridalveil Fall to the southeast. The westernmost of the Wisconsin terminal moraines lies a few hundred feet west of here.

4.3 Turn left across Pohono Bridge.

4.8 View of Rockslides across valley.

5.0 Road again crosses the westernmost Wisconsin moraine.

5.3 Junction with Wawona Road; turn right.

5.4 *Stop 2.* Turn left into parking lot. Walk along trail (about 1,000 feet) to viewpoint at base of Bridalveil Fall. Near viewpoint are fallen blocks of Leaning Tower Quartz Monzonite, Bridalveil Granite, diorite, and El Capitan Granite. On the cliff face at the lip of Bridalveil Fall can be seen a thick horizontal sheet of smooth-weathering Bridalveil Granite. Underneath is reddish rough-weathering Leaning Tower Quartz Monzonite, and to the east is dark diorite. Note that the lower part of Bridalveil Fall is in a slight recess flanked by buttresses. The borders of the recess are marked by the edges of slabs parallel to the surface, apparently the original continuations of these slabs across the face of the fall have dropped from the cliff and are represented by the cone of talus extending up the cliff to an apex just west of the base of the fall.

Return down the Bridalveil Fall trail and turn east on the trail crossing Bridalveil Creek. Looking ahead across the valley to the recess in which lies Ribbon Fall, one can see spalling in the upper part of the recess similar to that around Bridalveil Fall. After 0.3 mile the trail ascends the Bridalveil Moraine. Turn off the trail at the first switchback, climb to the top, and walk north along the crest of the moraine. This is one of six moraines at the lower end of Yosemite Valley recognized by Matthes. In the roadcut at the north end of the ridge can be seen boulders as much as eight feet across of Cathedral Peak Granite, marked by distinctive large phenocrysts of K-feldspar. These boulders must have been transported at least 13 miles from the nearest outcrop in the headwaters of the Merced River.

Return to the buses and continue east.

6.7 View of El Capitan across valley.

7.1 Junction with road to El Capitan Bridge. View of Sentinel Rock to the east, directly up the road. The forms of Sentinel Rock, Glacier Point, and the north face of Half Dome, are controlled by vertical joints trending east to northeast.

7.3 Pause at V-19 sign for view of El Capitan and Three Brothers across the valley. On the face of El Capitan the irregular boundaries of an intrusive body of diorite form a crude map of North America. This cuts an inconspicuous westward-sloping dike of gray rock, probably Leaning Tower Quartz Monzonite. The form of the Three Brothers is controlled by joints dipping obliquely westward.

8.9 View of Yosemite Falls across the valley.

9.4 Road junction at south end of Sentinel Bridge. Continue east, not crossing bridge. South of here are remnants of the Old Village, the center of commercial activity in the valley between the late 1850's and 1917.

9.5 Pause for a view to the east of North Dome, Half Dome, Royal Arches, Washington Column, and Glacier Point. The form of the Royal Arches, Half Dome, and North Dome is controlled by exfoliation of the Half Dome Quartz Monzonite, resulting from expansion due to unloading brought about by denudation.

9.8 Road junction; continue straight ahead.

10.5 Road crosses Happy Isles Bridge.

11.0 Road crosses Wisconsin moraine. View of North Dome straight ahead.

11.1 Road junction; bear right.

11.4 Road junction; bear right.

11.8 Road crosses rock avalanche that dammed Tenaya Creek forming Mirror Lake.

12.1 *Stop 3.* Parking lot at Mirror Lake. View of Mirror Lake, and of Tenaya Canyon to the east. Walk along trail to the northeast about 1,000 feet to see glacial polish and striae on Half Dome Quartz Monzonite. Well-formed books of biotite are prominent in this rock.

Return to parking lot and drive west.

12.8 Road junction; bear right.

13.0 "Indian Cave," north of road, is in coarse talus at the foot of the cliff.

13.2 View ahead of sheeting in the Royal Arches, formed by exfoliation.

13.6 Sugar Pine Bridge.

14.0 Road junction; bear right.

14.1 View ahead of flat-lying dikes of Half Dome Quartz Monzonite and pegmatite in Sentinel Granodiorite.

14.4 *Stop 4.* Church Bowl. View across valley of Glacier Point. In the cliff face west of Glacier Point, note the contrast between unjointed Half Dome Quartz Monzonite (Cretaceous) below, and jointed granodiorite above. In the center of the valley south of here as much as 2,000 feet of glacio-lacustrine debris overlies the bedrock (Gutenberg, Buwalda, and Sharp, 1956). In talus and in cliff faces on the north side of the valley at this stop dark-colored Sentinel Granodiorite is cut by gently dipping light-colored dikes of coarse pegmatite and Half Dome Quartz Monzonite at the margin of the large body of Half Dome Quartz Monzonite. In some of the dikes of quartz monzonite unequal concentration of dark minerals produces a nearly horizontal layering.

14.7 *Stop 5*. Parking lot at Yosemite National Park Headquarters. Visit to Museum.

15.4 East entrance to Yosemite Lodge parking lot.

Yosemite Valley. From *J. D. Whitney, The Yosemite Guide-Book, 1870.*

MINERALOGY OF THE LAYTONVILLE QUARRY, MENDOCINO COUNTY, CALIFORNIA

By Charles W. Chesterman
California Division of Mines and Geology

The Laytonville quarry is a locality where an unusual variety of minerals has been found in Franciscan glaucophane schists, including the three recently discovered new species, deerite, howieite, and zussmanite (Agrell, Bown, and McKie, 1965). The field trip to this locality includes no stops en route, hence no road log is provided. The geology along U.S. Highway 101, which is followed from San Francisco to the quarry, is shown on the San Francisco, Santa Rosa, and Ukiah Sheets of the State Geologic Map. Most of the rocks to be seen en route, as well as those at the quarry, belong to the Franciscan Formation, recently described by Bailey, Irwin, and Jones (1964).

The Laytonville quarry is in sec. 6, T. 20 N., R. 14 W., M.D.B.M., on the north side of U.S. Highway 101, about 5 miles south of Laytonville, Mendocino County (fig. 1). It was excavated by the California Division of Highways to supply rock for riprap along the embankment of Long Valley Creek nearby. The quarry was first worked in 1957, and since that time approximately 91,000 tons of rock have been obtained.

The rocks exposed in the quarry include both metamorphosed sedimentary and volcanic rocks of the Franciscan Formation (Jurassic and Cretaceous age). The list of minerals found here is long and impressive; seldom is it possible to find so many of the minerals characteristic of the glaucophane schists at one place.

GEOLOGY

The area in which the Laytonville quarry is situated is referred to by the California Division of Highways (Clemens, oral communication, 1965) as "Hell's Half Acre," a name that is justifiably applied to the area because it is essentially a large landslide. Such slides are common in the California Coast Ranges, and many, like this one, contain large and small masses of metamorphosed and unmetamorphosed Franciscan rocks randomly encased in a slumgullion composed of sheared and crushed Franciscan graywacke, siltstone, shale, chert, and greenstone, accompanied by serpentine.

The Laytonville quarry was carved in a single gigantic landslide mass of metamorphosed Franciscan rocks, which has retained its integrity although it has been somewhat removed from its original site.

Unmetamorphosed equivalents of the metamorphosed Franciscan rocks are exposed in the area surrounding the quarry. Bedding is preserved in the metamorphic rocks; the strike is N. 40° W., and the dip is 45° NE. The bedding in a prominent outcropping of white chert, about 500 feet in a southeasterly direction from the quarry, strikes N. 65° E. and dips 30° NW.

Faults are common in the area and two of them are easily observable in the quarry itself. One of these faults, exposed in the quarry face, forms the contact between metabasalt and metasedimentary rocks; the other, a transverse fault, has the effect of reversing the dip of bedding and foliation in the metabasalt (fig. 2) to a southwesterly direction.

The metamorphosed Franciscan rocks in the Laytonville quarry can be designated into two groups: (1) as metabasalt, and (2) as metasedimentary rock.

Metabasalt

The metabasalt is massive, sheared, fractured, jointed, grayish-blue in color, and comprises most of the steep quarry face. The blue color is due to glaucophane, which constitutes about 50 percent of the rock. Green colors, which are less prominent, are due to pumpellyite, clinozoisite, chlorite, and phengite. Other minerals present include garnet, lawsonite, sphene, aragonite, quartz, albite, and pyrite. Lying within the metabasalt, but not a part of this unit, is a lens about 5 feet thick composed of talc, actinolite, chlorite, and minor tremolite. This rock was probably derived from serpentine which crops out nearby.

The metabasalt is fine grained and in places exhibits a weakly defined foliation. Lawsonite occurs in idioblastic crystals as much as 2 mm in size. Glaucophane is in small interlocking prismatic crystals that range in size from 0.2 to 1.5 mm. Garnet is amber colored and occurs in idioblastic crystals that range in size from 0.5 to 2 mm. The garnet is unevenly distributed throughout the metabasalt, and it commonly occurs as narrow trains of small crystals associated with aragonite and albite cutting across the foliation.

Phengite, clinozoisite, pumpellyite, and chlorite tend to occur together as xenomorphic grains forming whispy streaks and small, thin lenses.

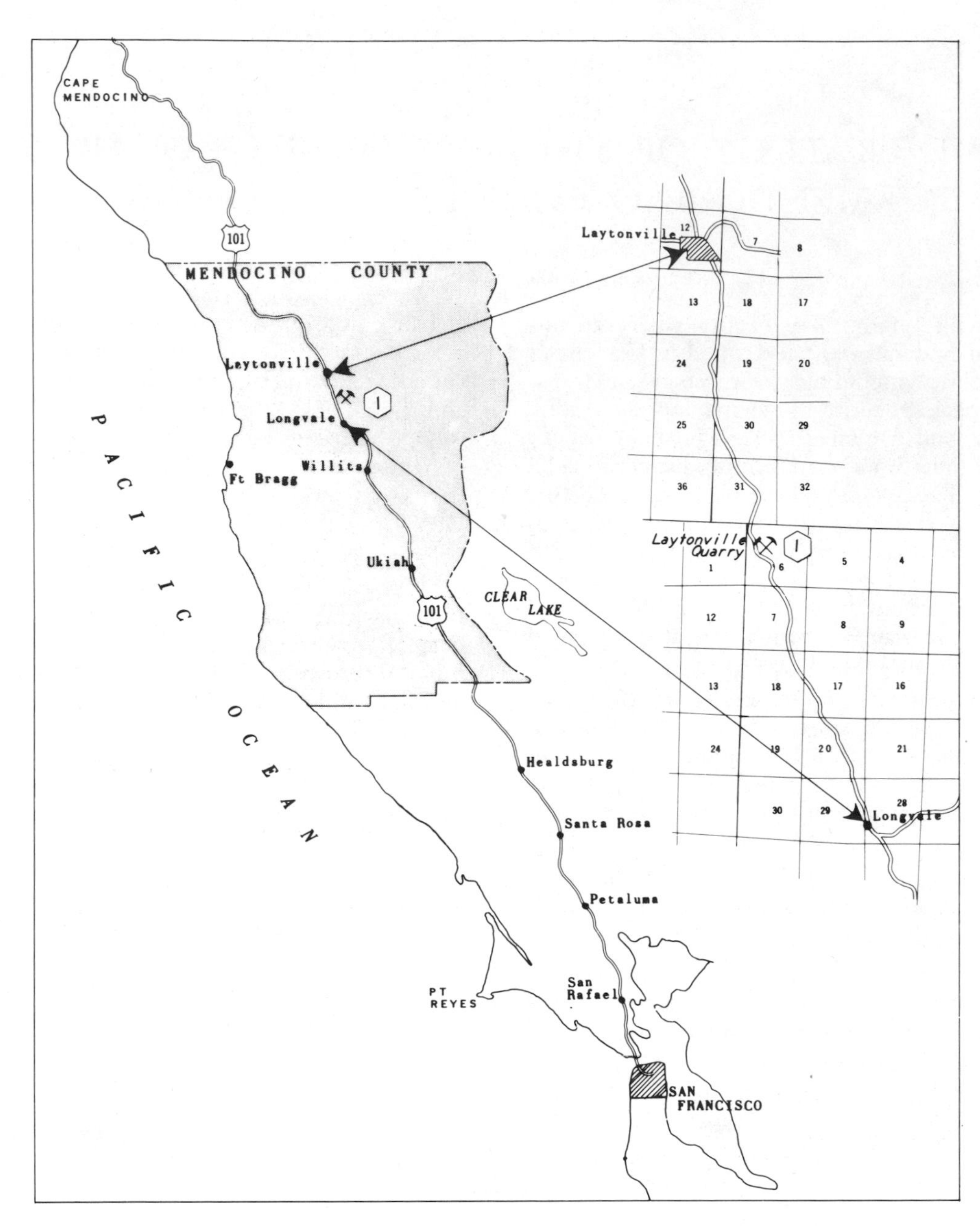

Figure 1. Map showing route of field trip from San Francisco to the Laytonville quarry.

Photo 1. Massive metabasalt (mb) in fault contact with foliated and thinly banded metasedimentary rocks (ms) at the Laytonville quarry. *Photo by John T. Alfors.*

Aragonite and calcite occur in small grains along shear planes, and calcite also forms narrow veinlets cutting across the foliation. Albite is in white and glassy subhedral crystals, which measure up to 1 cm across, occurring in veins.

Pyrite is ubiquitous in the metabasalt and occurs in idioblastic crystals that range in size from 1 mm to 1.5 cm. Sphene is in small idioblastic crystals and is a minor mineral.

Metasedimentary Rocks

The metasedimentary rocks include metachert, metashale, metaironstone, and metalimestone. Metachert appears to be subordinate in amount to the other metasedimentary rocks and will be described as a unit, and the metashale, metaironstone, and metalimestone collectively predominate as narrow interbeds in the metachert and will be treated as a unit also.

The metasedimentary rocks are moderately well exposed in the quarry wall, but are largely covered by rock debris on the quarry floor.

Metachert

The metachert is banded, with individual bands ranging from a few millimeters to several centimeters in thickness. The rock has a wide range in grain size and consists of quartz, stilpnomelane, crossite, riebeckite, aegerite, pyrite, deerite, zussmanite, and garnet. The quartz is abundant and shows a well-developed mosaic texture. It is in small grains that average about 0.5 mm in diameter. Stilpnomelane imparts a dark color to the metachert. Both ferri- and ferro-stilpnomelane occur in plumose and interlaminated aggregates with individual crystals ranging in size from a few millimeters to about 1 centimeter. The ferri-stilpnomelane, the more abundant of the two, is dark brown in color, while the ferro-stilpnomelane is pale greenish in color.

Garnet is spessartite-rich and is in orange-red, idioblastic crystals that range in size from 0.5 to 1.5 mm. Aegerite is yellowish green in color and occurs as small, stumpy prismatic crystals or as aggregates of radiating needles. Crossite is in dark, bluish-black prismatic crystals. Riebeckite occurs as bluish-black prismatic crystals as much as 1 cm long and 2 mm wide, and as aggregates of radiating greyish-blue fibers.

Pyrite is in small idioblastic crystals that tend to be deformed in a direction parallel to the foliation.

Deerite and zussmanite, two new minerals for California, appear to have developed best in the metachert which grades imperceptibly into the metashale and metaironstone. Deerite ($(Mg_{.08}Mn_{.86}Fe''_{10.9})_{11.84}(Fe'''_{5.89}Al_{.38})_{6.27}Si_{11.86}O_{39.95}(OH)_{10.05}$) is in black acicular and prismatic crystals that range up to 5 mm in length and 1 mm across. The crystals commonly occur in more or less parallel alignment, a feature which is not characteristic of the other dark prismatic and fibrous minerals in the quarry. Zussmanite ($(Na_{.07}K_{.92})_{.99}(Mg_{1.33}Mn_{.46}Fe''_{10.85}Fe'''_{.11}Al_{.34}Ti_{.01})_{13.10}(Si_{16.6}Al_{1.4})_{18}O_{42.2}(OH)_{13.8}$) occurs in medium-green tabular crystals that seldom are more than 1 mm across. It is not always possible to distinguish between zussmanite, chlorite, and phengite in the hand specimen. For this reason zussmanite could easily have been overlooked at other localities where similar assemblages of Franciscan metamorphic rocks occur.

Metashale, Metaironstone, and Metalimestone

These metamorphic rocks, which have been derived from fine-grained clastic sediments, are dark colored and have well-developed bedding and bedding-plane cleavage. The mineralogy of these fine-grained metasedimentary rocks is similar to that of the metachert, but, in addition, the metashale, metaironstone, and metalimestone contain phengite, grunerite, oligonite, ferroan-kutnahorite, and the recently discovered howieite. Phengite is pale green and occurs in small, shimmering platelike crystals which make up layers that range in thickness from a few millimeters to about 5 centimeters. The oligonite and ferroan-kutnahorite are two unusual carbonate minerals that occur in the fine-grained metasedimentary rocks. Oligonite occurs in small rhomb-shaped crystals associated with quartz, ferri-stilpnomelane, garnet, grunerite, and ferroan-kutnahorite. The oligonite is zoned, and an electron microprobe analysis indicates a core composition of approximately 4 percent $CaCO_3$, 46 percent $MnCO_3$, 40 percent $FeCO_3$, and 10 percent $MgCO_3$. The rim composition tends to be lower in $FeCO_3$ and higher in $MnCO_3$ and $CaCO_3$ (S. O. Agrell, oral communication, 1963). The ferroan-kutnahorite is granular, and an electron microprobe analysis of it indicates approximately 49 percent $CaCO_3$, 29 percent $MnCO_3$, 14 percent $FeCO_3$, and 8 percent $MgCO_3$ (Agrell, oral communication, 1963).

Howieite ($(Na_{1.03}Ca_{.02})_{1.05}(Mg_{.45}Mn_{2.98}Fe''_{6.41})_{9.84}Fe'''_{1.57}Al_{.62})_{2.19}(Si_{11.96}Ti_{.40})_{12.00}O_{31.3}(OH)_{12.69}$) is one of the more spectacular of the new minerals found at the Laytonville quarry. It occurs in dark-green to black-bladed crystals that commonly form plumose and interlaminated aggregates. Crystals of howieite up to 1 cm in length are common. From a first glance at a speçimen, one might easily mistake black stilpnomelane for howieite. However, a hand-lens examination will quickly reveal the prismatic character of the howieite as compared to the tabular nature of the stilpnomelane.

Grunerite occurs in brown fibrous and silky crystals. It is not a common mineral, but occurs associated with stilpnomelane, zussmanite, quartz, and oligonite.

Garnet is ubiquitous in the fine-grained metasedimentary rocks and has two distinct modes of occurrence: In separate idioblastic crystals that range in size from 0.5 to 1.5 mm and in thin, contorted layers and irregular streaks as much as 1 cm thick composed of small idioblastic and xenoblastic crystals. It is yellowish orange to pinkish orange in color and appears to contain both almandine and spessartite.

SUMMARY

No attempt will be made here to summarize the mineral paragenesis of the metamorphic rocks at the Laytonville quarry, primarily because the data presented here are based principally upon extensive field and hand specimen studies and upon limited microscope examinations. The metamorphic rocks exposed at the Laytonville quarry are similar in many respects to the type III metamorphic rocks that crop out in the Ward Creek area, near Cazadero, Sonoma County, California, which have been extensively studied by Coleman and Lee (1963, p. 260–301). However, no rocks of eclogitic composition have been identified at the Laytonville quarry or from the immediate vicinity of the quarry.

Based upon their study of the Ward Creek rocks, Coleman and Lee (1963, p. 284–288) have concluded that the basalt and sedimentary rocks were converted to glaucophane-bearing rocks under conditions of high pressure and low temperature. Although there are minor differences in the mineralogies of the metamorphic rocks exposed at the Laytonville quarry and along Ward Creek, one can assume that the paragenesis of the minerals at the two localities is comparable, if not the same.

REFERENCES

Agrell, S. O., Bown, M. G., and McKie, D., 1965, Deerite, howieite, and zussmanite, three new minerals from the Franciscan of the Laytonville district, Mendocino County, California: Am. Mineralogist, v. 50, nos. 1–2, p. 278.

Bailey, E. H., Irwin, W. P., and Jones, D. L., 1964, Franciscan and related rocks and their significance in the geology of western California: California Div. Mines and Geology Bull. 183, 171 p.

Coleman, R. G., and Lee, D. E., 1963, Glaucophane-bearing metamorphic rock types of the Cazadero area, California: Jour. Petrology, v. 4, no. 2, p. 260–301.

THE END

61917—650 1-66 5M